BIOLOGY AND THE FUTURE OF MAN

BIOLOGY AND THE FUTURE OF MAN

Edited by PHILIP HANDLER

President, National Academy of Sciences

New York
OXFORD UNIVERSITY PRESS
London   1970   Toronto

Figures 2-1, 2-2, 2-13, 2-16, 2-19 are from
J. D. Watson, *Molecular Biology of the Gene*.
Copyright © 1965 by W. A. Benjamin, Inc.

Figures 3-1, 3-6, 3-8, 3-11, 3-12, 3-13, 3-14, 16-2 originally appeared in
White, Handler, and Smith, *Principles of Biochemistry*, 4th ed.
Copyright © 1968 by McGraw-Hill, Inc.

Portions of Figures 9-3 and 9-6 from R. C. Truex, ed., are from
Strong and Elwyn's Human Neuroanatomy, 4th ed.
Copyright © 1959 by The Williams & Wilkins Co.

First printing, March 1970
Second printing, July 1970
Third Printing, September 1970

Copyright © 1970 by Oxford University Press, Inc.
Library of Congress Catalogue Card Number: 73:83029
Printed in the United States of America

PREFACE

Some years ago, the Committee on Science and Public Policy of the National Academy of Sciences embarked upon a series of "surveys" of the scientific disciplines. Each survey was to commence with an appraisal of the "state of the art" in a given discipline, i.e., a summary of the progress which has recently been made in approaching the major outstanding questions in that discipline. In addition, the survey was to assess the nature and strength of our national apparatus for continuing attack on those major problems, e.g., the numbers and types of laboratories, the number of scientists in the field, the number of students, the funds available and their sources, and the major equipment being utilized. Finally, each survey was to undertake a projection of future needs for the national support of the discipline in question to assure that our national effort in this regard is optimally productive within the framework of the resources which could reasonably be brought to bear. Reports of such surveys have been published in the fields of chemistry, physics, ground-based astronomy, mathematics, and computer science.

No parallel effort was initially undertaken for a biological discipline, largely because, whereas the physical sciences could usefully be fractionated along the conventional lines indicated above, no equivalent fractionation of the life sciences seemed rational or appropriate, while the task of surveying the entirety of the life sciences appeared to be of an appalling magnitude. Nevertheless, in 1966, it was determined that there is a compelling need for an equivalent survey of the life sciences, and it was decided to go forward with such a study.

As its initial undertaking, the Survey Committee on the Life Sciences, appointed by the Committee on Science and Public Policy, addressed itself to the "state of the art." It was soon agreed that the classical subdisciplines of biology are insufficiently instructive as approaches to current understanding and appreciation of life in its variegated manifestations. Accordingly, panels of distinguished scientists were assigned subjects, the titles of which were essentially identical to those indicated by the chapter titles of the present volume. The principal departure from conventional practice, omission of such categories as zoology, botany, and microbiology, is, in fact, a reflection of a significant philosophic departure.

Each panel was given a general "charge." The portion of that charge relevant to this volume was as follows:

"The prime task of each Panel is to provide a pithy summary of the status of the specific sub-field of science which has been assigned. This should be a clear statement of the prime scientific problems and the major questions currently confronting investigators in the field. Included should be an indication of the manner in which these problems are being attacked and how these approaches may change within the foreseeable future. What trends can be visualized for tomorrow? Which lines of investigation are likely to subside? Which may be expected to advance and assume greater importance? Which experimental approaches seem most promising at this moment in time? What new techniques seem ripe for application or in sufficient phases of development to be extremely promising?

"Are the questions themselves, or what today would constitute acceptable answers, likely to change significantly within the near future? Are there important problems within the field or promising investigational approaches which are currently being neglected? If so, why?

"Having stated the major questions and problems, how close are we to the answers? The sum of these discussions, panel by panel, should constitute the equivalent of a complete overview of the highlights of current understanding of the life sciences. It should *not* constitute a textbook. Much —indeed most—of the detailed knowledge ('facts') will be missing. But there should be a sufficiency to convey the reality of the ideas and concepts which are discussed.

"What will be the consequences of successful advancement of the sub-field? How will such success bear on other aspects of the life sciences or of the physical sciences? What may be the predictable effects in practical terms, e.g., in health, food production, or economics? In this regard, are there already significant advances which go unexploited for the benefit of man?

"The Panel must be highly aware of the audience to which its report is to be addressed. There is no desire to construct needless artificial constraints with respect to style or approach. The report must not be addressed primarily to the cognoscenti of the sub-disciplines concerned. In a general way, the audience should be viewed as a group of reasonably well-read scientists and laymen. Laboratory jargon, undefined acronyms, and undescribed theories must be avoided. Although the insights and overview to be presented should give some direction to the teaching of the life sciences at all academic levels as well as give some direction to research, the report should also be readily intelligible to a reasonably well-read physical scientist or interested non-scientist.

"If it is to be successful, the report must convey a sense of the excitement and enthusiasm of the practitioners of our disciplines and succeed in convincing scientists outside each specialty field that that field is important scientifically. To do so, it will be necessary to demonstrate that the questions which are asked, and the problems under investigation are both inherently interesting and have a bearing on the most important scientific issues characteristic of biology generally. At the same time, the report should provide some illumination of the coherence and integration of the field in question, as well as the relationship of that specialty to the total sweep of the life sciences and thus provide perspective even for the specialist. There should be developed a feeling for what is extremely important and what is relatively trivial. The greatest service the report can render is to share with its readers your sense of values as well as your love and enthusiasm for the pursuit of understanding of life in all its ramifications."

When these statements, prepared by the panels, were assembled, it became apparent that, collectively, they constitute an unique summary of current understanding in the life sciences. Although the initial purpose in drafting these reports had been to utilize them to prepare a relatively brief digest for inclusion in the final overall report of the findings of the Survey Committee, it was recognized that the public purpose would be well served if these panel reports, appropriately edited, were bound as a single volume and made available to all interested persons.

Accordingly, in a grueling one week session of the Survey Committee (whose membership also served as the Chairmen of the panels) on the campus of Williams College, each report was mercilessly exposed to the criticism of all other members of the Survey Committee. Each report was then rewritten and subjected to the searching, sometimes scathing, criticisms of the members of the parent Committee on Science and Public Policy. The reports were again revised in the light of this exercise. Finally, the Chairman of the Survey Committee, at Woods Hole, Massachusetts, devoted the summer of 1968 to the final editing and revision of the entire work.

As he goes through these chapters, the reader will encounter differences in style and in approach to the many aspects of the biological sciences, as well as a modest degree of overlap and repetition, deliberately introduced to permit browsing and freedom to read the chapters in any desired order.

As indicated in the "Charge" to the panels cited above, it was intended that this work could be read and comprehended by interested readers with little previous, directly relevant, scientific background. It is our hope that, in the main, this goal has been accomplished. But there are exceptions. Chapters 2 and 3 are, necessarily, presented in the language of chemistry; the subject matter with which they are concerned cannot be described otherwise. Whereas they should readily be comprehensible to those with a speaking acquaintance with chemistry, it is hoped that others will also find these two chapters understandable, albeit a modest expenditure of effort will surely be required. A general comprehension of these two chapters will markedly enhance and facilitate appreciation of many of the chapters which follow, but this is by no means imperative. We are confident that the reader who is uncomfortable with chemical detail will find much of interest and excitement throughout this work; he should feel free to browse as he pleases.

The plan of the book is simple. Chapters 1 through 13 deal with living phenomena at increasingly higher levels of organization—molecules, subcellular organelles, cells, tissues and organs, organisms, species, and ecosystems, as well as those phenomena which may be giving direction to the future. Chapter 14 is a chapter apart. Although most chapters make reference to specific items of equipment, no other experimental tool is granted a chapter of its own. It is out of our conviction that the use of the digital computer is on the verge of effecting as remarkable a transformation of the life sciences as it has in the physical sciences that we find it appropriate to include this chapter on the mode of operation of the computer and its applications to the life sciences.

Chapters 15 through 19 provide a series of illustrations of the manner in which understanding of living phenomena has been put to work in the service of man. These are but sample illustrations since, patently, the entirety of current medical and agricultural practice rests on this foundation. The specific illustrations presented were chosen for their drama, their historical significance, or for their current social importance. In our view, even this small selection amply justifies the expenditures of public funds for research which have made them possible.

Finally, there is offered an essay on Biology and the Future of Man. Although the initial text was drafted by the distinguished panel so charged, it was modified, edited, and revised by the Survey Committee, the Committee on Science and Public Policy, and, particularly, by the undersigned. The sentiments, evaluations, warnings, and recommendations recorded in this chapter reflect the thinking of all of those who have contributed to this endeavor.

Finally, I take this opportunity to record our sincere appreciation: to our executive directors, Dr. Herbert Pahl and Dr. Laura Greene, for their thoughtfulness, their untiring efforts, and their great patience with all the rest of us who participated in this enterprise; to the National Science Foundation, the National Institutes of Health, and the Smithsonian Institution whose financial support made this endeavor possible; to the Committee on Science and Public Policy of the National Academy of Sciences, and particularly its chairman, Dr. Harvey Brooks, who prompted this undertaking and whose thoughtful criticism gave it shape and intelligibility; to our publisher, the Oxford University Press; to all those scientists who drafted greater or lesser contributions to this volume, while foregoing royalties so that it might find the widest possible distribution; and to Mrs. Hope Jones and Mrs. Lora Whitfield who prepared the final manuscript copy while tolerating my working habits.

Philip Handler

Durham, N.C.
November 1, 1968

CONTENTS

Contents

BIOLOGY AND THE FUTURE OF MAN

Chapter 1

INTRODUCTION

"La vray science et le vray étude de l'homme, c'est l'homme."

PIERRE CHARRON

Traité de la Sagesse, Book I, 1601

Life is the most fascinating phenomenon within the ken of man, and its investigation has yielded among the greatest rewards in alleviating his brute condition. In Chapters 1 through 13 it is our purpose to provide an overview of present understanding of life in its variegated manifestations and in Chapters 14 through 20 to indicate some of the ways in which such understanding has been utilized for the benefit of mankind. No attempt has been made to be comprehensive; examples and illustrations have been chosen because of the drama of certain findings or for the insight they provide. Necessarily, much has gone unsaid.

The theme of this presentation is that life can be understood in terms of the laws that govern and the phenomena that characterize the inanimate, physical universe and, indeed, that, at its essence, life can be understood only in the language of chemistry. The reader who lacks facility in this tongue may find the two immediately following chapters rather heavy sledding. We hope that they are, nevertheless, comprehensible. Understanding of subsequent chapters is not dependent upon mastery of the contents of these earlier chapters, but a moderate effort on their behalf will enhance appreciation of the rest of the volume.

Until the laws of physics and chemistry had been elucidated, it was not possible even to formulate the important, penetrating questions concerning the nature of life. For centuries students of biology, in consider-

3

ing the diversity of life, its seemingly utter distinction from inanimate phenomena, and its general unlikelihood, found it necessary, in their imagination, to invest living objects with a mysterious life force, "vitalism," with which all living organisms were endowed. But in the late eighteenth century, Lavoisier and Laplace were able to show that, within the not inconsiderable limits of error of the methods available to them, the recently formulated laws of conservation of energy and mass were valid also in a living guinea pig. The endeavors of thousands of life scientists over the next two centuries have gone far to document the thesis thus begun. Living phenomena are indeed intelligible in physical terms. And although much remains to be learned and understood, and the details of many processes remain elusive, those engaged in such studies hold no doubt that answers will be forthcoming in the reasonably near future. Indeed, only two truly major questions remain enshrouded in a cloak of not quite fathomable mystery: (1) the origin of life, i.e., the events that first gave rise to the remarkable cooperative functioning of nucleic acids and proteins which constitutes the genetic apparatus, and (2) the mind-body problem, i.e., the physical basis for self-awareness and personality. Great strides have been made in the approaches to both of these problems, as summarized in Chapters 6 and 9. But the ultimate explanations are perceived very dimly indeed.

The pages to follow, in Chapters 1 through 13, therefore, are a record of the present "state of the art." Successively are treated such questions as: Of what chemical compounds are living things composed? By what means are the materials of the environment converted into the compounds characteristic of life? What techniques have been employed to reveal the structures of the huge macromolecules of living cells? How are living cells organized to accomplish their diverse tasks? What is a gene and what does it do? What are the mechanisms that make possible cellular duplication? How does a single fertilized egg utilize its genetic information in the wondrous process by which it develops into a highly differentiated multicellular creature of many widely differing cell types? How do differentiated cell types, combined to form organs and tissues, cooperate to make their distinct contributions to the welfare of the organism? What is understood of the structure and function of the nervous system? What is a species? How does speciation occur? What factors give direction to evolution? Is evolution still occurring? Is man evolving still and, if so, can he control his own evolution? What relations obtain among the species in a given habitat? What governs the numbers of any one species in that habitat? Are there defined physiological bases for behavior? What is known of the bases for perception, emotions, cognition, learning, or memory, for hunger or satiety? For few of these questions, today, can we provide ultimate answers; yet the extent to which these are approximated, even now, constitutes a satisfying and exciting tale.

In the space available, there is little opportunity to describe *how* the facts and concepts considered have been garnered in the laboratory or field. The popular press frequently presents descriptions of scientific "breakthroughs," while failing to indicate that no such event stands alone. Each research accomplishment is a bit of information in a large and growing multidimensional mosaic. The investigator is acutely aware of the history of the problem to which he has addressed himself and of the past and current contributions of others. Most successful demonstrations have occurred only when the time was right and the stage had been set. Frequently, the idea had been discussed in one or another sense before a definitive demonstration was available. And each bit of information that illuminates a problem reveals a yet deeper layer of questioning which remains to be undertaken.

Most particularly is it necessary to recognize the dependence of the investigator on his experimental tools. Indeed, the history of science, including the life sciences, is the history of the manner in which major problems have been attacked as more powerful and definitive tools have become available. Thus, living cells are invisible to the naked eye, appear as minute boxes or spheres with a denser nucleus by light microscopy, and exhibit an elaborate wealth of subcellular structural detail by electron microscopy. Techniques for isolation of pure proteins were developed in the 1930's and 1940's, but understanding of their structure seemed impossibly remote. Analytical tools such as electrophoresis (separation of molecules by virtue of differences in their electrical charge), ultracentrifugation (separation by virtue of differences in mass), chromatography (separation by virtue of varying affinity for adsorption onto diverse solid surfaces combined with varying solubility in diverse solvents), and appreciation of the specificity of action of certain hydrolytic enzymes permitted resolution of the linear sequences of amino acids along the strand that constitutes the protein chain. Without each of these tools, primary protein structure would remain a mystery. As they became available the tools were rapidly applied to the problem by a waiting battalion of scientists. But there remained the problem of deciphering the three-dimensional structure of these large molecules. It was already known that x-ray crystallography could establish the structure of much smaller molecules; a series of refinements were required before this technique could be applied to proteins. And, when these were made, there remained a seemingly hopeless task, a prodigious body of calculations required to convert the data into a model of a protein molecule. Fortunately, it was just at this time that the high-speed digital computer made its appearance. And the three-dimensional structures of proteins emerge as the triumphal accomplishment of this pyramid of scientific endeavor. Until all the stones had been laid, the apex would have remained invisible and unattainable.

Biology has become a mature science as it has become precise and quantifiable. The biologist is no less dependent upon his apparatus than the physicist. Yet the biologist does not use distinctively biological tools: He is an opportunist who employs a nuclear magnetic resonance spectrometer, a telemetry assembly, or an airplane equipped for infrared photography, depending upon the biological problem he is attacking. In any case, he is always grateful to the physicists, chemists, and engineers who have provided the tools he has adapted to his trade.

In Section II we will turn to the application of current knowledge and understanding to the purposes of human society. Again only glimpses of the totality are offered, but these should suffice to indicate how such understanding has been utilized to improve the nutrition of a burgeoning population, to understand and alleviate human, animal, and plant diseases, to minimize the despoliation of our environment, to conserve natural resources, and to protect man from the biological consequences of his own technology.

While glorying in how far we have come, these chapters will also reveal how large is the task that lies ahead. In the final essay on biology and the future of man are presented some of the major challenges for today and tomorrow. If these are met with vigor and determination, if man's technical capabilities are utilized to the full, a shining, hopeful future lies ahead. If the moral imperatives are not joined to scientific understanding, if apathy, indifference, and cupidity outweigh determination, man could be defeated by his own biology. The time of decision is at hand.

This volume is offered to all who would share the deep satisfaction afforded by insight into the nature of man and his myriad living relatives, to all who would understand and participate in the momentous decisions man must confront tomorrow.

Chapter 2

MOLECULAR BIOLOGY

This chapter will present an account of the area of biological research that has come to be known as "molecular biology." We begin by introducing the principal chemical compounds and processes that play central roles in the concepts of molecular biologists. This introduction makes possible a more informative description of how these concepts arose and evolved to the present level of sophistication and utility. Subsequent sections will consider the experimental findings and their implications in greater detail.

The Principal Components and Processes of Molecular Biology

A living organism is an entity that can utilize chemicals and energy from the environment to reproduce itself, can undergo a permanent change (a mutation) which is transmitted to succeeding generations, and by accumulation of numbers of such mutations can evolve into a distinctly new living form (a new species).

Reproduction and variation result from the behavior of *genes,* which reproduce themselves once each generation. Genes are the hereditary factors that are passed on from parent to offspring. Today, we know that a gene is a giant molecule of the class called deoxyribose nucleic acids, commonly abbreviated as *DNA,* a substance found in the nuclei of all cells. Ribose nucleic acid (*RNA*) is also found in all cells, principally outside the nucleus. It does not play a primary hereditary role in cells. However, certain viruses and tumor-inducing agents employ RNA as their genetic material. As we shall see, in cells DNA and RNA are primarily concerned with the synthesis of *protein* molecules. DNA, RNA, and proteins are the key substances of living things. The reproduction of cells and organisms, development of the multicellular organism, growth and maintenance of the cell, life itself, therefore, are all made possible by the properties of these molecules. Members of all three classes of macromolecules cooperate to constitute the genetic apparatus, which operates to synthesize the proteins characteristic of a given cell. All other aspects of the life of that cell are the consequence of the presence of the assemblage of proteins which have thus been constructed. *Molecular biology* is concerned with these central substances and their relation to each other.

DNA, RNA, Proteins

The proteins constitute the bulk of the macromolecules found in living cells. They serve many roles. Most importantly, they are the *catalysts* (called *enzymes*) which make possible the myriad chemical reactions necessary for cell function and structure. Proteins are linear *polymers* of *monomeric* units called *amino acids,* of which there are 20 different kinds. Figure 2-1 lists their structures, names, and commonly employed abbreviations. In proteins, the amino acids are condensed with each other, head to tail as it were, to form polypeptide chains (Fig. 2-2) containing a common backbone (shaded) to which are attached the side groups characteristic of each amino acid.

A centrally important demonstration was that each protein has its own *unique* sequence of amino acids (an example is given Figure 2-3). By this is meant that, at each position along the polypeptide chain, one and only one of 20 possible amino acids does, in fact, occur. To understand how such unique sequences can arise, we must now turn our attention to the structure of the other two macromolecules, DNA and RNA. Both are *polymers* of *monomeric* units called *nucleotides*. The four major nucleotides of DNA are shown in Figure 2-4. The two classes of nucleotides in DNA and RNA differ in the nature of the 5-carbon sugar (a pentose) which joins the base to the phosphate; these are deoxyribose and ribose respectively. For brevity one may denote these units A, C, G, and T or U. These monomeric units are connected into polymers—some DNA molecules contain 100,000 to 1,000,000 nucleotides in very long *polydeoxynucleotide* chains (Fig. 2-4). In polyribonucleotides, which are generally shorter molecules, T is replaced by U.

In the DNA molecule, two polydeoxyribonucleotide chains are twined together about a common axis. This is called a double helix

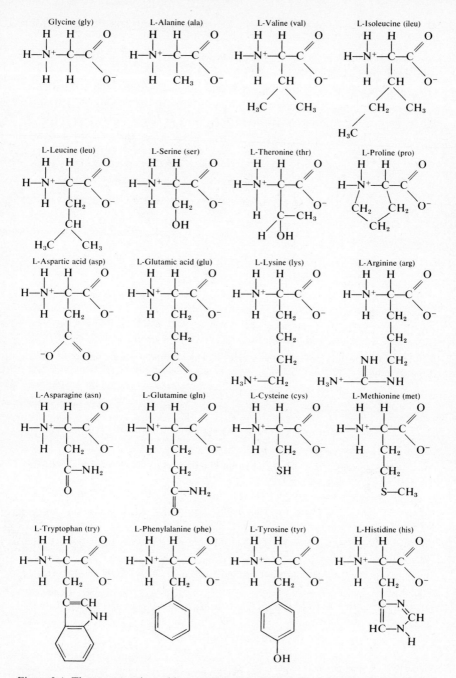

Figure 2-1. The twenty amino acids commonly found in proteins. The abbreviations shown in parentheses are used in summaries of amino acid sequences of proteins or their partial degradation products. (From J. D. Watson, *Molecular Biology of the Gene.* © 1965 by W. A. Benjamin, Inc.)

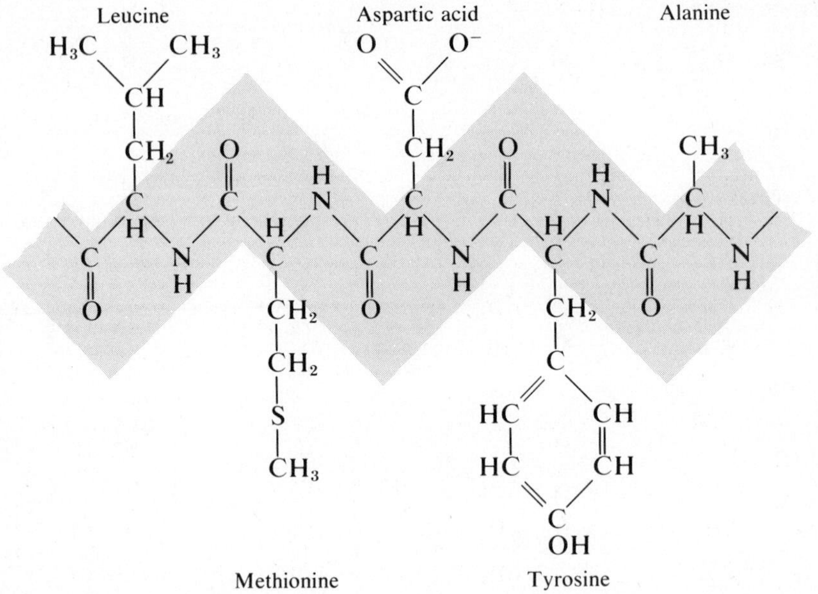

Leucine   Aspartic acid   Alanine

Methionine   Tyrosine

Figure 2-2. Polypeptide structure; the manner in which amino acids are linked in proteins. (From Watson)

Acetyl-**Gly**-Asp-Val-Glu-Lys-**Gly**-Lys-Lys-Ile-**Phe**-Ile-Met-Lys-**CyS**-Ser-Gln-**CyS**-**His**-Thr-
                                        10
                                                                    └────Heme────┘

Val-Glu-Lys-Gly-Gly-Lys-His-**Lys**-Thr-**Gly**-**Pro**-Asn-**Leu**-His-**Gly**-Leu-Phe-Gly-**Arg**-Lys-
20   30

Thr-**Gly**-Gln-Ala-Pro-**Gly**-Tyr-Ser-**Tyr**-Thr-Ala-**Ala**-**Asn**-Lys-Asn-Lys-Gly-Ile-Ile-**Trp**-
40   50

Gly-Glu-Asp-Thr-Leu-Met-Glu-**Tyr**-**Leu**-Glu-**Asn**-**Pro**-**Lys**-**Lys**-**Tyr**-**Ile**-**Pro**-**Gly**-**Thr**-**Lys**-
60   70

Met-Ile-**Phe**-Val-**Gly**-Ile-Lys-**Lys**-Lys-Glu-Glu-**Arg**-Ala-Asp-Leu-Ile-Ala-Tyr-Leu-Lys-
80   90

Lys-Ala-Thr-Asn-GluCOOH
100   104

Figure 2-3. The amino acid sequence of human cytochrome C. The residues in bold face are those which appear unchanged in the cytochromes C of more than 30 species studied to date including fungi, plants and animals. (From Matsubara and Smith, Journal of Biological Chemistry, *237:*PC 3575, 1962.)

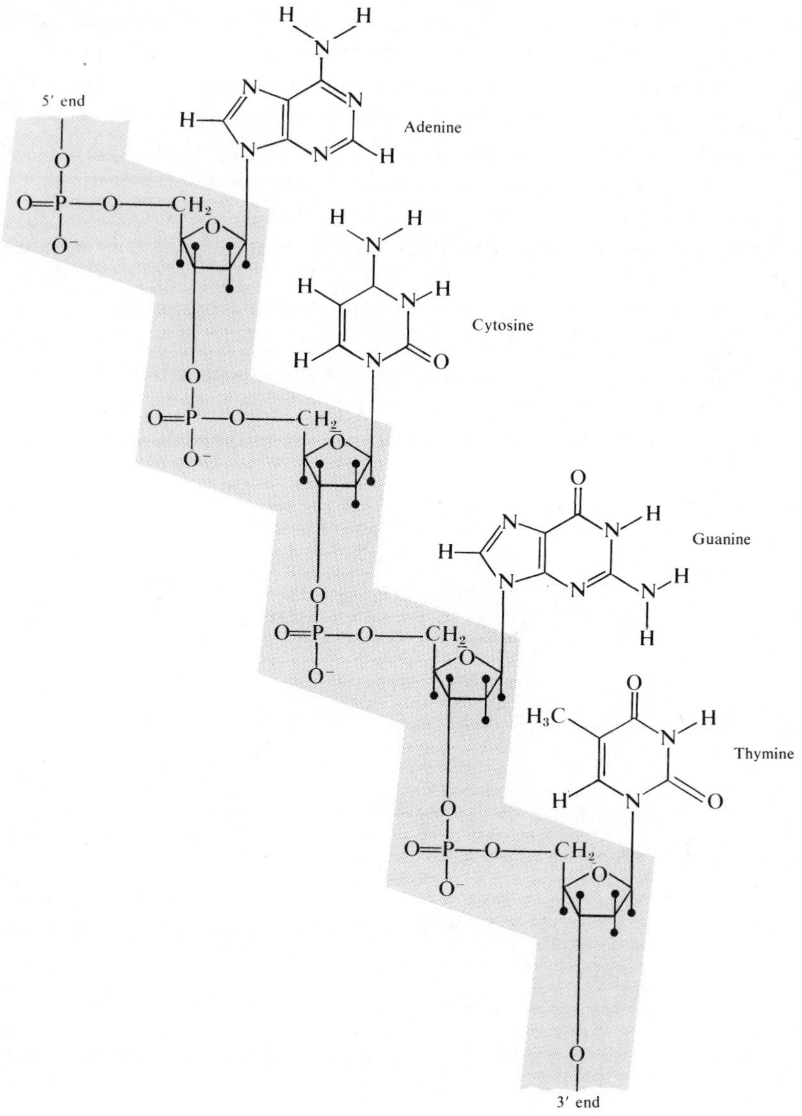

Figure 2-4. A tetranucleotide segment of DNA, illustrating the phosphodiester bridges as the backbone of DNA and the structures of the four bases of DNA. (From Watson)

(Fig. 2-5). This structure, an interpretation of x-ray crystallographic data, was proposed in 1953, and has satisfied the most demanding tests for 15 years. Figure 2-6 shows an electron micrograph of a single DNA molecule. Along the helix the nucleotides are "paired" in a precise way: A opposite T, and G opposite C. This is why the polynucleotide chains are said to have "complementary" sequences.

A gene is a unit of heredity that is identified by its end effect. In the earlier history of genetics this effect was noted as some easily apparent aspect of the organism, e.g., blue eyes or black hair. Study of viruses and other minute organisms has led to the demonstration that *individual genes are segments of DNA molecules.* All genes are made up of the same four nucleotides, but they differ from one another in the sequence of the four nucleotides. In this regard DNA is said to contain *information,* just as this sentence contains information in the sequence in which

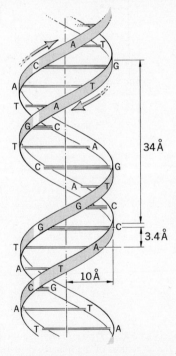

Figure 2-5. The double helical structure of DNA. The ribbons represent the deoxyribose-phosphate backbone chains. The opposing arrows indicate that one strand is running from the 5′ position of one sugar to the 3′ position of the next while the other strand is running in the opposite sense. The horizontal lines represent hydrogen bonds between opposing base pairs, two for each AT couple, three for each GC couple. (From I. Herskowitz, *Genetics,* 2nd ed. © 1962 by Little, Brown and Company.)

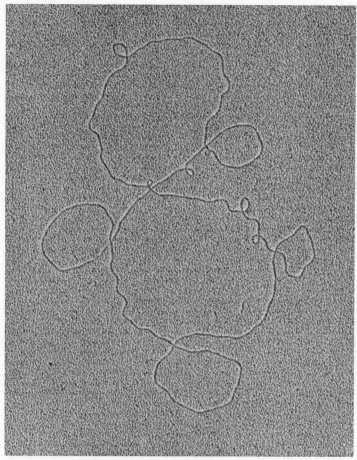

Figure 2-6. A single circular DNA molecule from Bacteriophage T7. (Courtesy of C. Thomas and E. L. MacHattie)

the 26 possible letters of the alphabet appear. The *genetic alphabet* is smaller; it contains only four letters, A, C, G, T. The information is encoded in the sequence of the amino acids in proteins; each gene corresponds to one protein. The huge DNA molecules can contain many genes, just as a sentence can contain many words. The entire genetic text of a simple organism can be contained on a single DNA molecule. The simplest *chromosomes* are single DNA molecules. Thus, a bacterial DNA of molecular weight 300,000,000 contains about 1,000,000 nucleotides sufficient to code for 330,000 amino acid molecules. Since an average protein chain contains about 100 amino acid residues, the

DNA could, maximally, specify the synthesis of 3,300 different protein chains. Larger or more complex chromosomes may be seen in the nuclei of cells just prior to cell division. These structures (Fig. 2-7) contain all (or most) of the DNA of the cell, but their anatomy is only partly understood at this time.

If, then, DNA is the material of which genes are made, it must (a) somehow assure its own perfect duplication as a cell divides to form two identical daughter cells, and (b) it must specify the structures of the proteins made in these cells.

When DNA is synthesized biologically it is said to *replicate* — that is, to produce copies of itself. This is accomplished by a process called

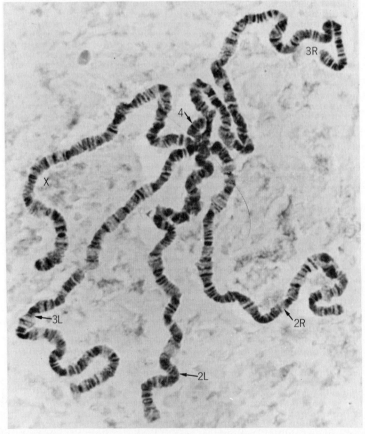

Figure 2-7. Salivary gland chromosomes of *Drosophila melanogaster,* showing the banding pattern. The arms are marked with their conventional nomenclature. (Photograph courtesy of B. P. Kaufmann)

template synthesis. The two complementary polynucleotide chains of a helix separate, and new polymer chains are made on the surface of the separated strands by adding nucleotides on to the growing ends of new chains. The specificity of each newly added nucleotide is directed solely by the nucleotide on the guiding "template" chain.

DNA, the primary information source, is never used *directly* to instruct the protein-synthesizing machines. Instead, working copies are made by a process called *transcription.* Transcription is like replication, but the result is not a copy of the DNA molecules, but a transcript (in complementary form) of a portion of one chain of the DNA molecule. The *transcript* is a single polyribonucleotide chain and is made by an enzyme called *RNA polymerase.* RNA chains made in this fashion that contain the information for protein molecules are called *messenger* RNA. The conversion of the information contained in a polynucleotide to the sequence of amino acids of a protein necessarily involves a *translation* from the 4-letter language of the nucleic acids to the 20-letter language of the proteins. Elegant experiments, which we shall describe later, established that each amino acid is specified by a triplet of nucleotides, called a *codon.*

Translation, in principle, requires the use of a dictionary; the biological dictionary functions in cells at the translational step from polyribonucleotides to proteins. The biological dictionary is a set of remarkable RNA chains to each of which is attached a specific amino acid. These chains can "read" the messenger RNA by means of an *anticodon triplet* complementary to the codon corresponding to the attached amino acid. This assures that the amino acid is inserted in the correct position in the growing polypeptide chain. The entire translational process, which occurs on a large spherical structure, the *ribosome,* will be described in greater detail.

Thus, overall, the gene (DNA) clearly specifies the protein. But without proteins, DNA cannot be made; without RNA, proteins cannot be made. Molecular biology is a drama with these as the three major actors, each owes its existence to the others.

The Emergence of Molecular Biology

Molecular biology began its emergence some 25 years ago with the fusion of biochemistry, microbiology, and genetics. The combination of both the methodologies and the body of information of these three disciplines forged powerful experimental and conceptual tools. To this was added the catalytic effect of a number of talented converts from the physical sciences who provided both particular know-how (e.g., x-ray analysis) and the kind of precise thinking that was now essential.

It will be useful to begin with a brief survey of the development of biochemistry, microbiology, and genetics up to the time of their union in the latter half of the 1940's. Necessarily, attention will be confined to those features that ultimately generated the logical necessity for their fusion. We have already noted that the principal initiating theme of molecular biology centered on the *informational* relatedness amongst the key macromolecules—DNA, RNA, and protein. The dominant theme that emerged was the recognition that the sequence of the amino acid residues of a particular protein was related to the sequence of nucleotides in a certain segment of DNA (the principle of *colinearity*). Each of the three component disciplines contributed information, materials, and methodologies which led to this central concept.

Biochemistry

Early biochemistry was, necessarily, a domain devoted to the study of the chemical compounds and processes occurring in the tissues of plants and animals. By the early 1940's the catalogue of compounds and reactions provided a satisfyingly detailed understanding of the composition of living material and the biosynthetic mechanisms involved.

Proteins and Enzymes. Of the macromolecules colinearly related to genetic material, the proteins were first identified as important constituents of living material. Their ubiquitous distribution was recognized early, and Berzelius showed remarkable insight in assigning the name proteins (i.e., first rank) to them. The connection between proteins and enzymes was not made with certainty for a long time after each was known. Here, biochemistry made early contact with microbiology, which provided the microorganisms as ideal experimental material for the subsequent development of modern enzymology. The demonstration in 1897 that a cell-free yeast extract could produce alcohol from sugar introduced the systematic study of metabolic pathways, biological reaction mechanisms, and the nature of enzyme activity. It is of interest that, as in several other important instances, this discovery was an example of performing the right experiment for the wrong reason. The brothers Hans and Edward Büchner, intending to study the toxicity in rabbits of a yeast extract, decided to "preserve" it—i.e., prevent putrefaction by contaminating microorganisms, by the addition of simple syrup. When they noted bubbling in this mixture, owing to production of CO_2, modern biochemistry began!

Even after the crystallization of urease in 1926, it was still not generally accepted that enzymes were proteins. The confusion was generated principally by the great sensitivity with which the catalytic property of an enzyme could be detected as compared with the crude methods for detection of its presence as a chemical entity. Thus, it was easily possible in the 1920's to purify invertase, the enzyme that catalyzes hydrolysis of cane sugar (sucrose), to the point where preparations showed extraordinarily high catalytic activities, yet no protein could be found by the analytical tests then available. By the 1930's this paradox was recognized and resolved.

Nucleic Acids. The history of the nucleic acids demonstrates the consequences of the early separation of biochemistry from genetics. Necessarily, biochemistry was not initially concerned with the problems of heredity. Nevertheless, having accepted the task of identifying all the chemical entities to be found in a cell, biochemists were forced to deal with the compounds now known to be the genetic material without, however, being in a position to delineate its biological function.

Nucleic acids were first isolated from white blood cells and sperm cells as complexes with proteins in 1872. The existence of both RNA and DNA was established soon thereafter. For a long time it was believed that DNA was confined to animals and RNA to plants. Indeed, DNA was commonly called "thymus" nucleic acid because the thymus was the most convenient starting material for the preparation of DNA. Similarly, RNA was often referred to as "yeast" nucleic acid. By the middle 1920's, it was finally recognized that both kinds of nucleic acids were to be found in plants as well as animals. By the early 1940's, it was established that DNA was one of the principal nuclear components and that RNA was to be found both in the cytoplasm and in the nucleus (Fig. 2-8).

The role of the nucleic acids as carriers of genetic information was not seriously entertained by many even as late as the middle 1940's. One of the difficulties stemmed from the wide popularity of the *tetranucleotide* concept of DNA. According to this theory, DNA was simply a monotonous repetition of one sequence of four nucleotides and hence could hardly be used to store information. It was not until the early 1950's that careful chemical analysis showed that the relative proportion of the four nucleotides in DNA varied from one organism to another, a finding that effectively disposed of the tetranucleotide concept.

By the late forties, biochemists had accumulated the information and know-how which permitted attempts to study the biosynthesis of macromolecules like proteins and nucleic acids. Inevitably, this brought biochemists into contact with those who were beginning to be concerned with the nature of the gene and its function.

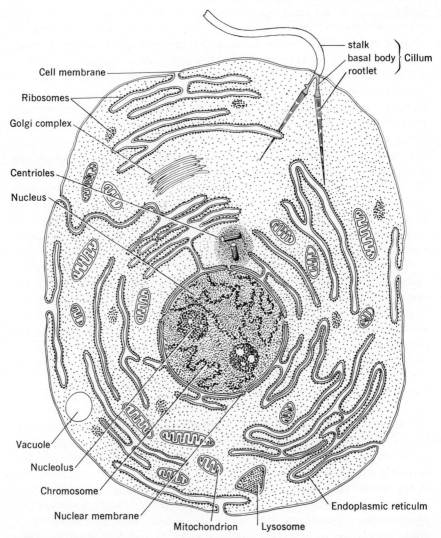

Figure 2-8. Modern diagram of a typical cell is based on what is seen in electron micrographs. The mitochondria are the sites of the oxidative reactions that provide the cell with energy. The dots that line the endoplasmic reticulum are ribosomes: the sites of protein synthesis. In cell division the pair of centrosomes, shown in longitudinal section as rods, part to form poles of the apparatus that separate two duplicate sets of chromosomes. (From W. T. Keeton, *Biological Science.* © 1967 by W. W. Norton & Co., Inc.)

Microbiology

The Founding of Microbiology. The evolution of bacteriology in isolation from genetics was largely determined by two factors, the smallness of bacteria and, strangely, their key importance to man. Their minute size, apparent simplicity, and lack of a readily observable nuclear apparatus led many of the early biologists to either ignore the bacteria or place them in a "chaotic" category, to which the usual biological laws did not apply. Because of these features and their ubiquitous distribution, the bacteria replaced mice and maggots as the center of the spontaneous generation controversy. Obviously, this question had to be settled before the hereditary mechanism of these forms could be taken as a serious object to study. It took such giants aṣ Spallanzani, Pasteur, and Tyndall to devise the necessary, completely convincing experiments.

Laying the ghost of spontaneous generation did not, however, usher in a rational genetic analysis. In fact, the work of Pasteur and Koch served to delay the inception of profoundly basic investigations into the genetics of bacteria! By demonstrating that bacteria were the causative agents of disease, these workers focused primary attention on the relation of bacteria to the health and welfare of man. Thereafter, many practical problems of pressing importance demanded immediate attention. With a few isolated exceptions, little effort was reserved for the investigation of the biological problems of microorganisms as living material.

When it did arise, the problem of bacterial variation became involved in a somewhat fruitless controversy between the *monomorphists* and *pleomorphists*. The pleomorphists argued that each bacterial species possessed a wide range of cellular forms, which was the consequence of a complicated life cycle. Depending on conditions, one and the same microorganism could, according to them, take the form of rods, spheres, or filaments. The monomorphists, followers of Koch, maintained that bacteria were constant in form. It is important to realize that the opposition of the Koch school to the pleomorphists stemmed from something more fundamental than pride in their own technical accomplishments. The entire operational nature of the Koch program would have been shattered into meaningless nonsense if the more expansive claims of the pleomorphists were founded in fact. How could one definitively decide that a given organism was the causative agent of a particular disease if, in the animal body, it was a gram-positive coccus, and on laboratory medium a gram-negative rod, or perhaps even worse, a green mold? The practical success of the Koch school assured victory to the monomorphists; and for a time, by a sort of "executive fiat," bacterial variation was ignored as a dispensable nuisance.

Nevertheless, the technical superiority of the monomorphists, which gave them the devastating advantage, provided the very techniques which proved that the pleomorphists were not entirely in error. No matter how carefully one follows the methods described for the isolation, purification, and maintenance of a pure bacterial strain, the appearance of heritable changes cannot be avoided.

Early Concepts of Bacterial Heredity. The types of variations bacteriologists had to deal with are relevant to the future development of biochemical genetics. Compared to higher plants and animals, microorganisms, including the fungi, are morphologically simple. As a consequence, microbiologists were, early on, compelled to use biochemical rather than morphological features to distinguish one strain or variety from another. They employed such cellular properties as reactions of cell surface to dyes, the ability to ferment a variety of sugars, nutritional requirements for individual amino acids, purines, pyrimidines, vitamins, etc. One need but open any classical textbook on medical bacteriology to observe the array of distinguishing characteristics of bacteria that are identified by biochemical events. For many years, bacteriologists employed these characteristics as useful diagnostic criteria without paying much attention to the mechanisms insuring their comparative constancy. These issues simply were not central to their purpose, and microbiology continued its useful development as an applied discipline.

Because of their biological material and their divorcement from the mainstream of genetic thinking, bacteriologists were often led to adopt a Lamarckian view of inheritance long after this model had been rejected by a majority of the biological community. Microbiologists had, for many years, been greatly impressed with the apparent genetic plasticity of microorganisms. It was, for example, easily possible to develop cultures that were resistant to various lethal agents simply by including them in the growth medium. Similarly, cultures capable of utilizing the sugar lactose could readily be derived from nonutilizers by passage through media in which lactose was the principal source of carbon and energy. It seemed that virtually any specific change desired could be brought about by introducing the proper agent. The feeling thus arose that these agents were *causing* instructional changes in the genetic makeup of the organism. Such observations appeared to support the earlier contention of Lamarck that environmental factors could influence the genetic material to direct the occurrence of those changes favorable to survival.

The temporary prevalence of this view derived in large part from the fact that microbiologists labored under what might be termed the "tyranny of large numbers." A bacteriologist can readily screen one billion individual cells, in one operation, and detect the presence of only a single individual possessing a particular heritable selective advantage. Under these circumstances, the chances are excellent for finding any particular type already present in the culture if it occurs by mutation of the parent strain with the usual mutational frequency of one in a hundred million. The situation is further exaggerated by the employment of intensely selective environments which eliminate the nonmutant (wild type) by lethal agents or prevent its growth by the absence of a required metabolite.

The Advent of Chemotherapy and Its Consequences. An article appeared in 1935 that, ultimately, drastically changed the attitude of microbiologists toward genetics and forced them to adopt a more critical viewpoint toward the mechanism underlying bacterial variation. This paper introduced Prontosil, the first of the sulfa drugs. By 1943, a number of derivatives became available and were being used effectively in clinics against a wide variety of bacterial infections. During the same period, the antibiotic penicillin entered as an important antibacterial agent, followed rapidly by others.

The role of medical bacteriologists began to change rapidly. Previously, they had been either glamorous "microbe hunters" or highly trained technical aides carrying out the complex tasks required for diagnostic decision. Prior to the advent of chemotherapy, the physician had to know the organism and its serological type so that he could prescribe the correct serum therapy, a procedure of limited utility attendant with some hazard. With the spreading use of antibiotics and chemotherapeutic agents, the information demanded by the clinician changed drastically. His prime concern was no longer identification of the organism and its antigenic type; the pressing need was for knowledge of the sensitivity and/or resistance of the infecting organism to the antibacterial agents available.

Shortly after the introduction of chemotherapeutics, with increasing and exasperating frequency clinicians encountered organisms that had become resistant and against which the miracle drug of a few months ago had become useless. Such findings brought the heredity problem to the fore in sharp practical terms. The mechanism by means of which bacteria became resistant to lethal agents was no longer an esoteric preoccupation of a few academics. The clinician had to know what precisely was going on. Only with this knowledge could he rationally decide whether to use two antibacterial agents simultaneously or serially. In this climate, bacterial heredity developed into a central issue which demanded resolution. By the early 1940's, medical bacteriologists were

prepared to heed the outcome of rigorous experiments designed to illuminate the genetic apparatus of bacteria.

At this very time a series of ingenious experiments were performed
to determine whether selective agents played any directive role in bacterial mutations. The first involved resistance to bacterial viruses and
established that the resistant mutants found in a series of independent
cultures grown in the absence of virus indicated that a *heritable* modification leading to resistance occurred *randomly* in the *absence* of the
lethal selective agent. To such experiments were added others using the
method of *replica plating,* which permitted the isolation and identification of pure resistant clones (a culture grown from a single parent cell)
from cultures that had never been exposed to the lethal agent. Bacteriology was no longer the last stronghold of Lamarckism.

It was finally accepted that bacterial mutation was no different from
that which had been observed in higher forms. The foundations of bacterial genetics were laid in classic investigations with *Escherichia coli,*
which demonstrated that the principles of Mendel's laws were also applicable to bacteria. Very soon thereafter, similar genetic recombinations in the viruses were discovered and developed as an experimental
tool. Both bacteria and viruses were added to the armamentarium of the
modern geneticist for further exploitation.

Genetics

The Early Isolation of Genetics. By virtue of the nature of their problems and experimental material, contact between biochemists and
microbiologists was made early in the development of each discipline.
But genetics developed without an early need for either of these disciplines. There was no pressing need for geneticists to adopt other methodologies or materials. The morphological variants of the fruit fly *Drosophila* and maize were adequate for their purposes until well into the 1930's.
However, while chemotherapy was forcing the microbiologists to
turn toward genetics, the success of genetics compelled the geneticists
to turn their attention to microorganisms as more suitable biological objects for the next stage of their investigations. Generation times are of
the order of an hour or two, instead of months, and enormous populations could be examined in a single test tube.

The initial goal of genetics was to specify the mechanism underlying
the laws of *transmission* of the differences of one generation to the next.
By the end of the 1930's this task was virtually completed. A clear and
logical distinction was drawn between the *genotype* (the array of genes)
and the *phenotype* (the array of resultant characters) being diagnosed.

It was recognized that it was the genotype only that was transmitted from one generation to the next. Consequently, the behavior of the genetic elements determined the rules of heredity. The original monumental discoveries of Mendel were confirmed and extended to include the recognition of *chromosomes* (Fig. 2-7) as the sites of linearly arrayed linked genes. Sophisticated and elegant methods were developed for the location of individual genes on the chromosome and resulted in the mapping of entire genomes. A vast amount of information was unified into a powerfully predictive theoretical structure based on the laws of recombination between and within chromosomes.

The success of formal genetic methods elevated the postulated fundamental entity, *the gene,* into one of the fundamental particles of biology, even though it had never been observed as a defined chemical entity. Increasingly meaningful examination of many aspects of living organisms required reference to the relevant genetic information. Questions of physiology and embryogenesis became involved with genetics as examples of variable expression of phenotype. In a more general sense, both the methods and the results of the geneticist pointed to the possibilities of solving a variety of problems which had previously appeared to be insoluble. They may be exemplified by a brief reference to replication, one of the central problems of biology.

The discovery of relatively stable genetic material which could undergo discrete heritable modifications abstracted the concept of self-duplication from the mass of biological observations so that it could be examined with greater clarity. Prior to these discoveries, and in some cases even subsequent to them, the cell was considered as a concatenation of interlocking interactions so controlled as to lead to further synthesis of like material. The obvious complexity of such a system and the inordinate difficulty that would attend any attempt at unraveling the multitude of reactions involved and their regulatory interactions precluded any serious efforts to do much about the problem. With the recognition of mutability and its significance, it became much more difficult to maintain this involved picture of self-duplication. It would have had to be supposed that the remarkable collection of integrated individual processes was so arranged that a modification of any one of them would permit the whole not only to continue to function but to do so in such a manner as to reproduce the modification. The discrete and particulate nature of the changes could be more readily understood on the assumption that cellular replication follows from the autosynthetic activity of a basic genetic material, which can exist in a series of alternative (allelic) states. All other cellular components arise then as a result of the directive or instructional activity of the genic elements.

The new concept to emerge from the discrete nature of genetic changes was *particularity*. What was most important was that the postulation of the genetic unit made it feasible to reduce the problem of self-duplication to the duplication of the gene. Essentially, what the geneticist predicted was that when the gene was chemically identified and its mechanism of replication deduced, the problem of the self-duplication of living material would have been solved.

The Advent of Biochemical Genetics. Understandably, the material used in the earlier stages of genetic investigation was chosen because it was convenient for the purposes the geneticist had in mind. The laws of transmission genetics were worked out with biological forms which possessed sufficient morphological complexity to provide a ready supply of easily diagnosed variations. One did not need to perform any sophisticated chemical tests to distinguish the red eye of the wild type from the vermilion-colored mutant of *Drosophila*. However, with the foundations of transmission genetics well established, attention began to turn to problems of how genes function. By the middle 1930's, geneticists had begun to ask how a change in a specific position on a particular chromosome of *Drosophila* could modify the eye color from red to vermilion? Thus, the mechanism of gene action became one of the central issues of genetics, and the approach to its resolution began to evolve.

In their very earliest discussions of gene function, geneticists were fully aware of enzymes and their key role as catalytic agents. It was natural, therefore, for them to initiate their analysis of gene function by correlating particular phenotypic differences with specific biochemical reactions. In 1923, Garrod, physician to the royal family of Great Britain, demonstrated that the human disease alcaptonuria is the consequence of a loss in the ability to oxidize homogentistic acid, an intermediate in the metabolism of the amino acid tyrosine, and that, further, this disease is a recessive trait whose inheritance followed the laws of Mendel. Thereafter he described five other conditions as "heritable disorders" of metabolism. In the middle thirties extensive investigations were undertaken which related specific genes to discrete steps in the biosynthesis of pigments in flowering plants; along similar lines were the studies of eye color mutants in the fruit fly, *Drosophila melanogaster;* two diffusible substances were identified as relevant intermediates in eye pigment production.

Gradually, it became apparent that the study of *gene function* required new biological material. The morphological complexity that made *Drosophila,* mice, and maize useful material for studying problems of gene transmission proved to be a disadvantage in this next stage of genetic investigation. It seemed likely that it would be an interminable task to unravel all the biochemical details that were behind the various morphological mutant phenotypes employed.

In 1941 the bold step was taken of inverting the experimental attack on the problem. Instead of waiting for the accumulation of information necessary to understand the biochemical basis of the complex morphological mutants of the higher forms, attention was turned to simpler microbial material. Here, the relation of phenotype to its biochemical basis was either known or, if unknown, much more directly accessible. For resolution, the only aspects missing were the genetic details, and these could be readily supplied.

At this time, sexuality in bacteria was still unknown. For a variety of reasons the bread mold *Neurospora crassa,* an ascomycete, was used for the combined biochemical and genetic analysis. The life cycle (Fig. 2-9) and basic genetic features of *Neurospora* were known. Further, it could be grown in a simple, chemically defined medium, making it a simple matter to isolate mutants which now required one or more nutrients, in addition to those in the simple medium which sufficed for the wild type. In addition, this organism possessed an admirable feature common to all ascomycetes and of enormous value to the geneticist. As may be seen from Figure 2-9, all of the products of each meiosis are conveniently

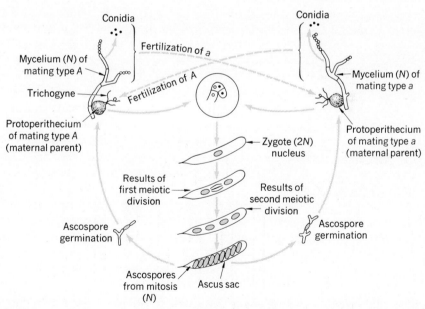

Figure 2-9. The life cycle of the bread mold, *Neurospora crassa.* (From Wagner and Mitchell, *Genetics and Metabolism,* 2nd ed. © 1964 by John Wiley & Sons, Inc.)

packaged in a separate little bag, the ascus. The task of determining whether a given character was assignable to one gene was thus made extremely simple. Suppose we make a cross between two stocks, one carrying the + allele and the other *P* allele of a particular gene. The original *diploid zygote* nucleus will be heterozygous +/P, carrying both. But when this nucleus undergoes the two meiotic divisions and the one mitosis described in Figure 2-10, the final eight-spored ascus must contain four haploid spores that carry P and four that carry +.

Numerous mutants with unusual nutritional requirements were collected. In each case, the mutant now required in the culture medium a compound that the wild type could make for itself. By that time, biochemistry had become sufficiently mature to have yielded much information concerning biosynthetic pathways. In a general way, such a pathway can be described as

$$\text{glucose} \rightarrow a \rightarrow b \rightarrow c \rightarrow d \rightarrow e \rightarrow \text{product}$$

where the product is an amino acid, purine, or vitamin, etc., and *a*, *b*, *c*, *d*, and *e* are specific chemical intermediates in the conversion of glucose to the product. Each mutant was found to be defective in one and only one reaction step along such a pathway—e.g., unable to convert

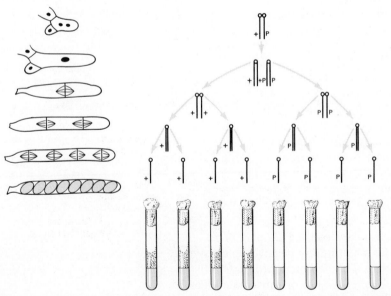

Figure 2-10. Chromosomal basis of gene segregation in *Neurospora*. The five cells arranged horizontally correspond to the five horizontal chromosome maps and show how segregation occurs. (From Beadle, Amer. Sci. *34*, 1946.)

$b \rightarrow c$, as indicated by the fact that b accumulated in the medium and the nutritional requirement could be met by any one of c, d, e, or final product. When such mutants were examined by the genetic method previously described, each was shown to result from a single gene change. The corresponding genes were located at specific positions on one of the chromosomes. It became evident that, with few exceptions, the absence of a *particular* biochemical reaction was always referable to a mutation in the *same gene*. The observations were summarized in the hypothesis, "One gene one enzyme," which became the slogan of biochemical genetics. The success of the work with *Neurospora* markedly influenced, both directly and indirectly, the further development of such research. It brought into sharp focus the gene-enzyme relationship as a key issue in the problem of how genes function.

From Biochemical to Molecular Genetics

Biochemical genetics was transformed to molecular genetics with the acceptance of the idea that genes were informationally related to their products by the colinear correspondence of their molecular structures, the central concept to which we have already referred. Three key findings made this possible. One was the chemical identification of genetic material as DNA. Second was the demonstration that DNA is a helical structure composed of a pair of complementary polynucleotide chains held together by a multiplicity of hydrogen bonds. Third was the demonstration that each molecule of the protein insulin exhibits a unique sequence of amino acid residues; this was followed shortly by similar demonstrations for other proteins.

Strangely, the identification of DNA as genetic material was accomplished before the actual birth of molecular genetics. Following up an observation made in 1928, an experiment was reported in 1944 which geneticists of the day may have dreamed about but hardly dared hope they would ever see. What was accomplished was the chemical purification of the genetic material from the cells of one strain of *Pneumococcus* and their permanent insertion into cells of a closely related strain. The former strain normally synthesized a specific polymeric carbohydrate which served as part of its cell wall. The latter, initially unable to do so, promptly began to make this carbohydrate after incubation with DNA of the former. Moreover, this property was retained through an indefinite number of subsequent generations.

This remarkable demonstration of genetic *transformation* should have illuminated for all biology the path to follow. In point of fact it had very little immediate impact, and this for several reasons. For one, the paper appeared at a time when the noninformational "polytetra-nucleotide" view of DNA was still widely accepted. Further, and ironically, the transformation experiment was carried out with bacteria, which were still not generally accepted as legitimate objects for genetic experimentation.

Finally, in 1952, an experiment was reported indicating that viral DNA contains all of the information required for the synthesis of a complete bacteriophage viral particle. This result, the transformation experiment, and a host of other observations convinced many that DNA is indeed the material of which genes were made. A year later came the dramatic announcement of the structure of DNA as a double-stranded helix held together by hydrogen bonds between the complementary base pairs (Fig. 2-5). Thus, by 1953, there were excellent reasons for believing that the general chemical nature of a gene was understood.

By this time, the task of determining the precise sequence of amino acid residues in insulin was completed; an accomplishment that generated two important logical consequences. This and the general structure of DNA stimulated the search for the biological dictionary which relates the linear structure of nucleic acids to that of proteins. The fact of unique amino acid sequences provided compelling evidence in support of the concept of protein-synthesizing mechanisms that entail instructional templates as key components.

The Biological Systems Employed in the Analysis of Gene Function

Several biological systems played key roles in the beginning attempts at understanding gene function and its control. They shared the feature that each permits the experimentalist to "turn on" particular groups of genes.

Enzyme Induction. Ever since 1900, it had been known that certain enzyme activities occur in cells of microorganisms only if the corresponding *substrates* (substances acted upon by the enzyme) are included in the growth medium. The term *enzymatic adaptation* (later changed to *enzyme induction*) was applied to this phenomenon. It seemed possible that this system offered an opportunity to examine how genes were turned on and off. In 1942 two groups, one using yeast and the other bacteria, began to exploit the potentialities of this system to analyze the control of gene function.

A decade of work by both laboratories established that enzyme induction actually involves de novo synthesis of the relevant enzyme protein; that is, neither the enzyme nor a preformed precursor is present in the cell before addition of the inducer, and enzyme protein is then totally synthesized from the pool of available amino acids. With this accomplished, it was possible to state with certainty that this system genuinely permits the study of gene function. Control of gene function is exercised by including or omitting specific small molecular weight compounds, called *inducers*. Subsequent events proved that the choice of enzyme induction as a model system for the study of gene function was a happy one. The data obtained led to the concept of RNA as the working genetic message and an understanding of gene regulation.

The Bacterial-Viral Complex. We have already noted that the bacterial viruses played an important role in the early attempts at understanding the nature of bacterial mutation. They continued to play a predominant role in molecular biology; with their aid, fine structure genetic analysis was pushed to its ultimate logical conclusion, culminating in the demonstration that two mutations could occur as close together as neighboring nucleotides of DNA. They served, however, another extremely useful purpose stemming from the following remarkable property: Minutes after a virulent virus injects its DNA into the host cell, the host stops transcribing its own genetic information. Attention is turned almost exclusively to the viral DNA, and the only RNA messages synthesized are those that represent copies of the viral genetic information. Thus, the experimentalist can stop the "reading" of one genetic "book" and initiate the transcription of another.

The Bacterial Recombination System. Mating between male and female bacterial cultures can be experimentally initiated. As sketched in Figure 2-11, the entrance of the genetic material is highly synchronized. If it is known where a specific gene is located on the chromosome, one can predict with precision when it will enter the cytoplasm of the recipient cell. By choosing the proper genetic constitutions of donor and recipient, it is not difficult to arrange the controlled introduction of particular genes into cytoplasms possessing a variety of informative properties. One can thus determine what intracellular components permit or prevent the expression of certain genes and how long these control processes take.

The Accomplishments of Molecular Biology

We now summarize in greater detail the ideas and facts that have emerged from recent research in molecular biology. The major thesis is that biological specificity—i.e., what makes an "organism" unique—is derived from information stored in its nucleic acid molecules. This idea has wide implications: It proposes a chemical interpretation of the

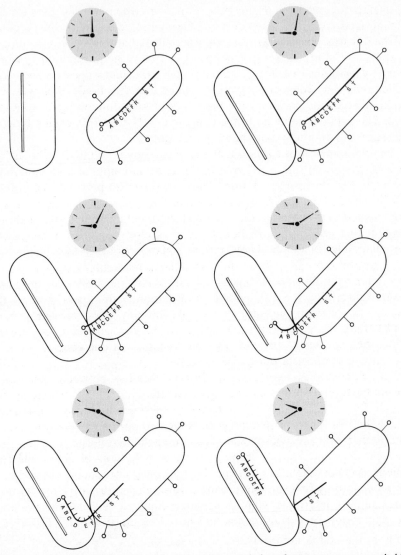

Figure 2-11. Sexual mating in bacteria. The order and timing of gene entry are remarkably constant among the cells of a given culture. (From "Sexuality in Bacteria," Wollman and Jacob. © 1956 by Scientific American, Inc. All rights reserved.)

origin of species; it explains mutations and provides a basis for the ultimate understanding of the laws of inheritance in chemical terms; it helps explain the regulated synthesis of molecules and, consequently, provides greater insight into the mechanisms of growth and development.

During the past 15 years, we have obtained substantial understanding of how information is stored and replicated in DNA molecules; how it is passed on to RNA molecules and finally to proteins; and how the three-dimensional structure of proteins depends upon the linear arrangement of their constituent amino acids.

The Nature of Genetic Information and How It Is Stored in DNA

To understand the concept of information storage in molecular structure and its subsequent readout, we must first examine the structure of nucleic acids in greater detail. DNA consists of a very long chain with a backbone made up of alternate groups of sugar and phosphate (Fig. 2-4). Attached to each sugar is one of four different bases: thymine (T), adenine (A), cytosine (C), or guanine (G). In most instances, two such chains are wound around each other to form a double spiral or helix (Fig. 2-5). The chemical bonds along each chain are extremely stable; the links between base and pentose and between pentose and phosphate are unlikely to be broken by ordinary changes in the environment. The two chains forming the double helix are held together through the bases according to specific chemical rules. T on one strand is always faced by A on the other, and C on one strand is always faced by G on the other. This restriction in the way the bases from one strand can join the bases on the other is a consequence of the specific molecular properties and size of each of the four bases. In this scheme G is referred to as the complement of C, and vice versa. Similarly A and T form a complementary pair. The bonds holding A to T and G to C are relatively weak; they are hydrogen bonds, $=N:H:O=$, and can be melted like ice. It is the huge number of such bonds along the two strands, the sum of many weak bonds, that results in the stable double helix. It is clear that the two strands of DNA contain the same "information" even though they are not identical in sequence; if the sequence of bases in one strand is known, that of its partner strand is automatically determined.

The pairing principle of A with T and G with C emerges as one of the fundamental theorems of modern structural chemistry. It provides the mechanism by which the base sequence of nucleic acids can be duplicated and transcribed. Complementary base pairing permits nucleic acids of whatever type to recognize and interact with each other. Further, pairing at this level is undoubtedly involved in the exchange of DNA between homologous chromosomes, the formation of circular DNA molecules from linear ones, and the translation of base sequence into amino acid sequence.

Indirect evidence has been accumulating for many years that genetic information is encoded in the sequence of nucleotides of the DNA helix. The wavelength of ultraviolet light that is most effective in causing mutations is the wavelength most effectively absorbed by DNA. Chemical reagents (mutagens) that react with the bases of the nucleotides to change their chemical form occasion "miscopying" or errors in replication, a topic to be discussed. Recently, direct chemical evidence has demonstrated that in one type of mutation there occurs substitution of one nucleotide for another. The accumulated information leaves little doubt that the genetic text is composed of a meaningful sequence of four letters (the four nucleotides) and that the sequence of these nucleotides constitutes the set of instructions for the biochemical machinery of the cell.

Molecular Hybridization

If a double-helical DNA is heated, the hydrogen bonds "melt" and are disrupted, and the two strands separate. If two separate strands having complementary base sequences are maintained at slightly lower temperatures under appropriate ionic conditions, a double-helical molecule is reformed. The degree to which a helix is reformed and the perfection of the new helix can be used to study the relatedness in the DNA's of different species.

Formation of a double helix will also occur between RNA and DNA strands providing they are complementary to one another (Fig. 2-12). If only portions of the strands are complementary, the unpaired portion of the RNA molecule can be removed by exposure to ribonuclease, an enzyme that hydrolyzes the backbone of free polyribonucleotides. In the last few years convenient and extremely sensitive methods have been developed for the detection of DNA-RNA complexes, thus fashioning an extremely powerful tool which permits the search for complementarity at the level of a single gene.

Some of the findings made possible by the use of that methodology are as follows: (1) *All* cellular RNA's, including messenger, ribosomal, and t-RNA, are transcripts of the DNA. (2) In any given segment of DNA only one of the two complementary strands is used as a template to generate RNA copies. (3) Invasion by a DNA virus results in cessa-

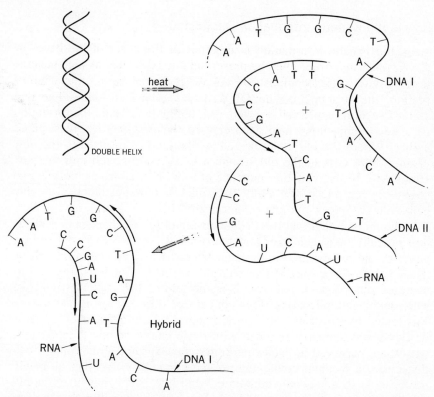

Figure 2-12. Hybridization of an RNA strand with one strand of a DNA helix. Hybridization occurs when the bases of the RNA can be paired with those of the DNA, using the same pairing rules as in DNA helix formation except that the uracil (U) of RNA replaces the thymine (T) of DNA.

tion of transcription of the cellular DNA and the onset of transcription of viral DNA. (4) Transcription of a genome is not a random process but occurs in an orderly manner, proceeding sequentially along the chromosome. (5) The nucleolus, a peculiar structure whose function was long unknown, has been shown to contain the DNA templates for ribosomal RNA. (6) Certain tumorous cells have been shown to harbor a viral DNA which can no longer complete the viral life cycle.

The exploitation of the RNA-DNA hybridization technique is just beginning. Many laboratories are using it in an attempt to understand the involvement of RNA and DNA in such diverse processes as embryogenesis and development, antibody synthesis, hormone action, and even the functioning of the central nervous system.

How Is the Genetic Information Duplicated?

Since the genetic information is inherent in the order of the bases in DNA, this same order must be preserved and replicated at each generation. How is this accomplished? As we indicated in the introductory section, the structure of the DNA itself supplies the clue. The two strands separate and each one acts as a template to guide the formation of a new companion chain according to the base-pairing rules stated earlier. Where the old chain has an A, then a T is inserted in the new chain; where C is in the old strand, a G is incorporated into the new strand, etc. In this way the sequence of four bases along each of the two strands is reproduced faithfully to yield two new but identical double helixes at the expense of the original helix (Fig. 2-13).

It should be noted that this "semiconservation" mechanism of replication predicts that each strand of the original duplex will be passed on *intact* to the two progeny that result from the first replication. Each of the progeny will consist of one old and one new strand. Figure 2-13 illustrates this process and describes the fate of the original strands in subsequent multiplications. This concept of the replication mechanism was tested by growing *E. coli* in a medium rich in C^{13} and N^{15} so that its DNA was similarly enriched with these heavy isotopes. Replication was then observed in cells permitted one further synchronous cell division in a medium containing normal C^{12} and N^{14} so that all newly synthesized strands would contain C^{12} and N^{14}. The behavior of the old and new strands, as well as hybrids between them, could then be followed by their positions in a density gradient as is detailed in Figure 2-14. The DNA then behaved as if it were built of $C^{12.5}$ and $N^{14.5}$, possible only if each double helix were built of one old and one new strand. The outcome completely confirms the semiconservative model predicted from the duplex structure of DNA.

Although this semiconservative form of nucleic acid replication represents the normal pattern, some variations on this basic mechanism have been discovered. In those cases where the genetic information resides in a single-stranded nucleic acid molecule, as in a few bacterial viruses, replication proceeds by first forming the complementary strand, thereby producing a double helix. The resulting helix then serves as the template to direct the formation of new single strands that are identical with the original.

From the mechanistic point of view, these replicating reactions represent a new kind of chemistry — template chemistry — and all life that we know is based on it. This exquisite capability of nucleic acids to direct

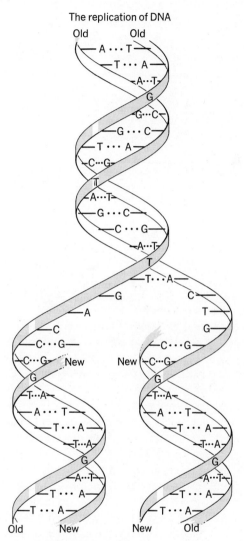

Figure 2-13. The original double helix is yielding two new helices, each of which consists of one old and one new strand. (From Watson)

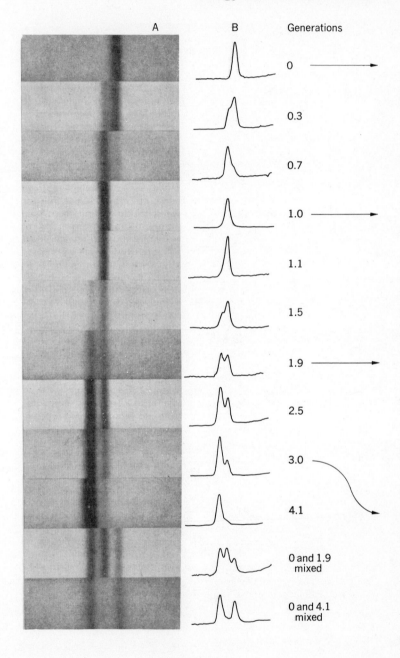

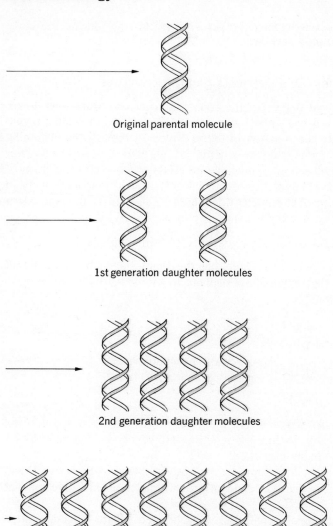

Original parental molecule

1st generation daughter molecules

2nd generation daughter molecules

3rd generation daughter molecules

Figure 2-14. Experimental evidence that DNA replication is semiconservative. Details in text. On left are shown ultracentrifuge data. As shown at bottom of figure, DNA in which all carbon and nitrogen are C^{13} and N^{15} is readily distinguished from that in which these are C^{12} and N^{14}. After one cell division only one "species" of DNA is present and it behaves in the centrifuge as if it were built of $C^{12.5}N^{14.5}$. (From Meselson and Stahl, Proc. Nat. Acad. Sci., *44*:671, 1958.)

their own duplication must have surely played a role during the early development of living systems.

Studies of Nucleic Acid Duplication in the Test Tube

If the full chemical details of the replicating reaction were ever to be finally unraveled, it was clearly necessary to isolate the relevant enzyme system and study the reaction in the test tube. A remarkable beginning toward this accomplishment was achieved in 1956. An enzyme system was isolated which could synthesize new DNA if old DNA were provided as a template. Synthesis occurred only if all components were in the medium. Each of the nucleotides must be present as the equivalent triphosphate—e.g., deoxyadenosine triphosphate, dATP:

$$\text{adenine-deoxyribose-phosphate} * \text{phosphate-phosphate}$$

Strand formation occurs by breaking the bond shown by the asterisk and connecting the remaining phosphate to the deoxyribose of the next nucleotide, so that

$$\left.\begin{array}{l} \text{dATP} \\ \text{dGTP} \\ \text{dCTP} \\ \text{dTTP} \end{array}\right\} \rightarrow \text{DNA} + \text{pyrophosphate}$$

Chemical analysis indicated that the product was indistinguishable from the template used to initiate the reaction. However, the synthetic DNA was abnormal in being branched.

For a long time, all attempts to synthesize a biologically active DNA failed. It took more than a decade of unremitting labor to resolve some of the difficulties.

Finally, an enzymic preparation was obtained which, indeed, synthesized a perfect, biologically active DNA. This experiment took advantage of a single-stranded DNA virus (ϕX174); the enzyme was shown to make a perfect complementary strand, which in turn served as the template for making biologically active DNA, providing convincing proof that accurate copying of DNA could, in fact, be achieved with purified enzymes in a test tube. However, the enzyme system available at present lacks some component that functions in the cell, since only one complement is made at a time in the test tube reactions. The duplex product must be artificially dissociated and a second reaction run to obtain the next complementary product.

Two years prior to these latest investigations with DNA the first synthesis of a biologically active nucleic acid was achieved using an RNA-replicating enzyme system induced in infected cells by an RNA virus. Accurate copies of the viral RNA were synthesized and shown to be biologically competent by their ability to produce complete viral particles in cells.

Thus the goal of a complete replicating mechanism functioning in a test tube has, in fact, been attained. In the RNA system, synthesis of active nucleic acid is continuous and extensive. If a single strand is used as a template, 500 billion product strands can be produced in 15 minutes.

In addition to providing an opportunity for studying the details of the replicating mechanism, the RNA-replicating system makes available a whole new area of investigation previously not attainable. *Clones* of mutant-replicating molecules have been produced for the first time. Potentially, one can now study the evolution of replicating molecules outside of cells, a situation that mimics early events in the genesis of living material. Darwinian selection experiments can be, and have been, performed to produce variant-replicating molecules which are defective for some segment of information necessary for the completion of the virus cycle. Some of these variants show features that make them excellent antagonists of normal viral nucleic acid. Similar studies should soon be possible in the DNA-replicating system. This line of investigation clearly opens up a completely novel approach toward a highly specific control of viral diseases.

Some Uncertainties About the Replicating Mechanisms

Although the general features of how the DNA structure is replicated are clear, we are still ignorant of many of the details. For example, despite the striking success achieved with the known DNA-synthesizing enzyme, there is the possibility that a different enzyme actually serves this purpose in the cell. Although chromosomes probably have beginnings and ends, it is not clear how the duplication process is initiated or finished. Of great importance is the task of learning how the reproduction of the chromosomes is timed with respect to the total process of cell division. Equally puzzling at present is how the complex chromosomes of higher forms are duplicated and how this process is integrated within the life cycle of the cell. Although the DNA component of complex chromosomes is also replicated semiconservatively, we are ignorant of how this process is coupled with the production of the basic proteins which are structural elements of the chromosomes, how the progeny DNA molecules are segregated among the daughter chromosomes, and how these events are synchronized with the mechanics of cell division.

Simple replication of each strand of the DNA is not the entire story in the replication of chromosomes. Even in bacteria additional features are discernible. Natural or artificial radiation and certain reactive chemicals are known to produce modification in the DNA structure. During subsequent replication, mutations or heritable defects are produced. Repair mechanisms do exist, however, whereby physically damaged regions of the chromosome can be removed and the appropriate segments resynthesized in their original state. There are known enzymes that can detect the defective regions of the DNA helix, excise them, and then regenerate on the template of the complementary strand the original of the altered sequence. Specific enzymes have been isolated which, respectively, catalyze the cutting of the DNA, removal of regions of a loose section of nucleotides, resynthesis of the original sequence (using the opposite strand as a template), and rejoining of the ends to reestablish continuity of the structure. These findings have great potential. Armed with them, it should be possible to utilize chemically synthesized polydeoxyribonucleotides to complete the synthesis of a DNA of completely known structure—to synthesize a new gene! And, one day, this may permit repair of hereditary diseases of man.

With regard to RNA viral replication, it seems certain that the replicating enzyme system has, in fact, been isolated, since virtually indefinite replication has been demonstrated. The precise chemical details of the mechanism used to produce complementary strands, and subsequently new viral RNA molecules, remain to be determined.

The Nature of the Genetic Code

In the introductory paragraphs it was stated that an informational relation exists between nucleic acids and proteins. The sequence of bases in a particular segment of DNA specifies the sequence of amino acids in a specific protein. Let us now inquire more closely into the nature of this relation and how the insight into it was acquired.

Recall there are 20 different amino acids, and hence during protein synthesis, at every position along the chain, one out of 20 possible choices must be made. Clearly, one nucleotide in the DNA or RNA would not suffice for each amino acid, since there are only four possible nucleotides and this would permit the specification of only four different amino acids. Two nucleotides per amino acid would likewise be insufficient, since then only 16 choices could be made. Clearly, in order to specify each of the 20 amino acids, the nucleotides must be "read" in groups of at least three or more.

The conclusion that three are indeed used emerged from a series of elegant genetic experiments employing the well-studied *rII* region of the genome of the T4 bacteriophage. After exposure to agents that induce deletions or additions of individual nucleotides, it was found that if one or two nucleotides were added at a particular location, all information beyond this point was garbled in translation. If, however, three nucleotides were added, only the small region being manipulated was modified; the remainder was correctly translated. Similar findings were obtained with deletions and combinations of deletions and additions. Thus emerged the concept of the *triplet codon*. Note that the use of three out of four nucleotides to specify an amino acid generates synonomy. There are 64 possible sets of triplets (4 for each nucleotide), and there are only 20 amino acids to choose from. Hence one should find that many amino acids have several synonomous triplets — i.e., several different triplets that code for one amino acid. In fact, this situation is found.

The next task was to ascertain the genetic dictionary specifying which triplet codes for what amino acid. By an astounding combination of luck and insight, a cell-free system was discovered which responded to synthetic nucleic acids by incorporating labeled amino acids into polypeptides. Thus, if one adds synthetic polyuridylic acid (a ribonucleic acid that contains only uracil residues) a polypeptide polymer containing only phenylalanine is synthesized. Thus was the Rosetta stone of biology discovered and deciphered; UUU of the nucleic acid language translated into phenylalanine of the 20-element language of the proteins. Several groups followed this lead, and by chemically synthesizing nucleic acids containing different bases, they were able quickly to establish other codons. The ultimate solution came from using isolated triplets of bases and showing that these caused binding to the protein-synthesizing particles of only a single amino acid; the final proof came from the use of synthetic nucleic acids of known base sequence which yielded proteins of defined amino acid sequence.

The result was the solution of the genetic code, one of the most significant achievements of molecular biology. Few, if any, would have predicted in 1960 that "the genetic dictionary" would be known in 1967! And yet today, if we were able to read off the base sequence from a gene, we could set down the order of each amino acid in the corresponding protein. In principle, proteins of any defined sequence can be synthesized.

The general features of the code are simple and are summarized in Figure 2-15. The base sequence of the nucleic acid is always translated starting at one end and then read three bases at a time until the specified protein chain is completed. Each of the 64 possible combinations of three adjacent nucleotides specifies either one of the 20 amino acids or a punctuation signal (start or end). A change in the base sequence of a given triplet creates a new triplet which either is a synonym or specifies a different amino acid. If a base is deleted or added to the sequence and the bases are still read three at a time, an entire new message is created and a new protein results. For example, in the sequence TCG, ATT, CGA, AGC . . . , if a *T* were inserted in the beginning, an entirely new message sequence, *T*TC, GAT, TCG, AAG, C . . . , would result.

It is difficult to overestimate the significance of knowing the genetic code and the fact that it appears to be essentially the same in all living things. We can, with this information, define the ways in which certain chemicals and radiation act as mutagens. We can chemically synthesize short lengths of nucleic acid corresponding to defined amino acid sequences. With knowledge of the code we can, among other things, gain new insights into how proteins and the code itself evolved, and how a variety of influences (particularly chemical) can cause misreading of the code.

2nd POSITION

		U	C	A	G	
1st POSITION	**U**	PHE PHE LEU LEU	SER SER SER SER	TYR TYR CT-1 CT-2	CYS CYS CT-3 TRY	U C A G
	C	LEU LEU LEU LEU	PRO PRO PRO PRO	HIS HIS GLN GLN	ARG ARG ARG ARG	U C A G
	A	ILU ILU ILU MET	THR THR THR THR	ASN ASN LYS LYS	SER SER ARG ARG	U C A G
	G	VAL VAL VAL VAL	ALA ALA ALA ALA	ASP ASP GLU GLU	GLY GLY GLY GLY	U C A G

(left axis label: 1st POSITION; right axis label: 3rd POSITION)

Figure 2-15. Each amino acid in a protein is specified by a nucleotide triplet in RNA, e.g. aspartic acid (asp) is specified by the triplets GAU and GAC. UAA, UAG, and UGA are utilized for punctuation, viz. to indicate when to terminate the chain.

The Transcription of Genetic Information

As already noted, DNA does not itself direct the assembly of proteins. Instead, the information in one strand of DNA is first transferred to a complementary strand of RNA molecule, which in turn serves as the immediate template for protein synthesis. The product of this process (*transcription*) is an RNA molecule called *messenger RNA* (Fig. 2-16). The transcription is similar to the duplication process: The two strands of DNA are separated, and one of them serves as the template for the formation of an RNA chain according to the same base-pairing rules outlined earlier; where DNA contains A, the growing RNA chain will receive U (the RNA equivalent of T), and where C is in the DNA, the RNA will contain G. When the entire gene has been transcribed, the base sequence in the RNA is complementary to one strand in the DNA and, therefore, identical with the other, except for the substitution of U for T.

Transcription is catalyzed by an enzyme (the DNA-dependent RNA polymerase) using activated precursors (ribonucleosidetriphosphates) of each of the RNA bases. Although general features of the process are known, many important questions are unanswered. For example, how does the enzyme recognize the beginning and end of each gene, namely, the DNA segment to be transcribed? How often does the enzyme transcribe a particular gene during any one cell generation? How do environmental and intrinsic factors influence how much and which messenger RNA is made?

These are not academic questions. Aside from the remarkable fact that we can today even pose these questions in such precise terms, they are the questions that must be answered before we shall understand the control of gene action. With this known we would be in a position to attempt resolution of the next order of problems — the mechanisms of

RNA transcriptions upon DNA templates

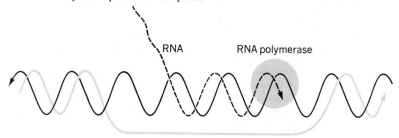

Figure 2-16. Attachment of RNA polymerase opens the DNA helix, and bases of ribonucleotides pair complementarily with those of one DNA strand. The RNA formed peels off as the strand grows by elimination of pyrophosphate. (From Watson)

growth and development and cellular differentiation in higher organisms.

These questions are being actively studied by molecular biologists. Investigations in the past decade of how cells regulate gene expression point to a mechanism whereby the protein products of certain genes function, not as enzymes, but as regulators of the transcription of other genes. The ability of regulator proteins to influence the expression of genetic information is, in turn, influenced by environmental and metabolic factors. In this way the cell possesses enormous flexibility for modifying both the rate of production and the kind of genetic messages available for translation; but how the signals are generated and how the regulation is actually effected are now only beginning to be known. Of considerable interest is how hormones, which have such profound effects on the target organs, participate in the regulatory processes. It is not unlikely that future research will demonstrate that some act at the transcription or translation stage and thereby alter both the qualitative and quantitative output of the genes.

The Translation of Genetic Information

Given a particular messenger RNA, how is it translated into a protein? Free amino acids cannot recognize their corresponding codons. Instead, each amino acid is first attached to a small RNA molecule (t-RNA). These t-RNA molecules are about 70 nucleotides and serve as *adapters* for binding to the codons. A given t-RNA molecule is able to bind only a single particular amino acid, and its structure contains a sequence of three bases that is complementary to the triplet for that amino acid. Some of these t-RNA molecules have been completely sequenced; an example is shown in Figure 2-17 of the t-RNA for phenylalanine. Note that it has a rather rigid structure which comes into being by folding of the molecule so that interval complementary regions are aligned and held by hydrogen bonds. The anticodon (AAG) corresponding to the triplet UUC, a codon for phenylalanine is indicated.

The matching process between the amino acid t-RNA and the messenger codons cannot occur in solution; rather, it occurs on large particles called ribosomes. It appears that ribosomes attach to messenger RNA molecules at their specific initiator signals, and then the amino acid t-RNA complex, which can recognize the initiator codon, is bound. This sets the reading frame, and now as the ribosome moves along the filament of messenger RNA each subsequent triplet codon comes into register, the appropriate amino acid t-RNA is bound, and the amino acid is polymerized onto the growing end of the protein chain. The whole process is diagrammed in Figure 2-18.

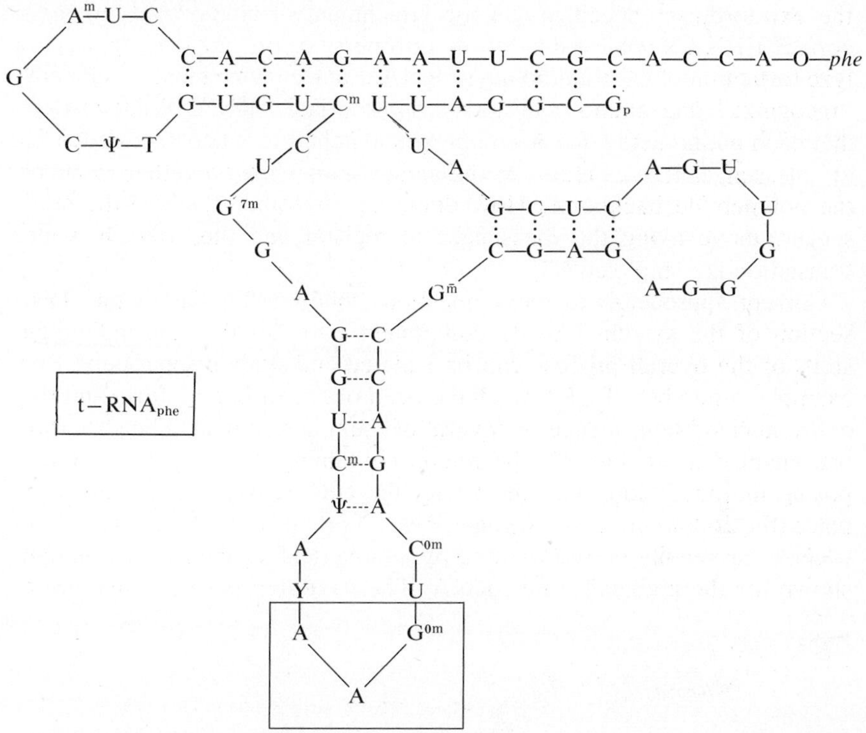

A^m—U—C

G

C—Ψ—T

C—A—C—A—G—A—A—U—U—C—G—C—A—C—C—A—O—*phe*

G—U—G—U—C^m U—U—A—G—G—C—G_p

U C

G^{7m} U A

G A—G—U U

A G—C—U—C G

$G^{\bar{m}}$ C—G—A—G A—G—G

G⋯C

G⋯C

U⋯A

C^m⋯G

Ψ⋯A

A C^{om}

Y U

A G^{om}

A

t—RNA$_{phe}$

Figure 2-17. Base sequence in the t-RNA for phenylalanine. Three-dimensional structure is created by internal base pairing at three loci. The reading triplet, to be base-paired with m-RNA is shown in box at bottom.

The protein chain grows one amino acid at a time. The sequence in which amino acids are polymerized is determined by the order in which messenger codons come into register and their matching by each amino acid t-RNA. This proceeds until a *terminator* triplet (Fig. 2-15) is reached, whereupon the completed protein is released by hydrolytic removal of the t-RNA still fixed to last amino acid in the chain.

Usually more than one ribosome is translating a given messenger RNA at a time. This is a situation analogous to what one might imagine if a tape recording were to be threaded through four, five, or ten tape recorders in sequence. Each instrument would reproduce the same message, in sequence.

These are the general features by which the base sequence in a messenger RNA is converted to an amino acid sequence in protein. Although we can see the basic design in the process, a chemical understanding of certain remarkable features has thus far eluded us. How is the extraordinary specificity in the attachment of amino acids to their correct t-RNA's achieved? This is a property of the enzymes that catalyze formation of each amino acyl t-RNA. Each enzyme must specifically "recognize" one amino acid and its appropriate t-RNA. What insures that each amino acid t-RNA complex is matched to its correct codon in the messenger RNA? How are the amino acids joined together to make the polypeptide backbone? How does the ribosome attach to the messenger, move along the messenger in register and then detach when translation is completed?

Current approaches to these questions follow a familiar theme: Dissection of the system into its component parts so that the individual steps of the overall process can be isolated and studied separately. For example, a number of t-RNA's have been obtained in pure form and the entire nucleotide sequence of several of them determined. The structure has enabled us to identify the region containing the three bases composing the anticodon—i.e., the triplet the t-RNA uses to recognize its place (the codon) on the messenger RNA. Perhaps not surprisingly, each t-RNA can readily be represented by a cloverleaf structure such as that shown for the phenylalanine t-RNA. The next step is to identify those

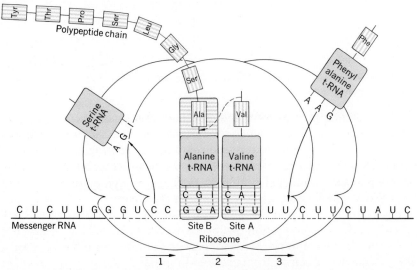

Figure 2-18. Translation. Protein synthesis on m-RNA threaded through a ribosome. The N-terminus of the protein is shown as the terminal tyr. The ribosome is moving along the m-RNA from left to right. It is just about to form the bond between alanine and valine. The uncharged seryl t-RNA is departing and the charged phenylalanine to t-RNA is arriving to be used next. (From "The Genetic Code:III," Francis Crick. © 1966 by Scientific American, Inc. All rights reserved.)

structural features required for recognition of the protein that catalyzes the attachment of the correct amino acid to the t-RNA.

At the heart of the translation mechanism is the ribosome; these nucleoprotein particles (containing RNA and proteins) were, until recently, the "black box" of protein synthesis. Ribosomes consist of two subunits, one about twice as big as the other. The present notion is that the smaller subunit is the component that binds the message, while the larger one binds the growing protein chain and the incoming amino acid t-RNA. Recent studies have begun to assign to the different proteins in the ribosome the various functions required for translation, initiation, binding to the messenger, peptide bond formation, etc. The information thus acquired may have important practical implications. It is these ribosomal proteins that seem to be the sites of action of a variety of antibiotics, and it is these proteins that are modified in certain genetically altered drug-resistant mutants.

To know how the ribosome works, it is important to know how ribosomes are made. Inasmuch as ribosomes are structurally complex, we can appreciate that the assembly of ribosomes is equally complex. Here, too, significant studies have been made in the last few years. In both bacterial and mammalian systems, some of the steps have been delineated.

We know that the RNA molecules in the ribosomes are coded for by specific regions of the DNA and that they are synthesized by a template mechanism in the same way as for messenger RNA and t-RNA production. However, the regulation of ribosomal RNA synthesis is different from that of messenger RNA. In some instances, certain bases of the ribosomal RNA are further modified; this is followed by a rapid and presumably stepwise accretion of the different ribosomal proteins (which themselves are coded for by genes) to form the finished particle.

As ribosomal structure is better understood, and constituent molecular species isolated and characterized, the nature of this assembly will be completely clarified. We shall then have a better basis for understanding how cells make proteins and, very likely, the basis for more rational approaches to modify and correct defects in this crucial process. That progress will be rapid is indicated by the fact that in the last few months the complete assembly of the smaller ribosomal subunit from its component parts has been achieved in the test tube.

Accuracy and the Role of the Protein Catalysts

Considerable emphasis has already been given to the role of complementary base pairing in the replication and expression of genetic information. One may ask whether this alone is sufficient to insure the high fidelity we know exists in the overall process. In the case of nucleic acid replication we know that proteins which catalyze the polymerization of monomer units also contribute to the specificity in matching the template base with the corresponding monomers. How polymerases minimize false copying is not entirely clear, but it is known that mutational changes in the structures of a polymerase can affect the accuracy with which a base sequence is replicated. Thus, the normal protein not only catalyzes the polymerization reaction but is also somehow involved in determining the fidelity of the copying process.

Transcription of genetic information into messengers also demands high accuracy. Mistakes at this stage, although not leading to a heritable change, produce faulty messengers which leads to modified proteins. The transcribing enzyme must also help insure correct readout of base sequence and help provide the basis for selecting the proper initiating point of transcription. The enzyme must recognize the specific site at which complementary base pairing is to begin. Errors in this recognition process would lead to the production of faulty messenger or the complete failure to produce any messenger RNA.

Translation of each triplet codon by the corresponding amino acid t-RNA's is also characterized by a low frequency of errors. In this instance the attachment of each amino acid to its cognate t-RNA is entrusted to specific proteins, which simultaneously distinguish each amino acid from the 19 others and the corresponding t-RNA from the 60 or so others. The subsequent correct matching of each amino acid t-RNA to its codon is monitored by still unknown features associated with the ribosome structure.

Each step in the sequence of information transfer can be interfered with or modified, thereby decreasing the fidelity of the overall process. We are only beginning to appreciate how this can occur naturally, such as by mutational alteration of the components of the readout system per se—i.e., polymerases, amino acid t-RNA synthetases, ribosomes— and how we may influence these processes from without, by drugs and manipulation of environmental conditions. Fooling these enzymes with substances that mimic natural substrates, or modifying the requisite enzymes to alter their specificity, offers a rational approach for external manipulation of gene expression.

Several of the possibilities noted have been achieved. Thus it is clear that the antibiotic activity of such potent medical drugs as chloramphenicol, streptomycin, neomycin, the tetracyclines (and many others) depends upon their ability to block one or another step of the translation mechanism. Thus, chloramphenicol and puromycin interrupt the normal process of protein chain growth. Streptomycin binds to ribosomes and modifies their ability to support normal protein synthesis, causing multiple errors in the reading process. Such studies have yielded a chemical understanding of a persistent medical problem—antibiotic resistance.

Molecular Genetics

The chromosomes of bacteria are smaller and simpler than those found in mammalian cells, and in certain cases they have been shown to be a single circular DNA molecule. Genetic recombination can occur amongst bacteria in the following variety of ways: (a) *transduction,* the introduction of DNA from another cell via a viral particle; (b) *sexual mechanism,* involving cell-to-cell transfer of the DNA; (c) *transformation,* the uptake of free DNA from the surroundings. In each case a single DNA molecule or a fragment thereof is transferred from one cell to another. Even two viral particles can exchange genes, provided that they infect the same host cell.

The discovery of genetic exchanges in bacteria and viruses initiated the activity now called *molecular genetics.* This is aptly named because the fundamental participants are DNA molecules themselves. Genetic maps have been constructed in many cases, and these maps have been identified with the DNA molecules involved. This implies that a single recombinant DNA molecule contains information that formerly resided in the separate parental DNA molecules. Recombinant DNA molecules are now known to be formed by breaking and rejoining DNA originating from the two parents. Breakage and rejoining of DNA molecules appears to be the basis for recombinant formation in higher cells as well. The enzymatic mechanisms of this fundamental and specific process are being intensively studied at the present time.

Breeding experiments with bacteria and viruses have revealed an unexpected connection between the two: Bacteria may sometimes contain viral genes, and viruses may sometimes contain bacterial genes. While a tiny viral particle can never contain all of the DNA of a bacterium, the converse is possible; bacteria may sometimes contain integrated in their own chromosome the complete genetic information of a virus. These are the *lysogenic* bacteria. We have, then, the distinct possibility that many bacteria or, indeed, any cell may contain the genetic information of viruses, yet undiscovered, as an integral part of their own genetic text. The mechanism of the insertion of viral texts into the DNA of the host cell, or vice versa, is by the process of genetic recombination just referred to.

What are the consequences of these exchanges? When a segment of bacterial DNA is incorporated into a viral DNA molecule, the resulting viral particle can inject this DNA into another bacterium where it can be incorporated by genetic recombination. This process, called *transduction,* is one of the important ways by which bacteria can exchange genes. From a technical point of view, transduction is a marvelous tool by which geneticists can analyze and manipulate the chromosomes of bacteria.

When viral DNA molecules are inserted into the bacterial chromosome, the lysogenic cell now has new genetic information. Some of these viral genes are expressed to produce virus-specific proteins. These confer new properties on the cell. For example, the bacterium that causes diphtheria does so by the production of a toxin that diffuses from the cell. It is now known that the ability to produce this toxin is the result of a viral DNA molecule carried as a cryptic segment of the host genome. Those strains of bacteria that can be cured of this DNA segment will no longer produce the disease.

A similar situation, of great medical importance, is drug resistance. It has been found that certain infectious bacteria (staphylococci, for example) will become simultaneously resistant to a number of different antibiotics used to combat them. The resistance has been shown to result from a viral DNA molecule that takes up residence in a formerly drug-sensitive cell. Thus, lysogeny has considerable medical as well as genetical significance.

These same concepts are probably important to an understanding of at least certain types of cancer. There are now many clear examples of tumor-inducing viruses. In some cases, the tumor-virus DNA can be shown by molecular hybridization to be present in the cells of the tumor and functioning to produce RNA. The parallel with lysogenic bacteria is too close to be ignored.

Tasks Ahead for Molecular Biology

In discussing possible future developments of biology at the molecular level, let us distinguish short-range and long-range goals. By short-range goals we mean the solution not only to problems likely to come, say, in the next five years, but also to those where fairly clear approaches are laid out and which are rather natural extensions of what is already known. The long-range goals will be sought by trying to apply to more complex biological systems ideas found fruitful on simpler ones. Not only will these goals take longer to reach, but the attempt is also more likely to bring surprises as these complex systems reveal new aspects of biology.

Short-Range Goals

Much is known of the pieces of machinery that function in transcription and translation. However, comparatively little is known with certainty of the detailed mechanism whereby the rates of these processes are controlled. The *processes* on which switches *might* operate to turn off and on the synthesis of large molecules can be specified generally; but exactly *where* the switches are in the cells, *what* they are, and details of how they function remain to be discovered.

It is an extraordinary feature of the genetic material that genes with a closely related function — viz., the enzymes for whose synthesis they are responsible participate successively in the metabolism of one amino acid — are occasionally (but not always) located close together in a cluster and that their functioning is regulated as a unit (referred to as an *operon*). A special example of this is that of genes encoding the formation of a group of enzymes that must act sequentially to make some substance that a cell needs for growth. How such coordinate genetic units are put under the same control, how the boundaries of such units are marked out, and how the products of these coordinate units function in a cooperative way are all still to be explained.

An example of how such problems are being worked out is the research being done on the regulatory group of genes in bacteria coding the formation of the enzyme *beta-galactosidase* (an enzyme that splits the sugar lactose) and two related enzymes (*lactose permease,* involved in the transport of lactose across the cell membrane, and *galactose acetylase,* with a still unknown role in lactose metabolism). The presently accepted model of how the lactose operon is controlled by its regulatory gene (i) is shown in Figure 2-19. Except under special circumstances, the genes that code for the three enzymes involved are kept shut off by a *repressor* (switch-off) which experiments reveal to be a protein. The whole group of genes can be turned on by certain small molecules, *inducers* (switch-ons), acting to block the effect of the repressor. Just recently a protein having some of the required properties of this repressor has been isolated from cells in which this group of genes were turned off. Even as this is being written, the functioning of this repressor is being worked out. It seems certain that this protein shuts off the transcription of its operon by binding at a specific locus on the "operator" gene. Exactly how it operates and which step it controls in the synthesis of this group of enzymes from the DNA level on will soon be known. It will be especially interesting to know how the repressor is turned from an "off switch" to an "on switch" by interaction with the small molecule inducer.

Thus far, relatively little has been done with the more complex situation in which genes concerned with the same biosynthetic pathway are not clustered. This situation has been observed both in bacteria and in higher forms possessing defined nuclei and chromosomal structures. The mechanism of coordinately controlling the activities of such scattered genetic elements remains to be elucidated.

Even simple cells that interact little with other cells (e.g., bacteria) have a complex program of events that lead regularly and repeatedly to cell division. To do this requires coordinated control of the synthetic

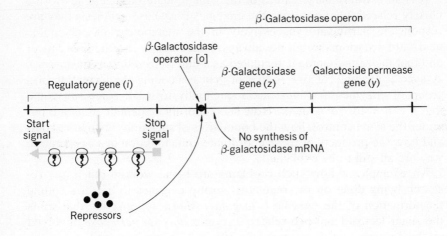

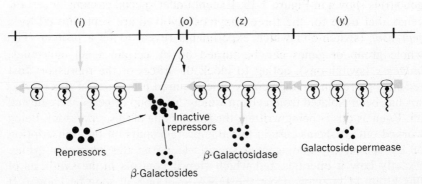

Figure 2-19. Repression and depression of an operon. In top figure, repressor protein, made by action of regulatory gene, binds to operator gene, and the other genes of the operon are not functional. Newly arrived substrate, below, binds to repressor protein which departs from regulator gene and the structural genes of the operon go to work. (From Watson)

machinery that makes *all* the components of the cell. How this program operates, how it can be interrupted, and the machinery commandeered by incoming viruses, for example, are challenging problems to be solved.

Other agents can also influence the program; for example, by various means most of the cells in a large population can be made to divide in synchrony, or spores can be set synchronously on the path to form dividing vegetative cells.

An interesting example of repetitive programming is the continued cycling of the light emission and division of certain unicellular organisms even in the absence of external signals. Where is the clock that controls this, and what are its parts?

A great deal is known now about how small molecules are made and even how certain of them are put together in orderly ways to form the high molecular weight polymers of living systems. It is also known that certain highly organized sub-structures of cells such as membranes, ribosomes, chloroplasts, and mitochondria, are formed by orderly combination of some of these polymers, together with low molecular weight components. On the other hand, comparatively little is known of the detailed structure of these organelles, how they are synthesized, how their synthesis is regulated, or what part is played by already preexisting structures in their further synthesis. In addition, little is known how these organized structures perform their cellular roles. The elucidation of these problems is a challenge for the future.

This is a small sample, then, of the goals for molecular biology in the near future. By and large we have included here some of the clearly indicated steps along paths already laid out.

Long-Range Goals

Even as advances are made in understanding the biology of the simpler organisms, attempts are being made to apply this understanding to more complex cellular systems. It has been one of the early lessons of molecular biology that many things are done in the same way in all living organisms, from the most simple to the most complex. This is a reflection in part of the fact that all known forms of life are based on nucleic acids and proteins. A most striking example of this unity is the discovery that except for minor differences the same triplet groups of bases are used for coding, transcribing, and translating genetic information in all living organisms examined. If this generalization holds, it constitutes by far the most compelling argument for the concept that all presently living organisms derive, by evolution, from a single, common primordial ancestor. Life may have originated more than once; but only one such event succeeded in a historic sense. In addition, the machinery for synthesizing proteins, the kinds of proteins synthesized, and how the proteins function are remarkably similar from bacteria to man.

The simplest organisms, the bacteria, lead essentially independent existences, and each individual of a population is much like the other. A relatively small number of genes, perhaps a few thousand, are sufficient for its needs. On the other hand, the cells of a multicellular organism are dependent on the others, each cell in its right place with its specialized function to perform.

During development of a multicellular organism from a single cell, differentiation occurs—that is, the many cells formed by subsequent division become specialized in function and arranged into organs to serve the whole organism. To do this requires precise and coordinated timing of the expression of genes in the large collection of cells that become these organs.

Since all cells of a multicellular organism start with the same genetic material (a few million genes for man) there is a problem of how the expression of each gene is programmed during development to allow the cells to form the intricate associations of complex organs, like the liver and the brain. How are cells of the nervous system connected to each other during development and the connections maintained? How do cells of other organs send signals to each other, and how are the signals received and processed? To understand these is part of the long-range problem.

Fortunately, much has been done to simplify mammalian cell systems so that the methodology of bacteria and bacterial viruses can be applied. A particularly fruitful instance is the development of tissue culture techniques for growing colonies from single animal and human cells. More recently, it has been possible to devise conditions that permit the cells to express an easily recognized differentiated function (such as the making of a hormone). With such cultures, effects of exogenous agents such as viruses, hormones, antigens, and chemotherapeutic agents can be studied without the complications of the heterogeneous cell population of an animal. Such cultures have, moreover, been very useful in ascertaining the molecular (or chromosomal) basis of certain human disorders.

In trying to unravel the complex programming of gene expression that is needed for different cells to express their specialized properties, the first approach is to determine whether the regulatory mechanisms unveiled by the research with bacteria function also in higher organisms. Is part of the programming done, for example, by small molecules sent from one cell to another to inactivate specific gene repressors or to react with already existing enzymes to change their activity? There are hints that the cell membranes are essential components in the receiving of signals that regulate cell functioning. It will be a real challenge to our ingenuity to identify the molecular components involved.

An interesting feature of the regulated state is that the cell can pass this state on to its descendants. Differentiated cells can, for example, divide and retain indefinitely their state of differentiation. This implies that not only is the DNA replicated faithfully at each generation but, in addition, its particular pattern of activity (or inactivity) is also replicated.

Toward the Synthesis of a Cell

One of the acid tests of understanding an object is the ability to put it together from its component parts. Ultimately, molecular biologists will attempt to subject their understanding of cell structure and function to this sort of test by trying to synthesize a cell. It is of some interest to see how close we are to this goal.

We have already seen that both types of genetic material, RNA and DNA, have been synthesized in the test tube. The same is true of proteins. In a prodigious tour de force of chemical technique, the protein hormone insulin was synthesized both in China and in the United States. Secretin, a small protein hormone of the duodenum, has since been synthesized, as have several hypophyseal hormones. Easier and automated ways of accomplishing the same thing are well on their way to development. Further and quite recently, active lysozyme, the enzyme that dissolves the cell walls of certain bacteria, has been synthesized in the test tube.

The fact that active proteins can be chemically synthesized from their constituent amino acid stimulates the hopes of those who dream of a man-made cell. According to our present understanding of protein function, the catalytic activity of an enzyme is a property of the three-dimensional structure of the protein molecule and depends, therefore, on the exact arrangement in space of the atoms that make up the protein. As will be described in the next chapter, it is now clear that, under certain conditions, the highly specific three-dimensional protein structure may experimentally be destroyed, with formation of a random, flopping coil. If this is returned to a normal environment, the normal, active protein spontaneously reforms. Thus, the three-dimensional conformation is entirely the obligatory consequence of the primary amino acid sequence.

An even more impressive example of self-assembly is the formation of active viral particles when the separated viral components are mixed together in a neutral salt solution. This experiment was first carried out with tobacco mosaic virus; the RNA molecule and the protein of the virus were separated and then allowed to reassemble to form a particle that is indistinguishable chemically and biologically from the normal virus. In this case, there is only one type of protein molecule that makes up the viral coat; to understand the assembly process, one must know how several thousand molecules of the same small protein can assemble with the large RNA molecule to form the active virus.

The most complex example for which the phenomenon of self-assembly has thus far been demonstrated is the bacterial virus T4. This is a structure that contains many different types of protein molecules, the synthesis of each of which is controlled by a separate gene on the viral DNA. By selecting a variety of different mutant viruses, it is possible to obtain infected cells which do not make complete viral particles but do make part of the total structure—heads, tails, tail fibers, etc. (Fig. 2-20). When these partial assemblies are mixed in solution, complete infectious viruses are produced. By means of different mutants it has been possible to work out most of the steps that are involved in the sequential assembly of this virus.

In many of these instances of self-assembly it is clear that the final structure can be reached only if the correct sequence of events takes place. The final structure cannot be formed until the subassemblies exist; the enzymes composed of several subunits can be formed only after the subunits are folded into their correct configuration, and it is possible that the final folding of the single polypeptide chain can take place only after the local structures along the proteins have been established.

It seems reasonable to generalize all of these processes of self-assembly by noting that, in each case, a well-defined sequence of events takes place leading to the final structure. Each separate step must occur with a free energy change lower than the others which are accessible to it. However, the sequential nature of the process means that the final structure may not be the one of lowest energy. The important point is that not only must genes be selected so that structures are active when they fold, but they must be selected so that the folding will take place sufficiently rapidly for all of the substructures to form and assemble with a speed adequate to account for the growth of the organism.

In summary, the studies described tell us that the rather complicated three-dimensional structures assumed by some polymers are a consequence of their primary sequence. Further, the interactions of these to form even more complicated multicomponent complexes are also determined by their chemistry. Thus far no new chemical and physical

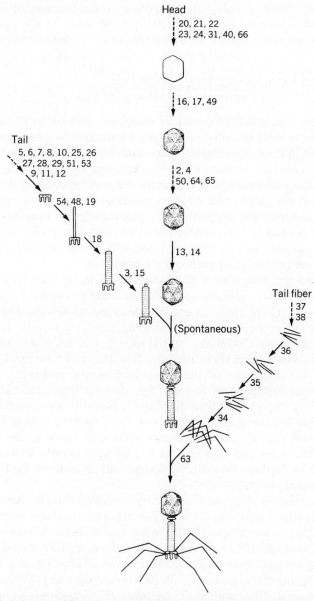

Figure 2-20. At bottom of figure is a complete virus particle. The viral genome itself conveys instructions for manufacture of its parts. Specific individual mutants of the virus, denoted by the numbers in the figures which represent the position of the defective gene in the chromosomal map of the virus, are unable to perform the specific operation shown on the arrow. (From Wood, Edgar, King, Lielausis, Fed. Proc. 27:5, 1968.)

principles *unique* to either the structure or the function of living material have emerged. Those who are hopeful about synthesizing a cell in the foreseeable future have every reason to retain their optimism.

A Detailed Example of a Long-Range Goal:
Cancer, Antibody Synthesis and Molecular Biology

To indicate the potential power of molecular biology in the service of man, we now wish to outline a proposed approach to a problem, chosen only as an important example, which combines an attack on the mechanism of antibody synthesis with an attempt to resolve the question of the origin and nature of some tumor cells. After defining the problem of antibody formation and briefly summarizing the known information, we shall describe the properties of certain malignant tumor cells (myelomas) which have an astonishing ability to synthesize antibodies. Finally, we shall propose two disciplines, immunology and cancer biology, that can be used to illuminate each other's problems.

Immunology. The science of immunology is in the midst of a blossoming not unlike that experienced by genetics and molecular biology about 15 years ago. There has been a tremendous growth fertilized by information from other areas of biology and biochemistry brought by investigators from many disciplines. In the next few pages is described some of what is now known about immunochemistry and how this knowledge impinges on a number of the most fundamental biological problems.

The original interest in immunology derived from medical practice, for the subject begins as a study of the reasons for increased resistance to infection following recovery from a first exposure. Thus, it has long been known that survivors of plague epidemics could safely remain in the infected cities and take care of the ill. Such empirical observations, bolstered by further controlled investigations, now form the basis of all immunization programs.

Studies, mostly done in this century, revealed the correlation of this kind of resistance to disease with the presence in the serum of a substance able to react *specifically* with, and reduce the infectivity of, the causative agent. This protective substance, a protein component of serum, is referred to as *antibody*. The serum of any animal is a concentrated mixture of very many proteins formed by many different organs of that animal. Electrophoretic methods of separating serum proteins from each other revealed a group of proteins called the gamma globulins. Antibodies proved to be among the gamma globulins.

The capacity of the organism to respond by producing a specific antibody as a reaction to each of an enormous number of foreign substances (*antigens*) is the *immune response.* Very large numbers of antibodies exist, all differing in their capacity to form specific combination with the particular antigen that led to their formation. This enormous variability poses special problems of the genetics, differentiation, and regulation of the cells that carry out these remarkable syntheses and comprise the immune system.

An interesting feature of antibodies is that except for their ability to react with the particular antigen, they are very difficult to distinguish from each other. Thus, they are all protein molecules, each almost identical with the other except for a small region, the combining site, responsible for its specific ability to attach to a particular antigen. How can the antibodies, which seem to be so similar as proteins, have such different combining sites? How can the cells of the immune system of the animal contain and regulate the extremely large number of similar genes seemingly needed to direct the synthesis of these proteins?

Let us consider how the recently elucidated structure of the antibody molecule indicates how the opposed characteristics of similarity and variability just described are expressed, particularly since these same structural comparisons of one antibody molecule with another yield clues about the determining genes. Recent experiments on the interactions of the cells that play a role in the immune response are beginning to hint at how this complex system performs and is regulated. So far, only the broad outline of the scheme is known.

The capacity to engage in the immune response results from an interplay of several different organs and of environmental triggers. In the maturing organism, cells of the bone marrow, thymus, lymph nodes, spleen, and white cells of the blood all interact by hormonelike substances or by direct contact. The capacity of a differentiating cell to form a single specific antibody out of the enormous number of possibilities available to the animal is a result of this complex reaction. Once the cell is set up to respond, it can be triggered to divide and make its specific antibody by introduction of a foreign substance (antigen) into the animal. The set of reactions, as far as they are known, in the maturing and developed adult can be described as follows.

Cells from the bone marrow that have reached a certain stage of development leave and travel via the bloodstream to the thymus. Here many divisions occur, apparently under the influence of a thymic hormone, and the cells make their commitment to the production of a single antibody. Cells so committed (called *lymphocytes*) now leave the thymus gland, wander into the bloodstream, and find their way to the spleen or the lymph nodes. These organs are highly organized structures made of several types of cells and are designed to remove foreign objects from the circulatory system. A variety of things can happen to a lymphocyte now residing in the spleen. If it should meet an antigen and make the encounter alone, it may be destroyed by it. This may happen for antigens in very low concentration. By this remarkable device, the body may be kept from making antibodies against body proteins that appear in the bloodstream in only trace amounts (e.g., the proteins of the thyroid or the lens of the eye).

On the other hand, if the antigen is there in larger quantity, another kind of cell is brought into action, the *macrophage,* which engulfs the antigen. Then, with bits of antigen stuck to its surface, the macrophage touches lymphocytes, finding finally the one ready to react to that antigen. This leads to multiplication of the lymphocytes and formation of large quantities of antibody. In addition, as the cells divide, certain of them are set aside in a more easily primed state (i.e., this time with a hair trigger), ready to respond quickly should the same antigen reappear. These primed cells seem to live in humans for many years. For such primed cells, very large quantities of antigen may be lethal, thus removing from the organism its capacity to respond to that particular antigen (the condition of "immune paralysis"). This device may be useful to prevent response of an organism to substances found in its blood in very large quantities—for example, its own serum proteins or red blood cells.

The preceding brief description of the interactions of cells of the immune system with each other and with external stimuli touches on many aspects of differentiation, genetics, and control of the cells composing a complex system. It will take a vast amount of work to fill in the necessary details. It is clear in any case that the kinds of phenomena observed in this system will be of great interest in studying other complex systems of interacting cells.

In addition, the understanding gained should produce clues to possible control points which will permit us to turn the immune response up or down as may be needed. Increasing the immune reaction would achieve an accelerated and augmented response to infectious agents or cancer cells. Conversely, repressing the immune mechanism would, for example, make transplantations of organs more successful; the same situation would also be of great medical importance in controlling those disease conditions caused by reactions of a person to his own body components (autoimmune diseases) or even to components in the environment, such as pollens (allergies). Some success in controlling the immune response has already been achieved.

Malignant Myeloma Tumors. The discovery first in humans and later in mice of a malignant tumor (myeloma) of the cells that form antibodies is another landmark in the explosive development of our understanding of antibodies and their formation. Moreover, this understanding has many implications for other kinds of mammalian cells and bears especially on how these cells express their different potentialities. Since, in addition, the myelomas are malignant cells, their detailed study should provide a clue to the control of their growth and possibly of other malignant cells.

Myelomas are recognizable in humans by an abnormal appearance of the bone marrow and blood cells and of the composition of the serum proteins. It is by the extensive use in hospitals and clinics of equipment and methods (e.g., gel electrophoresis of proteins) developed in research laboratories that the abnormality of the serum proteins is easily recognized. The disease of the marrow and blood is reflected in the excessive number of plasma cells, known to be the seat of manufacture of the immunoglobulins. The abnormality of the serum proteins is evident in the appearance of very large amounts of a single immunoglobulin. The immunoglobulins of normal serum are very heterogeneous, due to the very great variety of antibodies. On the other hand, the protein produced by a particular myeloma is exceedingly homogeneous, as if it were the product of a single cell and its descendants rather than of a diverse population. The purity of the myeloma proteins has made them extremely valuable for studying antibody structure. This cancerous condition, with the development of large numbers of cells all derived from a single one and all making the same protein, provides an enormous enrichment of this protein over the normal heterogeneous immunoglobulins. It thus became possible to purify a single protein from the mixture of proteins, a task that had seemed hopeless with the methods previously available in the laboratory. The purification attained has opened the way to a study of the amino acid sequences of individual antibodies. This information will lead eventually to the elucidation of their three-dimensional structures and the relation of their structure to the ability to serve as specific antibodies.

There was, at first, some question whether the myeloma proteins were true antibodies or some distorted related protein, for no activity as antibody could be demonstrated. Finding the matching antigen for the myeloma antibody seemed worse than hunting for a needle in the haystack. Recently, however, use of clever techniques has allowed the matching of several of the myeloma antibodies with their corresponding antigens and removed the earlier reservations about their not being "real antibodies."

An additional help in purifying antibodies and their component parts was the recognition that a long-known feature of the urine of a myeloma patient now had a simple explanation. In many such patients the appearance in the urine of a protein related to immunoglobulins had been noted. It was, naturally, thought to be a fragment of myeloma protein that had been degraded by passage through the kidney. It was instead found to be a normal *subunit* of the immunoglobulin produced in excess. This isolation in large quantities of the pure subunit, the smaller of the two different kinds composing an immunoglobulin molecule, allowed determination of its amino acid sequence and revealed the secret of the double theme of antibodies — plasticity and constancy. We return to this later.

While the incidence of human myelomas is not high, the human population is large and surveillance of its health is close; consequently, a large number of myeloma proteins have turned up. A limitation of the human material for study is that only small quantities of the cells that produce the myeloma are available.

This difficulty was solved by the extraordinary discovery that a condition exactly like the myeloma in humans could be induced in a laboratory mouse. Quite by accident in studying an unrelated phenomenon, it was observed that in certain mice there appeared a plasma cell tumor with low frequency. A young research worker at the National Institutes of Health, recognizing the great utility of having these tumors in laboratory animals, sought and found conditions for inducing these tumors with high frequency. Since the animals with the tumors were mice that had been so closely inbred that they accepted tissue grafts among themselves, the tumors, once induced, could be carried indefinitely in the laboratory by transplantation and used as standards anywhere in the world.

Analysis and Use of the Myeloma System. Two very interesting features of tumor induction stand as a challenge to our understanding. One is the mechanism underlying the ability of certain agents to induce the tumors. The other is the inheritance in the mice of the capacity to have these tumors induced. Strangely enough this capacity exists only in one strain of mice and seems to be transmitted in a straightforward genetic manner in crosses with other strains. It will be of great theoretical and practical importance to work out both of these aspects of tumor induction.

How are the mouse myelomas being used for research and what new uses can be envisaged? The fact that an enormous number of easily transplantable tumors can be induced, each making a single immunoglobulin or subunits, makes them extremely useful for a wide variety of problems. Some of these are outlined below.

Both human and mouse myelomas have already provided the key to the constancy and variability of the immunoglobulins. It was by determining the sequence of several myeloma light chains (the small subunit) that it became clear that each has a half that is constant from one myeloma to another, and a half that has differences characteristic of each myeloma. The same seems to be true of the heavy chain (the large subunit). Together the light and heavy chains form the combining site of the antibody molecules from their variable regions.

A development likely to follow from this will be the use of the myeloma proteins for x-ray diffraction analysis to yield the detailed configuration of the combining sites. These proteins provide the opportunity to make a structural analysis of a group of similar proteins with slight changes in them corresponding to different functions. The correspondence between structure and function could thus be determined with a new degree of refinement. We shall discuss at the end of the chapter a practical program for the selection of tumors useful for this purpose.

Not only will study of the myeloma proteins provide the structure-function relation indicated, but study of the tumors themselves will give insight into many problems of cellular regulation. While the myeloma cells are like ordinary plasma cells in their capacity to make antibody, they are different in two essential features. One, like other cancer cells, they are capable of indefinite division both in mice and, for some of them, in tissue culture. The other is that unlike normal plasma cells, which require contact of a precursor cell with antigen to turn on division and differentiation into an antibody-producing cell, the myeloma cells are independent of this requirement. It will be especially interesting to find the basis of this independence.

Several of the mouse myelomas have been adapted to grow outside the mouse in tissue culture. This opens the possibility of using these cells for physiological studies on either small- or large-scale cultures. For example, myelomas usually make and secrete an immunoglobulin. However, mutant forms can be isolated that no longer do so. Study in detail of the steps in the formation and secretion of immunoglobulin by the normal myelomas and of the blocked steps in the mutant ones will provide insight into processes like those carried out in many mammalian cells.

One of the developments that would enormously augment the utility of these cells for physiological and structural studies would be their adaptation to growth in large-scale cultures — e.g., hundreds or thousands of liters at once. In this way large amounts of cell components could be prepared and made available for study.

A final point that should not be overlooked is that these cultures could form primary standards to screen for effective chemotherapeutic agents to be used against the human myelomas, or which might have activity against other tumors.

The striking feature of antibodies — that they come in such an extremely large number of varieties while remaining very similar, and the recent understanding that this is a reflection of the combination between a constant portion common to all and another portion which supplies the variety—may not be restricted to structures of the immune system. There are other features of the cells of a complex organism that require wide diversity of similar structures. As example, the tags on cell surfaces that allow them to make the correct contacts in organ development may require a mechanism for making similar yet distinct cell coatings. Another instance is a nerve cell which must require a variety of tags to direct its contacts with other nerve cells and with muscles; similarly, cells of a given organ must have tags that direct them to reassociate even after being mechanically dispersed one from the other. The development of our understanding of the genetic basis for providing such an array of varieties in the immune system will influence our thinking and experimentation on other cellular features that also display a great deal of variety.

How might one imagine a project on a larger scale for exploiting the potentialities of the myelomas? There are so far in the United States not more than a handful of laboratories where the tumors are being induced and characterized. In each laboratory the manpower and cage facilities for mice needed are completely inadequate even for a program of moderate scale. Yet dozens of laboratories both in the United States and abroad already make extensive use of the few tumors characterized.

Among the mouse tumors, several hundred myeloma proteins had to be screened to find one with an antibody activity. A collection of myeloma proteins with known antibody activity suitable for crystallographic studies would require screening literally thousands of tumors, employing hundreds of thousands of mice.

It might be much easier to augment the utility of these tumors by a large-scale facility for the induction, characterization, and perhaps even determination of the amino acid sequences of many myeloma proteins. The accessibility of such a facility to the demands of workers in cellular biology could speed the pace of research in the problems of cancer, antibody synthesis, as well as related areas of embryology and cellular differentiation.

It will be evident that, in this proposal, little *immediate* use is made of our newfound understanding of the mechanisms of inheritance. Yet it should be understood that, without that understanding, this proposal could not have been conceived. The essence of the problem is an understanding of why and how myeloma cells overproduce a single antibody. This is an abnormality of the genetically controlled protein-making machinery of the cell.

Other potential applications of molecular biology could readily have been cited. Molecular biology provides the closest insight man has yet obtained of the nature of life—and, therefore, of himself.

Chapter 3

THE MATERIALS OF LIFE AND
THEIR TRANSFORMATIONS

A living cell is an unlikely object, vastly different from its environment. Large polymers predominate despite the fact that catalysts are capable of effecting their hydrolysis in the aqueous medium. Mineral ions, both anions and cations, are present in concentrations greatly different from that of the surrounding medium. Inside the cell are hundreds of molecular species not present at all in the bathing fluid. This object, born in a previous cell division, grows and divides again to give two identical daughter cells or, in the developing embryo, divides to yield cells specialized to the function of a new organ or tissue. In the adult certain specialized cells may never divide again but maintain themselves, in both form and function, for the entire lifetime of the organism of which they are a vital part. As revealed in detail in succeeding chapters, this cell is not a simple sac with a homogeneous mixture of contents. It is a wonderfully organized machine, with diverse parts specialized to accomplish specific tasks, the totality of which constitute the "life" of the cell.

These cellular substructures and the events they make possible can be described only in chemical terms. And this is equally true of the manner in which cells cooperate to form an organ, or organs cooperate to form an organism. This chapter cannot hope to present a detailed account of the current state of understanding of these structures or events. It will, however, attempt to summarize the highlights of current thought in these regards, offering a few selected examples in some detail. Those conversant with chemistry will find this chapter easily comprehensible: We hope that those who have had no experience in chemistry will make the attempt, though this will require patience and some effort.

Life is entirely dependent upon a few major elements: carbon, hydrogen, nitrogen, and oxygen. The myriad organic compounds characteristic of cells could not conceivably be usefully replaced by compounds formed from some other set of elements. The tetravalent structure of carbon, the covalent bond, the electrophilic properties of hydrogen, the nucleophilic properties of oxygen and nitrogen, are not to be found in equivalently useful form elsewhere in the periodic table. For example, a living system based on silicon instead of carbon offers insuperable difficulties, and this thought is not to be taken seriously. It is for such reasons, inter alia, that we believe that if "living" forms are to be found elsewhere in the cosmos, they will, in all likelihood, be based upon much the same chemistry as on Earth (see Chapter 5).

At its essence, life is made possible by the properties of a group of macromolecules. As we have already seen, the primary informational macromolecules are the deoxyribonucleic acids, the stuff of which genes are made (Chapter 2). The information so encoded is transcribed into complementary ribonucleic acids which serve variously as messengers, m-RNA, as the adapters which permit the message to specify individual amino acids in protein biosynthesis, t-RNA, and as part of the ribosomal protein-making machine by mechanisms yet to be ascertained, r-RNA. The ribosome and its enzymes, together with the cytoplasmic enzymes that bear the responsibility for fastening the right amino acid to the proper t-RNA, constitute an idiot machine which responds to instructions that arrive in the tape of messenger RNA. While the RNA survives in the cell, the proteins whose structures it encodes continue to be made. Hydrolytic destruction of m-RNA, catalyzed by a cellular ribonuclease, terminates the episode, but the "knowledge" of how to make this protein remains in the DNA, carefully protected in the cell nucleus to be drawn upon later when conditions warrant.

All other properties of the cell are the consequences of the battery of proteins synthesized by the genetic machinery. And they serve in a wide variety of roles. Some are purely structural, like the major protein found in mitochondria, or the collagen of bone and connective tissue, the keratin of hair and skin, and the fibroin of silk. Some serve as oxygen carriers, such as hemoglobin of red blood cells, myoglobin of muscle and the various pigmented proteins found in the blood or coelomic fluid of invertebrates. Some serve to coat DNA (the histones); transcription of genes in the organized nucleus requires that, in some fashion, the DNA be exposed by removal of the histone coat. Some are antibodies. Some are hormones. At the heart of living processes are those proteins that serve as catalysts — the enzymes which make possible and give direction to all of the synthetic and degradative processes of the cell. If the previous chapter was "An Ode to DNA," this chapter is "An Ode to Proteins."

Proteins

The chemical structure of all proteins is fundamentally the same. As already indicated, proteins are a linear array built of some 20 different amino acid residues which are united by covalent bonds resulting from head-to-tail condensation of adjacent amino acids. A protein molecule may contain one or several of such chains, and they may be identical or different in composition and sequence. The number of amino acid residues in a chain varies over wide limits, ranging from 20 to 30 in the case of some protein hormones, to several hundred in certain enzymes. *The specific chemical and biological properties of proteins are due to variations in the order in which their amino acid residues are assembled.*

All amino acids are of the same optical configuration, usually denoted as L-, except glycine which has no asymmetric carbon atom and hence is optically inactive. The joining of 20 different amino acids in a chain containing, for instance, 100 residues, which is relatively short for proteins, would allow for 20^{100} different combinations. Such a number is astronomically large. Even if there existed only one molecule of each kind, there would not be enough mass in this universe to accommodate all of these proteins. The actual number of proteins is very much smaller, perhaps of the order of 5,000 to 10,000 because only those that have a functional role and a selective advantage for the survival of the species are, in fact, expressed and have persisted.

Amino Acid Sequence. The determination of the chemical structure of a protein is a difficult undertaking. In 1953, the British biochemist Fred Sanger first demonstrated that the hormone insulin is not a random assembly of amino acid residues, but an orderly and unique arrangement of amino acid residues distributed among two chains which are held together by disulfide bonds (Fig. 3-1).

The strategy of such analyses is itself of interest. They are made possible by a variety of techniques. First, one requires knowledge of the molecular weight, obtained by ultracentrifugal analysis, and a precise, gross analysis of the protein indicating, per molecule of protein, the total number of residues of each of the 20 amino acids. Specific reagents

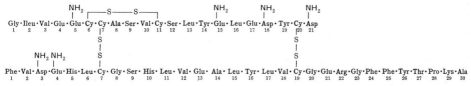

Figure 3-1. The amino acid sequence of bovine insulin. (From White, Handler, and Smith, *Principles of Biochemistry,* 4th ed., 1968, © McGraw-Hill, Inc.)

are available which can indicate the chemical nature of the amino acid at the amino terminus (left, as drawn) and carboxyl terminus (right, as drawn). Then advantage may be taken of the known specificity of hydrolytic enzymes such as trypsin, which cleaves bonds adjacent to an amino acid with a strong basic group, or chymotrypsin, which similarly cleaves bonds adjacent to an amino acid bearing an aromatic group. These would yield the two sets of smaller peptides shown in Figure 3-2.

In each case the peptides are separated and then analyzed by appropriate degradative procedures which remove one amino acid residue at a time but which can only be successfully applied to rather small peptides such as those shown. When the linear structure of each of the peptides is known, they may be fitted together like a jigsaw puzzle from the obvious overlaps. In the instance shown, only one solution exists to the puzzle.

Such sequence determinations have required some ten to fifteen man years for a single protein. Of the thousands of proteins that need to be characterized in such detail, there are hardly more than fifty for which this has been accomplished, and these are, in the main, relatively small proteins. Progress is likely to be accelerated in the near future, as the result of promising developments in automation of sequence analysis.

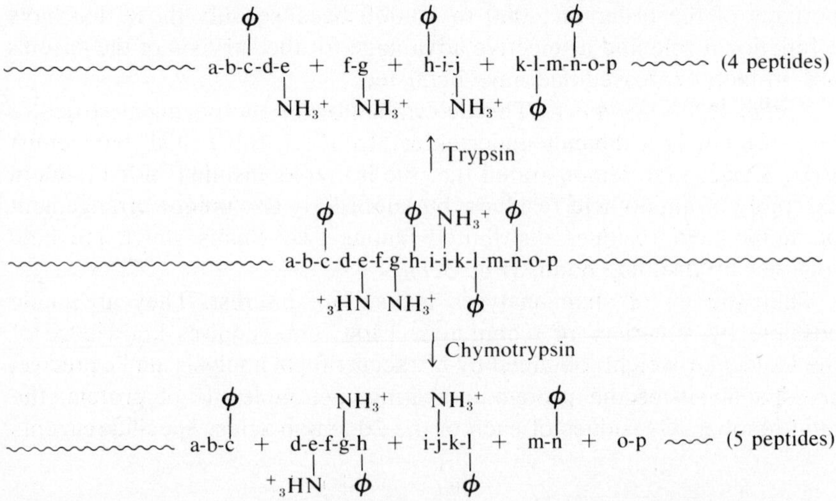

Figure 3-2. Determination of the amino acid sequence of a protein. In the center is shown a small segment of a protein in which the individual amino acids are designated as a through p. The enzyme trypsin catalyzes hydrolysis of the bond adjacent to an amino acid residue which bears a positive charge; chymotrypsin catalyzes hydrolysis of the bonds adjacent to amino acids bearing aromatic residues (ϕ). By analysis of the resulting smaller fragments, and examination of the overlaps, a unique sequence may be deduced for the original protein.

Protein Conformation. The linear covalent structure of a protein molecule is referred to as the primary structure. But, in fact, protein molecules are not simply linear strands of polypeptide chains. In nature the polypeptide chains of each protein are folded in a unique manner which brings the amino acid residues required for biological function into proper structural relationship to each other (Fig. 3-3).

There are essentially three basic patterns of folding that could be predicted from considerations of the known interatomic dimensions of model compounds such as amino acids and small peptides. In the regular conformation known as the *beta structure,* the polypeptide chains are fully extended; two or more adjacent chains held together by weak cross-links (hydrogen bonds) and can thus form layers or "sheets." Another regular conformation is the *alpha helix,* in which the polypeptide chain exists as a spiral analogous to the thread of a screw. This conformation is also stabilized by hydrogen bonds, parallel to the screw axis. Recognition of this structure required, among others, the bold realization that it involves a nonintegral periodicity, 3.6 amino acid residues for each full turn of the helix. In addition to these two regular and rigid conformations, polypeptide chains, of course, may assume loosely random orientations; in fact, a specific large molecule cannot be described by any one of these structures, but only by a combination of them.

This was first clearly revealed when the three-dimensional structure of myoglobin—a protein responsible for the binding of oxygen in muscle —was elucidated by x-ray analysis. Each of the few proteins for which the internal structure is now known exhibits a unique combination of alpha helices, beta structures, and "random" arrays. These are presently unpredictable but it is clear that they are dictated by chemical necessities originating in the primary structure. The stability of such a complex molecule containing thousands of atoms is determined by the multiplicity of forces operating within the structure and between the protein and its aqueous environment.

Three-Dimensional Structure. The greatest achievement in protein chemistry of the present decade is the determination of the three-dimensional structure of proteins by x-ray analysis. Protein molecules are too small to be directly visualized in all their detail by microscopy, since the limit of resolution of a microscope is approximately one half of a wavelength. For a molecule having a diameter of about 40 Å (1 Å = 10^{-8} centimeter) the light would have to be of the wavelength of x-rays, but since there are no lenses for x-rays, the indirect method of *x-ray diffraction* has to be used. In this procedure, the object has to be reconstituted by calculations from the patterns of the diffracted light. However, the relation of the phases to the object is unknown, and hence one

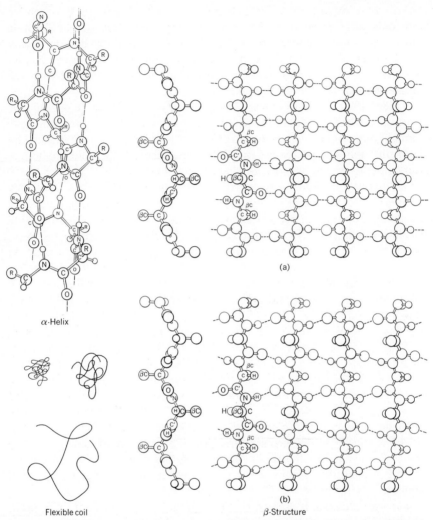

α-Helix

Flexible coil   β-Structure

Figure 3-3. Schematic representations of the major conformational structures encountered in proteins. The α-helix is a highly ordered structure whose dimensions and pitch are an intrinsic property of the structure of the protein backbone when stabilized by interactions between peptide bonds as shown by the dashed lines. Two forms of β structure are shown. Again, the general structure is determined by the intrinsic structure of the backbone of the polypeptide chain and is stabilized by interactions between parallel chains. The flexible coil exhibits no constant orderly structure; the final conformation is determined by interactions of hydrophobic residues with each other forming the interior of the protein with an orientation of hydrophilic residues on the exterior of the total structure. (From Tanford, *The Physical Chemistry of Macromolecules*, 1961. © John Wiley & Sons, Inc.)

doesn't know a priori whether one ends up with a real structure or with an "inside-out" structure. This is similar to a geographic contour map which doesn't distinguish the valleys from the peaks unless one has a marker. These markers in x-ray diffraction analysis are heavy metal atoms which are particularly electron dense and thus can be used as guideposts. The first task of the crystallographer, therefore, is to prepare heavy metal (platinum, lead, mercury) derivatives of the protein, which assume a crystal form identical with that of the native protein. Reconstruction of the three-dimensional conformation of the protein molecule from the diffraction pattern is a long and laborious procedure and requires both imagination and much computer time. But the final results more than warrant the effort required.

Sperm whale myoglobin was the first protein for which the complete three-dimensional structure was elucidated (Fig. 3-4). The structural determination of the related respiratory protein, hemoglobin, is now nearing completion.

There are four other proteins, each of them an enzyme, for which the three-dimensional structure is known with considerable certainty. These are lysozyme, a widely distributed enzyme that breaks up the cell walls of certain bacteria; ribonuclease, a pancreatic enzyme that hydrolytically degrades ribonucleic acids; and pancreatic chymotrypsin and carboxypeptidase, enzymes that catalyze protein degradation. At the time when this report went to press, the three-dimensional structure of the protein hormone, insulin, was announced.

Examination of the tortuous arrangement of the polypeptide chain within a protein molecule, such as myoglobin or lysozyme, raises the question of how such a structure is built, with such high precision, by the biosynthetic apparatus of the living cell. It now seems certain that the three-dimensional folding of the polypeptide chain is determined entirely by the primary sequence of the amino acids — that is, the mutual attractions of various amino acid side chains to each other: positive charges to negative charges, hydrogen bond donors to hydrogen bond acceptors, oily hydrophobic regions to other oily hydrophobic regions. The multitude of such interactions determines the way in which the final three-dimensional structure is achieved. Thus the information transfer DNA to RNA to protein not only contains the instructions for the primary structure of the protein but also determines its conformation. The simplicity of this process is elegant. When a sufficient number of such structures have been established, it should be possible to establish the governing rules and, thus, predict three-dimensional structure from knowledge of primary sequence structure — and, moreover, obviate what appeared to be one of the most difficult problems in biology, since it

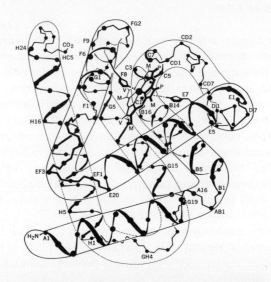

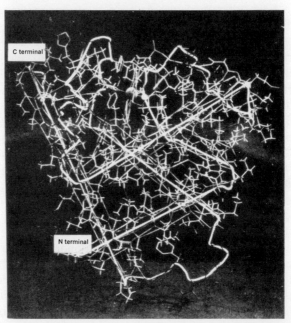

Figure 3-4. The three-dimensional structure of myoglobin as determined by x-ray diffraction analysis. A. The major sections of the polypeptide backbone indicating those sections of the chain which exist in α-helical form. (From Neurath and Bailey, *The Proteins*, 1961. © Academic Press, Inc.) B. A detailed representation of the same structure indicating the position of each atom of the molecule. The iron atom is the sphere in the upper central portion of the molecule and the small white sphere next to it represents a single water molecule. (From Kendrew, Watson, Strandberg, Dickerson, Phillips and Shore, Nature, *190*:669, 1961.)

describes the means by which a compact, three-dimensional structure is formed without the intervention of some complicated mechanical device. Meanwhile, it is evident that the biological properties of proteins are an expression of their three-dimensional structures.

This concept is strengthened by experience with proteins in which stable cross-bridges are formed between amino acids within the same polypeptide chain (see structure of ribonuclease, Fig. 3-5). Thus ribonuclease, a protein consisting of a single chain, contains 4 internal disulfide bridges. If these are opened by reduction in an environment in which the entire molecule exists as a random coil, and the conditions then reversed so that disulfides reform, more than 90 percent of the enzymic activity is regained. Yet, theoretically, there are 256 different ways in which the 4 disulfides could be formed from the 8 sulfhydryl groups of the molecule. Since, in all likelihood, only one of these could be enzymically active, viz., native ribonuclease, it is evident that it is the folding pattern determined by the primary structure which establishes the subsequent location of the disulfide bridges. This is an elegant and most elemental instance of the operation of the "principle of self-assembly" (see p. 80).

If the same experiment is conducted with insulin (Fig. 3-1), reduction breaks the disulfides that join the two chains, permitting their separation. Restoration of an oxidizing environment restores some insulin activity, but the low recovery indicates that the disulfides are reforming randomly and that all possible recombinations do indeed occur. This suggested that pancreatic islet cells must contain some additional "instructing" device to assure a good yield of insulin itself after the two chains were synthesized. But no such device could be found—and a much simpler and more elegant solution emerged. Pancreatic cells contain an additional protein which has been called *pro-insulin* for it is the precursor of insulin. As compared with insulin this may be drawn as

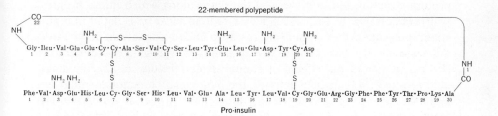

Pro-insulin

A 22-membered peptide connects the carboxy terminal of the B chain, alanine, with the amino terminal of the A chain. Clearly, the gene that codes for this hormone specifies the entire $30 + 22 + 21 = 73$ membered structure which, like ribonuclease, spontaneously and without directions or assistance, assumes the conformation that then assures formation of the disulfides found in insulin. When this compound is reduced so that the disulfide bridges open and then are allowed to rejoin, proinsulin is again formed in high yield. Thereafter, a hydrolytic enzyme, also found in pancreas, and seemingly specific to its task, hydrolytically removes the connecting 22-membered polypeptide loop, leaving the active hormone. The protein is initially synthesized as a single chain of amino acids, assumes spontaneously exactly the proper three-dimensional conformation and loss of the loop results in the final structure of insulin. Thus, the principle of self-assembly remains inviolate; the three-dimensional structure of insulin, including location of its three disulfides, is the necessary consequence of the sequence of amino acids in the polypeptide strand synthesized by the genetic machinery.

Thus, the insight afforded by the experience with ribonuclease guided this study of the anomaly of insulin behavior and led to the final, unexpected solution. It is of particular interest, also, that comparison of the A and B chains of insulins from diverse species reveals only a few amino acid substitutions, whereas the 22-membered connecting loop, which has no biological function but to assure proper folding of the chain before disulfide formation, shows a great many interspecies differences. This conversion of a protein from an inactive to the active form, by the splitting of a strategically located peptide bond, has been observed in other systems also. For instance, the digestive enzymes such as trypsin, chymotrypsin, or pepsin are secreted by the cells in an inactive precursor form in order to protect the tissue of origin from destruction by the very product they synthesize. The generation of enzymatic activity is an extracellular process and is mediated by a specific enzyme usually found in another tissue. This process is known as zymogen activation.

Structure-Function Relationships. The past successes in the field of protein structure indicate some of the paths along which future progress will probably lie. In the first place, a protein must be isolated in a pure state; the sequence of amino acid residues must be determined; the three-dimensional structure must be ascertained by crystallographic methods; and by studies of the effects of chemical modification of specific amino acid residues on biological activity, the biologically functional amino acid residues can be recognized. Such studies have proven to be particularly fruitful in the case of certain hydrolytic enzymes such as ribonuclease, chymotrypsin, lysozyme, or carboxypeptidase; but as yet, for no one protein have all of these procedures been applied to completion. These gaps are rapidly being filled, and a complete correlation between chemical structure and biological function will soon be at hand for several of these enzymes.

Enzymes

A living cell is a miniature chemical factory. Large polymeric molecules are degraded; others are synthesized. A relatively small group of organic compounds are accepted from the environment and utilized for the synthesis of all other organic compounds in the cell, including the monomers used for polymer synthesis. Other molecules are degraded to be discarded or reutilized. From some cells are released secretory products, made in the cell but to be utilized elsewhere—e.g., glucose, cholesterol, steroid hormones, protein hormones, antibodies, digestive enzymes. The details of the thousands of reactions involved include most of the major types of reaction known in synthetic organic chemistry—hydrolysis, dehydration, aldol condensations, alkylation, ammonolysis, acylation, oxidation, reduction, etc. None of these reactions proceed spontaneously at a rate commensurate with the demands of the living cell. Each reaction is catalyzed by an enzyme which, on its surface, specifies the reactants that shall participate and the manner in which they shall react. In most instances, in the absence of the enzyme the reaction would not even occur at a detectable rate. Even the seemingly simple and spontaneous process of the reversible combination of carbon dioxide and water to form carbonic acid occurs insufficiently rapidly to satisfy physiological requirements. The mammalian red blood cell and many other tissues contain the enzyme carbonic anhydrase, which accelerates this combination several thousandfold.

Enzymes are more effective than simple inorganic or organic catalysts. The rate advantage is of the order of 10^8 to 10^9, which in space is the same rate advantage that a man-made satellite has over a snail.

The first enzyme to be isolated in crystalline form was urease, barely 40 years ago, soon to be followed by the isolation of digestive enzymes from gastric and pancreatic secretions. The demonstration that these enzymes were in fact proteins provided the impetus for the development of protein chemistry, on the one hand, and for the study of the mechanisms by which enzyme catalysis occurs, on the other. Several hundred different enzymes have since been isolated in a high degree of purity. The vast area of macromolecular structure and function opened up as a scientific wilderness to be explored by theory and experimentation, and in the short period of 25 years, our understanding of enzymes and enzyme function has advanced from an image of a "black box" to a three-dimensional molecular entity in which thousands of atoms are each uniquely placed in position. Thus, in a few instances enzymatic specificity can now be described in precise structural and functional terms.

Enzymes are highly specific in their action. They can differentiate between optical isomers—that is, compounds that are identical in structure except that one is the mirror image of the other. Enzymes are sensitive to minor variations in chemical structure of the compounds on which they act, the substrates. They can sense the addition or deletion of a hydrogen atom, of a double bond, of a carbon atom, etc. They epitomize the principle of biological specificity on the molecular level.

The specificity of an enzyme resides in its "active site," that discrete region which is poised to receive the reacting compound, the substrate. Complementariness in shape, or "fit," is one of the major requisites for biological specificity on the molecular level. The other is chemical attraction of interacting sites. Because of the paramount importance of the process of enzymic catalysis, a somewhat detailed account of the present state of understanding of one enzyme, pancreatic ribonuclease, follows. As will be seen, the success of this analysis has been made possible by the availability of large quantities of the enzyme (grams rather than micrograms), which is then manipulated as an ordinary chemical and its reaction behavior studied. Such an analysis was impossible when enzymes could be had only in trace quantities sufficient to demonstrate their catalytic properties.

Ribonuclease

Ribonuclease (RNAase) catalyzes the hydrolysis of the phosphodiester bonds in ribonucleic acids, the bridges between the consecutive nucleotides in the RNA chain. By its action, the RNA is degraded into smaller and smaller fragments leaving, finally, a mixture of 3'-ribonucleotides. The bond hydrolyzed is that between phosphorus and the oxygen of the 5'-hydroxyl group of ribose.

This process is actually carried out in two steps. The first of these is the transesterification reaction yielding a 2',3' cyclic phosphate ester. The second step is the hydrolysis of the cyclic phosphodiester to yield the final product with the phosphate group linked to the 3 carbon of the ribose. This may be summarized structurally as follows, where R_1 and R_2 are bases in the RNA chain:

The relative velocities of steps 1 and 2 differ with ribonucleases from different sources. The need to form a cyclic phosphodiester as an intermediate in this overall process explains part of the specificity of ribonuclease. Deoxyribonucleic acid (DNA) is insensitive to ribonuclease since it has no hydroxyl group on C_2 of ribose, and thus cannot undergo the transesterification reaction.

The nonenzymatic hydrolysis of phosphodiesters has been studied to gain some insight into the enzymatic reaction. Thus:

The intermediate compound II, shown above (ethylene phosphate), contains a strained five-membered ring, and it hydrolyzes very rapidly owing to this strain. This poses a conceptual problem: If the ring of ethylene phosphate is so strained, what drives the reaction that forms that ring?

Cleaving a large molecule into two smaller ones is associated with an increase in *entropy* (a measure of randomness), and it is the energy change associated with this increase in entropy that drives reaction I. In simple solution, the hydrolysis of methyl hydroxyethyl phosphate (compound I) can be catalyzed by nitrogenous organic bases, notably imidazole. Thus 10 M imidazole (a very high concentration) enhances the rate of hydrolysis of compound I by a factor of 10^5. Can we then simply explain the action of ribonuclease as being due to catalysis by an imidazole residue close to the substrate binding site? Not quite. Because ribonuclease speeds up the rate of its substrates by about 10^{10} fold. We are therefore left short by an additional factor of 10^5. What phenomena span this gap?

Many studies with model systems have shown that attack by two catalytic groups acting in concert is vastly more effective than either acting by itself. We might therefore propose that the active site of ribonuclease could contain a *pair of imidazole* groups provided by residues of the amino acid histidine, so placed that concerted action is possible—i.e., when the substrate becomes attached to the enzyme, both imidazoles have access to the bonds in question. This might well effect an enhancement of hydrolysis of the substrate by a factor that approaches the known catalytic efficiency of this enzyme. While considering an ideal action site for ribonuclease one more refinement may be added. The phosphate group that links the ribose units of RNA bears one negative charge due to ionization of a proton. If our active site could bear a fixed positive charge so placed as to form an electrostatic tie-down for this negative charge on the phosphate, binding of the substrate in precise fashion to permit operation of the histidine residues would be vastly facilitated. The ϵ ammonium group of a lysine residue could provide this fixed positive charge. The mechanism we now propose is, then, as follows:

The alcohol group of the second nucleotide which is hydrogen-bonded to the imidazole nitrogen is then replaced by H—*OH* from the water, and we can now consider the second step—i.e., the hydrolysis of the cyclic phosphodiester, by the same pair of nitrogen atoms from histidine residues.

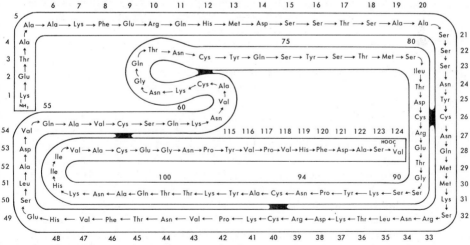

It is apparent that the mechanism proposed could accomplish the overall reaction; it should exhibit approximately the required catalytic efficiency and leave the active site ready for another catalytic cycle. In fact, a remarkable collection of data has been found to support it.

Ribonuclease is a single polypeptide chain of 124 amino acid residues: its complete amino acid sequence is unambiguously known. It contains 8 residues of cysteine which are joined by 4 specific disulfide bonds. The complete structure is shown in Figure 3-5.

Figure 3-5. The amino acid sequence of ribonuclease. Dark patches represent stable cross-bridges formed between amino acids within the same polypeptide chain. (From Smyth, Stein, and Moore, J. Biol. Chem. *238*:227, 1963.)

A graph of RNAase activity plotted as a function of pH shows a sharp peak at pH 7. Detailed analysis of this curve indicates that there must be two ionizable cationic acid groups at the active site. It is highly possible, then, that these groups are imidazoles, since proteins afford few other possibilities.

Iodoacetic acid (ICH_2COOH), which acts as a carboxymethylating agent, was found irreversibly to inactivate RNAase, yet did not seem to react with RNAase, whose tight three-dimensional structure had been opened by such reagents as urea (denaturation). Hence the residues in RNAase that react with iodoacetate only do so by virtue of the native configuration of this enzyme and could, therefore, be at the active center. Further support for this supposition arises from the fact that competitive inhibitors (compounds that can reversibly bind at the active site of the enzyme but are unaffected thereby, and hence prevent the enzyme from acting on the substrate while it is so engaged) of RNAase such as 3'-cytidylic acid serve to protect the enzyme against the action of iodoacetate.

RNAase which had been completely inhibited by iodoacetate was found to be a mixture of two proteins which could be separated from each other. One of these was found to contain a carboxymethyl group on the No. 1 nitrogen of the histidine in position 119 and the other on the No. 3 nitrogen of the histidine in position 12. Thus a given molecule of RNAase can be carboxymethylated at one position or another, but not on both, and not on either of the other two histidine residues in the enzyme. We must conclude, therefore, that histidine-119 and histidine-12 are especially reactive, they are probably at the active site, and the positive charge on one facilitates the carboxymethylation of the other in a reciprocal fashion, so that on any one enzyme molecule, one or the other, but not both, can be carboxymethylated.

RNAase is also very sensitive to Cu^{++}, being inhibited by 10^7 M of this metal ion. Detailed studies again suggest that the ligands which exhibit such high affinity for Cu^{++} in the native enzyme are the nitrogens of histidine-119 and histidine-12. From the structure of the copper atom, it can then be calculated that these histidine residues are approximately 5 Å apart.

If histidine-12 and histidine-119 are held in some specific orientation, one with respect to the other, and if they cooperate in causing one or the other to react with iodoacetate, then one might expect some stereospecificity to be associated with this alkylation reaction. This was confirmed by the finding that D-α-bromo-n-butyrate alkylates predominantly histidine-12, while the L-isomer of this compound alkylates predominantly histidine-119.

Reaction with one mole of 2,4-dinitrofluorobenzene (DNFB) per mole of enzyme causes irreversible inactivation of RNAase. The presence of either substrates or of competitive inhibitors of the enzyme protects against this inactivation. Hence, DNFB must modify some residue located at the active site. This single dinitrophenyl group was found to be on the ϵ amino group of lysine No. 41. Most importantly, whereas there are 11 lysine residues per molecule of RNAase, only one reacts with DNFB. Thus, this ϵ amino group must also be associated with the active site.

O-methylisourea can also form derivatives of the same ϵ amino group of lysine, but whereas the DNFB destroys the catalytic properties of the enzyme, O-methylisourea does not. The reaction is

$$
\underset{\text{O—CH}_3}{\overset{\text{O—CH}_3}{H_2N—C=N^+H_2}} \;+\; R—NH_2 \;\rightarrow\; R—N—C\overset{NH_2^+}{\underset{NH_2}{\Big/\Big\backslash}} \;+\; CH_3OH
$$

Note that there remains a positively charged group. Hence we must conclude that the lysine-41 at the active site of RNAase is probably important by virtue of the positive charge provided by its ϵ amino group.

If RNAase is treated with the hydrolytic enzyme subtilisin, a protease secreted into the culture medium by *Bacillus subtilis,* it is cleaved between alanine-20 and serine-21 (Fig. 3-5). This single cleavage separates single polypeptide chain into two chains, one 20-residue S-peptide and an S-protein 104 residues long. Nevertheless the RNAase retains its activity, an observation correlated with the fact that S-peptide and the S-protein adhere to each other with great tenacity, albeit by noncovalent bonds. However, by appropriate manipulation S-peptide can be separated from S-protein; these two fragments are completely inactive enzymically but, when mixed, readily recombine. The association constant for this recombination is $>10^9$. If the S-peptide is photoxidized with methylene blue, its histidine-12 is destroyed and the peptide will no longer restore activity to the S-protein. If the S-protein is similarly treated to modify histidine-119, no activity can be restored by S-peptide. Various fragments of the S-peptide have been chemically synthesized and tested for their ability to restore activity to S-protein. A fragment comprising residues 1 to 11 was totally inactive, whereas a synthetic peptide containing residues 1 to 13 was fully active, although it had much lower affinity for the S-protein than the complete S-peptide. Thus, the many small forces ordinarily operative in the three-dimensional folding of the protein suffice to attach the S-peptide in just the right place on the surface of the S-protein so that histidine-12 can usefully function in the catalytic cycle.

The collected evidence suggests that RNAase does in fact operate by the mechanism proposed from consideration of the hydrolysis of specific phosphate diesters. Histidine-12 and -119 act in a concerted fashion to carry out the transesterification and then the hydrolysis of the cyclic phosphodiester intermediate; the ϵ ammonium group of lysine-41 serves as a cationic tie-down for the negative charge on the phosphate and these residues are brought into precise juxtaposition at the active site by virtue of the specific folding of the other 121 amino acid residues of this protein. When the three-dimensional structure of ribonuclease was recently elucidated by x-ray analysis, these deductions were completely sustained. The specific groupings of the active site were found to have precisely the proper predicted relationships to each other; and in addition, the enzyme molecule showed a deep cleft which could accommodate the portion of the ribonuclease substrate that undergoes hydrolysis.

The organic chemist usually considers as final proof of structure the total synthesis of a molecule having all known properties of the compound in question. This proof has been recently provided by the controlled stepwise synthesis of a molecule, from individual amino acids, having all known chemical, physical and enzymatic properties of bovine pancreatic ribonculease. This extraordinary achievement represents the first synthesis of an enzyme by methods of organic chemistry!

This has been a rather lengthy summary of the current state of knowledge of this enzyme, all of which has been gained in the last decade. But this tale is of great significance. It removes the magic from enzymic catalysis while demonstrating the wondrous versatility of polymers formed by condensations of a few amino acids. And it illustrates our central thesis—life is the expression of the surface properties of the biopolymers.

Enzymes with Subunit Structures

Ribonuclease, chymotrypsin, lysozyme, and subtilisin, the hydrolytic enzymes that we have mentioned thus far, are composed of single chains. All function in digestion, outside the cytoplasm of a living cell. However, most enzymes operative in intracellular metabolic conversions are composed of several chains or subunits bound by weaker forces. Their active sites are seemingly distributed among segments of the various chains. Their biological functions, therefore, are dependent on the integrity, the three-dimensional structure, of the entire quaternary complex.

Moreover, the interactions between these subunits has proved to be an important aspect of the regulation of enzyme function. The earliest indication of this property was the behavior of hemoglobin. This protein is not an enzyme, but its functional behavior first indicated the consequences of subunit interactions in modifying functional properties. Figure

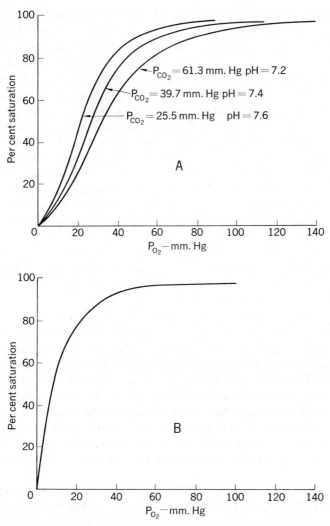

Figure 3-6. Oxygen binding by hemoglobin and myoglobin. Note the sigmoid character of the hemoglobin curves (A) which indicates that the presence of O_2 bound to some of its four subunits enhances the binding affinity for additional oxygen. In contrast, binding by myoglobin (B), which consists of a single chain much like one of the four units of hemoglobin, is represented by a hyperbolic curve, the simple expression of the normal law of mass action. (From White, Handler, and Smith)

3-6 shows the binding of O_2 to myoglobin and to hemoglobin as a function of oxygen pressure. Myoglobin, which exhibits a simple hyperbolic, oxygen binding curve, consists of a single chain much like those of hemoglobin. Hemoglobin, however, which exhibits a sigmoidal binding curve, is a tetramer which can bind four molecules of O_2, one at each iron atom; and as the curve indicates, the binding of oxygen to the first subunit enhances the affinity of the remaining subunits; binding of the second and third O_2 similarly increases the affinity of the remaining binding sites. Since each such site is on a different subunit, it is clear that attachment of O_2 must result in a conformational change in the subunit, which is then altered in its binding to the adjacent units. The simplest indication of this process is the observation that introduction of oxygen into a suspension of hemoglobin crystals cracks the crystals! The detailed nature of this rearrangement has been reconstructed by x-ray crystallography.

The subunit structure of many enzymes permits the fine regulation of their activity required for harmonious yet responsive metabolic activity. The details of this process are known for only a handful of enzymes but the generalities are now clear. To understand their import, consider the schematic set of events shown in Figure 3-7.

The starting material for many biosyntheses in almost all cells is the sugar glucose. If glucose is present in excess it can be stored as a polymer, glycogen, from which it can also be withdrawn as required. If these events are to match cellular requirements, the responsible enzymes, which catalyze the participating reactions, must be "turned on" or "turned off" as circumstances warrant. Similarly, the rate at which glucose is used for biosynthesis of a metabolic end product, such as the pyrimidine and purine nucleotides which occur in the nucleic acids, should be commensurate with the rate at which they are required. Let us examine two enzymes whose properties make possible such rate regulation.

Aspartic Transcarbamylase. The first step in the series of reactions that lead ultimately to formation of cytidine triphosphate (CTP) is the

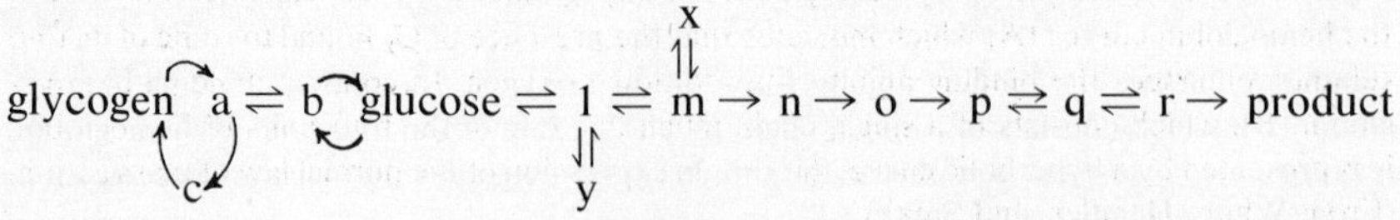

$$\text{glycogen} \overset{a}{\underset{c}{\rightleftharpoons}} b \ \text{glucose} \rightleftharpoons l \rightleftharpoons \overset{x}{\underset{y}{\underset{\Updownarrow}{m}}} \rightarrow n \rightarrow o \rightarrow p \rightleftharpoons q \rightleftharpoons r \rightarrow \text{product}$$

Figure 3-7. Schematic metabolic map of interconversion of glucose and glycogen and of conversion of glucose to a desired end product such as an amino acid, or a purine or a pyrimidine. Reaction $m \rightarrow n$ is the "committed" step in the latter pathway since compounds n, o, p, q, and r are of no utility to the cell except as intermediates in the formation of the desired product.

reaction between carbamyl phosphate and aspartic acid to form carbamyl aspartic acid.

$$H_2N—C—O—PO_3H_2 \quad + \quad H_2N—CH—CH_2—COOH \longrightarrow$$
$$\underset{O}{\parallel} \hspace{6.5cm} \underset{COOH}{|}$$

$$H_2N—C—N—CH—CH_2—COOH$$
$$\underset{O}{\parallel}\ \underset{H}{|}\ \underset{COOH}{|}$$

The enzyme that catalyzes this reaction has a molecular weight of 300,000. As shown in Figure 3-8, if reaction velocity is plotted against aspartic acid concentration a somewhat sigmoid curve is obtained. If the enzyme is treated with mercurials, it breaks up into identical subunits, molecular weight 33,000, which are even more active than the parent enzyme, and which yield the hyperbolic velocity plot expected for the simplest form of catalytic activity. In addition, however, there are identical subunits of molecular weight 17,000 each. These have no catalytic activity, but if the mercury is removed, they rejoin the catalytically active subunits to form native enzyme. Most importantly, if CTP is added, the

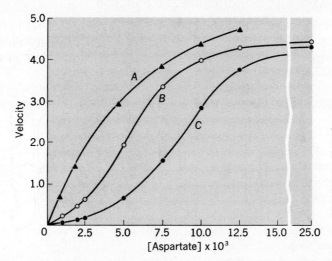

Figure 3-8. Velocity of aspartate transcarbamylase as a function of substrate concentration. Curve *A* illustrates the behavior of the enzyme in the presence of a mercurial. In this condition, the enzyme exhibits normal Michaelis kinetics and n = 1. The enzyme has been dissociated into separate catalytic and regulatory subunits. Curve *B* shows the behavior of the native enzyme; it is evident that n > 1. Curve *C* shows the effect of 2.0×10^{-4}M CTP. The curve is shifted on the abscissa: K is increased, reflecting a decreased affinity of the enzyme for substrate, i.e. a higher concentration of aspartate is required to attain the same velocity. (From White, Handler, and Smith)

kinetic behavior shifts from curve B to curve C, where the affinity of enzyme for its proper substrate is markedly reduced, as is the maximal velocity of the reaction. Thus, the second subunits create a binding site for CTP, and when this is so occupied, as shown diagrammatically in Figure 3-9, the enzyme is very markedly inhibited. If, therefore, the cell has enough CTP, the latter automatically prevents its own synthesis. This is a perfect example of the "negative feedback" principle which is so widely used in electronic engineering.

Glycogen Synthetase. A complementary process is found on the left side of Figure 3-7. In this figure, *b* is really the compound glucose-6-phosphate. The enzyme *glycogen synthetase,* which catalyzes formation of glycogen from uridine diphosphate glucose (*c* in Fig. 3-7), shows kinetics like those of curve *C* in Figure 3-8. In the presence of glucose-6-phosphate (compound *b*), the curve is now that shown as curve *B.* Thus, accumulation of glucose-6-phosphate, by *activating* the enzyme assures its own storage for later usage, an example of "positive feed forward." And again, this is made possible by the subunit structure of the enzyme.

Evolution of Enzyme Structure and Function

Since life began, the blueprints of protein biosynthesis have been undergoing change. Evolution has resulted in greater diversity on both the morphological and the molecular level. The pathways of metabolism

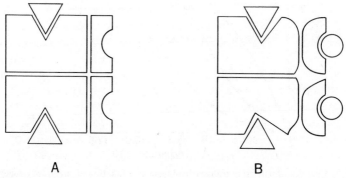

A   B

Figure 3-9. Schematic representation of allosteric inhibition. *A* shows the enzyme, constructed of two enzymic subunits with active sites at the angular clefts which exactly fit the substrate (triangles). The smaller subunits have no substrate binding sites but can bind the final product (circles) of the reaction sequence in which the enzyme participates. When the latter binding occurs, the structure of the reacting subunit is deformed, in turn deforming the enzymic units so that they no longer snugly fit the substrate. Hence, enzymic function is inhibited by the end-product of its catalysis.

have become more complex and the enzymes that control them more diverse and more specific. Yet the proteins and enzymes of our era still contain some of the structural and functional traits of their ancestry and thus have provided us with clues to their evolution.

Although the fidelity of protein biosynthesis is well-nigh perfect, the biosynthetic mechanism is under continued attack by mutations. The genetic message is protected against mutational consequences, at least in part, by the fact that more than one combination of nucleotide triplets codes for the same amino acid.

However, many mutations necessarily give rise to amino acid replacements in the protein product. Such replacements may be inconsequential, if they do not affect the biological function of the protein. However, when such replacements occur in the region of the active site, biological function may be modified or completely abolished. In the latter instance, if the reaction for which the enzyme is responsible is vital to the cell, in the homozygous state (both parental genes the same), this mutation is lethal. If the enzyme catalyzes a reaction that is not absolutely essential, such as those responsible for the ultimate degradative fates of amino acids, then a mutation at the active site can result in a disease of varying seriousness. More than three dozen hereditary diseases of man are known in which the specifically affected protein has been identified (see Chapter 16).

Two other situations may be recognized in which mutation leads to amino acid substitutions. Comparison of proteins fulfilling the same function in different organisms has revealed an astonishing degree of amino acid replacement. Thus, the protein cytochrome c, which is widely distributed in nature, but which is not an enzyme, is a chain of 105 amino acids. Examination of this protein from 30 species has revealed amino acid replacements in all but about 20 positions, most notably a single segment of 12 amino acids which appears to be the binding site for the enzyme that reacts with it. Significantly, and as might be expected, the further apart two species are on the evolutionary tree—i.e., the longer the time since they separated from a common ancestor—the greater the number of differences in their amino acid sequences. For example, human cytochrome c differs from that of chimpanzee, rhesus monkey, dog, tuna, moth, and yeast in 0, 1, 11, 21, 31 and 44 positions, respectively.

Studies of amino acid sequences have also provided a partial answer to the question, "Where do new proteins come from?" It is clear that the cells of highly advanced species have much more DNA than those of more primitive organisms. And they also have many more proteins. But how did this happen? One hypothesis has postulated that, from time to time, there occur partial mitoses, instances in which only one chromosome or only a part thereof undergoes replication. Later, when proper mitosis occurs, this DNA also duplicates. The cells in which this happens successfully then have four instead of two genes for a given protein. Since one pair will suffice, mutations in the other pair are of no consequence, and these genes are free to mutate in such fashion as to alter their function. Examination of the amino acid sequences of myoglobin and the α, γ, β, and δ chains of human hemoglobin makes it entirely clear that these have all come from a common ancestor, although all five are now represented by at least two genes. Indeed, from the number of amino acid replacements it can be said that they have branched from each other in just the order here listed. Many other dramatic illustrations of this principle are known. For example, the digestive enzymes trypsin, chymotrypsin and elastase, of the pancreas, as well as the enzyme thrombin, which participates in blood clotting, have similar basic structures with about half their amino acids held in common. The differences, however, have made possible their great differences in enzymic specificity, to the benefit of the species in which this occurred. Again the small octapeptide hormones of the neurohypophysis clearly derive from a common ancestral gene, but now have vastly different biological effects. And a similar situation is found in the close resemblance between glucagon, the blood-sugar-raising hormone of the pancreas, and the duodenal hormone cholecystokinin, which causes the gallbladder to contract. Finally we may note the resemblance between the amino acid sequence of lysozyme and that of one subunit of the enzyme responsible for synthesis of the sugar of milk, lactose. Both deal with carbohydrate substrates, but one catalyzes a hydrolytic degradation and the other, in conjunction with a second protein, catalyzes the reverse synthetic process. Undoubtedly many more such examples will emerge, since none of the foregoing were known a decade ago. But these examples amply establish the validity of the hypothesis that has been offered to explain where new proteins come from. They come from blueprints of old proteins.

Metabolism

A living cell is a busy, dynamic system. Unicellular organisms, under favorable circumstances, continue to grow and divide, a process that requires that there be synthesized and accumulated all of the materials requisite to formation of a new cell. Even if it is not so engaged, there is constant traffic, across its membranes, of ions and other solutes, and the cell must maintain the constancy of its composition. In the mature cells of the adult mammal there is constant need for the activity by which the cell makes its contribution to the organism; nerve cells conduct, muscle cells contract, kidney cells secrete, as do those of the endocrine and digestive organs, and the liver is a factory processing raw materials received in the diet and dispatching final products for use elsewhere in the body. The mechanisms involved in active transmembrane transport will be discussed in the following chapter. Here we shall be concerned with the more general aspects of biosynthetic activities, one aspect of those phenomena comprehended by the term *metabolism*.

Biosyntheses

We have already considered some of the general features of synthetic processes. They all take the following form:

$$a \rightarrow b \overset{\displaystyle x}{\underset{\displaystyle y}{\rightarrow}} c \rightarrow d \rightarrow e \rightarrow f \rightarrow g \rightarrow product$$

Here a is some compound readily available to the cell, such as glucose or a simple amino acid, and the product may be a purine nucleotide, a hormone, or cholesterol, for example; x and y are other products required by the cell, or intermediates in their formation; d, e, f, and g are intermediates in the pathway leading to the product. Each is a specific, defined chemical entity. All synthetic pathways are governed by a few rules:

1. Each step in the pathway is catalyzed by specific enzymes which, with rare exceptions, serve no other purpose in the cell.
2. The overall process, $a \rightarrow product$, proceeds with a net decrease in free energy (ΔF is large and negative).
3. Although individual reactions along the path are freely reversible, the overall process is not, because of one or more steps for which $-\Delta F$ is so large that these steps are essentially irreversible. The cell may be able to reconvert product to a but, if so, must utilize some other set of reactions to do so.
4. The pathway includes one reaction called *the committed step*, recognized by the fact that the product of that step, and all subsequent reactions, serves no purpose but ultimate conversion to the final product, viz., $c \rightarrow d$.
5. If the pathway is regulated by negative feedback, the product

serves as an inhibitor of that enzyme which catalyzes the committed step, e.g., the inhibition of aspartic transcarbamylase, previously described, by CTP.

During the past 30 years we have witnessed a spectacular rate of progress from almost complete ignorance of the pathways and enzymes of intermediary metabolism to a remarkably complete description of these cellular processes. Indeed most of the reactions involved in the synthesis and degradation of the important categories of cellular materials, including nucleic acids, proteins, carbohydrates, and lipids, have now been described.

As a result of these remarkable advances, we are now able to construct detailed and nearly complete charts which define the origin and ultimate fate of almost every component of the cell. "Metabolic maps" made their first appearance about 15 years ago, and have increased steadily in size and complexity. A recent version, which attempts to include only the major facets of intermediary metabolism, covers 10 sq ft of wall space, and contains approximately 1,000 individual reactions. Hundreds of laboratories have collaborated internationally in this effort. The rate of progress has been partially conditioned by the supply of investigators and of funds. More important than remedying these deficiencies, however, was the advent of the necessary tools — spectrophotometers, paper and column chromatography, radioisotopes and means for their detection, sophisticated manipulation of mutant strains of microorganisms. With these, the field blossomed and in a mere two decades came to maturity. The sum represents one of the greatest of human accomplishments.

A popular textbook of biochemistry, published in 1935, listed a total of 32 enzymes, nearly all of which are hydrolytic enzyme components of the digestive fluids. This work did not mention a single enzyme of cellular metabolism, and indeed at that time only a few intracellular enzymes had been described. In contrast, the report of a Commission on Enzymes, published in 1961, lists and names nearly 700 enzymes, each of which is known to catalyze a specific reaction, and at least 300 more have been observed.

An organic compound required by the cell and which it cannot make for itself from other materials is an *essential nutrient*. Animals can make for themselves all of the sugars, most of the fatty acids, all of the sterols except vitamin D, all of their purines and pyrimidines. But there are 10 amino acids, needed in substantial amounts, which cannot be so made — these are the essential amino acids, and the requirement for dietary protein is, in fact, a requirement for them. Undoubtedly primitive ancestors of the vertebrates could make these amino acids by reaction pathways like those operative today in green plants, but mutational loss of this ability occurred eons ago.

In addition there is a collection of organic compounds which occur in much lesser amounts and are normally synthesized by plants and micro-organisms but not by animals. These are the vitamins. Each serves a catalytic role, each is converted by the cell into a *coenzyme* and functions together with appropriate enzymes. Each coenzyme specializes in one type of reaction. For example, the coenzymes built from nicotinamide and riboflavin are used in oxidation-reduction reactions. Thiamine, as its pyrophosphate, ruptures and reforms bonds of the type

$$-\overset{\overset{\displaystyle O}{\parallel}}{C} - C$$

Pyridoxine (vitamin B_6) is converted to pyridoxal phosphate and is required for many reactions involving amino acids. Biotin is required for many reactions in which CO_2 is fixed into organic compounds. Folic acid is used for reactions in which

$$-CH_2OH \quad \text{or} \quad -C\overset{\displaystyle H}{\underset{\displaystyle O}{\diagdown}} \quad \text{or} \quad -C\overset{\displaystyle OH}{\underset{\displaystyle O}{\diagdown}}$$

is moved from one compound to another. And pantothenic acid, as coenzyme A, is used in acetylation and other acylations. Each coenzyme may be utilized repeatedly; hence replacement requirements are minute. Thus, a combination of protein enzymes which confer specificity and vitamin-containing coenzymes gives the cell its enormous chemical versatility.

One other class of coenzymes is noteworthy. These all involve the nucleotides commonly found in the nucleic acids. Thus uridine diphosphate is attached to glucose before the latter is converted to glycogen or converted to some other sugar. Indeed every one of the nucleotides of RNA is used as a coenzyme, doubling in metabolic brass as it were.

Energy-Yielding Processes

As we have seen, it is the change in free energy (ΔF) that successfully drives the multitude of metabolic synthetic pathways. Energy is also required to expel inappropriate ions, to contract muscle, to conduct, to secrete, etc. In all cases, the immediate source of energy is that available from hydrolysis of adenosine triphosphate (ATP) which occurs with an unusually large negative change in free energy ($\Delta F = -10,000$ calories per mole).

Adenosine Triphosphate (ATP)

How then is this compound made and utilized? Stated more broadly, how is the energy available to the cell from its environment utilized to drive the energy-requiring processes of the cell?

Use of ATP for Syntheses. Man-made machines use the energy of fuel combustion to accomplish work. Man himself also oxidizes fuel (carbohydrates and lipids) and uses the energy thus obtained to do work. But man-made machines do so by utilizing the heat released to expand a gas which, in turn, usually drives a piston. However, the efficiency of a heat engine is a function of the difference in temperature that can be achieved; the larger the difference, the greater the efficiency. And since man himself maintains constant body temperature, heat *qua* heat is unavailable for the performance of work, and some other arrangement is necessary. The heat we release to the environment is an end product, much like CO_2, water, and the components of urine.

Most of the "work" done in living cells is chemical work; the accomplishment is the synthesis of compounds required by the cell, syntheses that occur in a direction that is the reverse of that which would occur spontaneously in the absence of an energy source. To understand this arrangement, let us first assume the existence of ATP. How can the energy of this compound be used to synthesize an ester? Consider the endergonic synthesis of an ester and the hydrolysis of ATP to adenosine monophosphate (AMP) plus pyrophosphate (PPi):

1. $RCOOH + HO—R' \rightleftharpoons RCOOR' + H_2O$ $\Delta F = +5,000$ cal.
2. $ATP + H_2O \rightleftharpoons AMP + PPi$ $\Delta F = -10,000$ cal.

$$\Delta F = -5,000 \text{ cal.}$$

Under ordinary circumstances, reaction 2 would simply proceed, the solution would simply warm up, but no ester synthesis would occur. The statement that reaction 1 proceeds with a free energy change, ΔF, of +5,000 calories per mole means that spontaneously, in water, the reaction would run right-to-left, the ester hydrolyzing to its components. At equilibrium for each mole of ester there would be about 60 moles each of the acid and of the alcohol. The biological solution is the participation of a *common intermediate:*

3. $RCOOH + ATP \rightarrow RCO—AMP + PPi$ $\Delta F = -2,500$ cal
4. $RCO—AMP + HO—R' \rightarrow AMP + RCOOR'$ $\Delta F = -2,500$ cal

$$\Delta F = -5,000 \text{ cal}$$

The overall energy in 3 + 4 is that predicted for 1 + 2. But 3 + 4 can, and is, made to proceed on an enzyme surface, whereas there is no way reaction 2 can be made to drive reaction 1. This device, the common intermediate, is a feature of all biosynthetic pathways.

Biosynthesis of Adenosine Triphosphate

The utilization of the potential energy of ATP has proved to be an absolutely universal feature of living cells. Accordingly it seems likely that the earliest "living" systems capable of self-duplication must have employed this or a closely similar device. Quite conceivably ATP was in the primordial soup (Chapter 5). And for many years it must have been the prebiologically synthesized ATP which so served. Before this supply had vanished, there must have evolved some means for utilizing the potential energy of the environment—viz., the other organic compounds present in the medium—to achieve new ATP synthesis. Whatever form this may have taken, the simplest mechanism that has survived is the process of *fermentation* and its close analogue in animal cells, *glycolysis.*

These processes avail themselves of the potential energy of a pre-existing sugar, usually glucose. Without recourse to oxygen, the sugar is degraded in a series of consecutive reactions (a "pathway") with the production of ATP and, in yeast, ethyl alcohol plus CO_2, or in man and the bacteria which sour milk and make sauerkraut, lactic acid. In the process operative in human muscle, 13 independent enzymes are required to catalyze the overall process, for which the net reaction may be written as

$$\text{glucose} + 2\ \text{ADP} + 2\ \text{Pi} \rightarrow 2\ \text{lactic acid} + 2\ \text{ATP}$$

Because of the abundance of this system, and its enormous importance, these have been the most thoroughly studied of all intracellular enzymes. Of particular interest is the enzyme called phosphoglyceraldehyde dehydrogenase because on its surface is generated a high-energy compound which immediately permits synthesis of ATP. The enzyme itself can be crystallized with its associated coenzyme built from the vitamin nicotinamide, which is linked to the protein in a unique manner as follows:

$$H_2O_3-P-O-CH_2-CHOH-CHO$$

The bond between the substrate and the sulfur of the enzyme is a *high-energy bond* — that is, if it is ruptured by hydrolysis, a large change in free energy occurs. This compound may then, on the enzyme, be attacked by inorganic phosphate (Pi) to yield an enzyme-coenzyme complex plus $H_2O_3-P-O-CH_2-CHOH-CO-OPO_3H_2$, 1,3-diphosphoglyceric acid. On a separate enzyme surface, the phosphate esterified to the carboxyl of this compound (an acid anhydride) is transferred to ADP to form ATP, and the objective of the entire set of transformations is then achieved.

Photosynthesis

Clearly, the living world could not long have continued if it had available only the initial stock of organic compounds. One of the greatest triumphs of early evolution was the "invention" of a means of harnessing the energy of the sun so as to drive intracellular energy — requiring processes.

The term *photosynthesis* was initially employed to describe the process in higher plants whereby CO_2 and water are combined to make starch, a polymer of glucose, with liberation of oxygen:

(a) $6 CO_2 + 6 H_2O \rightarrow C_6H_{12}O_6 + 6 O_2$ $\Delta F = +686,000$ calories

Thermodynamically, this is an unlikely event, since so much energy is required, and the reverse process—familiar as the burning in air of paper or wood—is far more likely. And again, the key to such processes is the utilization of ATP and of chemical reducing power, via common intermediates. The pathways responsible have been elucidated in the past 15 years by the effort of a host of investigators. And the preceding reaction is more descriptively written as

(b) $6 CO_2 + 6 H_2O + 18$ ATP $+ 12$ NADPH $\longrightarrow$

$C_6H_{12}O_6 + 18$ ADP $+ 18$ Pi $+ 12$ NADP

Twelve separate enzymes are required to operate this process. If they are mixed in proper proportions with the ingredients shown in equation (b), carbon dioxide is indeed used to make glucose. The process occurs in the dark as well as in the light, so that, truly speaking, this is not a *photo*synthesis. The actual photosynthetic process is the mechanism whereby light energy is trapped and utilized for the synthesis of the ATP and the NADPH required for the CO_2 fixation pathway. NADPH is a coenzyme, built from nicotinamide, which can exist in an oxidized form, NADP, and can accept two electrons to yield its reduced form, NADPH.

All photosynthetic systems operate in a manner that can be described in the following equation:

(c) $H_2A + x$ ADP $+ x$ Pi $+$ NADP $\rightarrow A + x$ ATP $+$ NADPH

The nature of H_2A is variable. In the higher plants H_2A is H_2O, but in photosynthetic bacteria it may be an organic compound or even H_2S. In any case, reaction (c) is not spontaneously feasible; an external source of energy is required—the energy of the sun, transmitted as light. In every case, the process occurs in an especially organized subcellular organelle; in the higher plants, this is a chloroplast (Fig. 3-10). The latter is an organized set of membranes, crowded with water-insoluble lipids and containing the central pigment chlorophyll.

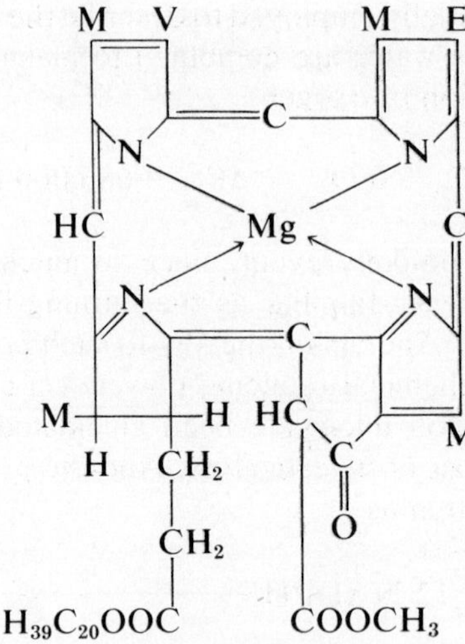

M = methyl
E = ethyl
V = vinyl
$C_{20}H_{39}O$ = phytyl

Chlorophyll a

Each functional unit has many chlorophyll molecules which harvest light in the manner of a light meter. The molecules are partially stacked in rouleau formation, e.g., a stack of coins, and regardless of which molecule initially receives the light quanta, the energy is transmitted by a process known as *induced resonance energy transfer,* within 10^{-9} second, to a specific chlorophyll molecule. This molecule is then photoactivated— i.e., an electron moves from the π orbitals to the exterior of an atomic shell and then is ejected, leaving behind a chlorophyll free radical. This terminates the truly photochemical event.

Also present in the substructures of the chloroplast is a series of compounds capable of gaining or losing an electron (electron carriers), each affixed to an appropriate carrier. The ejected electron passes from one to another of these, lodging finally in NADP, which becomes NADPH. But the chlorophyll free radical cannot again participate unless it regains an electron to replace that which was lost. As shown in Figure 3-11, in the photosynthetic purple bacterium, *Rhodospirillum rubrum,* this source can be an organic compound such as succinic acid or it can be H_2S. Thus, overall, succinic acid is used to chemically reduce (donate electrons) NADP, a reaction that is, ordinarily, thermo-dynamically not feasible. This is accomplished by the sum of two thermo-dynamically feasible processes: reduction of NADP by the electron from photoactivated chlorophyll plus reduction of a chlorophyll free radical by succinic acid or H_2S.

Associated with these events is another process known only in its

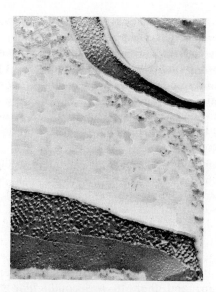

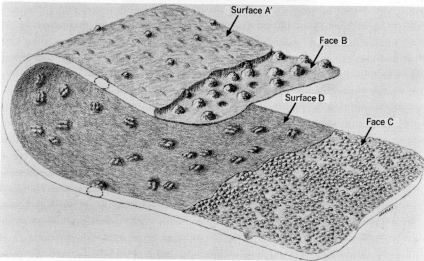

Figure 3-10. *Upper:* Electron micrograph of chloroplast lamellae, magnification 81,000×; *Lower:* Schematic diagram of chloroplast substructure. The technique of freeze-etching and electron microscopy have shown us both the surfaces of the thylakoid membrane (A and D) and the internal structure of the membrane, face B and face C. The definite assignment of chemical composition and function to the units within this membrane is a challenging field in photosynthesis research. (From R. B. Park, J. Cell Sci. *5:*299–313, 1969)

most gross detail, which is called *photophosphorylation*. Again this is a misnomer; there is only one photochemical event, the activation of chlorophyll. In any case, as electrons traverse the two electron pathways of Figure 3-11, approximately two molecules of ATP are formed per electron pair. No intermediates are known. The process is under almost feverish investigation, and there are many revealing experiments, but the essence of this mechanism remains elusive. However it happens, it provides the ATP which, together with NADPH, drives the formation of carbohydrate from CO_2.

In higher plants an additional complication is introduced. The amount of energy required to make possible reduction of NADP by H_2S is insufficient if H_2O is to be employed as the reductant. This was solved, in nature, by the cooperative functioning of two reactive chlorophyll centers, joined as shown in Figure 3-12. At the upper left is represented the reduction, by water, of a chlorophyll free radical, with formation of O_2. The electron ejected from this chlorophyll could not be used to reduce NADP. Instead, it is passed through a series of carriers (plastoquinone $\rightarrow$ plastocyanin) and then to a second chlorophyll free radical, designated as P_{700} (pigment which absorbs light maximally at 700 mμ),

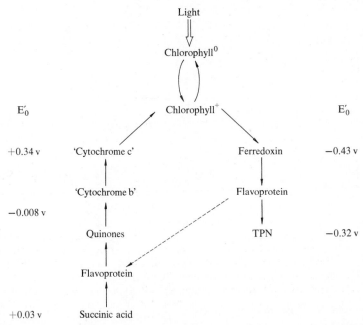

Figure 3-11. Path of electron flow in bacterial photosynthesis. (From White, Handler, and Smith)

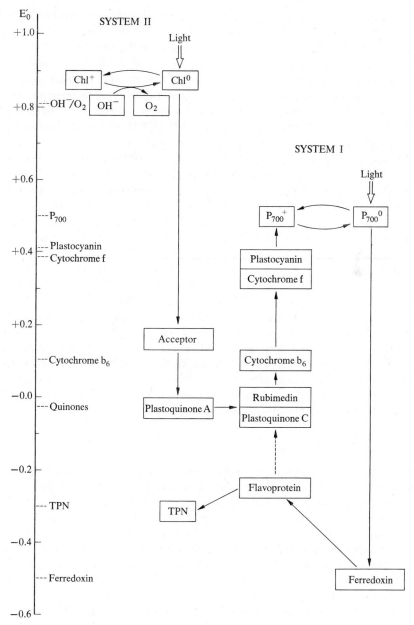

Figure 3-12. Path of electron flow in photosynthesis by higher plants. (From White, Handler, and Smith)

the electron from which is sufficiently energetic to reduce NADP. ATP is again generated in this system; in this case it occurs incident to the passage of the electrons from chlorophyll I to P_{700}, again yielding two molecules of ATP per electron pair.

Enormous effort has been required to establish this general picture. Identification of the intermediates noted in Figure 3-12 and their structures remains incomplete, as does understanding of the exact nature of P_{700}; and, of course, the nature of the ATP-generating events is obscure. An interesting property of the system is indicated by the dashed line connecting flavoprotein and plastoquinone C. If there is no NADP to accept the electron that came from activated P_{700}, a shunt is established and the electron continues on in its circuit, returning to the chlorophyll free radical. No reducing power is generated thereby, and CO_2 fixation would be impossible, but this cyclic electron flow does permit ATP formation in the usual way. Thus, when functioning in this mode, the chloroplast is a transducer which converts the electromagnetic energy from the sun into the chemical energy of ATP. Alternatively, instead of forming ATP, the same functioning system can use this energy to transport cations (Mg^{++}, Ca^{++}, K^+) against a concentration gradient, accumulating them inside the chloroplast. Or it can, instead, eject H^+ ions (protons) into the surrounding fluid. And the converse works also. If the chloroplast is exposed to ATP, a high concentration of protons, or other cations, a weak fluorescence at the wavelength characteristic of chlorophyll may be observed. Withal, no hypothesis adequately accounts for the actual working mechanism. Yet all of life on this earth is utterly dependent upon its continued success!

Oxidative Phosphorylation

When green, photosynthetic plants were well established, their activity generated the oxygen of the earth's atmosphere. Not until then was animal life possible, for the synthetic activities of these plants provide all of the raw materials of motile animal life—carbohydrate, amino acids, vitamins, as well as the oxygen required for respiration. As an energy source, animals can and do use the glycolytic system described earlier. But the yield of ATP in that system is minimal, 2 ATP per glucose molecule. With oxygen available, animal cells are enabled to utilize glucose for ATP production with enormously greater efficiency.

In effect, animal respiration—like that of plants in the dark—is the reverse of photosynthesis, except that no light is emitted. The overall process is

$$C_6H_{12}O_6 + 6O_2 + 38ADP + 38Pi \rightarrow 6CO_2 + 6H_2O + 38ATP$$

Rarely wasteful, in this case the system evolved by taking advantage of the existing capability of the cell to glycolyze. The glucose is cleaved in twain, with formation of two molecules of pyruvic acid in the cytoplasm by the usual glycolytic enzymes.

$$CH_3—\underset{\underset{O}{\|}}{C}—COOH$$

The pyruvic acid then enters a special organelle, the mitochondrion, the structure of which is presented in the following chapter. The strategy of what ensues is elegant in the extreme. The foregoing equation indicated that $6O_2$ are required per glucose, i.e., 12 O. Each oxygen atom may accept one pair of electrons. Accordingly, in the mitochondrion, the pyruvic acids are so manipulated, in a reaction series termed the *citric acid cycle,* as to permit 12 opportunities to withdraw an electron pair. Each of these, in turn, is utilized to reduce a nicotinamide-containing coenzyme. Within each mitochondrion there are hundreds of little substructures, each enclosed in a membrane within which there is arranged an electron transfer chain entirely analogous to that in chloroplasts and which probably evolved from them. Included in this chain is a series of electron carriers: a flavoprotein (built from the vitamin riboflavin), a series of iron proteins somewhat analogous to ferredoxin of the chloroplast, a set of quinones, and a group of cytochromes. The last resemble hemoglobin in their essential structures. Finally there is an enzyme called *cytochrome c oxidase.* Of all these components, only the latter can react with oxygen. Incidentally, it is this enzyme that readily reacts with cyanide, accounting for the great toxicity of this substance. The various components are not in free solution. They must be physically aligned so that electron transfer is facilitated and occurs in the proper order. And as this transfer occurs, just as in the chloroplast, ATP is formed, about three per electron pair. All indications suggest that the basic mechanism is essentially identical with that which makes possible ATP synthesis in the chloroplast. This process, oxidative phosphorylation, has been known since 1937; it was studied by various investigators until 1950 and has since been subjected to intensive scrutiny. But although much is known, the fundamental mechanism remains obscure and challenging.

The Biological Utility of Carbohydrates

Structural Roles of Carbohydrates

No class of organic compounds has a wider natural distribution than the carbohydrates. D-glucose, which is the immediate energy source for all of mammalian metabolism, is the most widely distributed and most prevalent organic compound known. Carbohydrates, both free and combined as constituents of complex structures, are found in the simplest unicellular animals, the most complex mammalian organisms, throughout the plant kingdom, and in general everywhere on the planet where living systems are found.

β-D-Glucose

Sucrose (current world production nearly 50 million tons per year)

Carbohydrates play many and diverse roles in cells, including their basic role as energy sources. They participate in antibody activity, they are found attached to a large number of enzymes and other proteins, ribose and deoxyribose are the backbone of nucleic acids, they function in blood clotting. But their unique function is to be fashioned into structural components, and it is only this aspect of the carbohydrates to which attention is directed here. The versatility of carbohydrates in this regard derives from the immense number and variety of possibilities. Consider only those sugars of 6-carbon atoms (hexoses). Because of the steric arrangements about an asymmetric carbon atom (an atom about which are disposed 4 distinct groups), there are 16 possible simple hexoses with an aldehyde function at position 1. Because the latter group spontaneously cyclizes, a new asymmetric center is generated, and there are thus 32 possibilities. If in addition one considers the possible number of keto sugars, of sugars in which an —OH group is replaced either by an acetamino function, $NH—CO—CH_3$ or even by a hydrogen, the total number of possibilities is vast indeed. Moreover, these can be linked by an ether bridge (properly, an acetal), between the carbonyl of one sugar and either the 6, 4, 3 or 2 hydroxyl group of an adjacent sugar, to generate a huge number of different possible polymers. And many have indeed been found. The simplest of these are built of but a single sugar as a repeating unit. This is true of glycogen and starch, which serve as storage forms of glucose for energy utilization in animals and plants. But it is also true of cellulose, the most abundant compound of nature, which serves as the cell wall of plants, and of chitin, which is used for the exoskeleton of insects and the cell walls of fungi.

Segment of polysaccharide structure
R=OH, cellulose; R=N—C—CH$_3$, chitin
H   O

But the enormous variety of carbohydrates arises from the possibility of heteropolysaccharides, in which the polymer embodies two or more different sugars as repeating units. An example of these is the *blood group substances,* which occur in or on the membranes of erythrocytes: the group B substance is built of *N*-acetylgalactosamine, *N*-acetylglucosamine, fucose, and galactose. Yet more complex polymers appear to coat cells of the nervous system and constitute a mechanism for "recognition" of matching cells in a circuit.

No aspect of chemistry has been more difficult than establishing the structure of the cell walls of bacteria. These have aptly been called "bag-shaped macromolecules" in that a single molecule actually envelopes the entire cell! This molecule, *murein,* is shown in Figure 3-13. Continued in three dimensions it is as large as the cell itself. Individual species have developed variations on this theme, but the basic pattern is constant.

Even more complicated is the "slime" surrounding some bacteria, slime that constitutes the antigen that elicits antibody formation when such cells invade an animal. This material is called a lipopolysaccharide. It has a lipid core, of unknown structure, to which is attached a polysaccharide built of a three-membered repeating unit of two heptoses and

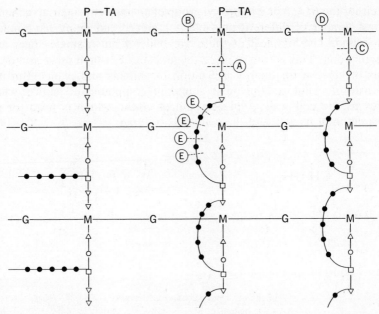

Figure 3-13. Polymeric murein as the basic structure of a cell wall. G = N-acetylglu-cosamine: M = N-acetylmuramic acid: P—Ta = phosphodiester to teichoic acid, △ = L-alanine, ○ = D-isoglutamine, □ = L-lysine, ▽ = D-alanine, ● = glycine. The pentaglycine chains to the left are in amide linkage to lysine but have not yet been connected to the carboxyl of D-alanine. The completed pentapeptide bridges are all shown connecting paral-lel polysaccharide chains in the plane of the paper. However, they can equally readily ex-tend to equivalent murein sheets above or below the plane of the paper and thus thicken and rigidify the wall. The encircled letters A through E represent the sites of action of specific hydrolytic enzymes obtained from bacterial sources. (From White, Handler, and Smith)

one eight-carbon sugar called octulosonic acid. To each of these three-membered repeating units is linked a single pentasaccharide of the structure

$$N\text{-acetylglucosamine-glucose-galactose-glucose}$$
$$|$$
$$\text{galactose}$$

And to the glucose of this unit is linked a large polymer of the structure

$$\left(\begin{array}{c}\text{abequose}\\ |\\ \text{—mannose-rhamnose-galactose—}\end{array}\right)_{n}$$

Thus eight different sugars are involved in this remarkable structure. Presumably, different bacterial species have built this material in variant ways, but it is thought that the general pattern is rather constant. What a challenge to the chemist! Although the names of the individual hexoses just cited may convey little to the reader, it will be appreciated that the physical and chemical properties of these compounds are generally rather similar, so that the task of deciphering the structure of such a lipopolysaccharide requires great ingenuity and highly sophisticated and sensitive techniques.

There remains the tasks of learning how such a molecule is assembled by the cell and extruded to the outside, and finally of understanding the advantages to the cell of a molecule thus assembled. Much of the task of unraveling the mode of biosynthesis has been accomplished in the past three years. Central to this process is a compound which has been called *bactoprenol:*

$$\underset{\displaystyle CH_3}{\overset{\displaystyle CH_3}{}}$$

H(H₂C—CH=CH—CH₂)₁₀—CH₂—CH=CH₂—O—P—O⁻

Bactoprenol Phosphate

This compound, a C_{55} terpene which is a linear sequence of 11 isoprene units, is esterified to phosphate. The long hydrocarbon chain is insoluble in water and is imbedded in the lipids of the cell membrane. In the genesis of the lipopolysaccharide, the final step, synthesis of the polymeric chains is accomplished by attaching the galactose of the repeating tetrasaccharide to the bactoprenol, in a pyrophosphate bond, then affixing the other three sugars in sequence. The bactoprenol then appears to rotate in the membrane, and the tetrasaccharide is then attached to the growing end of the polymer chain outside the cell. Rerotation in the membrane permits the beginning of a new cycle. Bactoprenol serves similarly in murein synthesis. After synthesis, in the cytoplasm, the fundamental repeating unit (*N*-acetylglucosamine in ether linkage to lactic acid, the carboxyl of which is in amide linkage to the pentapeptide) is linked through a pyrophosphate bond to bactoprenol, the second *N*-acetylglucosamine is then added, and this entire unit moved through the membrane to add it to the growing end of the cell wall structure.

Interest in these phenomena is not academic. It is precisely in the synthesis of such structures that bacteria differ from animal cells. Accordingly, interference with this system is an excellent approach to the development of antibiotics, since such drugs would be unlikely to affect mammalian metabolism. As we shall see, this is precisely how penicillin works.

Polysaccharide Synthesis

Enough has already been said to indicate a profound difference between protein and polysaccharide synthesis. Each amino acid in a protein is inserted according to the dictates of the genetic message. The polypeptide chain has a prescribed beginning and end. But this is not true of polysaccharides. They grow by addition of identical repeating units to the end of an existing chain. Occasionally, new chains are branched off and a new growing end begun. But there is no prescribed limit to this process, and it appears likely that size is dictated only by physical considerations.

Structure and Function of Lipids

The lipids comprise a wide variety of fatty cell constituents which are here grouped together because they are insoluble in water but soluble in ether and other organic solvents. These distinctive solubility properties are due to long water-repelling hydrocarbon chains and set the lipids apart from proteins, polysaccharides, and nucleic acids. Many bodily functions depend on the existence of water-insoluble molecules. Cell structure and cellular organization are inconceivable without physical boundaries and permeability barriers between extracellular and intracellular space. Moreover, various metabolic activities take place in different compartments within the cell. For these purposes nature has designed structural materials called membranes. Membranes consist chemically of both proteins and lipids, but they owe their water-insolubility primarily to their content of lipids. The most common components of cellular lipids are the fatty acids, hydrocarbon derivatives 16 to 20 carbon atoms long. In the tissues the fatty acids occur as esters combined with three principal types of alcohols: with glycerol they form the triglycerides or neutral fats, with glycerophosphophates the phospholipids, and with cholesterol the cholesterol esters. The three types of fatty acid esters serve separate and probably not interchangeable functions.

Triglycerides. Triglycerides are the principal fuel reserve in animal tissues. Foods consumed in excess over the bodily needs for maintenance and energy production are converted into triglycerides and deposited and stored in the form of tiny fat droplets in the various fatty or adipose tissues of the body. These fat reserves can be mobilized to be used as fuel sources when food intake becomes insufficient. By a process that is poorly understood, hormonal signals (e.g., adrenaline) cause triglycerides in adipose tissue to hydrolyze to free fatty acids. The latter travel in the bloodstream to liver and muscle to be oxidized for energy production. In this process, the fatty acid is degraded by removal of two-carbon fragments which enter the citric acid cycle operative in carbohydrate metabolism, and ATP is generated by the same mitochondrial system described earlier. The relative rates of these two opposing processes, fat deposition and fat mobilization from storage sites, are important factors in determining blood lipid levels. When these are abnormally high they may contribute to the deposition of fats in the blood vessels and therefore to degenerative changes that occur in cardiovascular disease.

The quality and consistency of fats (liquid or solid) are determined by the chain length (number of carbon atoms) and by the degree of unsaturation (number of double bonds) of their fatty acid components. Lard, containing mostly saturated fatty acids, and olive oil, containing largely unsaturated acids (oleic and linoleic acids), are extreme examples of the effect of fatty acid structure on the physical properties of triglycerides. As for the nutritional quality of fats, two aspects must be distinguished. All of the so-called edible fats, whether of animal or vegetable origin, and regardless of the degree of unsaturation, are roughly equivalent as energy sources; when metabolized, they yield approximately the same number of calories. However, animals reared on diets that contain only fully saturated fats develop severe deficiency symptoms. Only fats containing certain unsaturated fatty acids are nutritionally adequate. Linoleic acid, with two double bonds in an 18-carbon chain, and arachidonic acid, containing four double bonds in a 20-carbon chain, prevent this nutritional deficiency and are therefore known as essential fatty acids.

A partial explanation for the requirement of these fatty acids has recently been given by the discovery of the prostaglandins.

A prostaglandin

These novel fatty acid derivatives, which have hormonal properties, were first observed in minute amounts in the prostate gland but are now known to occur in many other tissues. Prostaglandins are made from linoleic and arachidonic acids. Since these two fatty acids are essential nutrients, it can be argued that the prostaglandins must play a vital role in metabolism and metabolic regulation. While it can be shown that the prostaglandins are indeed powerful pharmacodynamic agents affecting blood pressure, heart rate, and smooth muscle contraction, the specific function of the prostaglandins in metabolism is not yet known.

Prostaglandins have so far been isolated only from the tissues of higher animals, and it seems unlikely that they will be found in either plants or microorganisms. Yet highly unsaturated fatty acids occur in almost all forms of life. They must therefore have other essential functions.

One major consequence of introducing double bonds into a fatty acid chain is to lower its melting point. Stearic acid is a solid and oleic acid a liquid at room temperature. By varying the degree of unsaturation (the number of double bonds) in fatty acid chains, organisms may therefore modulate the solid or liquid state of cellular fats and thus maintain the appropriate physical properties of certain cell components in the face of environmental temperature changes. It has long been known that the seed oils of plants that grow in colder climates tend to be more highly unsaturated, obviously an advantage for survival.

Depending on the source, natural fats contain a bewildering variety of fatty acids differing both in chain length and in the number of double bonds. For example one organism alone, the phytoflagellate *Euglena gracilis,* contains 53 different fatty acids, and in relative proportions which depend critically on environment. Changing the fatty acid patterns thus seems to be a device for adjusting to the varying external conditions to which cells are exposed.

Phospholipids. Since, in many tissues and cells, the lipids are preferentially localized in the membrane fraction there is good reason to believe that lipids provide one of the principal structural elements for cellular boundaries which enclose cells or cellular components. When viewed in the electron microscope, cell membranes give the appearance of sandwich structures consisting of a double layer of lipid bounded on either side by sheets of protein. Although this physical image is very similar for membranes from a great variety of sources (the red cell, the chloroplast, the myelin sheath of nerve, or the bacterial membrane), their chemical composition and complexity differ vastly from case to case. Thus many bacterial membranes contain only one or two lipids, whereas

the membranes of the nerve cell or the chloroplast may contain 20 or
more different lipid types.

Apparently phospholipids are universal components of cell membranes.
These unusual substances contain phosphoric acid and a nitrogenous
base in addition to glycerol and fatty acids. The phosphorus- and
nitrogen-containing portions render the phospholipid molecule polar
or ionic and therefore water-attracting, while the hydrocarbon chains
of the fatty acid residues repel water molecules. Because of these opposing tendencies within the same molecule the phospholipids show the
exceptional property of dissolving both in an organic milieu and to some
extent also in water phases. For the same reason they form highly
oriented so-called micellar structures.

$$
\begin{array}{l}
CH_2-O-\overset{\overset{\displaystyle O}{\|}}{C}-R^1 \qquad R^1 \text{ and } R^2 = \text{long-chain fatty acids}\\[2em]
CH-O-\overset{\overset{\displaystyle O}{\|}}{C}-R^2 \qquad X = -CH_2-CH_2-N^+(CH_3)_3\\[1em]
\qquad\qquad\qquad\qquad\qquad\qquad or\\
CH_2-O-\overset{\overset{\displaystyle O}{\|}}{\underset{\underset{\displaystyle O^-}{|}}{P}}-O-X \qquad X = -CH_2-\underset{\underset{\displaystyle NH_3}{\overset{+}{|}}}{CH}-COO^-\\[1em]
\qquad\qquad\qquad\qquad\qquad\qquad or\\
\qquad\qquad\qquad\qquad X = -CH_2-CH_2-N^+H_3
\end{array}
$$

Phospholipids

How phospholipids affect the stability of cell membranes and what
role they have in determining permeability—i.e., the controlled passage of small molecules across the membrane barrier—is largely unknown. It seems likely that the specificity of the transport function
resides in the protein portion of the membrane lipoprotein, but phospholipids may contribute to selectivity by specifying the three-dimensional
arrangement in which the protein is held.

One promising approach to a better knowledge of membrane structure and function is to analyze in detail the membrane lipids from a
great variety of cells and cell components. Many striking differences
have been found, but it has not yet been explained how such differences

affect function. For example, the main phospholipids of bovine and other ruminant red cells are complex substances, related to the simpler phospholipids, known as sphingomyelins.

$$CH_3-(CH_2)_{12}-CH=CH-CH-CH$$

with the structure showing:

R—C—NH group (with C=O), OH on the lower left carbon, and the phosphate chain:

$$H_2CO-P-O-CH_2-CH_2-N^+\equiv(CH_3)_3$$

with O^- below the P, and R = long-chain fatty acid

A sphingomyelin

By contrast the major red-cell phospholipids of man and rat consist of the less complex phospholipids shown previously. Are these two types of phospholipids especially suited for the respective tasks the red cells have to perform in the blood of ruminants and nonruminants? Are these differences in red-cell chemistry possibly related to the fact that in ruminants the major fuel sources are short-chain fatty acids and not glucose, as in nonruminants?

The wide diversity of membrane chemistry is also tellingly illustrated by a look at the lipids associated with various subcellular units. The mitochondria and the chloroplast are intracellular organelles concerned with the task of generating ATP. In chloroplasts of plants, light energy is converted to ATP, whereas in animal mitochondria, ATP is generated by the oxidation of carbohydrate and fat. The machinery for these energy transformations consists of packages of electron-transport enzymes. Lipids provide the cement which holds the energy-producing enzyme components together in arrangements that follow a precise architectural plan. Yet the lipids used for this purpose in chloroplasts and in mitochondria are not the same. In the mitochondria, the simpler phospholipids we have already encountered are the most important membrane lipids. These are also present in the chloroplast, but most of the phospholipid consists of galactosyl glycerides in which the sugar galactose replaces the nitrogenous bases of the phospholipids. Present in chloroplasts also is a considerable amount of sulfolipid:

$$HO_3S-CH_2$$

(structural diagram of sulfolipid molecule with glucose ring and glycerol-fatty acid portion)

R¹ and R² = long-chain fatty acids

Moreover, the unsaturated fatty acids linked to the chloroplast lipid have a characteristic double bond structure of their own which is quite distinct from that of the unsaturated fatty acids in the animal mitochondria. Thus, a lipid environment is necessary for both photosynthetic and mitochondrial energy transformation, but the chemistry is of a special design for each case, apparently adapted for optimal efficiency of the two types of energy production.

Until relatively recently only a handful of phospholipids were known. With the introduction of more efficient and sensitive procedures for analysis and isolation, the list of newly discovered phospholipids is rising steadily. The structural prototype of phospholipids contains glycerol, fatty acids, and a phosphoric acid residue. Variations in the general structural design are achieved largely by the attachment of additional groups to the phosphate residue. These may be the nitrogenous compounds choline, ethanolamine, or serine; another molecule of glycerol or glycerophosphate; or various sugars. Intriguingly, some of these newer phospholipids occur only in minute amounts, so that one may suspect them to have some sort of a catalytic rather than a structural function such as that described earlier for bactoprenol.

Each molecule of phospholipid contains two, usually unlike residues of fatty acid. No restriction appears to exist on the type of fatty acid that can be present in a phospholipid. Variation of the fatty acid structures as well as of the residues attached to phosphate will therefore give rise to an almost unlimited diversity of phospholipid species with a correspondingly wide range of properties.

Cholesterol. All animal cells and many plants and microbes contain steroids. This is a special class of lipids, unrelated chemically to the triglycerides and phospholipids but similar in solubility properties. Like the fatty acids, steroids have many methylene or hydrocarbon groups, but these are arranged and linked together in a four-ringed structure and not as open chains. In animal tissues cholesterol is the major representative of this class of compounds.

Cholesterol

Cholesterol occurs in all animal organs and tissues and, along with the phospholipids, is concentrated in the membrane fraction of the cell. Especially large amounts of cholesterol are found in brain, nervous tissues, the adrenal gland, and some of the other endocrine organs. Cholesterol is widely known because it is suspected to cause hardening of the arteries (arteriosclerosis). Nevertheless, it should be emphasized that cholesterol is vital for the normal operations of animal cells. The functions of cholesterol are twofold. It is an obligatory precursor of other closely related steroids, and secondly, the presence of cholesterol seems to be essential for the integrity of some membrane structures in the animal body.

Cholesterol as a Precursor of Other Sterols. In vertebrates cholesterol, either ingested with the food or manufactured in the body itself, is modified to yield two other classes of steroids with well-defined physiological roles. The first are the bile salts, made in the liver and secreted by way of the bile duct into the intestine as aids in the digestion and absorption of dietary fats. Bile salts act like detergents or artificial soaps.

Deoxycholic acid, a bile acid

They serve to disperse or emulsify the water-insoluble fats. Chemically the bile salts of all animal species are similar but by no means identical. The greater the evolutionary gap between species, the greater the differences in chemistry. Practically nothing is known about the functional significance of these species-related differences in chemical structure.

A second type of sterol transformation takes place in various endocrine organs. In the adrenal gland, cholesterol is converted to cortisol and aldosterone, in the ovary to estrogens, in the testes to androgens, and in the corpus luteum to progesterone. Cholesterol is thus the common precursor of a wide variety of hormones which control and regulate many

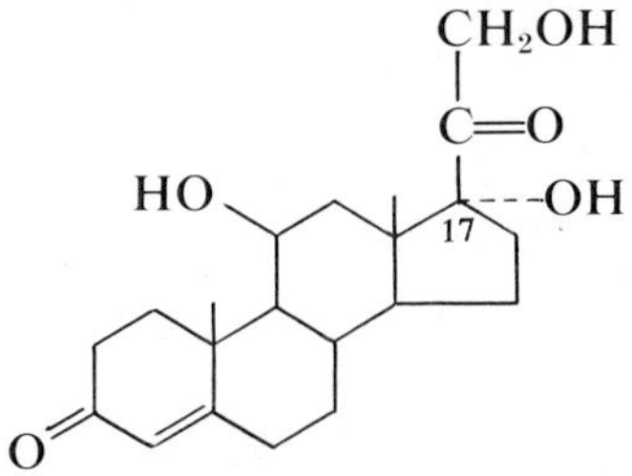

17α-Hydroxycorticosterone
(cortisol; hydrocortisone)

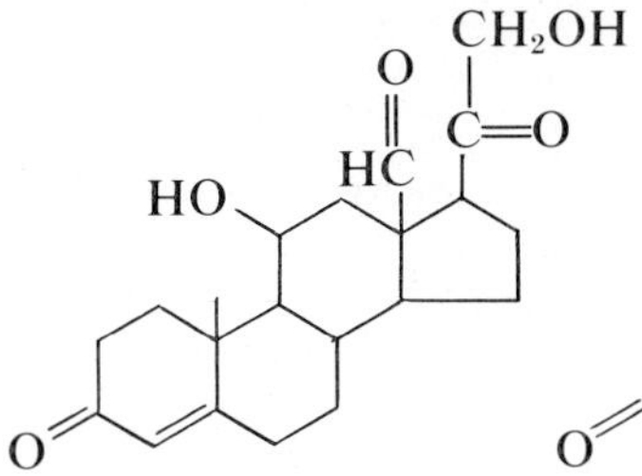

Aldosterone

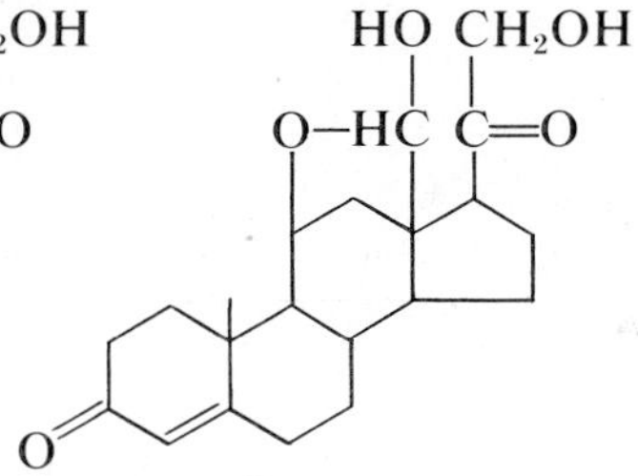

Aldosterone
(hemiacetal structure)

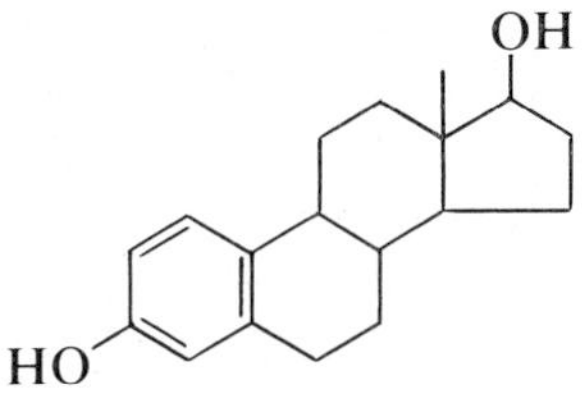

β-estradiol

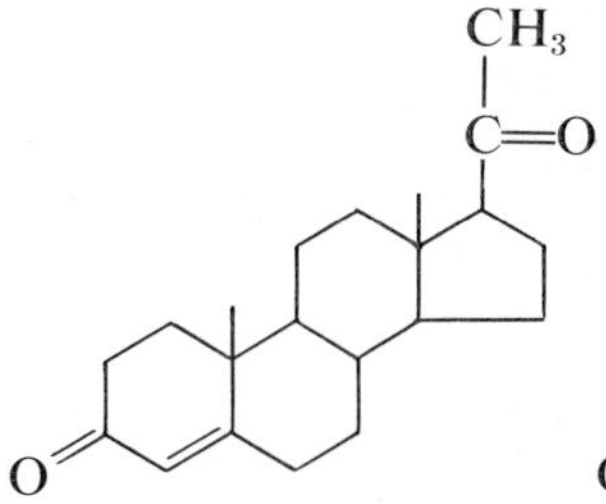

Progesterone

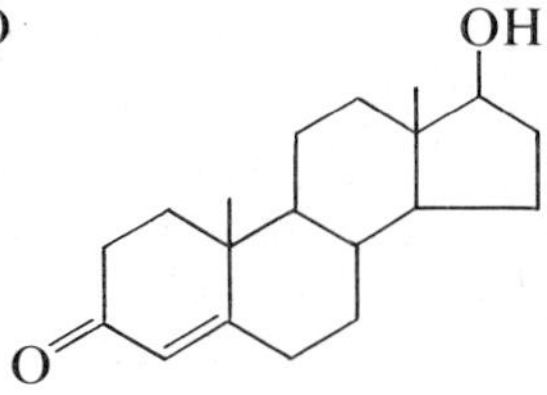

Testosterone

aspects of metabolism, of development, and of the reproductive cycle. The immediate mechanisms by which these hormones operate is not known but there is growing evidence that some of them participate in the control of enzyme synthesis at the chromosomal level.

Sterols and Membranes

Only a small fraction, probably not more than a few percent, of the total cholesterol in the animal body is needed for the production of bile acids and steroid hormones. Moreover, cholesterol is present not only in those organs in which it is chemically transformed but in all tissues and cells of the body. Thus the cholesterol present in muscle and nerve is not metabolized to any other substances. In animal tissues cholesterol along with protein and phospholipid is associated with membrane structures. However, its functions as a membrane component are probably different from those of the phospholipids. In contrast to phospholipids which have long and flexible hydrocarbon chains, cholesterol with its interlocking ring system is a compact, highly rigid, planar molecule. It is thought that these structural features are important in giving certain cell membranes mechanical strength. The mode of action of some newly discovered antibiotics supports this view. A class of antifungal substances, known as polyene antibiotics (nystatin, stipitatic acid), appear to exert their growth-inhibitory effects on yeast and other fungi by combining specifically with the sterol components of cell membranes. This interaction immobilizes and upsets the delicate membrane structure, making it leaky and more sensitive to external influences. The antifungal agents are specific in that they labilize only the membranes of cells that contain sterol. For example, not only do they inhibit the growth of fungi but they also make red blood cells very sensitive to hemolysis. On the other hand, the membranes of two groups of organisms, the bacteria and certain primitive unicellular algae, lack sterols, and these are also the only organisms that are completely resistant to the antifungal agents. The selective weakening action of the polyene antibiotics on sterol-containing membranes is a convincing argument for the important role of cholesterol and related sterols in membrane stability. Unfortunately, since animal cells also contain cholesterol, they are as sensitive to these agents as the fungi. Therefore the therapeutic use of the polyenes as fungicidal substances is restricted to external applications.

While bacteria, in general, neither make nor require sterols, the curious group of unusually small microbes known as pleuropneumonialike organisms or mycoplasma are an exception. The cells of these pathogenic organisms are plastic and of indefinite shape, since they lack the rigid murein cell wall common to all other bacteria. Interestingly many species of the mycoplasma group require cholesterol in their growth medium. The sterol is incorporated into the lipoprotein cell membrane, apparently to give some mechanical strength to a structure that in ordinary bacteria is stabilized and shaped by the rigid mucopeptide cell wall.

Comparative Aspects of Lipids

In the animal kingdom, only vertebrates carry out the complex process of cholesterol biosynthesis. Also, only vertebrates convert cholesterol to bile acids and steroid hormones. Insects and other invertebrates need a sterol, but they cannot synthesize it nor do they convert sterols to the bile acids and steroid hormones of the type found in vertebrates. At least one invertebrate steroid, the molting hormone ecdysone, is a product of cholesterol metabolism, but it is chemically quite unrelated to cortisone, estrogen, or any other vertebrate steroid hormone.

Ecdysone

The lipid materials elaborated by invertebrates as aids in fat absorption are also radically different chemically from the steroidal bile acids of the vertebrates. They are fatty acid-derived detergents (sarcosyl aminoacyl taurine) and bear, in fact, a close structural resemblance to some of the modern, man-made household detergents.

The curious fact that sterols and their derivatives are entirely absent in the bacterial phylum suggests that these molecules appeared relatively late in evolution. The bacterial cell differs from cells of higher organisms by having a more primitive anatomical organization, in particular by lacking the various membrane-bound intracellular organelles. Perhaps the invention of the sterol molecule and the development of the cholesterol pathway coincided with the various morphological innovations when the primitive bacterial cell evolved into more differentiated organisms.

Lipids, Nutrition, and Disease

Atherosclerosis is a degenerative disease process characterized by the deposition of lipids in the walls of arteries. There is a substantial if perhaps inconclusive basis for the view that a relationship exists between the incidence of this disease and the level of lipids in the diet. Statistical data tend to show that populations in the more highly developed countries are especially prone to this disease. Populations that enjoy a high standard of living in general consume high-quality foods, among which animal fats are prominent. In some individuals, at least, a high fat intake raises the level of lipids in the bloodstream, and this change in blood chemistry shows some correlation with the incidence of atherosclerosis. The views that excessive levels of dietary fats and especially of cholesterol are the major causes of atherosclerosis are supported to some extent by the results of feeding experiments with some animal species. The potential role of cholesterol is substantiated by the high frequency of atherosclerosis in persons with hereditary hypercholesterolemia. However, there is no convincing proof as yet that in humans lipids are the major or sole causes of this disease. More conservative medical opinion seems to tend to the view that apart from hereditary disposition, the total caloric intake and the overall composition of the diet are equally important influences in the incidence of arterial diseases. It is also possible that so far unrecognized derangements in lipid metabolism and not dietary fat alone are responsible for the lipid deposition in the arteries of susceptible individuals.

Regulation of Metabolism

A half century of research was required to establish the "metabolic maps," the reaction sequences by which energy is made available and by which cellular components are synthesized. Throughout much of this period it was vaguely understood that there must be mechanisms for the rate regulation of these processes. Certainly it seemed unlikely that each process simply races along at the maximal rate possible, governed only by the concentration of enzymes and availability of raw materials. But until the pathways were established, investigation of the rate-controlling mechanisms was not possible. Meanwhile clues were accumulating, for example: (a) Suspensions of mitochondria were noted to be incapable of oxidizing pyruvic acid or fatty acids if there were not available a supply of ADP and Pi. (b) Bacteria grown in a rich broth containing all of the amino acids were found to utilize these and synthesize none, although on other media they synthesize enough to maintain maximal growth rates. (c) Fatty acid and glycogen synthesis cease in the starving animal and recommence after ingestion of a meal. (d) Pasteur noted that the conversion of glucose to ethanol and CO_2, by yeast, is markedly reduced by the introduction of O_2, and many years later, others showed that animal tissues behave similarly. (e) The basal metabolic rate is increased by thyroid hormone and decreased by thyroidectomy. (f) The rate of O_2 consumption by man is determined by the work being done. The familiar act of panting during muscular exertion is patent testimony to this fact.

The past several years have made evident the principal mechanisms operative in these circumstances. Several of these have already been discussed, and only a brief recapitulation is offered here.

1. Regulation of cellular respiration is inherent in the process of oxidative phosphorylation. Whatever the details of this process, it is clear that electrons can flow from substrate through the mitochondrial carriers to oxygen only if, concomitantly, ADP and Pi are being used to make ATP. The "clutch" which couples electron transport and ATP synthesis is not understood, but it is patently operative. Indeed, it can be disengaged by various compounds. For example, dinitrophenol abolishes ATP synthesis and permits electron transport to proceed maximally, a phenomenon that is physiologically utterly wasteful. However, the reader will understand that this could be the basis of a "reducing drug" for the obese, literally permitting them to burn up their excess carbohydrate and fat. Were it not for highly undesirable side effects, this could constitute a useful therapeutic procedure. In the absence of such a drug, oxidation can proceed only when ATP can be made — viz., when the ATP-using systems, such as the contractile machinery of muscle, are utilizing ATP so that AMP, ADP, and Pi are accumulating.

2. Most synthetic processes are regulated by the negative feedback inhibition of the committed step in the pathway by a product thereof, as discussed earlier. This appears to include cholesterol synthesis in man. Although the product actually so engaged has not been identified, individuals who ingest copious quantities of cholesterol cease to synthesize their own because of such an inhibition of the conversion of hydroxymethylglutaryl coenzyme A to mevalonic acid, the committed step in this process. Similar events control the rates of purine and pyrimidine nucleotide synthesis and that of amino acids in plants and microorganisms.

3. Similar considerations also explain the Pasteur effect and the switching on and off of fatty acid synthesis. Both negative and positive controls are operative in these systems; the controlling events are summarized in Figure 3-14. Thus, all of these systems are inherently self-regulating, thanks to the properties of the participating enzymes. Moreover, no

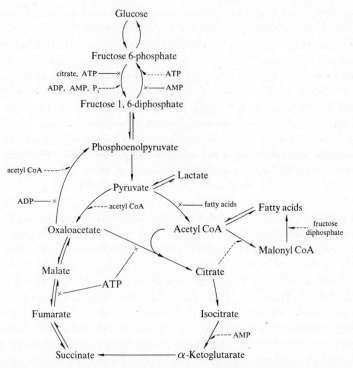

Figure 3-14. Self-regulation of the major energy-yielding metabolic pathways. ------◄
= Positive modifier; ——x = negative modifier. (From White, Handler, and Smith)

delays are involved, and each enzyme is immediately sensitive to a rise
or fall in the concentration of its substrate and of its modifiers.

4. As discussed in the previous chapter, many cells have available an
additional, much more slowly responsive control—regulation of the
synthesis, by the genetic machinery, of the very enzymes that participate
in a synthetic pathway. The most dramatic instances of such phenomena
have been observed in bacteria. But induction and repression of specific
protein synthesis in animal tissues is also well substantiated. A dramatic
recent example is the mode of action of vitamin D. It has been known for
30 years that this vitamin, in some fashion, facilitates the absorption of
calcium by the small intestine. Only in 1967 was it ascertained that
vitamin D, somehow, prompts the synthesis in intestinal epithelial cells
of a protein with great avidity for Ca^{++} and which is essential to active
transport of Ca^{++} from the lumen of the intestine. Similarly, the metabolic
consequences of several of the sterol hormones have been found to reflect
such induced enzyme syntheses.

5. Perhaps the most complex instances of regulation of a metabolic

system known are the events involved in the formation and utilization of glycogen, the storage polymeric form of glucose, in animal tissues.

This polymer is made by one enzyme and degraded by another. Each enzyme can exist, in the cell, in two forms, one of which is highly active, the other sluggish. In each case, this is the consequence of phosphorylation of the enzyme (esterification of the hydroxyl groups of serine residues in the protein) and of dephosphorylation. Remarkably, the seryl residue involved lies in a sequence of amino acids which is identical in both cases. But whereas the phosphorylated form of one, the synthesizing enzyme, is sluggish and dependent upon a high concentration of a positive modifier, the phosphorylated form of the degrading enzyme is highly active. The liver of a resting animal contains active synthesizing and sluggish degrading enzyme. If the animal is alarmed, is about to run, and hence requires glucose in its blood for muscular activity, the adrenal gland releases its hormone, epinephrine. In the liver, this activates an enzyme which catalyzes the conversion of ATP to a derivative called cyclic adenylic acid (3,5′ cyclic AMP). The latter in turn activates an enzyme that utilizes additional ATP to phosphorylate both the degrading and synthesizing enzymes, thereby turning the former on while switching off the latter. No more elegant a contrivance can be imagined!

Most importantly, it should be noted that this description of metabolic regulation could not even have been attempted three years ago. This area of investigation has proved to be richly rewarding, and it seems entirely likely that the most important, interesting, and useful information remains to be secured in the decades ahead. Enough has been learned to make it evident that the metabolic machinery of the cell is a finely tuned, tightly synchronized orchestra built to function, in the main, without a conductor. One of the triumphs of animal life is the evolution of a substitute for a conductor, the endocrine system, the hormones of which selectively modulate already ongoing activity, increasing or decreasing the volume from specific instruments (enzymes), so that the totality is harmonious and responsive to alteration in the basic score necessitated by the environment.

Some Biochemical Vignettes

The illustrations thus far presented have been concerned with those chemical events that are at the very core of cellular existence, of life itself. And, with but few exceptions, the phenomena that have been described are equally true of brain, muscle, or kidney; in fact, largely, they have also been true of plants and microorganisms. The chemistry of animals has also been explored at another level, the mechanisms and structures by which specialized, differentiated tissues and organisms make their unique contributions to the welfare of the total organism. Only a few instances will be presented; others will be encountered in the chapters that follow.

Connective Tissue

Although the vital aspects of the animal organism derive from cellular activity, much of the organism is, itself, essentially extracellular—e.g., the lumen of the gastrointestinal tract, the vascular system, and the extracellular space in largely cellular organs, much of bone, joints, etc. The very fact of organs of defined and constant size and shape indicates the presence of extracellular structure which binds it together. One form of tissue, connective tissue, is distributed throughout the body. It serves to tie structures together, to lubricate, to protect, to strengthen. In each instance, it is the product of the metabolism of cells derived from the primitive mesenchyme, usually the fibroblast. To accomplish its ends, this cell, and its derivatives, has at its disposal a battery of polymeric materials, varying mixtures of which are characteristic of such tissues as cartilage, tendon, arterial wall, intervertebral disks, the vitreous humor in the globe of eye, the corium just under the skin, the fluid of joints, and the mucous secretions.

At this writing there is only minimal, superficial understanding of the manner in which the chemical components of these structures relate to their biological functions. Attention, until recently, has perforce been focused on the chemical structures of these components. This has been a great challenge and the task is far from complete. The ubiquity of the connective tissue and its unique chemistry warrant a brief summary. Four major classes of polymer are found in connective tissue: (a) proteins; (b) protein-polysaccharides; (c) mucoproteins; and (d) mucopolysaccharides.

Only two major proteins are known, collagen and elastin. The former is the most abundant protein in the body. Composing a quarter to a third of the total body protein, it is unique in many ways. The fundamental unit is the most asymmetric biological molecule known, about 15 Å wide and 3,000 Å long, with a molecular weight of about 300,000. And this molecule, *tropocollagen*, is actually a triple-stranded helix with the strands being of slightly unequal length. These polypeptide chains are unusual in that they are the only protein in the body containing the amino acid hydroxyproline. The latter is not made, as such, in the body. Proline is incorporated into the protein chain as usual, and about 40 percent of the prolines in the already formed chain are then hydroxylated in a reaction for which ascorbic acid, vitamin C, is indispensable. Most manifestations of its deficiency reflect failure of this process. The strands of the helix spontaneously bind together after extrusion to the cell's exterior. Slowly, a small number of covalent cross-links form between them. Other such triple strands then align themselves in parallel, and again cross-linking slowly occurs. Yet other strands join these head to tail, because of the uneven lengths, and again cross-links form. The strands become fibrils, and the fibrils become the tough fibers of tendon or scar tissue. In the cornea the fibrils are all aligned in one direction and the cornea is transparent; in the sclera of the eye, the fibrils and fibers are intermeshed and crossed so that the globe is light-tight. When heated, these structures decompose (the hydrogen-bonded triple helix melts) and the resultant soluble mixture is *gelatin*.

Wherever it is obtained, the collagen fibers exhibit a periodicity by microscopy as if they had peaks and valleys along the surface. In the valleys are thought to be hydroxyproline residues. This structure offers one particularly useful property: When bathed in a supersaturated solution of calcium phosphate it serves as a "nucleating agent"; calcium phosphate, as hydroxyapatite crystals, precipitates out. And thus does the mineralization of bone occur. Again, biological function is an attribute of the unique structure of a protein.

Understanding of the protein-polysaccharides is meager. In outline plan they are as follows:

$$\begin{array}{ccccc}
 & & \text{protein chain} & & \\
\text{H}_2\text{N}\text{-----------}\!\!&\!\!\text{-----------------}\!\!&\!\!\text{---------------------}\!\!&\!\!\text{----------------}\!\!&\!\!\text{-----COOH} \\
 & \text{CH}_2 & \text{CH}_2 & \text{CH}_2 & \\
 & | & | & | & \\
 & \text{O} & \text{O} & \text{O} & \\
 & | & | & | & \\
 & \text{xylose} & \text{xylose} & \text{xylose} & \\
 & | & | & | & \\
 & \text{galactose} & \text{galactose} & \text{galactose} & \\
 & | & | & | & \\
 & \text{galactose} & \text{galactose} & \text{galactose} & \\
 & | & | & | & \\
 & (\text{AB})_n & (\text{AB})_n & (\text{AB})_n & \\
\end{array}$$

where (AB) is a repeating disaccharide. The best characterized protein-polysaccharide is chondroitin sulfate A. It is not clear how long the protein chain is; the shortest reported had a molecular weight of 10,500 (85 amino acid residues), to which was affixed six polysaccharide chains; the longest was ten times that. The polysaccharide chains are polydisperse, varying from 20 to 50 repeating disaccharides. In chondroitin sulfate A, the disaccharide is -glucuronic acid (1 → 3) N-acetylgalactos-amine sulfate, bound in 1 → 4 linkage to the next unit. Five different repeating disaccharides are known among this group of protein-polysac-charides.

Repeating subunit disaccharide of dermatan sulfate, heteropolymer from the protein poly-saccharide of cartilage.

Of particular interest, as a consequence of their structure, is the huge volume such a molecule can occupy (its *domain*). It tends to form a more or less water-filled sphere which serves as a trap for cations because of the –COOH and –SO_3^- groups. Calcium is particularly tightly trapped thereby, and it appears that mineralization of bone is the consequence of proteolysis of the protein, effecting release of the calcium, thereby creating a large increase in local Ca^{++} concentration, permitting nu-cleation to commence on the collagen.

The mucoproteins are the lubricants of mucus, the most carefully characterized being the mucin of submaxillary salivary glands. The latter is a linear protein chain of very great but uncertain length. Along its length, at frequent, close-packed intervals, are attached about 800 in-dividual disaccharides of N-acetylneuraminyl (2 → 6) -N-acetylgalactos-amine, with the hydroxyl on carbon 1 of the latter esterified to an aspartic or glutamic acid of the protein. This is the lubricant of the gastroin-testinal tract; its solutions are viscous and slimy.

Only one simple mucopolysaccharide is known, *hyaluronic* acid. This is a polymer which is built of only a repeating disaccharide, glucuronic acid-N-acetylglucosamine. In the eye it has a molecular weight of about 400,000; in the synovial fluid of joints about 2 to 10 million. In rheumatoid arthritis the molecular weight falls sharply; patients successfully treated with cortisone show a return to normal values. Again, the domain of this molecule is of biological importance; each molecule forms a sphere of effective radius 2,000 Å; in a 0.01 percent solution the domains of these molecules must account for the total volume! If more concentrated they must interpenetrate and, as in the eye, become extremely viscous and the solution almost rigid, thus maintaining the only slightly elastic shape — and hence the optical constancy — of the eye.

Only a beginning has been made in the study of the metabolism — the synthesis and degradation — of these versatile macromolecules. And already much of interest is evident. Two hereditary diseases of mucopolysaccharide metabolism — Marfan's and Hurler's diseases — have been established. The latter, gargoylism, may well have accounted for the "little men" of the Rip van Winkle legend. Aging is characterized by an increase in collagen cross-linking and a steady and consistent change in the composition of the protein-polysaccharide mixture of several tissues, changes that may, for man, give the direction and pace to "time's arrow."

The Eye

Visual perception is made possible by the remarkable structure of the eye. Light passes through the conjunctiva, cornea, aqueous humor, lens, and vitreous humor before impinging on the retina. All but the lens and retina are derivative of the mesenchyme and are variants of connective tissue. The plasticity of the lens is made possible by its content, a thick gel of a special group of proteins called *crystallins*. Interesting as these are, we shall here be concerned only with the manner in which light is perceived. Two special groups of cells in the retina are responsible: In the periphery are the rods, close-packed and responsible for vision in dim light. In the center are the cones, which operate in bright light and are responsible for color vision. The mechanism by which they operate is a magnificent adaptation of molecular structure to biological function.

In the rods is a protein termed an *opsin,* on which is affixed the aldehyde corresponding to vitamin A (retinal) which is in the unstable 11-*cis* configuration.

The absorption spectrum of this complex (rhodopsin) corresponds perfectly to the visual sensitivity curve of the eye in dim light. When a photon is absorbed, the retinal isomerizes to the stable all-*trans* configuration and comes away from its binding site on the protein, which then undergoes a change in its own conformation. This event then initiates the nervous impulse which passes up the optic tract to become part of the perceived image, but how it does so is unclear.

Color vision in the cones is an adaptation of the same mechanism. In-all-*trans*-retinal

Δ^{11}-*cis*-retinal

dividual cones each contain one of three pigments with absorption maxima at 430, 540, and 575 mμ, respectively. Each is an opsin combined with the same pigment, retinal; the differences in their absorption maxima, therefore, are due to the differences in protein structure, and it is these differences that permit color discrimination. *Color blindness* is the consequence of failure to make one of these three pigments. As in the rods, light of the proper wavelength causes isomerization of the 11-*cis* retinal with formation of the all-*trans* isomer and a conformation change which initiates the nervous impulse.

Fundamental to vision, therefore, are the molecular properties of the side chain of vitamin A and the subtleties in this process made possible by variations on the basic structure of the protein, opsin.

Insulin

The hormone insulin has played an exceptional role in the history and development of modern science. For the past 80 years, physicians, biologists, and chemists have been intensely interested in this pancreatic regulator of sugar metabolism. What has been learned about this hormone well illustrates the spectacular advances that science has made but also reminds us of the vast areas of scientific ignorance that still remain. In 1889, two physicians showed that the surgical removal of the pancreas in animals produces a sharp rise of the sugar levels in blood and urine, the symptoms long known to characterize human diabetes. The conclusion could be drawn that the pancreas elaborates a substance that regulates the metabolic disposal of sugar and thereby prevents sugar levels in the body from rising above normal.

For many years the search for this substance led nowhere until it was realized that insulin (so named later because it is produced by the "islet" tissue of the pancreas) is a protein which can be rapidly destroyed by enzymes released when pancreas was subjected to various extraction procedures. Eventually, in 1922, a very simple trick solved this problem. Treating pancreatic tissue with a mixture of acid and alcohol protected the hormone from denaturation and yielded active extracts capable of reducing the elevated blood sugar levels of the diabetic patient. From then on it was a matter of technology to process animal pancreas tissue and to obtain insulin preparations suitable for diabetes therapy. A few years later (1926) pure crystalline insulin of remarkable biological potency was obtained. As little as one millionth of a gram of insulin per kilogram of body weight was sufficient to lower the blood sugar level by one half.

The fortunate circumstance that insulin is small, perhaps the smallest molecule to qualify as a protein, and also that it was early available in a high state of purity, has been of the greatest historical importance. It was only logical that, for the first successful demonstration of the amino acid sequence of a protein, insulin, the smallest pure protein then available, should have been chosen. The elucidation of insulin structure, as described earlier, was based on principles that have remained exemplary for all subsequent work on the chemistry of proteins.

What made the structural determination of insulin so important was that it fully confirmed the basic ideas about protein structure, held since the days of E. Fischer at the turn of the century, that all the amino acid residues in a protein are linked together by peptide bonds. Apart from the disulfide bridges there are no other covalent bonds to hold the amino acid residues of insulin together. Any remaining doubts of this fundamental assumption have been allayed very recently. In organic chemistry it is often felt that the structure of a molecule cannot be regarded as fully proved until the molecule is prepared by an unequivocal synthetic or test tube procedure and then shown to be identical in all its properties with the material isolated from natural sources. A total synthesis of insulin has recently been achieved by chemists in three different countries, and again insulin has served as the testing ground for the trials and development of new methods. Just as the structural analysis of insulin was greatly facilitated by breaking it down first into smaller pieces, the A and B chains, the synthetic approach likewise took advantage of the double-chain structure of insulin. The 30-amino-acid A chain and the 21-amino-acid B chain were separately synthesized according to the blueprint which the earlier analysis of natural insulin had furnished. The products were then compared to the corresponding chains obtained by breakdown of natural insulin. No differences in properties could be detected. For the next step, the total synthesis of insulin, the knowledge was essential that the separated A and B chains of natural insulin will combine spontaneously to reform biologically active hormone. The same experiment was then done mixing natural A chain with synthetic B chain, and conversely natural B chain with synthetic A chain. Both experiments produced active insulin. Finally, fully synthetic insulin resulted when artificially produced A and B chains were allowed to interact. The first synthesis of a biologically important protein had thus been achieved, and the primary structure of at least one protein removed from the realm of mystery.

Profound consequences, both practical and academic, are likely to result from the total synthesis of insulin. First of all, it will be possible to determine how much of the insulin structure is necessary for biological activity. Secondly, all kinds of chemically modified insulins can now be produced by the techniques of organic chemistry. How these modifications will affect the potency and specificity of the hormone will be of great interest to see.

Insulins from various mammalian species differ from each other slightly in amino acid composition, yet insulin isolated from one animal species is as active in another species as it is in the species that produces it, in spite of the chemical differences. The amino acid replacements in the insulin chains are the result of the mutations that occurred in the course of evolution of the species. That such evolutionary modifications had no detectable effect on either biological activity or specificity tells us that in a hormone the overall structure is important, but not every single structural detail. Since the amino acid replacements that have occurred in the course of evolution did not improve the hormonal activity of insulin, at least in any obvious way, it is clear that mutations may occur and be transmitted to later generations even though they do not confer selective advantages.

As we have seen, the insulin molecule has taught us a great deal about various facets of protein chemistry. Equally if not more intensive efforts to understand the mode of action of insulin have yielded, however, only meager information. The most puzzling phenomenon of insulin action (and of the action of many other hormones) is the multiplicity of the effects that ensue when the hormone is administered to an animal. Injection of insulin reduces the level of glucose in the blood and urine. It increases the deposition of glycogen in liver and muscle. The synthesis of a number of enzymes catalyzing the formation of fats, polysaccharides, protein, and some nucleic acids is stimulated. Can all these effects be attributed to a single primary act that triggers or sets in motion several seemingly unrelated events? There is good evidence to believe that insulin facilitates the entry of glucose into the cell interior from the extracellular space, perhaps by opening or widening the spaces in the cell membrane through which glucose has to pass. The molecular mechanism by which insulin brings about this change in cell permeability is thought to be the crux of the problem. But an answer to this aspect of insulin action will not be sufficient to explain all the effects that are observed when insulin is given to an animal. There is as yet no obvious connection between glucose transport across cell membranes and the stimulatory effects of insulin on the synthesis of enzymes concerned with the formation of macromolecules.

Perhaps there should be more emphasis on those features in the insulin structure that are both prominent and unique—the fact that it contains two disulfide-linked polypeptide chains, which can be separated and which reform spontaneously, at least in the test tube. Is this reversible transformation also physiologically significant and, if so, can the separated A and B chains act individually? In other words, is insulin a dual hormone both chemically and functionally? Only when these and similar questions have been answered can there be consideration of a synthetic substitute for insulin.

Penicillin

The term *chemotherapy,* invented by Paul Ehrlich nearly a century ago, means the treatment of disease with chemical substances. This procedure is literally as old as civilization, although the biological basis or rationale for such therapy is even today relatively little understood. The ideal type of chemotherapeutic agent in infectious disease is one that has a very high affinity for the offending organism or parasite but relatively little affinity for the tissues of the host organism. Clearly the agent itself should be toxic for the infecting organism and nontoxic for the host.

In many respects penicillin is probably the closest approach to the ideal chemotherapeutic agent. It combines high bactericidal activity with a striking lack of host toxicity and an almost total absence of side reactions. Penicillin is usually classified as an antibiotic—i.e., a chemical substance of microbiological origin that seriously interferes with the growth or metabolic activities of other microorganisms.

There is little doubt that the remarkable potentialities of antibiotics, as related to their ability to conquer or control many of the most dreaded diseases of the early twentieth century, were so rapidly and fully exploited because of the stimulus provided by the Second World War. As a result of the fundamental research carried out on the structure, biosynthesis, activity, and production of penicillin, systematic worldwide antibiotic research has expanded at a phenomenal pace. Well over one hundred antibiotics which are significantly potent against a broad spectrum of microorganisms have been isolated in pure form. The triumph of the cooperation of biological, chemical, and medical research in translating a laboratory observation into a potent and useful therapeutic tool is in no way better illustrated than in the history of the development of the penicillins as medicinal agents.

The initial observation by Fleming in 1929 regarding the antibacterial activity exhibited by a culture of the mold *Penicillium* has been recounted many times. Nevertheless, the scientific climate at that period was such that these findings aroused relatively little interest for nearly ten years. The success of sulfonamide chemotherapy was partly responsible for directing further efforts toward the penicillin problem, but at the same time oriented the work along chemical (synthetic) lines, which were not fruitful until extensive biochemical and industrial problems had been overcome.

Structural studies by the joint efforts of several teams during World War II established the chemical formula of the natural penicillins as

side chain L-cysteine   L-valine   R = benzyl, *n*-heptyl and
                                                         2-pentenyl in penicillins G,
                                                         K, and I, respectively

structure of penicillin

These differed in the nature of the R group attached to the β-lactam ring, and subsequent efforts were directed toward possible modification of this function to produce acid-stable (suitable for oral administration) or more potent derivatives.

There were two key experimental findings which provided great initial stimulus. The first was the observation (made in the U.S. Department of Agriculture laboratory at Peoria) that the use of corn steep liquor in the culture medium increased the yield of penicillin nearly twentyfold. Further research revealed that the active ingredient was β-phenylethylamine, which served as a direct precursor of the benzyl group of the final product. In addition, it was recognized that the nature of the R grouping could be controlled to some extent by suitable additives and that compounds such as phenylacetic acid were very efficient precursors.

The second major development resulted from a systematic search for mutant strains of *Penicillium* which would provide higher yields of the antibiotic. A mutant produced by ultraviolet irradiation at the University of Wisconsin was found to give twenty-fivefold increased production of penicillin. The combination of these two findings with large-scale submerged culture techniques permitted a rapid expansion in production.* Concomitantly, greatly improved methods of isolation and purification were developed.

The impetus provided by the early therapeutic successes carried through until the early 1950's, although a steady research effort was maintained in an attempt to provide more useful variants of the drug. However, by 1950 a major difficulty had arisen. Numerous strains of *Staphylococcus* had become prevalent which were either resistant to benzylpenicillin or which produced an enzyme (penicillinase) which destroyed its antibacterial action. This problem, which rapidly assumed major proportions, was solved by a combination of techniques. Initial efforts concentrated on the 6-amino derivative (lacking the acyl-R grouping), which had been observed some years earlier as a by-product in the commercial manufacture of benzylpenicillin. Enzymatic synthesis of this compound was achieved, and it was used as the starting material for the synthesis of several "new" penicillins. A family of derivatives was prepared by this route which were active against previously resistant strains of staphylococci, although generally effective in a narrower spectrum of organisms.

It is interesting to note that although the antibiotic action of penicillin itself has been recognized for nearly a generation, the actual mechanism of action of this antibiotic is not yet completely understood. A pioneering study revealed that bacteria growing in the presence of penicillin excreted into the growth medium a series of ultraviolet-absorbing compounds whose composition directly reflected the composition of the bacterial cell wall. It was a logical extrapolation from this observation to conclude that penicillin interfered with some step in the formation of the bacterial cell envelope without at the same time interfering with other metabolic processes. As a result of this a continuing accumulation of unusable cell wall precursors led to the ultimate lysis and death of the bacterium. The actual enzymatic step at which penicillin acts is thought to

* The first clinical trial in the United States was in 1942. By late 1943, production had increased over a hundredfold, and the drug was becoming available for military use.

be the final stage in the assembly of murein, which involves the cross-linking of main chains by the short polypeptide chains containing predominantly glycine residues. A suggested mechanism of action is as follows: The penicillin molecule may be visualized as a two-headed structure containing a cyclic peptide to which is attached the highly reactive β-lactam ring. One end of the molecule (the peptide) mimics the structure of the natural cell wall precursor and is thus bound to the active site of the responsible enzyme, whereupon the free end alkylates a neighboring site on the protein and irreversibly inactivates it. Support for this mechanism is provided by studies that show that radioactively labeled penicillin is rapidly and irreversibly bound to cell surfaces after a brief exposure, which is nonetheless sufficient to inhibit the terminal step in cell wall assembly.

A rational basis for the design of new antibiotics, based upon the structure and biological action of penicillin, is still lacking. Even with some understanding of the knowledge of the mechanism of penicillin action, a design for this molecule will be feasible only after knowing the actual enzymatic step it is able to inhibit. If it were necessary to wait for such knowledge before undertaking clinical trials, we might be waiting yet; obviously some practical outlook is essential and continued "hit-or-miss" screening for antibiotics is a necessary and potentially rewarding avenue.

Conclusion

Exploration of the chemical basis for life has been an intense and fruitful endeavor. Proximate answers are available to each of the major questions posed by biochemists. And all those processes studied by the practitioners of the diverse subspecialties of biology—the subject matter of the remainder of this volume—can ultimately be understood only in the language presented by this and the preceding chapter. Understanding of living processes has expanded at a rate greater than that of any other area of science for two decades and has brought with it gains in the understanding and treatment of a host of human disorders. Impressive though this may seem, the tasks ahead are immense. As in other areas of science, attempts to answer questions have usually revealed only another, more sophisticated set of questions. But the rewards ahead are also predictably great, and we may look to tomorrow with eagerness and confidence. If these efforts are successful, the benefits to human welfare are incalculable.

Chapter 4

CELLS – THE UNITS OF LIFE

The cell is the basic structural unit of all living matter. Within a selective and retentive membrane, it contains a complete set of the different kinds of units necessary to permit its own growth and reproduction from simple nutrients. Each organism is composed of one or more cells; all the chemical activities that underlie the evolution of species and the development, growth, and reproduction of the individual, as well as many of the degenerative changes of disease, operate within this unitary, complex structure.

This central position of the cell in biological organization has been recognized for over a hundred years. Understanding of the nature of cellular life, and the experimental approach to the resolution of unresolved problems in such understanding, have been given sharp definition by the recent striking developments in the fields of molecular genetics and biochemistry. The new wealth of information concerning macromolecular chemistry and genetics of cells has provided insight into the controlled mechanisms by which cells grow, reproduce, differentiate, interact with their environment, or die. The convergence of high-resolution morphological studies with the analysis of increasingly complex biochemical studies has shown that the activities of a cell are based on a complex interplay, not of molecules alone, but rather of molecules organized into cellular subunits called organelles. Each of the various types of organelles has its own highly complex and specifically ordered substructure. It is the interplay of these substructures, mediated through the intracellular flux of molecules, that determines the behavior of the cell.

A major portion of the living material on this planet consists of unicellular organisms, including bacteria, fungi, algae, and protozoans. Such

131

unicellularity represents the more primitive state of life extending back perhaps as long as three billion years. While unicellularity is an evolutionarily earlier condition, even the simplest cells known are highly complex in function. Indeed, it may be argued that the major questions concerning how to achieve the paramount manifestations of life had been solved, albeit empirically, when the first self-reproducing organized cell made its appearance on this planet. The unicellular organisms have been extraordinarily useful in elucidating the basic structures and functions common to all living matter.

In multicellular forms of life, the processes of embryonic differentiation lead from the fertilized egg to the formation of cells of widely varying types and their organization into organs, highly diversified in both structure and function. The interactions of these cells during differentiation and in subsequent normal and abnormal function reflect the ability of the individual cell to respond to external stimuli, whether those stimuli involve direct contact with another cell, the action of another cell's products at the cell surface, or the penetration of such products into the cell.

Because of this pivotal position, the cell is the level at which many major problems of biology have converged and become amenable to experimental analysis. Their broad sweep is clear when we consider that they include the complex processes of cellular *growth, differentiation, regulation* of both growth and function, as well as the *pathogenesis* of disease.

Central to all these problems is the structural milieu within which these processes occur and which make them possible.

Principles of Cell Structure and Function

Cells are composed of a large number of well-defined subcellular structures and compartments, with discrete but complexly interrelated and coordinated roles. The biologist's concern with the structure and chemical composition of these organelles is based on the premise that such information will produce new insights into cell function, and that premise is being richly validated in many different ways.

The cell is divided into two main compartments, the nucleus and the cytoplasm. Two clearly recognizable and essential functions are expressed by the nucleus of every cell type: the replication of the chromosomes, and the release of genetic information to the cytoplasm by transcription into RNA. The nucleus is then definable as the compartment that contains the chromosomes, which are the site of DNA and RNA synthesis. In the "eucaryotic" cells of higher organisms the nucleus is surrounded by two membranes, while in the more primitive, "pro-caryotic" cells of bacteria (Fig. 4-1) and blue-green algae no nuclear membrane is detectable.

The cytoplasm surrounding the nucleus provides it with the energy and precursor material necessary for nucleic acid synthesis and nuclear replication, and in turn receives from the nucleus both the ribosomal and t-RNA necessary for the maintenance of cytoplasmic structure, and the genetic information in the form of messenger RNA necessary for growth and function. The cytoplasm is the chief site of lipid, protein, and car-bohydrate syntheses and the generation of energy.

Although the subcellular organelles are considered individually in the following discussion, any cellular activity, whether it be growth, division, differentiation, or secretion, obviously involves their complex inter-action; and unraveling the details of that interaction is one of the major tasks of current biological research.

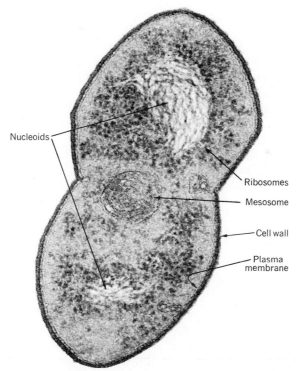

Figure 4-1. A photograph of a bacterium (*Diplococcus pneumoniae*) (at a magnification of 60,000) taken with the electron microscope. Various cell parts are identified. (From J. Jamieson, Proc. Nat. Acad. Sci. *52*:613, 1964)

The Nucleus (Fig. 4-1)

The nucleus contains the primary genetic material (DNA) of the cell organized into one or more chromosomes.

Nuclear Envelope. On rather inconclusive evidence, the nuclear envelope (of eucaryotic cells) is generally assumed to control or regulate the flow of materials between the nucleus and cytoplasm. Electron microscopic examination reveals two distinct membranes that fuse with one another at regular intervals to form an array of apparent openings, which could allow direct communication between the nucleus and the cytoplasm. RNA is known to move from the nucleus to the cytoplasm, and protein moves in both directions; electron microscopic observations suggest that this flow occurs through the pores. Further, in cells with extensive membrane systems in the cytoplasm, the outer membrane of the nuclear envelope is continuous with these cytoplasmic membranes at a number of points. The significance of this attachment is not clear. This is one of many instances in which the definition of a structure has preceded a clear definition of its function.

Chromosomes. Chromosomes become clearly visible in higher cells during mitosis (see Fig. 4-2). In the intermitotic interval chromosomes exist in such a highly unfolded form that they are invisible as discrete structures by light microscopy and are difficult to visualize on electron microscopic examination. The mitotic chromosome is a complex structure, containing DNA and protein with some accompanying RNA. At least in some bacteria, the DNA apparently exists as a single linear, double-stranded, helical molecule (in *Escherichia coli* roughly 1,200 microns long), with the two ends joined to form a closed loop. There is no evidence that DNA is interrupted along its length by non-DNA material. A similar arrangement has been observed in the DNA obtained from mitochondria and in some viruses. Although RNA and protein are not integral parts of the chromosome in a genetic sense, they are probably intimately involved in the regulation and expression of DNA function.

The chromosomes of larger cells obviously contain much more DNA than bacteria. Thus, the DNA in a typical mammalian chromosome is sufficient to make a double-helical molecule several centimeters long. Indeed, the total DNA of a human cell, if arranged as a single thread, would be about six feet long! One of the major questions now under consideration is whether the DNA in the chromosomes of mammalian cells is arranged as a single, continuous double helix or whether, instead, each chromosome contains many shorter discrete DNA molecules in some sort of highly ordered parallel arrangement.

In meiotic chromosomes in amphibians, the dimensions of a chromo-

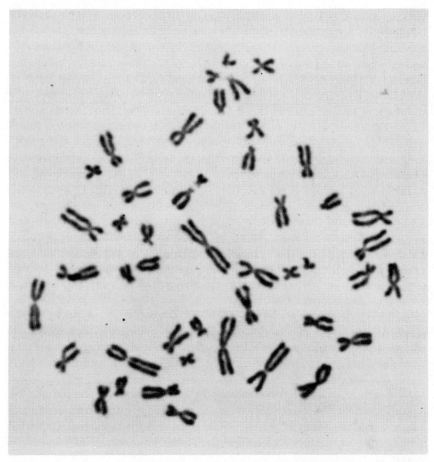

Figure 4-2. A photograph of a normal complement of chromosomes of a human female enlarged 15,000 times. The normal number of chromosomes in the human is 46. (Courtesy Michael A. Bender)

some denuded of its RNA and protein are consistent with the presence of a single double-helical molecule of DNA; kinetic analysis of its digestion by deoxyribonuclease also indicates the presence of only one helix. However, some inconclusive cytological studies of daughter chromosomes at mitosis suggest that they may contain more than one linear subunit.

Whether the unduplicated individual chromosomes of higher cells contain one, two, or many double-helical molecules of DNA, their mode of replication differs from that in bacteria or viruses in certain respects. The bacterial chromosome appears to consist of a single unit of DNA in which replication begins at a single point, and proceeds as a single wave through the entire length of the chromosome. In higher cells, however, DNA replication begins at many points within the individual chromosome. Thus, in a human cancer cell (HeLa), calculations based on the amount of DNA per chromosome and the rate of DNA synthesis indicate that, in the average chromosome, replication is proceeding in at least 125 points; and similar evidence has been obtained for the giant chromosomes of insects. The problem of the regulation of chromosomal replication is central, not only to normal cell function and reproduction, but to the mechanism of cell aging, and the escape from growth control that is characteristic of cancer (see later).

Little is known about the functions of chromosomal RNA and protein, or how they are arranged on the DNA molecule. There are certainly six kinds of histones (basic proteins) and several kinds of acidic and neutral proteins; these are assumed to function in the regulation of RNA synthesis (transcription), DNA synthesis, chromosome replication, and cell division. A major portion of the RNA detected in chromosomes isolated during the mitotic period appears to be ribosomal RNA which is adsorbed onto the chromosome rather than being an integral part of it. The importance of the histones for chromosome structure is underlined by the demonstration that they are synthesized only during the S period of the mitotic cycle simultaneously with the synthesis of DNA. Most, if not all, of histone synthesis probably takes place in the cytoplasm, the products moving rapidly into the nucleus to associate with DNA.

In the bacterial chromosome the DNA strand is "punctuated," by special nucleotide sequences, to permit the controlled transcription of single genes or blocks of genes. There is no definitive evidence of similar punctuation in the DNA of higher organisms, but there is inferential evidence of its existence.

Nucleolus. Another important difference between cells of bacteria and of multicellular organisms is the presence in the nucleus of the latter of one or more *nucleoli.* These structures, containing both RNA and protein in addition to DNA, are always located on a particular chromosome at a particular locus called the nucleolar organizer. The DNA in this region has been shown to contain the genetic information for the synthesis of ribosomal RNA. Curiously, the genes for the production of ribosomal RNA are apparently present in several hundred copies arranged in series. Whether the copies are identical, or whether slight differences permit the production of many slightly different ribosomal RNA's, is not known. Further, in amphibian meiosis, that section of the chromosome concerned with nucleolar formation is capable of multiple rounds of DNA replication independent of the remainder of the chromosome. This selective multiple replication of DNA (amplification) suggests that the chromosomes of higher cells may indeed contain many replicon units. The nucleolar DNA thus replicated in surplus leaves the chromosome, apparently to function in the production of the large amount of ribosomal RNA required in cellular growth. Much of the nucleolar RNA resembles that of ribosomes.

Chromosome Patterns (*Karyotype*). The number of chromosomes in the nucleus is characteristic of the particular species, 46 in man (Fig. 4-2). Further, each chromosome has a characteristic structure and size, evident during certain phases of the cell cycle, that distinguish it from most of the other chromosomes. Although several genetically different chromosomes may have virtually the same size and shape, making individual identification difficult, the differences in general are sufficiently marked to permit karyotypic analysis — i.e., the characterization of the chromosome complement by number, size, and structural features. Such karyotypic analysis has become increasingly important in relation to genetically determined developmental anomalies. For example, in Down's syndrome (unfortunately earlier termed mongolism) there is an extra copy of chromosome 21; and alterations in the number of the sex chromosomes (X and Y) are associated with abnormalities of sex development. Karyotypic analysis is important also in relation to cancer. Almost all cancer cells have an altered karyotype, suggesting a possible causal relationship. The karyotypic changes in cancer cells are usually quite varied. In chronic myelogenous leukemia, there is a specific and characteristic change, in that most cases show an abnormally small chromosome 21. The amount of chromosomal material lost (deletion) varies from case to case, and it is tempting to speculate that in the few cases with apparently normal chromosomes a deletion has, in fact, occurred but is too small to be seen by present methods.

Loss of DNA from one or more chromosomes should be expected to have gross effects on a cell, and most often this probably is lethal; why the loss of a small amount of DNA from a particular chromosome should lead to leukemia is unknown. Such visible changes in the karyotype are a special class of hereditary changes (mutations) which may occur long after normal fertilization of the egg, and they may affect the function of the many unknown genes present in a visible chromosome segment. Many other hereditary diseases are now known to be due to small alterations in single genes, which cannot be seen microscopically but are evidenced by loss or alteration of a specific protein (e.g., a particular enzyme or a particular kind of hemoglobin) corresponding to that gene.

The Cytoplasm (Fig. 4-1)

Virtually all the metabolic activities of the cell other than nucleic acid synthesis occur in the cytoplasm (e.g., protein, lipid, and carbohydrate syntheses, energy metabolism, and a varying number of specific functions characteristic of the particular cell type). The structural and metabolic arrangements required for such functions as contraction, movement, conduction of impulse, and secretion of cell products, are all properties of the cytoplasm. Not surprisingly, this portion of the cell varies more in structure and form among various cell types than does the nucleus. However, all cells have two cytoplasmic structural elements in common, the plasma membrane and ribosomes. The ribosomes are intimately involved in protein synthesis, and were described in detail in Chapter 2.

The Plasma Membrane of the Cell. Cells are separated from the environment by a membrane largely composed of phospholipids and protein. The details of their arrangement have been studied for years; although a number of theories have been proposed, the matter is very much *sub judice.* The entire complex forms a sheet approximately 70 Å in thickness, much too thin to be visible in the light microscope, but clearly discernible by electron microscopic observation. Whether the macromolecules forming the membrane fall spontaneously into a predetermined pattern by virtue of their stereochemical, configurational fit, or whether there are specific enzymes which join the appropriate macromolecular parts into their proper relationship in the whole, is not yet clear.

The plasma membrane is clearly not a static structure; its component parts are constantly undergoing turnover. In bacteria the formation of various specific transport systems in the membrane can be rapidly altered by adaptive responses to changes in the environment. Water and certain small molecules can apparently enter by diffusion through small, invisible pores; and the rate of entry of various lipophilic compounds appears to depend on their solubility in lipids, which form so large a fraction of the membrane. Most solutes, however, including sugars, amino acids, nucleosides, and inorganic ions, enter the cell largely by means of specific transport systems which accomplish transport across the membrane by the expenditure of metabolic energy. The detailed mechanisms of active transport are not clear. It appears that the specific carrier, a protein, to which a permeant is bound can rotate and face either side of the membrane; on the intracellular side the application of energy — e.g., by binding to the protein of ATP — to the protein changes its conformation in such a way as to decrease its affinity for the permeant, which is then released to the cytoplasm.

Schemes of this general sort have been proposed to explain the pumping of sodium and potassium ions across the cell membranes of such tissues as nerve, muscle, and blood. Active transport maintains a differential concentration of these ions inside and outside the cell that is essential for the normal function of these particular cells. The electrical potential across the plasma membrane established by sodium ion pumping together with low sodium and high potassium permeabilities in all cells, when modified, forms the basis for impulse conduction in specialized tissues such as nerve and muscle.

In some cases, passive transport by free diffusion of molecules into the cell is followed by an energy-dependent conversion to a form that is then unable to pass out through the membrane so that the molecule remains trapped in the cell. Such is clearly the case with nucleosides, whose entry is followed by esterification to phosphate, using ATP, to yield the trapped nucleotides. By such devices, materials present in low concentration in the environment are made available to the cell.

As the limiting structure between the inside and the outside of the cell, the plasma membrane is that part of the cell in most intimate and immediate contact with the environment. By virtue of its control of the passage of materials into and out of the cell, it has an important role in defining the ecological niche of the particular cell type, and in the adaptation of the cell to environmental change, a mechanism that underlies the entire process of development.

It is obvious that the plasma membrane is intimately concerned with the reaction of the cell to environmental changes, not only in terms of dissolved materials which enter into the cell, but in terms also of contact with other cells or structures, or with solutes that have a direct impact at the cell surface, rather than within the cell. Whether the "sensitive" compounds on the cell surface are a structural part of the plasma membrane, or compounds produced within the cell and bound to its external surface, is not known. In either case, interaction of the surface with the environment does have profound effects on cell metabolism. Thus, in cultured normal animal cells derived from mammalian tissues, contact between the surfaces of two cells results in an immediate, dramatic inhibition of their motility. Associated with this loss of motility, and equally important, is a striking reduction in the rate of protein, RNA, and DNA syntheses—i.e., the mutual inhibition of cell reproduction. How these effects are mediated by the surface contact remains to be determined.

These phenomena, easily observed in cells grown in culture, must play an important role in tissue formation and in the control of cell proliferation within a multicellular organism. The loss of this normal contact inhibition of motility and cell proliferation may be related to the induction of cancer, and is frequently accompanied by a change in the chromosomal pattern (karyotype) of the cell. The link between the chromosomal aberrations and the structural changes in the cell surface which are evidenced in loss of contact inhibition, and how both events are linked to the escape from the control over cell reproduction in vivo, are among the important unanswered questions in the genesis of cancer.

In some of the simpler bacteria the cytoplasm appears to contain only ribosomes and dissolved molecules, enclosed by the plasma membrane. The enzymatic machinery required for oxidative phosphorylation appears to be integrated within the plasma membrane, and much or most of the other metabolic activities of the cytoplasm take place in the structureless soluble phase. In higher cells, however, the cytoplasm of most cells contains a complex array of structures and organelles with specific metabolic functions in the cellular economy.

The Mitochondrion (Fig. 4-3). The mitochondrion is a vesicle bounded by two membranes. The inner membrane continues by projections and infoldings to form an extensive integrated complex of enzymes that conduct oxidative phosphorylation and thus generate biologically useful energy. The outer membrane is believed to mediate the interactions of the mitochondrion with the surrounding cytoplasm, including the movement of inorganic ions, the uptake of organic substrates, and, in particular, the release of ATP for use in energy-requiring processes elsewhere in the cell.

There has been considerable speculation as to how and when new mitochondria are formed during cell growth and division. Among the hypotheses proposed are (1) their de novo formation from the appropriate macromolecular precursors; (2) their formation from other membranous structures in the cell, such as the outer nuclear membrane or the plasma membrane; and (3) growth and fission of preexisting mitochondria. The last hypothesis is currently receiving most attention, because mitochondria have been observed to divide in living cells, and also because mitochondria have recently been shown to contain DNA, RNA, and ribosomes. The latter finding in fact suggests that at least some of the genetic information required for the synthesis of the mitochondrial proteins may be contained within the mitochondrion itself, rather than in the cell nucleus. The simplest mechanism of division to assure that each daughter organelle would have its own DNA could be a process similar to that involved in the division of bacteria. What controls this replicative process is not clear. It is clear, however, that the genes which code for several mitochondrial proteins are nuclear and are not present in the mitochondrial DNA, so that the significance of the latter is now uncertain.

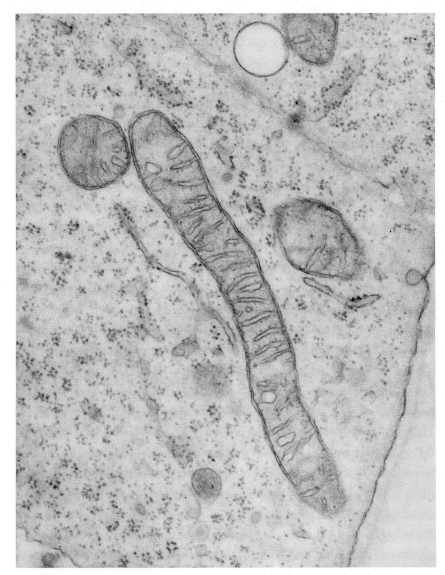

Figure 4-3. A mitochondrion in a cell of the epididymus of the mouse. Magnification 45,000 times, (Courtesy C. Flickinger)

The mitochondrion is not a free-living, autonomous suborganism within the cell, and its formation is governed, at least in part, by events in the nucleus.

Cytoplasmic membranes, referred to collectively as the *endoplasmic reticulum,* appear to be absent in bacteria, but are present in varying forms and amounts in all higher cell types. The structure varies from small vesicles scattered through the cytoplasm to tightly packed sheets that, in extreme cases, occupy most of the cytoplasm. The membranes of the endoplasmic reticulum appear to have a similar structure in all cell types, and closely resemble the plasma, nuclear, and mitochondrial membranes. Although a number of enzymes have been demonstrated in the endoplasmic reticulum, its function is not as precisely defined as that of other organelles. Different sections of the reticulum may in fact prove to have different functions, despite the basically similar structural configuration.

It has been suggested that the endoplasmic reticulum serves in the transport of materials within the cell, and particularly in the movement of newly synthesized proteins destined for export. It may be present in both a rough and smooth form, reflecting the presence or absence of ribosomes attached to its surface. The rough form is particularly prevalent in cells which are synthesizing protein for export (secretion). It is believed that protein synthesized in association with the membrane-bound ribosomes enters the space between adjacent folds, and is thence transported to the Golgi apparatus for "packaging" prior to release from the cell.

The Golgi Apparatus. The Golgi apparatus, poorly perceived by light microscopy, is composed of layers of membranes and vesicles, and is usually located in close proximity to the nucleus. This structure is most prominent in cells that secrete proteins to their exteriors, such as pancreas, liver and pituitary gland. Available information suggests that it has a role in "packaging" the proteins to be secreted; such a function has been clearly demonstrated in the case of pancreas cells in which digestive enzymes are packed into granules which migrate out of the cell. Recent results suggest that the endoplasmic reticulum and the Golgi apparatus may also be involved in the synthesis of new cell membranes required for growth.

Chloroplasts. The central role of plants as foods for animals is based on their unique capacity to use solar energy for the synthesis of utilizable carbohydrates, proteins, vitamins, etc. This the plant cell accomplishes through the presence of chloroplasts, cytoplasmic organelles unique to algae and higher plant cells, which contain the molecular apparatus for conversion of solar energy to chemical energy. Like mitochondria, the chloroplast is separated from the rest of the cytoplasm by two membranes and consists of a series of membranous layers within or on which are the compounds required to carry out the process of photosynthesis. The physical arrangements of the light-absorbing pigments (primarily chlorophylls), enzymes, and coenzymes in these functionally integrated structures are gradually being deciphered.

As with the mitochondria, experimental study has hitherto tended to deal with chloroplast function as a problem separate from chloroplast growth and reproduction. Growth and function are, however, obviously interrelated. Plants grown in the dark in a suitable medium containing carbohydrates fail to develop chloroplasts. Upon long deprivation of light, the chloroplasts of even a mature plant are reduced in size and complexity, and can then be stimulated to grow by reexposure to light of appropriate wavelengths. During normal growth it is thought that reproduction of the chloroplast occurs by fission. Again like mitochondria, chloroplasts contain DNA, RNA, and ribosomes that presumably carry and express genetic information for the formation of some or all the proteins unique to this organelle. How much of the structure and function of the chloroplast is governed by its DNA is unknown; clearly there is some degree of both independence of and dependence upon nuclear genetic information.

The Lysosome. Lysosomes, one of the most recent components of the cell to be discovered, are minute vesicles usually less than one micron in diameter and bounded by a single membrane. They are absent in bacteria, apparently occur generally in higher cells, and are characterized by their high content of digestive enzymes (hydrolases). Their role in the economy of an individual cell seems to be connected primarily with phagocytosis, the digestion of ingested polymeric materials, a prevalent function in heterotrophic cells; their role in maintaining the balance of cell populations in complex tissues (e.g., by autolysis) remains to be clarified. Certainly, the enzymes of this organelle must be kept apart from the cell proper, lest the latter be destroyed as it is postmortem.

The Cell Wall. Bacterial, fungal, and plant cells possess a rigid cell wall outside the plasma membrane. Strictly speaking, this is an extracellular structure, the components of which are synthesized and secreted by the cells. This protective wall allows the cell to maintain a relatively constant, intracellular osmotic pressure without lysing, in the face of a range of extracellular osmotic pressures which vary from fresh to sea water. The wall also provides a variety of specific receptors and antigens which interact with appropriate viruses and antibodies. Much has been learned recently about cell wall chemistry and about the enzymatic mechanisms by which the specific repeating units of wall polysaccharides are laid down, some aspects of which are described in Chapter 2. These studies provide models for studying the nature and formation of the all-important specific surface macromolecules of mammalian cells, which govern their survival in transfusion and transplantation, and must also guide their arrangement into tissues, but concerning which almost nothing is known. This will be a fruitful field of research in the next decade.

The Soluble Phase of the Cytoplasm. Although many biochemical activities of the cell occur within specific organelles, certain activities, such as glycolysis and certain phases of amino acid and lipid metabolism, are accomplished by enzymes in a relatively free state within the soluble phase of the cytoplasm. This phase also provides the ionic environment required to maintain the physical integrity of the organelles, brings the substrates necessary for their function, and transports the materials involved in their complex interactions.

Nuclear-Cytoplasmic Interactions

Of the interactions between cellular substructures, the most important is that between the nucleus and cytoplasm. This determines which genetic information is "transcribed" as messenger RNA for transmittal from the nucleus to the cytoplasm where it is "translated" into protein synthesis. The type and amount of such transmittal determines the structure and the functional activities of the cell. The conditions in the cytoplasm also profoundly influence the second function of the nucleus, the replication of the genetic material. This is the very essence of the control of cell reproduction.

The precise nature of the regulatory changes initiated in the cytoplasm by environmental conditions, and how that regulatory information is fed back from cytoplasm to nucleus, is a major unsolved problem in cell biology.

Cell Growth and Reproduction

In proliferating cells, each type of cytoplasmic organelle doubles in amount during the average cell life cycle, but it is not these increases that directly control cellular division. Cell division consists primarily of replication of the genetic material in the nucleus, and segregation of the genetic material at nuclear division into two functional nuclei.

The cell life cycle (diagrammed in Figure 4-4) is, for convenience, considered to begin immediately after nuclear division; but such a designation is clearly arbitrary, since in continuously proliferating cells, the cell cycle has no beginning or end. Following nuclear division, the next clearly definable event is the initiation of another round of DNA replication. In most cells a measurable period of time separates these two events, and is termed gap 1 (G_1) of the cell cycle. It is presumed that during G_1 the cell is preparing for DNA synthesis; but why this postulated preparation should require a relatively long G_1 in some cells, and an unmeasurably short time in others, has not been satisfactorily explained. The time occupied by DNA synthesis is called the S (synthesis) period. In most cells there is then a time gap between the completion of DNA synthesis and the onset of nuclear division, designated as G_2. In summary, the cell life cycle is usually divided into four subsections: G_1, S, G_2, and D (where D is the period of actual nuclear and cell division). More simply, the cell life cycle can be defined as alternate periods of gene replication (S) and gene segregation (D).

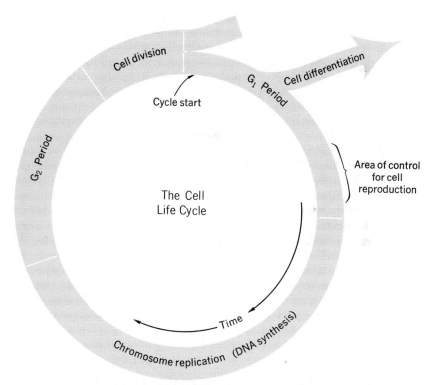

Figure 4-4. The diagram describes the progress of the cell through its life cycle. Cell reproduction is regulated by interruption of cycle progress at a still unidentified control point in the G_1 phase. The total time for one traverse through the cycle varies enormously from one cell type to another but is typically 10 to 15 hours in a mammalian cell undergoing unrestricted reproduction. See text for discussion of the cell life cycle. (Courtesy David M. Prescott)

The period preceding DNA synthesis (G_1) is an extremely important part of the cell life cycle, since it is in this G_1 state that cells usually come to rest when proliferative activity ceases for any reason. In the development of a multicellular organism, cell differentiation occurs in cells halted at this stage of the cycle; and the control of cell proliferation in fact appears essential to that development. In tissues in which new cells are required to balance physiological cell loss (epithelial tissues, blood cells, etc.), the balance is achieved by holding cells in the G_1 state for longer or shorter periods of time according to the immediate needs of the particular tissue. Following an acute loss of cells (e.g., after loss of blood, after wounding of the skin or other epithelia, or after partial removal of liver) there is an enormously accelerated cell reproduction to compensate for the large cell loss. The regulation of cell reproduction within each tissue is achieved by the tissue itself, presumably by synthesis and release of regulatory substances into the microenvironment. Specific information is scarce, and the mechanism of the control is yet another major unsolved problem in cell biology, and of obvious relevance to our understanding of embryonic development, organismic aging, and cancer.

Most present information concerning the regulation of DNA synthesis derives from studies on bacteria, in which the chromosome replicates as one unit with a growing point moving continuously from a single initiation site to the end. Following completion of such a round of replication, synthesis of a poorly understood "initiation protein" is required before another round can be begun. In the cells of higher organisms, with many chromosomes, each chromosome contains a large number of replicating units. Hence, the process of replication and its control must correspondingly be more complex. The transition from G_1 to S is a key aspect of the problem of growth control, since the regulation of cell reproduction is primarily the regulation of DNA synthesis.

The progress of a cell through its life cycle can be viewed as a series of sequentially ordered gene transcriptions, with correspondingly ordered protein syntheses, which control the timing of the various events. This sequence of transcriptions is assumed to constitute a closed circle, which, unless interrupted by some environmental influence, will continue indefinitely. Each phase must be initiated by a signal, a critical increase or decrease in the concentration of some key metabolite, and must be terminated by a similar or converse process. But these metabolites remain to be identified, as do the specific chemical processes they affect. It seems entirely likely that "timing" is the consequence of the sequential operation of a series of feedback loops, each of which creates the setting necessary for the next operation.

One final, additional organelle should be noted. After DNA replication is complete and chromosome organization has begun, there appear, at the two poles of the cell, bodies called centrioles from which radiate "spindle fibers," composed of a filamentous protein. These attach, in unknown manner, to the chromosome pairs. Thereafter, in wondrous fashion, the chromosomes align at the center of the cell, the fibers shorten, drawing the chromosomes apart, and new membrane forms, dividing the cell into two daughter cells. The elegant precision of this process is essential to cell duplication, but the underlying chemical events at the molecular level—the signal for fiber production, the mode of attachment, the mechanism of shortening, the signal and mechanism of new membrane formation, the fate of the fibers which then disappear, the mechanism of unfolding of the chromosomes—all remain to be established.

Differentiation and Specialization of Function in Cells

Another major problem is how cells derived from the same progenitor cell can differentiate into the wide variety of functionally and structurally specialized cells of the adult multicellular organism. Conceptually, this is not as puzzling as it was a few years ago. Recent findings have shown that, in bacterial cells, not all the genes are active under any given conditions; and specific mechanisms have been revealed which selectively repress or induce the activity of various genes or groups of genes. Such differential gene transcription, on a larger scale, provides a conceptual basis for understanding how different cells may inherit an identical genome but allow its unequal expression to develop the great specialization required to yield nerves, muscle, liver, etc.

The directive signals for differentiation, which are received by a cell from its immediate microenvironment, probably involve both accumulated cell products and as yet unidentified signal molecules originating from other groups of cells. Without knowledge of the composition of these signal molecules it is difficult even to speculate as to the regulation of their production, the means by which they are recognized, or the consequences of such recognition. Within the cytoplasm of the target cell the information received from the environment somehow directs a small, specific section of the genetic apparatus to the differential transcription of RNA, and the specific new proteins synthesized in consequence of that selective transcription effect a qualitative change in the cell (differentiation). One of the most useful experimental materials for the study of gene activation in larger cells is the larvae of certain diptera (flies). Because the chromosomes in certain tissues of these organisms are enormously enlarged by repeated replication of their DNA, activation of some genes during development can be detected by light microscopic observation as "puffs" at specific sites along the chromosomes. These are presumed to be areas on the chromosome where the histone has been detached from DNA, permitting access of the enzyme and substrates required for RNA synthesis. The hormone ecdysone, necessary for insect development, has been shown by this procedure to activate specific genes (cause puffs) at specific times in development. These observations have contributed substantially to the elucidation of principles of development of general applicability to all organisms and will be further considered in Chapter 6.

Cell and Environment

Nutrition. The simplest possible nutritional requirement of a cell is a source of nitrogen, mineral ions, carbon, and energy. Cells that can grow, reproduce, and function on so limited a "diet" must synthesize all the other types of molecules needed for their own purposes; their biosynthetic activities are correspondingly complex. Virtually all plant cells, many bacteria, and certain other microorganisms fall into this category. Other cell types are deficient to a varying degree in their biosynthetic capacities, and must compensate for these deficiencies by procuring organic molecules, or varying number and complexity, from the environment. Perhaps surprisingly, the scale of complexity in nutritional requirements does not parallel their evolutionary development. Thus, human cells in culture require essentially the same nutrilites (for survival and growth) as do some strains of *Lactobacilli,* the bacteria whose metabolic activities sour milk.

Assessment of the nutrition of an organism involves questions of not only what a cell requires but what it can use. Studies of cells in different nutrient environments, performed first with microbes and more recently with cultured animal cells, have revealed that "adaptation" involves the formation of specific enzymes to attack new substrates. It was the study of this adaptive process that revealed the general mechanisms of regulation of synthesis of specific macromolecules, and thus provided the background for our present concept of differentiation (p. 51). In any case, a list of nutritional requirements is a list of chemicals a cell must have and cannot make for itself. For all organisms this list is more remarkable for its brevity than for its length.

Radiation. Man's ability to produce ionizing radiations of ever increasing intensity, and to project himself into a radioactive environment, has made understanding of the biological effects of radiation of great topical importance. These effects are expressed primarily at the cellular level. The sensitivity of different cell types to radiation varies enormously. Those of man are among the most sensitive, whereas some protozoans are more than 1,000 times as resistant as human cells. The basis for this varying resistance is incompletely understood. One important factor is the ability of a cell to shield itself by chemical means against the chemical free radicals produced within the cell by ionizing radiation; another is the enzymatic repair of otherwise lethal damage to DNA. Although the examination of radiation damage tends to center on the genetic material, it is now clear that cytoplasmic damage can also be of considerable consequence, even in the energy range at which cell recovery eventually takes place.

One of the few objective means of assessing radiation damage, particularly at sublethal dosages, is the breakage of chromosomes. Cells generally are capable of a remarkable amount of chromosome repair within the first hours after exposure. Residual damage, with or without microscopically visible breaks, may result in cell death or ultimately in the induction of cancer. Why certain mutations or larger changes in chromosomes induced by radiation should lead to such a loss of control of cell reproduction is as yet unknown. Intensive radiation is required to produce serious damage to organs, because each organ contains a large number of cells which can function interchangeably. Each germ cell, however, plays a unique role in the formation of an embryo, and so mutations with serious consequences can be produced if even light irradiation reaches the germ cells.

Sensitivity to radiation varies greatly with the metabolic state of the cell. Actively proliferating cells are much more sensitive during early DNA synthesis, G_2, and division and least sensitive in the G_1 state (pre-DNA synthesis). Indeed, bursts of radiation, delivered during specific phases of the mitotic process, have been shown preferentially to damage different groups of genes. The reasons for these differences are not known. Nonproliferating cells arrested in G_1, such as differentiated cells in functioning organs, similarly tend to be appreciably more resistant to the effects of radiation; and the most resistant cells in the multicellular organism are those permanently arrested in G_1 (neurons, muscle cells, etc.). The important consequence is that the normal tissues that are the most severely affected by radiation damage are those in which there is the greatest need for new cells and in which there is normally a rapid rate of cell turnover (blood, intestinal epithelium, skin). This differential sensitivity of dividing cells is the major element in the effectiveness of the radiation treatment of cancer; unfortunately, radiation does not distinguish between cancer cells and normally proliferating cells.

Cell-to-Cell Interaction. Interaction between cells has wide-ranging effects which are most obvious and extensive in multicellular organisms. Such cell-to-cell interaction is, in fact, one of the distinguishing and essential features of multicellular organisms. Its importance is best evidenced by the diversity of situations in which cell-to-cell interaction plays a determinative role. The fertilization of an egg by a sperm cell; the complex process of differentiation and embryonic morphogenesis; the transmission of an impulse from one nerve cell to another or to a muscle fiber; the reaction of a target cell to hormones produced by cells at a distance; the contact inhibition of motility and of cell reproduction within certain tissues; the transmission of nutrients from one cell to another; the cooperative action of cells to produce an extracellular structure, such as the collagen matrix of tendons and bone: these are all examples of a fundamentally important and universal phenomenon. To what extent such interactions require specific adhesion of cell surfaces, rather than simple contact, and to what extent there must be exchange or passage of materials from one cell to another, can only be guessed. The mechanisms involved could be as diverse as the cell types involved and the nature of the response observed; but their elucidation is clearly central to the problems of biological organization and the pathogenesis of disease.

Cell Transformation. When mammalian cells are cultivated for many generations in vitro they frequently undergo alterations in their structure and their growth pattern, frequently associated with karyotypic changes. The term *transformation* is used to cover a wide spectrum of such alterations. Among the most interesting is a loss of contact inhibition (p. 213) and thus of a normal restriction of the extent of cell proliferation. Such cells frequently give rise to tumors when reinoculated into the animals from which they had been taken. Cellular transformation in the intact animal can be induced experimentally by irradiation, by exposing cells to carcinogens, or by certain "oncogenic" viruses; and, in some species more commonly than others, similar changes may arise spontaneously.

Biologists are only now beginning to recognize the profound importance of cell transformation. The fact that cancerous changes may be produced in cultured cells by agents known to cause cancers in the whole animal represents a major advance toward an understanding of this disease. A simple experimental system has, thus, just become available to study, in molecular terms, the massive changes in cell behavior that result from chromosomal aberrations, and to determine specifically which metabolic changes are responsible for the ability of certain transformed cells to produce tumors in the whole animal.

Virus-Cell Interaction. An understanding of the cellular processes induced by infection with animal viruses is important for progress in several areas of biological and medical sciences. First, about 60 percent of all illnesses are estimated to be caused by viral infection. Yet, clinically effective drugs are not available for viral diseases. The meager results of over twenty years of empirical searching for antiviral agents indicate that further knowledge of the fine structure of viral components and the molecular events involved in viral replication and virus-induced cell damage is required in order to design effective agents for the treatment of viral diseases.

Second, an understanding of the cancer cell and the neoplastic process in molecular terms, a hopeless pursuit several years ago, is now a realistic research goal for those studying tumorigenic viruses and the mechanism of virus-induced cell transformation. Because tumor-producing viruses can now be obtained in highly purified form and suitable "normal" cells in culture can be transformed into "neoplastic" cells, experimental systems are becoming available for a rational analysis of the molecular basis of neoplasia.

Third, a great potential of animal viruses is that they provide unique footholds within the mammalian cell for attacking these complex problems of cell function for which other approaches may be virtually non-existent. Viral infection is the only experimental procedure available by which a defined segment of genetic material can be introduced into a mammalian cell. Since viruses contain only a limited number of genes, from five to several hundred, it is technically feasible to analyze in detail the translation of specific viral macromolecules, and the intracellular controls of these processes, employing the virus-infected cell for experimental analysis.

More than 500 animal viruses of various sizes and degrees of chemical complexity have been discovered, containing either DNA or RNA, and multiplying or maturing in different parts of the host cells; over 300 of these can infect man. Most animal viruses have been tentatively classified into eight groups on the basis of biochemical and biophysical properties of the virion (the extracellular mature virus particle): four DNA-containing groups, the papovaviruses, adenoviruses, herpesviruses, and poxviruses; and four RNA-containing groups, the picornaviruses, reoviruses, arboviruses, and myxoviruses. Viral DNA's range in size from 3 million to 160 million in molecular weight, are double-stranded, and are either circular (papovaviruses) or linear. Viral RNA's have molecular weights ranging from 2 million for the picornaviruses to over 10 million for the reoviruses, the latter uniquely being double-stranded. This great variety in chemical composition, structure, and site of replication, presumably reflecting as well differences in replicative patterns and induced cellular modifications, endows animal viruses with a unique role in dissecting cellular function in molecular terms: by infecting homogeneous cell cultures one can experimentally insert viral genetic material of different types and sizes into defined intracellular regions and study the ensuing biosynthetic events.

Studies with representative members of the four DNA virus groups during the past five years have revealed the occurrence of the following series of events during an infectious cycle: (1) attachment of virus to specific receptor sites on the host cell; (2) uptake of intact virus into phagocytic vesicles and transport to cytoplasmic or nuclear (?) sites; (3) intracellular uncoating of viral DNA; (4) transcription of specific regions of viral DNA; (5) attachment of the transcribed product, viral messenger RNA, to cytoplasmic or nuclear (?) ribosomes; (6) synthesis of viral specific enzymes and other "early" proteins, utilizing the viral message on cellular ribosomes; (7) replication of viral DNA by enzymes of uncertain origin; (8) a second wave of transcription involving parental or progeny viral DNA or both; (9) translation of these viral m-RNA's to viral structural proteins and other viral specific proteins, some involved in regulatory functions such as "switching off" the synthesis of virus-induced "early" enzymes; and (10) the final construction of the virion, presumably by self-assembly.

While the overall replication patterns of the various DNA viruses are similar, the individual biosynthetic steps can differ considerably. Several interesting general patterns involved in the replication of most DNA viruses are the early inhibition imposed upon host cell macromolecular synthesis, the mechanism of which is unknown, stimulation of the activity of DNA-synthesizing enzymes, and the regulatory role of "late" viral gene products on "early" viral gene functions. Further analysis of these phenomena should provide insight into the mechanisms that regulate cellular and viral macromolecule synthesis. Hopefully, such information concerning regulatory mechanisms which operate specifically in viral infections may provide clues to the control of viral disease.

The biosynthesis of RNA animal viruses, especially poliovirus, has been intensively studied during the past few years and, although similar to that of DNA viruses in many respects, differs in several significant ways. As before, RNA viruses attach to cells, penetrate, and are uncoated. But the DNA-RNA transcription step, characteristic of DNA viruses, is bypassed. The parental viral RNA strand serves as a messenger RNA. It forms viral polyribosomes and directs the synthesis of viral-specific proteins, among which are (1) regulatory proteins which, in some manner, inhibit normal host cell RNA and protein synthesis, (2) a unique RNA-dependent RNA polymerase which catalyzes synthesis of new viral RNA (see Chapter 2), and (3) viral structural proteins. RNAase-resistant RNA structures, thought to be intermediates in viral

RNA replication, have been demonstrated with many RNA viruses.

Interferon is the name given to a cell-coded protein that is formed in response to infection with most DNA and RNA animal viruses. In sufficient quantity, interferon inhibits viral multiplication and, thus, may play a role in recovery from viral disease. Recent studies indicate that interferon acts by inducing the synthesis of a second cell protein which somehow prevents the association of viral m-RNA with ribosomes to form viral polyribosomes. Clearly, if a sufficient supply were available, interferon would have great therapeutic potential. Current research is directed toward means of eliciting maximal interferon synthesis in cell cultures.

Viral carcinogenesis provides a rational strategy for investigating the mechanism of neoplasia. Conversion of a normal to a cancer cell is thought to involve a permanent genetic alteration in some of the somatic cells of an animal. But the mammalian cell contains at least a million genes, and the identification of the altered genes in terms of gene products (i.e., the proteins and enzymes) without some suggestive clue poses insurmountable technical difficulties at the present time. However, the analysis of viral carcinogenesis greatly simplifies this problem. Cancer-producing viruses contain only between 7 and 50 genes, yet one or several of these genes can induce cancer in animals and transform normal cells to malignant cells in culture. Understanding of the functions of these relatively few viral genes should help to elucidate the nature of the carcinogenic process.

Indeed, significant progress has been made in understanding the mechanism of tumor induction and cell transformation by DNA and RNA oncogenic viruses. After they have invaded their host cells, the DNA tumor viruses, including 8 human adenoviruses (31 human adenoviruses are known), virus SV40, and polyomavirus, are not demonstrable as infectious in viral-induced tumor cells. However, the presence in these cells of virus-specific proteins ("tumor antigens") distinct from virion structural proteins argues for the persistence and functioning of at least part of the viral genome in the tumor cell. The direct demonstration of viral DNA in viral-induced tumor cells is a technically formidable problem, since a single viral gene would represent a very small portion of total cellular DNA, about one part in a million. However, it has recently been shown that tumor cells induced in animals by polyomavirus, SV40, and 7 different human adenoviruses synthesize viral-specific m-RNA as demonstrated by the formation of DNA-RNA hybrids when their m-RNA is mixed with pure viral DNA. A surprisingly large amount of the total m-RNA in the polyribosomes of adenovirus transformed cells is viral specific, 2 to 5 percent, suggesting that a small amount of viral DNA present in the tumor cell is preferentially transcribed while most of the host RNA goes unexpressed. The mechanism of this selective transcription operative in viral carcinogenesis may represent only a specialized case of the more general phenomenon occuring during cell differentiation, or it may occur by an entirely different mechanism. It seems likely that these viral m-RNA molecules are translated into proteins, some of which are responsible for the altered growth and antigenic properties of the tumor cell.

Host DNA synthesis is inhibited during the lytic cycle of infection with most DNA viruses. However, infection of nondividing cells with polyoma or SV40 virus induces the synthesis of host cell DNA during the lytic cycle, a phenomenon thought to be of importance in viral transformation.

A correlation has been uncovered between base composition and oncogenicity of DNA viruses. Nononcogenic human adenoviruses contain 55–61 percent guanine and cytosine, "weakly" oncogenic adenoviruses 50–52 percent, and "highly" oncogenic adenoviruses 48–49 percent. The oncogenic papovaviruses contain from 41 to 49 percent guanine and cytosine. Thus, those DNA viruses that possess a guanine and cytosine content closer to that of the mammalian cell (42–44 percent G + C) stand a better chance of being oncogenic. These findings may indicate that oncogenic DNA viruses possess DNA segments homologous to some regions of the host cell chromosome.

The oncogenic RNA viruses, including the avian and murine leukemia and sarcoma viruses, are capable of both transforming cells and replicating within the same cell. Particularly intriguing are those viruses that are defective in the genes for synthesis of viral coat protein; they transform cells without the production of infectious virus. Others are defective only within certain host cells. Coinfection of tumor cells induced by such a defective virus with a second virus ("helper virus") is required for the synthesis of infectious virus; newly synthesized virus then contains the genome of the transforming virus and the outer coat protein of the helper virus.

Vaccines. Vaccines, preparations that induce synthesis of antibodies against a specific virus, have been adequately developed. Nearly 200 years ago, Jenner developed a remarkably successful vaccine against smallpox. The currently available inactivated and attenuated poliovirus vaccines have virtually eradicated poliomyelitis in those communities where they are generally used. Vaccines effective in various degrees have also been prepared against yellow fever, rabies, measles, influenza, and adenovirus infections, although technical considerations often limit their usefulness.

Mechanisms of Drug Action. It is not appropriate to review here the wide range of studies on the action of pharmacological agents that affect the specialized functions of various cells and organs. However, since this report emphasizes the regulation of cell growth it seems pertinent to note that certain agents interfere with specific aspects of cell growth in a great variety of cells. Once the nature of that selective action has been delineated, these drugs, of interest primarily because they are clinically useful antibiotics, have proved to be sharp tools for the analysis of cellular function.

For example, actinomycin D, in both animal cells and bacteria, blocks the synthesis of all forms of RNA, on a DNA template, permitting an experimental approach to the survival time of messenger RNA. Protein synthesis on the ribosome is selectively blocked by chloramphenicol or tetracycline in bacteria, and by cycloheximide in animal cells; such interference makes it possible, for example, to define sharply the sequential appearance of new proteins in a virus-infected cell or during cellular differentiation. Streptomycin, which interacts with the ribosome, causes occasional misreading of the genetic code, which can even result in reversal of the effect of a mutation (phenotypic suppression). The ribosome is thus seen to influence the fidelity of translation; and the selection of streptomycin-resistant mutants, which have altered ribosomes, provides a tool for studying their structure and function. In bacteria, penicillin and certain other antibiotics interfere with specific reactions in biosynthesis of the cell wall, and have contributed materially to the analysis of that process.

Unsolved Problems in Cell Biology

Because the cell is the basic structural unit involved in both animal function and the pathogenesis of disease, the relationship of cell biology to human welfare is apparent in a general sense. Research in cell biology impinges in many significant ways on problems of nutrition, aging, and radiation exposure; on the production of antibiotics, hormones, and vaccines; on the storage of germ plasm. And disease processes in general reflect a breakdown in the normal function of groups of cells. In a very real sense, our lack of understanding of the causes of a particular disease, or our inability to prevent or correct a given pathological process, reflects an inadequate understanding of cell function and behavior.

The immediate objectives of most current research in the area of cell biology are not the solutions to these specific and particularized problems of human welfare, but rather to fundamental questions about cell structure and function. A number of the basic unsolved problems, and an assessment of progress, have been delineated earlier in this chapter.

Whereas much has been learned, much remains to be learned before we can truly understand such fundamental activities as cell growth and cell reproduction, cell differentiation, cell-environment interaction, chromosome structure, function, and replication; the function, growth, and reproduction of such organelles as mitochondria, chloroplasts, Golgi apparatus, membranes, and other cell elements. The chief hallmark of progress may well be that biologists have now learned to ask the right questions and are conversant with the language in which the answers must be framed.

It is clear that, for the moment, we have secured only rudimentary knowledge of the structure and function of the various components that make up the cell. We have no precise knowledge of the molecular architecture within any given structure, and we know little of how these structures function at the molecular level or how their functions are integrated at the cellular level. With the exception of a number of rather simple chains of enzymatic reactions, we know only in principle, not in detail, how cellular activity, from maintenance metabolism to growth and differentiation, is regulated.

For a considerable time to come a major part of research in cell biology must deal with the interrelation of structure and function in cell organelles. The assemblage of macromolecules to form a particular cell structure must be directed by the rules that establish and assure the functional integration of the component macromolecules to achieve an overall result—e.g., integrated assembly of enzymes, lipids—to form a mitochondrion with an overall purpose of energy production in the form of ATP. The regulation of the biogeneses of cell organelles and the rules that integrate these biogeneses to produce, in turn, cell growth, reproduction, or differentiation are matters about which knowledge is vaguest and need for understanding most important.

However, the preoccupation of cell biologists with these questions does not reflect a disinterest in the solution of practical problems. Rather, it derives from the fact that practical applications become possible only as the result of a broad understanding of the basic processes underlying cell behavior, and more often than not, in a totally unexpected way. There is simply no method of assessing a priori the ultimate utility of knowledge not yet attained; no shortcuts have been found that would obviate the need for this continued building of a wide foundation of information in cell biology on which to construct intelligent approaches to the solutions of problems of immediate practical importance.

To take only one example, a major area of research in cell biology over the past fifty years, and particularly in the past decade, has been the development of techniques for the cultivation of discrete mammalian cells outside the organism; yet the enormous practical value of that effort is only now becoming apparent. Cell culture has become indispensable to the study of viral diseases, the production of viral vaccines, and the prosecution of cancer research. Even in retrospect it is difficult to visualize how this development could have been planned more effectively.

Cell Biology and Cancer

In the past decade the importance of basic research on cell reproduction to the understanding of cancer has become sharply apparent. The formation of a multicellular organism such as man from a single fertilized egg occurs by millions of regulated cell divisions. As development proceeds, these become more and more restricted in number; and in the adult the production of new cells is finely adjusted to the death of old cells. The mechanism by which this precise balance between cell production and cell loss is achieved is not known; but a breakdown of control during development or in the adult results in a pathological imbalance, often with fatal results. Cancer is such an imbalance, resulting from the overproduction of altered cells which have escaped from normal controls.

The specific mechanism underlying this escape of the cancer cell from normal regulatory mechanisms is not known, but the problem now stands in much sharper focus in the light of important findings obtained during the past decade. The first recognizable sign that a cell has begun to reproduce is the beginning replication of the genetic material, deoxyribonucleic acid (DNA); in a multicellular organism the precise number of cell reproductions required to maintain the health of a particular tissue are achieved by regulating the number of cells allowed to enter upon DNA synthesis. In certain cell types, such as adult neurons and skeletal muscle cells, the inhibition of DNA synthesis is normally complete and irreversible, and there is no cell reproduction.

Because of its central role in cell reproduction, understanding of the initiation of DNA synthesis is clearly one of the most important problems in biology. The problem is, however, complex. It probably will be necessary to determine the arrangement of the replicating units of DNA within each chromosome—i.e., to understand the intricacies of chromosome structure. Nuclear-cytoplasmic interactions are involved, since cytoplasmic factors have been shown to influence rather specifically the onset and continuation of DNA replication. Also, the microenvironment surrounding a cell, in a tissue, for example, has a profound effect on whether or not a cell is permitted to enter DNA synthesis. Further, DNA is somehow involved in the control of its own synthesis. In ways that are largely unexplained, all these, and probably other factors as yet unknown, interact to determine whether a cell shall go through DNA synthesis and subsequent reproduction.

It is tacitly assumed by many investigators that a complete understanding of this process will be necessary before chemical tools can be designed which will be sufficiently specific to control the growth of cancer cells without interfering with normal cell reproduction. Clearly, an enormous amount of basic research still separates us from the design of such agents.

The long search for biochemical or biological differences between normal and cancer cells is finally yielding information that gives insight into the phenomenon of transformation, the mechanism by which a normal cell is converted to a neoplastic cell. Transformation can be brought about by exposure of cells, whether in the whole animal or in culture, to carcinogenic chemicals, to ionizing and nonionizing radiation, or to certain tumor-inducing viruses such as SV40, polyoma, and certain adenoviruses; and in cell cultures it may also occur "spontaneously." In the whole animal, transformation is evidenced by relatively uncontrolled growth and the appearance of a tumor. In cell cultures, "transformation" is evidenced in many different ways, in addition to the ability of the transformed cell to produce a tumor on inoculation into an appropriate host. One of these is a capacity for indefinite multiplication, as contrasted with the finite number of divisions possible for a normal cell. Another is a decreased susceptibility to the inhibitory effects of cell association on mobility and division. New antigens may appear, and specific biochemical activities may be enhanced. Which, if any, of these changes is causally related to the relatively uncontrolled growth in the whole animal is an open question.

One common denominator of the transformations effected by viruses, carcinogens, irradiation, or those that occur spontaneously is a change in the chromosome makeup, however small. It is now presumed by many that these chromosomal changes underlie the escape of the cancer cell from growth-regulatory processes, as well as all the other changes that may be seen in transformed cells. The amount of visible chromosomal change may vary enormously from one cell to another; and which particular genomic change, if any, is specifically responsible for the cancerous property is not known. In the case of chronic myelogenous leukemia, the chromosomal change is very small, for the karyotype appears normal except for a small deletion from one of the smallest chromosomes (number 21). Indeed, a change in the genetic material too small to be detectable cytologically could conceivably also result in transformation; such a submicroscopic genomic change has been detected as the probable basis for a particular type of cancer in the larva of the insect *Drosophila*.

In summary, the loss of control over DNA synthesis that underlies uncontrolled cell reproduction probably stems from a genetic change in the cell, whether the original causative agent is radiation, chemicals, viruses, or a "spontaneous" genomic change arising in the course of an abnormal cell division (chromosome breakage, nondisjunction, deletion, polyploidy, etc.). The fact that normal cells can be transformed in culture under controlled experimental conditions outside the animal provides a relatively simple system for the experimental analysis of carcinogenesis and growth regulation.

Investigations to evaluate the possible viral etiology of human cancer are just beginning. Viral tumor antigen preparations are being employed to test sera of cancer patients for antibodies against these viral-induced products. The helper virus approach is being employed to test human cancer cells for the possible presence of defective viral genomes. Purified viral DNA is being used as a reagent to detect the possible presence of m-RNA specific for certain viruses in human cancer tissues by the formation of DNA-RNA hybrids. Thus, the fruits of basic research in viral replication and carcinogenesis are being directly applied to the question of whether viruses cause human cancer.

Virus-Cell Interaction

Many fascinating problems, of both fundamental and practical significance, remain to be elucidated. Concerning the DNA viruses, the following problems need investigation: (1) Practically nothing is known about the mechanism of virus adsorption to host cell and the receptor sites involved. (2) Although the uncoating process has been well studied with the poxviruses, comparable information about the other three DNA virus groups is virtually nonexistent. (3) Where does viral protein synthesis take place in cells infected with the nuclear DNA virus groups (i.e., the papovaviruses, adenoviruses, and herpesviruses)—in the nucleus, as cytological evidence would suggest, or in the cytoplasm, as is the case with most cellular protein? (4) What selective advantage does viral-directed inhibition of the synthesis of host cell DNA, RNA, and protein serve for the invading virus? These inhibitions appear to be mediated by proteins in several cases, but the molecular mechanisms involved are obscure. (5) The mechanism of synthesis of viral DNA is not clear. Although poxvirus DNA, which is synthesized in the cytoplasm, is thought to be replicated by a viral-induced DNA polymerase, it is not known whether the viral DNA's of the nuclear viruses are synthesized by the cellular or viral-induced DNA polymerases. (6) Increases in DNA polymerase and thymidine kinase activities have been found in cells infected with poxviruses, herpesviruses, and papovaviruses, but not with human adenoviruses; however, the significance of these enzyme increases is not clear, and indeed the metabolic role of the ubiquitous thymidine kinase is unknown. (7) The possible existence of replicative forms of viral DNA has not been examined, although such intermediates are found in bacteriophage-infected cells. (8) Direct experimental proof of viral coding for induced enzymes in animal cells has not been attempted as yet. (9) There is no evidence as to whether virally induced RNA polymerase enzymes are induced for the transcription of viral DNA's. (10) Are specific virus-synthesizing structures formed for each of the different DNA viruses, as appears to be the case with the poxviruses and picornaviruses? (11) Present evidence indicates that the parental viral genome codes for early viral functions while progeny genomes code for the synthesis of virion constituents and for viral control mechanism. The molecular mechanism for selective and sequential transcription of the viral genome during the infectious cycle is completely obscure at the present time. (12) What is the mechanism of growth control by DNA tumor-producing viruses? (13) What does the natural homology, as judged from base composition, between some tumor virus DNA's and cellular DNA signify? (14) The identity and role of the tumor antigen in viral carcinogenesis is only speculative at present. (15) The functions of the large number of viral genes, as many as one to three hundred in some cases, are hard to imagine. Are all viral gene functions expressed during infection?

Concerning the RNA viruses, many questions of the same nature as just described for the DNA viruses remain to be answered. Furthermore, problems unique to the RNA viruses, such as the mechanism of RNA replication and the control of translation by polycistronic viral m-RNA, are now amenable to experimental analysis.

The queries and unsolved problems listed suggest that a complete understanding of viral infection in molecular terms will require not only considerably more incisive studies on viral multiplication, but also a fuller insight into cell function in general.

Although chemotherapy of viral diseases is almost nonexistent, the rapid progress in understanding of the many events characteristic of viral replication should provide the necessary information for the design of suitable treatments against viral diseases in the near future.

Vaccines and Immunity to Viral Diseases

Since there are no generally effective chemotherapeutic agents against viral diseases, man must rely on his immunity, either natural or acquired by the use of vaccines. Although most viral infections are self-limiting, suggesting that the host defense mechanism plays an important role in recovery from viral disease, the role of the immune response to viral infection is poorly understood. The role of serum antibody in acute and chronic viral disease is often uncertain and frequently harmful, inducing autoimmune disease. This creates difficulties with vaccine development; for example, parainfluenza and respiratory syncytial viral infections are among the most prevalent causes of severe respiratory tract illness among infants and children, but the testing and use of vaccines are complicated by the questionable protective role of serum neutralizing antibody. Clearly fundamental knowledge is badly needed on the host immune response to infection with various viruses.

Other difficulties and unsolved problems in vaccine development are (1) the periodic emergence of new influenza strains which necessitate the continued worldwide surveillance of influenza strains and the frequent development of new vaccine preparations; (2) the contamination of vaccine strains with other viruses, such as oncogenic SV40 in poliovirus preparations and oncogenic fowl leukosis virus in egg-grown vaccine viral preparations. (3) The oncogenic nature of certain human adenoviruses for newborn rodents prevents their use in vaccines to prevent frequent respiratory diseases in military epidemics (over 10 percent of recruits in military camps are hospitalized with adenovirus diseases). (4) The formation of "hybrids" between "normal" vaccine viruses and oncogenic regions of different viral genome, such as the adenovirus-SV40 hybrid, is a dangerous possibility. And (5) the large number of rhinoviruses, at least 60 distinct types, makes impractical the development of vaccines against these multiple causes of the common cold.

An encouraging possibility, offered by technical advances in the growth and purification of animal viruses, is the development of vaccines containing only noninfectious subunits of viral coat proteins, free of DNA. This would eliminate many of the problems concerning contaminating viruses, possible infectivity, and potential oncogenicity.

A much suggested cure of viral disease is the administration of interferon. However, at the present time this seems impractical on several grounds. The preparation of sufficient interferon to protect an individual is prohibitively expensive. Furthermore, viral infection most often is recognized clinically late after viral multiplication, when interferon administration would appear to be ineffective. Recently it has been reported that interferon can be induced experimentally by the administration of nonviral nucleic acids, especially double-stranded RNA preparations. The induction of interferon by nucleic acids or chemicals may be used to protect individuals suspected of being exposed to virus and may be of particular usefulness against those viruses where vaccines are not practical, such as the rhinoviruses.

A number of slow, chronic viral infections of animals are known, especially of the central nervous system. The possible viral etiology of chronic degenerative diseases of the central nervous system of man is an important area for future investigation.

It will be evident that the huge intellectual triumph of the past decade will, in all likelihood, be surpassed tomorrow—and to the everlasting benefit of mankind.

Chapter 5

THE ORIGINS OF LIFE

The Biological, Astronomical, and Geological Background

Biological Considerations

The origin of life is the most important and the least understood event of biological evolution. In view of the commanding interest that this subject has for scientists and laymen alike, it may be surprising that it has not, for the past century at least, been a major area for scientific investigation. The reason for this apparent neglect is simple: the problem has been too difficult. Only recently has it become possible to grasp the real meaning of the origin-of-life question, and it is doubtful if we fully comprehend it even now. Yet we are in a far better position today than ever before to address ourselves to it. Significant progress in untangling this puzzle has been made in recent years. This progress, stemming from advances in such diverse fields as cosmology, geochemistry, and molecular genetics, has reawakened interest in the problem. The sudden advent of the space age, with the search for extraterrestrial life as one of its prime objectives, has reinforced this interest.

In the past, discussions of the origin of life tended to be speculative exercises, often tinged with superstition. Only occasionally was the general obscurity illuminated by flashes of insight and meaningful experimentation. In modern times, the origin of life has become a problem for legitimate inquiry, subject to the same intellectual discipline as are other attempts to understand evolutionary processes — including the requirement for logical elaboration of hypotheses, avoidance of arbitrary assumptions, and recourse to observation and experiment. As with other historical investigations that attempt to reconstruct past events from present evidence, this one is subject to inherent limitations. Our knowledge of the terrestrial environment in the remote past is uncertain and, as the history of the question shows, is liable to drastic revision from time to time as new evidence accumulates. Furthermore, it is impossible to duplicate, or even approximate, the geological time scale, the variety of conditions, and the secular changes in these conditions that occurred during the earth's history. Thus, current discussions of the origin of life adopt the uniformitarian view that the evolution of the earth is a history of gradual change by processes that are still going on. But we cannot exclude the possibility that some unusual event, such as collision with a comet, all evidence of which has been destroyed, played a pivotal role in the origin of life. Because of such constraints, the most one can ever hope to claim for conclusions in this subject is a high degree of plausibility. In this respect, however, studies of the origin of life differ in degree, but not in kind, from other scientific investigations.

Historical Background. It is difficult to believe that there was ever a time when thoughtful men accepted the idea that the creation of life from nonliving matter was a commonplace event which could be induced at will. Yet from classic Greek times until the middle of the nineteenth century it was generally assumed that living organisms could arise spontaneously, without parents, from decaying organic material. The literature of these ages abounds in recipes for producing frogs, mice, scorpions, and other animals from mud or garbage. It was not until the latter half of the seventeenth century that this notion was disproved experimentally by an Italian physician and poet, Francesco Redi, who showed that maggots would not appear in meat if insects were prevented from laying their eggs on it. But the belief was revived in a new form following the discovery of the microbial world by the Dutch microscopist Leeuwenhoek in 1675. Redi's experiment did not seem to apply to the tiny and apparently simple microorganisms which many people believed were on the borderline between living and nonliving. We know today that these unicellular creatures are not simple at all: they are as complex as the individual cells of any higher organism, and the possibility of their spontaneous origin is just as remote as it is for any other cells.

It was not until 1861 that Pasteur succeeded, in a series of famous experiments, in proving (by essentially the same argument that Redi had used 200 years before) that bacteria can arise only from preexisting bacteria. The genetic continuity of all living things was thus established, and belief in spontaneous generation died out among educated people.

To most scientists, Pasteur's experiments demonstrated the futility of inquiring into the origin of life, and interest in the subject faded. Darwin wrote, in a letter to a friend: "It is mere rubbish, thinking at present of the origin of life; one might as well think of the origin of matter." (Nowadays, scientists do think of the origin of both matter and life.) Some of Pasteur's contemporaries suggested that life had no origin but, like matter, was eternal. We now know that this, too, is incorrect. Life is not one of the fundamental categories of the universe, like matter, energy, and time, but is a manifestation of certain molecular combinations. These combinations cannot have existed forever, since even the elements of which they are composed have not always existed. Therefore life must have had a beginning.

The modern view of the origin of life differs fundamentally from that of preceding centuries in that it concerns itself with the origin of these molecular combinations, rather than of organisms endowed with certain mysterious properties. Once this viewpoint is adopted, it is seen that we have to regard the origin of life as a historical incident in the evolution of the planet — i.e., as an event limited in place and time by prevailing physical and chemical conditions. The meaning of these statements will become clear as we proceed.

The theory that life arose on another planet — particularly a planet of another star — and was propelled to the earth by radiation pressure was once widely held. This theory is difficult to disprove, but it is extremely unlikely that organisms would survive the long exposure to cosmic rays and ultraviolet light that such a journey would entail. If life on another planet were found to be identical in all essential respects with life on the earth, then this theory, known as panspermia, would have to be reconsidered.

What Is Life? The most concise, unambiguous, and general definition of life that can be given at the present time is based on the *genetic* properties of living things. According to this view, the unique attribute of living matter, from which all of its other remarkable features derive, is its capacity for self-duplication with mutation. That is to say, living systems are systems that reproduce, that mutate, and that reproduce their mutations. Reproduction by itself is not a sufficient criterion for life. Many nonliving systems are self-propagating to a greater or lesser degree: crystals, for example, or even better, flames, which not only reproduce (by means of sparks) but also show metabolism and growth. Systems such as these increase by the same exponential law that describes the growth of living populations. But nonliving systems, being immutable, are incapable of evolution. Living things, on the other hand, are endowed with a seemingly infinite capacity to adapt themselves to the exigencies of existence. The endless variety and complexity of living organisms, the apparent purposefulness of their structure and behavior, are consequences of their mutability. *Any* system that has the capacity to mutate blindly in many directions and to reproduce its mutations must evolve.

Proteins, Nucleic Acids, and the Genetic Code. One of the major achievements of modern biology has been the elucidation of the chemical structures and mechanisms responsible for the genetic properties of living matter. These properties derive from two classes of compounds—proteins and nucleic acids. The nucleic acids are the ultimate self-replicating and mutable substances of living cells. They compose the genes, the bearers of the genetic heritage, in all species. This heritage consists of information, apparently all of it concerned, directly or indirectly, with the construction of protein molecules. The latter form the enzymes—the versatile and highly efficient catalysts that control the enormously complex chemistry of cells, including the production of the building blocks needed for the synthesis of more nucleic acids and proteins. The nucleic acids and proteins thus form an interlocking and interdependent system. Whatever is unique about living matter is inherent in this system.

Both nucleic acids and proteins are linear polymers of high molecular weight. The building blocks of the nucleic acids are the nucleotides, of which, in DNA, there are four kinds. Genetic information is encoded in linear sequences of these nucleotides, and with minor exceptions the same nucleotides are found in all known species. The genes of a man differ from those of, say, a horse only in the linear arrangements of nucleotides.

Proteins are made up of subunits called amino acids. There are 20 different kinds of amino acids in proteins, and again the same ones are found in all species, from viruses to man. As with the genes, the specific properties of protein molecules are determined by the linear arrangement of their constituent amino acids.

The logic of the gene-protein relationship is clear. Success in the struggle for existence depends on the ability of organisms to synthesize a large variety of specific proteins. But proteins are highly ordered, complex structures which must be built up from individual amino acids. If every generation had to discover for itself how to assemble amino acids in the correct order to produce useful proteins, survival would be impossible. Consequently, this information must be transmitted from parent to offspring, and a mechanism for storing and copying it is essential. Amino acid sequences cannot be copied directly from a preexisting protein—at least, no species that we know of has ever discovered a way to do this—but nucleotide sequences can be copied from a polynucleotide. Hence, instructions for assembling protein molecules are encoded in nucleic acids, and the latter are transmitted in inheritance.

One final element must be added to make the system work. This is a means for translating nucleotide sequences into sequences of amino acids. To accomplish this feat, living cells have a complex mechanism involving a number of special enzymes and several special types of nucleic acid. The details of this mechanism are not yet fully understood, but what it accomplishes is the translation of a message written in an alphabet of 4 symbols into one written in an alphabet of 20 symbols. An analogy would be a machine that translates messages from Morse code into English. (The analogy is imperfect because the biological mechanism not only translates but also assembles the proteins from their constituent amino acids.) Like the machine, however, the biological mechanism incorporates a dictionary sense that enables it to relate the two different sets of symbols. This dictionary is the "genetic code." Again, we find a remarkable similarity among living things: the code appears to be identical in all species.

The universality of the genetic code and the related fact that the nucleic acids and proteins of all species are built out of the same building blocks lead to the conclusion that all known organisms are fundamentally the same. Despite appearances, there is only one form of life on the earth. Life need have originated only once.

Must Life Be Based on Carbon Chemistry? It has been said that life is a property of carbon. If, as we have seen, life depends on the ability to store and replicate large amounts of information, and if such storage and replication require molecular complexity and versatility, then carbon is peculiarly qualified for this role. Carbon is unique among the elements in the number and variety of compounds it can form. This is not a merely parochial conclusion, derived from the fact that life as we know it is carbonaceous, but is based on the structure and properties of the carbon atom. Silicon is often proposed as a possible alternative to carbon for biological molecules. Silicon does not easily form large molecules in the manner of carbon, however, because of the weakness of the Si-Si bond and the great reactivity of most silicon compounds. In addition, silicon atoms do not make double bonds, so that $(SiO_2)_n$ is in no way comparable to CO_2, which has a central position in biochemistry. These facts explain why it is that silicon, although far more abundant on the earth than carbon, plays a very minor role in biology.

It is sometimes suggested that under conditions different from those that prevail on the surface of the earth, carbon could be replaced by other elements for biological purposes. It is difficult to assess these suggestions, since they have not been developed in detail. No explicit model of a world inhabited by noncarbonaceous organisms has yet been devised, a fact that is itself indicative of the difficulties encountered in attempting to dispense with the carbon atom. Until such a model has been constructed, or been shown to be impossible, one must adopt an attitude of undogmatic skepticism toward these conjectures.

Origin of the Earth

Cosmic Abundances of the Elements. The elemental composition of the universe is derived from spectral studies of the sun, stars, nebulae, and interstellar medium, and from chemical analysis of meteorites and the earth's crust. In Table 5-1 are displayed some representative values of the cosmic abundances. Hydrogen and helium together make up 99.9 percent of the atoms in the universe by number. The next most common atomic species, with abundances of 10^{-3} to 10^{-4} that of hydrogen, are, in order of abundance, oxygen, carbon, neon, and nitrogen. The overall composition of the solar system is essentially that of the sun, which contains over 99 percent of the mass of the system. The sun appears to be representative of a large class of stars whose compositions are similar to that shown for the universe as a whole, but significant diversity is found in the chemical constitutions of other stars. This diversity is related to the age of the star and the processes of element formation.

The relative abundances shown in Table 5-1 are well-understood in terms of stellar nucleogenesis. Beginning with a star composed of pure hydrogen, thermonuclear reactions in its interior generate He^4, and, as the star evolves to the red giant stage, successive nuclear processes construct C^{12}, O^{16}, Ne^{20}, Mg^{24}, etc. Neutron capture and other processes lead to the

Table 5-1. Cosmic Abundances of the Elements *
(atoms per 10,000 atoms Si)

Element	Abundance	Element	Abundance
H	3.4×10^8	Si	10,000
He	4.9×10^7	P	115
C	102,000	S	5,600
N	31,000	Cl	85
O	229,000	A	1,400
Ne	93,000	K	26
Na	565	Ca	560
Mg	9,800	Fe	2,700
Al	650	Ni	290
		Others	210

* Based on C. W. Allen, *Astrophysical Quantities*, University of London, The Athlone Press, 1963.

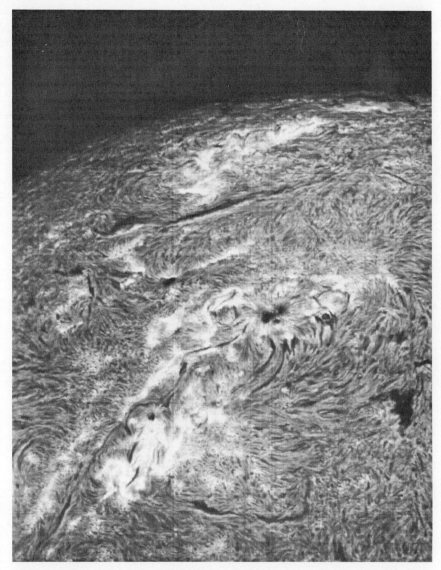

Figure 5-1. Photograph of the sun (spectroheliogram) taken in the light of the hydrogen α line, showing clouds of hydrogen gas. (From the Mount Wilson and Palomar Observatories)

observed distribution of other elements. These thermonuclear processes are very general, and we can therefore expect their occurrences throughout the universe even in regions and times we have not observed directly. The atoms so generated in the interiors of stars are then returned to the interstellar medium by hydrodynamic flow of material from the outer layers of the star, or from nova or supernova explosions of highly evolved stars. Thus, succeeding generations of stars formed from the interstellar material are increasingly enriched in heavy elements synthesized in the interiors of previous generations of stars. The sun probably contains some primordial hydrogen, but is composed mainly of material that has been through one or more previous stars. Radioactive dating of the earth and of meteorites, and theoretical models for the evolution of the sun, place the origin of our solar system at about 5 billion years ago. Our galaxy is, however, 10 or 15 billion years old, and, at the time of the origin of the solar system, the relative atomic abundances should have been essentially the contemporary cosmic abundances.

Origin of the Solar System. There is a variety of models of the origin of the solar system, but it can be fairly stated that no very detailed theory has won wide acceptance. All theories, however, are common in beginning with materials of approximately cosmic composition. The most popular view is that a cloud of cosmic composition called the solar nebula was condensed by gravitational forces out of the interstellar medium. The central condensation in this cloud became the sun, and peripheral condensations became the planets. Since the inner planets of the solar system, including the earth, have a distinctly atypical composition with respect to the light elements, some mechanism for the loss of hydrogen and helium must be devised. This loss may occur either before or during the condensation into planets of material in the inner solar system. Hydrogen in the solar nebula may have been carried outward by charged particles from the forming sun, or similar processes may have occurred during the formation of the planets.

The terrestrial abundance of the unreactive noble gases relative to, say, silicon is distinctly less than the cosmic ratios, except for Ar^{40}, which is radiogenic. This deficiency includes krypton and xenon, gases that are so heavy that their depletion from the earth suggests they must have been lost before the planet was formed.

This implies, as does other evidence, that the earth's atmosphere is of secondary origin. That is, the earth was formed out of solid materials which, except for small amounts of occluded gas, had no atmosphere associated with them. The atoms that later formed the atmosphere were combined in solid chemical compounds for the most part. These compounds were decomposed to gaseous products (or, in the possible case of ices, were evaporated) by the heat resulting from the release of gravitational energy and from radioactivity during and following the accretion of the earth. The liberated gases formed the earth's secondary atmosphere and the oceans. The enrichment of nitrogen relative to the rare gases in the present atmosphere implies that the former was originally held in chemical combination. It is possible that water was originally present as mineral hydrates which were subsequently decomposed by heating.

Evolution of the Earth's Atmosphere. A detailed knowledge of the foregoing processes has not been essential for the experimental work on prebiological organic synthesis to be described. The important conclusion is that the secondary atmosphere was reducing to a greater or lesser extent. This follows from the fact that the solar nebula and the primary atmosphere were both highly reducing. There is considerable controversy on how strongly reducing the atmosphere of the primitive earth actually was. The present atmosphere of the earth is oxidizing, with carbon present as CO_2, nitrogen as N_2, oxygen as O_2, and hydrogen as H_2O. A strongly reducing atmosphere would contain CH_4, NH_3, H_2O, and H_2. To assume that the primitive (secondary) atmosphere was oxidizing (CO_2, N_2, O_2) is unreasonable in the light of the discussion previously presented, and in addition makes it impossible to account for the prebiological synthesis of organic compounds, since such compounds cannot be synthesized in significant yield under oxidizing conditions. The same is probably true for an atmosphere containing CO_2 and N_2 without O_2.

The principal nitrogen species in the primitive atmosphere was probably N_2 rather than NH_3, because NH_3 is very soluble in water. The NH_3 would accumulate in the oceans, mostly as NH_4^+, provided the pH of the ocean was near its present value of 8.2. The major carbon species is a more difficult problem. The partial pressure of CO_2 was probably close to the present value of 3 times 10^{-4} atmosphere. This value is determined by a complicated set of equilibria involving the precipitation of limestones ($CaCO_3$), the pH of the ocean, and the formation of various silicates. It is reasonable to assume that similar processes took place on the primitive earth, if not at the beginning, then after a geologically short length of time.

The other species to be considered are carbon monoxide and methane. Carbon monoxide could be formed in the high atmosphere and from the outgassing of the interior of the earth. However, CO is a relatively reactive molecule. It would react in the ocean to yield formic acid by a base-catalyzed reaction and would also react in the atmosphere with various radicals. In particular, CO reacts with H atoms in good yield to give formaldehyde. The concentration of CO in the atmosphere would be determined by the rate of its production and its rate of reaction. It is difficult to give any realistic estimate of these rates.

Methane would be the thermodynamically stable species of carbon as long as the partial pressure of hydrogen was greater than about 10^{-5} atmosphere. However, the methane can react by nonequilibrium processes to give many products such as organic compounds, CO, etc. If the rate of organic compound synthesis was rapid, methane could be removed from the atmosphere faster than it was resynthesized, and the steady state partial pressure would be low. The various processes and their rates are not known. It is generally held that the CH_4 partial pressure was substantially higher than the CO or CO_2 partial pressures, but this is an area of considerable controversy. Nor are there reliable estimates of the early concentration of HCN in the atmosphere or the oceans.

In general, one considers that the synthesis of organic compounds took place after the earth was formed—that is, after all the matter that makes up the earth had accumulated. Actually, organic synthesis would have occurred while the earth was forming, and even earlier in the cosmic dust cloud. However, the mixing and heating that would have resulted from accumulation processes and outgassing either would have made these preformed organic compounds unavailable in the oceans of the primitive earth, or would have pyrolyzed them.

Two mechanisms have been proposed to explain the transition from a reducing to an oxidizing atmosphere: (1) the ultraviolet photodissociation of ammonia, methane, and water vapor, with the resulting preferential escape of hydrogen from the earth, and (2) green plant photosynthesis. At the present time, the rate of production of O_2 by photochemical processes in the upper atmosphere is slow compared to the production by plants.

The epoch of transition from reducing to oxidizing atmosphere cannot be accurately calculated from the theory of atmospheric escape, but rough estimates indicate that periods of up to a billion years are necessary for the escape of even relatively small quantities of hydrogen from the secondary atmosphere. The rate of this escape would have been highly dependent upon the temperature of the earth's surface and of the atmosphere. There is also some geochemical evidence suggesting that conditions were not oxidizing several billions of years ago, including the presence of uraninite (UO_2) and pyrite (FeS_2) in Precambrian sediments. These minerals are unstable in the presence of oxygen, but not all geologists are agreed that their presence is proof of a reducing primitive atmosphere.

Because of the absence of molecular oxygen and even small quantities of ozone from the primitive atmosphere of 4 billion years ago, there exists a significant possibility that solar ultraviolet light penetrated to the surface of the earth, particularly in the 2400–2900 Å range. This energy would have decomposed biologically important ultraviolet-absorbing compounds, such as purines and pyrimidines, exposed to it and would have been lethal for primitive organisms living near the surface of the ocean. The solar ultraviolet flux is reduced to tolerable levels at a depth of some tens of meters of pure water, or at more shallow depths in aqueous solutions of certain common organic molecules.

The appearance of green-plant photosynthesis, which probably occurred over 3 billion years ago (discussed later), led eventually to the accumulation of oxygen and ultraviolet-absorbing ozone in the atmosphere. This change must have radically altered conditions for life on the earth. It may well have triggered the explosive evolution of animal life which took place at the start of the Cambrian, 0.6–0.7 billion years ago, and also the colonization of the land.

Temperature of the Primitive Earth. The temperature on the primitive earth is not known, and, of course, there would have been considerable variation in temperature from the poles to the equator. A large amount of volcanic activity would not affect the temperature of the atmosphere and ocean, unless the whole earth melted, because the rate of radiation from the surface of the earth is quite high. The temperature of the atmosphere is determined largely by the incident energy from the sun and the radiation outward from the atmosphere. A realistic calculation of this heat balance is not possible for the primitive earth because the composition of the atmosphere is not known.

The synthesis of organic compounds and their stability place some restrictions on the temperature conditions of the primitive earth. We can say that the lower the temperature is, the longer organic compounds will persist before decomposition. Thus a temperature of 100°C would decompose almost all the organic compounds in a few thousand to a million years, depending on the compound. Some compounds (e.g., alanine) are stable for several billion years at 25°C.

Most of the organic syntheses that seem likely on the primitive earth can take place at 0°C. In the case of adenine synthesis, one of the steps proceeds in a water-HCN solution at the eutectic point (the lowest temperature at which the solution can exist in a liquid state, about −23°C). Low temperatures would slow the synthetic reactions from days at 25°–100°C to years or hundreds of years at 0°C, but such periods are short on the geological time scale.

In some reactions local high temperatures could be useful. Examples would be thermal decompositions requiring temperatures of 800°–

1200°C and a proposed synthesis of polypeptides which takes place at 100°–200°C. It is not clear whether such local high temperatures could have occurred on an extensive scale on the primitive earth, or whether they are in fact essential for any step in the origin of life.

The temperature on the primitive earth presents a curious problem. Because of the evolution of the sun, its luminosity was approximately 60 percent of its present value some 4 billion years ago. With the present atmospheric greenhouse effect, this implies that the global temperatures on the earth were substantially below the freezing point of water at the time of the origin of life. One possible solution to this problem involves the presence of larger quantities of infrared-absorbing gases than exist now, and it is notable that methane and particularly ammonia are just the appropriate gases to produce a larger atmospheric greenhouse effect than the contemporary one.

Energy Sources on the Primitive Earth. An atmosphere that is in equilibrium can yield no appreciable amounts of organic substances because all organic compounds (except CH_4 under reducing conditions) are thermodynamically unstable. This conclusion holds for both oxidizing and reducing atmospheres, with the exception noted. The organic compounds that can be produced by various processes to be described are thermodynamically unstable under the conditions in which they are formed, but many of them are kinetically stable and so will decompose very slowly. In a thermodynamically stable atmosphere a source of energy is needed to form activated molecules such as free radicals, ions, "high-energy" compounds (e.g., H_2CO, HCN).

The ultimate sources of energy for the synthesis of organic compounds on the primitive earth were the sun, gravitational energy, and radioactivity. The gravitational energy results from the potential energy released when an expanded dust cloud forms a solid body, and this energy would appear as heat in the interior of the earth, some of which would find its way to the surface of the earth in lava from volcanoes. Radioactivity also results in heating of the earth's interior and the emission of lava. Some of the radioactive elements would have been in the ocean of the primitive earth, but the amount was probably not large.

We cannot estimate accurately the amounts of energy available from various sources on the primitive earth. The present sources of energy on the earth are given in Table 5-2. It is evident that sunlight is the greatest source of energy, but only the small fraction below 2000 Å or 1800 Å can be absorbed by the CH_4, H_2O, NH_3, etc. Electric discharges form the next largest source of energy at the present time. The electric discharges include lightning and corona discharges from pointed objects. It is not clear whether ultraviolet light or electric discharges were the

Table 5-2. Present Sources of Energy on the Earth

Source	Energy (cal cm^{-2} yr^{-1})
Total radiation from sun	260,000
Ultraviolet light	
$\lambda < 2,500$ Å	570
$\lambda < 2,000$ Å	85
$\lambda < 1,500$ Å	3.5
Electric discharges	4
Cosmic rays	0.0015
Radioactivity	
(to 1.0 km depth)	0.8
Volcanoes	0.13

most important source of energy for the synthesis of organic compounds. Hydrogen cyanide has turned out to be an important intermediate in the simulated prebiotic synthesis of the purines and amino acids. Hydrogen cyanide is synthesized in good yield by electric discharges, but ultraviolet light is not efficient in this synthesis. We can say that electric discharges were probably important in the prebiotic synthesis of organic compounds at least to the extent that hydrogen cyanide was important.

There are considerable differences of opinion on the importance of cosmic rays, radioactivity, and volcanoes as energy sources for organic compound synthesis. The amount of radioactivity would have been greater when the earth formed, but most of this energy is dissipated in the rocks rather than in the oceans or atmosphere. We cannot make good estimates of the amounts of energy available from cosmic rays and volcanoes. The organic products obtained from these sources of energy are frequently similar to those produced by electric discharges.

Organic Geochemistry and Precambrian Fossils

It is estimated from various geological dating methods that the earth was formed about 4.5×10^9 years ago. This age for the earth is based on the age of the meteorites, and the different dating methods for the meteorites all give about the same age. The first hard-shelled animals appear at the beginning of the Cambrian, about 0.7 billion years ago. It is clear that life was present well into the Precambrian, a period lasting 3.8×10^9 years, but we cannot yet say how far back. The time when life started is an important number since it gives us the time scale for the organic synthetic reactions leading up to the origin of life.

There is difficulty in trying to find fossil remains of life in the Pre-cambrian. The first problem is that organisms without hard parts do not leave very clear indications of their remains. The second problem is that very old rocks have usually been heated at one time or another, and heating will destroy or greatly alter the organic remains and may also make the structural form of the fossil unrecognizable. However, there are a few Precambrian rocks which have not been heated, and a considerable amount of information has been obtained from these.

The principal Precambrian rocks that have been examined for their fossil remains and organic content are:

Nonesuch shale (1×10^9 years, northern Michigan)
Gunflint chert (1.9×10^9 years, southern Ontario)
Soudan shale (2.7×10^9 years, northeastern Minnesota)
Bulawayan limestone (2.7×10^9 years, Southern Rhodesia)
Fig-Tree chert (3.1×10^9 years, Transvaal, South Africa)

The Nonesuch shale contains hydrocarbons, porphyrins, and the isopre-noid hydrocarbons pristane and phytane. The latter are breakdown products of chlorophyll and possibly other biological molecules. The Gunflint chert contains normal paraffins (C_{16} to C_{32}), pristane, and phy-tane. In addition there are well-preserved fossils of microorganisms which are said to be bacteria and algae. The Soudan shale contains alkanes, pristane, and phytane as well as other isoprenoid hydrocarbons; no clear evidence of fossil microorganisms has yet been found. The Bul-awayan limestone is said to be a fossil algal colony and looks very similar to the limestones being laid down today off the Bahamas. Some hydro-carbons and fatty acids have been reported in this limestone. The Fig-Tree chert contains hydrocarbons, small amounts of pristane and phy-tane, and microfossils of bacterial and algal size and form (Fig. 5-2).

The interpretation of these results is not simple. The first problem is whether the samples analyzed are contaminated. Contamination can occur during handling, which does not seem probable in these cases, or during the long periods since these rocks were laid down. Contamination of these rocks could occur by absorption of organic materials from ground waters. If the rock was very compact and impermeable since it was laid down, such contamination would not take place. This seems to be the case with some of these old rocks, but we cannot be sure.

In the case of the oldest rocks, the possibility must also be considered that the observed structures are artifacts formed from inorganic minerals. For example, it is still uncertain whether the carbonate sediments formed today off the Bahamas are all biological or partly a nonbiological precip-itation. If they are partly nonbiological off the Bahamas, then a similar

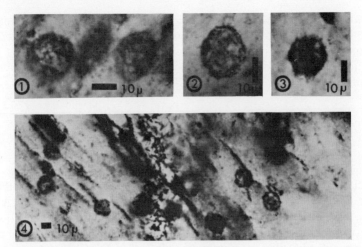

Figure 5-2. Three-billion-year-old alga-like fossils from the Fig-Tree chert. Fossil bacteria are also found. (From Schopf and Barghoorn, *Science 156:*508. © 1967 by The American Association for the Advancement of Science)

process could have formed the Bulawayan limestone. This possibility seems to be excluded for the Nonesuch and Gunflint fossils, however, and the authenticity of the Fig-Tree microfossils is supported by the chemical evidence, as well as by expert opinion.

If we accept that the organic material observed in these rocks was laid down at the same time as the rocks, and that the microfossils are authentic, then we can conclude that life was present on the earth 3.1 billion years ago. It also implies that the origin of life took place substantially before this, since the presence of pristane and phytane (which can result from reduction of the phytol side chain of chlorophyll) and other evidences of photosynthesis suggest that these organisms were already fairly advanced. We cannot say when in this period of 1.4×10^9 years (between 4.5×10^9 and 3.1×10^9 years ago) life started, since we do not know the rates of evolution.

Amino acids have been found in a number of rocks, principally limestones. No amino acids have yet been reported in early Precambrian rocks. Amino acids decompose by decarboxylation over long periods of time, but the rates are quite variable. Thus alanine is stable for several billion years at 25°C, but serine is stable only for several million. It has been shown that most of the protein amino acids are present in recent carbonate fossils, but usually only the more stable amino acids are present in the older fossils.

The field of organic geochemistry is quite new aside from petroleum geology. A great deal remains to be done. It is possible that the organic data will tell us something about the metabolism of primitive organisms in the Precambrian, although this type of information will be difficult to establish. The most interesting information to be obtained is the time scale for the origin of life and the rates of evolution of primitive organisms.

Laboratory Studies on Prebiotic Organic Syntheses

Synthesis of Amino Acids, Nucleic Acid Bases, and Sugars

The major organic components of the genetic system comprise the 20 amino acids of proteins, the purine and pyrimidine bases of RNA and DNA, and the sugars ribose and deoxyribose. The main objective of work on prebiotic synthesis so far has been the synthesis of these compounds from plausible starting materials under conditions presumed to be analogous to those on primitive earth.

A selection of amino acids including glycine, alanine, serine, aspartic acid, and glutamic acid has been obtained by passing an electric discharge through a mixture of ammonia (or nitrogen), methane, and water vapor above boiling water. Aldehydes were formed in the discharge, along with hydrogen cyanide, and these may have reacted with ammonia to give amino acids by the well-known Strecker synthesis:

$$RCHO + HCN + NH_3 \longrightarrow R{-}\underset{\displaystyle CN}{\overset{\displaystyle NH_2}{CH}} + H_2O \xrightarrow{\text{hydrolysis}} R{-}\underset{\displaystyle CO_2H}{\overset{\displaystyle NH_2}{CH}}$$

The yield of amino acids in these experiments was quite good, accounting for as much as 3 percent of the total carbon in the system.

It has long been known that the "hydrolysis" of fairly concentrated solutions of hydrogen cyanide gives a complex mixture of products including a considerable amount of glycine. It was subsequently found that aspartic acid, alanine, serine, and a number of other less certainly identified amino acids in addition to glycine could be obtained from cyanide hydrolysis. More recent work makes it clear that some glycine arises directly from the hydrolysis of hydrogen cyanide tetramer, while the remainder of the glycine and the more complex amino acids are obtained from the higher cyanide polymers. It has been claimed that peptides can be obtained directly from the polymer.

Both the routes described have subsequently been investigated quite extensively. The original claims have been substantiated, and the range of conditions in which amino acid synthesis is observed has been greatly extended. It is clear that other high-energy sources — e.g., an ultraviolet source — may replace the electric discharge. In addition aminonitriles corresponding to glycine and alanine have been isolated directly from the product of a discharge acting on an anhydrous methane-ammonia atmosphere. It is not at present possible to decide which route was the most important in prebiotic synthesis; the central role of cyanide in all pathways, however, is certain.

One important outcome of recent work has been the demonstration that amino acids are not produced under strongly oxidizing conditions — e.g., from CO_2, N_2, and water. This argues that H_2 or a reduced form of carbon must have been present in the atmosphere at the time when pre-biotic synthesis occurred. An attractive feature of these data is the fact that the amino acids synthesized in the laboratory under "primitive" conditions are the very amino acids which are most abundant in most proteins today.

Hydrogen cyanide is also the source of purines in a remarkable synthesis of adenine. If strong ammoniacal solutions of hydrogen cyanide are refluxed for a few days, adenine is obtained in up to 0.5 percent yield along with 4-aminoimidazole-5-carboxamide and the usual cyanide polymer. More recently a synthesis of adenine in up to 15 percent yield from hydrogen cyanide and anhydrous ammonia has been reported.

The mechanism of adenine synthesis in these experiments is probably

$$HCN + CN^- \longrightarrow HN{=}HC{-}CN \xrightarrow{\text{HCN}} H_2N{-}CH(CN)_2 \xrightarrow{\text{HCN}}$$

Evidence for all of the steps in this synthesis has been presented. Aminoimidazole carboxamide with cyanide gives hypoxanthine and with cyanogen gives guanine in up to 30 percent yield. Thus the biologically important purines are derivable from hydrogen cyanide and cyanogen.

The difficult step in the synthesis of adenine just described is the reaction of tetramer with formamidine. This step may be bypassed by the

photochemical rearrangement of tetramer to aminoimidazole carboxamide, a reaction that proceeds readily in contemporary sunlight.

A further possibility is that tetramer formation may have occurred in a
eutectic solution. High yield of tetramer (>10 percent) can be obtained
by cooling dilute cyanide solutions to between $-10°C$ and $-30°C$ for a
few months.

Potential prebiotic syntheses of pyrimidines have proved more difficult until recently. Traces have been obtained by reactions in which
three-carbon precursors such as β-aminopropionitrile are fused with
urea. More recently it has been shown that up to 35 percent of cytosine
may be obtained by refluxing cyanoacetylene with 0.1 M cyanate.
Cyanate is obtained from cyanogen by hydrolysis, and cyanoacetylene
is the most abundant nitrogen-containing product, apart from hydrogen
cyanide, obtained when N_2-methane and other similar mixtures are subjected to an electric discharge or high temperatures, so this mechanism
is not completely implausible.

Uracil is obtained in a similar way from propiolamide, but since hydrolysis of cyanoacetylene gives cyanoacetyaldehyde rather than propiolamide, we doubt that this has prebiotic significance. Uracil may have
originated from cytosine by alkaline hydrolysis, since this conversion is
known to occur slowly.

In summary the closely related family of molecules HCN, HC≡
CH—C≡N, and N≡C—C≡N suffice as raw materials for the synthesis
of glycine, aspartic acid, alanine, serine, and the biologically important
purines and pyrimidines. We believe that this is highly suggestive, since
these starting materials together with acetylene and diacetylene are
among the principal products obtained when reducing mixtures containing carbon, hydrogen, and nitrogen are subjected to high temperatures,
electric discharges, etc.

The synthesis of reducing sugars from formaldehyde under alkaline
conditions was discovered long ago. However, the process is very complex and incompletely understood. In simple solution, it depends on the
presence of a suitable catalyst: Calcium hydroxide and calcium carbonate are among the most popular heterogeneous catalysts; thallium hydroxide is a very effective homogeneous catalyst. In the absence of catalysts,

little or no sugar is obtained. Particularly attractive is the finding that, at 100°C, clays such as kaolin serve to catalyze formation of monosaccharides, including ribose, in good yield from dilute (0.01 M) solutions of formaldehyde.

There seems little doubt that the reaction is autocatalytic and proceeds in stages through glycolaldehyde, glyceraldehyde, and dihydroxyacetone, tetroses and pentoses to give finally hexoses including glucose and fructose. One proposed reaction sequence is

$$
CH_2O \rightarrow
\begin{array}{c} CHO \\ | \\ CH_2OH \end{array}
\rightarrow
\begin{array}{c} CHO \\ | \\ CH_2OH \\ | \\ CH_2OH \end{array}
\leftrightharpoons
\begin{array}{c} CH_2OH \\ | \\ C{=}O \\ | \\ CH_2OH \end{array}
\rightarrow
\begin{array}{c} CH_2OH \\ | \\ C{=}O \\ | \\ CHOH \\ | \\ CH_2OH \end{array}
\rightarrow
\begin{array}{c} CHO \\ | \\ CHOH \\ | \\ CHOH \\ | \\ CH_2OH \end{array}
\rightarrow \text{pentoses} \rightarrow \text{hexoses}
$$

reverse aldol

The composition of the mixture of products depends on the catalyst, pH, temperature conditions, and reaction time; almost all of the common sugars have been identified under appropriate conditions. Although the reaction has not yet been accomplished under prebiotic conditions, it seems likely that some mechanism was available to convert sugars to glycosides such as adenosine or uridine; these substances are very much more stable than the parent sugars and might survive for very long periods in aqueous solution. Alternatively, there may be a mechanism for synthesizing bases directly on sugars or conversely.

Dehydration Reactions and Polymer Synthesis

The second major area of research concerns the condensation of preformed amino acids to peptides, of preformed nucleic acid components to polynucleotides, and of nucleotides with phosphate to diphosphates and triphosphates. All of the reactions involved are dehydrations which, to take place in aqueous solution, must proceed against the normal free-energy gradient. Thus, either the reactions must be carried out in a solid phase or an effective mode of dehydration in aqueous solution must be employed. Three types of condensation have been attempted — thermal, photochemical, and chemical.

In general, the thermal condensation of amino acids to polypeptides does not proceed readily. However, if a mixture containing sufficient acidic or basic amino acids — for example, glutamic acid or lysine — is heated, then a good yield of random polypeptide is obtained. The prop-

erties of these polypeptides and their catalytic activity have been described in some detail; their relevance to the origins of life is still a matter
of debate. Of some interest is the observation that, if an appropriate mixture of amino acids is employed, the resulting polymer exhibits a low
order of activity as melanocyte-stimulating hormone. If the mixture is
lysine-rich, the polymer binds RNA rather tightly to form relatively
insoluble microspheres.

The thermal synthesis of organic phosphates by heating alcohols
with inorganic phosphates is well known, and the synthesis of nucleotides from nucleosides under these conditions is possible. The reactions
are rapid at 130°C but give yields of several percent in the course of a few
months even at 65°C – e.g., UMP from uridine and $Ca(H_2PO_4)_2$. However, there is one major difficulty – namely, that the most useful inorganic phosphates are of the type $M(H_2PO_4)$. It is difficult to imagine
prebiotic conditions sufficiently acid to permit the formation of these
dihydrogenphosphates. It seems just possible that $(NH_4)H_2PO_4$ might
have arisen from $(NH_4)_2HPO_4$ and brought about effective phosphorylation.

There have been several claims that nucleosides can be formed from
bases and sugars in the presence of phosphate or cyanide under the
influence of ultraviolet light. Some of these results are extremely difficult to understand and deserve more thorough exploration.

A number of reagents are widely used to bring about the required
condensations in anhydrous solvents; dicyclohexylcarbodiimide and
trichloromethylacetylene are well-known examples. It is believed the
anion of the acid attacks the condensing agent to form the active phos-
phorylating (acylating) species, which then reacts with the alcohol or
amine, e.g.

$$RN{=}C{=}NR + HPO_4^{2-} \rightarrow RN{=}C\begin{smallmatrix} \diagup OPO_3^{2-} \\ \diagdown NHR \end{smallmatrix}$$

$$RN{=}C\begin{smallmatrix} \diagup OPO_3^{2-} \\ \diagdown NHR \end{smallmatrix} + R^1OH \rightarrow RNH{-}\overset{\overset{\textstyle O}{\|}}{C}{-}NHR + R^1OPO_3^{2-}$$

In aqueous solution, water competes at two stages, e.g.

$$RN{=}C{=}NR + H_2O \rightarrow RNH{-}\overset{\overset{\textstyle O}{\|}}{C}{-}NHR$$

$$RN{=}C\overset{\textstyle OPO_3^{2-}}{\underset{\textstyle NHR}{\big<}} + H_2O \rightarrow RNH{-}\overset{\overset{\textstyle O}{\|}}{C}{-}NHR + H_2PO_4^-$$

Many of the condensing reagents to be discussed are quite selective at the first stage, but hydrolysis of the activated intermediate is a very serious problem for all reagents so far investigated.

The following table lists some "prebiotic" reagents which have been tested successfully in peptide, polynucleotide, or polyphosphate synthesis and some of the condensations achieved:

Reagent	*Reactions*
NCO^-	Inorganic Phosphate $\rightarrow$ Inorganic Pyrophosphate Uridine + Phosphate $\rightarrow$ UMP
$H_2N{-}CN$	Uridine + Phosphate $\rightarrow$ UMP 2 Glycine $\rightarrow$ Glycylglycine
$NH{=}\overset{\overset{\textstyle NH_2}{\|}}{C}{-}NH{-}CN$	Uridine + Phosphate $\rightarrow$ UMP 2 Glycine $\rightarrow$ Glycylglycine
$N{\equiv}C{-}C{\equiv}N$	Inorganic Phosphate $\rightarrow$ Inorganic Pyrophosphate Uridine + Phosphate $\rightarrow$ UMP
$HC{\equiv}C{-}C{\equiv}N$	Inorganic Phosphate $\rightarrow$ Inorganic Pyrophosphate Uridine + Phosphate $\rightarrow$ UMP

In general, yields amount to at most a few percent of the amount of condensing agent consumed, although up to 10–15 percent of uridine can be converted cleanly to UMP, e.g., by excess cyanogen.

The quantitative details of this work suggest that "prebiotic" condensing agents with ample free-energy are available, but that they lack the ability to discriminate between acceptor alcohols or amines and the excess of water always present in aqueous solutions. It has been suggested that adsorption on suitable minerals may have concentrated the active intermediates and hence favored condensation over hydrolysis. The only experimental evidence for such suggestions is the finding that cyanate brings about pyrophosphate synthesis from precipitated calcium phosphate, but not in homogeneous solution.

Biological Organization

One of the most challenging areas relevant to the origins of life is concerned with nonenzymatic template synthesis of polynucleotides and nonenzymatic polynucleotide-directed synthesis of polypeptides. The only positive result obtained so far is the joining together of two hexauridylic acid sequences to give a dodecanucleotide under the influence of polyadenylic acid. Both the experimental techniques and the conceptual background need extensive development before a more general attack on this problem is likely to be successful.

Concentration Mechanisms

If all the surface carbon on the earth (3,000 g/cm^2) were placed as organic compounds in the present oceans (274 liters/cm^2), a greater than 1 percent solution of organic compounds would result. So high a concentration of organic material in the primitive seas would simplify many problems in the origin of life, but it is generally felt that such a concentration is unrealistic and that the "primordial soup" was more dilute. If so, some concentrating mechanism may have been required to speed up chemical reactions. Several mechanisms have been proposed.

The simplest mechanism for concentrating nonvolatile materials is to evaporate the water. This could occur in tide pools or lakes. This process also concentrates the salts, and if these are in great excess over the organic compounds, the evaporated body of water is still not very concentrated in organic matter. Volatile compounds such as HCN and CH_3CHO cannot be concentrated by this process.

A second important concentration mechanism is the adsorption of organic materials on surfaces such as clay minerals or the water-air interface. This was undoubtedly an important process on the primitive earth, and a number of prebiological syntheses have been carried out using mineral surfaces as such catalysts. In one case the surface of calcium phosphate acted as both a catalyst and a reagent for the synthesis of pyrophosphate.

Freezing is another efficient concentration mechanism for some organic compounds. On freezing an aqueous mixture, salts and organic compounds do not enter the ice but concentrate in the liquid phase. This process was used for concentrating dilute HCN in one of the steps in the simulated prebiological synthesis of adenine. The efficiency of this concentration process for organic compounds in the presence of salts is not clear. This would be at least a three-component system, and the eutectics and their composition cannot be predicted.

More complex concentration mechanisms include membranes and colloidal droplets (coacervates). Membranes themselves cannot concentrate anything, but they can keep the enclosed solution from diffusing away once it has been concentrated. A membrane that can carry out active transport will concentrate materials, as present organisms do, but this is a complex process and is unlikely to have developed before life arose. Coacervates can concentrate some materials, and this process is in some respects similar to selective adsorption except that it occurs in the entire body of the coacervate colloid instead of just at the surface.

None of these mechanisms have been tested experimentally to show how they could have concentrated organic compounds for the synthesis of polymers such as peptides, polynucleotides, and other complicated structures. It is likely that each of these concentration mechanisms played some role in the origin of life, but no highly specific relevant example has yet been demonstrated.

Unsolved Problems

Although more work needs to be done, it is clear that nonbiological syntheses of many of the most important biological monomers have been achieved, starting with the constituents of the primitive atmosphere. It must be admitted that few of the laboratory experiments are completely convincing simulations of primitive processes, but enough progress has been made to indicate that this will be accomplished in the foreseeable future. Syntheses of peptide and phosphoester bonds have also been demonstrated, and the outline of a plausible route to polypeptides and polynucleotides can be given. It does not necessarily follow, of course, that the pathways discovered in the laboratory were taken by nature; but until evidence to the contrary is presented, we may consider these routes as possible. Since the free energies of formation of peptide and phosphodiester bonds are positive in sign ($\Delta F^\circ = 2\text{--}4$ kcal/mole for peptide bonds and 6 kcal/mole for phosphodiester bonds), the bonds are unstable in water and will hydrolyze spontaneously. This suggests that polymer formation did not occur in homogeneous solution, but on surfaces.

Origin of Self-duplicating Systems

The problem at this point is to discover a plausible route from the aqueous mixture of organic compounds—usually referred to as the "primordial soup"—to a self-replicating and mutable system. Since there are essentially no experimental data to go on, any discussion of this question is necessarily speculative. We shall not attempt to review the various hypothetical solutions that have been proposed, but shall discuss the general nature of the problem and suggest some possible approaches.

The difficulties surrounding this question are very great indeed, but they are eased somewhat by the consideration that duplication of the most primitive living things need not have been very rapid or very accurate. With an abundance of nutrients and few consumers, the primitive seas would have resembled a vast, rich, and underpopulated broth—an "aquatic Garden of Eden"—in which the struggle for existence was minimal. In such benign circumstances, reproduction need only have been efficient enough to prevent extinction of the species by occasional accidents. One can imagine that the original self-duplicating entities were linear polymers which had the capacity to serve as templates for organizing copies—or, more likely, complements—of themselves from activated monomers in their environment. The catalytic activity needed to combine the monomers might have been provided by inorganic ions or, perhaps, small organic molecules. These catalysts would have been inefficient by comparison with modern enzymes, but adequate under the circumstances.

In the course of time, mutations could have led to the accumulation of a great variety of such polymers in the primitive seas, but this process of replication and mutation would have led to a dead end unless the polymers had the capacity to bring about the formation of catalysts with novel specificities—or, alternatively, themselves had catalytic activity which was capable of being modified by mutation. In contemporary cells, as we have seen, the storage of genetic information is restricted to nucleic acids and the catalytic function to proteins. The translating mechanism that relates proteins to nucleic acids is an elaborate one. Unless the origin of life was a highly improbable event (a possibility that is not excluded), then this mechanism cannot have come into existence in anything like its present form, but must have evolved over a long period of time from a simpler one.

It is not obvious, however, what the simplest state of the system might have been. One conceivable answer is that the original polymers were polynucleotides which not only served as templates for their own reproduction, but also had a limited capacity to organize amino acids into polypeptide chains with catalytic activity. Alternatively, the original polymers might have been polynucleotides with some catalytic capacity of their own, or polypeptides capable to some extent of organizing complementary or identical copies of themselves in a genelike way. Such systems could easily have evolved into the mechanism we find today. None of these speculations is supported by present knowledge, but perhaps they are worth reinvestigating in the light of the aforementioned point that the most primitive organisms need not have been very efficient in any of their functions.

Some authors consider it more likely that the first organisms were not individual molecules, but polymolecular aggregates of one kind or another, separated from the surrounding medium by a definite phase boundary. These proposals are modeled on certain synthetic colloids which can simulate cell division and other cellular activities. The basic flaw of these models to date has been that they incorporate no real genetic mechanism. As we have repeatedly emphasized, the origin-of-life problem is basically one of explaining the origin of a genetic system.

Origin of the Genetic Code and Related Problems

The genetic code relates triplets of nucleotides (codons) to specific amino acids in the operations involved in protein synthesis. There are 64 codons, all but one or two of which are known to code for one or another of the 20 amino acids found in proteins. Since there is no obvious stereochemical relationship between the codons and their cognate amino acids, it is generally, but not unanimously, believed that the code assignments were essentially random choices. The apparent universality of the code is evidence of its great stability toward evolutionary changes. This stability does not require that the code have a stereochemical basis, however. It is easily seen that, once the code is established, any mutational alterations of the code words would almost certainly be lethal. The code is but one aspect of the complex mechanism by which genetic information is translated into proteins, however, and until the evolution of this mechanism is better understood, it would be premature to assert with confidence that the code assignments originated by chance alone. At the present time, there is no satisfactory hypothesis to explain the evolution of the protein-synthesizing mechanism.

A related problem is that of the monomeric composition of biopolymers. One of the implications of the spark-discharge experiment mentioned previously and of subsequent studies of organic syntheses under simulated prebiotic conditions is that, in many cases, the choice of particular substances for the formation of living matter was dictated by their availability. It follows from this argument, however, that if other compounds had been available, they also might have been used biologically. This raises an interesting problem, since there is reason to suppose that other substances suitable for protein and nucleic acid synthesis were, in fact, available on the primitive earth. For example, α-aminobutyric acid is a product of the spark-discharge reaction, and it is also formed metabolically by plants and animals, yet it is not found in proteins. This suggests that chance may have played a part in the selection of some amino acids for protein synthesis. Chance cannot have been the only factor, however, since the amino acids used for protein synthesis must obviously form a compatible set.

In all probability, chance determined which of the two optical enantiomorphs of the amino acids is found in proteins. It is reasonable to suppose that for structural reasons and also for economy it is advantageous for organisms to build proteins out of one optical form of the amino acids. The fact that the L forms are used for this purpose and the D forms excluded is almost certainly the result of an evolutionary accident — i.e., the original organism, from which all others have descended, by chance utilized L-amino acids for protein synthesis. Presumably, the organism would have been just as successful had it employed D-amino acids; chance dictated the choice. Alternative theories, which assume that life originated in an environment containing optically active amino acids, are much less plausible. The same conclusion applies to the optical configuration of the sugar moieties of the nucleic acids.

Evolution of Cells and Metabolic Pathways

The origin of cells is a more difficult problem than any of those considered above, since the molecular organization of the cell — in particular, the structure of membranes — is still obscure. As was mentioned earlier, some authors contend that various colloids prepared artificially in the laboratory can serve as models of living cells. These are dubious analogies, at best. If the history of the origin-of-life problem has shown anything, it is that an analytical understanding of living phenomena must precede attempts to reconstruct their evolution. Since we lack a deep understanding of cell membrane structure at the present time, the origin of cells must be considered a question for the future.

The position is different with regard to metabolic pathways. Metabolism consists of a network of chemical reactions, each reaction catalyzed by a particular enzyme. The structure and properties of the individual enzymes are determined genetically by a number of genes equal to the number of structurally different polypeptide chains in the enzyme—

usually one or two. Each metabolic pathway is thus governed by a particular constellation of genes. This raises the following evolutionary problem: A biosynthetic pathway has selective value only when considered as a whole, since, in general, only the end product of the pathway is useful to the organism. Intermediate steps in the synthesis of an amino acid, for example, have no value in themselves, and the corresponding genes by themselves would be selectively neutral or even disadvantageous. The pathway cannot have come into existence all at once, since the genes governing the pathway presumably arose by rare mutations, one at a time, from preexisting genes. But if these individual mutant genes failed to confer a selective advantage on their possessor, they would in all probability have been lost before the entire constellation could be assembled.

The solution that has been proposed for this problem is that biosynthetic pathways evolved pari passu with the disappearance of nutrients from the primitive soup. As each essential nutrient—e.g., amino acid— became scarce, a selective advantage would be gained by organisms capable of synthesizing it from potential precursors in the soup. The pathways thus evolved backwards, one step at a time, from the end product of the pathway toward the beginning of the reaction chain. For example, earlier we saw that aminoimidazole carboxamide is formed under presumed prebiotic conditions for the synthesis of purines. Today, this compound is a key intermediate in the enzymic pathway of purine formations. Each mutation would have been advantageous, since it made a new source of the end product available. According to this view, photosynthesis was the last pathway to evolve, since no advantage would have been conferred by this process until the organic materials of the primitive seas were exhausted.

The evolution of catabolic pathways does not seem to pose a special problem, since the reactions can be individually useful to the organism by supplying energy or intermediates needed for biosynthetic purposes.

The Search for Extraterrestrial Life

The Solar System: Moon and Planets

The search for extraterrestrial life has been announced by the National Aeronautics and Space Administration as one of the prime scientific objectives of the United States space program. Although no practical efforts along these lines have yet been attempted, space missions relevant to exobiology are in the planning and development stages, and substantial information relevant to exobiology can be expected in the next decade of space exploration. Exobiological methodology is naturally divided into three categories: (1) the remote and in situ characterization of a planetary environment, to test the a priori possibility of indigenous life, (2) remote and ground-based observations of extraterrestrial life, and (3) direct, in situ, observation of extraterrestrial life. These categories will be considered in turn.

Characterization of Planetary Environments. A wide range of techniques is available to the planetary astronomer in his attempt to characterize a planetary environment without actually landing a space vehicle on the planet. Observing stations on the ground, on stratospheric balloons, on ballistic rockets, in Earth-orbiting vehicles, and in lunar or planetary flybys and orbiters have all been utilized. The techniques include ultraviolet spectroscopy, polarimetry, and photography; visible spectroscopy, polarimetry, photometry, and photography; near infrared photography and high resolution spectroscopy in reflected light; far infrared radiometry and spectroscopy of emitted radiation from the planetary surface; and microwave radiometry, spectroscopy, and polarimetry. These techniques permit conclusions to be drawn concerning atmospheric and surface chemistry, surface granularity, the structure of planetary atmospheres, the surface and subsurface temperature distribution, and the ultraviolet flux at the surface—in short, concerning a wide range of parameters relevant for extraterrestrial life.

It is a simple matter to decide that some planetary environments may be hostile to terrestrial organisms. It is much more difficult to conclude that the environment cannot possibly be inhabited by indigenous organisms especially adapted to what for us seem very inclement conditions. The absence of oxygen, the scarcity of free water, higher or lower temperatures than we are accustomed to, high ultraviolet fluxes, all have conceivable adaptations. Very high temperatures probably exclude life because of the general problem of imagining an organic molecular structure which stably contains genetic information at elevated temperatures. Similarly, temperatures very close to absolute zero probably exclude life because of the exceedingly slow rate of chemical reaction. But in the broad intermediate range, we cannot be sure that life is impossible.

Mercury. The surface temperatures on the planet Mercury vary diurnally from over 700°K to below 150°K, but the microwave data indicate temperatures some meters subsurface which are approximately time invariant at about 300°K. Atmospheric pressures of a few percent that on Earth have been reported and disputed. Thus, subsurface temperatures are biologically clement, but because of its smallness, closeness to the sun, and distance from Earth, little else of biological interest is known about Mercury.

Venus. Information about the surface conditions of Venus can be obtained from its microwave emission. Venus radiates as if its surface were at a mean temperature of 700°K. A wide variety of radio and radar data are consistent with this interpretation, and no alternative nonthermal source of the microwave emission which is consistent with the data has been proposed. The temperatures at the subsolar point may be as high as 1000°K, although the exact figure is known very poorly. The temperatures even at the poles are probably above the normal boiling point and even the critical temperature of water. Mountains at average locales on Venus, high enough for the temperatures at their tops to be about 350°K, are inconsistent with the bearing strength of materials. There seems little escape from the conclusion that the surface temperatures on Venus are too high for the stability at least of familiar varieties of organic molecules, to say nothing of terrestrial organisms.

Several lines of evidence point to the clouds of Venus being composed of ice crystals at their tops and water droplets at their bottoms, although several other lines of evidence are apparently inconsistent with this view. No alternative cloud material consistent with all the data has been proposed, and substantial dispute on the composition of the clouds remains. Infrared radiometry has shown that the temperatures in the clouds are about 240°K, and toward their bottoms probably 270°K. Large quantities of CO_2 are known to exist in the atmosphere, as well as small quantities of water; nitrogen is suspected; oxygen has been reported, but not confirmed. Cloud pressures at the 270°K level are about 1 atm. The atmosphere of Venus is probably in convective equilibrium, and the microwave and radar data show the surface to be pulverized. Thus, the distribution of at least small quantities of dust throughout the atmosphere is reasonable, and a supply of minerals to the cloud bottoms is by no means out of the question. Therefore, the bottoms of the clouds of Venus may conceivably be reasonable habitats for organisms of the terrestrial type. The recent report of parts per million of HCl and HF in the atmosphere of Venus does not alter this conclusion.

The Moon. The surface temperatures on the moon range from about 100°C to about 100°K. Due to the almost total absence of an atmosphere solar ultraviolet light and solar protons and other charged particles probably strike the lunar surface unimpeded. The lunar surface can probably be excluded as a potential habitat for life. Subsurface conditions are much more clement; the average time-invariant temperature a few meters below the surface is about 240°K, and a subsurface permafrost layer of ice has been suspected. Because of the low subsurface temperatures, organic molecules produced early in the history of the moon are unlikely to have suffered thermal decomposition during the intervening few billion years, and substantial evidence on the early history of the solar system and on prebiological organic chemistry may be sequestered beneath the surface of the moon. It is difficult to imagine life beneath the lunar surface, however, because of the unavailability of light for photosynthesis.

Mars. The average surface temperature of Mars is about 210°K; but the diurnal and seasonal temperature fluctuations are very large, and equatorial summer noon temperatures of 300°K have been reported. The atmospheric pressure is about 10 millibars, largely carbon dioxide, although smaller quantities of nitrogen and argon may be present. Water vapor has been detected in variable amounts with a mean abundance of several times 10^{-3} g per square cm column. The nature of the polar caps is uncertain, both condensed water and a mixture of condensed CO_2 and H_2O having their advocates.

A variety of photometric, polarimetric, and spectrometric data suggest that pulverized iron oxide is a minor and possibly a major constituent of the superficial layers of the Martian surface. One of the iron oxides, goethite, is a mineral which is of possible biological interest. It contains water of crystallization, and is therefore a potential source of water for any hypothetical Martian organisms able to extract it. The density of water in goethite is about 0.4 g per cm^3, almost as large as the density of pure water. Goethite is also an extremely effective ultraviolet absorber, a property that could conceivably be useful to organisms living in unfiltered Martian sunlight. The actual presence of goethite on Mars is still in doubt, however.

Large elevation differences are suspected on Mars, and winds in excess of 100 miles per hour have been calculated, due in part to the large temperature gradients. Mariner IV photographic experiments have shown the surface to be heterogeneous on a large scale, and there is the possibility of biologically interesting microenvironments on the Martian surface and subsurface. A subsurface permafrost layer has also been suggested.

The character of the Martian environment is relevant to the problem of spacecraft sterilization. Sterility of exposed surfaces of spacecraft landed on Mars is necessary to prevent contamination of life-detection instruments carried on board. Aside from this, the possibility of contaminating Mars itself is a question that has received much attention. If any terrestrial microorganisms deposited on Mars are capable of dispersal and subsequent growth, substantial confusion of later biological experiments and even alteration of the Martian environment might ensue. However, thorough sterilization of the spacecraft is a costly endeavor. The *average* Martian environment is probably so hostile by terrestrial standards that no terrestrial organism could multiply there. There is, however, a difference of opinion on the likelihood of microenvironments either in time or in space on Mars in which terrestrial microorganisms could multiply. Further definition of these possibilities and improved knowledge of the sterilization policy of the Soviet Union would be useful in better assessing the need for thorough sterilization of the entire spacecraft.[1]

The Jovian Planets. The Jovian planets are by no means identical. But because the most information exists about Jupiter, and because from a biological point of view the similarities among these planets are very large, we will consider only Jupiter in this discussion, neglecting Uranus, Neptune, and Saturn. And because of its great distance from the sun, and the fact that we know practically nothing about it, no further mention will be made of Pluto.

Jupiter, as seen in the usual photographs, is actually being viewed at the cloud level. The composition of the clouds is most often said to be frozen ammonia, although this is inferential and not the result of any direct observations. The atmosphere is primarily hydrogen and helium, with small quantities of methane and ammonia detected. The cloud temperatures are 200°K or less. If any water were present in the Jovian atmosphere, it would be condensed out at this level. In fact, there is no way for water or atomic oxygen to escape from Jupiter, and therefore water below the clouds is to be expected. The average pressure at the visible cloud level is in dispute; estimates range from about one to several hundred atmospheres. Within this range of uncertainty, the atomic composition may be consistent with the cosmic abundances.

The atmosphere of Jupiter below the clouds is expected to be in convective equilibrium; therefore, some tens of kilometers beneath the clouds, biologically interesting temperatures may be achieved. There is also the possibility of liquid ammonia, ice crystal, and liquid water clouds at these lower depths. Because of the high pressure, the atmospheric density at these depths is considerable, approaching 0.1 g per cm^3. Because of the reducing nature of the Jovian environment, the production of molecules by such thermodynamic disequilibrium processes as ultraviolet radiation and electrical discharge within the clouds is expected. It has been suggested that the bright coloration of the bands, belts, and spots of Jupiter is due to the presence of organic molecules. Jupiter may in fact be a vast planetary laboratory of prebiological organic chemistry.

Remote Observations for Extraterrestrial Life. The observations made to date which are directly relevant to extraterrestrial life are small. On the moon, events of outgassing from the satellite's interior have been reported, including one in which the molecule C_2 was claimed on spectro-

___

[1] Mariners VI and VII, which successfully flew by Mars in July–August 1969, have clarified several of the questions discussed in this section.

scopic grounds. The precursor molecule of C_2 is most likely a simple organic molecule, and may point to the presence of such molecules beneath the lunar surface. Infrared spectroscopy of Mars had in the past revealed the presence of three bands observed in reflected light near 3.5 μ. These bands are at the same wavelengths that CH and CHO stretching bands absorb in many organic molecules. However, it has subsequently been found that two of these three bands are probably due to deuterated water in our own atmosphere. More recently other organic molecules in the Martian atmosphere have been reported by high resolution interferometric spectroscopy, but this report has not been confirmed.

A variety of features of Mars, including seasonal and secular changes, the coloration of dark areas, and the canals, have all at one time or another been attributed to life on Mars. However, in each case reasonable nonbiological explanations now exist. There is no compelling evidence for or against life on Mars.

Of the total mass of meteoritic debris that falls on Earth, about 1 part in 10,000 is composed of organic matter. Most of this organic matter is found in the carbonaceous chondrites. Among the compounds reported are *n*-paraffins, branched chain paraffins, cycloalkanes, isoprenoids, aromatic hydrocarbons, and long-chain fatty acids; reports of amino acids and purines have been disputed, and may be due to contamination. While it has been claimed that these molecules could only have had an extraterrestrial biological origin, substantial evidence exists that at least many of them can be produced by thermodynamic equilibrium processes at temperatures near 600°K, in hydrogen-depleted reducing environments. These conditions are not inappropriate for the early history of the meteorite parent bodies, presumably the asteroids.

The presence of morphologically well-defined "organized elements" contained within several varieties of meteorites have also been alleged to have biological significance or to be examples of extraterrestrial microorganisms. Some of these inclusions prove to be of inorganic origin, and others terrestrial contaminants — e.g., ragweed pollen. It has also been claimed that viable indigenous organisms have been extracted from some meteorites, but due to the serious contamination question, and for other reasons, this is very unlikely. Different research groups have claimed that saponified fractions extracted from some of these meteorites are or are not racemic. But the absolute value of the optical rotation under debate is extremely small, and there are several ways in which contamination can introduce optically active material. The difficulties experienced in testing meteoritic organic matter for biological origin indicate the care that must be taken in in situ planetary observations, and the great danger that contamination poses in the analysis of trace quantities.

In Situ Observations for Extraterrestrial Life. The next decade holds the possibility of flyby vehicles past Mars and Venus, the orbiting and landing on Mars of substantial payloads, and possibly flybys or orbiters around Jupiter. Such experiments could do much to remove areas of uncertainty discussed in the preceding paragraphs. Studies of Earth taken with the Tiros, Nimbus, and ATS meteorological satellites have shown that it is exceedingly difficult to detect even intelligent life on the daytime side of Earth at 0.1 km resolution. Ground resolution of 1–10 m permits a variety of biological detail to be discerned. Such a resolution is possible from orbit about Mars. In Earth's atmosphere methane is present in amounts some 30 orders of magnitude greater than that expected at thermodynamic equilibrium. This huge disequilibrium of a reduced gas in an oxygen atmosphere is due to biological activity. The presence of similar disequilibrium abundances of gases in the atmospheres of other planets might provide significant clues to the possibility of extraterrestrial life. This points up one reason for infrared spectrometers in planetary orbit. Such instruments could also detect local environments on Mars where the water abundance is large, and infrared and microwave radiometers could detect surface and subsurface hot spots. There are observations of very real biological interest to be performed from orbit, especially about Mars, and also from Earth.

A wide variety of experiments have been suggested for Mars landers including video scanning of the landscape, gas chromatography–mass spectrometry, microscopy and infrared spectrometry, optical rotatory dispersion, calorimetry, fluorimetry, monitoring of photosynthetic or metabolic labeled gas evolution or fixation, and tests of turbidity, pH, or catalytic changes in inoculated culture media.

Many of these experiments depend on whether one or another assumption about the character of possible Martian organisms is valid. It is clear that the more such experiments that are performed, the more likely it is that a significant characterization of the Martian environment and Martian biology, if any, can be obtained. For this reason, an automated laboratory capable of a real experimental protocol with contingency planning, successive experiments on the same sample, and some degree of control from Earth has been proposed. Another concept, currently being studied, is a roving vehicle which carries a complement of more stereotyped experiments. For the earliest missions, simple biological laboratories without roving capability can be expected.

All sets of observations described above can probably be performed more effectively in the presence than in the absence of a man, except for the danger of biological contamination. Manned lunar exploration has already been accomplished. Manned planetary exploration is unlikely within the near future.

In sum, one cannot be sanguine concerning the possibility of life in this

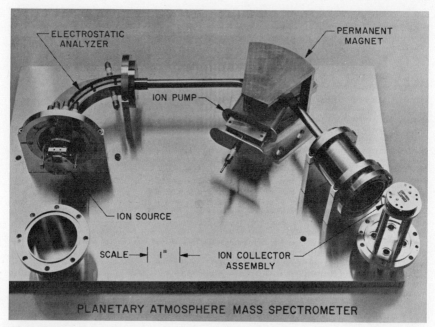

Figure 5-3. A mass spectrometer apparatus designed for analyzing the atmosphere of Mars during descent to the surface. The mass spectrometer is a double focusing magnetic sector instrument with a mass range from 12 a.m.u. to 90 a.m.u., built by the Jet Propulsion Laboratory, California Institute of Technology, under contract to the National Aeronautics and Space Administration. (Courtesy the Jet Propulsion Laboratory)

solar system other than on Earth. No positive evidence has yet been adduced, and the moon and all other planets appear to be decidedly hostile to life as we know it. Yet, because of the enormous potential rewards for our own self-understanding, it seems entirely appropriate that a systematic, continuing program exploring these potentialities be pursued with all the imagination that can be brought to bear.

Beyond the Solar System

The only life that might be detected beyond the solar system in the foreseeable future is intelligent life. There is no feasible method of observation from the vicinity of the solar system, with or without spacecraft, which could detect evidence of nonintelligent biology. Even the detection of planetary systems is extremely difficult. Furthermore, the only promising methods to detect intelligent life depend for success on rather gross manifestations of intelligent activity, such as the radiation of large amounts of power or major alterations of the natural physical structure of stars and planetary systems.

However, these limitations are not as serious as they appear at first glance. Given manifestations of intelligent activity no greater than we ourselves produce in the form of radio transmissions, existing terrestrial technology is capable of detecting such activities over distances as enormous as 1,000 light years, within which range there are 10 million stars. Some perhaps optimistic estimates of the abundance of intelligent civilizations suggest that within this sample there could well be more than one detectable civilization, and thus a significant chance of success in a serious search for such civilizations. Even a slight chance provides strong impetus for such a search, since the rewards of success would be very great indeed.

The most important consequence of success would be information on the results of the highest stages in biological and sociological evolution in an ecology completely independent of Earth, but at a stage of development at least equivalent to the terrestrial situation. Such information is surely not available in our solar system. It is of prime relevance to the most profound and ancient biological and philosophical questions of human civilization, the same questions whose partial answers or lack thereof have provided a major motivation for scientific research, and have given rise to various religions, philosophies, and political systems. Furthermore, data from other civilizations might show whether there are optimum end points to chemical and biological evolution, and whether there are preferred pathways of biological and cultural evolution. Undoubtedly, other data important to science and technology would derive from such a discovery.

In view of these potentialities, it may seem surprising that so little serious effort has been made to detect other civilizations. However, the lack of serious effort is rooted in a harsh reality. It is known that a successful search will require the application of major monetary and technological resources. Moreover, the data on which to base estimates of the amount and nature of the resources required are so poor that we cannot be certain of what is required for unequivocal success. Undertaking of such a program, as in all very costly programs, should await a convincing assessment of the resources required.

The difficulty in making such an estimate comes from our serious lack of information concerning those parameters that affect estimates of the number of civilizations in space. Some of the parameters affecting the estimate are sufficiently well known. These include the rate of star formation, the fraction of stars that *could* have planets at nearly constant radiation levels long enough to have permitted intelligent life to evolve, and the fraction of those planets likely to have conditions suitable for life. Weak parameters are the fractions of stars actually possessing planetary systems and the likelihood that natural selection will inevitably lead to the emergence of an intelligent species. Extremely weak parameters are the fraction of planets suitable for life on which life has actually developed, and the longevity of civilizations in a detectable state.

There are plausible theories which state that planetary systems are abundant. However, we are certain of the existence of only one system, our own. We have some evidence of the existence of a few other planetary systems probably containing dark companions of roughly Jovian mass, but more observations are required before we will be confident of their ubiquity. Such observations must be made from space. Similarly, whereas there are those who argue that the development of life is inevitable where conditions are appropriate, we have observed only one life-bearing planet, Earth. Again, the ease of the development of life can probably be determined by further laboratory studies of the kind described earlier and through foreseeable spacecraft missions, particularly to Mars, Jupiter, and Venus.

The likelihood of the emergence of intelligent life simply cannot be assessed. One can only admit the immensity of the universe, and the unlikelihood that either Earth or Man is unique. In any case, the acquisition of firmer data with respect to several of the weak parameters is within reach and depends on progress in biology and in the general space program. The last weak parameter, longevity of civilizations, is neither amenable to theoretical studies nor to observations, except of other civilizations themselves.

Thus, assessment of the effort required to detect other civilizations is in the unhappy dilemma of having to succeed before we can estimate the cost of success. Nevertheless, the probability that both planetary systems and life occur many times in the universe, and the profound nature of the question, appear to justify a substantial effort in this regard.

Such a search might require an expenditure of some $50 million over perhaps thirty years. The error in this estimate may well be a factor of ten in either direction, but it could be reduced greatly by the results of the already planned space program. This cost estimate assumes a search for intelligent radio emissions, the method widely considered most likely to succeed and at least cost.

Centering of interest on a radio search derives from considerations of economy in the transmission of information across space. Comparative studies of the cost of transmitting information have shown that electromagnetic radiation, radio frequencies in particular, is much less costly than the other plausible means, the transmission of matter, presumably through rocketry. The preference for radio frequencies over higher frequencies, such as optical frequencies, rests on the fact that radio photons are much less costly per bit of information than higher frequency photons.

The very lowest frequencies are unusable due to radio interference from natural galactic radio emissions.

Although economy may seem anthropomorphic and thus a dangerous concept to use in such analyses, the principles of economy must necessarily be important to other higher organisms, if such there be. The most probable carriers of interstellar information then seem to be radio waves. There is a further great advantage in the implementation of a radio search. If suitable techniques, already developed, are used, they are capable of detecting the ensemble of weak radio emissions that other civilizations might emit for their own consumption, even though no individual signals may be detectable. This greatly broadens the range of technological activity in other civilizations that would permit detection.

One short radio search for extraterrestrial signals was carried out in 1960 at the National Radio Astronomy Observatory. The negative results obtained confirm that the detection of other civilizations, if they exist, will not be very easy.

Although there are strong arguments favoring a radio search, it is clear that man is still at an early era in technological development. It could well be that new technological factors could make strong arguments for other modes of search. Thus it is at the least prudent to admit the possibility that evidence of other civilizations may appear through mechanisms that now appear unlikely, such as interstellar spacecraft or optical transmissions. For example, it has been proposed that very advanced civilizations might make major rearrangements of their planetary system so as to better use the natural resources of the system, particularly the energy of the central star. Pursuing this argument, whatever its likelihood, such arrangements could lead to quite unusual cosmic objects, and in some forms these objects would be observable only at wavelengths, particularly the infrared, where we presently have only limited capability.

A search for other civilizations may be regarded as a likely follow-on to space research already in progress or planned. But tests of these possibilities, when inexpensive or likely to produce useful information of other kinds, should be undertaken as soon as they seem opportune.

Results of a Survey of Radio Astronomers on Activities and Attitudes Toward the Search for Extraterrestrial Intelligent Life

In an effort to document the activity in radio searches for extraterrestrial intelligent life that has taken place or is planned, and to evaluate the attitude of radio astronomers toward such activities, the following questionnaire was sent to twenty-five major radio astronomy observatories:

1. Has your institution ever conducted an observational program aimed at the detection of radio signals from extraterrestrial civilizations, including searches for very short-term variations in the intensity of cosmic radio sources? If so, please briefly describe the scope of this program.
2. Does your organization have any plans for future studies of this kind? If so, please describe the proposed scope of such programs.
3. What is your opinion as to the general desirability of conducting such observational programs? How is this opinion influenced by the competition for telescope time by more conventional radio astronomical studies?

The replies, which were received from almost all observatories, give the following results:

Replies from astronomers all over the world were sober and serious, and reflected extensive thinking on the subject.

Two observatories have conducted sensitive and lengthy searches aimed specifically at the detection of extraterrestrial radio signals. One such search was conducted for two months at the National Radio Astronomy Observatory in 1960, and the other is a radio search presently in progress at the Shternberg Observatory in Moscow.

Other than the Soviet search now in progress, no observatory reported concrete plans for such activities in the foreseeable future. However, four observatories reported that they have major programs in the study of the variability of radio sources or in narrow frequency spectral line studies, both of which types of research use observing procedures which are well suited to the detection of extraterrestrial radio signals. These four observatories noted that in the analysis of their data they would remain alert for any evidence in the data that could be construed to be the result of intelligent activity.

With regard to the general opinion as to the desirability of conducting observational searches for extraterrestrial signals, there was a wide range of opinion. Of the twenty-one observatories that answered this question, fourteen expressed the strong positive opinion that such searches were very important and should be carried out. Considerable enthusiasm was shown in some responses, including those from some of the world's leading radio astronomers. The seven negative responses were generally accompanied by a justifying opinion that the probability of success was too low to warrant the investment of large personnel, equipment, and financial resources. There was no single response expressing the view that the detection of extraterrestrial life was impossible either because such life does not exist or because the technology was inadequate.

Those who held strongly that such searches should be conducted expressed several ideas as to how we might best proceed. Several, including some leading astronomers, maintained that a serious, well-funded search for extraterrestrial signals should be organized on a worldwide basis. Others felt that some fraction, say 10 percent, of the time of most radio telescopes should be devoted to such searches. It was felt that this would produce adequate activity in the search, without hindering progress in conventional radio astronomy. A few thought that the best hope was a chance discovery of extraterrestrial signals in the course of conventional astronomy work, and that we should simply make a great effort to be alert to this possibility in the analysis of data. All noted that the shortage of observing time on large radio telescopes was working strongly to hinder a development of significant searches for extraterrestrial signals.

In summary, although little activity has taken place, there is widespread interest in the conduct of searches for extraterrestrial intelligent life. A shortage of telescope time is inhibiting the implementation of such searches, and there is a feeling that observing time should be made available by either making limited use of existing telescopes or constructing new facilities.

Chapter 6

THE BIOLOGY OF DEVELOPMENT

It is the purpose of this chapter to convey a sense of both the accomplishments and the outstanding problems in developmental biology and to show how investments in research may help improve the quality of life in many ways, enriching endeavors from agriculture to medicine.

By development is meant the progressive changes that occur during an organism's life history. Each species exhibits a life cycle which, in familiar organisms, has the general form: fertilized egg, embryo, larva, adult, fertilized egg. In the perennial plants and vertebrate animals, among others, the mature organism passes into senescence – "old age" – after an extended period of reproductive life. Developmental processes are marked by progressive and cumulative changes at all levels of biological organization: molecules, cells, tissues, and organs.

Two features characterize developmental phenomena. First, developmental processes lead to more or less permanent structural change, while nondevelopmental processes such as muscle contraction or nerve impulse conduction involve only transitory and reversible changes in structure. Second, developmental phenomena are typically gradual and cumulative, spanning sizable segments of the life history, whereas physiological processes occur over relatively brief periods.

Yet a sharp demarcation between these two kinds of change cannot be drawn. Continuity between development and certain rapid processes is evident in the area of chemical synthesis, since the long-term control of what and how much material is synthesized is central to developmental change. At the other extreme there is a continuity between development and the slow course of evolution, a process that involves events taking place in a population of organisms over periods of many life cycles. New structural or physiological characteristics are available for natural selection only insofar as new modes of development can produce them. In the relative pace of its mechanisms, therefore, development grades into the rapid molecular reactions on one end and into the slow evolutionary process at the other. Just as the continuous presence of a chemically defined hereditary material, DNA, in successive generations of a species forms the basis of quantitative study of cause and effect in evolution, so does the presence of this same genetic material in all the cells of a developing organism form the starting point for a consideration of developmental mechanisms.

The recent advances in our understanding of heredity have altered the strategy, and also the language, of our approach to development. Knowing the genetic makeup of the fertilized egg, derived from that of its parents, one can predict many of the ultimate visible characteristics of the offspring. It is notable that genetic prediction can usually proceed successfully despite our limited knowledge of the mechanisms underlying the developmental events by which the fertilized egg gradually takes on its overt characteristics. Developmental processes could not be understood in complete chemical detail until the molecular nature of both the genes and the traits they govern had been elucidated.

When one contemplates inherited traits such as left-handedness, baldness patterns, earlobe structure, and so forth, the chemical basis of a trait or characteristic appears at first sight to be beyond understanding. Other inherited traits, however, were long ago recognized as having a relatively simple chemical basis. An albino, for example, has lost the ability to make body pigments. Since pigments are made by a series of chemical reactions, each reaction being catalyzed by an enzyme, the albino trait might be based on the malfunction or absence of one or more of these enzymes. A similar line of reasoning proved highly successful in now classical experiments on various forms of the bread mold, *Neurospora,* an organism in which mutations are easily induced with ultraviolet light. The mutant traits studied involved the inability of many strains of the fungus to grow on a simple nutrient medium. Such strains could be sorted on the basis of their inability to carry out particular enzymatically catalyzed reactions. As predicted, many inherited "traits" in the mold turned out to be based on enzymes — specific protein molecules — that were either defective or missing. Now, traits in many organisms can be ascribed to defects in specific proteins: these, in turn, as we have seen, reflect alterations in the structure of DNA.

Although it is important to know the genetic basis and intracellular machinery underlying the repertoire of developmental responses, even the fullest understanding of gene action in a bacterial cell will not completely elucidate the development of all cells, tissues, and complex organisms. What leads a fertilized egg to divide, and to produce daughter cells which become as unlike as bone and muscle, blood and nerve? It is these features that intrigue developmental biologists. We offer a few examples, selected on the basis of the following criteria: (1) They represent active areas of interest in developmental biology. (2) They illustrate the need for approaches at molecular, cellular, and organismic levels of organization and for appropriate means of integrating information from one level with another. (3) They illustrate one of the great generalizations of the last half century, that many biological phenomena occur universally. Let us dwell on the third point a moment, since it is basic to modern biology. Fundamental biochemical pathways are the same in cells of plants, worms, and men. The basic laws of heredity operate in lower forms of life just as they do in man. The behavior of cells – their mode of division, association, migration, specialization, and death – is also similar in the many forms studied.

In retrospect, such generalizations are almost obvious. But not all phenomena involving living things are readily observable and analyzable in all animal or plant forms. Certain organisms lend themselves particularly to the investigation of cell division or cell migration. In others, specific types of metabolic processes are most easily studied; still others are particularly suited for the study of heredity. The investigator therefore often chooses the organism or experimental "system" most likely to yield information on a particular phenomenon. For example, the early development of a newly fertilized egg is more easily observed in a frog egg than in a human egg because the frog egg is large, fertilized externally, and readily available for laboratory studies. Much, if not most, of what we know about development has been gained through studies on the widest variety of animals, plants, and microbes. Thus it is of strategic advantage not to restrict ourselves to the study of mice, rats, guinea pigs, rabbits, monkeys, and man. We must exploit such diverse forms as sea urchins, frogs, worms, sensitive plants, flies, jellyfish, fungi, ferns, algae, and salamanders, each of which displays one or more strategic opportunities to approach an aspect of development that is not amenable to investigation in other forms. There is ample reason to believe that, now, as in the past, studies of lower forms of life will yield important results with a bearing on human health and welfare.

Molecular Basis of Gene Expression

The properties of a specialized cell reflect the activity of its genes, located in the chromosomes. During each cell division, each daughter cell appears to receive an identical set of chromosomes, and hence an identical set of genes. Yet the various cell types of a multicellular organism differ from one another biochemically, morphologically, and physiologically.

A detailed knowledge of the biochemistry and morphology of normal development of an organism is essential if we are to understand the roles that genes play. An investigator concerned with tracing the complex pathway leading from gene to biochemical and morphological traits often chooses a developmental mutant as a starting point for his analysis, since such a mutant indicates that normal gene action—direct or indirect—is required for the particular developmental event. Many mutants interfering with normal development have been described, notably in corn, the house mouse, and the fruit fly.

There are mutations whose most obvious effect is at a behavioral level, as in the Japanese waltzing mouse. Other mutations are expressed at the level of tissue interaction. In several mutant strains of chick embryos, for example, lack of interaction between two tissues appears to be responsible for the failure of normal limb development. Still other mutations affect hormone production. The "dwarf" gene of the mouse, for example, affects a specific class of cells of the pituitary gland, and as a consequence these cells fail to produce the hormones that control the endocrine activities of the thyroid and adrenals. Dwarfism and sterility result from these hormonal disturbances. Several mutants of corn have an impaired ability to synthesize a major plant hormone, gibberellin, and their growth as a result is dwarfed and stunted. If gibberellin is supplied to such plants—for example, by spraying it on them—their growth closely resembles that of genetically normal plants without an external source of the hormone. In the same way, dwarfism and sterility of the mutant mouse can also be corrected by hormones obtained from normal pituitary. Such treatments do not "cure" the underlying disorders—that is, they do not repair the primary genetic lesions—they merely compensate for the consequences thereof. The mouse pituitary dwarf also illustrates two other important principles of developmental genetics. First, the malfunction of a tissue is not necessarily caused by malfunction of the genes of its own cells, but often by malfunction of genes of other cells. Thyroid and adrenal cells of the mutant mouse appear equipped to perform normally, provided that they receive the proper stimulus from the pituitary. Second, a single mutation often has multiple consequences—dwarfism and sterility, for example.

In the 1950's, stimulated largely by the discovery of the relationship between DNA and protein synthesis, students of development made their first major efforts to center attention on products that were "close to the genes." Employing the techniques of enzymology and immunochemistry, they began to study the pattern of synthesis of specific proteins. It is now clear that cells of different tissues of the same organism or individual differ by the presence or absence of specific enzymes. But, as we have seen, the genetic complements of these cells are thought to be identical. Since protein synthesis is under genetic control, the differing protein arrays are most easily explained on the assumption that not all genes are functioning in all cells at all times—that genes are expressed differentially. Many investigators are now studying the mechanisms underlying differential gene expression, the mechanisms whereby the activities of genes are regulated.

Not only may a specific protein be detected in some cells, and not in others; it may be present in different amounts in different cells. The absence of the protein may reflect the absence or modification of the structural gene determining the protein; it may be a consequence of the action of a regulatory gene which might determine the nature of the control systems to which the cell's synthetic machinery responds in making the protein; or it may reflect a control operating at a level beyond the gene.

What are the levels of control? First, the availability of genes (in quantity) may be different from cell to cell. This can occur as genes become "masked" and thus unavailable for transcription or, in certain cases, as multiple copies of genes are made available. We shall discuss recent evidence reported for this level of control. Second, the frequency with which a given gene is transcribed into RNA may vary. Evidence is accumulating from many organisms that this is a common way of genetic regulation, although we know very little about the mechanisms by which it is brought about. Third, transcribed gene copies may or may not be translated into proteins—that is, regulation might operate at the level of translation on the ribosome. Evidence is also accumulating that this type of control may be prevalent, not only during embryonic development but also in the stabilization of differentiating cells as they approach their highest degrees of specialization. Fourth, proteins, once formed, may not become functionally or structurally integrated within a cell. Still other levels of control may be envisioned.

On the basis of what we have said it would appear that the most direct assay of gene activity might be the rate of synthesis of RNA. Perhaps the most direct approach would be to analyze the RNA's containing the DNA code for specific proteins, the "messenger" RNA's. However, this task is formidable in view of the complexity of protein synthesis and the technical difficulties of selecting specific RNA's. It has become technically possible, however, to analyze an RNA that plays another role in protein synthesis but nevertheless is transcribed directly from the DNA.

A model of how RNA synthesis is controlled may thus be suggested, for example, by contemporary studies on the ribosomal RNA's (r-RNA's) and the genes that define their structure in the toad, *Xenopus*.

The ribosomes, cytoplasmic particles, consist of protein and at least three types of ribosomal RNA. Oocytes and embryos of *Xenopus* synthesize r-RNA at different rates depending upon the stage of development of the egg or embryo. Ribosomal RNA is formed in large quantities during oogenesis, and ribosomes are assembled during that period. When the egg becomes mature, however, r-RNA synthesis ceases, and resumes only well after development is initiated. Thus, the activity of genes for r-RNA must be controlled in a sensitive way during oogenesis and embryogenesis. The control of this activity involves not only the availability of genes for transcription but also the frequency with which available genes are transcribed.

Evidence from many laboratories shows that a spherical body in the cell nucleus, the nucleolus, is the site at which at least two types of ribosomal RNA are made. The most convincing demonstration of this was obtained in a mutant of *Xenopus* in which the nucleolus was completely absent, due to a deletion of part of a chromosome.

Embryos that are homozygous for the mutation—that is, in which the chromosomes derived from both egg and sperm are marked by the deletion—do not synthesize ribosomal RNA. The embryo contains enough ribosomal RNA made previously during oogenesis to support early development, but when, later, the embryo fails to make its own new r-RNA, it dies. The vast quantities of r-RNA synthesized during oogenesis are due to the presence of hundreds of nucleoli, which represent extra copies of the genes for ribosomal RNA. During the process of egg formation, all of these copies are synthesizing ribosomal RNA. Prior to fertilization, however, all of the extra nucleoli have entered the cytoplasm where they are nonfunctional. Somatic nuclei then contain only the normal number (2) of nucleoli. Somatic tissues, however, exhibit widely different rates of ribosome synthesis while containing the same number of genes for r-RNA. Thus, the rate of transcription of the r-RNA genes in different somatic tissues must vary.

How does one study control mechanisms in higher organisms? Although structural genes are adequately defined, the evidence for regulatory genes is scant. Hints that feedback control mechanisms do exist in higher organisms have come from a variety of sources, but categorical proof is lacking. The studies on ribosomal RNA synthesis in *Xenopus* might provide evidence that such phenomena occur. Three classes of ribosomal RNA are found in *Xenopus* oocytes. In the mutant *Xenopus* which does not synthesize r-RNA, a deletion removes the genetic material that defines the structure of two of these classes. However, the third class of r-RNA, for which the genes are not deleted, is likewise not synthesized. Thus it seems possible that, in the mutant, the failure of production of two types of r-RNA, owing to the absence of the genes, somehow feeds back and turns off the genes for the third type. There is ample evidence that there are continuing interactions between the nucleus and cytoplasm of the cells, since gene expression can be controlled or regulated by elements outside the nucleus. A few years ago the possibility was envisioned that one might study the interaction of some "control functions" within differentiated cell combinations by generating hybrid strains from the artificial fusion of embryonic cells.

Techniques have been developed for cell hybridization in which cells of different strains, or even from widely differing species, may be fused. We get a hint of the possibilities that emerge from such techniques in the following experiment. Cells from a black pigmented tumor (a melanoma) growing in a Syrian hamster were fused with unpigmented cells from mice. These cell hybrids were isolated and maintained in active division in cultures for up to 100 cell generations, and have thus far remained unpigmented under conditions in which the melanoma cells become heavily pigmented. Moreover, the activity of one of the key enzymes involved in pigment formation is suppressed. While these experiments have not been carried far enough to enable us to venture an interpretation of the mechanisms involved, they do suggest that in the unpigmented mouse cells the pathways from gene to pigment formation are blocked at some key point. Whatever the blocking mechanism, it suffices, in the cell hybrids, to block pigmentation in the component derived from the hamster tumor cells. Thus a kind of negative control appears to exist in this system.

What unique features of development have we considered thus far? We have seen that gene action in embryogenesis is dependent upon time or stage of development. Individual genes or blocks of genes are expressed as a function of time. Change builds upon change. One group of genes functions during the maturation of the egg, enabling the storage of products that will be used during the first hours after fertilization. During this latter period the egg divides; as it does, DNA is replicated again and again. During these replication steps, does the pattern of "masking" of the DNA change, enabling new genes to be expressed at the end of cleavage? Perhaps we shall have to think increasingly about—and to widen our search for—master genes which control a large domain of other genes.

Complex organs develop, not just cells or tissues. How are these activities coordinated? In part by master genes? As we shall see shortly, cellular interactions play an important role in the establishment of organized structures at the tissue and organ levels, but the possibility that master genes play a role must not be dismissed lightly.

Earlier we referred to the masking and unmasking of genes. If genes are masked, what is the nature of the "masking"? Although we have referred to the location of the genes in chromosomes (see Chapter 4), this discussion has tended to center on DNA alone. Obviously it does not exist alone but in a highly ordered complex with proteins. Do these proteins restrict the activity of DNA? If so, how? It is now possible to isolate complexes of DNA and protein, termed *chromatin*, in which the specific pattern of masking is undisturbed; for example, chromatins isolated from bone marrow and thymus retain biochemical characteristics specific for their origins. Thus, although we habitually equate genes and DNA, we must not forget that the DNA is part of a highly complex organelle. Basic studies of chromosome structure during development badly need to be refined and extended.

Molecular and Cellular Interactions in Development

We have considered the factors controlling the synthesis of nucleic acids and proteins. But cells are more than solutions of nucleic acids, proteins, and the other molecules of which they are composed. These constituents exist in ordered, regular configurations. Thus we may inquire, what factors determine the shape of a cell and the distribution of the organelles within it?

By now the patient reader will be familiar with the principle of self-assembly, a powerful guide to the understanding of biological processes, which has been shown to operate at increasingly complex levels, a few of which may be recalled. These include the spontaneous aggregation of two α and two β chains to form the tetrameric hemoglobin molecule; the spontaneous aggregation of 12 molecules of pyruvic decarboxylase, 6 molecules of dihydrolipoyl dehydrogenase and 24 molecules of a transacetylase, each with its own coenzyme, to form a "supermolecule" of molecular weight 5,000,000, superbly organized to accomplish the metabolism of pyruvic acid; the combination of three filamentous strands to form tropocollagen fibrils which then align side by side, and in register, to form tough fibers; the spontaneous reassembly of the DNA, protein coat, base plate, and fibrils to form a bacteriophage; the assembly of filamentous proteins to form cilia and flagella; and the yet more complex self-assemblage which leads to subcellular organelles. We are inclined to believe that similar self-ordering processes may play a large role in the organization of the myriad molecules that constitute a cell, but we have only begun to search for ways of exploring the molecular basis of the shape and polarity of individual cells. Are such processes involved in the formation of the chromosomes? Of mitochondria, the "power plants" of cells? Of cilia and flagella?

A form of self-assembly is also apparent at a higher level of organization, in the aggregation of cells to form tissues. When an organism containing several tissue types is experimentally dissociated into a mixture of individual cells, these cells can often reassemble into a pattern resembling that which they had in the original organ. The stability of cells in the embryo reflects both the properties of the cells themselves and the stability of their environment. During development, altered cell arrangements provide a continuously changing environment. Cells impinge upon and influence each other within that environment. We are just beginning to perceive the nature of those influences. Some may be diffusible, humoral influences. Others may require local specializations of the membrane at the site of cell-to-cell contact. The recent discovery that electrical communication between cells is correlated with some of these specializations suggests that junctional connections may be involved in the exchange of signals between cells.

Some of the principal features (and difficulties) in the study of cellular interactions are illustrated in contemporary research on the development of muscle, which is examined in the following section.

Cellular Interactions in Developing Muscle

During the earliest stages of development, changes may occur synchronously in all of the cells of the embryo irrespective of their eventual differentiation. At successively later stages, however, cells become progressively more divergent in their properties. During these phases we must focus our attention upon specific embryonic cell types. In what has been called "an astonishing stride forward in the history of biology," over fifty years ago Ross G. Harrison developed a new technique of tremendous power, that of tissue culture, establishing that cells could be grown outside the body. Only recently have techniques been refined to permit the derivation of *clones,* populations of cells derived by division from a single isolated tissue cell. However, most "established" strains of cells isolated originally from animal tissues and maintained continuously in culture are unsuitable for studies of cellular differentiation, since such cell strains rarely bear even the most tenuous resemblance to the major cell type of the tissue of origin. Such populations, during the course of their cultivation, lose the tissue-specific properties which characterize the cells of the original tissue. In order to study tissue-specific properties, and the manner in which they are acquired, it is necessary to apply cloning techniques to newly isolated embryonic cells. This goal was first achieved in studies of the growth and differentiation of embryonic skeletal muscle cells.

Early in the development of tissue culture as a research tool, Margaret and Warren Lewis demonstrated that fragments of embryonic chick skeletal muscle, embedded in clotted plasma, not only grow but form striated muscle. It is now clear that such cells develop equally well when grown by newer methods of cell culture in which the tissue is first enzymatically dissociated into its component cells. Cell suspensions prepared from the leg muscle of 12-day-old chick embryos attach to the bottom of the culture chamber, grow, and form a continuous sheet of cells. However, as the cell layer approaches confluency, large numbers of long fibers appear, which within a few days begin to contract spontaneously. The contractions suggest that the muscle cells have differentiated, but conclusive evidence is provided by the presence in the elongated cells of the cross-striated pattern and the contractile proteins typical of muscle. Thus embryonic muscle cells grown in cultures of randomly distributed individual cells are still capable of differentiating into structurally and functionally recognizable units.

Can a single cell give rise to a colony? By physically isolating a single primitive muscle cell and culturing it in a small glass cylinder, under conditions that exclude contact with any other cell, it was proved that the single cell can produce a colony of differentiated muscle.

During the first four days of culture, such cells divide every twelve to eighteen hours, producing small colonies of roughly fifty cells. The first indication of further differentiation is observed on the fifth or sixth day of culture, when the cells fuse to form multinuclear "myotubes." At successively later stages these multinuclear myotubes increase in length and number until by the end of the second week they form a colony of interlaced fiberlike cells. These colonies, which measure several millimeters in diameter, are apparent to the naked eye when appropriately stained. Not all of the single cells fuse, however; even at the end of the second week some remain, and continue to divide. However, the abrupt appearance of multinucleated myotubes is paralleled by an equally abrupt drop in the overall rate of proliferation. The nuclei in the developing myotubes no longer divide.

Muscle tissue contains two major cell types, the muscle cell itself and the fibroblast, which lays down the connective tissue framework of the organ. Mass cultures prepared by disaggregating embryonic muscle contain both cell types. Can one type be grown in the absence of the other?

It has long been known that fibroblastic cells can be grown clonally, and we have just noted that clones of muscle cells have been developed, suggesting that they do not require an interaction with fibroblasts. However, to clone muscle cells successfully, a "conditioned" medium had to be used initially — that is to say, a medium recovered from large cultures containing muscle fibroblasts was reutilized to grow clones from myoblasts. The medium appears to be altered by the activities of the cells themselves, making it more suitable for supporting muscle differentiation.

What is the nature of the conditioning process? It now appears that the fibroblastic cells secrete collagen which coats the surface of the culture dish, thereby enhancing muscle formation. At least, the conditioned medium may be replaced by spreading a thin layer of purified collagen on the surface of the vessel in which myoblasts are cloned. Whether collagen plays this role in normal development of muscle is yet to be determined.

Encouraged by the successful cloning of skeletal muscle, other workers are extending this approach to several other differentiated cell types of the chick embryo. Cardiac muscle, retinal pigment cells, and cartilage cells have also been cloned and subcloned, showing that these differentiated phenotypes are stably inherited through many generations. Each of these cell types has clearly recognizable features which permit ready identification of differentiated clonal type. It is important to realize that cells are sufficiently fastidious in their requirements that the techniques for cloning one type of cell may not lend themselves readily to other types. For example, until recently, the methods for clonally cultivating the differentiating cells of birds had not been applied effectively to mammalian cells. However, the past year has been marked not only by the successful cloning of differentiated rat liver cells but by the demonstration that they can be hybridized with established cell lines. Liver cells are especially intriguing because they are among the most complex in the diversity of their known biochemical functions. Does each liver cell make a large number of specific proteins — serum proteins like albumin, as well as enzymes? Or is the liver composed of a mosaic of cells, each pursuing one or a few specialized functions? It should now be possible to answer these questions.

Certain differentiating cells can divide and yet express their differentiation at the same time. We wish to emphasize this point: differentiation and division are not antithetical. Retinal pigment cells have been grown as clones from single cells while retaining their pigmentation and epithelial morphology. These cells have been subcloned six times, amounting to over 50 cell divisions, and have remained pigmented. Cartilage cells have been shown to retain their differentiated phenotype through at least 40 to 50 cell generations.

Many tissues go through a period of rapid cell division prior to specialization. Earlier observers of the formation of cartilage, muscle, and lens fibers, for example, had stressed the "mutual exclusivity" of DNA synthesis and differentiation. Instead of emphasizing "mutual exclusivity," however, we would stress the possibility that, in some cells at least, new transcription may *depend upon* an immediately preceding DNA replication. Among the several lines of evidence that might be brought to bear on this problem, none is more pertinent than that being derived from studies of cell transformations induced by viruses. This evidence can be summarized very briefly once the background of the work is made clear. Although the pioneering studies of Peyton Rous — on the chicken tumor that bears his name (Rous sarcoma) — established the role of a virus in causing a tumor, the full impact of the finding was felt only within the past decade when increasing numbers of virus-induced tumors came to light. During the same period, it was established that viruses could transform cells in culture. For example, if a piece of human skin is cultured, fibroblasts derived from it outgrow all other cells and soon one has a homogeneous fibroblastic culture. If the culture is inoculated with a tumor virus, transformed cells appear. The growth properties of these cells are greatly altered, and in particular they now proliferate rapidly. There is a loss of orientation of the cells; the transformed cells can produce tumors when returned to animals, and whereas normal cells synthesize abundant collagen and hyaluronic acid, the transformed cells synthesize very little. New tumor-specific products are made in transformed cells; their synthesis is permanent. These products are specific for the virus (they are the same molecules regardless of species of the host), but they are not components of the viral particle. Nongrowing cells are not generally susceptible to virally induced tumor formation, whereas rapidly growing cells and young animals are more susceptible.

It is now clear that one of the first critical steps in the production of such a tumor is the synthesis of cellular DNA. That is, the tumor virus first induces DNA synthesis, and most of the DNA made is of the type produced by the cell, not the virus. In fact, the Rous sarcoma virus is capable of initiating the incorporation of thymidine, a DNA building block, into mature muscle fibers in culture, fibers in which, as we have already remarked, DNA synthesis has normally stopped. Thus this virus does infect a nongrowing cell population, and in a sense restores some of the abilities associated with proliferation.

The full impact of these new findings is yet to be felt, but they do further strengthen the argument that for a major new differentiation or transformation, the cellular genome must be replicated, in whole or in part. In the process, new genes must be activated, or old ones reactivated, allowing the change in direction.

We have been emphasizing the relations of DNA synthesis, cell division and differentiation. Surely elucidation of the manner in which the cell life cycle is controlled will lead to a fuller understanding of the mechanisms of differentiation. Thus far, we have been able to see the relations between DNA synthesis and differentiation only in bold outline. As discussed in Chapter 4, we urgently require an intimate knowledge of the factors regulating cell division.

In concluding this section, we return to one of the questions that lie at the very heart of developmental biology: the nature of cellular interactions. Our example, muscle formation, illustrates two of the major problems that confront us. One is evident in the interactions of myoblasts among themselves, and the second in the interactions of myoblasts with other cells, notably fibroblasts.

The fusion of myoblasts to form a multinucleated myotube exemplifies, albeit in a specialized form, the surface interactions of cells. The origin of skeletal muscle by the fusion of myoblasts is not an artifact observed in culture, for crucial evidence has been presented recently that this process does occur in the intact animal. This evidence is sufficiently striking, and the method offers so much promise, that it should be introduced here.

It is possible to create in the laboratory a new kind of mouse, a mosaic of two discrete strains. The eggs of two distinct strains of normal mice are fertilized and allowed to begin dividing. Cells from these cleaving eggs are aggregated in culture, so that cells of the two strains are mixed, and the composites are then transferred to the uterus of a foster mother for further development. Hundreds of such mosaic embryos have survived as healthy adults. Here then is an ideal situation in which to test the hypothesis that the normal development of muscle involves fusion just as it does in culture. Earlier we recalled the fact that many enzymes are built of subunits. We can now put that information to immediate use. The two strains of mice used in the experiment contain clearly different forms of a specific enzyme, an enzyme known to be made up of subunits. If muscle fibers are made by fusion, then in the mosaic animals myoblasts of both "parental" strains should contribute to the muscle fiber. Thus a myotube should contain two kinds of nuclei in a common cytoplasm. Since it is the cytoplasm in which the polymerization of enzyme subunits occurs, we should expect to find three kinds of enzyme molecules in a myotube formed by fusion: enzymes of each original type, and "hybrid" enzyme built by combining subunits from the two strains. And that is exactly what is found (Fig. 6-1).

But, returning to our second problem, what mechanisms ensure that myoblasts normally recognize, and fuse with, myoblasts and not other

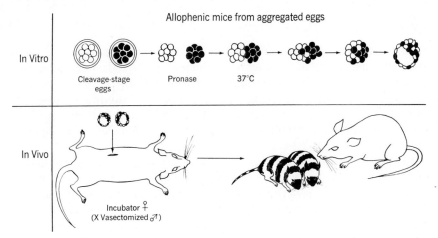

Figure 6-1. Diagram of the experimental procedures for producing mosaic mice. (From B. Mintz, Proc. Nat. Acad. Sci. *58*:345, 1967)

kinds of cells? How do migrating cells come to take up their ultimate positions? What are the properties of cell surfaces that ensure the orderly arrangements of cells within tissues? And how is it that certain types of cells, for example, lymphocytes, have the capacity not only to recognize cells from other strains or species of animals but to inhibit them? A detailed knowledge of the cell surface is badly needed.

As we have seen, recent experiments show that, at least in culture, the development of myoblasts is facilitated if they are allowed to interact with fibroblasts or with collagen, a product of fibroblasts. We do not know whether this particular interaction is required for muscle formation in the embryo. However, most students of development would be surprised if muscle formation occurred in the total absence of interaction with other cell types, for such interactions are one of the hallmarks of animal development. The initial steps in the organization of the nervous system, the formation of the lens of the eye, of the limb, of the exocrine pancreas and salivary glands, of the kidney and liver, all involve such interactions, in which one tissue directly influences the development of its immediate neighbor. A number of these inductive interactions are reciprocal. We know, from experiments in which membranes containing filters of known porosities are interposed between the tissue interactants, that many of these inductive interactions require the passage from one tissue to the other of a chemical substance. But of the nature of this substance, where it is produced and how it is received, we know very little. A sustained attack on this problem, one of the more difficult and fundamental in all biology, is essential in the coming decade.

Plants and the Tumor Problem.

In the similarity between crown gall, a plant disease, and cancer lies a striking illustration that research on almost any organism can have surprising relevance to human problems. It would, of course, be misleading to suggest that work with plant tissues is likely to lead directly to a cure or control for cancer, but such work has contributed to that aim by increasing our understanding of the origin and maintenance of tumors and neoplasms.

Clusters of cells that show disorganized and abnormally rapid— neoplastic or tumorous—growth can be readily induced in many plants by the crown-gall bacterium. Initially, wounded parts of the plant are infected with the bacterium, and the abnormal growth arises from the region of the wound. The induction takes place over a period of days and may be stopped at any time by a heat treatment which stops the growth of the bacteria but not plant tissue. The initiation of the tumorous state begins only at the time the cells adjacent to the wound start to divide in the normal process of healing the wound. Once this cell division process has begun, even longer periods of exposure give rise to tissues showing more and more rapid tumorous growth. One can thus obtain a gradient of response to the same inducing agent.

The exact nature of the inducing agent is unknown. It may be a product of the bacterium's metabolism or may be related to viral particles carried by it. In any event, the change it induces in the host tissue can be studied through an evaluation of the nutritional requirements of the tumors showing various degrees of response.

The most rapidly growing tumors (subject to the inducing agent for the longest periods) have a remarkable degree of nutritional independence. They can grow on a simple medium of salts and sucrose that will not support development of normal tissues. Under such conditions these tissues display organized growth indefinitely, even in the absence of the bacterium. The normal tissue, on the other hand, requires seven distinct kinds of organic chemical supplement to grow at a similar rate. Going up the gradient from normal to ever more rapidly growing tumor cultures, one finds fewer and fewer of these supplements required. It thus appears that the cells of the normal plant are usually slow-growing and organized, at least in part, because certain chemicals essential for division are neither made by the cells themselves nor provided for them by the activities of other regions of the plant. This stable condition is ended by tumor induction, which apparently confers the ability to synthesize many substances (Fig. 6-2).

Further biochemical study of the variety of new compounds ap-

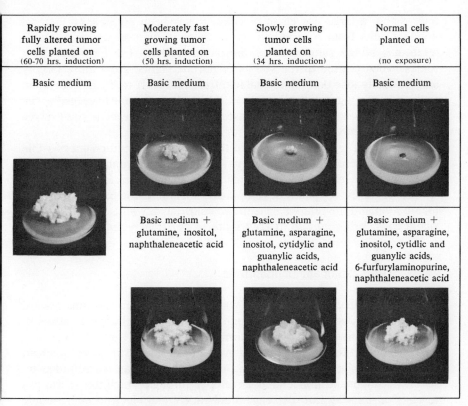

Rapidly growing fully altered tumor cells planted on (60-70 hrs. induction)	Moderately fast growing tumor cells planted on (50 hrs. induction)	Slowly growing tumor cells planted on (34 hrs. induction)	Normal cells planted on (no exposure)
Basic medium	Basic medium	Basic medium	Basic medium
	Basic medium + glutamine, inositol, naphthaleneacetic acid	Basic medium + glutamine, asparagine, inositol, cytidylic and guanylic acids, naphthaleneacetic acid	Basic medium + glutamine, asparagine, inositol, cytidlic and guanylic acids, 6-furfurylaminopurine, naphthaleneacetic acid

Figure 6-2. Types of crown gall tumor tissue formed following different periods of induction. (From A. C. Braun, Proc. Nat. Acad. Sci. *44*:344, 1958. Photograph by J. A. Carlile.)

parently produced by tumorous cells reveals that the enzymes involved in their synthesis have specific ionic requirements for proper function. This directs attention to the possibility that induction influences the ion-uptake machinery of the cells (most probably located in the cell membrane) and thereby indirectly influences metabolism toward the production of the nutritional factors needed for growth. Thus, in the course of evolution, higher plants have developed a set of specialized and highly regulated metabolic pathways. After tumor induction, controls are lost, and the cells appear to revert to a more primitive pattern.

A teratoma differs from a tumor in being more organized, with many differentiated cell types and even recognizable organs. Abnormality is still evident in the chaotic arrangement of these more or less normal parts. It has been shown in plant material that this trait is diagnostic of the individual cells of the teratoma, rather than some feature perpetuated only within a large aggregate of cells. It has been possible to take individual cells from a teratoma, grow them in culture, and reestablish teratomas of the same type as the parent culture. Further, such teratomas, when grafted to the shoots of normal plants, grow more rapidly and gradually lose their abnormal features and revert to the normal state. It has been suggested that some self-replicating particle inside the teratoma cells is unable to increase as rapidly as the cells themselves and thus is diluted out during the rapid cell division.

Therefore at least two aspects of the cancerous condition—a possible alteration in membrane function and the role of a self-replicating entity— can be studied effectively in plants. It is to be expected that several special features of plant development, including the absence of cell locomotion and the relative ease in the culturing of whole organisms from single cells, will continue to contribute to our understanding of cancer.

Fertilization and Implantation

The penetration of eggs by sperm was observed for the first time toward the end of the last century. Although in recent years the mechanisms of sperm entry have been partly clarified, particularly through extensive analysis of fertilization in marine invertebrates, we still have much to learn. Most animal eggs, including the human egg, are surrounded by several cellular and noncellular envelopes through which the sperm has to pass on its way into the egg. Biochemical and electron microscopic investigations have shown that this passage is made possible through the activity of material contained in a specialized structure of the sperm head, the acrosome. In a marine worm, for example, where the mechanism is particularly well known, the acrosome is "activated" upon contact between sperm and egg envelopes. Its contents then digest a canal through the egg envelope, providing a passage for the sperm. The agents that perform this digestion have been isolated from the sperm of mussels and worms, among other animal forms. Although there is some evidence for the existence of an enzyme with a similar function in mammals, it is not yet entirely convincing, and the rate of penetration allows doubt that a digestive process is the necessary and sufficient mechanism (Fig. 6-3).

Next, the plasma membranes that surround both egg and sperm fuse. This process has been studied in numerous electron microscopic investigations of sequential events in fertilization, again particularly well in marine invertebrates. It results in true cytoplasmic fusion of the two cells. The sperm nucleus, now inside the egg, moves toward the egg

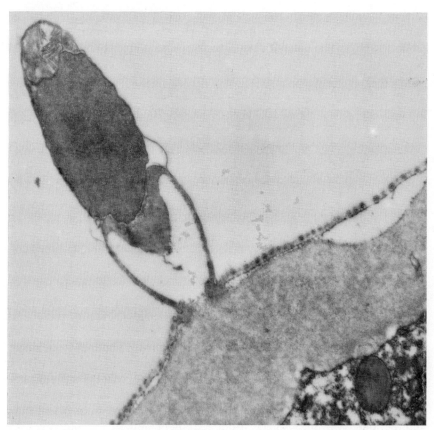

Figure 6-3. Electron micrograph of initial contact of sperm and egg membranes. Sperm plasma membrane meets egg envelope. Egg plasma membrane is still separated from sperm by egg envelope. ×36,000. (From A. L. and L. H. Colwin, *Cellular Membranes in Development*. © by Academic Press, Inc.)

nucleus, which also migrates to meet it. When nuclear fusion is accomplished, development of the fertilized egg, or zygote, is initiated.

While the mechanisms of sperm entry are fairly well understood, knowledge of a number of equally important aspects of fertilization is largely lacking. One of the most fascinating unsolved problems is the selectivity of fertilization. Sperm do not penetrate the eggs of all species indiscriminately. The membranes of gametes have unique properties which permit their fusion with each other but do not allow them to fuse with most other cells. The same or related properties may also be responsible for the high degree of specificity of fertilization. Sperm-egg interaction usually is restricted to the gametes of a given species; hybrid fertilization does not ordinarily occur. However, hybrid crosses fail for other reasons: The behavior patterns of species vary, so that mating may not occur. Or individuals of different species may mate, and the development may actually be initiated only to fail because of a chromosomal mismatch. Lastly, even within the same species, the unique properties of egg surfaces largely prevent entrance of additional spermatozoa once the first sperm has entered.

We have been discussing the mechanisms of sperm *entry*. But how does a sperm activate an egg? How is fertilization actually accomplished? At the molecular level, what are the first events that set the machinery for development in motion? Fundamental studies of these questions are being carried out using the eggs of marine invertebrates, for example, sea urchins. In these forms, as in several others that have been studied, the unfertilized egg contains not only large numbers of ribosomes but messengers (m-RNA) as well. However, this unfertilized egg engages in protein synthesis only at a very low level. The evidence, thus far, is interpreted as indicating that the messengers are stored in an inactive form. One of the primary, if not the most fundamental, roles of the sperm is to "activate" or release those stored messengers. Most of the events of early development appear to be maternally controlled; the genes of the maturing ovum, within the mother, act to provide both the machinery and genetic information needed for early embryogenesis. Accordingly, it appears that most of the program for early development is stored in the egg before fertilization. Thus there is a block to translation in the unfertilized egg—a block at the level of m-RNA and ribosomes and their interaction. New messengers, produced under direction of the new total embryonic genome, come into play only gradually. Thus the information for early embryogenesis comes from two sources: a program stored in the egg for a long time, and a program under the immediate control of those genes activated at fertilization, and thereafter.

After fertilization the mammalian embryo presents a special set of problems. It has, after all, a special relationship with its uterine environment. For several years now, investigators have sought ways of applying the techniques of molecular genetics to mammalian embryos, detached from the maternal environment and "living free" in culture. The idea has been popular for years—one hardly need stress either the light or the serious side of this part of the "Brave New World" theme. But it must be emphasized that acquisition of the ability to cultivate a mammalian egg under rigorously defined conditions straight through from fertilization to at least the time of implantation would have important consequences for fundamental research and, perhaps, for the future of our species. Techniques now being developed for the cultivation of mammalian embryos are providing the foundation for what should be an effective experimental approach to the study of the preimplantational stages of pregnancy in the mammal.

The fertilized mouse egg, for example, may be cultured to the early two-cell stage in a simple, chemically defined medium and from the late two-cell to the blastocyst stage, at which it normally implants, under similar conditions. However, the zygote (the fertilized egg) will not develop in culture straight through to the blastocyst unless it is exposed to the environment of the oviduct for a short period of time between the first and second cleavage divisions. Thus some event or molecular species peculiar to the oviduct plays an essential but still undefined role during early development.

The first cleavage division in culture requires that certain specific compounds which participate in energy metabolism, pyruvate or oxalo-acetate, be present in the basal medium. Cleavage will not occur with other common substrates such as glucose or lactate or in the absence of an energy source. If follicular cells (which surround the egg in the ovary) are placed in the medium with one-cell embryos, however, the first cleavage division does occur when lactate or glucose are present instead. Such evidence indicates that the follicular cells are able to metabolize these substrates and provide the fertilized egg with the necessary substrate to provide energy for cleavage. In addition, there is now evidence that utilizable energy sources, such as pyruvate, are secreted by the oviduct. Thus, the environment of the oviduct plays a vital role in providing the necessary energy requirements for the early stages of development in the mouse (Fig. 6-4).

After fertilization in the upper reaches of the oviduct, there is a delay before transport to the uterus begins. During this time cleavage begins, and continues as the dividing egg makes its way to the uterus. Transport itself requires at least a day. In many mammals the passage is completed in three to three and a half days after ovulation. The cleaving egg is propelled by muscular action of the oviduct and uterus, and the rate of propulsion is influenced by maternal hormones. Within the human uterus, the egg usually attaches in a restricted region, suggesting that there are mechanisms that influence its location. For example, within the rabbit uterus (which consists of two, long, tubular "horns") a solitary egg usually lodges near the midpoint of the horn containing it, whereas two or more eggs become equidistantly spaced along the horn. From each end of the horn and wherever it becomes distended by a growing egg within it, propulsive contractions arise and are propagated in each available direction. The contractions are believed to "milk" the eggs along

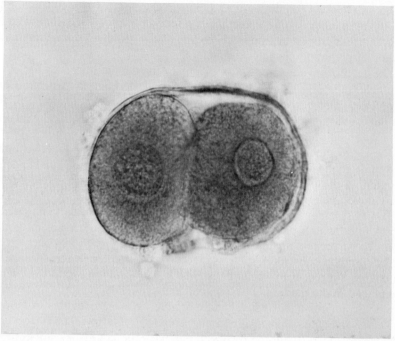

Figure 6-4. The human embryo at the 2-cell stage. (Courtesy the Carnegie Institution of Washington)

the uterine horn with the ultimate result that each egg has caused its neighbors to be repelled to a maximum, and consequently equal, distance.

But what "turns off" the transport mechanism? Experiments suggest that the expansion of the egg, which stimulated the spacing mechanism, simply continues and stops it. The expansion of the rabbit egg continues even after it comes to rest, and one wall of the uterus balloons out to accommodate it. Since it is always the same wall (the thinnest and free wall, farthest from the supporting structures of the uterus), one may suspect that the ballooning out has something to do with the eggs always attaching to that same wall of the uterus. Using the technique of looking into the uterus through a window and manipulating the egg inside, one gains the impression that the egg is grasped within the ballooned-out part of the uterus, moved up and down, and is thereby denied continued contact with the other walls of the uterus.

Not only is the privileged geographic region or wall of the uterus consistent for each mammalian species, but it is always the same pole of the egg that attaches there, the polarity of the egg becoming manifest when some of its cells form the embryo proper. The remaining cells of the mammalian egg provide for its protection and nourishment in various ways, including attachment to the uterus—a step of possible practical importance, since about half of human conceptuses fail to survive it. The normal development of that distinctly mammalian structure, the placenta, presents a number of paradoxes that invite exploration. It begins as an invasion through maternal tissues toward and around maternal blood vessels, but it is soon stopped. It joins two genetically different organisms, mother and fetus, providing physiological exchange between them (Fig. 6-5).

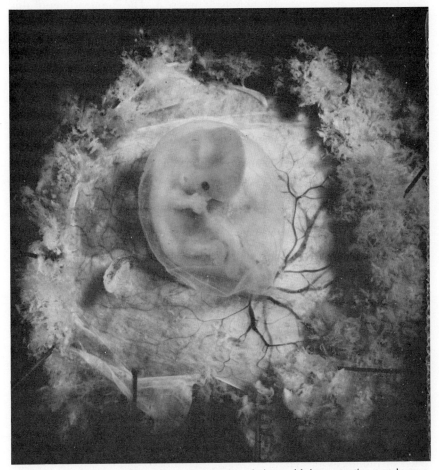

Figure 6-5. A 39-day human embryo showing its relations with its protective membranes. (Courtesy the Carnegie Institution of Washington)

In the genetic sense, the fetus is a homograft or foreign transplant; yet it is privileged to succeed. While it is true that we do not fully grasp the mechanisms underlying the rejection or survival of any transplanted organ, the "fetus as homograft" poses a set of special problems, whose eventual solution may contribute importantly to our understanding of organ transplantation as a whole.

Neurogenesis

The organization and function of the brain, and the manner in which these develop, are attracting ever increasing interest. The implications of this interest for better understanding of the human mind and of human behavior constitute one of the most exciting promises of science in this century. The questions being investigated are old: What is learning? Memory? Do we inherit these abilities? If so, how? Does memory depend on changes in the circuits of the brain? On changes in cellular chemistry? On changes in the properties of key molecules? How are the brain circuits established initially? How do they work? How are they modified by drugs?

The questions are old. But the optimistic hopes for really profound insights are new. The investigator of nervous functions has at his disposal an ever improving technology, the new optimism of molecular biology, and renewed confidence of biologists generally that the most complex and intricate phenomena of nature may continue to yield to their efforts.

Broadly interdisciplinary approaches now characterize investigations of the nervous system, some of which are highly analytical, component-oriented, while others stress the behavior of the system as a whole. The development of the nervous system has as yet been assayed only in a preliminary manner. There are several reasons why relatively few embryologists have attended to the nervous system, the extreme complexity of the final product being the most obvious. But those studies that have been undertaken have already produced some important insights and generalizations.

The search for the mechanisms that govern the construction of the nervous system during development will inevitably lead to more penetrating analyses of the development of function in this complex organ system. Developmental neuropharmacology, a field of inquiry just gathering momentum, will reveal the transient and permanent effects of each of hundreds of agents to which the embryo can be exposed at one or another stage in its development. At a still more complex level, the development of behavior patterns will be analyzed. This should reveal the sequence and patterns of emergence of behavior at all levels of complexity from neuromuscular activity to learning. It should also reveal to what extent we can predict or control the subsequent behavioral organization of an individual organism by elective input at specific stages during its maturation.

As is true of other organs and organ systems, the nervous system has its developmental origin in the interactions of embryonic cells and tissues. Through these interactions, some cells on the surface of the early embryo are induced to organize themselves into a thickened plate, which rolls into a tube and sinks beneath the surface. From this tube and from associated cellular masses, the entire nervous system arises. The essential events during this key phase of development involve the individual cells comprising the early rudiments of the nervous system. These cells typically spin out elongated cytoplasmic strands that become the adult nerve fibers. Before the embryonic nerve cells first send out their processes toward the periphery or to some station within the nerve centers, four interrelated events may be discerned: cell divisions; migrations of cells; changes in the shape, size, and content of individual cells; and the death and disappearance of already partly differentiated cells. Occurring in closely timed and precisely interlocking patterns, these events produce all the major features that finally characterize the adult nervous system — e.g., a recognizable neural axis with appropriately segregated parts, rudiments of cranial and spinal nerves, enlargements, foldings, and outpocketings that already foretell both the final gross form and the inner detail of localized cell groupings. The key point is that the final unity emerges from the coordinated activity of thousands of individual cells, each engaging in one or more of the four activities mentioned, each behaving as if it knew its place in the final structure, yet each subordinating itself to that structure.

Just as these developmental events are to be understood in cellular terms, so the function of the completed nervous system demands expression in the same terms. The human brain and spinal cord consist of billions of cells, all arranged in an orderly manner with precise interconnections, both structural and functional. Communication among nerve cells depends, of course, on the passage of nerve impulses. These arise in individual cells and are effectively transferred from cell to cell either by one cell directly exciting another or by an intermediate step involving a chemical transmitter. Small groups, or very large numbers, of nerve cells are thus brought into activity in highly selective patterns. Out of this complex of neural events emerges the coordinated product we call behavior.

In the early embryo, the young neurons develop sharp affinities and disaffinities for one another and for peripheral tissues. They reveal these properties both by entering selectively into specific cellular associations that become the interknit pathways and centers of the adult nervous system, and by selectively reestablishing some of these associations during nerve regeneration. The capacity of developing cells generally to enter complementary groupings lies at the basis of essentially all embryonic events at cellular and higher levels. The origin of these abilities and their nature are largely unknown.

There is increasing evidence that the developing nervous system plays an essential role in the development of a large number of organs. This role may be essentially trophic, as in the maintenance of the body musculature; cutting off the nerve supply to a skeletal muscle will cause it to wither. Frequently, the influence is more specific. Subtle details of muscle cell structure are apparently determined by the particular nerves that enter the muscle. The functional properties of sensory endings like taste buds are modified according the the specific neurons that innervate them.

Such influences on peripheral tissues appear to begin as soon as outgrowing nerve fibers reach them early in development. The question arises whether the periphery, in turn, exerts any influence in reverse on the nerve fibers that reach it. Are the nerve fibers that grow into a particular muscle already different from nerve fibers entering other muscles? Do they become different only after they are in the muscle? Do axons destined to carry sensory impulses from the skin "know" in advance the local area of skin they must innervate? Or do they enter the skin more or less at random, then in effect "learn" where they are? Efforts to answer such questions have shown that peripheral tissues exert highly specific influences on their nerve fibers. As a consequence, previously indifferent nerve fibers acquire properties reflecting the precise zones in which they terminate. The fibers become specialized, each acquiring its own particular "local sign."

In support of these general statements, consider the consequences of anatomically disarranging the normal interrelations between sensory nerve fibers and the skin. If this is carried out in a suitable animal, e.g., the frog, at a sufficiently early stage of larval life so that local sign properties have not already been stamped permanently on the neurons, the latter will acquire new properties in accordance with their new connections. A simple but instructive example, which may turn out to be much more complicated, is produced by rotating a large patch of flank skin in a frog tadpole. Turned through 180° and then allowed to heal in their new orientation, such skin patches become innervated again by the regeneration of sensory axons severed during the operation. But nerve fibers that once entered the flank skin near the back (dorsal) are now necessarily led into flank skin regions nearer the belly (ventral), and vice versa. Remarkably, residence in their new environments apparently imposes new properties on the regenerated neurons. Originally ventral axons now innervating dorsal skin acquire dorsal properties and presumably realign their interconnections with other neurons of the spinal cord. This may be demonstrated in the newly metamorphosed frog by irritating the dorsal past of the rotated piece (now, of course, lying ventrally). The frog's characteristic wiping response to this offending stimulus will usually be misdirected; it will be aimed at the back even though the stimulus was delivered to an anatomically ventral site (Fig. 6–6).

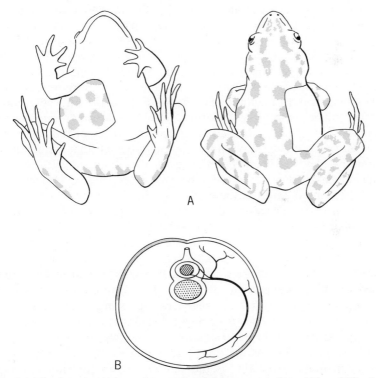

Figure 6-6. The frogs in (A) have skin patches that were rotated in mid-larval life. As the diagram in (B) suggests, the operation severed the sensory nerves to the skin. During healing the nerves regenerated into "foreign" skin. Stimulation of the rotated skin in adult life produced functionally inappropriate responses as explained in the text. (From M. V. Edds, Jr., "Neuronal Specificity in Neurogenesis," in *The Neurosciences: A Study Program.* © 1967 by The Rockefeller University Press)

A large body of evidence supports the conclusion that muscles confer unique qualities on motor nerve fibers, and sensory endings similarly influence sensory nerve fibers. Appropriate connections with neurons lying within the nerve centers are subsequently established in accordance with these specific properties of the peripheral neurons. That is, in the central nervous system the neurons independently develop specificities complementary to those of peripheral neurons. Highly precise inter-relations are then established between the two systems by selective matching of corresponding cell types. A surprising degree of specificity appears to be involved, extending to the level of the individual neuron in some cases.

Evidence to illustrate the extraordinary degree of this specificity in the case of central neurons may be drawn from the much studied visual system of frogs and salamanders. Well after embryonic development is complete in these amphibians, and the neurons that subserve their vision have long since acquired specific local properties, some of the nerve cells can nevertheless regenerate if their elongate axons are cut. When they do so, they go back to their previous end station. The capacity to regenerate is especially apparent in the neurons of the retina. The axons of these cells run through the optic nerve to the midbrain where, through contacts made with other neurons, impulses arising in response to stimulation by light are passed along to other parts of the brain. If the optic nerve is cut, its nerve fibers regenerate such that retinal neurons become reconnected with the midbrain. In so doing, small areas of the retina no larger than a few cells become selectively reassociated with equally restricted zones of the midbrain.

Strong support for this kind of statement comes from observations of the behavior of frogs or salamanders whose eyes have been surgically rotated through 180° at the same time their optic nerves were cut. When vision is recovered following nerve regeneration, the animal responds normally to the presentation of visual lures in all respects but one: it behaves as though every part of its visual field were upside down. Even more direct evidence that the regenerating axons actually reach their original end stations comes from neurophysiological studies. These show that tiny spots of light used to stimulate small areas of the retina produce recordable electrical changes in discrete zones of the midbrain. A map of this functional projection is the same after regeneration as it is in a normal, intact animal.

Taken altogether then, the evidence supports the view that neuro-genesis depends heavily on those properties of neurons that enable them to enter selectively into functionally critical groupings and intercon-nections. The developmental events are flexible and dynamic rather than static, but a high degree of fixed structural order is attained. The precise basis of all the properties summarized in the term *neuronal specificity* is highly conjectural. Such properties may arise from subtle chemical differentials graded over the surfaces of individual cells. This view, in fact, seems unavoidable. But the real question is what these molecular differences amount to, and how they relate to differential gene activity in the cells that possess them. In this sense, nerve cells—and the problems of neurogenesis generally—take their proper place in the broad spectrum of developmental mysteries.

The Photoperiodic Control of Flowering

The external environment—temperature, chemical composition, radiation, pressure, and so forth—affects many aspects of development. Sometimes the relationship between a particular external factor and development is highly specific, and an apparently trivial change in the environment can trigger whole developmental sequences. Such environmental effects provide means for directing life processes toward useful ends and, in suitable experimental systems, lead also to further knowledge of development. A specific illustration of these generalities is the photoperiodic control of flowering—the fact that, in many plants, the length of the daily exposure to light determines whether flowers and their associated structures can develop, and thus in effect controls sexual reproduction.

Photoperiodic control is often striking. Certain varieties of soybeans, for example, are "short-day plants." They flower only when the daily period of illumination is shorter than a certain number of hours, their "critical daylength." With a plant of this type, field sowings made successively throughout the early part of the season nevertheless all set seed at about the same time in the fall or late summer, after the natural daylength has fallen below the critical value. This happens even though individuals in the various sowings differ immensely in size; in fact, plants of this type kept artificially under continuous light may never flower, even when many feet tall. Conversely, such plants may flower when only a few inches high if grown from seed at short day illumination.

Not all photoperiodic plants are short-day plants—there are long-day plants and other types, as well—but all agree in one respect: flowering depends on particular conditions of light and darkness. Effects of this kind are obviously of practical importance for many industries based on plants. They also suggest a general explanation for the seasonal timing of many events in nature, since daylength changes with the time of year.

In addition, their significance in developmental biology is at least two-fold. First, the ability to turn a particular process — such as flower forma-tion — on or off is valuable in analyzing that process. Second, the very fact of such control suggests that there are probably many other situa-tions in which an elaborate sequence of developmental events may be initiated in a simple way.

A particularly challenging aspect of the photoperiodic control of flowering is known as photoperiodic induction — the fact that, in many plants, the effects of one or a few days' exposure to an appropriate day-length persist long afterward. This is easily studied in a common weed, the cocklebur, a short-day plant. Unable to flower if kept always under continuous light, the cocklebur will do so once exposed to even a single dark period more than nine hours long, even if it is immediately replaced in continuous light. The development of flowers and then seeds started by a single dark period continues for many months thereafter. No anatomical or biochemical test has, as yet, been discovered to distinguish between induced and noninduced plants immediately after the inducing dark period. Yet some basic change has been brought about, some self-maintaining or steady-state condition that governs the entire subsequent development without an additional external stimulus. Obviously, any insight into the nature of this induced state would be valuable.

A second little understood facet of photoperiodism is the translocation of the photoperiodic effect — i.e., its transmission from one part of the plant to another. With many short-day plants, for example, flowering takes place even if *most* of the plant is always under continuous light; it is sufficient to darken a single leaf in such a way that it alone under-goes a short day. One leaf in the appropriate daylength makes the entire plant flower. Indeed, a plant that has never been exposed to the ap-propriate daylength can be made to flower by grafting it to a plant that has been so exposed. The simplest explanation for such results is that a photoperiodic treatment favorable to flowering causes the production of some active material in the treated leaf or leaves. According to this hypothesis, the material then moves in the conducting tissues, even through a graft union, to the growing points of the plant, where it diverts cell development and differentiation from the nonflowering to the flower-ing pattern. To state it in another fashion, such results suggest the existence of a specific plant hormone that causes flowering. Alternative possibilities have also been suggested, particularly since no such hormone has as yet been conclusively isolated and identified. As with photo-periodic induction, additional understanding of the control of develop-ment will necessarily follow from a successful attack on this problem.

Considerably greater progress has been made in the studies of the role of light in the photoperiodic control of flowering. In suitable experimental conditions, flowering can be made to depend on very brief light treatments. For example, a short-day plant that flowers on a schedule composed of 10 hours of light alternating with 14 hours of darkness generally fails to flower if each dark period is interrupted in the middle by only a minute of light. Red light is the most effective region of the spectrum, and the effect of red light—the prevention of flowering, in this example—is annulled if the red exposure is followed quickly enough by a brief exposure to light of a slightly longer wavelength—"far red." Such results suggest the possibility of a single biological pigment which exists in two forms, one form preferentially absorbing red light and the other, far-red, with each form being converted to the other by light absorption. In the last few years, a protein-pigment complex with just these properties has been detected and isolated and named phytochrome. As was predicted from the fact that red and far-red light are known to affect many phases of plant development besides flowering, phytochrome appears to be universal in the higher plants. Its precise biochemical action is still unknown; it has been proposed that the molecule may change its conformation in going from one form to the other as a result of light absorption, and that this change of shape alters its participation in some crucial catalytic role—e.g., as an enzyme or as part of a membrane system. For this reason, phytochrome is now of prime interest not only in plant development but to biophysicists and biochemists as well.

No aspect of the photoperiodic control of flowering is less understood, nor potentially more significant, than the accurate timing involved. Careful experiments show that many photoperiodic plants can distinguish between periods of darkness with lengths differing by 15 minutes or less. Agreement on timing is observed even between plants kept at temperatures sufficiently different to change the rates of all the chemical reactions involved in plant metabolism. Thus the timing system is not a simple temperature dependent metabolic process, but there is little evidence as to what the mechanism might be, instead.

At least two points of general significance for biological research arise from consideration of the specific problems facing investigators of one single type of environmental effect, the photoperiodic control of flowering. In brief, they are the following:

Many of the experimental organisms used are of direct economic importance—soybeans, for instance. However, tactically, specific aspects of these problems are often best attacked in plants that are of little practical importance—cockleburs, in which induction is so persistent; varieties of morning glory, in which flowering hormone movement is easily observed; tiny duckweeds, which can be grown under completely controlled conditions; seedlings germinated in darkness, which have a very high phytochrome content. Full exploration of the field thus requires the use of many organisms, undoubtedly including some so far completely ignored; the same statement is almost surely valid for most areas in the life sciences.

Secondly, much of what seems most remote and specialized in the subject is in fact related directly to processes common to many other living things. On the molecular level, the discovery of phytochrome provides unique material for understanding the relationship between protein structure and function, a relationship of universal biological significance. On the cellular and tissue levels, photoperiodic induction is probably a particular instance of the specialized steady states that underlie many developmental processes, such as tumor formation; the hormonal mechanism proposed for flowering is analogous to mechanisms known in many animals. On the organismal and behavioral levels, photoperiodism regulates many processes besides flowering, nor is it even confined to plants. Day-length determines the reproductive activities of many animals, including mammals, birds, and insects. Though the light in these cases almost certainly acts through pigment systems other than phytochrome, the timing mechanism may indeed be universal, possibly having its basis in the innate rhythmic processes present in all multicellular organisms. Thus, knowledge concerning any of these specific topics can elucidate and be elucidated by research in areas that, at first glance, might appear completely unrelated.

The Interplay of Basic and Applied Research

Control over vital phenomena, particularly in matters of agriculture and medicine, is of major interest to man. Historically, control has been derived from traditional practice, from accidental discovery, and in some cases from the application of theory to a particular problem. The evolution of theory, in turn, has often been set into motion by an effort to explain the effectiveness of certain successful practical measures. Theory and practice continually interact. Within the life sciences medicine has evolved from the application of folk remedies to a point where a semipopular article can be entitled "Biochemistry and the Design of Drugs." Developmental biology has not come that far, but there is reason for optimism. To appreciate this position, one must recognize the importance of a continuing interplay between basic and applied research in developmental biology. As in the foregoing section, the number of examples discussed is limited, but the examples chosen illustrate that the flow of information must be reciprocal.

The Chemical Regulation of Plant Growth. For many years, investigators of the mechanisms of plant growth have studied substances with powerful specific effects on development. Some of these chemicals are naturally occurring, isolated originally from the plants themselves; some are man-made but with structures closely related to those of natural materials; others are quite unlike known plant substances. The use of such chemicals in farming and other activities based on plants has become widespread. Increasingly, particular chemical practices are not only useful, but essential and integral parts of the industries in question.

Synthetic compounds with structures or actions related to those of the auxins, the earliest known group of native growth substances, are useful in both agriculture and vegetation control. For example, the herbicide 2,4-dichlorophenoxyacetic acid (2,4-D) is selective against broad-leaved plants. Thus, it and related compounds are immensely useful in eliminating weeds among grasses, whether in wheat fields or suburban lawns, and in brush control. Such compounds are also valuable in having low toxicity for man, animals, and soil organisms, so that they generally do only what they are intended to do.

Many other growth regulators related to the auxins are in commercial use for purposes as diverse as causing flowering and fruiting, increasing fruit set, preventing fruit drop, thinning fruits, or defoliation. Such effects often make possible the extensive mechanization so important in many farm practices. Mechanical cotton-picking, for example, is vastly improved if the leaves of the plants fall off shortly before harvest. The pineapple industry depends on chemicals to control fruit maturity for the most efficient use of harvesting and packing equipment. The requirement for hand-thinning of fruits for optimum size and quality has been replaced at least in part by suitable sprays.

Plant growth regulators related to the auxins have been known and exploited for some time, and their use is still increasing. Entirely within the past decade, applications have developed from more recent research on two important groups of natural plant growth regulators, the gibberellins and the cytokinins.

Gibberellins applied to developing grapes lead to increased fruit set and looser clusters. The looser clusters are particularly important, for they permit better air circulation and resistance to fungi, better protection by insecticides and other sprays, easier harvesting, and cleaner fruit. Gibberellins have other uses, including that of speeding enzyme production in germinating grain, thereby significantly and profitably reducing malting-time in the brewing industries. Though this process is licensed only for the distilled liquor industry in the United States and not for beer, it is used widely for both in Great Britain and elsewhere.

Synthetic compounds related to the cytokinins are expected to play a valuable role in truck farming. These compounds slow the aging of cut materials by preventing protein destruction. Thus, they strongly enhance the keeping qualities of crops such as broccoli and spinach. Final licensing for widespread commercial use presumably depends on continued evidence of harmlessness or on the use of only naturally occurring cytokinins.

Studies on the accurate inhibition or retardation of various plant processes by completely synthetic chemicals have given rise to numerous applications. Inhibitors of bud growth, such as maleic hydrazide, also find use in the tobacco industry. It prevents the development of "suckers" (lateral branches from the base) after the plants have been topped, thereby facilitating mechanical handling and harvesting of the crop. Growth inhibitors simply prevent growth, but there are also many growth retardants — substances that alter the size and shape of the plants by interfering with stem elongation. These compounds are used to produce shorter, more robust plants, even under adverse conditions, as in the commercial production of pepper and tomato seedlings for later outside planting. For completely unknown reasons, several of these compounds also increase flower production in certain plants, notably azaleas and apples. In the former, at least, this use is already fully commercialized and it may become so in the latter.

The trend in all productive activities in this century is toward automation and accurate programming. This is increasingly possible in industries based on plants largely because of simultaneous and related developments in three fields: farm machinery, plant breeding, and the chemical regulation of plant growth.

Developmental Pharmacology and Toxicology. Pharmacology deals with drugs — drugs as seen by the organic chemist, by the physical chemist, by the biochemist and physiologist concerned with their mechanism of action, and by the physician treating his patient. Toxicology extends these concerns to the adverse effects of drugs on living systems. Recently there have emerged two growing subfields in these age-old subjects: developmental pharmacology and developmental toxicology.

As, at the molecular level, developmental biology and genetics form a continuum, so do developmental pharmacology and pharmacogenetics. These fields are moving, on the one hand, toward recognizing hereditary states in which responses to drugs differ from those usually observed and, on the other hand, toward determining to what extent the embryo, the fetus, and even the newborn animal, especially man, differ from the adult in their sensitivity and responses. At the molecular level, the two approaches hardly differ. An unwanted effect of a drug might be explained by a hereditary deficiency of an enzyme. Agents that produce only transient changes in the adult may permanently alter the animal when they are applied during a critical period in its development. An unexpected effect in a fetus might be explained in a number of ways; for example, an enzyme system present in the adult may not yet have developed, or possibly the development of a given system requires a different set of metabolic pathways than its maintenance and function in the adult. The requirements for making a muscle may be different from those for maintaining it.

A prominent example from the field of pharmacogenetics is the genetically determined sensitivity to the drug succinylcholine, which is used as a relaxant during surgery. Most patients have an enzyme that breaks down the drug, inactivating it, so that the paralysis lasts only an hour. However, some patients have an altered form of the enzyme; hence the drug is not inactivated, and the paralysis extends for ten to twelve hours, during which time artificial respiration may be required. Another example is the genetically determined sensitivity to the antimalarial drug primaquine; those who are affected suffer attacks of hemolysis—the release of hemoglobin from their red blood cells.

Most hazards to the fetus and newborn were discovered only after serious consequences drew attention to a specific drug. The thalidomide tragedy is a notable example. Other examples might be cited, however: When mothers are given coumarins or salicylates late in pregnancy, the blood-clotting mechanism in their newborn infants may be markedly affected, and severe or fatal hemorrhage may result. Infants frequently appear to be unable to tolerate the antibiotic chloramphenicol. The defect seems to lie in the absence or inadequacy of a mechanism for detoxifying and excreting it. Knowledge in these areas is primitive; there is a pressing need for new programs of basic research.

Toxicology, classically, has utilized knowledge of the toxic effects of chemicals in two ways: in preventing poisoning of man and other animals, and in employing *selective* poisoning to eradicate pests. Let us consider the second of these roles.

Modern agriculture requires the use of many chemical agents, including insecticides and rodenticides. The use of pesticides should be always based on selective toxicity, such as the rodenticide Norbormide, which is highly toxic to rats but not to many other species. One approach which appears to offer great promise, not yet fully realized, is the control of a pest by using its own natural products to limit its life cycles, thus preventing reproduction. Because these products are unique, side effects of other organisms are also avoided. For example, the hormones that regulate insect development have great potential for the control of insect pests. As discussed more fully in Chapter 7, on the functions of tissues and organs, it is already possible to prevent insects from reaching adulthood by administering the "juvenile hormone." This treatment leads to the formation of permanent larvae, which never reach the stage of reproductive maturity and therefore cannot produce offspring. Using another hormone, it is possible to force insect larvae into precocious metamorphosis; this latter method of insect control has potential in those cases where insects are harmful pests in their larval stages.

Reproductive Biology. Few areas demonstrate more forcefully the interplay of applied and basic research than does reproductive biology. This area is a fruitful combination of many disciplines, including anatomy, developmental biology, physiology, endocrinology, and biochemistry, and has had a profound impact on our lives.

Elucidation of the animal estrus cycle and its hormonal regulation has revolutionized animal husbandry and has contributed to increases in food production. Artificial insemination and the use of steroid hormones to synchronize estrus cycles of herds of cattle and sheep make it possible to inseminate all on the same day and from the same sire, improving efficiency and the quality of stock.

Normally a cow's or sheep's ovary releases one egg at a time, just as a woman's ovary does. Thus in its lifetime a female of these species may produce a dozen young. But hormones are now available to cause the animal's ovaries to release eggs en masse; these eggs, even 100 from a single female, may be fertilized, using semen from a single bull or ram. The early embryos may be transported, even across the sea to another continent, there to be implanted, each in the uterus of a different "foster mother," where it will undergo normal development. In short, beginning with a few highly selected mothers and even only one pedigreed sire, it is possible to shape the future generations of these animals at will.

As far as we know, there is nothing technically to prevent the application of these techniques to man, though the possibility, of course, raises immense moral and social questions.

It is not too farfetched to envision the day when we will be able to specify the genetic heritage of our children even more precisely. But whose eggs, whose sperm, whose genes will be selected? Who should provide the answer to these awesome questions? These questions will require the best efforts of all thinking men.

As we have seen, mammalian eggs can now be fertilized in vitro; this provides an opportunity to observe fertilization and to study the mechanism of action of agents designed to interfere with it for the purpose of population control. Some may ask whether there is still a need for such studies in the light of the increasing use of both hormones ("The Pill") and intrauterine contraceptive devices (IUCD's), and the announcement of preliminary successes with a postcoital pill. But existing techniques fall short of being completely satisfactory on several grounds.

First, in all these techniques the burden is placed on the woman; it would be desirable, for a number of reasons, to have a method in which the male could also assume responsibility. One promising lead may be provided by electron microscopic studies which have extended our knowledge of the cytological events in sperm formation. It appears that the clone of sperm that emerge from a single primordial spermatogonium remain connected by intercellular bridges during their development, separating only late in the process. Here is a step that might be vulnerable to blocking by a specific pharmacological agent, affording another opportunity for control of conception.

Second, although the use of hormones is a logical extension of basic research, too little is yet known of side effects of these same hormones, and it will be years before they can be fully assessed because some of the suspected consequences may develop only with chronic dosage. Moreover, the use of IUCD's arose almost entirely empirically. Although they are used widely, with substantial success, next to nothing is known about both the mechanism of their action and their side effects, some of which may be troublesome. This question urgently needs attention, and there are enough leads — such as apparently greater effectiveness of the larger designs of IUCD's — to permit rational efforts toward understanding and improved practice.

One additional important reason for continuing to acquire information is that, human nature being what it is, people like to change methods of birth control, even when the particular method being employed is satisfactory. In practice, a variety of methods will be required, since they will serve different psychological needs of the individuals who employ them.

The Interplay of Developmental Biology and Other Disciplines

As we have seen, the problems of development exist on many levels of complexity from the molecular to the evolutionary. Experimental approach to these problems has required a variety of tools and the diverse viewpoints provided by the interplay of various specialized disciplines. We have already emphasized the strength derived from the union of developmental biology with molecular genetics. Let us briefly consider a few additional examples.

One of the most promising is the relationship between developmental biology and virology. It was over fifty years ago that Peyton Rous discovered the tumorigenic virus that bears his name. It is less appreciated, however, that in those studies he used two techniques later to be developed further and exploited by students of development. One was the technique of transplantation of tissue fragments to the extraembryonic membranes of the chick embryo, later used by several generations of embryologists to study the ability of embryonic tissues to differentiate when isolated in a favorable environment well removed from their normal relations with other tissues. The second was the use of enzyme trypsin to liberate cells from clotted plasma on which they were growing, the forerunner of today's techniques of dissociating tissues into their component cells, now widely employed in studies of the manner in which embryonic cells interact in forming their characteristic patterns of tissue architecture.

But if virology contributed those techniques to the study of development, it was an embryologist, Ross Harrison, who provided the method that is widely recognized as one of the principal technical cornerstones of virology, that of tissue culture. Viruses may be now propagated in clonal lines of cells from a variety of sources, normal and abnormal; and clonally derived cells provide the most convenient and reproducible material for studies of the mechanisms of action of viruses in destroying or transforming cells.

Even now, several new developments offer promise of the future. One arises out of an idea already discussed — namely, that in order to transform a cell, a tumor virus must first stimulate the synthesis of the cell's DNA. With increasing numbers of clonal lines of differentiating cells available, it may be possible to determine just when in the life history of a cell it is susceptible to transformation, information that may shed some light on the mechanism of tumorigenesis. Moreover, since susceptibility to a number of animal viruses, apart from those that cause tumors, changes with time during embryonic life, we may learn more about virally induced congenital defects.

There is yet another twist to this particular story — potentially the most profound of all. It is now conceivable that we may use viruses as tools for repairing genetically determined congenital defects. It is known that the papilloma virus, a virus causing tumors in rabbits, induces in its hosts a specific enzyme, a form of the enzyme arginase. It has recently been observed that the blood of many of those men and women who have worked with this virus over the years contains this unusual form of the enzyme. What does this mean? The observation is interpreted as follows: The virus has entered the human hosts, but no overt signs of infection have been noted. However, a part of the viral genome, the part of the DNA encoding for the altered enzyme, has somehow become incorporated into the human cells. Thus this altered form of enzyme is produced throughout the individual's lifetime. It is clearly conceivable, therefore, that we might be able to "tailor" a DNA to fit a set of special circumstances. For example, to a fetus or newborn infant, known to lack a given enzyme, because it lacks the DNA encoding for it, we might add, with the help of a virus, the appropriate segment of DNA. This "ultimate in biological engineering" is not as farfetched as it seemed a scant decade ago.

The transplantation of embryonic tissues provides a starting point for another chain of interactions, those among developmental biology, immunology, transplantation biology (now almost a field in itself), and genetics. Mechanisms of antibody formation and the nature of the response of an animal to a foreign graft are considered in another chapter. However, it is intriguing to contemplate how the *absence* of a reaction was responsible for a series of important discoveries. Adults—goldfish, mice, and men—reject skin or kidney grafts, for example, from all but their identical twins (or members of the same highly inbred "isogenic" strain). Yet there are exceptions to this rule, the most striking being that grafts made between genetically dissimilar embryos succeed. It was the observation that the reactions of transplantation immunity are "missing" in embryos that led to the discoveries of actively acquired tolerance, discoveries that, in turn, fostered a new wave of research in the field. Moreover, it was the observation that chorioallantoic grafts of adult spleen, containing immunologically active cells, have an adverse effect on their embryonic hosts that in large part led to the discovery of the graft-versus-host reaction. And studies of the development of the immune response have helped clarify the role of that long enigmatic organ the thymus, which we now know to be intimately involved in the development of immunological mechanisms.

We may consider also the possibilities arising from studies of the regeneration of limbs and other organs in the lower vertebrates. An adult salamander, for example, can regenerate a lost limb. If nerves are prevented from entering the amputated region, however, the regeneration process fails. This observation in turn gave rise to a further question. In adult frogs, the limb does not regenerate. Could the failure be the consequence of too few nerves? The answer is yes. Augmenting the nerve supply to the amputation stump stimulates regeneration.

How soon will the information we are accumulating on the mechanisms controlling regeneration of limbs and organs in the lower animals enable us to formulate an attack on similar problems in man? This question is but one more among the many problems we can now formulate in meaningful terms. Consider too the opportunities we have to help lift the burden of congenital defects: prenatal diagnosis and therapy of many defects in the fetus increasingly will be possible; surgical procedures, already in use in some primates, will enable the removal of the fetus from the uterus for the correction of defects and its return to complete full-term development. As we learn more about the embryo and its uterine environment, prematurity will be reduced. We will more fully appreciate the impact on the fetus of bacteria and viruses, on the one hand, and of man-made drugs, on the other.

But to visualize the opportunities and to formulate the problems is only the necessary first step. Their solution will inevitably demand a depth and range of knowledge and technical sophistication beyond our present capabilities. The application and use of findings will require the most careful "social engineering" and moral wisdom of which man is capable. And it is likely that the very fact that such questions can be visualized today brands them as among the more conventional. The truly new developments of tomorrow cannot be imagined today.

We believe that this is more than an expression of faith. The approaches that are increasingly characteristic of the field should permit new ideas to be perceived and new syntheses to be effected more readily than before. These considerations should be weighed when we judge how our society shall determine the magnitude and direction of support of developmental biology, indeed of biology as a whole.

Chapter 7

THE FUNCTIONS OF TISSUES AND ORGANS

Tissues and organs of multicellular plants and animals are groups of cells which are specialized to perform some particular function for the benefit of the whole organism. Specialization imposes two requirements: (1) there must be some means of transport of materials between organs, and (2) there must be some way of relaying signals from one organ to another so that their functions may be regulated and integrated.

In higher plants and animals, vascular systems transport materials from one part to another. For example, in plants the products of photosynthesis are carried from leaves to roots, while absorbed nutrients are carried from roots to leaves. Both plants and animals have endocrine systems in which a chemical messenger, or hormone, formed in one organ governs the function of another. Animals have, in addition, a nervous system for quick communication and integration, and its function is, as we shall see, closely intertwined with that of the endocrine system.

This chapter will be concerned with research that is directed at (1) the basic mechanisms by which function is performed and (2) the regulatory mechanisms by which function is integrated. The first entails the reductionist approach, seeking ultimately to understand function in terms of chemistry and physics. The second is the synthetic approach in which parts analyzed by the first process are reassembled until one obtains a coherent view of the function of the whole organism. In actual practice, the two processes are never distinct. If one is studying the reabsorption of sodium by the kidney tubule, the reductionist trail leads to an analysis of the mechanism of active transport such as is described in Chapter 4. But in the course of this analysis one also discovers that the process of

241

active transport by individual cells is carefully regulated for the good of the whole organism.

Classically, students of animal physiology have addressed themselves to such major problems as the operation of the cardiovascular system, the mechanics of pulmonary respiration and its control, the various roles of the nervous system and the mechanism of nerve conduction, digestion and absorption in the gastrointestinal tract, mechanisms for preserving the constancy of the "milieu interieur," the extracellular fluid, including the operation of the kidney, the mode of action of muscle, sensory perception, and the integrative actions of the endocrine glands. Plant physiologists have been concerned with conduction of fluids, electrolytes, and nutrients, absorptive processes in root hairs, and photosynthesis. Somewhat detailed accounts of recent investigations in most of these areas will be found distributed throughout this book. This chapter will not, therefore, attempt a summary of the current state of knowledge in these areas, but rather, our concern will be the manner in which such problems are attacked.

We shall, therefore, illustrate the nature of physiological research by a series of examples. The first group, drawn from plant and animal physiology, illustrate accomplishments in the search for basic mechanisms, but in each instance the problems of control are touched upon. The second series, drawn from plant, insect, and animal endocrinology, illustrate achievements in the study of the processes that regulate function of the organism.

Basic Physiological Mechanisms

Growth of a Grain of Barley

The grain of the barley, as of any other cereal, consists of two main parts, the embryo and the endosperm. The embryo is the future barley plant. It contains a small root that will eventually develop into the root system of the adult plant, a small shoot with a short stem, a few leaves, and the growing point — an undifferentiated tissue that gives rise to more stem and leaves. The embryo is attached to the endosperm by a special structure, probably a modified leaf, a scutellum. The outside of the scutellum is covered with cells that can absorb organic nutrients (Fig. 7-1).

The endosperm is a nutritive tissue. It contains foodstuffs to nourish the young seedling until it is capable of securing its own food supply — organic food by photosynthesis and the necessary minerals by absorption from the soil by the roots. The foodstuffs in the endosperm are present

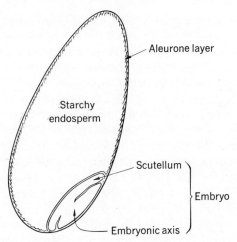

Figure 7-1. Diagram of a husked barley grain in longisection. The size of the embryo (scutellum and embryonic axis) is slightly exaggerated. (Courtesy J. B. Hanson)

in special storage forms, not directly available to the embryo; they must be mobilized by conversion into available materials which are then absorbed through the scutellum. The most abundant storage material is insoluble starch, which must be converted into simple, soluble sugars in order to serve both as an energy source and as raw material for diverse biosyntheses. This process of mobilization begins soon after the grain is allowed to germinate. About two weeks after germination the endosperm is an empty shell, devoid of any useful content and with no further function.

The first great advance in understanding of the mechanism of germination was the discovery, in the nineteenth century, that the interconversions of nutrients in organisms are catalyzed by enzymes. At first it was assumed that the embryo mobilizes the storage food materials by secreting enzymes in the endosperm. The secretion of the enzyme was thought to come from the scutellum, and various enzymes—such as amylases that convert starch to soluble sugar—were detected in the dissolving endosperm. However, the situation is more complex.

The endosperm consists of two morphologically distinct tissues: an inner portion which contains the starch, and a few outer layers, called the aleurone, which are free of starch but contain other materials, particularly proteins. Around 1890 it became clear that the mobilization of the endosperm was dependent on the aleurone. If the aleurone contributes the necessary enzymes rather than the embryo, an endosperm detached from the embryo should undergo the same changes as the endosperm of an intact grain. But this does not happen. Endosperms that are surgically separated from the embryo remain essentially unchanged for periods of time during which, under the same conditions of water and air supply and temperature, the endosperm of an intact seed is totally exhausted. Thus, all three parts (embryo, aleurone, starchy endosperm) must interact if the seed is to germinate.

The clue to the interaction among the parts of the seed was the recent discovery that when an isolated, inactive endosperm is treated with minute quantities of the plant hormone *gibberellin,* the nutrients of the endosperm are mobilized just as they are when the endosperm is attached to the embryo in the intact seed. The enzymes that break down the starch in the endosperm are not present in the aleurone before the gibberellin arrives; they are synthesized by processes initiated by the hormone. Furthermore, the embryo of the dormant barley grain does not contain any gibberellin; synthesis of the hormone begins about 24 hours after the grain has been supplied with water, air, and the right temperature for germination.

Gibberellin is not the only regulatory material released by the embryo. The scutellum in the nongerminated seed consists of rather uniform cells (except the epithelial layer); but shortly after the seed is allowed to germinate, there develop in the scutellum strands of tissue that are adapted for the transport of materials—the vascular strands. This development is also controlled by the embryo, but the control of vascular development in the scutellum and of enzyme formation in the aleurone is exerted by different parts of the embryo. Gibberellin is produced by the stem part of the embryo, the other messenger by the tip portion of its shoot and by its root. This second messenger, whose nature is still unknown, is released ahead of the gibberellin (about 12 hours after the seed has germinated), so that apparently the latter, when released in turn, can make use of the new pathway available for transport.

The picture at present is this: When the seed is allowed to germinate, by hydration, the embryo becomes capable of producing or releasing a messenger which causes vascular differentiation in the scutellum; then the embryo produces another messenger, gibberellin, which moves via those newly formed vascular strands in the scutellum to the aleurone and there causes the synthesis of amylase and other enzymes. The enzymes are released into the starch endosperm, resulting in mobilization of the stored foodstuffs in the latter. The mobilized foodstuffs are translocated to the embryo, via the scutellum and presumably again through the vascular strands formed in the latter in response to the first messenger; they enable the young seedling to grow and to become established.

A number of important questions still remain to be resolved, but the germination of the barley grain is one of the best understood cases of the interaction between organs and tissues in a higher plant and illustrates in a single grain of barley many of the questions and modes of answering questions used in the study of tissue and organ function.

The example points out an important general feature of research on tissue and organ function. The analysis started out with the whole organism, the barley grain. It then proceeded to the interrelation of its different organs and tissues, including structural changes of their cells, and it has finally been concerned with such questions as where and when particular materials—the hormone gibberellin and the enzyme amylase—are synthesized.

The problems of barley germination that are still unsolved reflect this trend even more succinctly. We now understand the overall functions and tasks of the different parts of the embryo. We would like to know how vascular differentiation occurs in the scutellum, how the cells change from ordinary cells into characteristic conductive elements. This is a problem of morphogenesis at the cellular level. We would like to know the nature of the early messenger that regulates the vascular differentiation; would like to know how it acts; and would like to know how gibberellin causes enzyme synthesis in the aleurone cells. The work at the organismal level is largely done; much remains at the cellular and molecular levels.

Incomplete though our knowledge may be, it can be applied to solution of practical problems. Gibberellin is used in the malting of beer. This use is based on the fact that the grain does not start to produce its own gibberellin until a certain time after soaking; production of amylase, which is an essential step in the malting process, is accordingly delayed. If gibberellin is added, amylase production and malting are accelerated with substantial savings for the brewing industry.

There are prospects of more widespread application of this knowledge of plant physiology. To document this, we must add another recently discovered fact. When barley grains are freshly harvested they do not germinate; they are dormant. Dormancy is caused by the presence of another hormone, *abscisin*. Abscisin counteracts the action of gibberellin on the aleurone in that it prevents the synthesis of amylase. It is likely that a balance between gibberellin and abscisin is an important factor in the control of dormancy in plants. In some cases, it is desirable to overcome dormancy and initiate early growth. In others, it can be advantageous to prolong dormancy. Thus, almost every year substantial losses are suffered by fruit growers because late frosts kill the open blossoms of apples, pears, or other fruit. Blossoms in these fruit trees are formed in fall, but remain dormant until spring, and in the dormant condition are not sensitive to freezing. If it were possible to extend the dormancy period until after the hazard of frosts is quite gone, such losses could be avoided. Knowledge of the relations between gibberellin and abscisin suggests that such control of dormancy should certainly be possible.

Contractile Tissues

In animals striated muscle moves the body, cardiac muscle pumps the blood, and smooth muscle churns food in the intestines. In each instance, muscle is a machine for converting chemical energy into mechanical energy, in modern parlance, a transducer. The complexity of such a machine becomes apparent when we examine how its functional parts must be fitted together. These include (a) fuel storage, (b) fuel distribution, (c) fuel consumption, (d) transformation of fuel energy to mechanical energy, (e) expression of mechanical energy in moving the part, and (f) control and regulation of all the foregoing.

And all of this must be accomplished by living cells which must also conduct all those processes imperative to the maintenance of cell life, per se. The present state of knowledge is insufficient to understand how these functions are fitted together in the heart. The failing heart cannot pump blood adequately; is it due to a failure of the fuel-synthesizing machinery? failure of fuel distribution? failure of fuel consumption? a defect in the contractile machinery? The answers cannot be given until the entire machinery of contractile tissue is understood.

Nonetheless, great progress has been made in the past twenty years; this has been achieved by concentrated attention on single functions and the use of the simplest and best muscle system to study these functions. All muscles work by the one-way process of contraction or shortening, and this is expressed in its purest form by certain types of striated muscle (e.g., the sartorius of the thigh) because all its cells are arranged in parallel and because it is relatively uncomplicated by other, interacting parts, as valves, chambers, etc. In such muscle, the action of the whole muscle essentially reflects the actions of the single cells constituting it, and the study of this type of muscle has greatly enhanced our understanding of the activity of contractile tissues.

The Contractile Process. A single muscle cell (or fiber) is a membrane surrounding a mass of sarcoplasm. Within this sarcoplasm are embedded the contractile elements, which, by shortening, bring about the contraction of the muscle. How do these elements shorten? What processes bring about this energetic contraction that enables muscle to perform mechanical work (Fig. 7-2)?

Our knowledge of the contractile process has been advanced brilliantly by combining knowledge and techniques from physics and chemistry

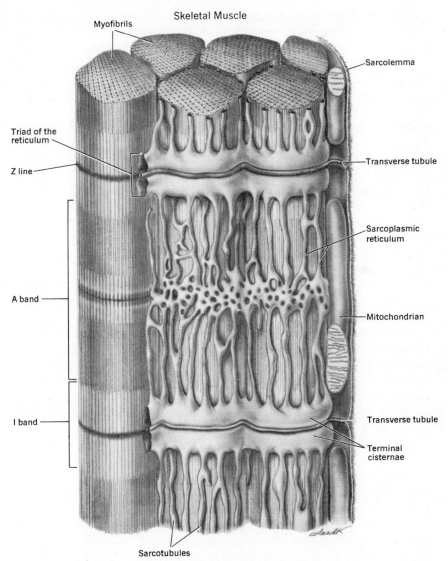

Skeletal Muscle

Myofibrils

Sarcolemma

Triad of the reticulum

Z line

Transverse tubule

Sarcoplasmic reticulum

A band

Mitochondrian

I band

Transverse tubule

Terminal cisternae

Sarcotubules

Figure 7-2. A skeletal muscle fiber. (Modified after L. Peachey, from D. W. Fawcett and S. McNutt, J. Cell Biol. 25:222, 1965. Drawing by Sylvia Colard Keene)

as well as biology. By high-resolution electron microscopy, the contractile elements have been shown to be composed of a double array of filaments, one set of thin and one set of thick, which are of the order of 100 and 200 Å, respectively, so arranged that each thick filament is surrounded by six thin filaments. When muscle is stretched, these two sets of filaments are pulled out from each other, whereas when muscle is contracted, they are telescoped into each other. X-ray studies of living, contracting muscle prove that the individual filaments, themselves, do not shorten. From this, the hypothesis has been proposed that the two filaments interact with each other to result in a "clawing" action to pull the filaments past each other. At present, this is the nub of the matter; what is this "clawing" action? A hint comes from extremely high-resolution electron microscopy and from x-ray diffraction, which show multitudinous "cross-bridges" between the filaments, suggesting that if all the bridges are identical the two types of strand can combine in a large number of relative positions, locked by the cross-bridges. In effect, this would serve as a ratchet.

The nature of this action can be elucidated only by study of the molecular structure of these filaments. The thick filaments are composed of a protein called myosin.

The myosin molecule, molecular weight 480,000, is an elongated multiple (2 or 3) stranded helix 1800 Å by perhaps 20 Å with a knob at one end. When isolated, the latter portion can catalyze the hydrolysis of ATP to ADP + Pi. The thick filaments, about 250 Å in diameter, appear to be cables formed by intertwining myosin molecules with the knobs of myosin more or less at right angle to the fiber axis. The thin filaments are primarily formed of another protein called actin. The unit of this protein is a simple globular unit, molecular weight 60,000. At the ionic conditions prevailing in sarcoplasm, this unit spontaneously polymerizes into a long filament of indefinite length, analogous to a string of beads, but with two such strands wrapped about each other in a double helix. This is the thin filament of the I bands of the myofibril.

Pure actin and myosin react rapidly to form a tightly bonded complex called actomyosin. One can but assume that the linkages involved are those of ATP; the two filaments slide across each other and relock. As this occurs, ATP hydrolysis takes place, and it is assumed that it is the ATPase activity exhibited by myosin and its larger subfragments which is responsible, particularly since this activity is exquisitely sensitive to its ionic environment. Withal, as of the moment, there is no clear understanding of how these interactions bring about movement of the filaments past each other. This important gap in the knowledge of muscle is the focal point for a great deal of intensive research today.

The Mechanochemical Couple. The action of the contractile elements requires energy, and the only source of this energy is the metabolic machinery of the cell located in the sarcoplasm. This is confirmed by electron microscopic observation that the seat of oxidative metabolism of the cell, the mitochondrion, is found in the sarcoplasm of the muscle cell. In what form is the fuel energy passed into the contractile elements? How do the elements utilize this fuel? How is the flow of fuel controlled?

As in all biological systems, in muscle, utilizable energy is in the form of the high-energy chemical bond. But striated muscle must accumulate a store of these high-energy molecules, and use this stored fuel in contraction, because a muscle deprived of oxygen and poisoned with drugs which prevent normal formation of ATP can still contract normally several times. In mammalian muscle, this stored energy is mainly in the form of a single compound, creatine phosphate (CrP). Upon demand, this molecule is used to form another high-energy compound, adenosine triphosphate (ATP) which can then be used energetically to drive the actin-myosin contractile process.

To illustrate the difficulty in ascertaining this information, a series of experiments may be described. A pair of muscles are prepared under identical conditions; they are deprived of oxygen and their metabolic machinery is poisoned. One of the pair is then contracted a number of times, then both are simultaneously frozen and analyzed for their content of energy-rich compounds. The results consistently show that CrP disappears in the activated muscle, but there is no appreciable change in the ATP content. The experiments were first done in 1936 and, over the years, repeated by many investigators using more refined techniques and better analytical methods, but all giving the same answer. But it was known that in the muscle there is a very active enzyme system which catalyzes synthesis of adenosine triphosphate at the expense of creatine phosphate according to the following scheme:

$$\text{CrP} + \text{ADP} \xrightleftharpoons{\text{enzyme}} \text{Cr} + \text{ATP}$$

Patently, this reaction *might* serve to replace any ATP being used in the muscle. That such was the case was shown in 1964 when a poison specific for this particular enzyme was found. Using this poison and preventing the above reaction, the same experiment gave the looked-for result, that ATP is the energy source directly used by the contractile system, for in this experiment it was ATP that disappeared in the proper amount for each contraction. Creatine phosphate, therefore, is a "storage battery" from which ATP can be rapidly formed and which is recharged, during rest, from ATP synthesized in the usual way by glycolysis and oxidative phosphorylation.

At the terminal end of the mechanochemical couple, therefore, it is the energy of the ATP molecule that is converted into mechanical movement by the actin-myosin system. But further, how is this flow of ATP regulated? It can be shown that a muscle, in a single contraction, is able to muster additional energy upon the demand imposed by a heavier load. But added energy means more ATP. This comes available, in part, from creatine phosphate and, in the main, by the acceleration of glycolysis and of oxidative phosphorylation, which is automatic in consequence of the increased concentrations of ADP and inorganic phosphate resulting from hydrolysis of ATP. Again, this is an elegant instance of inbuilt feedback control, sensitive to the changing requirements of the muscle cell.

The Excitation-Contraction Couple. A nerve impulse brings a message to the surface of the muscle cell calling for the muscle to contract. How does this message get to the interior of the cell so that all contractile elements can react? The muscle physiologist calls this the *excitation-contraction couple.* This story begins with the wave of excitation that sweeps over the muscle surface as the result of the impact of the nerve impulse. This "wave" consists of local alteration of the membrane such that sodium ions (Na^+) cross from the exterior and potassium ions subsequently leave the cell in approximately equal amount. A few thousandths of a second later, the entire cell begins to contract. How is this surface signal "felt" inside the cell? What is the link between the signal and the contractile process? Answers to these questions have come from several different lines of investigation.

The excitation begins as a local change in the muscle membrane when the nerve impulse arrives at the junction of the nerve end and the muscle surface. Once started, this local change of the membrane sweeps over the muscle surface as a self-propagated wave characterized by a sharp change in the flow of electrically charged ions through the membrane. This excitation can be brought about by agents other than the nerve impulse—e.g., an electric shock of sufficient intensity.

In a brilliant series of experiments, tiny microelectrodes with tips less than one micron in diameter were touched to the muscle surface, applying shocks too small to cause a general excitation. It was shown that local contraction responses could be obtained, but *only* at particular spots on the cell surface. Electron microscopy revealed these activating spots to be narrow but deep indentations of the surface membrane which penetrate deep into the cell. These have been termed the *transverse tubules,* and it is believed that the excitation changes of the surface membrane are carried inward by tubules, so that excitation is carried

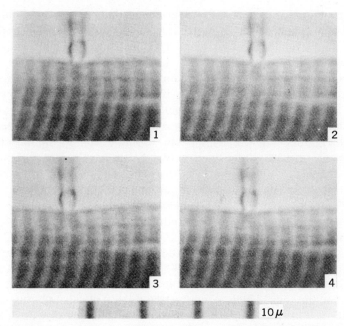

Figure 7-3. Edge of isolated muscle fiber from the frog with an ultramicropipette in contact. Polarized light, compensated so that the A bands appear dark. Pipette applied in 1 and 2 to an A band and in 3 and 4 to an I band. In each case, the left-hand picture was taken just before and the right-hand picture during a negative electrical pulse applied to the pipette. A contraction is produced only if the pipette is opposite an I band. Reference to Fig. 7-2 shows that the transverse tubules come to the surface of a muscle cell at the I band and not at an A band. (From Huxley and Taylor, J. Physiol. *144*, 1958)

deep into the cell into proximity with the contractile elements, the actin and myosin filaments (Fig. 7-3).

Further, the transverse tubules have a precise spatial relation not only to the contractile elements but also to another system of tiny tubes within the sarcoplasm, the *sarcoplasmic reticulum*. Swollen portions of this reticulum are found in close association with the transverse tubules where they are in proximity to the contractile elements. The functional meaning of these precise structural relationships has been clarified from an entirely unexpected direction.

Thirty years ago, the importance of ATP in muscle action was recognized when it was found that a muscle strip, killed and extracted in cold glycerol solution, was still capable of contraction when exposed to ATP. The contraction of this dead muscle was shown to be quite similar to that of the living cell, but unlike the living cell this muscle failed to relax after the contraction. Subsequently, it was found that an extract of chopped-up muscle could cause a relaxation of the contracted glycerinated muscle, and over the years a number of investigators gradually purified and isolated this "relaxing factor." To the surprise of all concerned, it turned out to consist of minute fragments of the membrane of the sarcoplasmic reticulum, and these pieces of membrane were found to exhibit an ATP-dependent activity that gathered up calcium ions from the surrounding solution. In effect, the sarcoplasmic reticulum seemed to be an energy-dependent calcium-sequestering device in the muscle cell. Calcium, in turn, has long been known to be required to maintain the normal activity of intact muscle. Most importantly, this ion has been shown to be necessary for the ATP-splitting activity of myosin. When the level of calcium is too low, the contractile protein fails to split the phosphate bond of the ATP molecule and, hence, fails to release the energy necessary for the contractile process.

The sequence of events in excitation-contraction coupling, therefore, may be reconstructed as follows: The excitation of the cell surface is carried to the interior of the cell by the transverse tubules. There, the flow of sodium ions somehow causes the release of calcium ions into the sarcoplasm. This sudden flood of calcium activates the myosin ATPase, which then causes the sliding motion of the filaments past each other so that they refasten in the shortened position. Then the reticular units begin to gather up the released calcium, reducing the calcium concentration to such a low level that the myosin no longer reacts with ATP, so the muscle relaxes until the next excitation sweeps over the muscle surface. But there is a great deal of speculation here. Not only do we fail to understand the relation of ATPase activity to the "ratchet" mechanism, we do not know how the excitation releases the calcium, where the calcium is released from, nor do we know really that the calcium-sequestering brings about the relaxation. These are important problems for current investigation.

From this brief account, it may be seen that a striated muscle cell, specialized to perform the simplest action of shortening in one direction, is still a complicated system. Smooth muscle is even more complex, both structurally and functionally, and this is the primary reason why less is known about the mechanism of its activity. For example, a single striated muscle fiber has one nerve ending and behaves as a unit. An equivalent amount of smooth muscle would consist of several hundred cells. A smooth muscle cell is quite small, and the arrangement of these cells does not have the geometric simplicity of the striated muscle fiber. There is considerable uncertainty about the innervation of these cells — whether each cell is individually associated with a nerve ending or not — so that questions of excitation, conduction, and coupling to contraction are fraught with difficulties. At the level of ultrastructure of smooth muscle, it is quite certain that the precise ordering of thin and thick filaments is not present. The thin filaments can be found, but thick filaments have not been seen. Surprisingly, however, the material to be expected in thick filaments, i.e., the protein myosin, is found in abundance, as well as the actin, so that the interaction of these proteins probably underlies the contraction process, but perhaps not as sliding filaments.

When heart muscle is examined closely at the level of the individual fibers, it is found to resemble striated muscle. The interdigitating thick and thin filaments are present, as are other structural features. But there is one great difference. The heart muscle fibers do not function as isolated individual units, for they are connected to one another by special junctions that allow excitation to pass from cell to cell, so that large masses of cardiac muscle act together as a unit. While interdigitating actin and myosin filaments may form the basis of the contractile process, other aspects of the muscle action, as excitation-contraction coupling, become extremely difficult to study and to understand because of these structural complexities. Furthermore, the heart as an organ consists of a number of parts, as chambers, valves, etc., and a coordinating system of conducting elements.

It is because of these structural complexities and the experimental difficulties they impose that progress has been slower in the understanding of smooth muscle and heart muscle. The great volume of literature on these systems has been concerned with their total performance, and the effects of hormones and drugs on this total performance. Such studies have a great empirical value, but when the question is posed, "How do these substances work?" the answer can be given only in terms of overall performance, and not in terms of basic mechanisms. For example, the effect of the drug digitoxin on the failing heart has been known for more than two hundred years, but the specific mechanism of its action is still unknown. The difficulties inherent in the question are illustrated by the following: The augmentation by this drug of output by the failing heart is well established, but this result is not obtained for the normal heart. Accordingly, the concept arose that there is a specific defect in the contractile mechanism of the failing heart which is corrected by the drug. More recent findings cast doubt on this, however, as direct measurements demonstrate that digitoxin does increase the contractility of the normal heart, but that peripheral effects of the drug reduce the blood flow back to the heart so that net increase of output is not shown. Thus, the indication is that the drug acts by increasing the contractility of the heart, and attempts have been made to localize this drug action by study-

ing the effect of digitoxin on the metabolism of the heart, on the actin and
myosin from the heart, etc., but the results of such studies have not been
definitive, and there is considerable disagreement.

As research continues, a full understanding of heart and smooth muscle
will be achieved, with consequent benefit to medicine and human health.
But this goal may well be reached by the study of entirely different types
of muscle, better suited for investigation of particular function, and the
information so derived examined and tested and applied to the less-suited
types of muscle.

The Intestinal Epithelium

The epithelium of the small intestine — a single layer of cells folded and
pleated so that, in man, it has a surface area of about 75 square meters —
is the site of absorption of nutrients. All the carbohydrate, protein, and
fat we eat must cross the epithelium to reach the blood and lymph. Although digestion has been studied for more than a century, the availability
of new techniques and new ideas within the past ten or twenty years has
cleared away many of the shadows of incomplete knowledge and unsub-
stantiated hypotheses; a reasonably clear picture of the function of the
intestinal epithelium is beginning to emerge, and it explains many hitherto
misunderstood digestive diseases.

To study carbohydrate absorption, lengths of small intestine are removed from experimental animals — the rat and the golden hamster being
most convenient — and maintained alive in oxygenated salt solutions. The
preparation is arranged so that the epithelium separates two solutions:
that on the luminal surface is equivalent to the contents of the intestinal
canal, and that on the serosal surface is equivalent to blood and lymph.
The basic units of carbohydrate of the diet are hexose (sugar) molecules;
the most common hexoses are glucose, galactose, and fructose. Hexoses
rarely occur in the diet as such; they are ingested as polymers of varying
length — thousands linked in the enormous branched chains of plant starch
and animal glycogen or only two joined in simple disaccharides such as
cane sugar (sucrose) or milk sugar (lactose). When carbohydrates are
placed in the solution bathing the luminal surface of the intestinal
epithelium, *only hexoses* are delivered into the serosal solution. No disaccharides or larger carbohydrates cross the epithelium.

Intensive study, facilitated by the availability of radioactive compounds, shows that of the hexoses only two, glucose and galactose, are
actively and rapidly transported across the epithelial cells; other hexoses
cross slowly and passively by diffusion. Glucose and galactose are transported by a chemical mechanism called a *hexose pump,* which is located

near the luminal surface of the cell. The details of this pump are obscure; available information is scanty but puzzling. It is clear that sodium ions must accompany the uncharged hexose. ATP is utilized as an energy source for the performance of this "work," but not stoichiometrically; many glucose and Na^+ ions enter for each ATP hydrolyzed. Clearly the properties of the epithelial cell membrane proteins are involved, but the real mechanism is obscure. In any case, this pump raises the hexoses to a very high concentration within the epithelial cells, and because this concentration is far higher than that of hexoses in the blood, the sugar molecules diffuse from the cells to the blood to become available for use by the body. The epithelial hexose pump has many characteristics in common with other pumps, but there are important differences. The intestinal sugar pump, unlike the glucose carrier of muscle cells, is not stimulated by insulin, and consequently sugar absorption is unimpaired in diabetes mellitus.

However, we do not eat carbohydrate in the form of hexoses; by far the largest fraction of the 200 to 800 grams of carbohydrate in the daily diet is in the form of enormous polysaccharide molecules (starch or glycogen) or of disaccharides (cane or milk sugar). The older explanation of how these large molecules are transformed to hexoses was simple: hydrolytic enzymes secreted by the digestive glands split the larger molecules into smaller ones. This explanation is still partially valid. The amylases of human saliva and of pancreatic juice do catalyze the hydrolysis of starch and glycogen. If a tube is passed into the human duodenum so that intestinal contents can be withdrawn for analysis, and if the subject is then fed starch, the bulk of the carbohydrate recovered from the intestine 10 minutes after feeding is found to be reduced to small molecules. But only 10 to 20 percent of the hexoses in starch is ever liberated as single hexose molecules ready for absorption; the remaining 90 or 80 percent is in the form of disaccharides.

There are many enzymes (disaccharidases) within the intestinal epithelium which hydrolyze disaccharides: sucrase which splits cane sugar into its constituent hexoses glucose and fructose, lactase which splits milk sugar into glucose and galactose, and maltase which hydrolyzes the disaccharide, derived from glycogen and starch, into glucose. These enzymes are *not* secreted into the lumen of the intestine; they are an integral part of the microvilli which form the "brush border" of the epithelial cells, hence they lie between the lumen of the intestine and the hexose pump. Disaccharides in the lumen diffuse into the brush border where they are hydrolyzed to hexoses; then they are picked up by the hexose pump and translocated to the blood.

It has been known for a long time that some babies cannot tolerate milk. When he is given milk, such a baby's intestines bloat, he has copious diarrhea, and his stools are strongly acid. If the problem is not quickly recognized and properly treated, the baby dies of dehydration and malnutrition. The immediate cause of milk intolerance has recently been discovered: the baby cannot digest lactose, the disaccharide of milk. Undigested and unabsorbed lactose rapidly ferments within the intestinal lumen; among the products of fermentation are acids which stimulate motility of the intestinal tract and carry water and salts out into the frequent stools. The baby cannot digest lactose because the single enzyme lactase is missing from the brush border of his epithelial cells. An instrument called a biopsy capsule can be passed by way of the mouth into the small intestine; by means of a trigger mechanism within the capsule a tiny piece of intestinal epithelium can be snipped off without harm to the patient and removed for microscopic or chemical analysis. Study of biopsy specimens shows that of all the disaccharides only lactase is missing; therefore, lactose of milk is the only sugar that cannot be split and its constituent hexoses made available for the hexose pump. If lactose is removed from the diet and another sugar substituted, manifestations of the inability to digest lactose disappear. Absence of lactase from the brush border is hereditary; the child is deficient in the gene that governs synthesis of the enzyme. Surprisingly, this principle also extends to the digestion of proteins. The pancreas secretes into the intestinal lumen a battery of enzymes which catalyze protein hydrolysis, each with a different specificity, rupturing bonds adjacent to basic, acidic, or aromatic groups. This results in a mixture of small peptides. Digestion is again completed in the brush border, which also has an armamentarium of enzymes that, in sum, assure that only single amino acid molecules remain. These are then absorbed by three or four distinct pumps of varying specificity.

The Kidney and the Internal Environment

The very bulk of an animal isolates most of its cells from the external environment; its cells, unlike a unicellular organism, cannot draw oxygen and nutrients directly from the external environment and discharge their wastes into it. To provide for exchanges of their constituent cells, animals have developed an internal environment. Individual cells, tissues, and organs are enclosed with a sheath which separates and protects them from the external environment. Through this sheath sensing devices gather information about the surrounding world, but within it each cell is bathed in a fluid which provides its immediate or internal environment.

By regulating the properties of their internal environments, animals have largely freed themselves from the vicissitudes of the external environment. By maintaining constant chemical composition, constant temperature, and constant nutrient supply within their internal environments, animals can live a free and independent life.

Groups of organs and tissues form a set of transport systems between the external and internal environments. The respiratory apparatus brings oxygen from the air to the alveolar membrane deep in the lungs. Oxygen diffuses across the membrane into blood which is pumped through the capillaries of the lungs by the right ventricle of the heart. Oxygen combines with the hemoglobin of the red blood cells, and the oxygenated blood is gathered into the left ventricle of the heart, which drives it through the distributing system of arteries and arterioles into capillaries, which penetrate all tissues. Oxygen then diffuses from red blood cells through the capillary wall and the very thin layer of extravascular interstitial fluid to the respiring tissue cells. Food is engulfed and chemically processed within the digestive tract; the constituents to which it is reduced—glucose, amino acids, fatty acids, and monoglycerides—are transported by the intestinal mucosa from the lumen of the small intestine into the blood and lymph, making them available throughout the internal environment for nutrition of the cells. Products of metabolism (carbon dioxide, nitrogenous wastes, and heat) are gathered by the blood from the internal environment and transported to organs and tissues capable of disposing of them.

The organ par excellence in regulating the constancy of the extracellular environment is the kidney. The function of the kidney is not to make urine. It regulates both the volume and composition of the internal environment; urine is the residuum discarded in the process of regulation.

Nothing was known about the function of the kidney until its anatomy was worked out, in the 1840's, by William Bowman, then a boy of twenty. Bowman found, by the most elegant dissections, that the kidney is composed of some millions of functional units, the nephrons, arranged in parallel. Arterial blood arrives at the nephron through an afferent arteriole and is delivered to a compact tuft of capillaries. On the distal side of the capillaries is an efferent arteriole through which blood must pass to leave the capillaries. The tuft of capillaries is surrounded by a fluid-filled capsule—*Bowman's capsule*, after its discoverer. The capsule drains into a long, convoluted proximal tubule composed of a single layer of thick cells. In mammals the proximal tubule is next connected with a thin-walled tube arranged as a long hairpin loop, the loop of Henle, which is accompanied by a similar loop of capillary blood vessels, both of them dipping deep into the medulla of the kidney. At the end of the loop is another convoluted tubule, the distal one, formed like the proximal tubule of thick cells. Both proximal and distal tubules are surrounded by venules which receive blood from the efferent arterioles and which empty their contents into the renal vein. The distal tubule ends in a thin, straight collecting duct which lies alongside the loops of Henle. The collecting duct empties into the pelvis of the kidney, which in turn delivers its contents to the ureter and urinary bladder.

This structural form suggests function. The tuft of capillaries and its surrounding capsule could be a filter in which water and crystalloids of plasma are driven by pressure of blood within the capillaries through the capillary wall into the surrounding capsular space. This filtrate of plasma could flow down the system of tubules draining the capsule, and there some of its constituents could be saved by being reabsorbed and transported into the renal venous blood. Or substances could be abstracted from renal venous blood by the tubular cells and secreted into the fluid contained within their lumen. Whatever is left in the collecting duct would then be the urine which reaches the bladder. From inspection of its architecture, such might be the function of the kidney. And, for nearly eighty years, no more was really known about the subject than is summarized in the last hundred words. After the first World War came a series of experiments which established the general truth of the speculation but also, like all good experiments, opened the way to entirely unexpected concepts and practical results.

Is the glomerulus really a filter? This can be broken into two subsidiary questions: (1) is the pressure difference across the walls of the glomerular capillaries high enough to separate an ultrafiltrate of plasma from the proteins of the plasma by filtration, and (2) is the fluid within the capsular space actually an ultrafiltrate of plasma (plasma minus its protein complement)?

The glomeruli of the living anesthetized frog and of the mudpuppy *Necturus* can be visualized under the dissecting microscope. Keeping a glomerulus under direct observation, an extremely fine glass pipette, connected with an injection device and a manometer, was inserted into the capsular space. Injection of fluid into the space raised the pressure on the outside of the capillaries, and when the capillaries were seen to collapse, the pressure outside the capillaries was known to be slightly higher than the blood pressure within them. By this means blood pressure in the capillary tuft was found to be about 60 percent of arterial blood pressure, a value far higher than the pressure in other capillaries of the body and more than enough to effect continued ultrafiltration. The second question was answered by withdrawing minute amounts of fluid from the capsular space and comparing its composition with that of an ultrafiltrate of plasma of the same animal. The extreme smallness of the samples demanded the most delicate analytical methods, and ten years were occupied in obtaining definitive results. At the end it was unequivocally demonstrated that a series of solutes—total electrolytes, glucose, hydrogen ions, chloride, urea, uric acid, and so forth—had the same concentration in the glomerular fluid as in an ultrafiltrate of plasma. Thus these fundamental facts of renal physiology were nailed down for good.

If it is an ultrafiltrate of plasma that flows from glomerulus into the renal tubules, where and how is it modified by tubular action? This question has been answered by the application of similar micropuncture methods, first to the tubules of frogs and *Necturus* and more recently to those of rats, dogs, and primates. The concentration of glucose in plasma, and therefore in glomerular fluid, is usually about 90 mg/100 ml. If one samples fluid in the proximal tubule one finds that the concentration of glucose at the beginning of the tubule is the same as in plasma and is zero at the end of the tubule. All glucose filtered through the glomerulus is normally reabsorbed by the cells of the proximal tubule and is transferred into renal venous blood. This accounts for the fact that there is usually no glucose in the urine. The distal tubule, which under ordinary circumstances receives a fluid containing no glucose, is incapable of reabsorbing it. If two micropipettes, one to deliver a glucose-containing fluid to one end and one to collect fluid from the other end, are placed in a distal tubule, the amount of glucose collected is found to be the same as the amount delivered. Thus, if any glucose escapes reabsorption in the proximal tubule, it will not be reabsorbed in the distal tubule and will escape into the urine.

The load of glucose imposed on the proximal tubular transfer mechanism is equal to the rate of glomerular filtration of fluid (ml/min) times the concentration of glucose in the filtrate (mg/ml). One would expect the ability of the proximal tubule actively to transfer glucose to have some upper limit, a transfer maximum, T_m, and this is in fact the case. If the load exceeds the transfer maximum, that part of the load exceeding the T_m is delivered into the urine. Hence, glucosuria can arise for two reasons: (1) the load may increase until it exceeds T_m, or (2) the T_m may be reduced. The former occurs in diabetes mellitus in which plasma glucose concentration and therefore the filtered load are very high; the latter occurs when the tubular transfer mechanism is poisoned by the drug phlorizin.

As the result of a vast number of micropuncture and related studies, there now exists a detailed knowledge of the topography of kidney function. We know which substances are reabsorbed at which segments of the tubules, where the osmotic pressure of the urine, and therefore of the internal environment, is adjusted, and where the ionic exchanges that regulate the acid-base status of the extracellular fluid are controlled.

The total osmotic pressure is one of the properties of the internal environment most closely regulated by the kidney. When the body's water load increases and the osmotic pressure of blood plasma falls, the kidney excretes dilute urine, saving salts and disposing of water. When intake of water is low and osmotic pressure rises, the kidney excretes concentrated urine. A dehydrated man can excrete urine whose osmotic pressure is about four times that of his plasma, but in this respect his kidney is far inferior to that of the desert kangaroo rat. This animal does not drink water; he can manage with a water supply consisting only of that contained in his dry food and that produced by his oxidative metabolism. This is because he can excrete urine fourteen times more concentrated than his plasma.

The development of the hairpin loop system of the kidney parallels the ability of animals to conserve water by excreting concentrated urine. An engineer suggested that the loop system might be a countercurrent multiplier—long known in heat engineering as a device for multiplying small temperature differences to create a large temperature difference. Other loop systems in the circulation were already known to operate as countercurrent multipliers. In man, in diving mammals, and in the tuna, loops in the peripheral blood vessels conserve body heat so that body temperature may be kept above that of cold surroundings. In some fishes, similar loops enable gaseous oxygen to be secreted from blood into swim bladders for adjustment of buoyancy. Following this suggestion, investigation quickly established that the loop arrangement of the nephron is, in fact, an osmotic countercurrent multiplier which establishes a region of very high osmotic pressure at the tip of the loop. Since the collecting duct which delivers the final tubular urine to the pelvis of the kidney lies parallel to the loop and has its terminal orifice in the region of high osmotic pressure, the high osmotic pressure surrounding the collecting duct tends to draw water away from the final tubular urine. This, of course, saves water for the body.

The extent to which water can be drawn from the final tubular urine depends not only upon the magnitude of the osmotic gradient but also upon the permeability of the walls of the collecting duct to water. Their permeability was found to be governed by a hormone long known to control water excretion, the antidiuretic hormone (ADH) of the neurohypophysis (posterior pituitary), whose mechanism of action had hitherto been a mystery. In diabetes insipidus, due to failure to secrete this hormone, humans may excrete as much as six gallons of urine per day! A few milligrams of this hormone, a small polypeptide, afford complete protection. Recent studies have shown that a rise in osmotic pressure of the internal environment is sensed by "osmoreceptors" in the hypothalamic part of the brain; these cause the release of ADH from the posterior pituitary gland. Upon reaching the kidney by way of the blood, the hormone increases the permeability of the wall of the collecting duct so that water is withdrawn from the tubular urine within them, leaving normally concentrated urine to be excreted. When the osmotic pressure of the internal environment falls, ADH secretion stops, and the walls of the collecting duct become less permeable to water. Then the osmotic gradient is incapable of withdrawing water from the fluid within the collecting duct, and dilute urine escapes into the bladder.

A series of parallel but entirely distinct studies established the overall, quantitative facts of renal physiology. The principle is simple, and in practice it can be applied to intact, unanesthetized animals with the result that human kidney function can be measured.

Suppose a substance X is present in blood plasma, either naturally or as the result of intravenous injection, which is freely diffusible through the glomerular membrane. Hence, its concentration in the glomerular fluid is the same as its concentration in plasma $[X]_p$; if the plasma concentration is measured, its glomerular concentration is known. Therefore, the rate at which it is filtered is equal to the glomerular filtration rate (GFR) in volumes per unit time multiplied by the concentration in plasma water: $(GFR)[X]_p$. Suppose further that X is neither reabsorbed from the tubular fluid nor secreted into the tubular fluid as it passes down the tubules. Then all X filtered, and only X filtered, appears in the urine. If the rate of urine flow is U volumes per unit time and the concentration of X in the urine is $[X]_u$, the rate of excretion of X is $U[X]_u$. This is, if our suppositions are correct, equal to $(GFR)[X]_p$:

$$(GFR)[X]_p = U[X]_u \quad \text{or} \quad (GFR) = U[X]_u \div [X]_p$$

Since three of the four quantities are measurable, the fourth, (GFR), can be calculated. A few substances are known to meet these specifications, most notably inulin, a polysaccharide of fructose obtained from the Jerusalem artichoke. With its use the rate of glomerular filtration is now readily determined.

In a 160-pound man the rate of glomerular filtration is 120 to 125 ml a minute, or about 180 liters a day. Since total blood plasma volume is 2.8 liters, a volume equal to the whole volume of plasma is filtered 65 times a day. Almost all of the water and its solutes are reabsorbed as the filtrate passes down the tubules, for the usual urine output is about one liter a day. The fact that the kidney deals with such stupendous volumes has important implications for understanding of the way the kidney regulates the internal environment. If the problem is to dispose of an additional liter of water, the kidney need reduce its rate of water reabsorption only by half a percent. Patently, renal regulatory mechanisms embody wonderfully delicate adjustments. How regulation of these processes may go wrong in disease and how it can be manipulated for therapeutic purposes is illustrated by renal handling of sodium.

Under ordinary circumstances daily dietary intake of sodium varies over a wide range. Sodium is the major ionic and osmotic constituent of the extracellular fluid, and in order to keep the composition and volume of the extracellular fluid constant, the kidney must excrete an amount of sodium essentially identical with sodium intake. Sodium is filtered in the glomerulus; since its concentration in this filtrate is 145 mEq per liter, about 26,000 mEq or 600 grams of sodium ion enter the renal tubules each day. Normally, all but a few grams of filtered sodium is reabsorbed, most of it in the proximal tubule and the rest in the distal tubule and collecting ducts. At these latter sites, reabsorption of sodium is coupled with secretion of hydrogen ions by the tubular cells. This is a major process by which acid-base status of the internal environment is adjusted; one sodium ion (Na^+) is reabsorbed for each hydrogen ion (H^+) secreted.

When the heart begins to fail, regulation of sodium reabsorption by renal tubules is impaired. This is the consequence of the following sequence of events. Changes in blood flow through the kidney, resulting from the hemodynamic consequences of heart failure in some manner, stimulate the kidney to secrete the proteolytic enzyme renin into the blood. Renin attacks a protein in plasma, thereby releasing the oligopeptide angiotensin, the most powerful of known vasoconstrictive agents. Angiotensin not only raises arterial blood pressure but it stimulates the cortex of the adrenal gland to secrete the hormone aldosterone. Aldosterone, in turn, stimulates the mechanism for tubular reabsorption of sodium. As a result, the kidney reabsorbs an inappropriately large amount of sodium, daily excretion falls behind daily intake, and the body content of sodium increases. This, in turn, necessarily causes an increase in extracellular fluid volume, and the patient with congestive heart failure becomes waterlogged with edema fluid, evident particularly as swelling of the extremities.

From these considerations, there emerge two ways to afford symptomatic relief to a patient with congestive failure. One is simply to restrict sodium intake, hence the well-known low-sodium diet. The other is to promote increased excretion of sodium despite the exaggerated physiological processes which make for retention. One possibility is to inhibit the mechanism which accomplishes the tubular exchange of H^+ for Na^+. The enzyme *carbonic anhydrase* is known to be essential to this renal acid secretion mechanism. It catalyzes the hydration of carbon dioxide, the ubiquitous product of cellular metabolism, to produce carbonic acid.

$$CO_2 \xrightarrow[\text{anhydrase}]{\text{carbonic}} H_2CO_3 \rightarrow H^+ + HCO_3^-$$

Carbonic acid in turn ionizes to give a hydrogen ion and a bicarbonate ion. Cells of the collecting duct then secrete the H^+ into the urine in a 1:1 exchange for Na^+, which is returned to renal venous blood along with the bicarbonate ion. Inhibition of carbonic anhydrase would limit the availability of H^+ ions, and Na^+ reabsorption would be correspondingly reduced. Carbonic anhydrase was known to be inhibited by some sulfonamide drugs, sulfanilamide for example. Years of research by chemists working with biologists led to synthesis of several compounds, related to the sulfonamides, which powerfully inhibit carbonic anhydrase and have minimal undesirable side effects. Administration of these drugs reduces acid secretion by the kidney, and sodium that otherwise would have been reabsorbed pours out into the urine, bringing with it the edema fluid. Today such diuretics are routinely used in the management of congestive heart failure and of other diseases which involve excessive sodium retention.

These studies on kidney function demonstrate one important feature of physiological research: one approaches a problem where one can get at it. Frog and *Necturus* glomeruli were studied because they were accessible. Results obtained on them were generalized to other animals, but it was not until much later that the generalization was proved valid for a mammal. The generalities and quantitative aspects of renal dynamics were largely ascertained in the dog. No one has ever actually directly demonstrated that the human glomerulus is an ultrafilter, yet we can safely think and act as though the demonstration were complete, thanks to the experience gained in countless studies of comparative physiology.

It is worth recounting that there are also limitations in the validity of extrapolations from species to species. Occasionally, evolution produced alternative effective solutions to a common problem. We have noted the manner in which the countercurrent mechanism enables mammals to elaborate urine decidedly more concentrated than the plasma from which it derives. Marine birds are constantly confronted with this problem. Their only source of free water is the sea with four times the sodium concentration of plasma. And each dive for fish necessarily results in swallowing some seawater. The least salty water they encounter is the flesh of the fish in their diets. But bird kidneys give no evidence of an apparatus appropriate to this task. The clue to the solution was the observation by a comparative physiologist that, after a fishing expedition, a considerable volume of fluid would flow off the tip of the beak of a gull or albatross while resting on a dock pile. Examination of this fluid revealed that it was even more concentrated than seawater. Moreover, each bird always released fluid of the same composition. Further inquiry revealed that this fluid is the product of a "salt gland" in the nasal passages of all marine birds. This gland lacks the versatility of the kidney; it cannot vary the concentration of its secretion with varying circumstances. Instead it can vary the volume of a secretion of fixed, high concentration. When the sodium concentration in plasma, increased by absorbed seawater, is restored to normal by removal of the highly concentrated secretion, the secretory process terminates—a completely logical, highly successful solution to a problem which, if unsolved, would never have permitted the evolution and broad distribution of some of the most distinguished of all birds—gulls, terns, albatrosses, boobies, etc. The mechanism of this remarkable secretion, discovered only a few years ago, is today under intensive scrutiny.

Cardiac Output in Exercise

When he is at rest a normal man's heart pumps 5,000 ml of blood a minute into his arteries, the cardiac output. His heart rate is about 70 beats a minute, and therefore the blood ejected by each beat, the stroke volume, is 70 ml. With exercise, the cardiac output can increase to about 20,000 ml a minute; the heart rate rises to 180 beats a minute, and the stroke volume to 110 ml per beat. In addition, the force with which the heart contracts is greatly increased, with the result that the stroke volume is ejected more rapidly and at a higher pressure.

The research that enables us to state precisely the cardiac output of a man, how it varies in exercise, and how it changes in disease is one of the most brilliant accomplishments of physiology. Of this long and entrancing tale, we will describe only the measurement of cardiac output and the means by which the heart meets demand for increased output in exercise.

Let us designate cardiac output as CO liters per minute. Venous blood flows at this rate into the capillaries of the lungs. If the amount of oxygen in venous blood is V cc per liter, then the rate at which oxygen arrives at the lungs in venous blood is (V)(CO) cc per minute. In the lungs the venous blood picks up oxygen and becomes arterial blood. The rate at which blood is oxygenated we can designate as O_2 cc per minute. Arterial blood leaves the lungs at the rate of CO liters per minute, and it contains oxygen at a concentration of A cc per liter. Thus the rate at which oxygen leaves the lungs is (A)(CO) cc per minute. The rate at which oxygen leaves the lungs must be equal to the rate at which it reaches the lungs in venous blood and as gaseous oxygen:

$$(A)(CO) = (V)(CO) + O_2$$

Rearranging, we have

$$(A)(CO) - (V)(CO) = O_2$$
$$(CO)(A - V) = O_2$$
$$CO = \frac{O_2}{A - V}$$

The theory is childishly simple, and one can calculate cardiac output if three quantities are measured. It is easy to measure O_2, which is the rate of oxygen consumption. Since all arterial blood is alike, a sample of arterial blood obtained, with suitable precautions, from any artery, allows measurement of its oxygen concentration, or A. The problem is to measure V, for the only place at which venous blood is thoroughly mixed so that a representative sample can be obtained is in the right ventricle which delivers mixed venous blood to the lungs through the pulmonary artery.

The way to obtain a sample of mixed venous blood from a man is to introduce a flexible radiopaque catheter into the right antecubital vein, at the elbow, to thread the catheter into the superior vena cava, and then with fluoroscopic control to persuade the tip of the catheter to pass into the right atrium and then through the tricuspid valve into the right ventricle. Once the tip is in place, a sample of mixed venous blood can be withdrawn while an arterial sample and the oxygen consumption are simultaneously being obtained. The first person who had the courage to attempt this, in man, was a German physician who, sitting in front of a fluoroscope, threaded a catheter into his own heart. The technique was adapted and developed with the result that cardiac catheterization for measurement of cardiac output and of pressures within the chambers of the heart is now a routine diagnostic procedure in many hospitals.

The heart has two means by which its output can be adjusted: one is the intrinsic ability of the heart muscle, or myocardium, to increase the force of its contraction when it is stretched, and the other is its response to stimulation through sympathetic nerves. The first property can be studied only if the influence of nerves and hormones is abolished or rigidly controlled. To do this, the heart and lungs of an anesthetized dog are separated functionally from the rest of the animal, and the heart is kept alive by being supplied through the right atrium with blood from a reservoir. This supply of blood resembles normal venous return, and its rate of return and the pressure with which it flows into the heart can be varied at will. The blood flows from the right ventricle through the lungs, where it is oxygenated, into the left ventricle. Contraction of the left ventricle forces blood into the aorta, and in the heart-lung preparation the aorta is cannulated and attached to devices which measure the cardiac output and the pressure. Since the heart rate can be counted, stroke volume can be calculated.

Isolation of the heart allows its volume to be measured. As the ventricle relaxes in diastole it fills with blood. At the instant that marks the end of diastole—just before the ventricle begins to contract again—the volume of blood within the ventricle is at a maximum; this is the *end diastolic volume*. As the ventricle contracts it ejects the *stroke volume*. It does not, however, empty completely; a *residual volume* remains.

If venous return is raised in a heart-lung preparation, pressure within the ventricle is increased during diastole. Since the heart in diastole is a distensible structure, increased diastolic pressure increases end diastolic volume. The fundamental property of heart muscle is then displayed: an increase in end diastolic volume is at once followed by increased force of myocardial contraction. As force of contraction increases, stroke volume, and therefore cardiac output, rises. In this manner cardiac output is immediately adjusted to match venous return. This description of the ability of the myocardium to contract more vigorously as end diastolic volume increases is called the *law of the heart*.

But the myocardium can also be made to contract more vigorously without change in end diastolic volume. Fibers from that branch of the nervous system known as the sympathetic nervous system reach the heart. Some of the fibers end near the cells whose intermittent electrical activity sets the pace of the heart, the pacemaker, and others are distributed throughout the myocardium. When sympathetic fibers are stimulated, they release at their endings the hormone norepinephrine. This hormone increases the rate of firing of the pacemaker cells and thereby accelerates the heart. In addition it greatly augments the strength of contraction of the myocardium at any end diastolic volume. Sympathetic fibers also go to the adrenal medulla where their excitation causes secretion of the hormones epinephrine and norepinephrine into the blood. These hormones, on reaching the heart, back up the effects of the nerves to the heart by accelerating and augmenting the heartbeat. Hence, cardiac output rises.

The two means by which the heart adjusts its output to demand were discovered by the customary scientific method of dissecting a complex organism into its constituent parts. When we seek to answer the question, "What actually happens?" we must return to the whole organism. How much, if anything, the law of the heart contributes to increasing cardiac output in exercise can only be answered by measuring end diastolic volume in an exercising animal. This is a very difficult task, but it has recently been accomplished by a combination of techniques derived from biological sciences ranging from bioengineering to open-heart surgery. An elaborate set of transducers can be placed within and around the heart of an anesthetized dog. These are designed to measure the dimensions of the heart throughout the cardiac cycle, to measure pressures within the veins, the chambers of the heart, and the aorta, and to measure the cardiac output. Signals from the transducers are recorded outside the animal. After the animal has fully recovered from surgery, all aspects of its cardiovascular function can be measured while it is lying at rest, running down the hall of the laboratory, or exercising on a treadmill.

Such measurements show that when a dog's cardiac output increases in exercise, its end diastolic volume does not increase. Consequently, the law of the heart is not called upon. It is stimulation of sympathetic fibers to the heart and to the adrenal medulla that augments the force of myocardial contraction, and stroke volume is increased by diminution of residual volume. As nearly as one can tell from necessarily more restricted experiments, the same conclusions apply to man.

The fact that the law of the heart is not called upon in these circumstances does not mean the law has been repealed. It is still a valid explanation of many adjustments of the healthy and the diseased heart. Sometimes, particularly when he is under nervous strain, the heart of a normal man will have an extra beat, an extrasystole, interpolated in the regular sequence of cardiac cycles. Because an extrasystole occurs shortly after a normal beat, the ventricle is only partially filled; its end diastolic volume is low, and its contraction is feeble. Heart muscle is refractory to further stimulation during its contraction, and the refractoriness occurring during an extrasystole prevents the next normal wave of excitation arising in the pacemaker from stimulating the heart. Consequently, there is a pause in the heart's rhythm following an extrasystole—the compensatory pause. During the pause the ventricle fills to a greater extent than it does during the regular rhythm, and its end diastolic volume is large. The result is that the next beat following an extrasystole is abnormally strong. The apex of the heart hits the front of the chest during the heart's contraction, and the apex beat of the contraction following an extrasystole is felt as a strong thump in the chest. Persons who do not understand the physiology behind this are frequently alarmed by the thump, whereas a physiologist is reassured that his heart is capable of responding to abnormal end diastolic volume with appropriately increased strength of contraction.

Absorption and Bulk Transport in Plants

The nutritional economy of plants is quite different from that of animals. Animals get their food in highly concentrated form, by eating plants or other animals. Plants obtain theirs from extremely dilute sources in the inorganic environment, taking up, in essence, one molecule or one ion after the other. And because they can do so, they are therefore the prime accumulators of nutrients from the environment.

The two main classes of raw food materials of plants are (1) the carbon dioxide of the air, which is converted, by the process of photosynthesis, under the use of light energy, to organic compounds, primarily sugars, and (2) the mineral nutrients of the soil. In all cases the nutrient molecule or ion is brought to the plant by the simple process of diffusion; there, is it trapped at a reactive site, this mechanism being powered by energy derived from metabolism, and usually transported into the cell and in many cases then to other cells, tissues, and organs of the plant.

Carbon dioxide is mainly fixed in the interior of the leaves. The gas first diffuses through special openings (the stomata) into the leaf, then through the membranes that surround the living contents of the cell into the latter and finally, through a similar membrane, into the chloroplasts where the trap is sprung. The trap in this case is the substance ribulose diphosphate (a sugar coupled with two phosphate molecules); in a rapid, enzyme-catalyzed reaction the carbon dioxide molecule combines with a ribulose diphosphate molecule to produce 3-phosphoglyceric acid. This is further reduced to sugar, and a complicated recycling process feeds out another trapping molecule, to replace the one just used, so that the process can start over again. (See Chapter 3.)

The mineral nutrients such as phosphate or potassium are absorbed by the roots. They are present as charged ions in the soil solution. Their diffusion stops at the cell membrane which, in plants as in animals, is normally impenetrable to ions. Here the nature of the trap, the system for active transport, is unknown. Some membrane constituent, commonly called a "carrier," is presumably brought to an active state by an input of respiratory energy. (See Chapter 4.) The activated carrier binds the ion, and the carrier-ion complex can move within the membrane, and when it is appropriately located its surface can discharge the ion out of the membrane and into the cell interior.

Transport through the cell membranes of roots is not all one way. Roots also excrete a variety of substances, including metabolic products and enzymes. One of the most striking examples is excretion of herbicides (weed-killers) which, when applied to the leaves, may be excreted by the roots. In some weeds, this serves effectively as a mechanism for detoxification, for it removes a poisonous material from the body of the plant.

The bulk transport of fluids in plants is along pressure gradients, just as in animals. However, in the case of water transport by transpiration, the actual gauge pressures along the gradient will be negative. At present it is thought that the evaporative loss of water at the leaf mesophyll leads to increased curvature of the menisci at the air-water interfaces of the submicroscopic pores in the cell wall. The increased tension produces a tractile force at the top of the enmeshed water column which the plant-soil continuum provides, and water flows along the pressure gradient established from soil to root to leaf. A path of low resistance, and hence rapid transport, is provided by the dead, interconnected cells of the xylem. In recent years studies of this transport process have been handled from the viewpoint of water potentials, rather than tensions per se, and the energy inputs are calculated from dissipation of absorbed radiant energy in evaporation. However, there remain conceptual problems in relating thermodynamics to hydrodynamics; and further experimental inquiry into the physical state of water in transpiring plants is needed. Viewed as whole, is the water continuum of the plant at reduced pressure, and is cell growth accomplished in a mass of "stretched" water?

Transport of foodstuffs from photosynthesizing leaves to roots, fruits, and growing buds occurs through the phloem. Here the cells are living, but the cytoplasm is altered from that of vegetative cells and is interconnected along the axis of the line of cells. Transport is thought to be by mass flow of concentrated solution, largely of sucrose. By an active metabolic process, solutes are pumped into the phloem cells at the leaf, and flow as a solution through the linear array of anastomosing cells to the receptor tissue where the solutes are removed by adjacent living cells. Differences in solute concentration between source and sink are believed to provide osmotically the required pressure gradient. However, all this is hypothesis, and not accepted by everyone. An alternative hypothesis proposes an active transport of the sugar through the interconnected cytoplasm, with any water movement simply reflecting the osmotic consequence of moving solute in an aqueous medium.

The long distances involved from leaf to root, seem, at first thought, to be incommensurate with forces of the magnitude here considered. That net flow does occur in both directions is self-evident. What must be appreciated is that the work is done, not by a single large and powerful pump, but by the sum of a very large number of minuscule pumps. But, as we have so frequently concluded, much remains to be done before true understanding of these mechanisms has been gained.

Control of Function of Tissues and Organs

An animal or plant is more than a collection of cells and tissues; it is an integrated being, the function of whose tissues and organs is regulated to serve the purpose of the whole organism. In both plants and animals, integration and regulation are performed by their endocrine systems;

chemical messengers are synthesized and secreted by one group of cells and are carried to other groups of cells where they initiate, regulate, or suppress the functions of their targets. We have seen how gibberellin governs the development of the seed. In animals, nervous and endocrine systems act jointly to control the entire life cycle.

Glandular Physiology: Integrative Functions, Neuroendocrine Phenomena, and Mechanisms of Hormone Action

The human body represents a wondrous unit of myriads of cells, tissues, organs, and systems all functioning in harmony. The interworkings of these parts is of remarkable complexity. Nature leaves few critical requirements for life to the whims of organisms. Just as all that is required to keep a modern automobile going is the occasional adding of fuel and oil, all that the body requires by voluntary act is the ingestion of food and water and elimination of accumulated wastes. Mechanistically considered, all else is automated and self-regulating. We have a thirst mechanism that tells us when we need water, a hunger mechanism that signals mealtime, and a satiety mechanism that warns us when we have had enough. Other vital processes such as the beating of the heart, breathing, temperature control, and the regulation of the chemical composition of our body fluids are automatically regulated.

It has long been known that the nervous system interlinking all parts of the body plays a major role in keeping internal order and coordinating functions. What was not appreciated until little more than a generation ago is that hormones or chemical messengers circulating in the bloodstream are of transcendent regulatory importance.

The hormones come from glands which discharge their secretory products into the bloodstream. Structures classically considered as the ductless or endocrine glands are the thyroids, parathyroids, adrenals, pituitary, ovaries and testes, and the islets of the pancreas. Several other structures, including the pineal body, the gastric antrum, and the duodenum, meet most of the requirements for classification as parts of the endocrine system. New hormones and new sources of internal secretion are constantly being uncovered as science advances. The endocrine system is responsible for such major functions as the proportionate growth and development of the body, the regulation of intracellular metabolism, the maintenance of the constant composition of the bathing body fluids, the appearance of puberty and support of all reproductive functions including pregnancy, parturition, and lactation, and the identifying characteristics of the sexes. Hormones are also critical to the establishment of normal behavior patterns and essential to the learning process. Acute removal of the adrenal, parathyroid, and pancreatic islet secretions is quickly followed by death of the animal. Although an animal can live without the other hormones, its ability to reproduce and the quality of its life are impaired. Thyroid deficiency in the adult human, for example, reduces the subject to a state bordering on idiocy.

The most revolutionizing endocrine discovery of recent years is that certain nerve cells respond to neural signals by secreting hormones into the bloodstream. Thus the major integrative systems of the body are themselves functionally interlocked on a scale hitherto undreamed.

Interplay of neural and endocrine mechanisms is well illustrated in the regulation of the mammalian female reproductive system. Among seasonal breeders, young are born and raised at a time of year favorable in terms of warmth, food supply, and a protective environment. The series of bodily and behavioral events that lead to mating and pregnancy is clearly anchored to changes in the environment. The exciting stimuli usually relate to photoperiodicity, ambient temperature, food, visual perception, odors or sounds, or any combinations of such external stimuli. The beneficial effect on egg production of extending the day by artificial light is well known in agricultural practice. Among wild birds, the female generally requires the attention of the male before she will engage in nest building and egg laying. The female pigeon must perceive the visual image of her mate in order to produce crop milk for the young. With rats and mice even the mere matter of crowding can completely disrupt the reproductive processes and prevent or eliminate sexual behavior. Mice are also especially sensitive to sexual odors. A female mouse who has mated with a male of her own strain and colony does not become pregnant if, within 24 hours, she senses the odor of a male mouse of a different strain. (See Chapter 10 for a fuller discussion of this topic.) Her pregnancy is blocked by suppression of pituitary support of the corpora lutea, which leads to failure of implantation. The important fact in all these situations is that the environmental stimuli perceived by sensory receptors in the brain are translated to chemical signals which are secreted by nerve cells in the region of the brain called the hypothalamus. There, neuroendocrine secretions, termed *releasing factors* (RF), are transmitted to the pituitary gland via the very short hypophyseal portal veins. Specific releasing factors bring about the release (secretion) of the pituitary gonadotropins: follicle-stimulating hormone (FSH) and luteinizing hormone (LH). FSH stimulates the development of ovarian follicles, each of which bears an egg cell. LH effects the rupture of mature follicles and release of eggs; it also converts each ruptured follicle into a new glandular structure, a corpus luteum.

The ovarian cycle is composed therefore of a follicular phase, an ovulating phase, and a luteal phase. With each phase there is not only a shift in the hormones that stimulate the ovary but a shift in the nature of the hormones secreted by the ovaries. Thus during the follicular phase the ovaries secrete estrogens which promote growth of the uterus, whereas during the luteal phase progesterone produced by the corpora lutea prepares the uterus for reception of the fertilized egg and the intrauterine development of the fetus. This sequence in ovarian hormone production is also responsible for changes in sexual behavior that bring about mating at the proper time to ensure fertilization of the ovum.

When these events were first studied, it was thought that the pituitary and ovary were linked in a closed negative-feedback regulatory mechanism. Ovarian hormones secreted under the stimuli of pituitary gonadotropins were presumed to act back on the pituitary to suppress the secretion of gonadotropins. It is now quite clear that the ovarian hormones act, not on the pituitary, but on the brain proper to suppress the production of the hypothalamic hypophysiotropic releasing factors. There appears to be an RF for FSH and another for LH. These neurohormones are of great potency and are made and secreted only in minute quantities. They have been extracted from the hypothalamuses of great numbers of sheep and identified biologically in hypophyseal portal blood of rats, but their chemical structures are entirely unknown.

The releasing factors can be administered experimentally by intracarotid injection or by infusion directly into the pituitary gland; under these circumstances all of the expected sequelae are obtained. Viewed in toto the ovarian regulatory mechanism consists of a reflex neuroendocrine arc with the primary center of control located in the hypothalamus. The hypothalamus receives information through two pathways: ovarian hormone feedback and nervous impulses of exteroceptive or psychogenic origin. Such information prompts the hypothalamus to effect the cyclic discharge of neuroendocrines. Capillaries draining the area where releasing factors are synthesized collect into short veins, the hypothalamic portal system, which go to the pituitary gland and again break up into capillaries. It is through this local system of blood vessels that releasing factors reach the pituitary gland and bring about the secretion of gonad-stimulating hormones in an orderly sequence that governs the ovarian cycle.

Studies in the rat indicate clearly that the cyclic aspect of hypothalamic control of pituitary function is lacking in the male. Ovaries grafted into intact males develop follicles but fail to ovulate, whereas ovaries grafted into males castrated at birth exhibit the normal ovarian cycles as they would in intact females. This led to the important discovery that the male gonad effects a sexual differentiation of the hypothalamus in late fetal or early neonatal life. Newborn female rats exposed to testis hormone, as by implanting testes or injecting an androgenic steroid hormone, are sterile for the reason that their masculinized hypothalamuses are arrhythmic and unable to secrete enough LH to effect ovulation. This information clearly indicates the importance of protecting the female fetus or infant from indiscriminate exposure to any of the androgenic steroids that are in common clinical use.

The evidence for hypothalamic control of reproductive functions has been further strengthened in recent years by a variety of different experimental approaches. Electrolytic lesions placed in particular minute areas of the hypothalamus interfere with specific functions of the anterior pituitary, thus showing that each of the release factors originates from a given, unique locus. In some instances, gentle electrical stimulation of a given locus will increase the secretion of a particular gonadotropin. This has been especially well demonstrated in respect to LH release as evidenced by ovulation. In yet another approach, the implantation of minute crystals of estrogen or testosterone directly in these hypothalamic loci exerts a damping effect on pituitary stimulation of the gonads. Transecting the pituitary stalk disrupts the portal blood supply to the anterior pituitary and abolishes the secretion of FSH and LH until the portal vessels regenerate. Pituitaries transplanted to another site fail to secrete FSH or LH, but such functions return when the glands are retransplanted to a region beneath the brain where they can reestablish vascular connections with the median eminence region of the hypothalamus. Collectively, this evidence provides overwhelming support of the concept of neuroendocrine regulation of reproductive phenomena.

Mechanisms of Hormone Action. A few hormones have been available since the turn of the century, and numerous others have been studied intensively for lesser periods, yet the fact remains that we do not know how any hormone acting as a chemical messenger conveys its signal to a responding cell or tissue. The actions of growth hormone, thyroid hormone, and insulin are each very widespread and may include nearly every tissue in the body. Other hormones stimulate only a particular tissue or organ. The determinant of response is not the hormone but the sensitivity of the tissue or target organ to a particular hormone. The basis of this sensitivity remains totally unknown. Some target organs take up and bind the hormone but other, nonresponsive tissues may do likewise. Usually the hormone must continue to be present to sustain the response, but in a few instances only its initial presence will suffice to trigger off a whole series of reactions that proceed in the absence of the hormone. All hormones are very specific in the kind of response they induce. Despite these seeming advantages in studying the mechanisms of action of hormones, the actual modus operandi remains elusive in every instance. Only three general mechanisms appear attractive: (1) A hormone may bind to some component of the plasma membrane or of one of the intracellular membranes, thereby altering permeability characteristics. (2) A hormone may bind to an enzyme protein and thereby alter its catalytic properties, particularly the effect of modifying compounds in the environment. (3) A hormone may serve as an inducer, i.e., a derepressor of the biosynthesis of one or more proteins.

Evidence has been adduced in support of each of these hypotheses for various hormones. Most compelling are the instances in which such hormones as insulin, cortisol, estrogens, and androgens have been shown to elicit the biosynthesis of diverse enzymes, each compatible with overall observed metabolic effects. Once again, this may not be descriptive of the ultimate mechanisms, since it is not at all clear that these hormones, themselves, serve as derepressors; the possibility of intermediaries in this process is entirely open. But increasing evidence indicates that it is at this level that many endocrine effects are initiated. For example, there is the report that RNA from an estrogen-stimulated uterus, in turn, stimulates an untreated uterus, much as does estrogen itself.

One other development in endocrine mechanisms warrants description in this brief summary, the existence of a compound which seems to warrant consideration as an "intracellular hormone." The compound is $3'5'$-cyclic adenosine monophosphate, which is formed from ATP by the action of an enzyme termed phosphoadenosine cyclase. This compound has been independently discovered in several connections. For example, the release of glucose from storage as liver glycogen is stimulated by epinephrine, the hormone of the adrenal medulla. The immediate effect of epinephrine is to activate the adenosine cyclase of liver; the resultant cyclic adenylate, in turn, activates an enzyme that activates glycogen phosphorylase, the agent that degrades liver glycogen to glucose units. In another context, ACTH, a trophic hormone of the anterior pituitary, stimulates the adrenal cortex, which then makes its various hormones. And again, ACTH appears to operate by stimulating adenosine cyclase activity; thereafter, all else follows. In a third instance, the antidiuretic hormone of the neurohypophysis, which alters the permeability of renal collecting ducts to water, stimulates the formation of cyclic adenylate. Indeed, application of the latter compound to frog skin or bladder exerts the same effects as does the hormone. How these three hormones stimulate the enzyme that makes cyclic adenylate in these respective tissues, and how this substance then affects its receptors, remain to be established, but it is clear that this compound warrants consideration as an intracellular hormone. And it seems highly likely that it will be found to participate in many other physiological processes.

Insect Endocrinology. As we have seen, one of the most important advances in understanding of endocrine systems was the realization that some hormones are released from specialized nerve cells. These neuro-endocrine cells serve as a link between the nervous and endocrine systems. They are part of the nervous system, so they can be excited by messages originating in the sense organs which detect changing conditions inside and outside of the animal. Frequently, the secretions released by the neuroendocrine cells into the blood stimulate conventional endocrine organs, whose products then act on other tissues of the body. Some of the most important work leading to the recognition of neuroendocrine cells was done by the relative handful of scientists who study the endocrinology of invertebrates. Several lines of investigation were involved in this development; insect endocrinology will be taken as an example (Fig. 7-4).

Insects are encased in a relatively rigid skin, which serves both as a covering and as a skeleton for support. To grow in size, they must periodically molt this external skeleton. Experiments done many years ago showed that molting would cease if the insect's brain was removed, but the full significance of this observation was not understood. Molting could be restored if the brain was reimplanted into another part of the animal's body, suggesting that a chemical is released from the brain to trigger the molt. Other investigators who examined stained sections of the brain found that some of the large nerve cells contain prominent granules. This suggested that these cells may be manufacturing large amounts of specific, albeit unidentified, chemicals. Each neurosecretory cell has a long process, or axon, that runs out of the brain and ends in a specialized organ that is abundantly perfused with blood. The granules manufactured in the cell body migrate down the axon and are discharged into the blood at the axon ending. These neurosecretory cells are the source of the hormone that triggers the insect's molting; if they are destroyed, while the rest of the brain is intact, molting ceases. The demonstration that the neurosecretory cells in the insect brain release a hormone stimulated many other studies, and neuroendocrine cells have since been described in animals of every sort. This is one of the characteristics of the life sciences: results with one group of organisms may greatly influence understanding of all organisms.

Further studies showed that the brain hormone does not act on all of the insect tissues, but serves only to stimulate a second endocrine organ, the prothoracic gland. The stimulated prothoracic gland releases a steroid hormone, ecdysone, which acts on the tissues of the body to produce all of the changes characteristic of the molt.

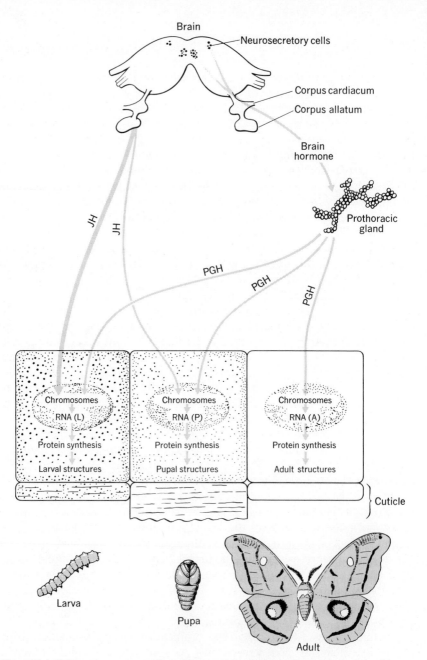

Figure 7-4. Schematic representation of insect endocrinology. (From H. A. Schneiderman and L. I. Gilbert, "Control of Growth and Development in Insects," Science *143*:325–33. © Jan. 1964 by American Association for the Advancement of Science)

Figure 7-5. Three stages of insect development. (Prepared by F. White from a color transparency by M. V. Williams)

The most advanced insects have a complicated life history. Butterflies and moths, for example, hatch from their eggs as caterpillars or larvae. The caterpillar undergoes a series of molts; each time, the animal emerging from the shed exoskeleton is a larger caterpillar. At the end of larval life, the caterpillar molts again, but this time emerges as a quite different sort of animal, the quiescent pupa. The pupa is a transitional stage in metamorphosis between the larva and the adult moth or butterfly. The pupa molts to an adult, which emerges and then expands its wings. Some of the tissues in the adult are formed by reorganized larval cells. But some of the adult organs, like the wings, were formed early in larval life and maintained as specialized packs of cells segregated in the caterpillar's body. During larval life the future wings grow slowly, but at the time of the molt to the pupa, there is a spurt of growth, and the small packet of cells grows into a wing. At the same time, other larval tissues, like the silk glands, die. Their cells are broken down and their substance is reused in the synthesis of other adult tissue (Fig. 7-5).

These processes—the multiplication of some cells and the death of others—are also controlled by hormones. In the insect's head, just behind the brain, is a pair of small organs, the corpora allata. If the corpora allata are removed from a young caterpillar, a tiny pupa is formed at the next molt. The pupa can develop normally and form a midget moth. When corpora allata are implanted into a caterpillar at the end of larval life, the next molt yields a giant caterpillar instead of a pupa. If active corpora allata are implanted into a pupa, it molts into a second pupa instead of a moth. The corpora allata therefore release a hormone with the remarkable property of braking progress in development. It is aptly called the *juvenile hormone*. In normal development, the juvenile hormone is present throughout larval life, so that at each molt the animal simply forms another caterpillar. At the end of larval life, the corpora allata stop secreting juvenile hormone. When the animal next molts, it forms a pupa and then goes on to become an adult.

The way in which these hormones—ecdysone and the juvenile hormone—interact to regulate cellular activity is a key problem in biology. The question is how these chemicals can cause some cells to multiply, others to differentiate, and yet others to die. Some hints about the mechanism have been obtained. The cells of certain insects—the flies and their relatives—have giant chromosomes. The giants consist of hundreds of parallel chromosomal threads. They are large enough to be seen and studied in the light microscope. At certain spots the chromosomes are swollen or "puffed." At the puff the threads are loosened and separated; there is an enhanced synthesis of RNA and of proteins. Apparently the puff represents a region at which the genes are especially active. The puffs shift from point to point at different times of the life cycle. When ecdysone is injected into a larva, new puffs appear on the chromosomes within fifteen minutes; the pattern of the puffing is that of a larva about to undergo pupation. These hormones may act by regulating the activity of certain genes and hence the fate of the cells. There are still difficulties and uncertainties about this interpretation, but this is a most important clue about how endocrines act to control growth and development.

The exact chemistry of the naturally occurring juvenile hormone is still unknown, though the problem is being worked on by many laboratories. Extracts made from certain insects can duplicate the effects of juvenile hormone, and these extracts have been highly purified. The hormone is most certainly a large lipophilic molecule. However, a few years ago a species of insect that lives on certain trees in central Europe was found not to respond to the hormone extracts. Some of the insects were brought to this country for further investigation. There were immediate difficulties. They did not grow properly in the United States;

they never became adults. Indeed, they behaved as if they were being exposed constantly to juvenile hormone and were extremely sensitive to it. It turned out that the critical factor came from a paper towel placed in each of the rearing bottles. The paper towels contained a substance that acts on the insects like their own juvenile hormone, and thereby prevents them from reaching adulthood. The source of this factor was the pulp of a North American fir tree used in paper manufacture. (The active substance has been identified as todomatuic acid methyl ester.) No wonder the insect lives only in Europe, since it cannot coexist with the fir tree. More importantly, this discovery emphasizes the potential usefulness of juvenile hormonelike substances as insecticides. Compounds that act like juvenile hormone, have no effect on other animals, and yet prevent insects from reaching adulthood are, potentially, the ideal insecticides for field use.

At first glance insect endocrinology might seem like a specialty far removed from the cares of man. However, studies in this area have led to important advances in our understanding of the relation between nerve cells and hormones, of the control of cellular growth and death, of the mechanism of hormone action, and also of how we may better control insect pests.

Plant Endocrinology. The idea of chemical communication between different parts of a plant was proposed about 1880 by the German plant physiologist Sachs, but for a long time the idea did not find acceptance. Among the reasons for this was undoubtedly the fact that plants do not possess specialized endocrine organs, and that it seemed possible to explain any interrelations between different plant parts on the basis of simple nutrient supply. Plants obtain their organic food by photosynthesis which occurs in the leaves but obviously not in the roots; the fact that roots are unable to grow if detached from the shoot seemed easily and fully explained by the lack of the products of photosynthesis. While correct, this proved not to be the complete picture; the roots of plants depend on the shoot not only for the major products of photosynthesis—sugars and amino acids—but also for other materials which are required in much smaller amounts, particularly certain of the materials which in animals are called vitamins. In plants, these can in fact be called hormones.

In addition, it is now recognized that parts of plants synthesize hormones which play an essential role in the growth, development, and differentiation of plants. The first such hormone was discovered in 1928. Tips of the first leaves (the coleoptiles) of oat seedlings were placed on blocks of agar gel, and the hormone—which was soon after christened *auxin*—was trapped in the agar. Then botanists, who before that had been so hesitant to accept the existence of hormones in plants, went all the other way. They were so fascinated by auxin that they tried to interpret all phenomena of plant growth with this single hormone; little effort was directed at the search for other hormones.

It must be admitted that there were some good reasons for this single-mindedness. Auxin proved capable of performing a surprising variety of actions. It promotes the growth in length of the main shoot of a plant and also the growth in thickness of the stem, while at the same time inhibiting the growth of lateral shoots (branches), at least in some plants; it causes formation of roots in cuttings and formation of flowers in at least a few plants; it is essential for fruit growth. It certainly did seem capable of regulating very many if not all individual growth processes of plants. As late as 1954, some authors were arguing that auxin was the only plant hormone.

In the middle 1950's, however, this situation changed. Several other plant hormones were recognized, first (1955–56) the gibberellins and the cytokinins; more recently (1965–66) abscisin; in addition, it became apparent that a simple, well-known gas, ethylene, functions as a hormone in plants, so that at present we recognize five major hormones or groups of hormones in plants.

However, the feature that was apparent already with auxin, and distracted botanists for over twenty-five years from searching for additional plant hormones, remained true also with the newer plant hormones. None of these substances has a single, clearly defined function; they all are active in a *variety* of different processes of growth or development. The gibberellins are active, among other processes, in stem and leaf growth, seed germination, the growth of some fruits, the formation of flowers in numerous plants, the determination of the sex of flowers in certain plants, and the termination of dormancy conditions. The cytokinins affect root and bud formation; they are, like the gibberellins, capable of overcoming dormancy in some plants; and they have the interesting property of rendering plants less sensitive to all kinds of unfavorable conditions, such as shortage of water, low and high temperatures, and the effects of weed-killers. Abscisin is a hormone which generally seems to *reduce* the growth activities of plants and to induce dormancy. This effect can, however, again be observed in a variety of organs (buds, seeds, perhaps flowers). Similarly, ethylene seems to affect the growth of shoots, leaves, fruits, and perhaps also other plant organs. The idea is emerging that the growth and development of many, if not all, plant organs is regulated, not by a single hormone, but by several plant hormones simultaneously. In this regulation, the *ratio* of the hormones may be of very great importance. For example, if a particular plant tissue (tobacco stem pith) is treated with a mixture relatively rich in auxin and poor in cytokinin, it will form roots; if the ratio is reversed, the tissue will form shoot buds; if the ratio is intermediary, the tissue will not form any structures but will continue growing in an undifferentiated manner.

The results summarized in this section were obtained either by removing the source of the hormone in the plant and registering the latter's responses, or by treating plants, plant organs, or plant tissues with the plant hormones, either singly or in combination. The removal of the hormone source was accomplished either by excision—the classical technique in endocrinology—or, particularly in the case of the gibberellins, chemically: a number of chemicals have been discovered which selectively suppress the synthesis of gibberellin in the plant and can thus be used to reduce the level of this hormone in the latter.

In the study of plant hormone action by means of hormone application, the technique of tissue and organ culture has played an increasingly important role. Plant biologists have gradually learned to grow nearly all important organs of the plant (roots, shoot tips, leaves, flowers and some flower parts, embryos, and fruits) in the test tube and have also been able to culture in the same manner undifferentiated tissue derived from different organs. The advantage of this technique is, of course, that the organ or tissue is removed from the supply of hormones (and also of nutrients) from other parts of the whole plant, so that the effects of a given hormone, or a combination of two or more hormones, can be studied without interference from the rest of the plant organism.

The discovery of several types of plant hormones, on the one hand, and the finding that several, if not all, of these hormones interact in numerous different growth processes of the plant, on the other, again pose the question of the action mechanism of the plant hormones. But, again, knowledge is still very fragmentary. In the case of both auxin and gibberellin it has been shown, in elegant experiments, that these hormones render the walls, which surround all plant cells, less rigid and thus capable of more growth (stretching).

We have already noted that gibberellin causes synthesis of amylase and other enzymes in barley aleurone; thus, in this case it is apparent that the hormone is activating the appropriate genetic information present in the cells, although it is not clear whether it functions at the transcription or the translation step. For other actions of gibberellin and auxin we cannot safely say that the hormone is acting in this manner, but there is evidence that its action depends on the concurrent synthesis of nucleic acids and of protein: if these processes are inhibited (which can be accomplished by certain selective agents) the effect of the hormone on the growth of the tissue is greatly reduced. Cytokinins have been recognized as constituents of transfer RNA, the adapter for attachment of amino acid molecules to the growing protein chain; how this finding relates to the action mechanism of this group of hormones remains to be determined.

In retrospect, we see that research in plant endocrinology shows the same trend that was emphasized in the introduction to this chapter. It started exclusively as work with whole plants or their organs or tissues but presently includes an ever increasing amount of work at the molecular level; the ultimate answers to the question, "How do plant hormones work?" can be couched adequately only in molecular terms.

This trend is important from another viewpoint. Comparing plant and animal endocrinology there are certain clear differences, although these differences, as they appear to us now, are of a quantitative rather than a qualitative nature. Plants do not have special endocrine organs as do animals. Auxin and gibberellin are produced in such different organs as the young leaves at the shoot tip, in the root tips, and in the developing seeds; cytokinins in roots, young seeds, and possibly also elsewhere in the plant. Plants have fewer hormones than animals. Whereas most mammalian hormones exhibit unique, clearly defined functions, all plant hormones presently identified have a multitude of overlapping functions, leading to the belief that they do not act singly but in concert with one another. However, as research in plant endocrinology moves increasingly to the molecular level, we find an increasing number of similarities. Most striking is the fact that both plant and animal hormones may exert their primary effects on the genetic apparatus responsible for protein biosynthesis.

The Future of Research in Physiology

At any one time some fields of research are fashionable, and others are neglected. Then quite suddenly new ideas and new methods applied to a neglected field result in an abundant harvest. It is almost impossible to tell where this will occur, for neglected fields tend to be invisible before they are cultivated. In 1930 no one could have predicted what was about to happen in renal physiology, a field that was stimulated by the efforts of a few inspired investigators. Sometimes, however, efforts can be deliberately directed to solution of particular problems. The history of respiratory physiology in the past 25 years is an example of the explosive growth of useful knowledge occurring because physiologists tackled an urgent problem.

The Physiology of Respiration—Integrated Synthesis of a System

The inspiratory movement of the chest creates a pressure gradient which causes air to flow through the respiratory passages into the alveoli, the smallest subdivisions of the lungs. These gas-filled spaces are separated by a thin membrane from venous blood driven through the capillary blood vessels of the lungs by contraction of the right ventricle of the heart. Oxygen from the inspired air diffuses across the membrane into the blood and combines with hemoglobin in the red blood cells. At the same time, carbon dioxide contained in venous blood—carbon dioxide produced in the tissues and collected by venous blood—diffuses from the blood in the lung capillaries into the air spaces of the lungs. Blood returns from the lungs to the left ventricle of the heart, and the oxygen-enriched blood is pumped through the arteries to supply the tissues with oxygen. Upon expiration the lungs become smaller, and gas is forced from the lungs; carbon dioxide is carried into the expired air. Study of these processes is, in essence, the science of respiratory physiology.

Before World War II, respiratory physiology was not a totally neglected field, but work in it was proceeding at the leisurely pace of prewar science. The coming of war posed a respiratory problem demanding urgent solution. In combat flying it is absolutely essential not to let the enemy get above you. In those days the height a plane could reach was largely limited by the respiration of the man who flew it. As one goes up, the quantity of oxygen in a cubic meter of air decreases; despite reflex increase in rate and depth of breathing, the amount of oxygen delivered to the arterial blood decreases, and tissues, particularly the brain, suffer from lack of oxygen. A pilot breathing air is already adversely affected at 10,000 feet; his night vision is impaired, and his judgment may be unreliable. For a pilot breathing pure oxygen the limit is somewhere between 36,000 and 40,000 feet. The question asked physiologists was, "What can we learn about respiration which will allow a pilot to climb a few hundred feet higher?" There were, in addition, a group of related problems, for example, the possibility of economy of weight. During expiration some oxygen contained in the lungs is blown out along with carbon dioxide and is wasted. This is unimportant at ground level, but when oxygen must be carried in heavy tanks on prolonged missions or when armament or fuel must be sacrificed for oxygen, economy of oxygen may become a critical factor.

The obvious need to know about respiratory physiology mobilized men, money, and machines. The few senior scientists already working in respiratory physiology were joined by men with established reputations in other fields. A second group, profoundly important for the future, was composed of graduate students who had not yet made a commitment to a particular line of research and of physicians in the early stages of their medical training. All members of this latter group brought with them some specific scientific or engineering skill acquired outside the course of their regular medical education. The supporting funds, provided by the wartime OSRD, the armed services, and academic department budgets, were trivial compared with modern R and D funds.

Study of respiratory problems requires accurate and rapid analysis of gas samples. At the beginning of the war the best instruments available could analyze only a spot sample of gas, and a highly skilled man took at least seven minutes to analyze the single sample for oxygen, carbon dioxide, and nitrogen. The demand for adequate instrumentation was met. A nitrogen meter was invented by a medical student at Penn who had premedical training at Caltech and experience as a radio "ham." An oxygen meter—which has since had important industrial applications—was invented by a famous physical chemist, and a carbon dioxide meter came out of the kind of garage-in-the-backyard industry which has spawned many great corporations. At the same time physiological techniques—for example, cardiac catheterization allowing blood samples to be withdrawn from the heart—were refined so that they could safely be used on man.

New ideas and new ways of looking at old problems—the inevitable consequence of the steady application of first-class intellectual ability—brought new advances. The celebrated "alveolar equations" were developed, which predict exactly what will happen to the gases in the lungs under any conditions provided a few relatively simple measurements are made. The equations are, in fact, nothing more than the law of the conservation of matter applied to respiration, and they are so simple they are now taught to first-year medical students; however, the type of thinking they represent had not previously been applied to respiratory problems. By adding measurement of blood flow through the lungs and data on the concentration of oxygen and carbon dioxide in arterial and venous blood, it became possible to describe in quantitative terms the whole process of respiratory gas exchange beginning with ventilation of the lungs, diffusion of gases across the membrane dividing the gas spaces from the blood, the distribution of blood in the vessels of the lungs, and the transport of gases from the lungs to the tissues. Moreover, at every step, identification and quantitation of abnormal function became possible. Three examples of this which later became important in medical practice are the measurement of maldistribution of gases in the lungs occurring in emphysema (abnormal distention of the lungs), measurement of blockade of diffusion of oxygen from the lungs to the blood occurring in some kinds of cancer of the lungs or in the poisoning resulting from breathing beryllium dust, and measurement of distorted relations between flow of blood through the lungs and ventilation of the lungs occurring in many cardiovascular or pulmonary diseases.

By the end of the war the military problems had largely disappeared; either they were solved insofar as physiology could solve them, or they had been eliminated by engineering solutions such as pressurization of cabins or of flying suits. There remained, however, a tremendously powerful armamentarium of ideas and techniques. Most important of all, there was a group of able, enthusiastic young men familiar with these ideas and methods waiting to apply them to problems of respiration in health and disease. These men and their successors have revolutionized a branch of physiology, and with momentum that has lasted to the present day they have created a new medical specialty. The use of knowledge of respiration in diagnosis and treatment of disease is described in Chapter 16.

Thus, under the right conditions, effort was successfully directed to the solution of a specific problem. And this can be done again. Furthermore, the yield of useful information and the effect on the development of science may be far greater than anticipated. The necessary ingredients are a sense of urgency, a supply of competent and appropriately trained brains, and a field ripe for exploration. If a sufficient number of mature scientists can be persuaded that a problem demands their full attention, important results are likely to be obtained. Once this becomes obvious and once younger men are trained in the field, very rapid growth of knowledge may occur. The history of respiratory physiology is not unique; cardiovascular physiology, for example, has gone through a parallel development. A field that was neglected between about 1920 and 1945, the study of the digestive tract, appears just now to have started on the upward phase of growth; a few senior men and women have contributed ideas and have trained a group of brilliant pupils who are early in lifetimes of productive work.

The tasks facing anyone who sets out to find and cultivate a neglected field are, first, to identify the field and, second, to capture the attention of scientists. The prevailing mood in the scientific community is that a scientist's curiosity will, unaided, lead him in the right direction. But there are acceptable alternatives. And occasionally, when a field has grown sterile, when only derivative, nonexploratory research is in progress, it would be well to allow it to lie fallow awhile, until new ideas, techniques and insights provide reinvigoration and a sense of direction.

Cardiovascular Physiology and the Enhancement of Understanding

The motto of physiological research is *Quanto? Quando? Quo Modo?* What happens, when, and by what means? Research begins with the accurate description of an event; then it is explained in terms of the next more fundamental level of understanding. We gradually push the analysis to the level beneath which with the tools, mental and physical, we cannot go. Then we must await new opportunities.

In 1887 an English physiologist recorded by means of two electrodes on the chest and back and a slow galvanometer the changes in electrical potential on the surface of the human body which accompany the heartbeat. This was the first electrocardiogram. The underlying potential changes were more rapid than the instrument recording them, and to remedy this a Dutch physiologist invented the fast string galvanometer— not the first nor the last time the requirements of physiological inquiry have improved physical instrumentation. Then came a period of very rapid advance in dissection and analysis of the electrocardiogram. Potential changes were recorded directly from the heart of an anesthetized animal, and the electric wave of excitation which originates in the pacemaker at the sinoauricular node was carefully and exactly mapped as it swept over the heart. Experimental analysis then showed what each aspect of the electrical changes meant in terms of excitation and conduction through the heart muscle. Variations in disease were analyzed in terms of the electrical events. Application of engineering principles showed how the potential changes arising in the heart are represented by the electrocardiogram recorded on the surface of the body, and a vast amount of clinical observation correlated features of the electrocardiogram with diseases of the heart. This work remains enormously revealing and useful. But, eventually, it ran out of intellectual excitement at the point where it was forced to say that the electrical waves "just happened."

The next advance was literally a penetration to a deeper level of understanding. An extremely fine glass electrode was thrust into the heart, and the transmembrane potential of a single muscle fiber was recorded. Thus the basic electrical event from which the electrocardiogram is derived could be recorded. When a ventricular cell is at rest it has a steady transmembrane potential, the inside of the fiber being about -90 mV with respect to the outside. Upon excitation, the membrane suddenly depolarizes, and the potential difference reverses, with the inside of the fiber becoming about $+30$ mV with respect to the outside. Then the fiber slowly repolarizes and eventually reaches the resting state. The sum of all these potential changes as seen by external electrodes is the electrocardiogram.

Not all cardiac cells are alike. When a cell in the sinus pacemaker region is impaled, the transmembrane potential does not stay constant during the interval between action potentials; it slowly drifts toward zero. When it has reached a particular voltage, the threshold, the cell suddenly depolarizes, and a fully developed action potential follows. This action potential is then conducted over the rest of the heart and excites it to contract. The rate at which the heart beats is obviously determined by the rate at which the resting potential drifts toward zero. If it drifts quickly, the threshold is soon reached, and an action potential soon occurs. If it drifts slowly, the next action potential will be delayed, and the heart will beat slowly (Fig. 7-6).

But what chemical events underlie these changes in potential? At the next more fundamental level of analysis, the heart action potentials and the drift of the pacemaker potential have been found to depend on the permeabilities of the membrane to potassium and sodium. Although there are some differences peculiar to the heart, a description of potential changes in terms of conductances of potassium and sodium across the membrane of the cardiac cells could be given in much the same terms as those used to describe the function of nerves in Chapter 9. We have now reached the limits of present understanding; these changes in permeability, conductance, and ion movements are entirely real, but their initiation and the mechanism of propagation remain obscure. The next step will be to discover and to describe in terms of the configuration of molecules in the membrane what causes the changes in permeability. This will certainly be done soon—but beyond will lie still another unanswered question.

In recent years progress in understanding tissues and organs has come far faster than the most optimistic would have dared to predict. There are three reasons for the rapid advance: labor, ideas, and techniques. Science is usually extraordinarily time-consuming. Weeks, months, or even years of effort may be needed to produce the data summarized in a single line in a table in a scientific paper. A substantial increase in the number of investigators and the amount of time they are able to give to research have greatly speeded the gathering of vital information.

To understand how tissues and organs work, we must first understand the cells that make them up. The rapid developments in molecular and cellular biology, the chemistry of the living state, have provided a series of powerful ideas. This new knowledge is just now being applied to tissues and organs. Because of the backlog of new generalizations we can anticipate substantial further advances in our understanding of tissues and organs.

Progress in science has been paced by the development of tools that

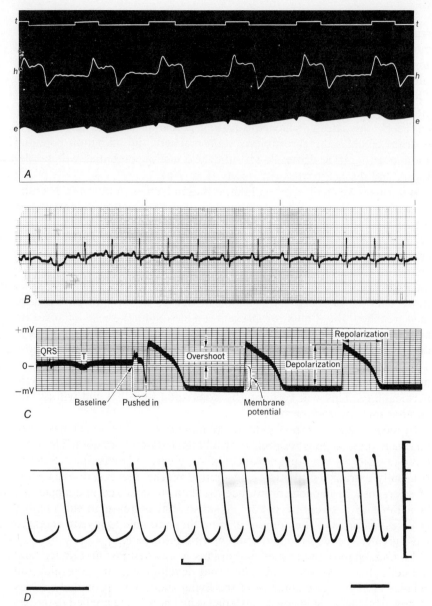

Figure 7-6.

extend man's senses. In recent years there have been great steps forward in technique. With electronic instruments we can measure events occurring in fractions of a thousandth of a second. A variety of devices have been developed that can be placed on or near an organism, without interfering with normal function, and allow us to record rapidly, by telemetry, changes in fluid flow or in pressure voltages, gas concentrations, or other physiological variables. The measuring instruments can be attached even to freely moving animals and the data broadcast to a remote receiver. Extensive experimentation can be undertaken without seriously disturbing the organism or its normal function. It may well be that the principal payoff of the remarkable developments in microminiaturization of electronic devices, spurred by the national space program, and made possible by the advancement of solid-state physics, which was largely supported by the Defense Department, will be found in applications in the study of human physiology and prosthetic devices for the ailing or injured.

Further Developments in Synthesis of Physiological Processes

At the same time that study of function of tissues and organs is carried to the level of molecular biology and biophysics, we will increase our

---

A. The first published human electrocardiogram.
       t = time in seconds
       h = arterial blood pressure crudely recorded
       e = electrocardiogram recorded with relatively slow
          galvanometer
       (From A. D. Waller, J. Physiol. *8*:229–34, 1887)
B. A normal human electrocardiogram recorded with a rapid galvanometer
C. The first published transmembrane potential of the heart. Sequence of events as a microelectrode is pushed into a normally beating frog ventricular fiber. At the start of the record as the needle approaches the fiber a surface electrocardiogram (QRS, T) is recorded. This is followed by an iso-electric baseline, then movement artifact and a sudden swing of voltage as the needle penetrates the cell. At this point the fiber depolarizes and an action potential follows. Two more action potentials are recorded. (From Woodbury, Hecht, and Christopherson, Amer. J. Physiol. *164*, 1951)
D. The effect of sympathetic stimulation on pacemaker potentials in the sinus venosus of the frog heart. The rapid phase of depolarization is too fast to give a recordable trace on the face of a cathode ray oscilloscope. After the repolarization has brought the voltage to the baseline the transmembrane potential begins to drift slowly upward. Compare this with the record in C made from a cell not spontaneously beating in which the transmembrane potential remains constant between action potentials. When the drifting transmembrane potential reaches a threshold value, the cell fires by depolarizing. Between the breaks in the bottom line sympathetic nerves to the heart were stimulated, and the rate of drift of the transmembrane potential increases, and heart rate accelerates. (From Hutter and Trautwein, Nature *176*, 1955)

knowledge of the means by which control of function is exerted. If, for example, we learn the means by which plant hormones are synthesized, we will comprehend the means by which the controller of plant function is itself controlled. Now that transport of water and salts into and within plants is reasonably well understood, the next step is to study the synthesis and transport of organic constituents. The factors that regulate biosynthesis of cellulose, which forms the bulk of the plant and is the basis of its support, remain to be investigated. Since plant hormones control both form and function of a plant by regulating the deposition of cellulose, success in this line of study will reveal the means by which growth and maturation of the whole plant and of its fruit are determined. This could place in our hands rational means of controlling entire orchards.

The way in which blood circulates is now understood in considerable detail, but intensive study of regulation of the circulation is just beginning. When a man exercises, his cardiac output and heart rate increase, as we have described. Much is known about the components of this response. The heart rate rises, because nerve impulses liberate a hormone at their endings within the heart muscle, and this hormone accelerates the rate of change of the membrane potential of a few pacemaker cells. But we do not understand how the *total* response to exercise is regulated. In fact, a man's heart rate rises in anticipation *before* he begins to exercise, while that of a whale or porpoise declines dramatically as it begins its dive, and this emphasizes the major role the central nervous system plays in regulating the circulation. Research along these lines requires methods that can be applied to intact, unanesthetized men and animals. Such methods are being developed; the heart rate of a greyhound chasing a rabbit or of a sounding whale can be measured. The methods devised for such studies will be particularly useful for the study of the pathophysiology of the human circulation.

We can expect these studies to reveal hitherto unknown links in the control systems just as study of the regulation of heart rate led to discovery of chemical transmission of nerve impulses by acetylcholine and norepinephrine—one of the most fruitful discoveries of physiology. Similar revolutionary discoveries doubtless remain to be made. After the general principle of a control mechanism is discovered, we are often astonished by the diversity of detail in the way the principle is applied. Nerve impulses regulate the peripheral resistance in the circulation by liberating transmitter hormones which act on smooth muscle of blood vessels. Yet in one vascular bed the transmitter, epinephrine, causes contraction of smooth muscle and vasoconstriction, whereas in another vascular bed the same neurohormone causes relaxation of smooth muscle and vasodilatation. Such examples could be multiplied indefinitely, and major tasks in the study of control are to identify diversity and to understand its basis.

The remarkable complexity of physiological function can no longer be comprehended in simple terms. Consequently, new tools are being used in the study of the interrelations of parts and the behavior of whole organisms. Some of the tools are conceptual — among them, control systems theory drawn from engineering, advanced probability theory, the mathematics of compartmental analysis. Some tools are new types of sensing devices which measure function continuously, and other tools are the electronic devices ranging from simple operational amplifiers to the most elaborate computers, which handle and reduce the data obtained or even control the course of the experiment itself. Three examples will show how these tools help us to understand control.

We know that the output of insulin by the beta cells in the pancreas is somehow regulated by the level of blood sugar and that the rate of output of insulin in turn regulates the blood sugar level. To determine exactly how the blood sugar level controls insulin output, one can measure, almost continuously, the concentration of insulin in blood flowing from the pancreas and the rate at which that blood flows. One can also measure continuously the concentration of sugar in the arterial blood flowing to the pancreas, and cause that concentration to vary at different rates. The data obtained indicate that the rate of insulin release is a function, not only of the absolute level of blood sugar, but also of the rate of change of blood sugar concentration, and that the pancreas responds with a characteristic delay. The data are simply too numerous and the questions asked too complex to be handled by ordinary computation. When the data are fed to a computer there is developed a differential equation, containing three terms, which accurately and comprehensibly describes this one aspect of physiological control.

The mean arterial blood pressure is the product of the total peripheral resistance, a function of the caliber and expansibility of the arterioles and the cardiac output. Total peripheral resistance is controlled in an extremely complex way by hormones and by the nervous system. In order to study it one must measure variations in blood pressure while the cardiac output is constant. But factors that change peripheral resistance also change cardiac output in an unpredictable way. The problem can be solved by an arrangement in which the experimental animal is on line with a computer. The system continuously measures cardiac output as well as mean arterial blood pressure and total peripheral resistance. When a deliberate experimental perturbation changes peripheral resistance — and therefore cardiac output — the computer commands the appropriate adjustments which will keep cardiac output constant. Alternatively, the system can be set so that mean arterial blood pressure is held constant in the face of changes in both cardiac output and resistance. Thus the control system provided by the computer allows us to isolate and study a physiological control system in a manner hitherto impossible.

The arterial system consists of a large number of branched tubes of greatly differing radius. The walls of the tubes are distensible, but their distensibility varies in a complex way with their radius. Blood is injected into the arterial system by the heart intermittently and within a complex pattern of changing velocity and pressure. Blood leaves the arterial system at a rate controlled by the peripheral resistance, which in turn is partly controlled by both mean blood pressure and the rate at which blood pressure changes during the cardiac cycle. Furthermore, the walls of the arteries vibrate, and pressure waves sweep along them from the heart to be reflected from the ends of the arteries in a way that varies with the arterial pressure, the length and radius of the artery, and the distensibility of its wall. A mathematical model of the system can be set up on a combination analogue-digital computer, and the performance of the model can be compared with the actual behavior of the arterial system. When the model agrees reasonably with actuality, the computer and experimental animal can be combined to ask questions of the model. For example, the physiological feedback system which senses the rate of change of arterial blood pressure and changes cardiac output and peripheral resistance accordingly can be replaced by an electrical and mechanical analogue. Then if the living system continues to behave in a normal fashion we can conclude that the characteristics of the analogue — its time constants, its sensitivities and so on — accurately describe those of the feedback loop it has replaced.

Studies like this, elaborate though they may seem, are only the primitive beginnings of future physiological work. There is a vast array of unanswered questions to which these or still more elaborate methods will be applied, and we may confidently look forward to a rapid increase in the depth and comprehensiveness of our understanding of function of tissues and organs and eventually whole plants and animals.

Chapter 8

BIOLOGICAL STRUCTURES – FROM MOLECULES TO MAN

Contemporary anatomical science can be defined as the study of biological structure as it relates to function, and as the investigation of modulations of structure in response to temporal, genetic, and environmental factors. It has as its major goals an understanding of the architectural principles on which living organisms are constructed, the discovery of the structural basis for the functioning of the various parts, and a comprehension of the formative mechanisms involved in their development. It encompasses the study of long-term changes of structure in the course of evolution; changes of intermediate duration in development, growth, and aging; and those shorter-term changes that are associated with different phases of normal functional activity. And it deals with structure at all levels of biological organization from whole animals and plants and their organ systems to cell organelles and macromolecules.

The scientist so engaged may employ such procedures and instruments as dissection and direct visual observation; mensuration and radiological analysis; cinematography and electromyography; light and electron microscopy; histochemical techniques; tissue and organ cultures, micromanipulation, and differential centrifugation—in short, any and all methods that may illuminate the intimate relation of form to function. As the range of visible structure was extended first by the light microscope and later by the electron microscope, the major focus of anatomical research shifted correspondingly. More than ever with the coming of the electron microscope, the morphological approach has enriched biological research. This chapter will offer a series of examples of the manner in which enhanced appreciation of structural organization has contributed to the broad advancement of understanding of living forms.

293

The Microscopic Structure of Living Organisms

The Diversity of Cell and Tissue Architecture

The enormous diversity of plants and animals and their remarkable adaptations to specific ecological conditions are of deep interest to the ecologist and to the student of evolutionary biology. But nature has been equally prodigal in the diversity of cellular subunits specialized for specific functions in the internal economy of the organism. Among the traditional goals of biology have been establishment of the identifying morphological characteristics of the many cell types of higher plants and animals; discovery of the functional significance of their visible specializations; and comprehension of the architectural principles that underlie the varied patterns in which cells are associated to form multicellular functional units.

Morphological discoveries are an indispensable part of the informational substrate for the functional studies of the physiologist or biochemist. The microscopist has often been first to define new problems or describe the relations essential to the design of meaningful experiments. In many instances, the physiological experiments come many years after the morphological descriptions of the pertinent structure. For example, the sarcoplasmic reticulum of skeletal muscle was revealed by Veratti with classical cytological techniques in 1902, but the experiments implicating this tubular system in muscle relaxation and the coupling of excitation to contraction came a half century later.

Microscopic studies of progressive thickening of plant cell walls led plant physiologists to a consideration of the synthesis of wall components, the composition of which is of vital concern in many uses of plant materials. More than half a century later, refinement of techniques has linked the synthetic processes involved to specific cellular organelles. Similarly, the chlorophyll-containing plastids first observed in the nineteenth century, became the foci of investigations of photosynthesis, the process by which plants utilize energy from the sunlight for the synthesis of organic molecules. Quantitative aspects of this vital process can now be related to specific features of the molecular organization of the plastids. The discovery, twenty years ago, of special nerve cells in the brain of fishes that possessed cytological characteristics of secretory cells led only recently to understanding of the humoral control of pituitary gland function (including the regulation of water balance, parturition, and milk ejection) and to the general recognition that the function of most nerve cells depends upon their capacity to secrete either neurotransmitter substances or hormones at their endings. The parafollicular cells of the thyroid, described forty years ago by Nonidez, are now understood to be the site of elaboration of the new hormone thyrocalcitonin, which plays an essential role in regulation of blood calcium concentration. Microscopic and experimental analysis of the interrelations of the parathyroid cells, bone-absorbing cells, and thyroid parafollicular cells has led to the identification of osteopetrosis (Albers-Schönberg disease) as an endocrine disorder and has suggested rational approaches to its treatment.

Some specific functions are performed by cells that are migratory and widely dispersed in the animal body. Examples are the lymphocytes and plasma cells that are essential to the immunological defenses of the organism, and the reticuloendothelial system, a widely dispersed population of cells which clear the blood and tissues of foreign proteins or invading microorganisms. Cells of great physiological importance may comprise only a small fraction of the cell population in a large organ. Discovery of the significance of such cells is dependent upon morphological methods that either assess their function in situ or achieve their segregation from other cell types. In plants, factors of disease resistance of tremendous economic importance in agriculture do not depend upon the specialized properties of migratory cells, but they do appear to correlate with specific structural details which make some resistant cells distinguishable from their nonresistant counterparts. In situ microscopic analysis is therefore of as much significance in plants as in animals.

Regrettably the methods of microscopic anatomy are, for the most part, qualitative. However, the key to an understanding of function, in some instances, may lie in the topographical relations or mechanical interactions of the parts. Perhaps nowhere is this more obvious than in the ear, where transduction of the energy of sound to nervous impulses depends upon the intermediate mechanical events of vibration of the auditory ossicles and of the basilar membrane and the attendant deformation of the hair cells. An adequate explanation of the mechanism of hearing is thus utterly dependent upon knowledge of the spatial relations of structural components and the mode of engagement of moving parts. It is equally apparent that the integrative function of the central nervous system depends upon its "wiring diagram,"—i.e., the location and pattern of interconnection of millions of neurons of specific functional types.

Outstanding among the many significant discoveries of the past decade with the electron microscope has been an unexpected solution to the old problem of muscular contraction. The myofibrils were seen to be built of two interdigitating sets of filaments that change their relative positions in different phases of the contraction cycle. Their changing relations fully account for the previously observed grosser shifts in the pattern of cross striations. It was these studies that led to the widely accepted sliding-filament hypothesis of muscle contraction. In the long history of speculation on this subject, numerous models of contraction had been proposed. The idea of two sets of filaments sliding past one another had apparently never occurred to anyone, but as soon as the existence of two sets of filaments was demonstrated in high-resolution electron micrographs, the possibility of shortening by a sliding mechanism was immediately obvious.

A final example of the interdependence of morphological and physiological studies is seen in recent advances in understanding of transepithelial transport. The linings of the small intestine, kidney tubule, and the gallbladder are capable of transporting fluids in the absence of an osmotic gradient or even against a substantial, artificially induced gradient. This important property long defied adequate explanation. Studies of the ultrastructure of these epithelia have now suggested a possible mechanism. In some of these transporting epithelia, the cells are firmly attached to one another near the free surface, but their lateral surfaces are free to separate, leaving intercellular clefts of variable width. Other epithelia with similar properties show elaborate infoldings of the cell bases creating a labyrinthine system of narrow extracellular spaces at the base of the epithelium. Such basal labyrinths and the narrow intercellular clefts are both tightly sealed toward the free surface, but toward the fixed surface they are closed only by the basement membrane which underlies the entire epithelium. Consideration of these structural relationships led to formulation of a new theory of fluid transport across epithelia and to construction of a model on which this theory could be tested. The model assumes a confined space between two membranes or diffusion barriers, arranged in series and having different properties. It is proposed that the first membrane has a restricted permeability to solutes but is more permeable to water. The second barrier is presumed to be nonselective and freely permeable to both. If solute is actively transported across the first membrane into a confined space between the two barriers, then the solute would exert a greater osmotic pressure across this first membrane than across the highly permeable second barrier. Water would, therefore, cross the first membrane by osmosis, building up a hydrostatic pressure in the confined space which, in turn, would force water through the second barrier. The structural analogue of the first membrane of the model is the lateral or basal membrane of the epithelial cells. The confined space corresponds to the intercellular clefts or basal labyrinths, and the second barrier is represented by the basement membrane and connective tissue subjacent to the transporting epithelium. Thus it is now believed that the transport of water is not itself an "active" process but is a consequence of active secretion of ions into the intercellular spaces.

This is clearly not the only mechanism employed in nature to achieve this result, for both single-celled and multicellular plants can accumulate high concentrations of specific substances against strong osmotic gradients without the morphological specializations described for several of the transporting epithelia of animals. The development of this concept nevertheless provides an interesting example of the way in which descriptive anatomical studies provide a framework of structural reality that sets limits upon speculations concerning mechanism and leads more directly to the design of the crucial experiments. The demonstration that the model was indeed able to transport water against an osmotic gradient provided, in turn, a functional interpretation for surface specializations common to a number of such epithelia, an interpretation that could not have been arrived at by morphological methods alone.

Localization and Chemical Characterization of Tissue Constituents and Cell Products

Possibly the most distinctive feature of the morphologist's approach to an understanding of the organism is his preoccupation with the *localization* of functional events. In the preparation of his specimens for microscopic examination, he goes to great lengths to maintain the parts of the cells or tissues in their normal spatial relations. The morphologist's concern with structure leads him to see events as individual rather than statistical and to seek to localize them with respect to visible structural components at the tissue, cell, and subcellular level. An important approach to such problems is afforded by histochemistry – a collection of methods for the chemical identification of certain proteins, carbohydrates, enzymes, metabolites, and secretion products in thin sections of tissue.

Localization of a particular constituent is commonly accomplished by incubating tissue sections with appropriate chemical reagents. Under the proper conditions, a colored or electron-dense reaction product is precipitated in or very near the place where the substance or enzymatic activity of interest resides. The site of the product can then be visualized with light or electron microscopes and related to particular cell types or even to intracellular organelles.

A number of the more specific chemical reactions for nucleic acids, carbohydrates, lipids, and proteins have been adapted for use on tissue sections. In some instances the specificity of these histochemical methods can be improved by comparing the distribution of reaction product with that obtained following pretreatment of the tissue section with a specific enzyme that removes the constituent being studied. Glycogen, for example, is colored a deep magenta when reacted with p-dimethyl-aminobenzaldehyde and sulfite after periodate oxidation. It can be differentiated from other carbohydrates that give this same staining by demonstrating its removal from tissue sections with amylase. Similarly, RNA can be differentiated from DNA and other constituents because of its specific removal by the enzyme ribonuclease. By virtue of their specific ability to catalyze oxidation of 3,4-dihydroxyphenylalanine, the pigment-producing cells, melanocytes, can be identified histochemically at a stage when they still lack melanin granules and are therefore colorless. The localization of histamine in mast cells of connective tissue and the precursors of 5-hydroxytryptamine in argentaffin cells of the gastrointestinal tract has been accomplished by histochemical methods.

Histochemical localization of a wide variety of enzymes (e.g., dehydrogenases, phosphatases, esterases) has been achieved by incubating tissue sections with substrates that lead to the formation of insoluble reaction products that can be directly visualized or which can be subsequently converted to a colored or electron-dense derivative. Thus, histochemical localization of the enzyme, acid phosphatase, within lysosomes provides a reliable method for the identification of this organelle, which does not have distinctive morphological characteristics. The enzyme nucleotide phosphatase can be used similarly to identify the peripheral cisternae of the Golgi apparatus. The histochemical localization of cholinesterase in the motor end plate of muscle provides a valuable means of revealing these physiologically important structures which are otherwise difficult to find.

An increasing number of histochemical staining methods are finding important applications in diagnostic pathology. It is evident that histochemistry, both at the light and electron microscope level, will contribute greatly to our knowledge in the future.

By attaching fluorescent dyes or electron-opaque markers to antibodies, it has been possible to take advantage of the exquisite sensitivity and specificity of antigen-antibody reactions to localize certain proteins or complex carbohydrates in the tissues. Antibodies to specific proteins (antigens) are prepared by standard immunological methods, and the antibody gamma globulin is then separated and conjugated to a fluorescent or electron-dense marker. When applied to tissue sections, the labeled antibody is then selectively bound to the site of antigen localization. Using such immunohistochemical procedures, the cell types concerned with hormone production in the pancreatic islets have been identified: insulin in the beta cells, glucagon in the alpha cells. The same approach has contributed to resolution of the confusion concerning the specific cellular sources of hormones in the pituitary gland. Inasmuch as specific antibodies can be prepared against a wide variety of proteins including enzymes and hormones, immunohistochemical methods promise to have wide applicability.

An extraordinarily valuable method for localizing substances and tracing their movements with time is *radioautography,* which depends upon injecting into animals radioactive precursors of tissue constituents and subsequently visualizing, in tissue sections, the sites of their radioactive emissions. A common application of radioautography involves labeling of cell nuclei to identify the sites of origin of new cells and to follow their subsequent migrations. The substance thymidine can be used by the cell nucleus in the synthesis of new DNA. Thymidine can be radioactively marked by incorporating into its structure tritium, the radioisotope of hydrogen. When labeled thymidine is injected into an experimental animal, it is taken up by the nuclei of cells that are preparing for division and built into the genetic material being synthesized. The nucleus thus becomes permanently "labeled" and will differ from other nuclei by its emission of beta rays. Thin slices of the animal's tissues are prepared for microscopic examination some time after the injection of the labeled compound and are coated with a photographic emulsion. After a suitable period of exposure the beta emissions from the labeled nuclei will reduce silver in the overlying photographic emulsion, producing black grains that reveal to the microscopist the location of the cells that were preparing for division (and hence incorporated thymidine) at the time of the injection. Tritium-labeled compounds are especially useful because of the low energy characteristics of the emitted beta particles, which travel only a limited distance, and hence they activate the silver grains only in the immediate proximity of the radioactive sites. Quantitation of the radioactivity can be accomplished by counting the number of individual silver grains per unit area of tissue section.

A wide variety of radioactive compounds have been used in radioautographic studies. Their selective uptake and incorporation into nucleic acids, proteins, and carbohydrates have been followed, and their subsequent intracellular and extracellular localization determined. In one of the earliest uses of radioautography, the selective uptake of iodine by the thyroid follicle cells and its subsequent incorporation into thyroid hormone was followed by giving I^{131}. This subsequently developed into a useful clinical procedure in evaluation of patients with thyroid disease.

The incorporation of tritium-labeled amino acids into the specific proteins of the pancreatic acinar cell has been followed radioautographically, and the subcellular sites of enzyme synthesis, storage, and release have been identified. Within a few minutes after the administration of the labeled amino acid, radioactivity is localized in the region of the endoplasmic reticulum. Subsequently the radioactivity is concentrated in the Golgi area of the cytoplasm where the newly synthesized protein is packaged in the form of secretion granules. When the pancreas is stimulated, the labeled secretion granules release their contents through the free cell surface and into the duct lumen. Radioautography will continue to be one of the most valuable techniques in the armamentarium of the histologist and cytologist for the localization of metabolic events in cells and tissues.

Several instruments permit quantitative analysis at the cell level under conditions where the interrelations of the cell and tissue components are preserved. By microspectrophotometry, changes in the concentrations of specific chemical constituents of cells with distinctive absorption spectra have been determined under different physiological and pathological conditions. The x-ray probe, the laser beam microprobe, and the computer-linked microspectrophotometer are likewise being used in studies involving cell identification and quantitative localization. The flying spot microscope and television microscopy, coupled with line scanning devices and spectrophotometric techniques, afford new methods for studying intact living cells. These techniques are presently being used in studying the state of key enzymes and coenzymes in living cells under varying conditions. By micromanipulative procedures substances can be injected into individual living cells, or components such as the nucleus can be surgically removed or transferred from cell to cell. Using frozen-dried tissue sections, groups of cells, individual cells, and even parts of single cells have been microdissected under the stereoscopic microscope. The component cellular layers of the retina have been separated, individual nerve cells isolated, individual glomeruli removed from kidney, and the insulin-producing islets have been dissected from pancreas. These minute samples of tissue can be weighed using a quartz-fiber microbalance, and can be analyzed for their enzyme or hormone content.

Living cells are astonishingly diverse in the details of their structure, and hence in their functional attributes. A rich armamentarium of analytical devices now permits intensive investigation of their fine structure under all relevant physiological circumstances.

Dynamics of Organized Cell Populations and the Movements of Their Cells and Products

The availability of radioelements for use as biological markers, and the development of the method of radioautography for visual localization of such markers in the tissues, introduced the time dimension into research in microscopic anatomy. Radioautographic studies have clearly defined three distinct categories of cell populations: static cell populations (e.g., neurons, cardiac and skeletal muscle); expanding cell populations (e.g., connective tissue, liver, endocrine glands); and continually renewing cell populations (e.g., hemopoietic tissue, epidermis, intestinal epithelium).

Among the most interesting applications of radioautography to problems of cell population dynamics have been the studies on the life history of intestinal epithelial cells. The dividing cells in the lining of the intestine are concentrated in crypts between the intestinal villi. In radioautographs prepared from samples of intestine taken on the day of injection with tritiated thymidine, only the cells in the crypts are labeled. One day later the labeled cells are found to have moved to the base of the villi; and in specimens taken four days after injection, they are near the tips of the villi. By the fifth or sixth day the labeled cells have been cast off into the intestinal lumen. Thus new cells, constantly forming in the crypts, are displaced upward along the sides of the villi and are eventually shed at their tips. The daily loss of cells from the small intestine of a rat is estimated at 1.3 billion, and from the entire gastrointestinal tract the total number of cells lost per day may approach 2 or 3 billion. Proportionally greater losses are reported for man. These results have important implications for gastrointestinal physiology and pathology and for understanding the events that accompany the normal aging process.

Investigations of the movements of labelled cells are also changing our concepts of the role of cell migration in embryonic development. It has been possible to establish the time of last division of the various classes of neurons found in the adult brain and to trace the route of their migration during development. Typical neurons undergo their final cell division within the primitive ependyma, the layer lining the cavity of the embryonic neural tube. They then migrate outward through an intermediate matrix zone and into the peripheral mantle zone of the neural tube, where they differentiate. Many regional modifications of the basic pattern of cell migrations are being found, corresponding to structural and perhaps to functional specialization of different brain regions in the adult. The cerebral cortex has been shown to form in an inside-out fashion. Neurons that arise and migrate earliest take up stations in the deepest layers, while later arrivals migrate past these cells already in place and go to more superficial layers. The factors that guide these migrations and determine the final configurations remain to be explored. It will also be of interest to discover what role these migration patterns play in establishing the specific synaptic interconnections of neurons upon which the integrative function of the nervous system depends.

The origins of the cells responsible for immunological defense against disease have also been clarified by radioautographic methods. Evidence has been obtained for two populations of lymphocytes in the body, short-lived ones found in bone marrow and thymus and long-lived lymphocytes found in other lymphoid organs such as the spleen and lymph nodes. Migration of lymphoid cells from one organ to another has been shown to be more extensive than was hitherto suspected. Indications are that the thymus may be a source of lymphocytes that migrate via the bloodstream to take up residence in other lymphoid tissues. These are believed to be the immunologically competent lymphocytes that proliferate in response to antigen and become the source of antibodies.

Adaptation of radioautographic methods for use at the electron microscopic level of resolution has made it possible to localize the intracellular sites of synthesis of protein and to follow its migrations within the cell. For example, incorporation of the tritium-labeled amino acid leucine into protein in the cell bodies of neurons can be demonstrated within minutes after its administration. In samples taken at successive time intervals, the protein synthesized in the cell body is shown to migrate continuously along the nerve process (axon) toward the periphery, thus confirming the axoplasmic flow postulated earlier on the basis of constriction experiments. The physiological significance of this flow is now under intensive investigation.

Translocation of Substances Between Compartments Within the Organism

Microscopy permits definition of the limits of various "compartments" within the organism: intravascular and extravascular; intracellular and extracellular. At a finer level, the cell is, in turn, partitioned into a number of recognizable compartments delimited by membranes: a given substance may be in the nucleus or the cytoplasm; intramitochondrial or extramitochondrial; within the canalicular endoplasmic reticulum or in the surrounding cytoplasmic matrix. By use of supravital staining with dyes that penetrate living cells or with particulate markers, such as amorphous carbon, it has been possible to follow, visually, the movements of various substances between these compartments. Application of this approach made it possible to delineate the lymph vascular system and to demonstrate the capacity of some cell types to ingest particulate matter by the cellular activity called phagocytosis. This led to recognition of the reticuloendothelial system – a widely dispersed population of scavenger cells which put their phagocytic capacity to use in the defenses of the body against invasion by microorganisms. The permeation of most tissues by blood-borne colloidal dyes, in contrast to their exclusion from the brain, led to the concept of a *blood-brain barrier* and drew attention to the existence of important local differences in vascular permeability. These and many other significant findings were achieved by use of particulate markers whose movements were followed with the light microscope.

With the advent of the electron microscope, it became possible to visualize particles of very much smaller size. Thus, administration of exogenous electron-opaque particles of molecular dimensions permitted study of such physiological problems as the pathway of intestinal absorption and the mechanisms of exchange between the blood and the tissues.

Movement of naturally occurring particulates has been traced to establish routes of cellular secretion. For example, the liver plays a decisive role in the metabolism of lipids and in the maintenance of the lipid levels of blood plasma. The main vehicle for the transport of water-insoluble lipids is the low-density lipoprotein of the blood plasma which is synthesized in the liver. Lipoprotein occurs in the form of spherical particles of a size easily resolved in electron micrographs, thereby permitting visual demonstration of the intracellular pathway of its synthesis and release. Isolated livers of fasted rats were perfused with physiological salt solution containing bovine serum albumin and linoleic acid as a precursor for lipid synthesis. By examining electron micrographs of biopsies from the perfused livers taken at successive time intervals, particles of lipoprotein were seen initially at the ends of profiles of the granular endoplasmic reticulum, later in the smooth-surfaced reticulum and Golgi complex, and still later at the cell surface where they were being discharged into the sinusoidal blood vessels. Micrographs of material recovered from the perfusate revealed a uniform population of particles identical with those seen developing within the cells; these were independently identified as very low-density lipoprotein. Visual evidence was thus provided for cooperation of the granular and agranular reticulum in the synthesis of a secretory product of the liver which is essential in the metabolism of lipids.

A problem of long standing has been to understand where and how large molecules leave capillaries and how they enter cells. In recent years, much attention has been given to the importance of *pinocytosis*, a process wherein a large molecule lodges on the exterior of the cell membrane, which invaginates locally forming a minute cup around the foreign material; membrane constriction and fusion close the opening of the invagination, and the material in question is then in a membrane-enclosed vesicle within the cell interior. Dissolution of the membrane then releases its contents. Electron microscopy of the capillary wall has demonstrated that the capillary endothelium in muscle is continuous save for intercellular clefts 50 to 150 Å wide at the edge-to-edge junctions of neighboring cells. These narrow slits have been interpreted as passages through which solutes might traverse the capillary wall. Attention has also been focused upon small vesicular inpocketings of the luminal and basal cell surfaces which are interpreted as a submicroscopic form of pinocytosis by which the endothelial cells might take up fluid in bulk and transport it across the capillary wall to be discharged into the perivascular spaces.

By means of particulate markers, it has been shown that both of these pathways may be involved in exchange across the capillary wall. Ferritin is a protein, normal to liver and spleen, of molecular weight 450,000, which contains 23 percent iron and, hence, is electron-dense. Ferritin administered intravascularly enters the small vesicles at the luminal surface and can be observed discharging at the abluminal surface. These 90 Å ferritin particles are not found in the intercellular clefts; hence they seem to be transported only by pinocytosis. It may be, however, that they are too large to be representative of the behavior of many of the important naturally occurring substances that are transported under normal physiological conditions. A recently developed method for detection of the enzyme peroxidase in electron micrographs has made it possible to use this smaller protein molecule (molecular weight about 40,000) as a tracer. Peroxidase has been found not only to enter the minute pinocytosis vesicles but also to traverse the intercellular clefts. It appears, then, that the pinocytosis vesicles and the intercellular pathways demonstrated morphologically may correspond respectively to the "large pore" and "small pore" systems which have been postulated on the basis of physiological studies.

These ingenious methods have now been extended to the identification of the site of the barrier that excludes many substances from the brain. In the past, some have thought that it was in the capillary wall itself, while others attributed the block to the relations of the glial cell processes that surround the brain capillaries. When peroxidase is injected intravenously, essentially none passes into the brain substance. On the other hand, when it is injected into the ventricles of the brain, it rapidly permeates the narrow extracellular spaces throughout the nervous tissue. The blood-brain barrier has thus been shown to reside in the capillary wall itself. In the brain capillaries in contrast to those of muscle, the clefts between endothelial cells appear to be sealed, preventing escape of peroxidase through this path. These capillaries also exhibit very little bulk uptake and transport by vesicle formation. Thus, by demonstrating the nature of cell-to-cell contacts, by establishing the dimensions of the intercellular spaces, and by tracing particles from one compartment to another, sophisticated morphological studies in recent years have contributed significantly to understanding of important physiological processes.

Production and Ordering of Extracellular Tissue Components

The cells of higher plants and animals are enmeshed in an extracellular stroma of amorphous, crystalline, or fibrous components that support and bind together functional units and serve to maintain the integrity of the organism as a whole. Many research efforts are now concerned with the intracellular sites of synthesis and mode of secretion of such materials as cellulose, chitin, pectin, collagen, bone matrix, and elastin and with the conditions necessary for the extracellular aggregation of the molecular subunits into their ultimate forms. Also intensively investigated are the factors involved in the ordering and orientation of extracellular fibers in a pattern that provides maximal strength with minimal material and which is adapted to specific local requirements.

The structural analysis of collagen, the principal extracellular fiber of animal tissues, has proceeded in the past decade from the dissection of such gross structures as tendons and ligaments, through microscopic description of fiber bundles of diminishing size, to electron microscopic identification of the cross-striated unit fibrils and the isolation and visual identification of the tropocollagen macromolecule, 3000 Å long and 15 Å thick. This molecule in turn has been degraded into three intertwined polypeptide chains, and the chemical analysis of the sequence of the constituent amino acids in these polypeptides is well advanced. Collagen fibers can be disassembled into their macromolecular subunits and reconstituted in vitro into fibers identical with those occurring in the intact animal. By varying the conditions of their reaggregation, fibers can be formed with patterns of cross striation not yet observed in nature. Thus by reductional analysis we have come to know in detail the general principles of the ordering of this extracellular animal protein at all levels from the molecule to the gross structural component of the whole organism. These fundamental advances are of great theoretical and practical importance not only for biology and medicine but for gelatin and leather technology as well.

The cell types involved in the production of collagen have been identified. By labeling amino acid precursors of collagen with radioactive isotopes, the intracellular pathway for synthesis has been traced in radioautography of fibroblasts, and as expected, ribosomes on the endoplasmic reticulum are first involved in the synthesis of the polypeptide chains. These are concentrated, modified, and combined in the Golgi complex. From there the product is transported in vacuoles to the cell surface to be released as triple-stranded tropocollagen molecules. In the extracellular spaces these spontaneously associate in a highly regular fashion to form collagen fibrils. As noted in Chapter 3, the fibrils and fibers built up from tropocollagen slowly form covalent, rigid cross-links, thus constructing the tough material characteristic of tendon and scars. This process occurs under the influence of the copper-containing amine oxidase of plasma. In the animal disease *lathyrism,* which is characterized by gross skeletal deformities, the collagen fibers and fibrils appear to be much narrower than normal; indeed the collagen may even be soluble. This disease is the consequence of ingesting the pea *Lathyrus odoratus,* which contains β-amino proprionitrile, a potent inhibitor of the amine oxidase. Patently, restriction of the intake of this pea is both therapeutic and preventative. Such studies have relevance to human connective tissue diseases such as arthritis.

Studies of wound healing have shown that the tactics of regeneration are basically a matter of mobilization and movement of reparative cells. It is evident that the freedom of these cells to move depends upon the nature and the abundance of the extracellular components of the connective tissue around them. Until recently there was little evidence that cells had the capability to depolymerize connective tissue ground substance, which consists mainly of the polysaccharide hyaluronic acid, or to degrade collagen in order to permit the cells to invade the site of injury. In studies on the resorption, remodeling, and new growth that is involved in the metamorphosis of tadpoles, evidence has now been obtained that the enzyme hyaluronidase may be released from mesenchymal cells, resulting in a depolymerization of the ground substance and a fraying out of the collagen bundles. At the same time, the epithelium of the tadpole tail releases a collagenase which initiates a degradation of collagen that is continued by proteases contributed by the mesenchymal cells. Collagenolytic activity has also been detected in the mammalian uterus, in bone, and in healing skin wounds. The enzymes involved in amphibian metamorphosis are activated following thyroxin administration, while the activity of the collagenase of bone is enhanced by administration of parathyroid hormone. These studies provide new insight into the interplay of biosynthesis and degradation in the development and remodeling of complex tissues and suggest that the appropriate balance between these processes may be under continuous hormonal control.

The major manifestation of hypervitaminosis A, in man and experimental animals, is markedly increased fragility of bones with frequent and multiple fractures. Treatment of embryonic cartilage in organ cultures with excess vitamin A has demonstrated the ability of the bone-forming chondrocyte to break down the components of the surrounding cartilage matrix. This effect appears to depend upon the release of proteases and other enzymes from intracellular structures identified as lysosomes. This lytic action, evoked by vitamin A, can be prevented by administration of agents known either to stabilize the membranes of lysosomes or to inhibit the action of some proteases. These investigations clarify both the cellular basis for the chondrolytic events in normal ossification as well as the mechanism by which excess vitamin A affects bone growth. To extrapolate from results on the in vitro modification of extracellular matrix to diseases of man would be premature, but the suggestion is clear that some of the tissue damage observed in diseases, such as arthritis, may possibly be due to release of lysosomal enzymes.

Plant cells are also surrounded by amorphous and fibrous components. The fibrous substance cellulose is probably the most abundant extracellular organic component on earth and forms the base of the wood, paper, and much of the natural cloth industries. The amorphous components, including the so-called pectic substances, are of considerable importance in the food-processing industry. Though chemically different, cellulose is formed by cellular processes remarkably similar to those involved in formation of collagen in animal tissues, and the orientation of the extracellular fibers is somehow determined by the cell. The important role of cellulose in plant growth is not widely appreciated. In the elongation of a root or stem, for example, the cylindrical organ extends because it is composed of thousands of cylindrical cells each increasing in length. Unlike that in animals, organ elongation in plants is a direct function of cell elongation. The growing plant cell contains a remarkable internal pressure (90 lb/sq. in.), some six times that in a household pressure cooker, and the cell grows as the wall slowly yields to this pressure. A cylinder giving way to internal pressure is normally deformed by enlargement of its center to approximate a sphere. That this does not occur in cellular subunits of elongating plant organs is attributable to the presence of reinforcing circumferential strands of cellulose that run like belts or hoops around the cylindrical cell. Their oriented reinforcement confines and redirects the growth pressure into an elongation of the cell. How the cell is able to determine this particular orientation of the extracellular fibrous components is now under investigation. Evidence has been obtained that a microtubular component of the cytoplasm is involved, for if the formation of these is suppressed by the drug colchicine, adaptive orientation of cellulose fibers fails and the cells grow into spheres. Interestingly enough, this same microtubular component of cytoplasm seems to be involved in the determination of the shape of animal cells. Because the internal pressures in animal cells are very small and the membrane not strong, the tubules can act directly in shaping the cell. In plants which have a high internal pressure and a strong wall, they appear to act indirectly by exercising some control over the orientation of extracellular cellulose fibers.

Adaptive Changes of Tissues in Response to Environment

Among the most remarkable and distinctive properties of living tissues is their reparative capacity and ability to respond to changes in their environment by adapting their structures in ways appropriate to the altered conditions. In this challenging area, research may be concerned with the mechanisms of initiation and limitation of growth or regeneration; with adaptive transformation or metaplasia; with compensatory hypertrophy; and with the means by which tissues sense and respond to environmental change or to reduction in their mass. Knowledge of the regulatory mechanisms involved in these phenomena is basic to an understanding of all forms of normal and abnormal growth, including cancer.

In its simplest form, compensatory growth merely involves cellular enlargement or hypertrophy with use, as is seen in the biceps of the boxer or the legs of the ballerina. In other instances it consists of increase in cell numbers or hyperplasia, as in regeneration of the liver and of various endocrine glands. In the enlargement of one kidney after removal of the contralateral kidney, the compensatory growth must, of necessity, involve a feedback mechanism capable of specifically communicating the effects of the loss to the remaining tissue. In most instances it is not known whether the communication is via humoral or nervous pathways, but in recent years progress has been made in the study of one example which may serve as a model for others. Studies of the regulation of the formation of red blood cells have been particularly revealing. Functionally compensatory production of erythrocytes occurs after hemorrhage and during exposure to low oxygen tension such as occurs at high altitude. In the case of blood loss, the deficit of circulating erythrocytes, per se, does not directly stimulate blood cell production. It is the resulting insufficient oxygen transport to the tissues which is sensed by the kidney, which then releases a substance called erythropoietin. The latter stimulates the blood-forming tissue in the bone marrow. Histological and immunohistochemical methods are now being applied to the problem of localizing the cellular site of production of this humoral agent as well as its mode of action. It is not unlikely that other examples of appropriate response to functional demand will be found to be mediated by blood-borne factors.

More puzzling are those examples of growth or structural alteration that seem to take place as direct responses to changes in the physico-chemical conditions or mechanical forces of the immediate environment. After experimental distension of the gallbladder by ligation of the common bile duct, the proliferative activity of the bladder epithelium rises in twenty-four hours ten- to twenty-fold. This mitotic stimulation is thought to be a response to the increased functional demand for concentration of bile rather than the direct effect of mechanical distension. But the sensor is unclear. In other examples, where the tissue is weight-bearing, it is difficult to avoid the conclusion that the mechanical pressures stimulate growth directly. "The soles of my boots grow thin, but the soles of my feet grow thicker the more I walk upon them," said D'Arcy Thompson in posing the problem of the reaction of living systems to functional demand. It is not any clearer today how pressure or abrasion brings about local increase in proliferation of epidermal cells to produce a callus. Here no known chemical signal is involved, but the locally applied mechanical stress seems to elicit the response. In another familiar example, a change in application of force to bone brings about a slow reordering of the internal trabecular architecture such that the new arrangement of bone spicules is more efficient than the old in resisting the altered pattern of stressing. This remodeling process involves both a local deposition of new bone and an equally selective reabsorption of old bone. How mechanical force can be translated into local activation of cells for synthesis or for lysis of bone matrix is still completely unknown.

When main vascular channels are occluded by disease, more blood flows through small collateral channels that bypass the obstruction, and in time, these small vessels respond to the increased hydrostatic pressure or increased volume flow, by growth. As a consequence, they are able to carry more blood, and adequate circulation is maintained around the obstruction. Patently, changes in local hemodynamics stimulate proliferation of cells and synthesis of the new extracellular materials necessary for the enlargement of the vessel lumen and increase in the thickness of its walls. Neither the nature of the primary sensor nor the manner in which it triggers hypertrophy is understood. Yet, knowledge of the mechanisms regulating growth of collateral vessels might well have significant application in improving circulation to the heart muscle in coronary artery disease.

Electron microscopy has revealed that structural alterations in the organism in response to functional demand extend to the subcellular level of organization. The phenomenon of *drug tolerance,* which necessitates increasing dosage to achieve the same biological response, has been known for many years. For a wide variety of drugs, it was recognized that this reflected an increased enzymic capacity of the liver to metabolize the drug, usually by oxidation, occasionally by methylation, hydrolysis, or acetylation. The responsible enzymes were known largely to occur in the *microsome* fraction of cells broken open by homogenization. The microsomes in turn were known to be derived from the smooth membranes of the endoplasmic reticulum. When phenobarbital is given or any one of a large variety of other lipid-soluble drugs that are metabolized in the liver, the cells of that organ engage in a remarkable hypertrophy of the cytoplasmic membranes comprising the smooth endoplasmic reticulum. This change in the hepatic cells is an *adaptive* response that increases their efficiency in metabolizing a wide variety of drugs, since the enzymes concerned exhibit only a low order of specificity. The mechanisms by which compounds, never encountered in nature, induce these changes in the structure and enzymic complement of the liver cells is a subject of active investigation. The ability to use drugs to induce the formation of new cytoplasmic membranes can be employed to increase the efficiency of the liver in carrying out certain other normal functions that depend upon the enzymes that reside in these membranes. This effect also has obvious pertinence to the growing problem of contamination of our environment, for chlordane and several other hydrocarbon insecticides are among the most potent inducers of increased drug-metabolizing enzymes. Incidental exposure of humans to these substances, even in small doses, may therefore influence their response to other drugs given for therapeutic purposes.

The morphological investigation of the adaptive responses of plants are of equal interest. In many instances the limits of adaptive cellular hypertrophy and hyperplasia, together with the associated modifications of their functional responses, determine both the natural distribution of plants and the geographical range of those species that are agriculturally important. The aberrations of growth occurring in certain plants in response to compounds such as 2,4-dinitrophenol (2,4-D) are the basis for the widespread use of herbicides. Responses of cells in specific regions of plants to other compounds results in defoliation which, in addition to its military applications, now finds peacetime use in harvesting of cotton. The observation that the form and distribution of some plant cell organelles can be varied greatly by manipulating the environment leads directly to the possibility of identifying the cause of certain plant growth deficiencies by direct anatomical study. The cellular responses of plants to injury also warrant serious investigation. To take a single example, the wounding of the developing capsules of the opium poppy results in the production of opium from which a whole series of drugs with important medical applications are derived.

One of the more striking and economically significant responses of organisms to changes in the physical environment is found in the initiation of flowering in plants by changes in day length. The physiology of this process is discussed in Chapter 6, on developmental biology, but the phenomenon is relevant here because it poses the kind of problem that will continue to occupy developmental anatomists for many years. How does a specific agent, a flowering hormone made active by day length, bring on specific and well-defined changes in gross structure? In the case of plants there is an undeniable chain of causation between day length and a shift from the production of leaves to the production of flower structures such as the ears or tassels of corn. The future of plant anatomy will be much concerned with exploring the nature of the cellular activities that act in harmony to produce both vegetative and floral development, and with discovering how a single diffusing agent, a hormone, can shift the developmental anatomy from one pattern of growth to the other. Problems of this general sort – how small molecules can exert such profound effects on organ structure – remain unsolved, indeed, almost unapproached throughout biology.

Detection of Specific Environment Stimuli

Among higher animals the mechanisms for perception of the environment and for processing sensory information in the nervous system are highly differentiated and structurally of great complexity. A variety of mechanical stimuli (touch, pressure, sound), chemical stimuli (taste, smell), and photic stimuli operate through a variety of processes in the sense organ to become transformed (transduced) into nervous impulses. So intimately is the structure of the sense organ linked to its special functional characteristics that an adequate understanding of one is unthinkable without an equal understanding of the other. As in other fields, studies of structure at the electron microscopic level have led to major advances in knowledge of the sense organs in health and in disease.

Perhaps of greatest significance has been progress in understanding the receptor cells and synaptic structure of the retina. Particularly noteworthy are the relationship of rod and cone receptor cells to ciliated epithelium, and the lamellated character of the cytomembranes associated with the photosensitive pigments in the outer segments of these highly specialized cells. Electron microscopy has recently resolved the important question of the nature of other retinal cells which exhibit slowly developed potentials (nerve impulses) but not fast spikes. These have proved to be synaptic nerve cells which possess no axons, but are not neuroglia cells, as earlier believed by some. The discovery by electron microscopy of previously unsuspected reciprocal synapses in such anaxonic neurons in the retina and olfactory bulb has produced a new dimension in the field of nerve cell interaction.

In the auditory system, approaches to the function of the receptor organ of Corti have been changed in spectacular fashion by the discovery that there are two major receptor cell types, and that they are innervated in different fashion by centrifugal nerve axons from the brainstem as well as by the centripetal or sensory axons. Not only is understanding of the neural aspect of audition utterly dependent on precise anatomical information, but the renewed interest of physicists and communication engineers in the transducing mechanism of the ear has stimulated a closer investigation of the vibrating component of the organ of Corti, the basilar membrane, and other structures concerned with the conversion of sound energy to nervous impulses.

One of the most unusual conceptual reorientations in the field of sensory physiology was induced by morphological studies which showed that taste receptor cells have a life-span of only several days and must be continually replaced. Although this remarkable fact was suspected from conventional microscopic studies as early as 1922, experimental studies with colchicine-blocked mitotic division and with radioautography of tissue treated with tritiated thymidine have recently demonstrated continual formation of taste cells as a basic characteristic of the taste system. This poses a fundamental problem of neural organization, since specific chemical sensitivities to salt, sweet, bitter, and acid substances have been demonstrated for different taste receptor cells as well as for different neurons. It is believed that as a new taste cell is innervated by a nerve fiber (which may have just lost an old receptor cell contact), it may receive information from the nerve which establishes the code determining the excitation by the receptor cell in response to a particular chemical stimulus. Presumably, the central organization remains unchanged.

Microscopy has continued to clarify the organization of muscle spindles. These are receptor structures in muscle which are crucial components of the complex feedback from muscle to the central nervous system that makes possible the postural adjustments of both static posture (standing, sitting) and the complicated dynamic postural changes essential to all types of movement. These receptor structures are composed of two main types of fine muscle fibers that are encapsulated and separated from the larger muscle fibers which form the muscle mass proper. Two types of sensory nerve fibers and an independent motor supply from small nerve cells in the spinal cord combine to produce a functional unit which is both highly responsive to stretch of the muscle and modulated by nervous influences from various levels of the nervous system.

There are specialized structures in smooth and in hairy skin, as well as in deeper structures, which constitute the anatomical basis for cutaneous and deep sensibility to touch and to other mechanical or thermal stimulation. The widespread distribution of nerve endings of this type (Merkel's corpuscles) has been confirmed, and the association of the nerve fiber endings with specialized receptor cells containing granules as of yet unknown significance has been one of the more provocative electron microscopic discoveries in this field. Histochemical methods directed at basic problems of receptor function require much more active exploration. As an example of the potential of this approach, histochemical staining for cholinesterase provides a convenient microscopic method for establishing the number and location of sensory endings (Meissner's corpuscles) in any part of the skin, as well as the functional integrity of this sensory structure in diseases of the skin. In the pathetic hereditary affliction of children known as familial dysautonomia, the exploratory use of the histochemical method for cholinesterase quickly established that the sensory deficiency in this disease is not associated with degeneration or serious derangement of the peripheral components of the sensory system.

Higher Levels of Organization of the Nervous System

The nervous system is the prime regulator of body functions, the organ of mental and emotional activity, and the seat of the greatest number of incapacitating and feared diseases. Man's attempts to understand the nervous system entered the modern scientific period not long before the turn of this century, when microscopic studies first mapped, in broad outline, its basic plan of cellular organization and laid the morphological foundations for all of the neurosciences, from psychobiology to neurochemistry. In the present era of accelerated biomedical research, novel experimental approaches and powerful new instrumentation have had great impact upon studies of the nervous system and have established the neurosciences as the area, next to molecular biology, most likely to yield new discoveries of prime importance. The revolution in neurophysiology made possible by intraneuronal recording with microelectrodes has demonstrated an urgent need for knowledge of the location and connections of nerve cells that is even more precise and detailed than that provided to date by classical neuroanatomical investigations. We are, therefore, witnessing a vigorous revival of traditional morphological methods of structural analysis, but now, more than ever, directed to the solution of specific functional, behavioral, and pathological problems. Morphological studies are rapidly being extended from the higher levels of intercellular organization that have long been the concern of neuroanatomy, to the submicroscopic specializations of the contact surfaces of neurons, their internal organization, and the functional changes in their cell organelles. The details of these and related studies are the principal concern of the following chapter.

Comparative Vertebrate Morphology

The macroscopic study of biological structure is concerned with the recognition and analysis of the principal general plans of construction of animals and with the progressive specialization and adaptation of these plans in the course of development and evolution. The field encompasses the whole range of living and extinct forms. Thus it has much in common with systematics and evolutionary biology which deal with the origin of species and the diversification of life. However, comparative morphology is more directly concerned with form and with structural mechanisms.

There continues to be a great need to extend established concepts and traditional techniques to new biological material. For example, biologists in general are increasingly requiring reference information on the detailed structural organization of numerous forms which have heretofore been neglected, such as fish and certain primates (viz., the baboon) which are now becoming essential in some fields of medical research.

The present vitality and promise of this field of biology rests, however, upon imaginative investigations that are much broader in concept than in the past and which often involve integration of anatomy with one or more of the related fields of physiology, ecology, engineering, and mathematics. Training of the comparative morphologist in more than one area of science, interdisciplinary collaboration, and a willingness to adopt techniques of other fields are increasingly demanded to achieve the correlations that make structural observations more meaningful and provide valuable new concepts and perspectives. The central focus of comparative vertebrate morphology has veered away from an unselective cataloguing of encyclopedic information toward problems involving biological principles.

Two common approaches to the structural problems related to evolution involve either studies on long-term changes of form within a single group or investigations that concentrate on a single functional process such as locomotion or feeding as it occurs in a broad range of animal groups. In the first approach one is concerned with the entire biology of a group in relation to other animal groups. Deductive reasoning is used to determine the environmental, genetic, and selective factors involved in morphological change. Much research has centered upon determining how groups enter new ways of life and how these groups have successfully invaded populated environments — as, for example, the movement of fish into the great lakes of Africa or of north temperate salamanders into tropical lowlands. Studies are made of the adaptive structural events associated with such changes, their functional correlates, and their effects on the behavioral pattern. In these comparative studies that concentrate on a single functional process, this activity is analyzed in a wide variety of animal groups in an effort to determine how various factors may produce either similar or different structural modifications. Thus the mechanical system of the jaws of freshwater fishes may be analyzed to outline the way in which different environments produce divergent effects within one group. On the other hand, a particular environment may elicit a similar adaptive response in unrelated groups of animals. In the depths of the Amazon River, for example, certain fishes, frogs, and turtles have all evolved very flat broad skulls and associated modifications of feeding behavior that favor their survival as inhabitants of the river bottom.

Another group of problems that have engaged the attention of vertebrate morphologists are those concerned with feeding mechanisms: the capture and kill methods of raptorial birds; the correlation of structure of the bill with feeding habits of other birds; the mouth parts and jaw mechanisms of snakes and fish. New attention is being given to problems of aquatic locomotion both in fish and in mammals. The hydrodynamics of body shape in porpoises, the biomechanics of their propulsive movements, the flow of water over the skin, are matters that have been of interest not only to biologists but to naval architects and rheologists as well.

The availability of electronic computers has created renewed interest in problems dealing with the shapes of organisms and their structural components. Modern instrumentation and statistical methods have brought a new dimension to the understanding of biological variation, the explanation of growth changes, and the genetic and selective influences that may underlie the final form of organisms.

For example, recent studies of the evolution of the shoulder in mammals employing classical morphological methods have consolidated our knowledge of the relationships between the structure of the region and its function. They have, however, produced few insights not already glimpsed by workers of a generation ago. On the other hand, the application of computer techniques to comparisons of the shape of the shoulder in animals as widely different as bats, sloths, kangaroos, monkeys, and man has made it possible to reduce confusing multidimensional data to easily visualizable two- and three-dimensional models. Such models have confirmed previous findings but in addition have provided entirely new insights into the kinds of processes that underlie changes in shape during evolution. They have suggested, for instance, that the myriad shapes of the shoulder in mammals may be the resultant of a very small number of morphogenetic mechanisms. Insights into the evolution of the shoulder in man have been obtained from computer studies of living forms, from interpolating into the computer results, data from fossils, and through the "invention" by the computer, of hypothetical evolutionary intermediates. In the short history of the development of computers it has only been since 1965 that the instruments have reached a stage where they have become easily utilizable by biomorphologists. Studies such as those outlined here are therefore in their infancy. It seems likely that the progress in sophistication of these instruments and increasing familiarity with their use may produce a scale of research in this area that will have profound effects upon our understanding of the mechanical principles of animal structure and of the evolutionary process itself.

Though dissection, observation, and mensuration remain basic and indispensable methods in comparative morphc'ogy, the field has been rejuvenated by new and more complex methods adopted from other fields. To these classical procedures have been added high-speed cinematography for the study of feeding, swimming, running, and flying mechanisms. Fluoroscopy and radiography are increasingly used for analysis of movements of deeper-lying structures in living animals. Techniques of proportional enlargement and reduction, and three-dimensional reconstruction of intricate structures have been adopted from the graphic arts. Force transducers, sensitive strain gauges, and photoelastic techniques for experimental stress analysis have been taken over from engineering for use on problems in functional morphology. Telemetering of electronic sensing devices permits studies of musculoskeletal dynamics in free-ranging living animals. Applications of various methods of photoelastic analysis have given new information about the patterns of force operating in such irregularly shaped objects as bones and have demonstrated the mechanical efficiency of specific shapes of bones that would otherwise defy explanation. Some of these studies have provided valuable clues to the meaning of differences in shape of the same bone in animals as the result of the evolution of different functions. Other studies have been put to practical use to assess the mechanical efficiency of proposed interventions of the orthopedic surgeon for correction of human deformities.

An especially active research area has been the comparative anatomy of sense organs and sensory physiology. The discovery twenty years ago of the use of pulses of supersonic sound for echolocation by bats led to comparative studies of the frequencies and frequency modulations of many chiropteran species under different conditions of obstacle avoidance and pursuit of prey. The existence of this remarkable physiological counterpart of man's sonar systems has raised fascinating new problems on the anatomical and physiological specializations of these species for phonation at the high frequencies used, and the adaptations of the external and internal auditory apparatus and brain for reception and interpretation of the signals. These investigations have interesting implications for the design of man-made navigational and detection devices, with application ranging from military tactics to auxiliary sensors for sightless humans. Mechanisms similar in principal have developed in the course of evolution in a number of unrelated animal groups. The use of sound for navigational echolocation and capture of prey has been demonstrated for porpoises and whales. The anatomical basis for production of sound by these species that lack a laryngeal organ remains a subject of investigation. The discovery of their intelligence and facility for learning, and their purposeful use of sound for communication, as well as navigation, has led to recent anatomical studies of the porpoise brain intended to identify the neurological basis of their special skills.

Comparative microscopic studies are increasingly suggesting mechanisms that eluded earlier gross morphological investigations. For example, the capacity of certain lizards to climb apparently smooth vertical surfaces has in the past been variously attributed to secretion of an adhesive, creation of suction, or development of electrostatic charges. Electron micrographs now reveal on the scales of the undersurface of the digits as many as a million and a half infinitesimally small spicules or setae in each square millimeter. Each of these in turn branches repeatedly and terminates in several hundred minute spatulate endings. As a consequence of this remarkable specialization, the total amount of surface in contact with the submicroscopic irregularities on the substrate is enormous. Inasmuch as frictional force is proportional to the area of actual contact between two objects, the ability of these creatures to walk across the ceiling now appears to be largely explained by this surface phenomenon.

Among the most tangible benefits from comparative morphological studies at the histological level are discoveries of animal species having specialized organs that are uniquely favorable for experimental analysis of functions less well developed or inaccessible to experiment in man. Examples of these are many, but enumeration of a few will suffice. The discovery of certain kinds of fish whose kidneys lack glomeruli was of inestimable value to physiologists in studying the respective contributions of filtration and secretion in the formation of urine by the nephron. Certain other fish have made a large contribution to our understanding of diabetes and the regulation of carbohydrate metabolism by virtue of the fact that the exocrine and endocrine portions of their pancreas are not intermingled as in mammals, but segregated in separate organs. This fortunate circumstance, which is of no taxonomic or evolutionary interest, has nevertheless been of great practical value in that it permitted extraction of insulin from pure islet tissue and experimental ablation of the endocrine portion of the pancreas without disturbance of the rest of the gland. As we have already noted (Chapter 6), the recognition of the long loop of Henle in the renal tubules of the kangaroo rat was a most important clue to the mechanism for concentration of urine.

Anatomy and Evolutionary Biology of Primates

To fully understand man and his place in nature, it is important to complete the fragmentary record of his evolution and to study in considerable detail the other members of the order to which he belongs. These tasks are far from complete.

The past forty years have witnessed increasing numbers of discoveries of fossil remains of primates, including such forms as the Australopithecinae, which are of great importance because of the light they throw directly or indirectly upon certain critical phases in the evolution of the Hominidae. Divergent views persist as to their exact zoological affinities, but when better information becomes available as to their geological age, their habitat, and the phylogenetic significance of some of their morphological features, these differences will be resolved. Within the past ten years, this area of investigation has been revitalized by rich new finds of fossil hominids in South and East Africa. The careful anatomical studies now in progress of both fossil and living primates promise to fill important gaps in our knowledge of man's forebears. Current thinking about the rate of human evolution has recently undergone some modification owing to application of the potassium-argon method for dating volcanic rocks. Results of this method have added to the early Pleistocene period an additional million years representing forty to fifty thousand generations. Further progress in unraveling man's past will require not only much more paleontological evidence but, for accurate interpretation of the fossil record, much more comprehensive knowledge of the functional anatomy, behavior, ecology, and physiology of living primates. The analysis of the long past history of man and his related ancestors should provide insight into the evolutionary processes through which modern man is passing, and possibly hint at his future genetic potential.

Erect posture is probably the determinant evolutionary change that separated man from the other primates. Numerous studies are in progress to discover the factors that express these changes. Cinematographic and direct observations of various nonhuman primates in their natural habitats are correlated with laboratory studies of their hands so as to ascertain the relationship between form and function. The presence of a particular thumb muscle plays an important part in producing the human capacity to grasp implements. Studies on the hip joint of primates are providing valuable clues as to whether this joint is a specifically responding organ and whether its muscular system responds to the postural needs of the species. Such information provides extrapolative data for interpretation of the fossil record.

Some of the anthropoid apes have been studied more or less systematically, particularly the chimpanzee and gorilla. But the deficiencies in knowledge of the morphology of the orangutan and gibbon, and most of the Old and New World monkeys, are great. The bulk of the information available pertains to the skeleton, somewhat less being known about the soft parts, and surprisingly little about the central nervous system. The latter deficiency is particularly regrettable, for the only truly unique primate character is the striking tendency toward a high degree of development of the brain—the remainder of the body remaining relatively unspecialized. With the current rapid development of interest in behavioral studies, there is an increasing need for basic neuroanatomical studies on primate species other than the ubiquitous macaque and squirrel monkey. In experimental psychology, the closest behavior analogies are between man and the chimpanzee or gorilla, but unfortunately anatomical knowledge of the brain of these species is very fragmentary.

Concern is often expressed over the degree to which basic research in medical science depends upon observations on a very small number of species, mainly laboratory rodents, cats, and dogs. Despite the far-reaching unity of nature at the cellular level of organization, the physiological responses and disease susceptibilities of these species are often sufficiently different that experimental results on them cannot be applied directly to man. Thorough study of the gross and microscopic anatomy and physiology of several small species of primates is needed to provide information essential to the increased use in medical research of species more closely related to men.

In addition to their obvious superiority for investigations on behavior, functional morphology, learning, conditioning, social organization, and certain diseases, the subhuman primates offer special advantages for studies on endocrinology and reproductive physiology, for they alone share with man a menstrual cycle instead of an estrus cycle. Their extensive use in basic and applied research aimed at the control of human fertility can, therefore, be expected.

Various monkeys comprise single species (e.g., rhesus, langur) made up of several races having a very wide geographical distribution. They live under greatly varying conditions of climate and altitude. From a study of anatomical and physiological characteristics of races from different climatic zones, valuable information might be gained on the capacity of primates to adapt to environment without the benefits of culture.

Still more profitable and urgent are anthropological studies on structural and functional adaptations to climatic conditions among the few remaining isolated populations of primitive humans exposed to harsh environments. A number of productive studies are in progress on the tribes of New Guinea, the Aborigines of Australia, and the Bushmen of Africa. Studies of body form, pigmentation, hair, blood groups, cytogenetics, physiological responses to heat and cold, disease susceptibility, and many other characteristics are needed before the opportunity is lost, owing to the breaching of geographical barriers, the progressive interbreeding of mankind, and the inexorable spread of civilization.

Applied Human Anatomy

Description and illustration of the structure of the human body as revealed by dissection has made a continuing contribution to human knowledge since the fifteenth century. Indeed, the early application of this knowledge laid the foundation of medical science. Significant advances in clinical medicine still stem directly from past and recent anatomical research. Advances in medical and surgical technology not infrequently give practical value to anatomical details previously considered to be of purely academic interest. Before those developments in anesthesiology that made possible prolonged surgical procedures in the open chest, there was no need for detailed knowledge of the segmental anatomy of the lung. The development of a capability for intrathoracic surgery stimulated investigations of the lung lobules and their vascular architecture that have provided the basis for successful surgical treatment of localized pulmonary disease. Similarly, anatomical researches on the development and topography of the heart found ready application when open-heart and transplant surgery became possible. New knowledge of the precise location of the impulse conducting tissue now guides the surgeon's needle in avoiding creation of heart block during closure of a low atrial septal defect. Descriptions of the development and anatomy of the adult ear have been essential to the striking achievements of modern intraaural surgery for the amelioration of deafness.

Advances in radiological techniques have opened up new possibilities for the analysis of both static and dynamic relationships in the living body. The movements of the structures involved in swallowing can now be analyzed fluoroscopically in slow motion so as to permit the diagnosis of defects in this process that are not discernible with conventional x-ray techniques. The ability of radiologists to make advances in applied research of this kind is clearly related to their depth of training in anatomy. No part of medicine depends more directly upon a firm knowledge of anatomy than surgical repair of extensive injuries. Successful restoration of continuity of tendons, nerves, and blood vessels can scarcely be accomplished without such knowledge. Recent successes in reimplantation of severed extremities emphasize its potential rewards.

The classical problem of the musculoskeletal basis of man's bipedal locomotion continues to challenge the imagination and ingenuity of anatomists and has resulted in application of methods of steadily increasing sophistication. The early dissections and accurate observations on the origins and insertions of the muscles involved in walking were followed by studies of the classes of levers and their mechanical advantage. Interest then turned to high-speed cinematographic analysis of running and walking, and more recently to cinefluoroscopic studies of the joint movements. With the development of electromyography (the recording of the electrical activity associated with contraction of individual muscles) and with the availability of sensitive strain and pressure sensing devices, the study of locomotion has entered a productive new phase. Now with electrodes placed over particular leg muscles, and pressure detectors on heel, ball of foot, and great toe, the sequential activation of the muscles can be accurately timed in relation to the phases of heel, foot, and toe contact observed in simultaneous cinematographic recordings of the step. Such studies establishing the manner and degree of participation of the various muscles and the pressures and tensions developed in normal locomotion are now being extended to patients with flat feet and other alterations of anatomical relations that result in disturbances of gait.

Progress in the emerging field of bioengineering often requires considerable knowledge of human anatomy and its variations. Man evolves far more slowly than his ability to modify his mechanical environment. With any major technological advance in military or industrial equipment, new problems of human engineering arise. Anatomists, physiologists, and engineers are called upon to help adapt the design of machines to match the natural capabilities of man so that their combined efforts will be safer and more efficient. The design of aircraft for suprasonic speeds, automobiles for maximum highway safety, manned equipment for agriculture and industry, and clothing, involves consideration of normal human measurements and their variations, reach and range of joint movement, muscular capabilities, and speed of reaction in various positions. Man's desire to operate under hitherto unexplored conditions of gravitational force and deceleration has led to studies of tolerance of bones, joints, and soft tissues to vibration and compressive and shearing forces. The design of capsules for travel in space has raised bioengineering problems such as optimal position of operator and of instrument panels and the anatomical effects of prolonged immobilization and weightlessness.

A new branch of human engineering has come to the fore, with the advances in surgery and the development of metals and plastics that induce minimal tissue reaction. This is the branch of technology that is developing machines to substitute for the function of organs—artificial kidneys, mechanical devices for temporary or enduring replacement of the pumping action of the heart, the construction of artificial heart valves. All of these are requiring reexamination of the pertinent anatomy to gain a better understanding of the function of the normal parts and to plan the most favorable method for placement of the prosthetic devices. A novel application of electromyography is exemplified in efforts now being made to construct an artificial arm and hand wherein the electrical activity of muscles in the amputation stump will be detected and used to activate motor-driven mechanical displacements of the prosthesis which will simulate normal arm movements. If successful, this will give the amputee an immediately useful prosthesis without extensive reeducation. In a country where trauma related to traffic and industrial accidents and to military action is steadily increasing, research of this kind promises to yield results of great practical value.

Gross anatomy, the oldest of the sciences, now presents fewer problems that can be solved by the time-honored techniques of observation, section, and dissection, but the prevailing view that anatomy is a classical subject devoid of intellectual challenge is a misconception. In the examples presented we have endeavored to illustrate how methods from other fields, such as electronics and mathematics, and new instruments, such as telemetric devices and computers, are opening up for investigation a whole new range of problems in biomorphology. Until this new concept of morphology becomes more widely recognized, able young scientists will continue to be unaware of its expanded research opportunities. There is a real danger that the numbers who do recognize its potential may be too small to maintain the subject as a viable field of inquiry or to ensure imaginative and stimulating teaching to future generations of students.

Chapter 9

THE NERVOUS SYSTEM

Many of us are curious about the brains of animals, be they spider, fish, or dog, because we are fascinated by the way in which the nervous system controls the complex actions of even the simplest creatures. Above all, most of us have a special interest in the human brain because if we knew more about it, we would be closer to understanding ourselves.

The task of the neurological sciences is to learn how the brain works. What strikes one most forcibly in thinking about the human brain is that it is made up of more than 10^{12} cells (a million million) and that the interconnections between these cells are many times more numerous still (Fig. 9-1). The nervous system continually receives, transforms, stores, and updates information concerning the world about us. It is through the interactions of nerve cells that we have an awareness of the world around us and are capable of learning and remembering, of feeling and acting.

How does the brain function and how does its functioning lead to behavior? The task of studying brain functioning is, at first thought, staggering. Fortunately this task can be experimentally simplified in a number of ways, and with these simplifications we have been able to gain increasing insights into brain functioning.

Perhaps the most remarkable simplification has resulted from the development of techniques for studying the activity of individual nerve cells. From studies of single cells it is apparent that the building blocks of the different regions of the vertebrate nervous system, and indeed of all nervous systems, are everywhere about the same. What distinguishes one region from another, and one brain from the next, is the way the building blocks are put together. Using this cellular approach, we have

324

gained some insight into the more complex problems of how visual or other sensory stimuli are sorted out at various levels in the brain, and we are even beginning to learn about the detailed organization of the cerebral cortex. We now know that the cells in the cortex are organized into elementary groups, arranged in narrow vertical columns, whose function it is to perform a particular "transformation" of the neural message. As a result of these studies one can begin to appreciate why the cerebral cortex needs so many cells. It is not that the actions mediated by individual cells are trivial; rather, it is because the cortex receives such an enormous amount and variety of information from the sensory apparatus at the body surface (eyes, ears, nose, skin) that huge numbers of cells are required to handle and to transform this information so that it can be used for perception and for action.

A second development which has simplified the study of brain function is the finding that the brains of relatively simple animals, or even ganglia — parts of their brains containing only several thousand cells — manifest a variety of interesting behaviors which are analogous to those found in higher animals. This development has led to a renewed interest in the comparative biological approach with the purpose of using the less complex and more accessible brains of lower animals as model systems for studying the mechanisms of certain elementary features of behavior.

Future developments will continue to depend upon imaginative simplification of naturally complex situations. It is also becoming increasingly clear that if future research is to reach a new and expanded level of understanding of the nervous system, vigorous interaction with other disciplines will be essential. For example, interaction with molecular biology can provide an extraordinary opportunity for developing new biochemical and genetic approaches to brain function. As will be evident in the following chapter, a merger of concepts and techniques of the neural sciences with those of experimental psychology holds great promise for future advances in understanding of perception and learning. Only the barest beginning has been made in utilizing the knowledge available from these rapidly growing neighboring disciplines, but it is already clear that interdisciplinary efforts will be essential for gradually bridging the gap between the function of individual cells and groups of cells, on the one hand, and between groups of cells and psychologically meaningful behaviors, on the other. It would be naive to expect quick results. New tools have to be fashioned and new approaches developed. But those engaged in neural science sense an unusual excitement in the air.

This chapter attempts to summarize where we now stand and to indicate some of the directions in which the neural sciences will move in the next decade.

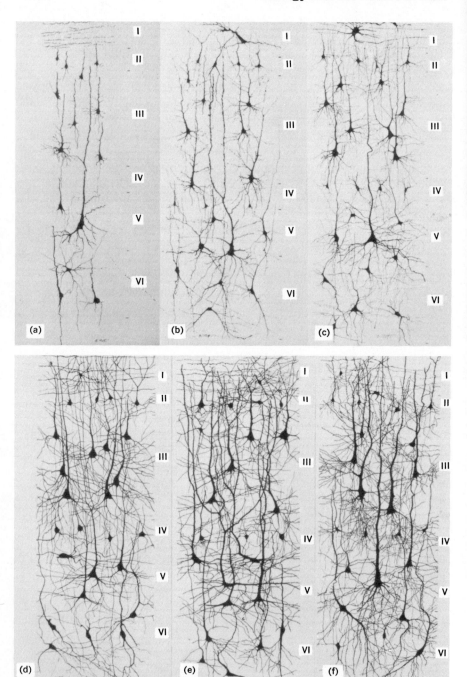

Structure, Function, and Chemistry of Cells in the Nervous System

The Structure of the Neuron

All neurons have an irregular shape and consist of a cell body with numerous processes, the axons and the dendrites, which vary in prominence from one class of neurons to another. Each neuron is a structural and functional entity, separate from but interacting with others. An example of the much studied motor neuron is shown in Figure 9-2. *The dendrite-cell body region* is that part of the neuron which most commonly receives the contacts, or synapses, projected to it by the processes of other neurons. For some cells, such as the motoneurons of the spinal cords, the number of other cells from which contacts are received may number in the thousands, while for others the number is very restricted. Each of these contacts influences, by virtue of conducted nerve impulses and transsynaptic action, the excitability of the recipient neuron. The properties of the dendrite-cell body region are such that they enable the cell to sum, or integrate, all the influences that converge on it.

The interest of the cytologist is concentrated on the cell body of the neuron, for here are the nucleus and the *Nissl bodies,* masses of granular endoplasmic reticulum. As compared with other cells, the nucleus is extraordinarily large. It has the same quantity of DNA as do other cell nuclei, and thus presumably the same number of chromosomes as do other diploid cells in the organism. The nucleolus is also large and often associated with accessory clumps of chromatin, the so-called sex chromatin.

Figure 9-1. Ontogenetic development of human cerebral cortex. The complexity of the interconnections of cortical neurons can be illustrated by studies of the ontogenetic development of the human cerebral cortex. This figure illustrates histological sections stained with the Golgi-Cox method. The six layers of the cerebral cortex are indicated in roman numerals.

| a: newborn; | b: 1 month; | c: 3 months; |
| d: 6 months; | e: 15 months; | f: 24 months |

Although the number of neurons does not change significantly, there is a progressive increase in the neuronal arborization which is particularly dramatic between 15 and 24 months. (Reprinted by permission of the publisher from Jesse LeRoy Conel, *The Postnatal Development of the Human Cerebral Cortex,* Vols. I–VI. Cambridge, Mass.: Harvard University Press. Copyright Vol. I – 1939 by the President and Fellows of Harvard College, © 1967 by Jesse LeRoy Conel; Copyrights Vol. II – 1941, Vol. III – 1947, Vol. IV – 1951, Vol. V – 1955, Vol. VI – 1959 – all by the President and Fellows of Harvard College)

The cell-body cytoplasm contains masses of granular endoplasmic reticulum, the protein synthesizing machinery of the cell (the Nissl bodies), which are basophilic to optical microscopy because of the high concentration of ribosomes. The nerve cell is unusual only in possessing large amounts of this material. The protein that the cell produces is destined for export down the axon or out of the cell, rather than for distribution among its progeny, since adult nerve cells do not divide. A large mammalian neuron synthesizes about a third of the protein in its cell body every day; the fate of this protein is a major unsolved problem. By a variety of methods it has been shown that the protein synthesized in the cell body under nuclear control moves out into the processes extending from it. This "axoplasmic flow" has been shown by tracking the movement of newly synthesized protein which has been labeled with radioactive amino acids, as well as by other means; the mechanism of this movement is not known. The axon itself is devoid of ribosomes, cannot synthesize protein, and eventually dies once it is separated from the cell body.

The axon is cylindrically shaped and small in diameter relative to the cell body. It may extend in length from a fraction of a millimeter to one meter, and serves to conduct the action potentials generated in the cell body-axon hillock portion of the neuron to its terminal contacts, in a repetitive code of all-or-none impulses. The axon is an evolutionary development for the rapid transmission of information, not for integration or transformation.

The axon contains two types of longitudinally oriented structures, the neurofilaments, fine threads of protein about 100 Å in diameter, and equally fine microtubule system of unknown origin. These extend from the cell body to the terminals. The terminals of axons in the central nervous system are small bulbous enlargements containing a cluster of mitochondria and numerous small vesicles. Typically the vesicles are concentrated against the surface membrane of the ending. This specialized apposition of two nerve cells is called a synapse, and it is at this point that impulses are transmitted from one cell to another. The general structure of synapses will be discussed later.

Signaling in Neurons, the Transfer of Information and Integrative Action in Single Elements

Study of the electrical activity in single neurons in the brain has provided powerful evidence that the complex organization of the nervous system is based upon a precise and selective interconnection of neurons, many of which are present and operative at birth. Functional connections need

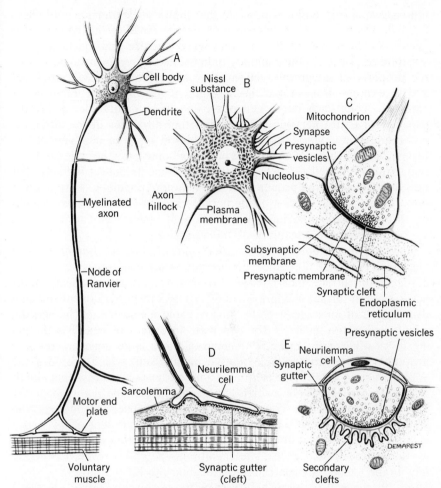

Figure 9-2. Diagrams of a motor neuron of the ventral horn of the spinal cord. (A) The neuron includes a cell body and its processes (dendrites and axons). Within the cell body, there is Nissl substance, nucleus, nucleolus, and axon hillock. The axon collateral process branches at a node of Ranvier. (B) Several axons form synapses on the cell body and base of dendrites; motor neurons are densely covered with such synapses. Some have an excitatory, others an inhibitory action. (C) A chemical synapse as reconstructed from electron micrographs, including synaptic vesicles in bulbous ending, mitochondria, presynaptic membrane, thick subsynaptic membrane on the postsynaptic side, and the synaptic cleft which is 200–300 angstrom-units wide. (D) Enlargement of a portion of the motor end plate region of (A). (E) Cross-section through (D). (From Charles R. Noback, *The Human Nervous System,* © 1967 by McGraw-Hill, Inc.)

not be permanent, and it is possible that they can be unmade and others formed, although the mechanism and circumstance of this change, if it occurs, is unknown. Studies of the nerve impulse and the local post-synaptic responses in the cell body indicate that a given neuron possesses the property of integrative action—the capacity to process all its input and to express in its output the net influence of the many influences it receives. Thus each nerve cell possesses in miniature the integrative capacity of entire nervous systems, but the intricacies of the latter are not readily understood by a simple addition of large numbers of the former. The problem of integrative action encompasses the action of large populations, as well as their constituent elements, and it is likely that new and undiscovered properties of the action of populations are of great importance in the function of the nervous system. Nevertheless, as will be discussed later, the integrative action of single elements is funda-mental, and now reasonably well understood.

The Resting Membrane Potential and the Action Potential. The electrical potential difference across neuronal membranes can be re-corded with intracellular microelectrodes. At rest, a neuron maintains across its cell surface a difference of 60–70 mV, resulting from an unequal distribution of ions across the semipermeable membrane of the neuron, which leaves the inside of the cell with an excess of negative charge. As in all other cells, the maintenance of these large ionic gradients is accomplished by the cell's oxidative metabolism, which provides the ATP, which in turn drives a coupled active transport process that simul-taneously expels the Na^+ which leaks into the cell and pumps back the K^+ which diffuses out. This transport process causes the internal con-centration of K^+ to be ten or more times higher than that of the extra-cellular space and that of Na^+ and of Cl^- to be ten times lower than that of the extracellular space. The membrane potential results from the membrane's much higher resting permeability to K^+ than to Na^+. Alter-ations in the resting permeability to different ions, by either electrical or chemical stimuli, produce alterations in membrane potential. In turn, changes in the membrane potential produce changes in ionic permeabili-ties.

If the resting potential is reduced by a certain critical voltage, usually 10–15 mV, a point is reached at which an explosive all-or-none change— the nerve action potential—occurs. It is the potential across the cell membrane that intitiates and determines cell permeabilities. The action potential results from a sudden reversal in the characteristic Na^+/K^+ selectivity of the membrane. The fuller understanding of these ionic permeability changes responsible for the membrane potentials and action potentials, as well as synaptic events, has probably been the major advance in the field during the past two decades.

The potential change produced by the action potential is propagated along the whole length of the axon without decrement: each active patch of membrane produces a current flow which is more than adequate to depolarize the next patch, which in turn depolarizes the not-yet-active region ahead of it.

The Initiation of Impulse Activity at Sense Organs. A nervous system gains information about the external world, and about the internal state of the organism in which it resides, by virtue of incoming, or sensory, nerve fibers. The peripheral terminals of these neurons are often distributed in sheets such as those of the retina, the cochlea, or the skin, and thus are exposed to the external environment. Their centrally directed branches enter the central nervous system. The peripheral endings are in many cases in close relation to other cells, frequently nonneural, whose special function is to translate or transduce external energy of one form or another into impulses. For example, in the retina the cones and rods collect light energy which initiates the chain of chemical reactions described in Chapter 3, which in turn leads to permeability changes in the adjoining nerve membrane. These changes cause current flow, depolarization, and the generation of nerve impulses. In mechanoreceptors of muscle, the cochlea, or the skin, the mechanical deformation itself leads to this sequence of events. Details of the transducer mechanism are not known, but it is clear that, first, the quality of the sensory stimulus—the form of energy—determines whether a given afferent nerve fiber will be activated by it, though the nature of this selective action is obscure; second, the spatial and temporal pattern of the stimulus is transformed into impulses of varying patterns and frequency.

The study of sense organs, the sensory transducer process, and the encoding in first-order afferent neurons has been pursued by many workers, and the events in many sense organs have been described in considerable detail. Some of the important problems remaining to be solved at the level of mechanism are the following: (1) What molecular rearrangement occurs in the membrane of the nerve terminal, evoked by some form of impinging energy, which leads to changes in its permeability? This is a special case of one of the more general and most important problems in membrane physiology. (2) Why is it that this molecular rearrangement is evoked at lower threshold by one form of energy for one class of nerve endings and by other forms in others? The possibility exists that this differential specificity is due to special properties of the nonneural cells that surround nerve endings, and these deserve further intensive study at the level of molecular mechanism. (3) What is the nature of the influence of afferent nerve fibers upon the development of the nonneural peripheral tissues they innervate? When regenerating nerve fibers reach the tissue they normally innervate, they evoke in that tissue a rearrangement leading to the formation of a sense organ—e.g., the formation of "tactile organs" in the skin when reinnervated by a "cutaneous nerve," and of taste buds in the epithelium of the tongue when regenerating "taste fibers" reach it. Is the influence of a *particular* set of nerve fibers upon the tissue important, or does the tissue rearrangement into a "sense organ" occur when it is innervated by *any* set of fibers?

These and many other problems of a related nature still confound us, and it is obvious that we still understand little of the basic mechanisms of the transducer process. The problem of neural coding will be discussed in a later section.

There are two mechanisms for synaptic transmission by which signals are exchanged between nerve cells, one chemical the other "electrical." The former seems to predominate for synapses in the vertebrate brain, but the fact that electrical transmission is clearly established for many invertebrate synapses and in some vertebrate ones opens the possibility that it also is an important transsynaptic mechanism at mammalian synapses.

Chemical Synaptic Transmission. At a chemical synapse the nerve impulse travels to the terminals of a neuron by means of the conduction mechanism previously described. Depolarization of the terminal by the action potential causes the release of a chemical "transmitter" substance in small multimolecular "packets" from the nerve terminal into the intercellular space. The transmitter diffuses to the next cell, usually separated by a gap of several hundred Å, and there it combines with receptor substances, in or on the postsynaptic membrane. This combination leads in some unknown way to permeability changes in the membrane of the postsynaptic cell. Depending on the chemical structure of the transmitter and the chemical nature of the receptor substances ("sites"), the induced permeability change leads to either excitation or inhibition. Chemical synapses can be recognized with reasonable certainty in the electron microscope.

This cell junction is characterized morphologically by an interspace, the synaptic cleft, about 200–300 Å deep, which intervenes between the apposing surfaces of the presynaptic terminal and the postsynaptic cell. Thus it is clear that in the chemical synapse the two cellular units are simply in apposition to each other and are not in continuity (Fig. 9-1c).

A second characteristic of chemical synapses is the presence of small vesicles, sometimes in great numbers, clustered in the terminal enlargement of the axon. These are bounded by a unit membrane and either have a clear content or contain a smaller dense granule. The vesicles are thought to correlate with the quantal release of transmitter chemicals at the synapse, and hence they are considered one morphological sign of chemical synapses.

Identification of certain chemical transmitters with specific types of synaptic vesicles has proven difficult. What is reasonably certain is that some terminals with clear vesicles are cholinergic (acetylcholine is the transmitter substance), and some vesicles having extremely small dense centers are adrenergic (norepinephrine is the transmitter substance). Pharmacological studies on vesicles isolated by differential centrifugation tend to agree with this correlation. Synaptic vesicles, however, occur with granular centers having different sizes and densities. In addition, synaptic terminals with a mixed population of clear- and dense-centered vesicles are very common in the central nervous system. A better understanding of these vesicles awaits further refinement of fractionation methods and further recognition of other transmitter chemicals.

A number of other unsolved or only partially resolved problems concerning the synaptic vesicles can only be listed here. What is their origin, are they produced in the nerve terminal or in the cell body and transported to the terminal? Is the transmitter synthesized in the vesicle or merely concentrated in it? Can the vesicle be used again after it has discharged its load of transmitter? What is the mode of discharge? Must the vesicle fuse with the surface membrane of the terminal in order to discharge its content? Does the vesicle have a role in uptake of transmitter from the intercellular space or synaptic cleft? How is the discharge of transmitter coupled to the presynaptic electrical potential changes that accompany the invasion of the terminal by the action potential?

In the neurons of the brain, each presynaptic cell exerts one of two influences on the postsynaptic cell. It either excites, i.e., it leads to initiation of an impulse, or it inhibits, preventing or depressing the ability of the cell to discharge. On most neurons there are both inhibitory and excitatory synapses, the balance of their influences determining whether a neuron will or will not generate an action potential or whether its frequency of discharge will increase or decrease.

Interestingly, the basic mechanisms for excitation and inhibition are similar. In both types of chemical synapses, transmitter substance is secreted by nerve terminals, and in each the transmitter increases the permeability of the postsynaptic membrane for *selected* ions only. At excitatory synapses the transmitter increases the permeability to certain cations (Na^+ and K^+) whose movement will reduce the membrane potential and cause current flow which sets up impulse propagation. At inhibitory synapses the transmitter increases permeability for small ions (K^+ and/or Cl^-) which keeps the membrane potential below threshold and thereby prevents impulse propagation.

Whether a neuron will cause excitation or inhibition in the next cell cannot always be attributed to the chemistry of the transmitter alone. Differences in the properties of the receptor may be equally important. For example, the motor nerve terminals at skeletal muscles secrete acetylcholine which combines with specific receptors at the endplate. This leads to a simultaneous flow of Na^+ and K^+ ions across the membrane in the end plate, causing a depolarization and conducted impulses, which in turn lead to an activation of the contractile mechanism in the muscle. In the heart the same transmitter, acetylcholine, liberated by nerve endings of the vagus, causes an increase in the permeability for K^+ alone, leading to inhibition.

Functionally, synaptic regions add and subtract the converging influences which are exerted on the cell by inhibitory and excitatory impulses. The individual graded synaptic potentials seem to shift the "excitability" of the cell and consequently the readiness of the neuron to discharge is either increased or decreased. This is the cellular basis for integration.

At chemical synapses the ionic permeabilities are controlled through the secretion of a transmitter, which in turn causes the graded synaptic potentials. The synaptic potential therefore differs from the explosive "all-or-none" nerve impulse whose ionic permeabilities are regulated not by a chemical mediator but by the potential fields across the membrane and whose permeability mechanism is regenerative so that, once triggered, it invariably runs its full course.

The complex tasks of the nervous system are carried out by the use of a relatively small number of mechanisms: the excitatory and inhibitory synaptic events for local integration of opposing influences and the conducted event for transmission of the information to more distant points. Although the types of signals that are used for the complex activity of the brain are relatively few (the various synaptic potentials and conducted impulses), the underlying variables in terms of neuronal properties are extensive. For example, the chemistry, and therefore sensitivity to various drugs, of "chemical" and "electrical" synapses differs, and that also is true for various inhibitory and excitatory processes. This has important consequences because the proper recognition of the physiological properties will determine the experimental approach for an analysis or for control of nervous activity.

The chemistry of synaptic transmission is but part of the wider subject of the chemistry of nerve cells. The principal problem is how to gain insight into those aspects of chemistry that relate to the specific and specialized performance of neurons. After decades of interest and work, only acetylcholine and norepinephrine have been proven to be transmitters in the peripheral nervous system in mammals. Evidence of equal weight is now available that γ-aminobutyric acid serves as an inhibitory transmitter in crustacea, and evidence exists for a transmitter role of serotonin in several invertebrates. These compounds are also found in high concentration in mammalian brains, and will probably turn out to be transmitter substances there as well.

Understanding of neurochemical transmission requires clarification of the processes for *synthesis, storage, release,* and *termination* of the activity of a neurochemical transmitter as well as for *interaction* of the chemical with its *receptor.* Our current concepts of these processes are derived by extrapolation of findings in a variety of tissues and species.

As mentioned previously, synaptic vesicles probably play a role in the synthesis as well as storage of transmitters. The action of the transmitter that has been released is terminated by enzymatic destruction (acetylcholine is hydrolyzed), by active transport back into the neuron from which it was released (norepinephrine), and by diffusion away from the receptor sites.

While neurotransmitters are released into the synaptic cleft, other substances are synthesized in specialized nerve cells and stored in larger vesicles or granules; they may be secreted into the blood in response to a nerve impulse. In mammals, neurosecretory cells in the hypothalamic nuclei are thought to control the function of the anterior pituitary, and thus provide a means for neural control of growth and differentiation, reproductive cycles, metabolic balance, etc.

It is evident that in spite of the remarkable advances in our knowledge of neuronal structure and function, most basic problems relating to neuronal chemistry remain unsolved. Extension of detailed information concerning transmitters should, one day, create a more rational basis for chemical modification of behavior and the treatment of its abnormalities.

The Structure and Physiology of the "Electrical" Synapse. "Electrical" synapses are junctions between cells in which the pre- and postsynaptic cells are linked by a pathway which enables current, a flow of ions, to pass readily from the interior of one cell to the other. Here, the same mechanism of current flow that operates in axonal conduction also transfers excitation to the postsynaptic cell.

In contrast to chemical synapses, electrical synapses are characterized morphologically by the absence of or a marked reduction in width of the synaptic cleft. The surface membranes of the apposed pre- and postsynaptic cells come close together and may even fuse. These junctions, therefore, resemble the close or tight junctions of epithelia, of smooth muscle, and of cardiac muscle. They have been found in the brains of crustaceans and of fishes, the spinal cord of the frog, and the ciliary ganglion of birds. In the past year, two examples have been discovered in mammals, in the retina of monkeys and in the lateral vestibular nucleus of the rat, but physiological correlates have not yet been obtained. In several of these examples—the ciliary ganglion of birds, the Mauthner cell of fishes, and the lateral vestibular nucleus of the rat— the synapse is of a mixed (chemical and electrical) type with some appositional zones characterized by vesicles and the closed synaptic cleft, both sharing the same surface.

The recognition of two types of transmission between neurons has had important consequences in current views of the communication between cells in the brain. The chemistry and pharmacology of "chemical" and "electrical" synapses differ, and these differences have to be considered in any experimental (or therapeutic) approach to the nervous system.

In addition to electrical excitatory transmission, a specialized electrical inhibitory mechanism has now been found in the axon cap region of the Mauthner cells (large neurons in the medulla) in the goldfish. Similar inhibition has not yet been seen elsewhere.

The electrical synapses which at first seemed only to serve for spreading of impulses between neurons now appear to have a broader significance. They have been found widely distributed among various cells, even those which do not generate electrical signals. The fact that they may be involved in basic cell interactions has attracted the attention of workers in the field of embryology and cancer research.

Neuroglial Cells: Structure, Physiological Properties, and Hypotheses Concerning Glial Function

These cells differ in many structural aspects from neurons and make up perhaps 40 percent of the bulk of the brain. They outnumber neurons by a factor of ten and are interspersed among them and also line the ventricular cavities of the brain. In the peripheral nervous system they are represented by one cell type, the Schwann cell, which surrounds the nerve cell bodies and their processes and produces a distinctive coating, the myelin, around a large proportion of the axons. In the central nervous system the neuroglia are represented by three cell types: ependymal

cells, astrocytes, and oligodendrocytes. The "microglial" cells apparently
are not true natives of the nervous system.

In spite of their predominance in the brain, glial cells will be treated
only in passing. They have been studied extensively by classical microscopists and lately by electron microscopists. At least one role is known
for Schwann cells and oligodendrocytes, but almost nothing is understood of the function of ependymal cells or astrocytes. Oligodendrocytes
and astrocytes are really well differentiated only in birds and mammals.
In other animals, both vertebrates and invertebrates, the cell types are
less distinct, but it seems from what is known now that their role will
turn out to be similar in various species.

Oligodendrocytes, like the *Schwann* cells in the periphery, produce
the myelin coating around axons (Fig. 9-1a). Myelin forms an insulation
around the axons, interrupted only at the nodes of Ranvier; it speeds
conduction by forcing the ionic currents to flow through the nodal region.
Thus the impulse "jumps" from node to node. In invertebrates high
speeds of conduction are achieved by making the diameter of axons large.
Myelinization results in a saving of space for a greater number of communication channels which can be smaller and still transmit at high speed.

The *ependymal cells* are ciliated cuboidal or columnar and line the
cavities of the brain and the central canal of the spinal cord. In the
choroid plexuses they produce the cerebrospinal fluid that fills the cavities
of the brain and flows out into the subarachnoid space. The ependyma
is the remnant of the original embryonic epithelium from which the
brain develops.

Astrocytes are characterized by a wealth of radiating branching
processes, which insinuate themselves among the other cellular elements
of the nervous system. Their sheetlike expansions enfold certain nerve
cells and particularly the dendrites with their adherent synaptic terminals.
Astrocytes tend to have accumulations of glycogen both in the cell body
and in the processes. The astrocytes send processes to the surface of the
brain and to the basement lamina surrounding blood vessels, where they
are often attached to one another by means of tight junctions.

The role of astrocytes is not known, although their physiological
properties have now been studied in tissue culture, in some invertebrates
and in amphibians. Like neurons they are cells with a resting potential
dependent on a differential distribution of ions, principally K^+. They do
not, however, participate in signaling, as do neurons; nor are they essential, in the short run, for conduction, as axons deprived of their glial
covering continue to give signals for hours or longer. When neurons
conduct impulses, however, the glial cells that surround them become
depolarized. This effect is caused by a leakage of K^+ out of neurons,

the ions accumulating in the narrow 150–200 Å clefts between the cells. The physiological activity evoked in glial cells by the K^+ depolarization is not known.

Many hypotheses concerning the role of astrocytic neuroglia had been proposed at the turn of the century or earlier. Amongst the more popular are the following: (1) Neuroglial cells serve as structural support for neurons. (2) They provide essential nutrients for neurons. (3) They "insulate" neurons from each other or prevent the spread of transmitters from synapses. (4) They have a role in repair when neurons become injured, or they replace them when they disappear. Unlike neurons, the glial cells can divide and they are known to participate in the formation of scar tissue. (5) Glial cells are supposed to be part of the "blood-brain barrier" system which prevents some molecules in the blood from reaching the nerve cells.

There are numerous other suggestions for a role of neuroglial cells, and some have become generally accepted, probably because they are of old standing. However, critical experimental evidence is lacking. In view of the fact that astrocytes take up a large part of the volume of the nervous system, our ignorance of the role of these cells is both remarkable and deplorable.

The Central Nervous System

Understanding of the functional properties of individual neurons, such as excitation, conduction, and synaptic transmission, has advanced rapidly during the past twenty years. The major unresolved problems relate to neurochemistry and to the molecular rearrangements within the membrane which lead to the ionic permeability changes underlying the action and synaptic potentials. There is every reason to believe that imaginative efforts during the next decade will lead to greatly improved understanding of even these problems.

However, when we consider the function of the brain as a whole, problems of much greater magnitude are encountered. First, we face the problem posed by an extraordinarily large number of cells which are highly interconnected and are organized into systems superimposed in hierarchical fashion, yet cross-connected at many levels. Second, we face the problems posed by an organ concerned with an extraordinarily complex set of functions: the recognition and recording of sensory data, their storing, comparison of these data with previous sensory experiences, and the formulation of decisions which lead to effective actions.

Fortunately, there are some rudimentary clues to understanding even these enormously complex problems. As we have noted, studies with a variety of animals and in different regions of the same animal suggest that the fundamental properties of neurons are everywhere qualitatively similar. Yet different brains have greatly differing capacities for generating behavior. What separates one brain from another, what makes us consider one to be simple and another highly developed, is the difference in the *number* of neurons that compose them and *their interconnections*. Stated another way, nervous systems differ from each other not so much in their components but in the way in which these components are organized. In retrospect, this finding is perhaps not surprising, since with the same components one can build either a simple calculating machine or a complex computer, the difference between the two being determined by the number of components employed and their interconnections. But the function of a brain as a system cannot be simply understood by merely adding up the functional properties of its individual neurons. As a result of the many permissible types of interconnections of individual cells, even simple neural systems manifest emergent properties which cannot be intuitively predicted from knowledge of the individual members. An understanding of the system properties of different types of neural organizations is therefore an essential prerequisite for understanding the whole brain.

Ideally, studies of the brain should involve observing a large number of interacting elements simultaneously, in order to reveal the properties of large systems of neurons. At the moment, this is technically impossible. As a result, investigators have adopted one of two complementary strategies. The first is to study brains with small numbers of cells in order to obtain simultaneous information from a significant fraction of the total population, in the hope of elucidating some general principles of neural organization which might be relevant to large neural systems. The second is to work with subsystems of known connections in large brains and to study sequentially the responses of a large number of the elements at each level to a given stimulus pattern and to infer the transformations that have occurred from one level to another. The two approaches are complementary. The first approach is designed to study, in biophysical detail, the mechanism of information transformation at a given level of neural action. This approach will be described in the next section. The second approach, which will be considered in a later section, offers the opportunity of studying larger and more complex integrative systems.

The Study of Small Brains

A great advantage of studying small brains is in using them as models for exploring general problems which for technical reasons cannot be investigated in the more complex mammalian brain. For example, it is highly useful to have a simple preparation in which a new learning task, say a conditioned reflex, can be generated and in which all the anatomical pathways involved in both the unconditioned and the conditioned responses are known and can be adequately studied at the cellular level with physiological, anatomical, and biochemical techniques. This type of preparation would be useful not only for gaining insights into the cellular mechanisms of learning and memory, but also for studying sensory perception, discrimination, and control of motor movement, the behavioral prerequisites of learning. Indeed such preparations would also be instructive for studying abnormalities of behavior produced either by abnormal manipulations of external stimuli or by selective ablation or pharmacological or electrical interference with neuronal function. Clearly such a well-worked-out preparation is not at hand, but its development is no longer technically inconceivable.

It is, of course, an assumption that the neural mechanisms of learning in a small brain will be in some way comparable to those in the brain of man, but, at the very least, knowledge of the neural mechanisms of learning in invertebrates will establish hypotheses for testing in larger brains.

Types of Small Neural Groups

Nervous systems differ in the *number* of their constituent elements. The central nervous systems (CNS) of higher vertebrates contain about 10^{12} neurons, while those of most invertebrates contain only 10^4 or 10^5 cells, and some contain as few as several hundred cells. Thus one can select for study nervous systems that differ in numerical complexity by several orders of magnitude (Fig. 9-3). Perhaps even more relevant for the study of neural integration than total number is the fact that some invertebrate nervous systems contain small organized groups of cells capable of generating rather specific behavior. For example in crustaceans, a ganglion consisting of only nine interconnected cells provides the rhythmic beat for the heart. Segmental invertebrate ganglia, which control much more complex motor reflexes, may contain as few as 400–1,000 cells. For example, the lobster ganglion shown in Figure 9-4 has built into it a complex system of sensory-motor organization. A good beginning has been made in tracing the connection of its individual nerve cells as well as in identifying them chemically. In insects there are some preliminary findings that suggest that a very simple type of avoidance learning can be accomplished by a segmental ganglion containing only 3,000 cells. Nervous systems also differ in the *size* of their *constituent neurons* (ranging from 3μ to $1,000\mu$) and in the *efficacy of individual connections*. For example, in the ganglia of the marine snail, *Aplysia*, single neurons may reach a millimeter in diameter. Since no class of animals is advantageous for all purposes, a number of different preparations have been developed because of their suitability for particular types of problems. One of the major tasks in the next few years is the further development of some of these preparations by combined anatomical, biochemical, physiological, and psychological methods.

Some groups of neurons are concerned primarily with sensory functions, others with motor functions, while a third type is primarily associational. In the first part of this section, we will examine one or two examples of each of these functional types to see what patterns of connections are commonly found in neural aggregates. In the second part we will consider some general properties of neural groups.

Sensory and Other Afferent Groups. The sensory systems provide the brain with information about its external environment. As a preliminary step to perception, the sensory information is encoded by the nervous system. The information must then be still further transformed before it can lead to motor action. In addition to encoding the incoming information, there are afferent systems which appear not to participate directly in perception but whose function it is to disseminate the meaning of information to nonsensory structures, for storage and for subsequent motor action. In some simple sensory aggregates it has been possible to isolate and record from several receptor units simultaneously and to study the interaction among them. It has also been possible, in some systems, to record individually from all, or most, of the first-order sensory interneurons, which are fed by a population of receptors.

Studies of these simple sensory and afferent systems has provided a couple of general principles: (1) the afferent input is distributed widely to various regions of the CNS, and (2) a great amount of sensory transformation occurs at the earliest points in the sensory pathways, as a result of lateral interactions between adjacent elements. When excitatory, lateral interactions lead to facilitation and synchronization of the activity in adjacent members of a neural population. When inhibitory, lateral interactions lead to spatial contrast. Lateral inhibition has been studied in a large number of neural systems, and perhaps most intensively in the

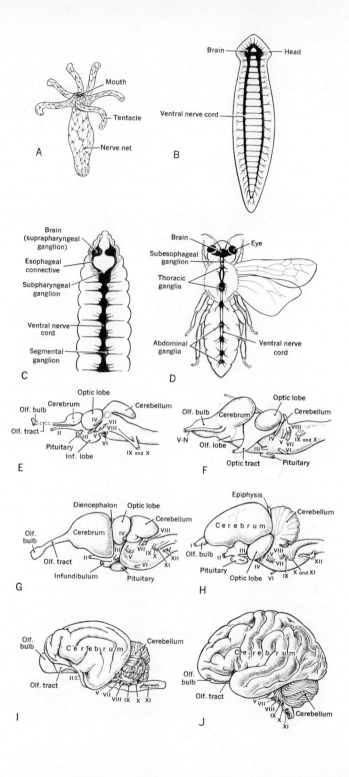

A

Mouth

Tentacle

Nerve net

B

Brain

Head

Ventral nerve cord

C

Brain
(suprapharyngeal
ganglion)

Esophageal
connective

Subpharyngeal
ganglion

Ventral nerve
cord

Segmental
ganglion

D

Brain

Eye

Subesophageal
ganglion

Thoracic
ganglia

Abdominal
ganglia

Ventral nerve
cord

E

Olf. bulb

Cerebrum

Optic lobe

Cerebellum

Olf. tract

IV

VII

VIII

II

III V

VI

Pituitary

Inf. lobe

IX and X

F

Olf. bulb

Cerebrum

Optic lobe

Cerebellum

V-N

Olf. lobe

III

IV

V

VI

VII

VIII

IX and X

Optic tract

Pituitary

G

Olf.
bulb

Diencephalon

Optic lobe

Cerebrum

Cerebellum

IV

VIII

Olf. tract

II

III

V

VI

IX

X

XII

XI

Infundibulum

Pituitary

H

Epiphysis

Cerebrum

Cerebellum

I

Olf. bulb

II

III

V

VIII

XII

Pituitary

IV

VI

IX

X and XI

Optic lobe

I

Olf.
bulb

Cerebrum

Cerebellum

Olf. tract

II

V

VII

VIII IX

X XI

J

Olf.
bulb

Cerebrum

Olf. tract

V

VII

VIII

IX X

XI

Cerebellum

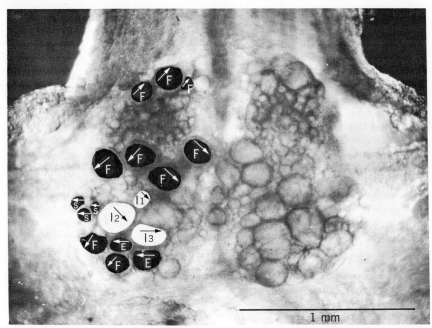

Figure 9-4. Lobster ganglion. This photograph shows both the physiological and chemical architecture of a segemental ganglion from the nerve cord of the lobster. The functional role of some of the nerve cells as well as their specific connections to various muscles was determined experimentally in the living animal. After their physiological function had been established specific cell bodies were removed for chemical study. In the left section of the figure several neurons have been outlined and marked according to their function. Those in black are excitatory neurons controlling extensor (E) or flexor (F) muscles. Chemical analysis of three inhibitory neurons (I_1; I_2; I_3), marked in white, showed them to contain within their cytoplasm a high concentration of gamma aminobutyric acid which acts an an inhibitory substance at synapses. (From Otsuka, Kravitz and Potter, J. Neurophysiol. *30*, 1967)

Figure 9-3. Phylogeny of the brain. Phylogenetically, there is a progressive increase in the complexity of the central nervous system. This is first apparent in invertebrates (A–D) as a centralization of nerve cells into ganglia and a fusion of several of these into a brain. In the vertebrate brain (E–J) there is a further trend toward encephalization of function as manifest by the progressive increase in the size of the cerebrum in higher forms. The drawings are not to scale.

A. Hydra; B. Planaria; C. Earthworm; D. Bee; E. Codfish; F. Frog; G. Alligator; H. Goose; I. Cat; J. Man.

(A–D reprinted from *Animals Without Backbones* by Ralph Buchsbaum by permission of the University of Chicago Press. Copyright 1939 and 1948 by the University of Chicago. All rights reserved. E–J from R. C. Truex, ed., *Strong and Elwyn's Human Neuroanatomy.* Fourth edition © 1959 by The Williams & Wilkins Co., Baltimore) visual system of the horseshoe crab, *Limulus*. It will be described in detail as a prototype.

When small spots of light are used to examine the response of the eye of *Limulus* one can show that the receptor units (ommatidia) are *not* independent in their action. Although the activity of any given receptor unit is principally determined by the light shining on its facet, this activity is significantly modified when light is shone upon neighboring receptor units causing them to become active. The receptor units are mutually inhibitory; excitation in one unit produces inhibition in all the surrounding neighbor units. The *spatial spread of inhibition* is such that it is most effective for the nearest units and falls off sharply with distance. The *intensity of inhibition* in the surrounding units increases in proportion to the logarithm of the intensity of illumination of the reference receptor unit. Thus the strength of the inhibitory influence exerted by a particular receptor channel on neighboring receptor channels depends both on the effects of the stimulus on the reference channel and on the inhibitory influences from its neighbors. The strength of this influence depends, in turn, on the neighbors' level of activity, which is partially determined by the inhibition that the reference receptor elements exert on them. These interactions occur simultaneously in each member of the interacting population, resulting in a dynamic interdependence of all.

The mutual inhibition is mediated by recurrent collaterals of the axons of eccentric cells which synapse on the axons of neighboring eccentric cells, providing an anatomical pathway for negative feedback.

This anatomical arrangement provides an example of a major principle in the dynamic organization of neural populations, *the balanced opposition of excitatory and inhibitory tendencies in molding patterns of neural activity*. Recurrent inhibition is a specifically interesting form of this principle of opposition. It illustrates the integrative utility of even fairly nonspecific interactions. In the *Limulus* eye, inhibitory influences exerted quite indiscriminately by receptor channels on their neighbors have the effect of enhancing contrast in the visual image. If each unit in the mosaic of receptor channels inhibits the activity of its neighbors to a degree that is greater the more strongly it is excited, then brightly lighted elements will exert a stronger suppressing action on dimly lighted neighbors than the dimly lighted neighbors can exert on the sharply lighted element. Consequently, the disparity in the activities of the two channels will be exaggerated, and brightness contrast will be enhanced. If the inhibitory interaction is stronger for near neighbors in the retinal mosaic than for more widely separated ones, such contrast effects will be greatest in the vicinity of sharp light discontinuities in the retinal image, and the outline of objects imaged on the retina will be sharpened.

Thus the pattern of neuronal activity generated by the action of light and by boundaries between light and dark is transformed in a physiologically important way by the mosaic of receptor channels, at a very early point in the analysis of sensory input. Lateral inhibition, of which recurrent inhibition is a special form, occurs in many neural systems, motor as well as sensory. The complex transformations carried out by large neural systems are executed in part by repetition of a limited number of elementary mechanisms, of which this is an example, occurring in complexly divergent and convergent channels.

Interneuronal Populations. Sensory Interneurons. Any neuron not classified as a primary afferent fiber or a motoneuron falls into the general class of interneurons. From this point of view the entire mammalian nervous system might be viewed as a galaxy of interneuronal arcs superimposed upon themselves and interposed between input and output. Obviously some reduction in the experimental field is required to study the properties of interneuronal populations, and here the study of small brains has been particularly valuable. Interneurons have been studied in the greatest detail in the nervous system of the crayfish. Here "afferent interneurons" can be grouped into two classes: (a) segmental interneurons which respond only to first-order input to the anatomical segment of the animal in which they reside, and (b) multisegmental interneurons which respond to input reaching them from several segments via a number of sensory pathways and other interneurons. A single sensory stimulus may activate a dozen or so interneurons. For example, stroking a single patch of hairs on the dorsum of one of six abdominal segments activates one segmental interneuron and a number of multisegmental interneurons which serve the reference segment as well as adjacent ones. Afferent interneurons thus provide a parallel representation of a particular sensory area in varying spatial combinations with other areas. Moreover, afferent input mediated via multisegmental interneurons is distributed widely, including channeling to the higher integrating levels as well as to efferent pathways at various levels. Overlapping communication lines provide an economical means of approaching functional redundancy (which permits greater tolerance of injury and a greater uniformity of threshold) while still keeping sufficient contrast in channel function (especially by the comparison of activity in parallel channels) to signal different degrees of specificity and complexity.

Command Interneurons. At some stage beyond primary and interneuronal sensory processing, activity evoked by sensory stimuli engages effector interneuronal pools. Some of these have a remarkable influence upon the behavioral patterns of the animal. For example, single "command" interneurons in the crayfish can excite flexor motoneurons, inhibit the peripheral inhibitor of flexion, excite the peripheral inhibitor of extension, and inhibit extensor motoneurons. That is, the discharge of this single cell influences at least 120 motoneurons and elicits the full pattern of tail flexion. Other individual command interneurons are even more potent, and produce coordinated postural adjustments which involve several segments. The discovery of command interneurons in the nervous system of the crayfish and of some other invertebrate animals is of great interest, for it illustrates the extraordinary effectiveness with which individual cells can control behavior. No matter how large the brain, there must be a series of points between the central transformation of sensory input and the evolving pattern of the motor output when a *decision* is made. That a single cell can trigger such decisions provides an unexpected help in analyzing interconnected cell systems.

Effector Groups. The nervous system is capable of generating four classes of effector responses: (1) the contraction of skeletal muscle for postural adjustments and for movement, (2) the modulation of smooth muscle activity for the integrated functioning of the internal organs of the body, (3) the release of hormone, and (4) the control of the secretions of glandular epithelium. We will limit ourselves here to effector aggregates of the first type and examine a group of motoneurons in the mammalian spinal cord which innervate a synergistic group of muscles.

The function of the different motoneuron pools is to translate afferent messages coming into the CNS from the outside world (which have been elaborated and transformed by sensory and interneuronal aggregates) into appropriate action upon the environment. The function of the final motor outflow from the brain is to provide fine control of movement. This is accomplished by a combination of precise connection and by recurrent inhibition.

The motoneuron pool is one of the "final common pathways" in the nervous system and is thus a site of great convergence of neural information. Information may come to motoneurons directly from the periphery, through only one synapse (monosynaptically). More commonly, motoneurons are engaged through many earlier relay synapses (polysynaptically). Frequently the same information is mediated through both types of channels. In addition to receiving excitatory synaptic action tending to discharge it, a motoneuron also receives inhibitory synaptic action tending to prevent it from discharging. The activity of motoneuron discharge leading to the activation of muscular contraction is therefore determined by an integration of the total information available at a given time. This is accomplished by weighing and adding the effects of the different synaptic input over its surface. Not all synapses of a given class (e.g., excitatory) converging upon a given motoneuron are of equal value.

Moreover, the relative efficacy of synapses on motoneurons, as on other cells appears not fixed but labile. Synapses may change in efficacy as a result of maturation, as a result of use, as a result of pathological conditions such as those produced by drugs and disease, and presumably as a result of experience (learning). The ability of synapses to vary in efficacy is called the "plastic" properties of synapses and will be further considered later.

In a sense, the final decision for motor action resides in the integrative capability of the motoneuron, in its ability to mix and add excitatory information of various degrees and from different sources and subtract from it the sum total of inhibitory information. If the integrated excitatory synaptic action exceeds the inhibitory synaptic action by a certain critical minimum, the motoneuron discharges and the muscle contracts.

The level of activity in a motoneuron depends not only upon the net excitatory and inhibitory influences reaching it, but upon the activity of its neighbors as well. Vertebrate motoneurons send inhibitory recurrent collaterals to their neighbors in a manner similar to those in the receptor mosaic of the *Limulus* eye. In the motor systems, the function of this recurrent inhibitory system is to isolate functionally cells that are anatomically near each other, a feature that increases the fineness of motor control. Thus, the mechanism of contrast enhancement is found in a variety of neural systems.

General Properties of Neural Aggregates

Specificity of Neural Interconnections. Information comes into the nervous system via specific receptors and emerges via specific motoneurons, along individual and specific communication channels. The question naturally arises as to what degree a highly ordered specificity of pathways and of connections exists in the central parts of the nervous system. The problem has now been examined in a number of animals with small brains, and in each case a great deal of specificity has emerged. For example, the central nervous systems of the crayfish, the lobster, the leech, and *Aplysia* have some cells that are highly distinctive in appearance and functional properties (Fig. 9-3). These cells can be recognized in preparation after preparation on the basis of specific location, physiological, morphological and/or biochemical properties, as well as specific connections with other cells. For example, in the crayfish the stretch receptors are predetermined in number, functional properties, and anatomical connections. The efferent outflow to muscles is mediated by a small and constant number of fibers (two to six, depending on the muscle). The motor fibers can be further distinguished from each other by their

effects on muscle, either inhibitory or excitatory. The specificity for
sensory and motor neurons also appears to exist for interneurons. While
random connections may play a role in the functioning of neural aggregates, this role is likely to be minor. The predominant findings available speak for a specifically "wired" and genetically predetermined nervous system.

In view of this rather strong suggestion, two further problems arise.
First, how is this specific wiring accomplished during the early development of the nervous system? How do the outgrowing nerve cells manage
to form and maintain appropriate end organ terminations in the periphery
and appropriate synaptic connections in the central nervous system? How
do the genes carry enough information for all the connections? Second,
given rigidly specific connections, how can modification of neural action
of the sort involved in learning occur? For neither of these questions is
much information available. However, as a result of a number of investigations, the interrelated concepts of the trophic and plastic properties of neurons have been developed and have proven to have heuristic
value.

Trophic Functions of Neurons. The term *trophic functions* of neurons
refers to the influences that neurons exert on the structures they innervate. Although trophic influences are mediated via synaptic connections,
their action is not necessarily related to electrical activity at the synapse.

The idea that neurons exert trophic actions on other neurons and on
muscle comes primarily from studies of *redeveloping* synapses following regeneration. In only rare cases has a developing synaptic function
been successfully studied. The future growth of this area will continue
to depend upon contributions from developmental biologists. Moreover,
since neurotrophic influences represent part of the general problem of
cellular differentiation, the application of the concepts and techniques of
molecular biology are likely to have a major impact on this important
area.

Trophic interactions have been best studied in the spinal motor horn
cell where it has been possible to show two types of functions mediated
in the forward direction, from motoneuron to muscle. One of these determines the size of the chemosensitive area of the muscle membrane;
the other contractile properties of the muscle. These can be explained
by postulating that a number of specific chemical substances are im-
parted by motoneurons to the muscles they innervate. The release of
these substances cannot be simply related to the detailed pattern of impulse traffic in the neuron. Thus, in addition to transmitting neural information, synapses transmit chemical influences to the tissues they
innervate. Indeed, there is evidence that the chemical influence appears

to be transmitted in both directions. If an outgrowing nerve cell can impart a specific influence on the structures it innervates, and if these structures can in turn influence the growth and functioning of the neuron, then these processes could indeed serve as effective regulators in the embryological development of the nervous system. The trophic substances could provide the types of chemoaffinities necessary for the development of highly specific connections.

Lower vertebrates have remarkable regenerative capacities and have provided excellent models for testing these ideas. For example, if one cuts the optic nerve of a fish or frog, the nerve regenerates and normal vision returns. By combining optic nerve section with removal of part of the retina, it is possible to prevent a portion of the optic nerve from regenerating and to follow in detail the course taken by the remaining regenerating optic nerve fibers. Do the outgrowing nerve fibers have multiple opportunities to make synaptic contacts among the dense populations of neurons they encounter in the optic tectum? Of the many opportunities available, the fibers refuse all but the appropriate ones. Incorrect zones in the tectum are consistently bypassed and left empty, and only when the outgrowing fibers reach the appropriate cells in the appropriate part of the optic tectum are synapses formed. This specificity suggests that presynaptic terminals of the optic nerve fiber and the specific tectal neuron it innervates must have a complementary specificity so that the appropriate pre- and post-elements of the synapses are attracted to each other.

This attraction appears to be due to chemical affinities present during growth rather than to the functional pattern of neural impulses produced by experience or learning. In amphibians it is possible to rotate the eyeball 180 degrees on its optical axis. When reinnervation takes place, the visual responses of the frog are 180° inverted. The resulting maladaptive responses, such as snapping for food in the wrong direction, persist indefinitely without correction, indicating that optic nerve fibers remain connected to their initially appropriate tectal cell despite the functional inappropriateness of these connections.

These findings strongly support the notion that the major connections of the nervous system are established under genetic control and develop in the absence of learning. Indeed in the mammalian visual system it has been possible to show that intricate cortical connections are present and to a large degree functional at birth. The basic morphological structure for complex behavior is therefore apparently built into the nervous system under genetic control, and seems to develop as a result of a specific chemical affinity between afferent connection and central nuclear regions. What is all the more intriguing about chemical trophic influences is that they are essential for the development of appropriate connections in embryogenesis, and for the maintenance and regulation of these connections in later life as well.

Plastic Properties of Neurons. If the connections of the nervous system are largely specified genetically, how do functional modifications occur in the brain? The environment continuously produces modifications in the behavior of the organism. How is the modifiability of behavior consistent with a rigidly wired brain? These are the types of questions neural scientists confront as they begin to examine this complex biological problem.

The study of learning begins with the fact that a variety of neural networks can undergo persistent changes outlasting the initiating stimulus, changes that are electrophysiologically detectable. Although this neuronal plasticity is analogous to learning on the organismic level, the two concepts are not identical. In fact, the detailed study of the actual learning of an organism is, at present, beyond the technical limits of neural science. The concept of plastic change is primarily useful in defining a necessary neural component of learning (long-term change, analogous to information storage) which can be approached experimentally.

The question posed at the beginning of this section has therefore been approached experimentally in the more restricted sense of what constitutes plastic change in the nervous system. A number of realistic answers to this question have now been suggested. One is that although most connections in the nervous system are genetically specified, a small number of neurons with unspecified (blank) connections are set aside specifically for learning. Another possibility is that the connections are specified but their value, or efficacy, is not. A third possibility is that plastic changes, although mediated via connections, may reside not in the connections but in some other parameter of neural function, such as changes in the number of trigger zones, or in the spontaneous activity pattern of neurons.

Of the three possibilities the second, that of change in synaptic efficacy, has received the most consistent support. In a number of systems the efficacy of synaptic transmission can be significantly increased, at least for periods of time ranging from many minutes to several hours. The facilitatory changes are usually confined to pathways that have been stimulated, but in some systems there can occur a transfer of facilitation from one pathway to another. Whereas some pathways show prolonged synaptic facilitation following stimulation, others may show prolonged synaptic decrements, and still other pathways show facilitation at one frequency of stimulation and decrement at another.

Changes in synaptic efficacy have been demonstrated in elementary synaptic systems and have been studied in considerable detail. Perhaps the most striking and important finding has come from a comparison of electrical and chemical synapses. The finding is that following a high rate of activity, changes in synaptic efficacy occur in chemically operated synapses and not in electrically operated ones.

The mechanisms for neuronal plasticity so far uncovered describe an intermediate range of temporal events, lasting from minutes to a few hours. The time course of these phenomena is parallel to that for a short-term memory in an intact learning organism. So far, no mechanisms have been uncovered which might provide permanent or even long-term changes in neural function. Yet clearly these are the most intriguing and important features of learning in higher animals. A beginning in this direction has been provided by research which involves chronic rearrangement of normal sensory inflow into the nervous system. These procedures produce persistent changes in neural function, but none of them has yet been examined in sufficient detail to specify their mechanism. There is nonetheless the intriguing possibility that these long-term changes might involve some trophic function comparable to those that have been postulated to function during neural growth and development. Such trophic influences could, for example, alter the efficacy of synaptic transmission or change the property of a silent postsynaptic cell so that it becomes spontaneously active.

The Structure and Function of Higher Nervous Systems

Animals with large brains are distinguished by an extraordinary development of their capability to gather information about their environment, to act upon it, to think abstractly, and to communicate among themselves. In addition, animals with large brains also have exceptionally good homeostatic regulation of bodily function. A characteristic feature of animals with large brains is an extraordinary development of their cerebral cortex, which becomes so large that numerous enfoldings (sulci) become necessary to handle its greatly expanded surface area (Fig. 9-5).

Information gathering, action upon the environment, and bodily homeostasis are represented within large brains by systems that can be specified anatomically and studied separately. Studying these systems individually is a necessary simplification and serves as a preliminary step for a later attempt at resynthesis which hopefully will allow an understanding of the more holistic aspects of brain function. Even now the level of understanding in some systems has progressed to the point where some analytic studies of behavioral functions can be carried out in the waking

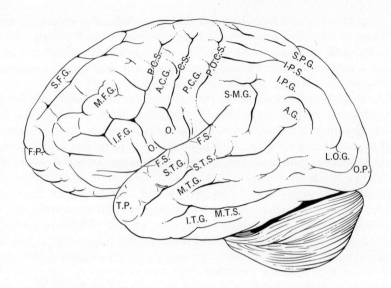

A.C.G.	Anterior central gyrus
A.G.	Angular gyrus
C.S.	Central sulcus (Fissure of Rolando)
F.P.	Frontal pole
F.S.	Fissure of Sylvius
I.F.G.	Inferior frontal gyrus
I.P.G.	Inferior parietal gyrus
I-P.S.	Inter-parietal sulcus
I.R.	Island of Reil
I.T.G.	Inferior temporal gyrus
L.O.G.	Lateral occipital gyrus
M.F.G.	Middle frontal gyrus
M.T.G.	Middle temporal gyrus
M.T.S.	Middle temporal sulcus
O.	Operculum
O.P.	Occipital pole
P.C.G.	Posterior central gyrus
P-C.S.	Pre-central sulcus
P.O.C.S.	Post-central sulcus
S.F.G.	Superior frontal gyrus
S-M.G.	Supra-marginal gyrus
S.P.G.	Superior parietal gyrus
S.T.G.	Superior temporal gyrus
S.T.S.	Superior temporal sulcus
T.P.	Temporal pole

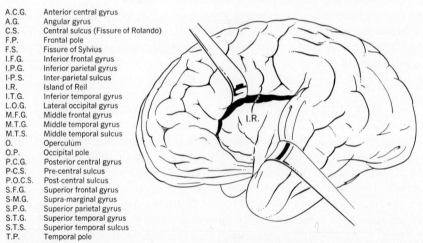

Figure 9-5. Lateral view of the surface of the human cerebral cortex. The surface of the cerebral cortex presents irregular grooves called sulci or fissures and elevations known as gyri or convolutions. In different individuals each hemisphere may show slight variations. The major fissures divide the cerebral hemispheres into lobes. (Redrawn from F. H. Netter, *CIBA Collection of Medical Illustrations,* Vol. I, *The Nervous System.* Copyright The CIBA Collection of Medical Illustrations by Frank H. Netter, M.D.)

brain, so that the interaction *between* systems, characteristic of brain function, can be studied. It is the preliminary and detailed study of individual systems that will make this broader study of interacting systems increasingly possible.

In the next three sections we will consider the sensory systems concerned with sensation and perception, the motor systems concerned with action upon the environment, and the intercalated systems of the brain concerned with homeostatic regulation.

The Sensory Systems: Neural Mechanism in Sensation and Perception

Our brain has contact with the world around us only through our sensory receptors. Our experience of the world is therefore not a replication of reality but an abstraction of it accomplished by the sensory receptors and by the later neural transformation within the brain.

The sheets of peripheral receptors (e.g., touch, pain, vision, audition) are represented in the thalamus and cortex in an orderly, topographical manner, and this provides an anatomical representation of the external world within the highest levels of the nervous system (Fig. 9-6). Recent cellular studies have shown important similarities and differences in the functional organization of the various sensory systems. For example, both the somaesthetic and visual cortex are organized into narrow vertical columns running from the cortical surface to the white matter. The cells in a column are specific to receptive field position and submodality in the somaesthetic cortex and to receptive field position and axis of orientation in the visual cortex.

In the visual cortex, for example, all axes of orientation are represented for each receptive field position. The cortex must therefore provide cells for a vast number of peripheral representations, and it is this fact that allows one to understand why large numbers of cells are necessary to normal cortical functioning.

Studies have been carried out at different subcortical and cortical levels within both the somaesthetic and visual systems to examine the transformation of neural activity along the system. In the somaesthetic system the major transformation for signaling the intensity of a touch or vibratory stimulus occurs at the receptor; the subsequent neural pathways have linear properties and are designed to produce minimal loss or distortion of the incoming signals. In the visual system, a major transformation also seems to occur at the receptor stage, but even more remarkable transformations take place at higher, cortical synaptic levels.

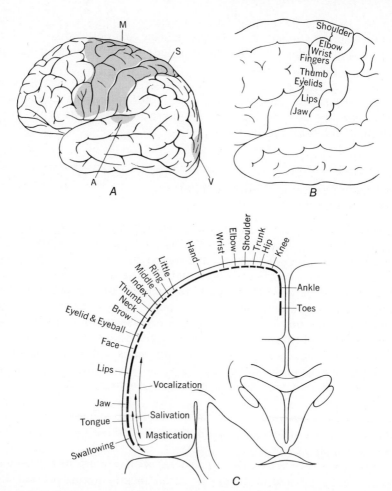

Figure 9-6. Localization of function in the human cerebral cortex

A. Approximate location of sensory and motor areas on the surface of man's brain. *M:* Motor; *S:* Somesthetic; *A:* Auditory; and *V:* Visual. This diagram does not indicate the full extent of either the visual area, which extends into the cleft behind the two hemispheres, or the auditory area, which is buried in the Sylvian fissure.

B. General representation of the body in the motor area on the surface of the human brain.

C. Detailed representation of the body as seen in a cross section of the brain at the level of the central sulcus. There is an orderly and systematic representation of the body musculature in the motor cortex. ((A) from D. O. Hebb, *A Textbook of Psychology.* © 1958 by W. B. Saunders Co. (B) from Truex. (C) from Truex's modification of Rasmussen and Penfield, 1947)

Of the five special senses we will consider only somaesthesis (touch, pain, temperature, and position sense) and vision.

The Somaesthetic System. Peripheral Somaesthetic Mechanism. One of the most striking findings in recent studies of somaesthetic sensation is that in response to variations in the intensity of a stimulus, the firing frequency of afferent fibers obeys the same mathematical relationship as does somaesthetic perception in man. This implies that the major transformation of the incoming message occurs in the first-order fibers and that the CNS responds to variations in the intensity of a stimulus in a linear manner. This finding draws our attention to the importance of neural coding in first-order fibers. Indeed, it is likely that the principles of coding that we find here will have general validity and will apply as well to coding within the brain. We will consider here two aspects of neural coding: (1) the types of transformation that occur in neurons, and (2) the modality specificity of individual information channels.

1. *Neural transformations in afferent fibers.* The afferent fibers use an all-or-none action potential for signaling and therefore function as a pulse-operated system. How can information be coded in such a system? Recent research has given us some important leads.

a. *By changes in frequency.* A single axon signals changes in the intensity of a stimulus by a change in its frequency of discharges per unit time. This code is widely used in nervous systems, and recent correlated studies of somaesthetic perception with first-order input indicate that it is the main way in which intensity of the stimulus is signaled.

b. *By evaluating the profile of frequencies of discharge in a population of elements.* The population profile provides a contour map in the afferent pathways to the brain which represents the contoured spatial position and extent of an external stimulus.

c. *By taking the time derivative of the frequency profile.* A central mechanism might read direction or velocity acceleration by sampling across a population of neurons which is changing its frequency profile with time.

d. *By evaluating the internal structure of the neural message.* Messages of different informational content in two trains of impulses may be signaled by differences in the position of the signals in each train. The two trains can then be compared during each measuring unit of time.

To establish that a code impressed at the first-order level has functional meaning, one must also show that it is relevant for sensation. This points up the need for a quantitative study (psychophysics) of the commonly available laboratory animals, especially primates.

2. *Modality specificity of individual information channels.* To what

extent are different submodalities of somaesthetic sensation (e.g., touch, pain, temperature) mediated by separate and specific afferent fibers?

A great body of evidence has recently accumulated to indicate that there is a great deal of *functional* (modality) specificity. Thus afferent fibers show a clear-cut *preferential* sensitivity to specific types of somaesthetic stimuli, although anatomically different receptor types cannot be parceled out as subserving different modalities. Of special interest is the recent demonstration that some fibers are selectively sensitive to stimuli that damage tissue. This is the first clear demonstration of a group of fibers which could specifically mediate pain sensation.

Central Somaesthetic Mechanisms. The modern study of the CNS mechanisms in somaesthetic sensation is based upon the extensive knowledge of the electroanatomy developed during the past decades and upon the recent quantitative studies of sensory transduction and first-order coding, described briefly above. Current studies are attempting to elucidate the neural transformations of sensory input at successively higher regions of the somaesthetic systems, including the sensory areas of the cerebral cortex. The methods used in these studies are mainly electrophysiological. The first method is that of single-unit analysis, in which the investigator attempts to characterize the action of large populations of neurons by a sequential study of individual elements. The second method is the recording of slow wave electrical events, within or in the vicinity of the populations that generate them. The latter method is now primarily useful for electroanatomical and topographical studies, but it has great potential value because it can be applied harmlessly to the brains of human subjects. A newly developed method is to study unanesthetized and freely moving animals by means of implanted recording devices. With this technique and the development of psychophysics, we may hope for a complete characterization of the spatial and temporal patterns of neural activity within a sensory system during such perceptual events as differential discrimination.

Using these techniques, work on integrative action within the central somaesthetic systems has in recent years been marked by a number of major advances. The first concerns the functional role of inhibition. There is no peripheral inhibition within the somaesthetic system; inhibition enters for the first time at the first central relay. By comparing the response properties of afferent fibers with those of central relay neurons, it becomes clear that inhibition has important functional consequences. Whereas the receptive field of a primary afferent fiber (the area of skin which, upon stimulation, effects the firing rate of the fiber) is exclusively excitatory, the receptive field of a central relay cell has a central excitatory zone surrounded (or flanked) by a belt of inhibition, which permits greatly enhanced two-point discrimination.

A second major advance is the recognition that the different parts of the somaesthetic system, the lemniscal and anterolateral systems, possess markedly different functional properties; the former preserves modality specificity and the precise spatial attributes of the stimulus, and the latter seems especially concerned with pain and the affective qualities of stimuli.

A third fundamental contribution is the demonstration at the cortical level of the lemniscal system of at least two types of functional organization. First, there is a gross topographical organization: different regions of the sensory cortex are devoted to processing information from separate parts of the body surface, providing the substratum for spatial discrimination. Second, there is a finer-grained organization of the cortex within this topographical pattern. The cortex is organized into narrow vertical columns running from surface to white matter, and the *columns* of cortex are specialized to process information related to a specific submodality. For example, superficial and deep sensations generated within any given region of the body would be selectively distributed to separate small columns of cortex, all within the appropriate topographical area.

Taken together, these advances provide a basis for further, more analytic and quantitative studies which promise to yield much more information about how quality and intensity of sensation are coded, and about the detailed synaptic arrangements by which the sequential transformations are achieved. Ultimately, there is hope of learning what changes in the nervous system accompany states of attention to sensory stimuli, what pathways and mechanisms mediate both normal and pathological pain sensations, and, finally, how sensory information is handled at integrative levels beyond the primary cortical receiving areas.

The Visual System. Studies similar to those carried out in the somaesthetic system have also been carried out in the visual system; here the receptive fields undergo even more complex transformations.

Early studies using evoked potentials showed that the retina projects in an orderly fashion upon the visual cortex. Microelectrode studies, performed more recently, have illustrated that changes in configuration of the receptive field occur at various levels of the visual system. As we shall see, these studies have also suggested how such changes in receptive field properties can come about and have therefore been generally useful in indicating how the brain abstracts information from its external environment. Finally, these studies provide additional insights into the functional organization of the cerebral cortex.

In the visual pathways the receptors, the rods and cones, end on the bipolar cells which, in turn, synapse on retinal ganglion cells. The axons of the retinal ganglion cells enter the brain via the optic nerves, the optic chiasm and optic tract, and end in the lateral geniculate body. The cells of the lateral geniculate project onto the striate cortex, area 17, and the cells of this cortex in turn project onto cortical areas 18 and 19.

As is the case in the somaesthetic system, it is possible to outline a receptive field for all cells so far studied in the visual system (i.e., an area of the retina which upon stimulation either excites or inhibits a visual cell). The first neural elements in the mammalian visual system whose receptive fields have been successfully studied are the ganglion cells of the retina. The receptive fields of retinal cells are circular in shape and look much like targets or donuts, having an "on" or "off" center and an annular antagonistic surround region. A cell with an "on" center receptive field has an inhibitory surround region, and cells with "off" center receptive fields have an excitatory surround region. The most effective excitatory stimulus for cells with an "on" center receptive field is therefore a circular spot covering the entire central (on) region of the field. If the stimulus is enlarged to include any of the annular surround region, the effectiveness of the stimulus is reduced because of the mutual antagonism between the center and surround regions. From these properties of the receptive field we learn that a retinal ganglion cell does not primarily signal the *intensity* of light reaching it from a given part of the retina but the *contrast* between the intensity of illumination in the center of its receptive field as compared to that of the annular surround region.

At the next synapse, in the lateral geniculate, the receptive field resembles that of the retinal ganglion cell. However, at the first cortical synapse (area 17), the receptive field changes dramatically in its configuration. Small spots of light which were effective in stimulating retinal ganglion and geniculate cells are practically ineffective. To drive cortical cells, the stimulus must have linear properties (bars, lines, rectangles, etc.).

There are several kinds of cortical receptive fields, and these can be grouped into two general classes (1) simple and (2) complex.

Cortical cells with simple receptive fields resemble geniculate cells in that their receptive fields can be described in terms of discrete excitatory and inhibitory zones. However, the receptive field is rectangular and not circular, and the effective stimulus is not a spot of light but a bar (or a line) with a specific inclination—e.g., a vertical, horizontal, or oblique axis of orientation. For example, the most effective excitatory stimulus for cortical cells with a simple receptive field may be a bar with a receptive field orientation of twelve to six o'clock projected upon a particular retinal position. This rectangular excitatory zone is framed by a rectangular inhibitory zone. How is such a receptive field built up? The simplest explanation is that a cortical cell with a simpler field receives its input from a set of geniculate cells having appropriate properties ("on" center) and similar retinal positions.

The most striking feature of the cortical cell is that it is much more particular in its stimulus requirement than the retinal ganglion or geniculate cell. For a stimulus to be effective on a cortical cell it must have (1) the proper retinal position and also (2) the proper shape and (3) the proper axis of orientation. Since all areas of the retina have to be presented in all orientations and for several stimulus types, we begin to see why the cortex needs so many cells for its normal functioning.

A further feature distinguishes cortical from geniculate cells. Geniculate cells (with rare exception) respond only to stimulation of one eye, whereas cortical cells tend to respond to both eyes. At the level of the first cortical synapse we therefore find the first evidence for binocular fusion so characteristic of vision in higher animals.

The next category of cells encountered in the cortex are those with *complex* receptive fields. For these cells the effective stimulus is again linear, it must have the correct orientation, but its exact position in the receptive field is not important. Again we ask how is the receptive field of the complex cell built up? The simplest explanation is that cells with complex receptive fields receive excitatory projections from a set of simple cortical cells. This idea is supported by the following findings. The visual cortex is organized into vertical columns which run from the surface of the brain to the white matter, very much like those we have encountered in the somatic sensory cortex. Within any one column one finds both simple and complex cells, and the properties of the simple cell are just what are needed to account for the properties of complex cells if one supposed that the complex cell in the column receives all of its input from the simple cells in the column. The column thus appears to be the elementary unit of neural organization in the cortex and serves to bring cells together so that they can be appropriately interconnected in order to generate a cell with a higher-order receptive field.

Cells in area 17 project to both 18 and 19 where the visual message undergoes still further processing, with the end result that some cells have hypercomplex receptive field properties and respond only to a highly specific stimulus, such as a corner.

Areas 18 and 19 are also organized into vertical columns. Cells within a column are both complex and hypercomplex, and again the properties of the complex cells are just what are needed to account for the hyper-complex ones, if one assumes that a hypercomplex cell receives its input from the complex cells in its own column.

These studies of the changes in the configuration of the effective stim-ulus at various levels in the visual system provide us with a remarkable insight into how the cortex abstracts essentials from sensory stimuli. For example, the function of the hypercomplex cells suggests that they serve as a detector of curvature; they indicate changes in the direction of a line. This suggests that lines may be analyzed by measuring *changes in* contour much as light intensity is analyzed by measuring *contrast* between light and dark.

Finally, these studies inform us about the role of the regional subdivi-sions of the cortex. In the case of areas 17, 18, and 19, each accomplishes one or more specific transformations of neural activity. Moreover, this transformation occurs in each of the cortical areas within specific co-lumnar systems in which the information is primarily conveyed in a ver-tical manner with little lateral dissemination of information.

All of these elaborate transformations of the neural message depend upon conventional neural mechanisms of the sort that have been de-scribed in previous sections of this report: action potential, excitatory and inhibitory synaptic potentials, and specific convergent and divergent connections.

Perhaps the most remarkable aspect of these studies of somaesthesis and vision is that they suggest that the immense task of understanding the neural basis of perception is only immense; it is no longer incompre-hensible. Indeed, what we have learned so far about the neural mecha-nisms of perception is that, once understood, the details are not only elegant but beautifully simple.

The Motor Systems: Action Upon the Environment

The capacity of man to modify and control his environment sets him apart from all other forms of life. As Herrick pointed out, "A young salamander larva or tadpole is well equipped with sense organs. He has nearly as many ways of sensing what is going on around him as we have, but the number of things that he can do about it is surprisingly small."

The evolution of the vertebrate brain, culminating in a system that can control its environment and even itself, has, to a large extent, in-volved evolution of those parts of the nervous system that extend the range of *action upon* rather than *reaction to* the environment. Under-standing of the human brain, even in its most complex intellectual functions, may be advanced if it is approached as an organ that has evolved as a system to allow adaptation to and control of the environment. Sperry has put forth this point of view most lucidly: "Instead of regarding motor activity as being subsidiary, that is, something to carry out, serve, and satisfy the demands of the higher centers, we reverse this tendency and look upon the mental activity as only a means to an end, where the end is better regulation of overt response. Cerebration, essentially, serves to bring into motor behavior additional refinement, increased direction toward distant, future goals, and greater over-all adaptiveness and survival value. The evolutionary increase in man's capacity for perception, feeling, ideation, imagination, and the like, may be regarded, not so much as an end in itself, but as something that has enabled us to behave, to act, more wisely and efficiently."

The term *motor systems* is applied to the neuronal organizations converging upon the motoneurons, the final common paths to effector organs. This organization consists of two parts, segmental and suprasegmental.

Segmental Mechanisms Controlling the Motoneuron. How is the motoneuron controlled? Work begun by Sherrington late in the nineteenth century showed that impulses in afferent fibers associated with specialized receptors within the muscle itself play a major role in controlling the activity of the motoneuron. Of special importance among these muscle receptors is the *muscle spindle*, a receptor in which the afferent endings coil around specialized muscle fibers (the *intrafusal* fibers) which, by contracting or relaxing, can regulate the sensitivity of the receptor. In the 1940's it was found that the intrafusal fibers of the muscle spindle were under the control of a specialized group of small spinal cord motoneurons, the so-called fusimotor (gamma) neurons. The muscle spindle is a receptor that provides information about muscle length, and the activity of the fusimotoneurons maintains the spindle in a state of sensitivity in spite of the variations of length associated with shortening or stretching of the muscle in which the spindle is located. The operation of the muscle spindle is thus somewhat analogous to the operation of the pupil, which controls the total light entering the eye so as to allow optimum operation of retinal receptors.

The muscle spindle afferent fibers synapse directly (i.e., monosynaptically) on motoneurons innervating the muscles in which the spindle is situated. When a muscle is stretched, its spindle afferents are excited and the resultant afferent impulses act to excite the motoneuron via the classical monosynaptic reflex; contraction of the stretched muscle results. Thus, stretch of a muscle sets up a muscular contraction which tends to counteract the stretch, thereby acting to maintain a stable posture of the skeletal parts to which the muscle is attached. Activity of the spindle afferents also inhibits (via an intermediary interneuron) the motoneurons of antagonistic muscles.

In addition to having local (or segmental) terminations, spindle afferents project to relay stations which transmit information about muscle length to the cerebellum, cerebral cortex, and other components of the central motor apparatus. These impulses do not lead to conscious experience in man, as is shown by the fact that subjects undergoing muscle surgery (under local cutaneous anesthesia) are quite unaware of changes imposed on muscle length. Conscious awareness of the position of our limbs depends on information arising in joint afferents rather than muscle afferents.

A segmental overview of the motor systems must include not only the motor neurons but also the surrounding population of generally smaller nerve cells connected with the latter, the interneurons. The interneuronal pool is an important mechanism of impulse distribution to the motor neurons; its intrinsic organization appears to determine the major patterns of motoneuronal excitation and inhibition, which in turn control posture and coordinated movement. The interneuronal pool therefore serves as a bridge between the higher levels of the CNS and the motor unit. There is some indirect evidence for a somatotopical organization in the interneuronal pool of the spinal cord in the sense that interneurons associated with motor neurons innervating the musculature of the trunk are located medially in the gray matter, while those related to the motor neurons of the extremity are found more laterally. Many further organizational details of this complex distribution mechanism remain to be elucidated.

In contrast to the detailed information known about certain reflex pathways, little attention is now given to the more holistic aspects of spinal cord function. For example, it is not possible today to give any better description of the spinal cord mechanisms in stepping, walking, or running than those provided by Sherrington and his school, more than thirty years ago. There is need for a renewed attack upon the overall regulatory mechanisms of the spinal cord. Such an effort would be especially timely, for many of the methods now used in the study of the segmental and peripheral motor apparatus can be applied to man and used in an analysis of the normal state and its alterations by disease.

Forebrain Mechanisms Controlling Posture and Movement. The dramatic discovery that electrical stimulation of the motor cortex would elicit contraction of muscles in both experimental animals and conscious man initiated a century of study of the localization of function within the brain (see for example Figure 9-6). For a long time electrical stimulation of the brain served as a geographic tool for studying motor systems. The results obtained with electrical stimulation, combined with experimental anatomical studies, have revealed the location and topographic patterns of the neural systems which play primary roles in the control of posture and movement. These are (1) the reticulospinal, rubrospinal, tectospinal, and vestibulospinal systems which take origin from the brainstem and end upon the segmental interneuronal and motoneuronal pools; these systems appear to mediate influence of cerebellar and forebrain origins upon the spinal segmental apparatus; (2) the basal ganglion system, a huge collection of neurons whose functions are poorly understood and whose fibers end via multisynaptic systems of the ventral thalamus and mesencephalon upon the brainstem reticulospinal systems; (3) the motor cortex, from which take origin the extrapyramidal system which feeds downward via the basal ganglia and the brainstem reticular formation, and the pyramidal tract, a long-fibered system projecting directly upon the segmental apparatus, which in higher primates and in man gains a powerful monosynaptic control of the initiation of action upon the environment.

None of these so-called motor systems are entirely independent of each other. The organization of the "motor systems" is thus characterized by massive convergence of fiber pathways, originating at several or all major levels of the brain, upon certain strategically located descending "channels" such as the rubrospinal and reticulospinal systems.

Studies of higher motor systems have lagged behind studies of higher sensory systems. The reason for this disparity lies in certain basic differences in the way in which these two systems are organized, and it is because of these differences that experimental approaches that have proven highly productive in elucidation of how the brain handles sensory inputs have been considerably less productive in telling us how the brain elaborates motor output. For example, natural stimulus patterns for a sensory system can be systematically delivered by the experimenter, whereas natural stimulus patterns for the motor system must be generated within the nervous system itself.

Fortunately these stumbling blocks have not prevented major advances in knowledge of the physiological anatomy of certain components of the motor areas of the brain. In particular, much has been discovered concerning both the cerebellum and the motor cortex. These studies have told us a great deal about how the various elements of these areas are "wired" together.

The cerebellum has been referred to as the "head ganglion of the proprioceptive system." It is the major terminus of afferent systems which convey information about limb and body position arising in the vestibular apparatus of the ear and in the muscle afferents. The cerebellum receives weaker inputs from other sense modalities. In mammals the cerebellum also has major inputs from the sensorimotor areas of the cerebral cortex, and it is thus "informed" both as to limb and body position and as to the pattern of impulses leaving the cortex aimed at producing a movement. The output from the cerebellar cortex arises from a group of large neurons called Purkinje cells, cells whose axons terminate in the cerebellar nuclei, whence second-order axons pass to brainstem and midbrain nuclei, where they end on third-order neurons projecting either to the cerebral cortex or to the spinal cord.

The cerebellum has been compared to a computer which receives (1) inputs describing the current status of the system, and (2) inputs describing desired modifications of the system (i.e., movements). Given these two classes of inputs, it is said to compute the patterns of muscular activity necessary to achieve the desired change in the state of the system. One may make an analogy with an automatic gunsight, which is given information as to (1) current status of the system and (2) location of target, and which then automatically sets azimuth and elevation so that the projectile will hit the target. The enormous amount of computation which must take place automatically in the course of normal movement may be imagined if one considers the case of a quarterback who, in the process of being overwhelmed by an opposing lineman, spots a receiver and *as he is falling* to the ground heaves the ball with perfect accuracy at a moving target. Even the marvels of present-day microelectronics and servocontrol cannot yet produce a machine which can perform with such accuracy, for the number and complexity of computations required of the quarterback's brain in this situation are truly staggering. Visual, vestibular, joint, muscle, and tactile inputs must be evaluated, integrated, and used to select those motor units which must become active and to specify the discharge frequency of each motoneuron.

As a result of recent anatomical and neurophysiological work we know much about the internal wiring of the cerebellar computer, but we know very little about the consequences of its activity when the system is operating normally—i.e., when the organism is carrying out normal movements. Do cerebellar neurons act only to correct errors in movements *after* they have been initiated, or do they also set the stage for accurate movements *before* the motor unit has been put into action? What is the function of the massive projections which interconnect cerebellum with the motor regions of the cerebral cortex? These are pressing questions both from the standpoint of physiological science per se and from the standpoint of the light that answers might cast on the pathogenesis of the disorders of movement associated with cerebellar disease in man.

Phylogenetically, the cerebellum is the oldest of the three major components of the higher-level motor control system which will be considered in this discussion. The second component which, like the cerebellum, reaches its greatest size in man is the *corpus striatum,* a section of the brain containing the caudate-putamen and the globus pallidus. These structures (part of the complex referred to as the basal ganglia) are of great significance, for disorders of these structures are associated with the clinical entities of parkinsonism, paralysis agitans, Huntington's chorea, athetosis, and a number of other serious neurological disorders. Of all regions of the brain, the corpus striatum is, by general agreement, the most deserving of the title *terra incognita.* Surgical lesions of this structure do not reproduce the disorders that follow infectious or degenerative damage to its components in man. We know that the corpus striatum is richly interconnected with other parts of the motor system, but we have not identified the functions subserved by these interconnections. Actually, most of our knowledge as to the function of the corpus striatum comes from the clinic. But what are we to make of a disorder such as parkinsonism in which the patient (1) can run better than he can walk, (2) has a tremor at rest but not during movement, and (3) reports an odd loss of normal volitional impulses to movement? It is in dealings with such patients that we become most acutely aware of our ignorance of how the brain controls the muscles.

The motor areas of the cerebral cortex have been more extensively investigated than any other component of the higher-level motor control system. The motor cortex (like the somatosensory cortex) is organized somatotopically — with regions for hand, leg, face, etc. (Fig. 9-6). Destruction of regions corresponding to a particular body part is followed by paralysis of that part. The motor cortex does not represent all parts of the bodily musculature equally; the hands and face (including the tongue) have the most extensive representation, and the musculature of the trunk is represented very weakly. Effects of lesions of the motor cortex reflect this differential representation, producing most pronounced effects on fine hand movements and (in man) on speech.

Following lesions of the motor cortex there may be remarkable recovery of function, particularly if the lesion occurs relatively early in the life of the organism. The mechanisms underlying this recovery of function have not yet been elucidated, though present knowledge suggests several possible mechanisms whereby it might occur. A motor cortex lesion in the right hemisphere which destroys the hand area eliminates most but not all motor cortex neurons controlling movements of the left hand. Neurons related to the right hand remain both within other parts of the damaged hemisphere and within the opposite hemisphere (not all descending axons from the motor cortex cross to the opposite side of the spinal cord). Thus, recovery of function might depend either on the function of remaining hand-neurons within the damaged cerebral hemisphere or on noncrossing hand-neurons in the undamaged hemisphere. Recovery might also involve a change in the role of neurons that prior to the lesion had had only weak connections to motor units of the hand. The cerebral cortex is remarkably plastic, and it is possible that motor cortex neurons that were predominantly concerned with the musculature of shoulder or elbow (and only weakly associated with hand musculature) might shift their functional connections following a lesion and come to have control over muscles of the hand.

Experiments could be carried out to compare the relative importance of these alternative mechanisms in recovery from the effects of brain lesions, and the results of such studies would help us to understand a whole class of clinical disorders in man — disorders resulting from traumatic and vascular lesions of the brain.

Prospects for Research. The most urgent need in the present state of knowledge on motor systems is research concerning the workings of the higher motor control apparatus. This need cannot be met by carrying out experiments in anesthetized or immobilized animals; it is essential that neuronal discharge patterns in higher levels of motor systems be studied in moving animals. Of course, this need has long been recognized. Sherrington was well aware of it sixty years ago when he wrote that "By combining methods of comparative psychology . . . with the methods of experimental physiology, investigation may be expected ere long to furnish new data of importance toward the knowledge of movement as an outcome of the working of the brain."

Granted that advances in knowledge of the motor function demand observations of activity patterns of neurons during physiological movement, what specific areas seem most promising? After what has been said about the contrasts between motor and sensory systems, it may come to the reader as a surprise that several of the areas that seem promising for work on motor systems are similar in general terms to the areas suggested earlier in this chapter for new research on sensory systems. Two of several promising approaches are the following:

Determination of Significant Dimensions of Movement. There are no modalities of movement in the sense that there are modalities of sensation, but there may be some aspects of movement according to which motor activity can be scaled so as to allow its description and analysis. The determination of these aspects of movement will depend on studies in both man and laboratory animals. Just as there is a need for development of psychophysical techniques that can be applied to studies of sensory mechanisms in animals, so is there a need for techniques that allow studies of highly skilled movements in animals.

Electrophysiological Studies in Moving Animals. The section on sensory systems pointed to the great potential value of simultaneous electrophysiological observations and psychophysical measurements of the animals' sensory performance. For motor systems this approach is not only desirable, it is essential. A beginning approach along these lines has been made in studies on activity of individual motor cortex and cerebellar neurons during learned hand movements in monkeys. The techniques of operant conditioning and automatic training make it possible for monkeys to learn a great variety of precise manipulations, and advances in the art of microelectrode recording now allow recordings from single neurons (in cortex, cerebellum, or basal ganglia) during the performance of these learned movements. With these techniques it is possible to answer many questions, several of which are listed as examples: Does the activity of neurons in the region in question precede or follow the movement? Is activity differentially related to learned as compared to reflex movements? Is activity related to force, velocity and/or acceleration? Does activity correspond to steady-state (tonic) or transient (phasic) aspects of movement? These studies complement those aimed at isolating the neurologically significant dimensions of movement, for if neurons in the cerebellum are related to one dimension of movements and neurons in the motor cortex to a quite different dimension, then these two dimensions will have been established as neurologically independent and significant aspects of movement.

The Intercalated Systems: Homeostatic Regulation

Between the major sensory and motor systems there exists the great mass of the central nervous system, composed of subsystems organized for the regulation of intrinsic brain functions and for the control of the function of other organs.

Intercalated systems are particularly voluminous and diverse in the forebrain where they are represented by (1) the "association areas" of the cerebral cortex which separate the sensory and motor field; (2) the limbic system, a vast, heterogeneous array of large neural structures in the medial and basal walls of the cerebral hemispheres; and (3) the corpus striatum.

The *association areas* of the cerebral cortex are particularly extensive in primates and man and cover large parts of the frontal, parietal, and temporal lobes. Much like the more easily specifiable cortical regions (visual, auditory, and somaesthetic cortices), these large cortical fields receive massive neural connections from well-defined thalamic cell groups, but unlike the specific sensory areas, which receive their major fiber connection from the visual, auditory, or somaesthetic thalamic nuclei, the association areas receive more heterogeneous connections. The cortical association areas also receive afferents from adjoining cortical fields, and the overall organization indicated by the still fragmentary anatomical data suggests that they are placed largely in series with the specific sensory cortices. *It thus appears that the association areas may be involved in the elaboration of specific sensory information into percepts of varying complexity.*

The association areas of the cerebral cortex have been relatively inaccessible to the modern cellular neurophysiological analyses that have proven successful in studying the main sensory systems, because of the difficulties in establishing the effective sensory stimuli. What little is understood about these vast regions of cerebral cortex has come largely from clinical and behavioral studies of the deficits resulting from pathological destruction or surgical ablation of the regions. The neurological and behavioral findings support the notion that the association areas are involved in higher integrative mechanisms. In man, certain lesions of the posterior parietal cortex, for example, may cause inability to recognize written words, despite the absence of blindness. Large lesions involving parietal and temporal regions of the left hemisphere result in loss of the capacity for propositional speech, although there is neither paralysis of the musculature involved in verbal articulation nor apparent loss of any specific sensory modality. There is, moreover, suggestive evidence from observations during neurosurgical operations that a large region of the posterior temporal cortex is important for the storage and recall of visual and auditory memories. These and numerous related findings emphasize the need for a better understanding of those neural mechanisms of information handling that lie beyond the specific sensory systems of the cerebral cortex.

An animal's response to its environment is not exclusively determined by cortical mechanisms. Of particular importance, and most intensively studied, among these largely subcortical systems is the limbic system.

The term *limbic system* refers to a large, heterogeneous array of neural structures extending from the cerebral hemisphere into the diencephalon and beyond it into the midbrain. At the level of the hemisphere, the limbic system is represented by the hippocampal formation, a primitive cortical structure, and the subcortical amygdaloid complex. Surrounding these structures is a ring of intermediate cortex, the so-called gyrus fornicatus, which appears to constitute a major reciprocal link between the limbic system and the neocortex. The components of the limbic system each have strongly developed reciprocal connections with the hypothalamus, the rostral subdivision of the brainstem reticular formation. The hypothalamus is involved in homeostatic regulation — i.e., in the maintenance of stability in the internal dynamic environment of the body. The hypothalamus performs this function (1) in part through its modulation of lower levels of the brainstem reticular formation which controls, via appropriate motor neurons, autonomic functions such as respiration, heart rate, blood pressure, etc., and (2) in part by its critical influence upon the pituitary, the master gland of the endocrine system. The hypothalamus also plays a leading role in the normal diurnal and seasonal cycles in the organism's general activity levels. More recently, animal experiments have produced convincing evidence of yet another aspect of hypothalamic function, long suspected from clinical observations — namely, a determining influence upon "moods," the internal "feeling" states that are subjectively experienced as pleasure, pain, anxiety, or sadness and are objectively correlated with certain behavioral attitudes. It thus appears likely that the limbic components of the cerebral hemisphere play a leading role in the programming of behavior by determining the set of priorities among the various available responses of the organism to its environment.

Much like the cortical association areas, the limbic system has been studied primarily with behavioral and clinical neurological techniques. Studies of hypothalamic mechanisms have led to the development of an active and highly productive branch of the neurobiological sciences, neuroendocrinology. Neurophysiological studies of the role of the cerebral components of the limbic system (hippocampus and amygdala) so far have been conducted almost exclusively by methods recording integral rather than individual neuronal activity states. As with the cortical association areas, a major obstacle to a more cellular analysis lies in the complexity of the adequate environmental stimuli. Inadequately explored is the possibility of a more specific afferent driving force, suggested by anatomical findings indicating olfaction as the sensory modality that has the most direct access to the limbic system. The intricacies of the limbic system pose a formidable challenge to neurobiologists, for there is good reason to believe that it holds important clues for understanding animal and human behavior.

Two Examples of Homeostatic Regulation. The brain performs two types of regulatory function. One is *intrinsic* and concerns the brain's regulation of its own excitability. The other is *extrinsic* and concerns the regulation by the brain of other organ systems.

Intrinsic Regulatory Functions of the Brain: Sleep, Wakefulness, and the Conscious State. The relation of the brain to the mind, and the meaning of conscious experience, has influenced philosophical and scientific thinking since early history. Central to the mind-brain problem is the question of consciousness; indeed consciousness may be the only possible means of achieving appropriate regulation of large brains and may represent the most elaborate example of a general biological regulatory mechanism concerned with the control and direction of action.

Even now we can still only crudely describe the various states of consciousness or levels of *awareness*. For example, there are certain publicly observable attributes of consciousness: attention, the manipulation of abstract ideas, the capacity of expectancy, self-awareness and the awareness of others, the overt demonstration of aesthetic and ethical values; and finally perception and memory.

Consciousness is variable, and certain of its levels and transition states are susceptible to experimental manipulation. Neurophysiological research begins with the simplifying assumption that levels of consciousness may be equated with levels of awareness, which are themselves determined by the distribution of excitability levels in the brain. Of these levels the two sleep and wakefulness, and the transition states between them, are those most directly subject to experiment. During the past thirty years a considerable amount of research has been carried out in this field, and the increase in its understanding has been spectacular.

The controlling systems. The brain contains a neuronal system that serves to regulate neuronal excitability. This system has an extraordinarily wide distribution extending from the higher regions of the brain to the motoneuron. It is phylogenetically old and occupies part of the tegmentum of the medulla, pons, and mesencephalon, projecting upward upon their telencephalic distribution network the generalized thalamo-cortical system. A descending projection, the reticulospinal system, serves to funnel excitatory and inhibitory influences from the forebrain upon the spinal segmental apparatus. This large system lies parallel with and receives collateral input from the great afferent systems, and it appears to set the ongoing levels of excitability of cells of the cerebral cortex, the basal ganglia, and other large gray structures of the forebrain. It was therefore natural to suppose that these systems are potently concerned in regulation of the sleep-wakefulness cycle, and indeed this is the case.

The nature of sleep. Sleep is a state of consciousness, which differs from alert wakefulness by a loss of critical reactivity to events in the environment. Sleep in mammals and in birds appears to be a special case of a very general phenomenon of cyclic changes in activity levels which all animals display. A great deal of evidence has now accumulated that these cyclic events and the sleep-wakefulness cycle in particular are, in mammals, neural phenomena. Thus the main thrust of research of the last decades in this field has been aimed at understanding the controlling neural mechanisms.

The remarkable changes in cerebral action associated with sleep-wakefulness transitions are not limited to the level of consciousness. There are changes in muscle tone, reflex thresholds, etc.—all signs of altered CNS excitability. These changes are, however, selective in nature, for there is no general diminution in the overall activity of the brain. There is, for example, no important change in cerebral blood flow or oxygen consumption, and no overall decrease in the activity of cortical neurons. This points up a central problem: why the necessity for sleep? What processes—replenishing or otherwise—does the brain require for continued life which can proceed only during sleep? Is it the metabolic replenishment of synaptic transmitters by short-axon cortical cells? Suggestions such as this and many others are currently under study, but no answers are available.

The most intriguing recent observation in this field is the finding that spinal fluid taken from a goat that has been kept awake for several days contains a material of low molecular weight which induces deep, natural sleep in other animals. If confirmed, this offers enormous potential, not only for understanding of the mechanisms involved in sleep, but for the development of the ideal sedative or anesthetic.

Other than behavior, the most readily observed physiological variable that can be correlated with level of awareness is the electroencephalogram, which has become the major tool for research in this field, particularly in humans. Its usefulness would be further increased were its basic mechanisms fully understood.

CNS mechanisms controlling the sleep-wakefulness cycle. Two important discoveries underlie modern concepts of the CNS mechanisms involved in sleep and wakefulness. The first is that slow (8/sec) rhythmic electrical stimulation of the generalized thalamocortical system entrains the electroencephalogram (EEG) in rhythmic oscillation, and provokes all the behavioral signs of sleep, and that more rapid stimulation of this same system or of the ascending reticular system which impinges upon it "desynchronizes" the EEG and wakes a sleeping animal. The second is that deafferentation of the forebrain by a midbrain transection leaves it with electrical and behavioral signs of continuous sleep, while transection of the brain below the medulla leaves intact the sleep-wakefulness cycle. These two observations and studies that have followed them in the past decade have led to the proposition that sleep is due both to a withdrawal of driving input and to an active process originating in the brainstem which tends to drive the forebrain electrical activity in slow rhythmic oscillation and to produce sleep. Sleep is therefore exclusively neither an active nor a passive process, but a combination of the two. Much of current research is aimed at clarifying the nature and the mode of operation of these two reciprocally active mechanisms.

As early as 1936 it was known that sleep is not a uniform state, for it is frequently interrupted by outbursts of desynchronization of the EEG, rapid eye movements, and a profound loss of muscle tone elsewhere. These have now been correlated with the times during sleep when dreams occur. Observations of the sleep patterns of human infants show that at birth this "sleep with rapid eye movements" occupies a majority of the sleeping time, with a gradual reduction in its prevalence with maturation. In adult life the outbursts occur at cyclic intervals during a night's sleep. The mechanism of these burstlike changes in forebrain activity and their physiological meaning is obscure. It is now known that the structural connectivity of synapses in the forebrain and particularly in the cerebral cortex depends upon continued patterned activity. Can it be that the domination of the sleeping infant by this form of activity is actually a maturating process, a substitute for the continued sensory input of the waking adult life?

We list here without further discussion some of the major problems in this field of research. First and perhaps most important is that of the function of sleep, just alluded to. Is sleep necessary for the imprinting or learning function in a brain? What is the role of the hypothalamus in the CNS mechanisms governing the sleep-wakefulness cycle—for a number of other cyclic alterations of function in mammals depend upon the hypothalamus? What is the relation between the antagonistic brainstem mechanisms, one that promotes forebrain desynchronization and wakefulness, the other forebrain synchronization and sleep? What is the interaction between chemical and neural factors in sleep?

A very different approach to the problem of consciousness is exemplified by the recent studies on the interrelationship of the cerebral hemispheres in which the corpus callosum, a bundle of perhaps 10^8 fibers that interconnect the left and right hemispheres of the mammalian brain, is cut. Under these circumstances, the functioning of each hemisphere remains intact—and quite independent. Learning in each hemisphere becomes totally dependent upon its own sensory input, with no crossover unless each receives identical input. For example, such an animal can be taught, with one eye, that a given signal represents the availability of food, and subsequently, with the other eye, taught that quite a different signal so indicates. Thereafter, it will continue to respond to these signals entirely in accord with which eye is left uncovered. In a dramatic instance, prefrontal lobotomy was performed on only one side of a "split-brain" monkey. When introduced into a cage containing a snake, this subject cowered with fear when one eye was uncovered, and completely ignored the snake when the other eye was employed. These studies have found practical utility. Surgical separation of the hemispheres, by cutting the corpus callosum, has been accomplished in patients with certain forms of epilepsy who are thereby returned to a semblance of normal life. Examination of these patients shows that they, too, are clearly under the control of two independent half-brains, with no fusion of visual inputs. These studies have demonstrated that in man each hemisphere is capable of independent conscious awareness. Surgery has left these people with two separate minds, indicating that these higher functions are not the exclusive domain of the major hemisphere. Such studies offer high promise in revealing the highest orders of organization of the brain.

Extrinsic Regulatory Function of the Brain: Regulation. The free and independent life of animals depends upon the constancy of their internal environments. The homeostatic regulation of that environment has been intensively studied at the molecular and integrative levels. We will comment only on the role of the central nervous system in these regulations.

The constancy of the internal environment depends upon control systems employing the principle of negative feedback. In many of these control loops the central nervous system is of major importance. This is true not only because it regulates the regulators, but because it is at this link that both rapid and slow adaptations to behavioral or environmental demands are made. In these control operations the CNS frequently employs an additional mechanism quite different from that of the signaling systems previously discussed. That is, certain of its cells are chemoreceptors, sensing the concentration of substances in the intercellular spaces of the CNS (e.g., water, or thyroid hormone) and, on the basis of that measure, changing in the physiologically appropriate direction their own *secretion* of a neurohormone which regulates a regulator. Thus all the problems of chemoreception and neurosecretion, at the cellular and molecular level, discussed in earlier chapters, are pertinent to the control mechanisms under discussion. Certainly the discovery of this neurohumoral or glandular function of the hypothalamus in regulating the anterior pituitary gland, and thus the secretion of trophic hormones by the latter, is one of the most important recent developments in the understanding of homeostasis.

The importance of this field of research for understanding mechanisms operative in health and disease is evident from a simple listing of some of the functions thought to be controlled in this way:

1. The reproductive cycle, sexuality and sexual behavior
2. The basal metabolic level, appetite and thirst, and associated appetitive behavior
3. Water and electrolyte metabolism, and hydrogen ion concentration
4. Cardiac output and peripheral resistance, and thus the rate of blood flow through tissues and organs
5. Respiratory rate and volume, and thus tissue oxygenation and CO_2 concentration

The role of the CNS in these matters is not confined to homeostasis. That is, centers within the CNS concerned with regulating the regulators, or regulating directly an effector, are themselves open to regulating influences from other parts of the brain. For example, cells of the hypothalamus may measure the level of thyroid hormone in their surround, and in turn change their own rate of secretion of a hormone, thereby regulating the formation of thyrotropic hormone by the anterior pituitary. There is no reason to doubt that these chemoreceptive cells are also influenced in the usual way by neural signals reaching them over synaptically related inputs. Thus it is at the CNS level that interactions in these regulator loops may occur over and above the general oscillations which tend toward homeostasis. Their importance in normal adaptation to other than usual demands, in the genesis of disease, and particularly in the somatic and visceral accompaniments of neurotic behavior can hardly be overestimated.

Yet very little is known about the influence of higher levels of the nervous system upon these neuronal regulators (or vice versa) which are usually located in phylogenetically old portions of the forebrain, the hypothalamus and the brainstem. A typical question for study, for example, might be this: in what way does the limbic lobe influence the hypothalamic regulation of the ovarian cycle and the secretion of sex hormones, and thus sexual behavior and its various sublimations? Clearly this field of the relation of the brain in regulating the autonomic and endocrine systems is of first importance for clinical medicine and for psychiatry.

Problems such as the one stated above are for the moment beyond solution. Progress depends upon the development of methods for the simultaneous observation of total behavior, brain activity, and the physiological variables regulated. These "visceral" functions of the

CNS are of vital importance in determining behavior, and deserve more intensive study in the future. They should not be lost sight of in the present concentration on signaling mechanisms in sensation, perception, and cognitive functions.

Relation of Neural Science to Medical Sciences

Psychiatry. Neural science stands to psychiatry and neurology as physiology and biochemistry stand to medicine: *it must provide the basic knowledge and concepts for understanding human behavior and its abnormalities.* Whereas the impact of neural science upon neurology has been extraordinary, its contributions to psychiatry so far have been small. Early pioneers in neural science were strongly motivated by the hope that knowledge of brain structure would lead to a detailed understanding of mental disorders and that the major categories of mental disease could eventually be correlated with specific morphological changes in brain tissue. This approach has repeatedly been thwarted. No useful general organic theory of behavior disorder has been formulated, and we are still far from such a formulation. On a more limited scale, however, some progress has been made.

A major part of the forebrain, the so-called limbic system, has now been identified as a neural mechanism dominantly involved in affect, mood, and motivation. Selective surgical interventions (e.g., cingulectomy) interrupting certain specific neural circuits in this major brain area have recently been shown to be effective in the treatment of some chronic depressive disorders in man. The recently developed surgical management of temporal lobe epilepsy, a disease in part characterized by extreme and occasionally dangerous fluctuations of affect, is based on the same rationale. It is entirely possible that more detailed neuroanatomical and neurophysiological data will lead to a greater variety of effective psychosurgical procedures.

The advent of the tranquilizing and antidepressant agents has caused a major advance in the treatment of the major psychoses. Although these drugs are the products of empirical research, and their modes of action are presently not understood, future developments in neurochemistry and pharmacology are certain to produce a significant increase in our understanding of these agents and of the mental illnesses they ameliorate.

Recent developments in the neurophysiological understanding of sleep mechanisms have had a major impact on clinical studies. A most important discovery was the finding that dreaming was highly correlated with only a certain phase of sleep, that associated with rapid eye movements and an activated electroencephalogram. The availability of an objective correlate of the dream state has revolutionized clinical studies of sleeping and dreaming, permitting studies of dream frequency, dream content, and dream deprivation both in normal man and in persons with psychiatric disorders.

Finally, clinical studies of the interrelations of hormones to emotion derive heavily from the basic experimental studies that demonstrated the existence of glandular neurons in the hypothalamus and their relationship, via direct neural and vascular links, to the posterior and anterior pituitary.

Neurology. Recent advances in the neural sciences—principally in physiology and chemistry of the nervous system—have had a significant impact on current practices in neurology.

The perfection of adequate recording amplifier systems has been responsible for the development of clinical electromyography. Basic knowledge about the conduction of the nervous impulse, transmission at the neuromuscular junction, and the structure and functional properties of muscle has been applied directly to diagnosis of disease in the peripheral nervous system. In addition, the application of averaging techniques to improve signal-noise ratios has made it possible to study selectively conduction in sensory nerves in man; averaging has also proved useful in studies of the scalp-evoked potential in man which also promise new diagnostic applications.

The elucidation of the segmental organization and control of the muscle length tension servo system has had an important impact on studies of movement disorders. The use of procaine to block gamma motoneurons in the study of clinical states of spasticity and rigidity is a good example. Recent experiments suggesting the existence of two distinct gamma motor fibers—one exerting control over the tonic and the other over the phasic response of the spindle afferents—may lead to selective permanent intervention on the system considered responsible for altered tone in extrapyramidal diseases.

The techniques for acute and chronic stimulation and recording from brain structures, first developed in animal studies, have revitalized thinking in almost every part of modern clinical neurology, particularly in clinical electroencephalography, the study of epilepsy, dyskinesias, and the localization of function. The functional specificity of discrete cerebral loci for movement and sensation in man has been firmly established; indeed, recently, complete memories have been elicted from stimulation of the temporal cortex. Effects of ablation of discriminative function in primates has led to the modern concepts of the relationship of the two cerebral hemispheres, the importance of primary and secondary cortices, and the concept of compensations for lost function.

The development of methods for subcortical recording in man now makes it possible for neurosurgeons to localize with greater accuracy the pathophysiological locus in many cases of focal epilepsy. Recent research into the cellular mechanisms of the epileptiform discharge promises to generate a more detailed understanding about this common disease state.

Studies of thalamocortical circuitry and the connections to the basal ganglia have increased knowledge about the role of the generalized thalamocortical projection systems in the maintenance of consciousness and the generation of the intrinsic brain rhythms. From these basic studies have evolved more recent approaches to regional surgery for the alleviation of involuntary movements, most notably those of Parkinson's disease and dyskinesia.

Advances in neurochemistry have focused on elucidating the basic metabolic derangements in the organic encephalopathies. Particularly noteworthy is the current success in preventing irreversible mental retardation in phenylketonuria, nicotinic acid and thiamine deficiency states, cretinism, and to a lesser degree in galactosemia and maple-syrup urine disease.

The development of an allergic encephalomyelitis in animals has served as a model of multiple sclerosis and provides a basis for the theory of an immunological causation for the disease, currently under investigation. Discovery of a demyelination factor in the cerebrospinal fluid of patients with this disease and its quantitative variation during therapeutic trials might provide a response that could be objectively assayed; the criteria for therapeutic response in patients with this disease are notoriously difficult to evaluate.

Medicine. A primary goal of the physician is insight into how abnormalities in function which are associated with disease may be prevented, controlled, or reversed. Because the various organs of the human body function in concert, a disturbance in one may cause disturbance of another. Many systemic diseases in which the primary lesion is outside the nervous system also secondarily involve the nervous system. Thus diseases of the liver, kidney, cardiovascular system, digestive system, endocrine organs, etc., as well as vitamin deficiencies and toxins, cause metabolic or circulatory disturbances in the nervous system with consequent neurological or psychiatric manifestations. Conversely, the important role of the nervous system in control of the respiratory system, gastrointestinal system, cardiovascular system, endocrine organs, etc., is firmly established, and the relationship of disturbances in emotional state to so-called psychosomatic disorders is well recognized.

There is obviously a great deal of overlap among the clinical sciences of neurology, psychiatry, and medicine. It is also apparent that, in the future, understanding of how the nervous system functions will provide the clinician with valuable approaches to the prevention and therapy of a variety of disorders that involve the nervous system.

Chapter 10

THE BIOLOGY OF BEHAVIOR

Scientists of diverse background and training, today, are investigating the ways in which animals, including human beings, behave toward each other and toward their environment. This group of "behavioral biologists" includes zoologists, physiologists, psychologists, psychiatrists, anthropologists, and others. Some observe whole animals; others do experiments on small parts of the nervous system. Some study the physiological mechanisms of behavior in adult animals; others study the development of behavior in embryos. Some engage in theoretical problems, and will use any particularly appropriate animal as a tool; others are fascinated by particular kinds of animals. Some approach animal investigation primarily as a means of understanding human behavior; others have no conscious concern with the social usefulness of their work. Yet the sum of their endeavors, their interrelated work, illuminates in diverse ways the behavior of organisms toward their environment.

In this chapter we will show how this work, starting from different points of view, interested in different animals, and formulating different problems, is gradually building a coherent picture of the way in which behavior evolves and develops, and of the physiological mechanisms that make behavior possible.

Animal Behavior and Human Behavior

Behavioral biologists do not assume that animals are just simpler versions of human beings and that experiments with animals are merely substitutes for experiments on humans. Humanlike motives, feelings, or insights are not attributed to animals without the strongest possible evidence, since all aspects of human life are pervaded by human characteristics which derive from features of our situation (the use of speech and the transmission of culture by socially developed symbolic language) and are quite unknown in even the highest animals. Moreover, just as animals are different from human beings, nonhuman animals differ from each other. The structure, physiology, and behavior of a one-celled animal like the amoeba are very different from those of a bee; and a fish and a monkey probably differ from each other in equally fundamental ways.

On the other hand, human beings *are* animals who have evolved from nonhuman forebears, and just as there are differences which must be carefully recognized, there are also similarities between humans and other animals which must not be overlooked. Higher animals, such as chimpanzees, use tools in ways that suggest the origins of communication by gestures and of human language. Under certain circumstances, they may cooperate with each other in ways that suggest the consciousness of each other's intentions. Further, the nervous and endocrine systems of animals are progressively more like those of humans the closer they are in the evolutionary scale; and many human behavioral capacities are similar to those of lower animals and based on similar physiological processes.

Behavioral biologists pay attention to both the continuities and the discontinuities between human beings and lower animals; and both the similarities and the differences are sources of understanding and insight. Some experiments with animals lead to the discovery of processes that are then found to exist in the same form in humans; others reveal differences between humans and other animals, such that the comparison increases our understanding of both levels. All work in behavioral biology, whether with humans or with animal subjects, ultimately increases our understanding of the whole world of living beings.

The Animal in His Environment

The first group of research problems to be presented are those having to do with the analysis of the relationships between animals and their natural environments.

The Selection of Habitats

The observer of animals in nature is aware that each species of animal is to be found in a limited habitat. One kind of flycatcher may be found only in open fields; a closely related one lives only in dense forests. One species of bird may always be found creeping on the trunk of a large tree; another usually creeps on the branches. One species of squirrel lives only in trees; a close relative only in burrows in the ground. A fish that is found only in running streams may have a relative that lives only in lakes. What keeps these animals from going into the "wrong" habitat? The problem is most clearly shown by those animals, such as many birds and fishes, which migrate every year for great distances from their birthplaces, and which, when they return home at the beginning of their breeding season, unerringly *choose* to settle in the characteristic habitat of their species, even though other habitats seem equally available.

An example of one such study, which reveals some of the important aspects of the problem, involves the habitat choices made by individuals of two strains of a species of *Peromyscus,* the deermouse. One strain inhabits the forested areas of Michigan, the other the prairie. Mice of both strains were obtained both by live-trapping and from stocks long reared in the laboratory, imposing selection pressures radically different from those obtaining in the wild. The testing procedure was to measure, by automatically monitored treadles, the amount of time individual mice spent in varying portions of a 1,600-square-foot enclosure. Half of the enclosure was woodland, and half an open field. The variables, therefore, were heredity (offspring of field or laboratory derived parents) and early experience (young reared in fields, woods, or lab).

With the field strain a regular choice was made of the field over the woods environment, regardless of whether the young themselves were reared in the field, woods, or lab. Field-rearing, however, did strengthen this preference. Laboratory stock originally derived from field-dwelling mice were more malleable: if laboratory-reared, they do prefer fields; if woods-reared, however, no significant preference for either woods or fields develops. Apparently, 12–20 generations of laboratory-rearing reduced the degree to which the animal responds discriminatively to the appropriate habitat. In the "normally" reared mice, the early (field) experience serves to strengthen the characteristic strain preference.

A similar result was obtained in studies of foliage preferences of chipping sparrows; with this species, too, one particular rearing experience augmented the "natural" preference, while a contrary experience lessened this preference. The general significance of these results, aside from their relevance to the question of *how* such habitat constancy is maintained, lies in the additional evidence provided for the existence of internal constraints that determine the effectiveness of particular external influences. Their practical significance lies in the fields of game management and conservation, where the need to establish species in new or different areas may be thwarted by ignorance of the behavioral processes involved in habitat selection.

Social Organization and Mating Systems

Group behavior of animals, including the dynamics of animal aggregations and the structure of animal societies, has been studied in a social context and, for the sake of understanding and interpreting the individual behavior of animals, based upon their biological and experiential history and upon the conditions under which they live. Some of these include the interactions of animals of the same species, as in mating or in overcoming environmental obstacles through group interaction. In the simplest cases this latter may amount to no more than conditioning the medium in which they live by absorbing, precipitating, and diluting toxic substances. In more complicated situations, the physical conditions of the environment are more directly controlled through group behavior, as in the case of the termites' nest, the beehive, the wolf den, or the human house. As early descriptions of animal aggregations and societies were compiled and compared, phylogenetic affinities and hierarchies were seen, and the development of societal organization among animals was interpreted as an evolutionary phenomenon leading to better adaptation of the societal species. Simple organisms, such as protozoans, aggregate both because of common origin in a restricted area through a succession of binary fissions, and because each reacts to gradients of light, temperature, and other environmental factors in much the same way. This makes conjugation easier to achieve by ensuring physical proximity and enhances the possibility for compounding genetic variability and thereby for the evolution of the species.

From the very loosest aggregates of this kind to the more cohesive ones found in vertebrates, to the highly structured and biologically differentiated ones found in social insects, one sees a loose analogue to the evolution of the complex multicellular organisms. The simplest beginnings of multicellularity consist in little more than cell aggregates which, in the course of evolutionary time, developed a specialization of structure and function whose beginning stages are relatively simple but which lead eventually to large and complex organisms whose capacities in all respects are many magnitudes beyond what could be achieved with lesser levels of organization. Carrying the analogy one step further, social insects with biologically differentiated castes which have specialized function have been viewed by some biologists as superorganisms. Such societies are integrated by means of biological communication devices and behavioral capacities that are very largely represented in the genome. Selective advantages in these instances cannot readily occur in consequence of the success of better endowed individuals in leaving progeny, since the link between generations is relegated to a small number of individuals belonging to the reproductive castes, while the success and survival of the group depend upon the presence and performance of the sterile castes as well. Further evolution of such forms is necessarily slow.

Many vertebrate groups form their societal bonds on the basis of early experience and as a result of the later development of dominance hierarchies and territorial tendencies. In some birds, early social bonds are formed as a result of exposure to an adult member of the species, normally the mother, at a certain time in early post-hatching development. There is some evidence that these bonds have a determining influence on later mating preferences. While many other vertebrates appear to form their early social bonds and to arrive at their species identification in a somewhat more flexible manner, there do appear to be sensitive periods in early social development that are unusually important in these regards.

The principle of social dominance, which was initially most thoroughly studied in domestic hens, appears to hold for many other groups of vertebrates as well. Such groups, when organized in a dominance hierarchy, are more effective in exploiting their environment and in leaving progeny than are disorganized and continuously disrupted groups. Organized flocks of hens eat more food and lay more eggs than similar flocks in a state of social disorganization. In many vertebrate forms, social dominance is a determining factor in the mating structure. Among sage grouse in the western United States, for example, where mating occurs seasonally in a restricted territory, a very small proportion of the males are involved in almost all of the active mating. Similar situations obtain in many mammalian groups. The genetic consequences are that the gene pools of such populations are sampled in so nonrandom a fashion that some gene combinations could become easily fixed in the homozygous condition. Primate societies are no exception. Social dominance plays a major role in the organization of many monkey and baboon troops and also has implications for the mating structure of the groups. As recent primate experiments have shown, social deprivation of the infant from its mother, or of the juvenile from its peers, can result in irreversible deficits in social behavior. Such studies have generated hypotheses regarding the genesis of various types of social behavior in human beings, particularly with respect to the personality structure of the adult who was an "unloved" child, and have also provided evidence about the development of structure of societies at the near-human primate level which may shed light on the beginnings of human sociology.

Regulation of Populations

Animal numbers in a given region are relatively constant. While they may fluctuate from year to year, particularly with changes in the environment, the fluctuations are often transitory and, over longer periods, trivial. Three theories of population control have been advanced to account for this relative constancy, two of which are intimately bound to an understanding of animal behavior. The first theory attributes relative constancy to periodic natural catastrophes which decimate populations with such frequency as to prevent them from exceeding some particular limit. This is the "density-independent" view of population control. A second view argues that population growth is density-dependent — i.e., that the *rate* of growth of a population is smaller the larger the numbers of animals. The mechanisms whereby this regulation by negative feedback is managed may vary; as numbers increase, the food supply may be outstripped which, in turn, would increase mortality or decrease fecundity; high densities can attract predators, which then become more efficient harvesters of this prey; crowding resulting from a rise in numbers may bring about physiological changes, for instance, changes in adrenal gland activity, with a resultant decrease in fecundity and viability.

This last observation has been of particular interest to students of behavior because such physiological effects of "crowding" are, to some degree, determined by the frequency of either certain kinds of social intercourse or the presence of certain signals. In locusts, "crowding" is signaled by tactile stimulations; prodding a locust with a glass rod is apparently behaviorally indistinguishable from actual physical crowding. For some birds acoustic signals may be of primary importance in defining the presence of other members of the species; for some rodents, odors are the primary cues; for others, such as prairie dogs, the frequency of individual encounters among members of the same coterie (which encounters stimulate "kissing") are primary. The effects of crowding, however perceived, may be to promote dispersion, to inhibit reproduction, or to increase the vulnerability to death after subjection to stress. There is evidence that these effects may persist for one, two, or even three generations in the absence of the original provocation. The challenge to students of behavior is to develop models that would allow prediction of the variables by which crowding is signaled and of the effects of this crowding. The general significance of this problem to *Homo sapiens* scarcely requires mention.

The third theory of control argues that organisms have evolved a "code," in the form of social or "epideictic," including territorial, behavior displays, that (a) provides each individual with information on the size of the population and (b) affects his behavior in an appropriate fashion so as to anticipate and avoid food shortage. The evidence cited in support of this notion is open to other interpretations, and it is believed by many that the supporting arguments are themselves faulty. Nonetheless, this is yet further evidence of the importance ascribed by students of behavior to the behavioral concomitants of population growth whether these are endocrinologically or socially mediated.

Finally, we must remind ourselves that populations may have minimum as well as maximum sizes. The observation that some social species cannot reproduce unless their numbers exceed a certain minimum has refocused attention on the role of social stimulation in initiating and maintaining the reproductive state.

Orientation and Homing

Appropriate spatial orientation to their surroundings is one of the most characteristic behavioral attainments of animals and men. Many animals orient themselves by sensory mechanisms or behavioral discriminations quite different from those ordinarily recognized in human behavior. Hence they have often posed perplexing mysteries, and despite considerable progress in recent years, many important unsolved problems remain. Direct human relevance is often clear. For example, echolocation is employed not only by bats and marine mammals but also by blind men. Echolocation enables bats with brains weighing less than one gram to locate and intercept minute flying insects within a fraction of a second. But only very limited echolocation is yet achieved by the human blind. If this gap could be narrowed, the handicap of blindness would be significantly reduced.

Many migratory animals pose rather elementary questions for which there are, as yet, no adequate answers: Which aspects of their environment provide directional information? And what sensory channels convey this information to the central nervous system? Some animal species with highly developed powers of locomotion migrate over such long distances that their travels are limited, not by their navigational ability, but by the dimensions of our planet—or at least by the extent of its habitable portions. Such birds as Arctic terns and some of the shearwaters migrate several thousand miles. Even penguins, swimming at the ocean surface, cover hundreds of miles, often under severe climatic conditions with severely restricted visibility. To achieve an adequate understanding of the sensory bases of these migrations, and the ecological and motivational needs they satisfy, will require broadly based investigations involving not only behavioral scientists in the strict sense, but zoologists, ecologists, and experts at home on the expanding frontiers of instrumentation.

Mammals as distantly related as bats, seals, whales, and caribou also migrate for long distances under sufficiently difficult conditions to pose serious problems of orientation, motivation, and behavioral ecology. Sea turtles swim across large fractions of the oceans to locate relatively small islands where they lay their eggs on a few suitable beaches. The phenomenon of long-distance migration is receiving more experimental attention than many others, but even here only a modest beginning has yet been made. Increased effort devoted to the tagging and recapture of fishes has demonstrated both increasing magnitudes and regularities in fish migrations. But we still know almost nothing about the orientation behavior of the millions of eels that migrate through thousands of miles of ocean waters, although this has been recognized as a classic problem of orientation behavior for half a century.

Some marine invertebrates also migrate extensively. Squids have been shown to migrate for many miles; spiny lobsters exhibit homing behavior; the giant squids of the deep sea remain wholly beyond the reach of our techniques for studying their orientation behavior or anything else. Vertical migrations are widespread in pelagic animals throughout enormous areas of the oceans. Such migrations are most evident as the daily vertical movements of the "deep scattering layer" which reflects underwater sound. We do not know at all adequately which animals make up the deep scattering layer, but the magnitude of vertically mobile echoes demonstrates beyond question that this form of migratory behavior is an important concern of behavioral scientists as well as oceanographers.

Insect migrations typify the theoretical significance of broadly based comparative studies of migratory behavior and similar phenomena. Because most insect migrations have been generally believed to result from passive carrying of these small creatures by moving air masses, no one troubled to look for active migration. Locust migrations have been notorious in the Middle East and North Africa since Biblical times because of their destruction of human crops. The goal of these migrations is unclear, but they are not solely dependent upon wind direction and velocity. Recent behavioral investigations have led to important improvements in control measures. A sustained cooperative program of tagging monarch butterflies by enthusiastic amateurs has demonstrated migrations up to 1,000 miles and in directions that cannot be accounted for by passive transport. These significant findings show what can be expected from intensive study of other strong fliers such as dragonflies,

moths, and butterflies other than the monarch. But the drive and navigation of these migrations remain to be established.

Patently, a broad comparative outlook is of great importance as behavioral scientists inquire more deeply into migratory and orientation
behavior. Not only do the sensory mechanisms involved in orientation
require penetrating analysis; equally significant are questions of motivation, genetic programming in relation to individual learning, and the
ecological advantages of migration that must be present to offset the exer-
tions and hazards in such extensive travels.

Homing behavior is closely related to migration, and a pronounced
homing ability has been found in most groups of animals that migrate
extensively, whenever they have been investigated adequately. Homing
has usually been studied by artificial displacement of animals for considerable distances. Speed of return and the proportion returning have
been the standard criteria of homing performance. In recent years, new
techniques such as following from aircraft and radio tracking have
disclosed the actual routes traveled and some elementary aspects of
behavior en route. This approach requires considerable expansion
and technical improvement in the instrumentation available. It is evident
that orientation behavior cannot be effectively investigated until the
major part of it can at least be observed; in the case of homing and
migratory behavior this means tracing the actual routes by which the
animals travel. Radar has been employed with considerable success to
observe the migrations of birds, and more recently insects and bats as
well. In most cases bird echoes have been accidental by-products of
radar development, and much more effort has been devoted by radar
designers to their elimination than to adapting radar systems to maximize
echoes from animals traveling through the air. Enough has been learned
with radar designed for other purposes to warrant a serious effort to
design and construct radar systems specifically adapted for studying
birds and other animals during migration and homing.

It is important to learn whether behavior similar to that revealed by
homing experiments also occurs under natural conditions when animals
are accidentally carried to unfamiliar surroundings by unusual winds or
currents. More research is needed on the relationship between the
homing efforts of a displaced animal and the behavioral adaptations that
probably relate it to familiar surroundings. Many animals behave differently in known territory than in strange areas, whether this be the
home cage of a laboratory mouse, the defended territory of a breeding
bird, or, according to one hypothesis, the odor of a home stream selected
by migratory fishes such as salmon. This behavioral role of familiar

territory may be important in the adaptation of animals to domestication or the laboratory niche. Social interactions deserve investigation in relation to migration and homing. How much of homing behavior is due to the displaced animal finding itself in the territories of aggressive conspecifics? Are the flight calls of nocturnal migratory birds part of an extended network of social communication? How do social structures of migratory animals change during the annual cycle that may include a breeding habitat, long migrations, and a winter area where breeding activity is absent?

The sensory basis of homing after displacement in an arbitrarily chosen direction presents even more challenging problems to behavioral scientists than long-distance migrations, because the latter can be explained, in part at least, by orientation in a roughly constant compass direction based upon the sun or stars. Such sun or star-compass orientation behavior requires compensation for the apparent motion of celestial bodies due to the earth's rotation. Such compensation has been well demonstrated in a wide variety of invertebrate and vertebrate animals, and it is closely related to "biological clocks." Homing after arbitrary displacement, on the other hand, requires an animal to select the homeward direction as well as to keep moving in that direction. As the late Gustav Kramer aptly expressed the matter, "We know how some animals obtain the equivalent of a compass, but we know almost nothing about how, in homing, they obtain the equivalent of a map." The clearest evidence that goal-directed homing does in fact occur has stemmed from simple observations of initial headings of birds immediately after release in unfamiliar areas. Such data require much more extensive reinforcement than they have yet received from studies of the subsequent orientation of homing animals after they have moved too far from the release point for direct observation. Observations from aircraft and radio tracking have partly supplied this need, but much more can and should be done along these lines.

While the limited evidence available points toward a major role of celestial navigation by the sun and/or the stars, three important categories of ignorance remain to be dispelled: (1) Can any animals achieve goal-directed, as opposed to unidirectional, orientation by means of celestial cues alone? If so, what sensory mechanisms permit the required precision of time measurement and angular acuity for observing the position and movements of the sun, moon, stars, or other celestial cues? (2) To what extent have we overlooked environmental cues that guide animals in migration or homing and which may lie within the sensory capacities of the animals in question, and possibly those of men as well? The polarization patterns of the blue sky were believed not long ago to be useless for animal or human orientation, but it is now clear that bees and other animals do orient themselves by polarized light, and there is evidence that such patterns are discernible to unaided human vision. (3) Are there unsuspected forms of sensory contact between animals and their environments that remain to be discovered? The orientation of certain fishes by electric fields generated by their own weak electric organs was just such a surprising discovery less than twenty years ago. We would still remain completely ignorant of this phenomenon but for the inquiring research work of zoologists concerned at the most basic level with orientation behavior.

The discovery and subsequent detailed investigation of echolocation (biological sonar) has dispelled such former mysteries as the rapid and agile flight of bats in total darkness and the ability of porpoises to navigate in dark or turbid waters. But even here our blinders may not be fully removed. Orientation behavior based on such an unfamiliar sensory and perceptual mechanism tends to resist incorporation into contemporary common sense. This in turn hampers scientific inquiry by restricting fruitful speculation and consequent questioning of nature in new and sometimes decisive ways. The ramifications of research on orientation behavior are surely unpredictable; they may well continue to yield significant surprises.

Evolution, Inheritance, and Development of Behavior

A major area of research in behavioral biology is concerned with the evolutionary history and ontogeny of behavior—that is, how behavior changes over the generations, how it is transmitted from each generation to the next, and how it develops in each generation during the growth of an individual from egg to adult.

The Functions of Behavior

When we inquire about the biological utility of a particular behavior pattern we assume that the behavior is not an accidental feature, or a side effect, hence that it has itself been subject to selection. In fact, however, it is quite possible for certain traits to be maintained even when they cannot be shown to increase fitness. For instance, the European pied flycatchers that inhabit Spain differ from their more northern relatives in various details of 17 behavior patterns, though their habitats appear identical throughout Europe. No "reasons" for these differences have been made apparent. Experimental demonstrations that behavior patterns do contribute to increased fitness are obviously more satisfying than such appeals to negative evidence. Nonetheless, the function of behavior patterns has been more usually a subject for speculation than for experiment. Notable exceptions are the demonstration that the habit of certain gulls of removing broken eggshells from their nest reduces their visibility and, hence, vulnerability to marauding crows; or that the habit of nesting in clumps leads to a reduced loss of young compared with nesting in a more solitary or peripheral location. In many instances, the behavior in question may not be amenable to direct experimental manipulation. Recourse is then had to inferences from comparative studies. This has, indeed, been one of the oldest areas of research in animal behavior, but also one of the most deficient in rigor. However, with an increased understanding of the logical basis of inference and statistical procedures, students of behavior are again finding comparative studies useful.

Thus, it was noted that the kittiwake, a cliff-nesting gull, differs from other gulls in several ways, all apparently related to the peculiar problems of nesting in a limited area on a steep cliffside. No direct measure of the value or function of these distinctive behavior patterns was possible, but fortunately another previously unstudied species of cliff-nesting gull, the swallow-tailed gull, was found on the Galapagos. It was, then, interesting to establish whether information concerning the kittiwake could be used to predict the behavior of the swallow-tailed gull, since some of those elements of kittiwake behavior serving the function of cliff-nesting ought also to be present in other cliff-nesting species. In fact, the kittiwake and swallow-tailed gull do share a number of behavioral characteristics which can reasonably be related to the problems of cliff-nesting.

Artificial contrivances or models have begun to provide a basis for understanding the function of particular elements of behavior, just as the wind tunnel has been used to reveal the function of deviations in the shape of an airfoil. This has been particularly true for analyses of the biological functions of acoustic signals; sounds readily lend themselves to analysis and synthesis, and the responses of animals to artificial sounds can be tested. The use of films and videotape is being exploited for analysis of the "meaning" and function of certain expressions or movements. Rhesus monkeys, for instance, react appropriately to the facial expressions of other rhesus monkeys, even when these are displayed on a TV screen, permitting an analysis of the function of particular elements of the facial movements. Such studies are a logical sequel to the studies by the early ethologists of the function of certain species-characteristic features of plumage or morphology, such as the wing patterns of ducks or the moustache stripes of some woodpeckers.

A final note concerning studies of biological function of behavior patterns must include a reference to behavior patterns that serve to preserve the genetic distinctiveness of species. One major means for maintaining a barrier to hybridization is through species-specific behavior patterns, particularly those patterns important in courtship and mating. Such patterns or displays are often intimately associated with the conspicuous markings referred to above. They represent a major function of behavior patterns which, in any other context, might be useless if not inimical. It is worth conjecturing that certain apparently maladaptive features of human behavior represent vestiges of these often persistent patterns.

The Inheritance of Behavior

In the immediate post-Darwinian period, much emphasis was placed on the natural selection of behavioral characters, as these were assumed to be a part of the biological makeup of a species and of paramount importance in both intraspecific and interspecific competition. During the ensuing years, the lability and modifiability of many aspects of the behavioral repertoire of higher animals suggested that the behavioral characteristics were not as strongly genetically determined as had previously been assumed.

The advent of quantitative genetics and its extension to polygenic systems, which make incremental contributions to intergrading characters which can also be influenced by environmental variables, made it possible to reanalyze the problem. Several methodological procedures have been followed. One has been breeding selection for behavioral capacities of various sorts. These have included maze performance in rats, aggressiveness in mice, dogs, guinea pigs and rabbits, and geotropic responses in fruit flies, to name only a very few. The very fact of the ability to alter these aspects of behavior by breeding selection is itself evidence for an underlying genetic basis for the behaviors in question. Most genetic analyses have revealed that these behaviors are affected by many genes; none conform to a simple Mendelian model. In some instances, it has been demonstrated that each chromosome may make a contribution toward a given behavioral phenotype, providing further evidence that many genes are involved.

In other studies it has been demonstrated that individual genetic substitutions do affect particular behavioral characteristics. There was considerable literature in the twenties showing that simple Mendelian ratios could be obtained from such "traits" as position preference in coach dogs, wildness in rats, susceptibility to sound- or smell-induced seizures in deer mice, and many others. These results are not irreconcilable. There is no reason why a behavioral phenotype should not occur on a variety of genetic bases, such that a genetic substitution at any one of a number of loci could affect it. There is also no reason to suppose that any test of behavior arising through observation or experimentation should be isomorphic with the way in which the organism is organized genetically in this respect. A given behavioral deviation may result from any one of a number of genetic causes or from experiential or physiological events that have differed from one individual to another and would have produced behavioral differences even if these individuals had been of the identical genotype.

It has been demonstrated that there are profound individual genetic differences among members of the same species, which affect their susceptibility to environmental variables. For example, early handling in rats and mice produces effects on later behaviors that can be described by average scores in a genetically mixed population. Individuals within such a population may, however, have different sensitive periods, so that the time when a given set of stimuli would be maximally effective in producing a later change in behavior in one genotype would not be the optimal time for another. The direction and magnitude of the effect during the optimal sensitive period, or, indeed, whether any effect is produced at all, is also genotype-dependent. The same life experience applied to two genetically different members of the same species will not necessarily produce equivalent behavioral results.

Genes that affect behavior may also affect a variety of other characteristics. Such "pleiotropic" effects (i.e., side effects) of genes have often been postulated. This has been especially true of genes controlling pigmentation in rodents and other mammals which have also been related to wildness, aggressiveness, seizure susceptibility, etc. In some instances, these presumably pleiotropic phenomena have been shown to be connected by linkage rather than resulting from manifold effects of the same gene. On a more complicated level, body type, genes, and behavior have shown intercorrelations presumed by some to be causal. Such statements are found both in the medical literature and in the literature of experimental biology. In one such study, the hypothesis was advanced that certain genes determine the endocrine balance and that the endocrine balance is in turn responsible for differences both in body type and in behavior. Through genetic approaches, it has been possible to reshuffle the genes by crossing the extreme types and extracting a large offspring population. If the genes having to do with body type do not determine those aspects of behavior attributed to that body type in correlation studies, then it should be possible to dissociate and recombine various body types and behaviors. This is, in fact, what happened.

An example of behavioral effects attributed to marker genes is the association reported between the "pigment dilution" gene in the mouse and various behavioral abnormalities, including susceptibility to convulsive seizures. A biochemical mechanism was related to the behavior both in theory and through correlations. However, thoroughgoing genetic analyses have revealed that in this instance, as in many others, the association is through linkage and that separate genes are involved in pigment dilution and susceptibility to convulsive seizures.

Even where pleiotropy is rigorously demonstrated, whether a given effect of a gene is associated with several phenomena or not is also a matter for investigation. It may be that despite the very close correlation between a gene, intervening morphological and physiological events, and two different aspects of an organism's characteristics, the relationship between the variables is collateral, each depending on a different effect of the gene, rather than lineal.

Where there are a multiplicity of genetic bases for developmental phenomena affecting behavior, and where the behavior in question can also be induced in "normal" genotypes, depending upon physiological insult, environmental stress, and other extreme conditions, correlations between environmental events, physiological and morphological findings, and behavior are even more difficult to interpret. The use of inbred strains and isogenic stocks and the use of controlled genetic substitutions on such constant backgrounds are bringing order into what was until recently a field more notable for speculation than for its rigor. Attempts to analyze the connection between multiple variables and behavior were purely correlational and based on the manipulation and control of only a few of the relevant events.

In human studies, the major methods necessarily involve pedigree analyses, studies of populations in which there is high consanguinity, studies of population isolates existing in relatively small numbers and with reliable genealogies, studies based on various degrees of genetic relationship within families (cousins, full sibs, half sibs, etc.), and studies of twins. To these may now be added a variety of studies in which some of the abnormalities found show familial tendencies associated with chromosomal aberrations.

Twin studies, though legitimately criticized on many grounds, have provided a great deal of interesting evidence regarding the heritability of behavior in humans. Usually, they have not been adequate to suggest a clear genetic mechanism but merely to establish that genetic factors are involved. One problem has been that of defining more or less natural units of behavior that have been the product of evolution, rather than relying upon arbitrary measures invented by psychologists that may not have isomorphic relationships with genetic capacities. As illustrated in connection with some animal experiments, where sensitive period in relation to early environmental stresses may be temporally different in different genotypes, and where the ultimate behavioral effects of experiences capable of changing later behavior are also genotype-dependent, the complexity of the investigation that needs be done in order to understand genotype-environment interaction is beyond that usually conducted. However, by the same token, this also demonstrates that sensible research in this area can be done. In a number of instances, the developmental mechanisms that are affected by the genes have been identified and related to the genotype-environmental interaction.

Domestication has produced interesting genetic behavioral results. Wild animals, by comparison with their domestic counterparts, are notoriously wary. That is to say, they have a low threshold of response to environmental novelty and a rather extreme reaction to it. The survival value of this wariness in the wild is self-evident. Among many species of wild animals, there is an effective system of communication, through physical postures and vocalizations, which appears to be acquired and understood very quickly and, in some instances, upon the first presentation. The adaptive value of this phenomenon is again easy to imagine. Under domestication both the behavior repertoire and the reaction to it are very often fragmented. In many dogs, for example, some aspects of threat behavior that may be seen in wolves and coyotes are there, but others are missing, and the missing components are not the same in different individuals, even where the history of rearing and social experience has been quite similar. The meaning of the threat is also variable in two respects in the domestic dog by comparison to his wild cousins. One respect is that of intent. The wild animal generally "means what he says," whereas his domestic counterpart may or may not, as judged by his behavior. Another facet is the ability to recognize the meaning of a postural attitude or a vocalization, which is again lost in a hit-or-miss way when one compares many domestic species with their wild counterparts. All of this suggests that these aspects of behavior are genetically independent and that selection in the wild has kept them intact. The relaxation of selection for these attributes under domestication has permitted a wider range of genetic variability in these regards.

The Development of Behavior

One important source of understanding of the behavior of adult animals is the careful study of the development of behavior, starting with earliest prenatal life, and of the influences that affect the ways in which behavior develops.

The investigators whose work furnished the background for current studies of behavioral development studied the earliest behavior patterns, which provided understanding of some basic principles of behavioral development which are still widely applicable. Later, ingenious new techniques made it possible to watch the development of behavior in chick embryos within their eggs, and to study the movements and responses of the embryos of cats, rats, and guinea pigs, *in utero,* at various stages of prenatal development. Some of the ideas derived from such observations have been verified on human fetuses.

In addition to studying in parallel the development of the nervous system and of behavior, and analyzing the correlations between these two, it is also possible to interfere with the development of the nervous system and to observe the effects of such interference upon the subsequent development of behavior. Experiments in which parts of the embryonic central nervous system of amphibians have been transplanted into "host" embryos show that specific parts of the embryonic nervous system are able to establish connections with embryonic muscle and to develop the ability to regulate the movements of the muscles, in the absence of any contact with higher centers of the central nervous system. More recent experiments show that certain aspects of the motor activities of chick embryos can develop even though the nervous system is damaged in very early embryonic development in such a way that no sensory information reaches the central nervous system from the musculature. This implies that some of the motor patterns are integrated entirely within the central system, rather than being reflexly formed by stimulation from outside.

The newborn human infant has been the object of intensive study in recent years. Studies of the visual responses of newborn humans have shown that the ability to perceive forms is probably present in a primitive form at birth, and that simple learned responses can be shown during the first few days, or even the first few hours, of life. It has also been shown that individual differences in responsiveness to stimulation, which are to some degree the basis for the development of individual differences in temperament, are already present in the newborn child. The idea that the newborn child is a blank slate, whose characteristics depend entirely upon experience, and the contrary idea that the human infant does not learn anything significant until some appreciable time after birth, are giving way to an appreciation of the importance both of initial individual differences and of the earliest experiences; longitudinal studies are now under way in which a number of individuals are being followed for a long period to observe the stability during development of the earliest observed individual differences and the importance during development of early experiences.

The importance of early experience in the development of later behavioral capacities has been the subject of a massive experimental assault in recent years. If rats are handled by an experimenter or are subjected to stress situations early in life—i.e., before or shortly after they are weaned from their mothers—they will, when adult, be noticeably different from normally reared animals with respect to emotional responsiveness and with respect to many aspects of behavior which are affected by emotional responsiveness, such as ability to solve complex problems, manner of responding to other members of the species, tendency to explore the environment, etc.

Fundamental capacities, such as the ability to reach for a visually perceived object, also seem to depend upon relevant early experience. If a young cat or monkey is prevented from visually perceiving the consequences of his voluntary movements, the adult will be deficient in visual-motor coordinations. Rhesus monkeys reared during early life without normal social association with other monkeys of their own age are strikingly abnormal in social and sexual behavior when adult. Their responses to other monkeys in conflict situations, their sexual responses to monkeys of opposite sex, and their maternal responses to their own offspring are all noticeably distorted as a result of the distortion in their early social experience. The implications of this work for studies of human social development are obvious.

A striking example of the effect of early experience upon later social development is to be found in the so-called "imprinting" of certain types of birds. If, during a certain "sensitive period" which occurs within a few hours after hatching, a duckling sees a moving object other than its mother, it may for a very long time afterward, perhaps permanently, prefer to follow and associate with the object to which it has thus become "imprinted" than the normal object, viz., another duck. Kittens reared in isolation for the first few days of life may be permanently unable to associate normally with their siblings or to relate normally to their mother. The mother, in turn, by her reaction to the behavioral abnormality of the abnormally reared kitten, may contribute further to the abnormal direction of its development.

Studies of the effects of early experience upon behavioral development converge with studies of behavioral heredity. It can be shown that the effects of early experience are different in different strains of mice or rats, and thus that the expression of the hereditary factors that make for the differences between strains also depends upon the early experience of the individual animal. This means that, in one kind of environment, heredity may be a very important determinant of certain types of behavior patterns, while in other types of environment it may not be so important. Conversely, the effects of early experience may be very important with respect to certain behavior patterns for one type of mouse or rat, while for another type of mouse or rat the effects of early experience on the same behavior may be negligible. This type of research throws the whole problem of interaction between the effects of heredity and those of environment into a much more illuminating framework than was previously available.

In sum, these studies strongly indicate that an understanding of the behavior of any organism requires careful consideration of the early development of its behavior and of the events impinging upon the organism during that development. Animal studies such as those described here give a crucially important background for the understanding of clinical and social problems in the development of human behavior.

Physiological Analysis of Behavior

A major goal of behavioral biology is to analyze the behavior of humans and other animals in sufficient detail to understand the nature of the underlying mechanisms. Hopefully, such understanding may facilitate both prevention and cure of undesirable, abnormal behavior. In order to do this, we must understand the physiological processes which, in interaction with social influences, determine behavior itself. A concerted and many-sided attack is now being carried out on the problems of the ways in which the nervous system and the endocrine system influence behavior.

Biological Rhythms

Biological rhythms, which cover a large range of frequencies, from 1/msec up to 1/several years, have been described at all levels of biological organization. They may be classified also according to functional systems such as rhythms in single cells or small cell aggregations (e.g., pacemaker of the heart, rhythmic impulses from the brainstem), in organs (e.g., blood circulation or the endocrine system, the latter exemplified by the ovarian cycle), in the whole organism (e.g., diurnal and annual rhythms), or even in populations (cycles in population size). In the past, segments of this "spectrum" have been studied quite independently (e.g., rhythms in the central nervous system by neurophysiologists, diurnal and annual rhythms by either ecologists or physiologists, ovarian cycles by endocrinologists). Recently, however, increasing attention has been paid to general features of mechanisms, common to many kinds of rhythms. In addition to basic similarities in mechanism, interaction between different rhythms has been observed, indicating a hierarchical system of interdependent frequencies for at least parts of the spectrum.

A system in which rhythms are observed may represent either a passive system which is susceptible to imposed oscillations, or an active system which is capable of self-sustained oscillations. Within the same biological unit, e.g., the circulation, both types of oscillations may exist concurrently by interaction of central nerve impulse rhythms with passive reactions to lung excursions. Rhythm studies in this field are typical examples of application of cybernetics to biology.

Most rhythms of higher frequencies, e.g., the EEG and the heartbeat, originate within the organism. The ovarian cycle is an example of an endogenous rhythm of lower frequency. Only rhythms that correspond to rhythms of equal frequencies in the environment can hypothetically be considered to be driven from the outside. Potentially, these include the tidal, diurnal, lunar, and annual rhythms. Of these, only the diurnal or "circadian" rhythms have been studied to an extent that models could be developed which allow a mathematical formulation. Most probably, what is known of circadian rhythms can be applied to a large extent to the other three "environment-matching" rhythms.

Nevertheless, all experimental evidence favors the hypothesis that circadian rhythms are basically of internal origin in the individual. Under conditions of constant temperature and light, they continue undamped with an average period which (a) deviates slightly from 24 hours and (b) depends on the environmental conditions (e.g., on light intensity, noise level, temperature). This "circadian" period normally becomes entrained to exactly 24 hours by means of pacemakers in the environment. Similar "circa-periods" and mechanisms of entrainment have recently been demonstrated for tidal, lunar, and annual rhythms.

Real progress in the field has been made in the past twenty years by treating circadian (and other) rhythms as self-sustained oscillators in a technical sense. Pertinent questions which are only partly answered today are: Which environmental factor is capable of entraining a circadian rhythm? What are the mechanisms of entrainment? What are the general features of entrained and free-running rhythms? Available information has been summarized in two models, the predictions of which are presently under test.

Of great importance for medicine are recent findings demonstrating circadian rhythms in sensitivity to drugs and other harmful stimuli such as x-irradiation. More information on those daily rhythms of responsiveness could influence understanding of physiological and pathological processes while contributing to the practical art of how and when to treat patients. In applied physiology, knowledge of circadian rhythms is prerequisite to solving problems with respect to workshifts, modern jet travel with its rapid transition across time zones, and space flight.

Numbers of rhythms of frequencies other than those discussed so far have been described, especially in man. Some are doubtful or at least not rigorously proven. Others seem real enough but there is no clear conception of underlying mechanisms. With regard to human annual rhythms such as birth rate and suicides, more intensive and extensive studies comparing different populations at the same latitude and subgroups of the same population at different latitudes should yield most interesting results.

Physiology of Motivation

Understanding the nature of human and animal motivations and the basic biological mechanisms underlying them has been the goal of recent approaches to a variety of questions concerning instinctive behavior, drive and satiation, reward and punishment, pleasure and pain, and certain physiological regulations. These efforts have included studies of hunger and thirst, sexual and maternal behavior, aggressive and social behavior, as well as temperature regulation; they have been concerned with issues in the reinforcement of learning and performance; they have aimed at the elucidation of underlying physiological mechanisms; they have been concerned mainly with animal behavior, but they also include the study of man in both physiological and psychological aspects, in both normal and abnormal regulations and motivations.

The basic theme of these investigations, and therefore their promise for the future, has been the elucidation of the neurological mechanisms underlying the behavior. Through such study, motivated behavior can be related to physiological regulation; the internal environment and its endocrine, metabolic, chemical, and physical makeup can be related directly to the nervous system, and vice versa; and the many learned and unlearned factors that control motivated behavior can be uncovered and organized into a meaningful whole. Out of these advances comes not only a basic scientific understanding, but the distinct possibility of practical application in the medical and social control of obesity, sexual deviation, aggression, and other disorders of motivation as well as in the development and management of normal, healthy drives and motivations.

The efforts made in the investigation of the basis of hunger and thirst will illustrate the approach, the achievement, and the practical possibilities. It is self-evident that these two forms of behavior—eating and drinking—are finely regulated by some exquisitely sensitive feedback system. The sensitivity of the control need not be as great for water as for solid-food intake. As seen in Chapter 7, the kidney is fully capable of adjusting the composition of body fluids in the face of a wide range of water intake. But there is no really equivalent mechanism for solid intake. Failure to ingest sufficient calories results in combustion of body tissue if there are no fat stores. Excess caloric intake cannot be excreted; it is deposited as fat. The sensitivity of this control is evident in the fact that a 150-pound man, eating 2,000 calories per day, consumes about 350 pounds of solid food per year. A 5 percent error in regulating intake would mean a weight gain or loss of 17 pounds of dry weight plus its associated water, about 30 pounds more, or one third of initial body weight in one year!

Investigation of the basic neurological mechanisms has revealed, within the hypothalamus at the base of the brain, excitatory and inhibitory mechanisms that work reciprocally like the accelerator and brake of a car in control of the final behavior. Thus destruction of the excitatory mechanism in the lateral hypothalamus results in refusal to eat or drink to the point where an animal will starve to death in its home cage in the presence of its usual food and water. Conversely, destruction of the inhibitory mechanism in the medial hypothalamus will make an animal double or triple its food intake with the resultant gain in body weight. In further definition of the excitatory and inhibitory mechanisms is the additional finding that arousing them by electrical stimulation through chronically implanted electrodes can cause the converse effects: stimulating the lateral hypothalamus will cause the satiated animal to eat promptly, and stimulating the medial hypothalamus will cause the hungry animal to stop eating. Opening up a new approach is the further finding that manipulations of the excitatory and inhibitory mechanisms may be performed chemically by injection of substances into the hypothalamus through pipettes which are chronically implanted in the brain. Thus, the local anesthetic procaine will cause temporary overeating when injected into the medial hypothalamus and temporary refusal to eat when injected into the lateral hypothalamus, even in the same animal. Conversely, injection of an excitant, strong salt solution, produces eating in the lateral hypothalamus and inhibits it in the medial.

Are there specific chemicals that can selectively activate the lateral and medial hypothalamus? Can a specific hormone or metabolic substance be identified, or could serum from a hungry animal produce eating and serum from a satiated animal inhibit eating? Sex hormone introduced in the anterior hypothalamus evokes sexual behavior even when the dose is so small as to have no effect when administered intravenously. Serum from lactating rats can produce maternal behavior in the virgin female. It seems likely that there are chemoreceptors in the hypothalamus, selectively responsive to minute amounts of naturally circulating key compounds, just as there are "osmoreceptors" and temperature receptors. But to what are the appetite centers in the hypothalamus normally responsive? If one knew, it should become possible to develop drugs, to be ingested orally, that would control overeating and undereating.

Central neural mechanisms such as the excitatory and inhibitory mechanisms of hunger obviously must be under the control of many factors known to influence appetite and eating, such as the smell, sight, and taste of food, fullness of the stomach, environmental and body temperature, and indeed habits of food preference and aversion. Many of these factors have been investigated singly and in combination in animal studies, with the result there is now a picture of how the peripheral physiology of the organism affects the central nervous system and, thus, these aspects of behavior. For example, in the ingestion of a meal consisting only of glucose, voluntary intake increases with concentration, due to the effects on the taste receptors; but beyond isosmolar concentrations, ingestion declines with increasing concentration because of the discomfort of osmotic effects in the stomach. By use of a liquid diet, taste and oral factors prove to be unessential for the basic regulation of intake, for animals can be trained to press a lever to feed themselves via an implanted stomach tube. They select rationally in accord with the degree of hunger and the caloric density of the diet. Experiments on the regulation of water intake suggest that even the stomach may be bypassed, for animals regulate intake remarkably well when part of their intake goes directly into the circulation through an implanted venous catheter and part of it is available by mouth each time the animal presses a lever.

Approaches of this sort have now been extended to human subjects expected to press a switch to obtain liquid diet into the mouth through a stainless steel straw or directly into the stomach by an indwelling catheter. Man's ingestion under these circumstances is remarkably similar to the animals', and he regulates well. Similar studies have yet to be performed with intravenous feeding. With such experiments in hand, it is now possible to study patients with feeding disorders: the obese, the anorexic, the depressed, the brain-damaged. The scientific questions that may be asked of man are unlimited, and it should be possible to study the subjective aspects of appetite, the role of social factors, culture, and individual experience in the production of food preferences and aversions, in the cause of overeating and overweight.

Such motivational processes provide the basis of reward or reinforcement. The hungry animal not only eats, but will work for food and will learn to do whatever leads to food. In this sense, food reinforces new learning. At one level of description, we can say hedonistically that the reinforcer for man is pleasure, and animals and man tend to learn what is pleasurable. At another level, we can specify the operation of a reinforcer in objective, behavioristic terms and say quantitatively how much behavior of what strength and with what probability will occur as a function of the amount, kind, and schedule of reinforcement. At another level, we can learn what neurological mechanisms are concerned and get new insights into the whole reinforcement process. For example, an animal can be trained to press a lever to close an electric circuit to stimulate a limited region of his brain through an implanted electrode. The animal "works" for brain stimulation much as it works for food. In that sense, the brain stimulation is positively reinforcing or rewarding. In other loci, the brain stimulation is aversive, and the animal will work to be relieved of it and learn to press a lever promptly to turn it off. This is like negative reinforcement or the escape of punishment. In still other loci, the brain stimulation is without reinforcing effect and is said to be neutral.

The striking thing about such reinforcement through direct self-stimulation of the brain is that the positive and negative loci are much the same as those concerned with the control of motivated behavior. Thus, there is great promise that the nature of reinforcement will be elucidated and related to neurological mechanisms in motivation. Through such investigations we should gain understanding of the keys that shape and control behavior.

Similar questions may be asked about still other types of motivated behavior at both the scientific and practical levels, and indeed they are being approached in the study of man in connection with sexual and parental behavior, and aggression and social behavior. The future lies in the control of animal and human populations, in the prevention of extinction and substandard existence; and the scientific issues in the study of motivation are central to the future success of our species.

Fighting and Antagonistic Behavior

It has been known for more than three decades that electrical stimulation of selected sites in the mammalian brain can cause intense emotional displays involving "aggressive" or "fearful" patterns of behavior. Parallel studies have disclosed regions of the brain where local destruction enhances or diminishes such reactions. However, only within the past few years has a unified approach to the study of such problems been undertaken — an approach that seeks a complete-as-possible description of aggressive or fearful patterns as they occur in the natural habitats of the individuals or species concerned.

When not living a life of relative ease in the laboratory, the vast majority of animals are involved to varying degrees in performing those fearful, defensive, or aggressive patterns which enable them to evade animals that would prey upon them, to maintain access to their food supply, and to interact with members of their own kind. Information about such basic patterns of survival can best be gained through field research, which not only provides descriptions of critical behavior sequences but also clarifies the stimuli that elicit them. Thus, for the student of the physiological substrate of aggressive, defensive, or fearful behavior in the rhesus monkey, it is imperative to know the natural enemies of the species and the range of responses performed by rhesus monkeys when confronted by such predators. It is equally critical to understand the structure of rhesus monkey society and the meaning of the varied postures, facial contortions, and vocalizations emitted in the social context.

Physiological scientists have often failed to appreciate the extent of intraspecific aggression, or its significance in maintaining an orderly social group, where the members are best protected against predators' attack, where the territory can best be defended against intruders in competition for food or living space, and where the genetically sturdy members of the group can be selected for reproductive activity. In a society such as that formed by a group of rhesus monkeys, the bulk of aggressive or fearful behavior is directed at other members of the species. Yet, despite their formidable strength and biting capacity, very little physical damage is ultimately done to either the aggressor or the victim of aggression. Study of the manner in which gesture and countergesture substitute for actual destructive conflict has become a most rewarding area of research.

That such information is crucial to proper interpretation of brain stimulation or lesion effects is supported by recent evidence which demonstrates the interaction between the laboratory test situation in which an animal is observed and the result of physiological intervention. Electrical stimulation of a given region of the brain may produce an aggressive attack if the subject is concurrently presented with a model of a predator, but merely result in random locomotion if the model is omitted. Further, each species may have its own characteristic technique for dealing with aggressive interchanges. Interpreting flailing claws and biting teeth may seem a simple matter, but all aggression is by no means that obvious, and the detection and proper identification of more subtle changes in tail elevation, ear position, or turning of the head require detailed understanding of the species in question.

A large portion of the research currently under way in this field involves the electrical stimulation of selected brain structures through implanted electrodes connected to the current source by flexible wire leads. Successful work has been accomplished in this manner, and more valuable information will be forthcoming. However, technological innovation could open further routes of research. It is of particular importance in complex social situations to have the subjects as unfettered as possible and capable of free movement in the environment. Continued improvement of radio-frequency stimulation techniques should permit wireless stimulation. It is already being employed in several laboratories studying social interactions in monkey colonies. Stimulation of the brain by local injection of drugs should also prove highly fruitful, although this technique is just beginning to be applied to the analysis of fighting and fleeing. Finally, it seems probable that automatic recording procedures, for recording electrocardiograms and electroencephalograms, utilizing telemetry technology with freely moving animals will find increasing utility in this research area. Such recording procedures, employed while subjects are interacting in aggressive-defensive encounters, have already provided valuable preliminary information regarding significant changes in circulatory function and electrical activity in particular regions of the brain.

The Endocrine System and Behavior

Substantial progress has been made in the past few years in the analysis of the relationships of the endocrine system to behavior.

It has long been known that male and female sexual behavior may, in most animals, be eliminated by castration and may be reinstated by the administration of male hormone to males and of female sex hormones to females. Refined techniques have recently made it possible to implant very small amounts of sex hormones locally into particular loci in the brain, and thus to ascertain exactly *where* these hormones act upon the brain. Parallel study of the effects of such local administration of hormones and of the effects of equally precisely localized destruction of small amounts of brain tissue are yielding increased understanding of the neural mechanisms controlling reproductive behavior and of the ways in which these mechanisms are influenced by hormones. By the use of synthetic hormones labeled with C^{14} or H^3, it has been demonstrated that the sex hormones are indeed taken up by specific points in the brain, and that there are probably specific cells which are sensitive to, and which have an affinity for, the sex hormones.

The relationship between the endocrine and nervous systems is a two-way street. Not only do hormones circulating in the blood affect behavior by their effects upon specific parts of the brain, but it is now clear that the brain controls the secretions of the endocrine glands through its connection with the pituitary gland, which in turn controls the secretions of the other endocrine glands. The hypothalamus is the part of the brain most immediately involved in the regulation of sexual behavior, most immediately sensitive to sex hormones, and most directly involved in regulating the activity of the endocrine system. Hence, it is in the hypothalamus that the reciprocal effects of the endocrine and nervous systems upon each other are integrated.

Since the brain controls secretion by the endocrine glands, it is not unexpected that external stimuli, including social stimuli acting through the brain, cause changes in endocrine secretion. Many examples of such effects are now known. For example, stimulation of the mother's nipples by the suckling young mammal causes the pituitary to secrete the hormone which stimulates the mammary glands to manufacture more milk. By this means, the mother is stimulated to keep secreting milk as long as she nurses her young. The route by which this stimulation reaches the pituitary gland through the brain is now fairly well known. Analysis of this phenomenon in mice, rats, and dairy animals has illuminated the mechanisms involved in nursing and weaning in mammals, including humans. For example, a mother rat secretes lactogenic hormone in response to the sound and smell of her hungry young even when she is not in direct contact with them.

Another example of regulation of endocrine secretion by external stimuli acting upon the brain is to be found in the effects of odors from male mice upon the ovarian activity of female mice. The female's perception of these odors can affect her estrous cycle, as well as the physiological mechanism by which a fertilized egg becomes implanted in the uterus. The odor of a male of her own strain keeps her on a regular estrous cycle and permits implantation. The odor of a strange male interrupts the estrous cycle and, as long as 24 hours after mating, will prevent a pregnancy.

Related effects can be demonstrated vividly in birds, which are more sensitive to visual and auditory stimulation, and much less sensitive to olfactory stimulation, than are mammals. In birds, visual and auditory stimulation from a courting male can affect the activity of the ovary of a female without direct contact between them. Further, association with the nest and eggs induces equally striking changes in endocrine secretion, which cause further changes in the behavior, so that the progression of behavioral changes from courtship to nest-building to laying of the eggs to sitting on the eggs to rearing the young is the result of a series of endocrine changes, which are themselves partly stimulated by the changing social situation.

The endocrine system also plays a role in the *development* of the nervous system. Male and female nervous systems are different from each other: a male mammal does not readily show female sexual behavior when injected with female sex hormone, and the female does not easily show male sexual behavior when injected with male hormone. Thus, differences in the behavior of males and females is the result not only of the fact that males and females secrete different hormones, but also of the fact that the loci in the central nervous system which react to these hormones so as to give rise to the relevant behavior patterns also differ in males and females. In a recent dramatic series of experiments sex hormones were injected into pregnant female guinea pigs or monkeys, and the behavior, when adult, of the offspring that thus received the hormone treatment when they were fetuses was then studied. These experiments have demonstrated that it is possible to change the nervous system from male to female, or vice versa, by treating it with appropriate hormones when it is an embryo or newborn, as measured by the ability of the animal to respond appropriately to sex hormones when it is *adult*! In general, the developing nervous system responds to the embryonic hormonal situation by developing into a male or female type in much the same manner as the embryonic sex organs respond by becoming male or female organs. This line of experimentation has opened up a wide range of possibilities for understanding various types of sex differences and for understanding and possibly controlling clinical abnormalities of sexual development.

The fact that a behavior pattern is induced by the injection of a hormone does not mean that it springs full-blown from the brain, unaffected by the animal's previous experience. Many experiments have shown that, in different kinds of animals, previous experience influences the sexual behavior induced by injecting sex hormones into castrated animals. It seems to be true that the higher the position on the evolutionary ladder, from the lowest mammals to man, the more important is the effect of previous experience, and the less important is the immediate presence of sex hormone, in determining various aspects of reproductive behavior. Here the study of behavioral development and the study of the effects of the endocrine system upon behavior converge, so that it is impossible fully to understand the organization of the behavior patterns without understanding both the physiological mechanisms operating in the adult and the way in which these mechanisms, and the behavior patterns influenced by them, have developed during the individual life of the organism.

Behavioral biology has thus contributed to, and benefits from, recent advances in understanding of the physiology of the endocrine system.

Emotions and Stress

In the face of difficult and distressing life situations man reacts with a variety of responses which tend to prepare him to cope with the threatening situation. These adaptive responses occur on various levels of organization and appear to involve every system of the body. The nervous and endocrine systems are of primary importance in these responses.

We have already noted that the brain controls the endocrine system through a link between the hypothalamus and the pituitary gland. A particularly interesting direction of neuroendocrine research in recent years has involved the elucidation of influences from higher brain centers upon the hypothalamus and through it upon the anterior pituitary–adrenocortical system. Attention has chiefly centered on the limbic system, the great limbic lobe of Broca, completely enveloping the brainstem; it consists of the oldest cerebral cortex from an evolutionary viewpoint, as well as subcortical structures. Several workers have shown that stimulation of various limbic areas through chronically implanted electrodes in waking mammals, including primates, can produce substantial increases or decreases in the circulating concentration of adrenocortical hormone.

A considerable body of evidence in recent years indicates that the anticipation of personal injury by man may lead to important changes not only in thought, feeling, and action, but also in endocrine and autonomic processes, and hence in a wide variety of visceral functions. Much work has centered on the changes in adrenocortical functioning in association with emotional distress. Investigators have generally found the adrenal cortex to be stimulated, via the brain, under environmental conditions perceived by a person as threatening to him. Usually such personally threatening conditions precipitate clearly detectable emotional distress. In some studies, it has been possible systematically to correlate the extent of emotional distress with levels of adrenocortical hormone of the cortisol series in blood and urine, each assessed independently. Work in this field has profited greatly by the development of reliable biochemical methods for measuring steroid hormones, epinephrine, and their derivatives.

Several hundred persons have been studied in various laboratories under conditions of moderately intense distress. The results are quite consistent, showing significant elevation of adrenocortical hormones in

both blood and urine over the observations made under nondistress conditions. Moreover, many persons have been studied on repeated occasions, and the elevated adrenocortical hormone levels have been found
to be quite persistent when the distress remained unabated. With relief
of distress, substantial fall in corticosteroids has been observed. Though
the data are less adequate, similar studies relying upon newer biochemical
methods for measurement of epinephrine (adrenaline), norepinephrine,
and aldosterone, under conditions of emotional distress have yielded
similar results. Thus, it now appears likely that emotional distress in
man is associated with elevated blood and urinary levels of four series
of adrenal hormones reflecting increased secretory activity by both the
cortex and medulla of this gland.

We may summarize the evidence concerning adrenal function under
conditions of psychological stress as follows: (1) there is an important
set of brain regulatory functions acting upon the adrenal gland, particularly through brain structures in the hypothalamus and limbic system;
(2) elevations in plasma and urinary adrenal compounds are regularly
observed under circumstances perceived by an individual as threatening to him; (3) there is a positive correlation between the degree of distress experienced by the individual and the tendency toward hormone
elevation; (4) consistent individual differences have been observed, both
in the range within which each person's adrenal hormone levels fluctuate
under ordinary circumstances and in the extent of adrenal response to a
difficult, disturbing experience. The fact of consistent individual differences in adrenocortical response to environmental conditions touches on
the important problem of differential susceptibility to psychological stress.
The precipitation and exacerbation of a variety of illnesses have been
associated with emotional crisis — not only psychiatric disorders, but a
rather wide range of medical problems. Yet it is abundantly clear that
many individuals undergo the common stressful experiences of living
without developing such disorders. There are good reasons for anticipat-
ing that a great variety of genetic and environmental factors contribute
to the formation of consistent individual difference in stress response and
hence to differential susceptibility. A promising line of inquiry is now attempting to relate genetically determined differences in the metabolism
of hormones to behavior under stress.

Arousal, Alertness, and Sleep

It is a commonplace observation that animals and man are not continuously active in their environments nor reactive to the welter of stimuli
around them. Not only does each individual organism filter by selective
attention the stimuli to which it will respond, but the rise and fall in alert-

ness through relaxation to sleep may lead to the exclusion of most if not all stimulation. These changes in reactivity depend both on external changes such as the daily cycle from light to dark, and on endogenous or internal functioning of the nervous system, particularly the nonspecific system in the brainstem, the midbrain reticular formation. Animals with damage in the reticular formation show a chronic condition of deep sleep. This part of the brain, in fact, receives collaterals from various sensory pathways of the forebrain. The reticular formation acts as a gating mechanism which determines, in part, what message will get through to the higher brain areas. The activity of this area of the brain, therefore, is essential to "consciousness" or "self-awareness."

An important technique in understanding the arousal functions of the reticular formation comes from recording the electrical activity of the brain, the electroencephalogram, in awake, behaving animals. The relaxed unreactive animal or person often shows a steady regular wave pattern in the EEG, the so-called alpha rhythm. Upon stimulating the reticular formation, this pattern shifts to one that is typical of the aroused and alerted animal, a record of high frequency and low amplitude waves. For example, the first time a novel stimulus is presented to an animal, he turns his head, pricks up his ears, and gets up to approach or investigate the sources of stimulation. Pavlov, the Russian physiologist, was one of the first to describe this "orienting" or "what is it" reflex. The EEG record shows the "aroused" wave pattern like that initiated by reticular stimulation. This appears to be a physiological sign of orienting or attending behavior. In addition to the reticular formation, other structures, such as the thalamic nonspecific nuclei, are also involved in brain arousal, albeit with somewhat different characteristics. It has been suggested that the reticular system controls general arousal from wakefulness to sleep, but that the thalamic system is more specific in action and controls shifts of attention.

Upon repeated presentation of all but the very strongest stimuli, behavioral and EEG orienting as well as evoked potentials of the sensory pathways and their cortical projections gradually diminish and eventually disappear. This disappearance, called habituation, is a mechanism that protects the organism from overstimulation. This process has been studied rather extensively because it seems to be a primitive form of learning.

That the reticular formation may have a more subtle effect upon attention was shown by a discrimination experiment in which normal, awake monkeys were stimulated through electrodes chronically implanted in the reticular formation. They were given only a brief glimpse of two objects and then had to reach through a trap door under the correct object to obtain food reward. Both the number of correct responses and the speed of response to these stimuli improved during reticular stimulation. The brain itself, therefore, modulates how it will respond to stimuli that come to it through sensory channels.

In addition to the EEG changes during arousal and attention, continuous recording shows a progression of changes in electrical brain activity as an animal goes to sleep. The EEG of relaxed man changes from the regular 10 per second alpha rhythm through a stage of low voltage, fast activity, Stage 1. This then fades into Stage 2, consisting of "sleep spindles" characterized by a moderate amount of high voltage, slow activity, and Stage 4 by almost continuous high voltage, slow activity. These four stages do not, however, represent a continuous and steady progression from activity to sleep and inactivity. Upon closer examination, the Stage 1 EEG response resembles that of the aroused organism and, in addition, is associated with rapid eye movements (REM) but no other bodily movements. Eye movements during wakefulness or sleep can easily be recorded without disturbance to the individual by small electrodes placed near the eyes to monitor continuously the electrical activity generated by eye movements. The REM's of sleep are quite similar to those movements associated with visual perception in the waking state. These occur not only in man but also in many animals. Stage 1, with REM, differs from Stages 2, 3, and 4, which comprise a single state of sleep with inactivity and regularity of physiological functions such as breathing, heart rate, etc. The REM's are signs associated with dream activity in man and presumably a similar process in animals. REM's can be used as objective signs of dreaming; subjects can be awakened during a dream sequence, using the REM signs, which permits more immediate recall and a more accurate report of dream content.

Of particular interest is the relation of the REM periods to the need for dreaming. In one experiment, sleep was interrupted at the start of every REM phase so that the individual did not experience dreams for several nights. This was followed by a compensatory period of excessively long dream periods when the subject's sleep was uninterrupted on later occasions. Similar observations have been made on animals, indicating that this is not a unique characteristic of the human brain. When the organism is so deprived it shows signs of disturbance and emotional upset until dreaming is again permitted.

Although there have been suggestions that sleep is a period to permit recovery, many neural units of the nervous system can recover quickly from activity without sleep. Sleep seems to reflect some special process of the nervous system not yet understood, but which may in fact have a chemical basis. As noted earlier, an extract of cerebrospinal fluid from an animal which has not been permitted to sleep will put an awake animal to sleep when injected directly into the brain ventricles. There is some indication that two neurohumors, each produced by a different region of the brainstem, are involved. Norepinephrine may cause REM sleep and serotonin may play a role in deep sleep. The possible effect of such chemical agents in controlling not only sleep and activity but imagery and hallucinations as well as disorders of perception and attention and other forms of behavioral pathology is an intriguing lead for future research.

Learning, Conditioning, and Memory

The learning process is one of the unique properties of the living organism; it is one of the outstanding properties of the central nervous system; it is one of the major modes of adaptation to the environment, particularly among the vertebrate animals; and it is a basic aspect of the highest of all functions of man, intelligence. Simply put, learning is the process whereby behavior is modified in experience; it is a measurable and lasting change in behavior produced by a specifiable set of environmental circumstances.

While there are several varieties of learning, some requiring many trials, some only one or a few trials, all learning can be reduced to specific parameters, operating under four principles: (1) there must be *contiguity* in time and space of the items learned (stimuli to be associated with other stimuli, stimuli to be associated with responses); (2) typically there must be *repetition* of the items associated, despite the rare occurrence of one-trial learning; (3) there must be *reinforcement,* whether it be reward or punishment or simply the reflex evocation of a response, for with reinforcement the learned response grows, and without it, it decays (extinction, forgetting); (4) there must be an *interference* or inhibition process to produce forgetting, presumably by covering over or "locking up" memory rather than destroying it, for lost memories can be recovered, and there is much evidence that the basic process of learning is permanent.

To understand the nature of learning and its functional basis in the nervous system, investigators have undertaken a variety of approaches. One line of attack is to examine learning in different species to see where it emerges in evolutionary development and what properties an organism must have to achieve different kinds of learning. A second approach is to interfere with the nervous system and see if the ability to learn or the ability to remember what was previously learned is seriously impaired by interfering with the nervous system. Damage to the brain, the administration of drugs, direct inhibition of chemical processes within brain cells, electrical stimulation of the brain, and production of convulsions within the brain are some of the methods used to interfere with learning and memory. Together these two approaches constitute the major avenues to the understanding of the biological basis of learning.

Phylogenetic and Comparative Studies. Learning has been studied in animals at all levels of the evolutionary scale, from paramecium to octopus, from fish to man. However, it has been difficult to establish an unqualified instance of learning below the level of the worms, where already a true synaptic and ganglionated nervous system and specialized receptor and response mechanisms have developed. Learning in such simple organisms may be possible, but has not been demonstrated. Even at the level of worms, there is much doubt about the reality and stability of learning. This, despite the fact that a complex literature has grown up around the flatworm (the planarian) purporting to reveal chemical mechanisms underlying learning. The field of planarian learning is controversial; many insubstantial and unverifiable claims have been made, and many a mature scientist outside of psychology has been disappointed and turned away from the problem.

No doubt, the roach and the octopus can learn simple problems as rapidly as more complex organisms. Thus far, however, it appears that they can *only* learn simple problems. Now that these organisms are also being studied electrophysiologically, and their neural structures investigated by electron microscopy, there is the promise that the learning process may be related to the physiological properties of individual nerve cells, to their fine structure and molecular composition.

The major change during evolution is in the complexity that the organism can handle in learning. These new properties of learning are dependent upon the phylogenetic development of more complex receptor and integrating mechanisms, laid over old neural structures which can still accomplish the simpler aspects of learning. The epitome of learning comes in man, who, with the gift of language, can learn and remember symbolically, endowing him with an immense capacity for the absorption and storage of information, available for an endless variety of uses. Out of these raw materials are built the human properties of reasoning and intelligence, seen only in rudimentary form in the infrahuman animals.

The phylogenetic approach allows the scientist to solve problems in the study of learning by taking advantage of unique properties of specific organisms. Sometimes, it is a relatively simple organism that serves his purpose; sometimes a particular facet of learning and its underlying mechanism can be seen only in an organism with a complex brain. Some organisms are uniquely suited to electrophysiological or biochemical approaches. Some are suited for anatomical and neurosurgical work involving the ablation of different parts of the brain before or after learning. Simple organisms sometimes provide the basis for developing a model of the learning mechanism, while complex organisms give a clue to the far reaches of the learning process. All provide the basis for building, out of experimental work, different theoretical conceptions of the learning process and its underlying biological mechanisms.

Neurological Approaches to Learning. Classically, neurological approaches were designed to answer two simple questions, one concerning the locus of learning within the brain and the other concerning the nature of the change in nerve cells that occurs in learning. The neuroanatomical approach usually entails neurosurgery with the hope of removing the tissue involved in a particular instance of learning so that either learning is prevented or previous learning (memory) is lost. However, there is a more important aspect of the brain lesion approach: Are there lesions that disrupt the normal organization of the brain and, if so, is learning or memory disrupted in some way? Electrical stimulation of various loci in the brain, through implanted electrodes, might also disrupt learning and memory. So would a discharging epileptic focus, whether from a tumor or an experimentally implanted irritant. So might a spontaneous, massive or *grand mal* convulsion or one produced chemically or by passing an electric current through the brain. So, theoretically, could other major alterations of brain states such as deep anesthesia of certain types.

The results of a large number of studies in which brain lesions have been made show that the locus of learning, in the vertebrate animal at least, is elusive indeed. No one lesion, even a sizable one, produces permanent amnesia or inability to learn. But they do produce disruptions of varying degree and, under the right conditions, amnesias for recently learned material. Thus a lesion of the visual cortex may produce an animal that fails in a previously learned brightness-discrimination test. But the animal can relearn the habit normally without its visual cortex, presumably using subcortical visual structures. If these subcortical structures are then removed, the animal learns again with other structures, albeit this time more slowly. Thus is revealed a series of levels of the nervous system that can mediate the same habit, and the data suggest that learning may occur at a number of different loci within the brain.

Other experiments reveal other principles. If the lesion is made within hours after the learning and isolates the hippocampus, there will be very little memory compared to the case where the same lesion is made days after the learning. It appears that the hippocampus is crucial for memory in its early stages but not its later stages of formation.

The time factor in memory formation is also revealed in other studies.

Animals subjected to a convulsion shortly after a learning experience show little memory of the experience, but the same convulsion given many hours after learning has no effect on that memory. Similarly, memory may be lost following the administration of the antibiotic puromycin, an inhibitor of protein synthesis, directly into the hippocampal area of the mouse brain if the treatment occurs within a few days of the learning experience, but not if it occurs five or six days after learning.

These and many other experiments indicate that memory formation is a multistage affair, spread over a considerable range of time. Furthermore, the biological mechanisms mediating the memory and the locus of the memory within the brain both may change over time. Thus, a convulsion can disrupt memory only over a period of minutes after its formation, presumably by interfering with the electrical activity of brain cells mediating memory. The antibiotic puromycin is still effective after a few days, presumably by disrupting a chemical mechanism mediating memory.

In yet another set of experiments, removal of the vertical lobe of the octopus results in an animal that can remember a learning experience for fifteen minutes to an hour, but cannot remember for two hours. Similarly, human patients with bilateral damage to the temporal lobe can recall an experience that occurred fifteen minutes earlier, but cannot recall the same experience an hour later. In both cases, the mechanism for temporary storage of memory is intact, but the mechanism for long-term storage of new learning is lost. Older memories, formed before the temporal lobe damage, are not impaired by these lesions, so the mechanism for permanent storage is also intact in the human cases; it is transfer from the short-term to the long-term mode that is impaired.

Thus, learning and memory occur in a number of different structures of the brain, and there is no one locus. This is confirmed by studies in which the electrical changes that take place in the brain during learning are rewarded. Such investigations have only recently been attempted, but if they indicate one thing, it is that changes take place in many loci and at many levels of the brain simultaneously and in succession.

The lesion, convulsion, and drug studies also indicate that memory goes through a number of stages of formation over a period of time after learning and in a number of different loci. Furthermore, it is likely that different physiological mechanisms represent the "memory trace" at different times. Current evidence suggests that memory may be mediated by patterns of electrical activity in the brain in the early minutes after learning and that these patterns may be disrupted by convulsions. Later, over the next few days or more, memory may be mediated by chemical changes in nerve cells and still later, perhaps, by grosser but still fine anatomical changes.

The question, then, of the nature of the change that occurs in learning should be rephrased to focus on a variety of possible biological changes, in a number of loci, and in an orderly progression over time, with each change dependent upon the previously occurring one. Past thinking has suggested a number of possible biological mechanisms that might be responsible for mediating memory. While these ideas are still quite speculative, they may be listed here. (1) Electrical circuits in the brain may be set into action by a learning experience and be self-sustaining for a period of time. (2) Physiological changes may take place in the connections between nerve cells, the synapses, so that previously ineffective connections may become available for the mediation of memory. (3) There may be anatomical changes at the synapses, such as outgrowths or sprouting of connecting terminals. (4) There may be chemical changes, either in the chemicals that mediate transmission across synapses, or in the coding of information within large molecules inside nerve cells.

This last notion of coded information within nerve cells has received much attention within recent years with recognition of macromolecules as repositories of "information"—e.g., DNA, RNA, proteins, and even polysaccharides. The concept applied to learning and memory is that experience may be "coded" in a large molecule, perhaps RNA; and through the role of RNA in directing the steady production of specific proteins, large numbers of specific memories may be preserved. Such a concept would require an understanding of how the events that occur are coded in macromolecules and how the code is translated into a specific physiological mechanism that underlies the learned behavior. Thus far, neither the input nor the output side of the coding mechanism has been investigated, but there have been a large number of investigations directed toward demonstrating that such a coding mechanism is operative.

Unfortunately, most of these experiments aimed at demonstrating the coding mechanism have been insufficiently conclusive. Thus it has been claimed that RNA, fed to senile patients, counteracts the forgetfulness of old age. Or that flatworms can acquire the effects of a learning experience by eating other flatworms that have undergone training. Or that a learning experience obtained by one rat can be preserved in an RNA extract made of its brain and transferred to an inexperienced rat by injecting the extract intraperitoneally. These claims are presently regarded with great suspicion and are taken seriously by only a small group of investigators.

Fortunately, there have been a few excellent investigations that have advanced knowledge in a substantial way. The antibiotic puromycin will inhibit gross protein synthesis in the brain by 75 percent or more for eight to ten hours after it is injected into the brain substance. Such a dose of puromycin will also eliminate memory of a learning experience in mice. If the puromycin is administered only to the posterior regions of the brain, involving the hippocampus and entorhinal cortex, it must be injected within two days to be effective. If it is injected into the middle and front parts of the brain as well, it is effective up to five weeks after the learning experience. Weak doses of puromycin that do not inhibit protein synthesis by 75 percent or more, or that inhibit for less than eight hours, are not completely effective. Puromycin that has been split and has lost its ability to inhibit protein synthesis is also ineffective.

On the other hand, acetoxycycloheximide, another drug that will inhibit protein synthesis in the brain by 80 percent or more and for as long as ten to twelve hours, albeit by a quite different mechanism, is ineffective in blocking memory in mice. So it is not protein synthesis per se. It is necessary to look at ways in which the action of the heximide and the puromycin differ. The mechanism by which puromycin inhibits protein synthesis results in disruption of polysomes with a decrease in working RNA. The heximide does not work this way and, in fact, prevents polysomes from breaking up and thus allows RNA to be maintained, statically. The heximide can counteract the effects of the puromycin; when the heximide is injected into the brain along with puromycin, the polysomes and the RNA are preserved and memory is maintained, despite inhibition of protein synthesis.

This type of investigation provides very important insights into the mechanisms of memory and, more than that, offers the tools for further probing of the mechanism. Successful investigations along these lines should, one day, also provide insight into and avenues of approach to the broader questions of intelligence and mental deficiency.

Sensation and Perception

Behavioral biology is continuously trying to apportion those aspects of behavior that are spontaneously generated by the organism, and those that are under more or less direct control by environmental stimuli. Much of this control is channeled through the organism's sensory equipment; to a large extent it is correct to say that any given species lives in the particular world defined for it by its own sensory apparatus. To understand the biological basis of behavior, in animal and man, thus requires elucidation of the general physiology of sense organs and sensory pathways, combined with an awareness of the lessons one might learn from observing the great diversity of sensory mechanisms in different species.

This field of sensory physiology — the general and comparative study of information processing in living organisms — cannot be summarized adequately in these few pages. Instead, we shall identify those aspects of current work where developments appear to be especially rapid and significant, or where there seems to be especial promise of further discoveries.

Comparative Studies of Sense Organs. The variety of sensory receptors that have been identified in different species is constantly growing. Many species respond to aspects of the environment to which man is altogether insensitive; photoreceptor structures found in insects and crustaceans distinguish the angular polarization of light; acoustic receptors in bats and other lower mammals are sensitive to ultrasound which cannot be perceived by the human ear. So-called weakly electric fish emit regular electric pulses and sense with their body surface those deformations in the electric field which are produced by objects in their immediate environment. Chemical receptors in vertebrates and invertebrates are often found in unlikely places, on appendages (as on the barbels of bottom-feeding fish) or in small clusters (as in various insects). The extremely low concentrations to which these cells can respond and the high degree of specialization of these miniature organs make them excellent models for a more general biophysical approach to receptor processes.

The same is true for certain special organs that are found in man as well as in other species. Thus, the olfactory apparatus remains essentially unknown, since we are still ignorant of the precise nature of the physical-chemical stimuli for olfaction and of their transformation to patterns of nerve impulses in the olfactory organ. Moreover, many other species exhibit an exquisite acuity for odor-bearing substances; in some cases the impact of only a few molecules suffices to influence behavior. Some investigators are, in fact, convinced that progress toward an understanding of this relatively neglected sense might also contribute to those basic mechanisms that underlie memory, since in most vertebrates, central processing of the olfactory input engages nervous structures that seem to play some role, as yet undefined, in the acquisition of more persistent memories for past experience.

Even for the study of man's distance receptors, which bear strong resemblance to corresponding organs in other species (visual and auditory receptors), rigorous application of the comparative approach can yield important clues about the ways in which the sensory input is processed at different levels within the sensory systems. Thus, it is important to note that some cephalopods, with their large image-forming eyes (which have evolved quite independently of the vertebrate eye), consistently confuse certain mirror images. Such apparent anomalies in the shape-recognition process may yield clues for an explanation in terms of the neural process by which shapes are classified.

Clues in Behavior. In identifying sensory capacities in different species in all their diversity, naturalistic field observations and laboratory experiment play a complementary role. Clues to the existence of an unusual arrangement can occasionally be detected by paying close attention to certain intraspecific relations, as those between predator and prey. Thus, certain nocturnal moths have evolved specialized acoustic receiving cells selectively sensitive to the supersonic cries of bats that prey upon these moths. Careful, critical consideration of animal camouflage, as seen by protective coloration or cryptic attitudes, is bound to yield hints about the organization of color and form perception in those animals that prey on the camouflaged species.

Feature Detectors: Vision. One of the most promising recent developments, however, is the discovery of "feature detectors" in the visual and auditory systems of amphibians, birds, carnivores, and primates. Recent studies of the visual apparatus of frogs, pigeons, rabbits, cats, and monkeys have revealed individual nerve cells with selective sensitivity to certain simple patterns: lines and directions of lines, corners, movement, direction of movement, color. There are hints of a systematic processing of visual input into elementary components, with the possibility of hierarchical elaboration of increasingly complex patterns, by what has been called "cascade specification."

Much remains to be done to determine the levels in the visual nervous systems of different species where this sort of feature extraction can take place: movement detection apparently can be accomplished in the rabbit retina but involves midbrain and cortex in higher mammals. Nor do we know, at this time, how far the feature-extracting processes, in any species, can go toward specifying perceptual inputs: Can the system be extended to specify, for instance, a particular face among a thousand faces? Some essential aspects of the pattern-recognition process appear to lie beyond the feature detectors that are known so far.

Feature Detectors: Audition. In audition, similar observations are still more recent and much less complete. However, it is apparent that the bullfrog auditory nerve is especially attuned to certain components of the frog's croak, and that in the cat, auditory neurons in the brainstem have preferential firing patterns to certain complex frequency and intensity-modulated sound sequences. Such discoveries were possible only by virtue of a concerted search for what might constitute natural adequate acoustic stimulation for these species, in contradistinction to the noise bursts and pure tones which had been the principal physical stimuli employed in physiological acoustics in the past.

The continuing search for complex feature detectors in the auditory system may well extend to man, where linguists have disclosed a surprising universality of certain aspects of language. Despite the obvious diversity of linguistic forms, all languages share the major distinctive features that generate phonemes; and all languages are syntactic, with similarities of syntax probably exceeding the differences. It is thus tempting to think that specifically human feature analyzers might be found in the language areas of man's brain, accounting for the universal phonemic features that have been disclosed, the ease of initial learning of any language by young children, and the specificity and relative persistence of language loss after certain brain lesions in the adult.

Somatic Sensation: Major Tasks for Research. Work in somatic sensation and its neural correlates offers still other opportunities for fundamental discoveries. Much has been learned about the information-carrying capacity of first-order neurons in transmitting signals about vibratory frequency of mechanical deformation of the skin in monkeys. These discoveries fit well with what has become known about the capacity of intact man to detect and scale such stimuli in psychophysical experiments. In both sets of studies, the sensory system seems to work with astonishing precision, being close to the theoretical limits of efficiency.

Physiological investigation of higher levels of the somatic-sensory system has revealed a considerable specificity of pathways, so that individual cells in the thalamus and cortex are selectively sensitive to touch in a particular area of skin (their cutaneous receptor fields) or to movement at a particular joint, over a particular range of motion and in a particular direction.

Yet, many major questions remain. It is still not clear how these pathways represent submodalities such as temperature and pain; in fact, it remains a matter of intense controversy whether pain is a specific quality of somatic sensation, with correspondingly specific pathways, or a product of interaction between different types of pathways, so that the resulting pattern would convey pain.

The question of how location of stimuli on the body surface or within the body is mediated by the central nervous system is likewise far from solution. The multiple maps in the thalamus and cortex disclosed by electrophysiological methods may be necessary for achieving such localization of sensory impulses, but they are probably insufficient. Orientation to one's own body and to external space is extremely vulnerable to brain injuries in areas of the parietal lobes that lie well outside the primary projection regions.

Sensory Interaction. It is not clear how various submodalities of somatic sensation interact with one another and with vestibular input, which is known to go massively to the parietal lobes. Nor do we know in general much about the way in which, in perception, we integrate information from other senses with that from somaesthesis. In the forebrain of mammals, many neurons can be found which are open to influence from more than one sensory channel; some proof exists that some of these polysensory units are plastic, in the sense that they modify their activity in response to signals in one modality with signals from others. Such observations open the possibility of finding direct evidence of a functional mapping of different sensory systems into one another, as a result of use. In such intersensory integration, active movement of the organism may play a crucial role.

The Role of Movement. Unfortunately, however, the neurophysiology of movement is in an even more rudimentary state than that of sensation. Experimental and clinical neurology have delineated the major pathways for execution of movements in the central nervous system, especially in higher animals and man, but the initiation of so-called voluntary movements, their patterning into sequences, and the acquisition of skilled movement, all remain complete mysteries at present. Some help may come from recent experiments on the motor cortex of nonanesthetized and lightly restrained monkeys in whom microelectrodes are implanted in a manner analogous to those used for recording sensory potentials in single cells. Individual motor neurons can be identified in the cortex which fire in relation to the onset of "spontaneous" movement in, say, the animal's hand, and in proportion to the effort exerted by the animal in moving the hand against a variable load.

Still other cortical units have been discovered (in the frontal eye fields of the monkey) which fire at the *cessation* of a spontaneous eye movement, as if they were signaling to lower levels of the nervous system that a particular end position has been reached, permitting another phase of a motor sequence to be initiated. Here again, great expectations may be realized from efforts correlating the microphysiology of the nervous system with observations of ongoing behavior.

Efferent Control. A particularly pressing problem, in this respect, is the presumed role of efferent control mechanisms in perception—i.e., the control of sense organs by the central nervous system. Earlier demonstrations of such downstream modulatory influence within visual, auditory, or somatic-sensory pathways have been called into question, but it is evident that animals and man can selectively attend to certain stimuli at the expense of other sensory information, can be distracted or bored, or can become habituated or dishabituated—all processes clamoring for the discovery of their neural correlates.

Possible Role of Centrifugal Regulation in Perceptual Constancies and

Illusions. Some of the most refractory aspects of perception might ultimately be understood by invoking such descending control mechanisms.
Thus, the so-called constancies of size might be understood if one could
prove that such motor impulses as those for convergence or accommodation might interact with visual input processing at some level of the visual
pathway in such a manner that near objects are reduced and more distant objects are increased in size.

The relative stability of perceived space poses similar problems. The
fixed arrangements of feature detectors for verticality and horizontality
in vision actually make it harder, not easier, to understand why verti-
cals remain subjectively vertical during voluntary head and body tilts,
unless one assumes some systematic transformations of the visual input by the postural system. Equivalent assumptions may need to be made
to understand the subjective stability of the world during voluntary eye
movements.

Similar central effects have been invoked from time to time in order to
account for some of the perceptual illusions. For centuries, illusions in
perception have remained unexplained, particularly those classified as
geometric-optic illusions. It has been repeatedly suggested that some of
these effects might not be unrelated to the normal constancies in perception—e.g., the tendency of human and animal observers to rescale
seen objects approaching at various viewing distances, so that the object seen nearby does not grow nor the distant object shrink as much
as ordinary geometric perspective would predict. Some illusions may
turn out to be caused by such rescaling tendencies running off in exaggerated fashion. Whether such an approach is fruitful or not, any biological theory of perception will ultimately have to account for illusions and
constancies as instances of general perceptual laws.

*Sensorimotor Coordination: Complementary Role of Deprivation
and Rearrangement Experiments.* For behavioral biologists concerned
with the boundary region between perception and motor control, two
types of experiments have a special promise: those involving *deprivation* (reduction in sensory input, particularly early in an organism's
life) and those involving *rearrangement* (of spatial or temporal relations)
between the organism and his sensory environment.

Most deprivation studies on higher mammals have to be currently reevaluated, since they were done before the discovery of feature-extracting mechanisms in the forebrain. The feature-detecting cells in the visual
cortex of kittens, and presumably of baby monkeys and human infants
as well, are present at birth, but they atrophy with prolonged visual deprivation resulting from rearing the animal in darkness or diffuse light.
Such experiments are therefore irrelevant to the classical question about

the role of experience in the origin and maintenance of visual form perception.

However, it is possible to provide a type of deprivation that avoids this experimental difficulty. One can deprive very young animals (e.g., kittens) of all opportunity for self-produced movement, arranging their rearing conditions so that they are seeing their environment while they are passively being moved but do not see it while they move themselves. Under such circumstances profound disturbances of visual-motor coordination and of form and depth perception are induced, which are nonetheless reversible upon subsequent exposure to a visual environment in which the animal is permitted to move actively about. It is likely that the acquisition of visual-motor coordination (whether proceeding normally or artificially delayed) involves the building up and storage of correlations between self-produced movements and their perceptual consequences.

Complementary to deprivation studies are experiments employing rearrangement. If one fits a normal adult with distorting and displacing spectacles and permits him to walk actively in a structured optical environment, his visual-motor coordination will adapt to the displacements, and perceived distortions (e.g., induced curvature or tilts of objectively vertical lines) will diminish as a direct function of such active exposure. In contrast, if the same exposure period is spent by the observer while being moved about, passively, in a wheelchair, little or no adaptation ensues. Such observations suggest that adaptation to rearrangement requires active movement or, differently put, that active movement contains sensory information which passive movement lacks.

One possible approach to the physiological difference that must underlie these different perceptual-motor consequences of active and passive movement would be to assume that active movement involves more than the sending of motor commands to the muscles; in addition, a corollary set of signals goes from central motor to central sensory systems, presetting the sensory mechanisms for those changes in the input that are to be expected as consequences of the perceiver's own motion. The postulation of such corollary or motor-to-sensory discharges is prompting a diligent search for unorthodox neuroanatomical connections and for corresponding electrophysiological effects. Whatever the outcome of this search, some physiological distinctions of active from passive movement will have to be specified.

Hemisphere Differences. The relative roles of the two hemispheres of the brain have been a subject of interest for a century. Combined application of verbal and nonverbal tests is particularly necessary, since earlier views on hemisphere differentiation and dominance have been called into question. It used to be believed that left and right hemispheres (halves of the brain) in most adults were equivalent in function, except for the addition of language mechanisms in the left hemisphere, in the majority of cases. Instead, it is becoming increasingly evident that the two hemispheres stand in a relation of reciprocal specialization, with certain nonverbal aspects of performance depending more on the right hemisphere than on the left. So far, no anatomical or physiological correlates for this reciprocal specialization have been found, but the search continues, although hampered by the obvious fact that such hemisphere specialization is absent in animals below man.

We believe that particularly rapid progress in neuropsychology can be expected when studies on men with brain injuries and on animals with experimental ablations proceed together in the same laboratory. Studies of lesions or ablations can then find their place as "defect" experiments next to those studies that involve rearrangement or deprivation. In the defect experiment, one studies the living system after the elimination of one of its parts, in order to determine how performance proceeds in its absence. In the rearrangement experiment, some parts of the system are actually or virtually interchanged (e.g., in fishes or amphibians, eyes are rotated in their orbits, or limbs interchanged, while in higher forms auditory input may be reversed by pseudophones, or visual input altered by displacing or inverting spectacles); the extent and limit of functional adaptation to such rearrangement is then investigated. In deprivation studies, one isolates the organism from its normal input, either early in development or later, in order to see how function proceeds in the absence of particular sensory inputs.

Split-Brain Studies. Much recent experimentation on lesion effect in animals and man employs the device of cutting the long pathways between the two cerebral hemispheres, thus depriving each half-brain of some of the direct input from the other. Animal preparations of this sort permit experiments on transfer of sensorimotor reactions from a practiced to an unpracticed hemisphere. Cutting the cross-connections between the two cerebral hemispheres has also been reintroduced in treating certain forms of epilepsy in man. In such patients, information processing can be studied separately, up to a point, in a verbal (left) and a relatively nonverbal (right) hemisphere. While dramatic in outcome, these split-brain studies do not supersede the older approaches to functional localization in various lobes of the brain, such as the problem of the occipital lobes and visual function, and corresponding functions for other lobes and subregions of the brain.

The Occipital Lobes and Visual Functions. Renewed efforts at elucidating the effects of occipital lobe removals are all the more timely, since it is in the occipital regions that most of the information on feature detectors has been obtained. It has been assumed, until quite recently, that only reactions to the total amount of light remain following removal of all of the primary visual cortex in the monkey, but new experiments suggest, in addition, a capacity for discriminating speckled fields from any shade of gray and, possibly, some ability to track small visual objects.

The role of old visual centers, such as the roof of the midbrain in higher forms (carnivores, primates), in mediating these and perhaps other residual visual capacities after cortical loss is still as controversial as it was a hundred years ago. Yet the problem can and should be attacked by animal experiments and by careful observations on brain-injured man.

Inferolateral Temporal Neocortex: Role in Visual Discrimination Learning. Equally promising is further analysis of the role of temporal lobe structures in the processing of visual information; such analysis should proceed by fractional ablations and electrophysiological techniques. For some time it has been known that bilateral removal of inferior and lateral neocortex in the monkey produces impairment of visual discrimination learning which seems specific to that sensory modality. Quite recent work suggests that a more posterior focus in this temporal region causes a subtle perceptual deficit, while a more anterior focus produces a deficit of visually mediated learning.

Such observations of differential localization of symptoms are essential preliminaries for an inquiry into the underlying functions: Do the temporal lobe foci represent higher stages in a series of hierarchically ordered steps of visual-input processing, or do they rather act back upon the primary processes in the occipital lobe and elsewhere? Detailed physiological studies may bring an answer, provided we can pose the behavioral question in rigorous terms.

Other Functions of Temporal and Parietal Lobes. Analogous questions may be asked about the role of the more rostral temporal lobe structures in audition, and about that of the anterior parietal lobe in somatic sensation. For carnivores, subhuman primates, and man, one question has remained unsolved for a century: Are there ever specific impairments in object recognition, so that an animal or man might see (or feel, or hear) things the way he did normally before the cerebral lesion was incurred, yet fail to understand what he perceives, and this in the absence of sufficient intellectual deficit to account for such a modality-specific failure of recognition? In order to prove the existence of such a postulated selective breakdown in recognition, one needs a thorough quantitative assessment of elementary sensory capacities for the modality in question. No study, thus far, has met this requirement.

The Riddle of the Frontal Lobes. Frontal lobe syndromes remain similarly elusive, but are potentially revealing of the functional organization of the brain in higher mammals. A paradox seems to exist here in that the principal symptoms, after removal of certain frontal structures in the monkey, are unequivocal but extremely difficult to interpret in functional terms. In contrast, symptoms of massive frontal lesions in man are variable but may suggest interpretations that might apply to man and monkey alike.

Monkeys with bilateral frontal removals have severe difficulties on delayed-response and delayed-alteration tasks, yet it is still not clear, in spite of numerous experimental variations of these tasks, *why* the bifrontal monkey continues to fail. For man, delayed-response tasks are too simple and thus insensitive to focal lesions; but there are difficulties with voluntary searching for objects in complex arrays, and there are defective perceptual judgments in the presence of conflicting input (e.g., judgment of visual vertical with body tilted); all of these seemingly disparate symptoms strongly suggest that a root difficulty might lie in the way in which the perceiver has to take his own actions into account.

Very recent experiments with prismatic spectacles in monkeys suggest, indeed, that bifrontal lesions selectively abolish capacity to adapt to these distorting media; the only other lesion found effective, so far, in this respect, involves the head of the caudate nucleus. As they stand, these studies prompt one to pursue certain earlier conjectures about a possible role of frontal structures in a corollary discharge (from motor to sensory systems) and thus in the integration of active movement and perception. These problems are at a stage where they are ready for much more intensive study than they have received until now.

"Limbic" Structures. The same is true for the remarkable behavioral consequences that appear after injury or surgical insult to certain mesial temporal (limbic) structures in man — profound and lasting amnesias, which are observed in previously normal cases without any corresponding changes in perception, in vigilance, or in motor control. Similar memory disorders are sometimes seen after trauma to the upper brainstem or to the tween-brain (diencephalon), although in these instances the syndrome tends to be less selective.

The amnesia found in patients with surgical destruction of the hippocampal zone and surrounding regions is best characterized as a preservation of short-term memory mechanisms combined with nearly total loss of capacity for establishing long-term traces. Such a dissociation of effects suggests that the transition to long-term traces requires some special mechanism, which is still entirely obscure. Here as elsewhere, continued work on the behavioral effect of brain lesions and ablations can prepare the ground for a needed physiology of higher functions.

It is clear that we are still short of even the most elementary understanding of neural correlates for memory or language, for deliberate action or thought. Yet the beginnings of an understanding of perception and of motor control are there, and the importance of the ultimate goal is so obvious that much more effort should be directed at basic brain-behavior studies than has been expended thus far. If man ever hopes to understand himself, he will have to understand his brain.

Coordination of Movements in Invertebrates

The relatively small number of nerve cells composing the total nervous system of an insect—probably less than the number in one retina of a mammal—has made it possible to take technical steps in analyzing the nervous mechanisms of coordinating muscular activity that are not practicable at present with the more complex nervous systems of vertebrates.

Reflex Coordination. Illustrative of the promise in this area is the fact that one group of investigators, using special staining and electrophysiological methods, has been able to identify the precise motor nerve cell bodies in a cockroach ganglion that supply each of the several muscles in the leg. It is significant that this preparation is being widely used for motor learning studies. When these are correlated with the anatomical localization work, interesting findings are expected.

Spontaneous Activity. Earlier it was believed that all animals' actions were reflexive in the Sherringtonian sense—that is, that each action could be referred to a specific sensory stimulus pattern. This leads to the logical conclusion that an animal would be immobile in the absence of sensory input. Students of animal behavior, in particular the European ethologists, reached the conclusion, on considerable indirect evidence, that animals were frequently spontaneously active, showing appetitive or search behavior as the result of changes in internal state rather than in response to specific stimuli from the outside world. Insect central nervous systems can be dissected out of the body, thus severing all sensory connections, and remain active (generating nerve impulses) for days. It was shown as early as 1931 that this is a common phenomenon, and spontaneous activity has since been found in many types of sense cells when deprived of their normal modality of stimulation. Earlier there was a tendency to dismiss this spontaneous nervous activity as biological "noise" having little behavioral significance. More recently, many experiments have demonstrated its importance, and attempts are being made to correlate it with appetitive behavior. Denervation of the terminal ganglion in several insects increases both sexual "search" behavior and the electrical activity of appropriate motor ganglion cells. The flight movements (flapping of the wings) in locusts occur in a fully coordinated manner after the appropriate motor ganglia have been deprived of sensory input. This does not mean that sensory input has no role in these actions. In the case of the locust, sensory input (information telling the nervous system that the wings are being flapped) increases the strength of the wing movements. Yet the fact remains that this input is not necessary for the action. Similar conclusions have been reached from experiments with coelenterates and worms. This type of finding is of great theoretical importance in understanding the relation of nerve function to behavior.

Point Stimulation and Adaptive Behavior. This topic, again, has seen striking advances from work on insects. A number of specific actions having an obvious adaptive function can be elicited by punctate electrical stimulation of the central nervous system of the cricket. Thus, cleaning movements, flight, even different kinds of songs (chirp patterns) associated with courtship and aggression in the male cricket can be obtained by precise stimulus patterns applied to localized areas of the brain. These promising experiments confirm and extend earlier and more crude observations using the opposite technique—brain ablations.

Sensory Information and Action. The parsimony of neurons in insect nervous systems has permitted much more precise analysis of the relation between sensory input and behavior. When only one or a few neurons normally provide the animal with the total span of a given sensory modality, it is possible with today's electrophysiological techniques to decode and analyze all the information available to the central nervous system through this modality. This allows one to proceed with confidence in tracing the central pathways with which these sensory nerve fibers connect and, hopefully, to disentangle the neural set involved in the behavior.

Caterpillars are commonly highly specific in their choice of food plant, often refusing all but one plant species from among dozens presented. It has recently been shown that this specificity is determined by taste endings on the maxillary palps. Electrophysiological studies on certain species demonstrate that there are only four taste receptor cells on each palp. The "acceptance response" is determined by a unique pattern of impulse discharge in these four axons, all other patterns leading to rejection of the material in contact with the mouthparts. This finding has obvious practical significance in connection with the control of plant pests, as well as great theoretical importance. Related studies on the feeding responses of flies are now reaching the stage of analysis of central nervous mechanisms. The same can be said about extensive studies of the reception and central actions of insect sex attractants.

The adults of certain moth species are preyed upon by insectivorous bats. They have ears capable of detecting the ultrasonic cries made by their predators. These cries are made by the bats when echolocating — that is, using their sonar system to avoid obstacles and find their flying prey in darkness. The moths' ears serve as a countersonar system, and acoustic stimulation elicits several kinds of evasive reaction. Each ear is supplied with only two acoustic sense cells — another example of neural parsimony in insects. This simplicity of sensory input is making possible a neurophysiological analysis of the central organization of nerve cells responsible for the various types of evasive behavior shown by moths in the presence of hunting bats.

These few examples illustrate the potentialities of invertebrates, with their simpler nervous systems, for analyzing the sensory, central, and motor mechanism of behavior.

The Biology of Mental Deficiency and Disease

The concepts outlined in this chapter, as well as research results in many other areas, are being brought to bear upon the problems of diagnosis, prediction, prevention, and cure of mental and behavioral abnormalities.

The first stages of research into any deviations from the normal involve the description of the deviation, so that one begins with the description of syndromes and progresses, with wider experience, to a taxonomy of syndromes. The taxonomy, when applied to individual instances, takes on the features of a series of Procrustean beds to which individual instances may be fitted — more or less. The problem, especially in the behavioral realm, is to be certain that the various investigators working with a "given" condition are actually talking about the same thing. In the evaluation of the controversy over some of the genetic studies of schizophrenia and some of the biological researches having to do with infantile autism, the problem of diagnosis and classification is a very crucial one. Even where the taxonomy and syndromy are clear, the causes of a given syndrome may be manifold and complex. This is often easier to demonstrate with animal materials than with humans. Hereditary predispositions to convulsive seizures in mice can occur on a variety of different genetic bases, some of which interact quantitatively so that two genetic substitutions make the odds of having seizures much greater than either one alone, whereas others do not interact in this way. Palliative measures effective for one genotype are not necessarily effective for another. In addition, many other factors resulting from accident or disease can predispose to seizures on a nongenetic basis. However, the syndrome itself is practically indistinguishable for a large variety of distinct underlying causal mechanisms.

A one-gene substitution that produces an abnormality of glutamic acid metabolism in the rat brain results, among other things, in a lessened ability of the animals affected to learn mazes. This can be corrected by the administration of sodium glutamate. Other genotypes with similar performance deficits, but with normal glutamic acid metabolism, cannot be helped in this way.

Research into biological correlates of mental disease is being carried forward vigorously in the hope that chemotherapy or other forms of biological manipulation may be able to correct some clinical conditions and, hopefully, provide a more direct way of manipulating behavior than do present methods of psychotherapy. The identification of important neural transmitter substances, and the demonstration that their metabolism can be affected by certain classes of compounds, and the empirical findings that some substances affecting these transmitters have palliative effects on a variety of aberrant behaviors, have led both to practical results through a variety of "tranquilizing" drugs and to further research based on the strengthening of the hope, aroused by these findings, that detailed studies of neurochemical and neuroendocrinological events will permit a still closer correlation with behavioral states and thereby provide both understanding and the possibility of amelioration and control. Relationships among some of the indoles and catecholamines, γ-aminobutyric acid, glutamic acid, acetylcholine, and various aspects of behavior have been well described on a correlational basis. The interrelationships between some of these transmitter substances and the actions of hormones have also been elucidated in certain cases. Manipulation of the levels, within the brain, of some of these substances by drugs and antimetabolites has produced alterations in visual and perceptual states, both in animals and in man. The metabolic systems involved in the synthesis and degradation of most of these substances are under active investigation. Genetic differences in the capacities to release certain steroid hormones, to synthesize, bind, or destroy certain neural transmitters, and to affect other neurochemical events are now known. In some instances, genetic substitutions produce very local differences in some of these capacities in different parts of the nervous system. In other instances, the eventual level of a transmitter substance is not affected, but the ontogeny deviates from normal in that the time at which the normal metabolic capacity is reached may be early or late. Biologically controlled materials, from both animal genetics and occasional human anomalies that are extreme and involve an easily identifiable major factor, are now becoming available, and cannot but enhance our understanding of many of these mechanisms in relation to behavior. These biological developments are certain to affect psychiatric practice and to provide a means of control in psychopharmacological research that would be impossible if the correlation were merely between signs and symptoms of a disease state and neurochemical analysis.

Conclusion

In the foregoing essay, we have outlined the ways in which a large and heterogeneous group of scientists, of varying backgrounds and interests, working with varying techniques and at various levels, are constructing an intricate network of interrelated ideas and information which is gradually producing a clearer and more comprehensive picture of the biological bases of the behavior of all the members of the animal kingdom, from the simplest to the most complex. If this picture seems incomplete and less than satisfying, the reader should be heartened by the fact that 90 percent of the information presented has been extracted from biological work since World War II and that the correlation of behavior with neurophysiology and neurochemistry has attracted some of the brightest and most fertile minds in science during the past decade. Hence, there is confidence that this has been but the earliest, if most painful, installment payment on a promissory note.

Chapter 11

WHAT IS ECOLOGY?

Ecology has been called "the study of complex systems," which it is —but of course all biology is that. A familiar definition is that ecology is "that branch of biology that deals with the mutual relations between plant and animal organisms and their environment." That is not wrong; the key word, *mutual,* stresses the fact that, as a rule, the most relevant part of an organism's environment is other organisms.

Let us stick with this definition for the time being. Its language leads directly to a model as shown in Figure 11-1, where x is an organism, and the arrows stand for mutual relations of at least three kinds: physical $\leftrightharpoons x$, physical $\leftrightharpoons$ biotic, biotic $\leftrightharpoons x$. Ecologists favor this model, and use the word *ecosystem* for any patch of nature, real or conceptual, that displays these kinds of relations.

Actually, ecosystems worth studying are *both* real and conceptual. A typical one, somewhat hypothetical, which has recently gained prominence for its social implications, is shown in Figure 11-2. The diagram, a sort of flow sheet, purports to sketch the "population dynamics" of a small mammal, such as a woodmouse or a rabbit, as the abstract "system" moves through a year's time. One advantage of showing it this way is to get away from the too-pat hierarchy of "levels of organization"— individual, population, society, biotic community, ecosystem—into which ecology is divided by the textbooks. Such a diagram also reminds us that everything an ecologist does can also be called something else— anatomy, physiology, behavioral biology, or simply zoology or botany. What is essential, if a system is to be meaningfully described as an ecosystem, is that two or more complex systems interact, and be studied simultaneously as they do so. It follows (because of the key word *mutual,*

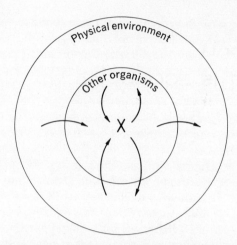

Figure 11-1. Diagram of a model of an ecosystem.

represented by the double arrows) that the physical environment, too, is a complex changing system; other names for things that ecologists do, therefore, can be *bio*meteorology, *bio*geochemistry, and *biological* oceanography.

Note, in the diagram, that the mammal *body* contains a complex system, the *endocrine* system, and is contained within another complex system, the *population,* which is linked to still other systems, here hinted at only by the words "resources," "winter," and "spring." (Predators and diseases, and all genetic systems, are neglected in this model.) It is the interaction between systems that concerns the ecologist; in cybernetic language he is looking for coupling, gating, amplification, delayed feedback, or some new sort of interaction.

Note also that the system, as diagrammed, centers around the liver—itself a complex system of endless fascination. Evidently, then, the more complex systems that interact with livers could be abstracted further. The body and the population, for instance, could be represented schematically as a coupled pair of high-pass filters, acting to damp seasonal fluctuations in the state of a rabbit's liver. So it can be misleading to say that ecology *starts* with the individual organism, as if it were a black box. For an ecologist, the "minimal unit of relevant complexity" varies with the problem in hand.

This point needs emphasis, because it is often misunderstood. Ecologists are as likely as other biologists to study organic molecules and their physical chemistry, but a molecular system must be clearly linked to something beyond "the cell"—as insect sex attractants and other airborne substances are linked to a system of programmed behavior—

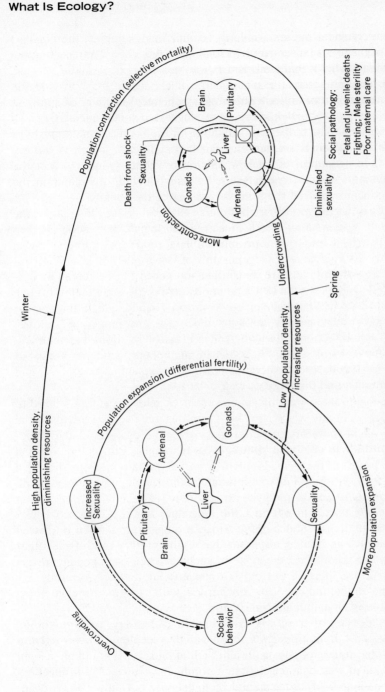

Figure 11-2. Schematic diagram of the annual population cycle of a small mammal, conceived as controlled by and controlling the brain-pituitary-adrenal-gonad system. (From Edward S. Deevey, in Bresler, J. B., *Environments of Man*, Addison-Wesley, 1968)

to be of ecological interest. Taking enzymes as examples, the catalase activity of the livers in Figure 11-1 would probably not tell much about the social behavior of a mammal. But in another context, dehydrogenases, found in sulfur bacteria of soil and the deep ocean, may provide the key that unlocks the entire system of geochemical cycling, of sulfur at any rate. As an eminent oceanographer suggested some time ago, and as studies with sulfur isotopes tend to confirm, the bacterial metabolism of sulfur is as important on earth as is photosynthesis, which is the enzymatic hydrogenation of carbon dioxide by green plants. In fact the two enzymatic systems cooperate, i.e., "are coupled," to maintain the oxygen concentration of the atmosphere and of the oceans.

Look again at the model of relations in Figure 11-1. As long as x, "the organism," is something like a pine tree, ecologists are encouraged to play with such a model. The trouble we have in accepting the definition that led to it arises over the generality of the model. It is not too restricted, as many models are, but rather too general to be genuinely useful. To see why, let the set of x's be one kind of organism, mankind. Then "physical $\leftrightharpoons x$" will embrace all environmental science, including human physiology and geography. "Biotic $\leftrightharpoons x$" will encompass agriculture, forestry, and infectious disease. And a class of relations between x's, of no great moment when x is, say, sea cucumbers, suddenly looms so large as to take in all the social sciences, not excluding psychiatry, and presumably art and theology as well.

The recognition of a *social* environment as relevant makes it hard to define ecology in any way that is both rigorous and useful. Perhaps social relations ought therefore to be left out—over the protests of the ecologists who discovered social pathology in mammals. But leaving art and theology aside, is the ecology of man so very different from that of a social insect? Or of a nonhuman primate? Anthropologists, at least, think not. Like architects and psychiatrists, they occasionally *label* themselves ecologists. It is not just the language, but the basic concepts, of ecology that they find helpful. Since ecologists, too, have borrowed such concepts as homeostasis, feedback, energy flux, etc., from other fields, we can appreciate their use in social science or in geochemistry.

We therefore identify ecologists, rigorously if not very usefully, as those who are simultaneously concerned with two or more complex *living* systems in significant interaction.

In thus denying that ecology is a branch of biology, or of anything, we deliberately limit ourselves to one kind of ecology: *environmental biology*. That much, of course, *is* a branch of biology. It could have been the heading of this chapter, but that would have begged the question, "what is ecology?" Environmental biologists are not only keenly aware of other kinds of ecology, but are increasingly drawn into them as their own research widens.

We would not have struggled so hard to define ecology if it were not for the more important question, "what good is it?" Ecologists are trained to focus on the interfaces between systems—on problems that fall between the cracks of "basic" sciences. They have little patience with distinctions between "basic" and "applied" research. Everything they do is an application, while everything they learn about the operation of a complex system is more or less immediately applicable. Until recently, most applications have been narrowly economic, as when the Norwegian highway department saved millions of kroner by asking an ecologist, who knew where certain "snow plants" grow in summer, where the alpine snowfields would lie longest in winter.

As knowledge grows, however, ecologists can take more comprehensive views of larger ecosystems. And the ecology of nonhuman species, when adequately studied, turns out, nearly always, to include man or his works as relevant, if not primary components of environment. That has never been truer than it is today, as artificial ecosystems replace natural ones nearly everywhere. We may suspect that it has always been true, ever since Neolithic man began to use fire to domesticate his environment. "Pristine nature" is thus at best a relative matter, and sometimes a misleading illusion. As human activity interpenetrates all ecosystems, all ecology tends to become human ecology; and applicability increases steadily and automatically. It extends, now, to the major problems of human society, from water resources and environmental medicine to regional planning and preventive psychiatry.

This means, of course, that effective applications of ecology are surrounded by political and moral questions whose resolution is itself a set of problems in applied ecology. It is instructive to think of the new ecology as Thoreau's ambiguous legacy. Thoreau's concept of Concord was what we now call a "model ecosystem," though he formulated and studied it in advance of all the technology we believe to be necessary in such studies.

Ecologists, however—at least the ones we know—are modest men and women. Most of them are more at home in the forest or on shipboard than in the councils of government, and they are well aware that they are biologists, not universal geniuses. They believe, because they know how richly the multidisciplinary approach pays off, that scientific specialization is insufficient in itself, and that ecology (under whatever name) is *the* science of the twenty-first century. But they know—better than most, because they are close students of recent environmental history— how short a distance their science has come, and how excruciating are the problems that they will be expected to solve. Ecology is concerned with what kills rats, or grows deer and trees, and tells us why some lakes turn green before they die. But can ecology also cure wars, clean up the atmosphere, and banish ghettos?

Ecologists know that in most of the world, especially in the tropics and the southern hemisphere, environmental biology has not yet passed the stage of inventory and survey, and is far from ready to grapple with the galloping degradation of the human habitat. As limnologists and oceanographers, they have greatly improved their ability to navigate and observe and analyze and even to comprehend aquatic systems, but as to "farming the waters" to "feed the world's billions"—well, all the well-publicized manganese nodules in the deep ocean cannot make up for the lost opportunity to domesticate the blue whale. What we find really new in ecology, in the past ten years, is the possibility of coping with large terrestrial systems, on the scale of a forest, a drainage basin, or a desert, using the input-output approach that has been so successful in understanding lakes, estuaries, and coral reefs. And this possibility exists mainly because of a cluster of five new technologies—tracer geochemistry, remote sensing, automatic monitoring, computer simulation, and mass production of chemical analyses—all of which, of course, were developed in other sciences.

These sober reflections lead us to temper our public statements about the benefits of ecology, but they do not diminish the enthusiasm with which ecologists embrace their frustrating, fascinating, increasingly expensive, and increasingly rewarding jobs. In what follows we give a few examples, from a broad spectrum of recent research, of the specific tasks and findings of *environmental biology,* the kind of ecology we know best.

Areas of Research in Ecology

Environmental Challenges to Individuals

Physiological Ecology. Physiological ecology blends the laboratory orientation of the physiologist with the field viewpoint of the ecologist. For the physiologist, the "individual organism" is literally a single animal or plant body. For the ecologist, the individual is usually the *species,* one of dozens that are more or less similar and of millions that are different, and the compelling question is, "How does this species function *in its natural environment?*" Thus the ecologist, though equally concerned with the aberrant individual and the exceptionally severe environment, is less interested in a physiological mechanism for its own sake than as an example of diversity—as one of the endless series of small changes that nature has rung on broadly familiar themes. With this attitude, the physiological ecologist is especially ready to study diversity where he finds it, i.e., in nature, before he creates it, perhaps prematurely or unrealistically, in the laboratory. He is also both more aware of the differences between animals and plants, or between invertebrates and vertebrates, and less committed professionally to one group or another, than is the classical physiologist.

Because animals have nervous systems, and generally move about, their behavior is inseparable from their physiology. As one result, modern ethology, which has strongly influenced modern psychology and psychiatry, has arisen as a direct extension of physiological animal ecology. (Its founders, of course, rejected both the physiology and the ecology of their day, but that is one of history's ironies.) Plants, however, are no less interesting in their vegetable immobility. Not only do they perform several unique reactions—photosynthesis, plus several varieties of organic decomposition—without which animal life would be impossible; many woody plants also record their own histories of growth in a variable environment. Unlike many experimental biologists, who can take evolutionary history for granted and treat recent history as irrelevant, the plant ecologist can never forget the explicitly historical nature of his data.

Navigation and Homing. No one who has seen a forty-pound salmon fling itself into the air again and again in a vain effort to surmount a waterfall can fail to marvel at the strength of the instinct that draws the salmon upriver to the stream where it was born. How do salmon remember their birthplace, and how do they find their way back, sometimes from thousands of miles away? These questions have economic and political interest, because dams athwart their routes have cut heavily into salmon reproduction, and the diminished numbers have affected the fisheries of many nations.

Cooperative studies by Japanese, Canadian, and American scientists have shown that salmon are incredibly intermingled, during their sea phase, over thousands of miles of the northern Pacific, only to sort themselves out as spawning time approaches and to head for their streams of origin, be it in Asia or North America. To understand such far-ranging fishes, it is not enough to know the physical and chemical characteristics of the stream and oceanic habitats. We must know well the conditions beyond the horizon, where the fishes have spent their adult lives, their reactions to those far reaches and to the intervening ocean—and perhaps to the celestial bodies they may use in navigation. Finally, we need to acquaint ourselves fully with the sensory abilities and mechanisms that permit the fish to perceive the environmental conditions and to react appropriately.

Salmon literally "smell (or taste) their way home." Each home stream, from the plant and mineral oils of its drainage basin and of its bed, acquires a unique organic quality which young salmon learn in the early weeks of life, and recognition of which remains imprinted throughout their adult lives. That a unique stream factor exists and that fish can be conditioned to respond to that factor have been fully verified in the laboratory. The chemical nature of the odors, however, has not been identified.

The details of the salmon's journey through the changing salt concentrations and variable currents of the estuarine waters, to reach the mouth of the home river system, are still vague, but we can expect to learn more through ultrasonic tracking. Having successfully entered the main river, the salmon selects the tributary that carries the home odor and continues the upstream journey. We presume the odor track is picked up only intermittently, and that the fish does not stay within an odor cloud, for its olfactory sense should soon be fatigued. Constant exploratory testing, rejection of an inappropriate action, and correction of an off-target course are, of course, characteristic of all cybernetic systems, including proximity fuses, but the details of the salmon's information-processing system are still obscure, apart from the fact of location within the central nervous system.

The energy requirement of this extraordinary journey has recently been studied in sockeye salmon, using laboratory and field techniques that have long been familiar in the study of migrating birds and butterflies. Caloric expenditures, of course, vary with the velocity and temperature of the river, so neither the basal nor the cruising metabolism are particularly informative. Salmon observed during their migration swam 600 miles up the Fraser River in British Columbia, taking almost three weeks for the traverse. By the time the female salmon, which do not feed during migration, had reached the spawning grounds, they had expended 96 percent of their body fat and over 50 percent of their protein. Comparison of field data with measurements in an artificial stream revealed that energy was expended by the average migrant at 80 percent of the maximum possible rate, leaving very little reserve for emergencies. This narrow margin of safety provides a clue as to why only one more small dam on a river may cause a salmon run to collapse.

We chose the salmon to illustrate navigation and homing, rather than birds or bees, because men (like birds but unlike most mammals) inhabit a visual world, and usually forget that most animals do not. The salmon's exquisite ability to discriminate odors is not unique, and its world of waterborne odors is probably not particularly rich. Insects live in and respond to an odorous atmosphere that is probably far richer than any stream or lake, and many of them produce their own odors (pheromones) for a wide variety of purposes. As sensory environments for fish and for insects, however, both water and air are equally vulnerable to odorous pollution.* The study of pheromones and other ecologically relevant odors is in its infancy. The gas chromatograph is a powerful tool, newly available, but an older technique—classical conditioning, by which the animal is taught to teach the investigator what it can discriminate—will continue to tell the gas chromatograph what to look for.

Desert Animals. When aquatic vertebrates came on land, some 400 million years ago, they gained access to a richer supply of oxygen and a greater variety of foods (including, eventually, each other). But as part of the price they paid, water became a scarce resource. Devices for conserving body water are nowhere better shown than in hot deserts, where excessive demands for evaporative cooling may seriously over-strain the scanty supply. Many small rodents simply avoid the harshest aspects of the desert by remaining in their thermostatic, humid burrows during the day, emerging to feed and explore only at night. Most desert mammals have exceptionally effective kidneys, which produce a highly concentrated urine, thereby conserving water. Not surprisingly, the native marsupials of the Australian desert are far better adapted than the sheep preferred by Australians, and their biochemical devices for conserving water are more varied, more bizarre, and potentially more profitable to man, than those of cacti and other succulent plants.

Though hot in the daytime, deserts can be cold at night. Many rodents and several birds respond by turning down their thermostats and abandoning the homeothermic state. By permitting body temperature to approach the environmental temperature, the temporarily torpid animals considerably reduce their energy and water requirements. This abandonment of an otherwise precious device, homeothermy, may be in response

---

* We cite here one of Samuel Taylor Coleridge's more apposite poems:

COLOGNE

In Köln, a town of monks and bones,
And pavements fanged with murderous stones
And rags, and hags, and hideous wenches,
I counted two-and-seventy stenches,
All well defined, and separate stinks!
Ye nymphs that reign o'er sewers and sinks,
The river Rhine, it is well known,
Doth wash your city of Cologne:
But tell me, nymphs, what power divine
Shall henceforth wash the river Rhine?

to seasonal heat and aridity (aestivation), to seasonal low temperatures (hibernation), or to short periods when food is in low supply (daily torpor, as in hummingbirds and pocketmice). As rainfall in the desert is erratic, and production of seeds and insects is related to rainfall, the energy and water saved by reducing body temperatures allow these animals to maintain themselves for prolonged periods of scarcity. Even when active, many desert animals drink no water, but obtain their entire supply from seeds and other dry vegetation.

Large birds and mammals cannot avoid the impact of desert conditions by utilizing microclimates or by hibernation, but face the harsh thermal environment by widening their tolerance to dehydration and to high body temperatures. Camels and ostriches exemplify both adaptations. Furthermore, these large animals are highly mobile and can seek out surface water when their limits of dehydration are approached.

Lizards are abundant and conspicuous members of most desert communities. Although the body temperatures of resting lizards tend to reflect the environmental temperature, the active animals maintain a remarkably constant range of temperature by behavioral adjustments. They move into and out of sun and shade, they change their posture and orientation to the sun, and, internally, they make adjustments in the circulation of blood to the skin. When it is necessary to cross hot rock or sand, they do so with extreme rapidity, many of them on tiptoe. A lizard's eggs, of course, are particularly susceptible to water loss, and many desert species are ovoviviparous, retaining the eggs in the oviduct until they hatch. A few, mainly in Australia, have foreshadowed another precious mammalian patent—true viviparity, with exchange of fluid between mother and fetus across a placenta—though solid food is apparently still provided by the reptilian yolk sac.

Though remarkable in their number and perfection, physiological adaptations for desert life are not really unique; they are extensions of devices common to other terrestrial vertebrates. A viviparous lizard is still a reptile, and a hibernating rodent is still a mammal. Much the same lesson—that adaptations are cumulative, but rarely dramatic in themselves—is taught by physiological studies in other extreme environments, such as high altitudes or high latitudes. Deep diving, as by whales and porpoises, provides other examples. All the remarkable things that whales do while diving—collapsing their lungs, shunting blood away from muscles, accumulating lactic acid in the blood, acquiring and later paying off a huge oxygen debt, and so on—have parallels in seals or even in human sprinters. But the whales do more of these things, and do them better or longer or with less damage, and the perfection of the end result is far more impressive than any of the contributory processes.

Trees and Water. The growth and survival of plants is critically dependent on the supply of moisture to their roots. When soil moisture is abundantly available, growth is limited chiefly by the fertility of the soil and the solar energy that provides the heat and light necessary for photosynthesis. However, when midday temperatures and radiation exceed a critical level that varies with the nature of the plant, the plant's conducting system can no longer transfer water from the soil fast enough to replace evaporation from the leaves, and water tensions are set up within the plants. Suction forces equal to minus 16 atmospheres have been measured in the tops of redwood trees under normal moisture conditions. When internal water stress becomes too great, stomata close, slowing water loss but also shutting off carbon dioxide uptake and release of oxygen. This stops production of organic matter. Thus plant communities are closely dependent on the balances of heat and water in the area they occupy.

In eastern North America, and even more in drier areas, variations in tree growth are large from year to year, depending primarily on the water supply available during the growing season. More precisely, daily water deficits within the tree override other processes that regulate growth, and thus largely determine how much new wood can be formed and when during the growing season it is laid down. Not only the amount but the quality of the wood produced is related to the plant's internal water supply. Abundant water late in the growing season has been associated with increased width of the latewood band—the dense portion of the annual ring—in several species of pine.

Methods are not yet available for large-scale monitoring of internal water relations of trees, though diurnal changes in trunk diameter can be measured by sensitive instruments, and the problem is of the order of the detection of microseisms on wave-pounded shores. In a more indirect attack, however, additions and depletions of soil water, implying variations in internal water stress, have been detected and monitored by micrometeorological methods. Much has been learned about the production of growth-regulating substances and the formation of wood cells under different degrees of water stress. Such data have been synthesized in a computer program that mimics the cell-by-cell development of a tree's annual ring. New developments in color photography and in airborne scanners sensitive to infrared radiation have made it possible to detect incipient water stress—and many other features of importance in hydrology and forestry—from the air.

Increased understanding of the role of climatic conditions in altering tree-ring development leads to better understanding of past climates. Records as long as six thousand years, long preceding any instrumental data, are currently under study in bristlecone pine. Where water stress is a dominant climatic feature, shorter-lived but more widespread and less demanding trees such as ponderosa pine give highly probable reconstructions of former weather and climate. Such information, coupled with detailed fossil analyses and with close study of present-day climatically controlled boundaries of distribution, should make it possible to predict the more important biological effects of weather modification.

The Abundances of Living Things

The numbers of animals and plants, for the ecologist, are meaningful only when expressed in relation to some other parameter. "Numbers/ resources" is ideal, but hard to quantify if the resources are not also numerical. "Numbers/area," or *density*, is the ratio the ecologist usually has in mind, which is why "numbers," "density," and "population size" are commonly used as if they were interchangeable. Density, of course, is the most elementary statistic of quantitative ecology; if the ecologist is unable to measure it accurately, as he often is in the field, he is obliged to estimate or even to assume it, before he can think further. What invariably strikes him, as soon as he has a density in mind, is the extraordinary constancy of *average* densities. Insects and other pests do have outbreaks, and weeds do invade open fields, and there are short- and long-term trends over time, notably including *ecological succession*. Nevertheless, in the temperate zone, where winter is very different from summer, no observer can fail to be impressed by the year-to-year constancy of innumerable species, insects and weeds not excepted. What this comes to, if one takes a population of beetles, for instance, is that the product of the probability of death and the probability of birth, summed for beetles of all ages over a generation, comes out at an average value of 1.0, a theorem owed to the actuaries Dublin and Lotka. The more one thinks about those probabilities, and the many uncertainties that affect them (especially the changing age structure of the population, and the different ways that larvae and adult beetles can die), the more astonished one is. Something regulates densities within remarkably narrow limits. For many ecologists, that "something" is the central problem of environmental biology.

A priori, one can say that there are two main kinds of regulation, internal and external. Completely external controls, such as bad weather, pesticides, or natural catastrophes, will reduce all densities alike, whether they were rising or falling before the catastrophe; though often very important because very useful, such external controls may not be very interesting or exciting, intellectually. Predators and food supplies, however, are external controls that may or may not be independent of the density of the population controlled; and if they are not independent – if predator and prey populations interact in coupled oscillation, for example – then the control is internal to the interacting system, if not to the prey alone. Most interesting of all are the many clear cases (nearly all confined to the laboratory) where a population regulates its own numbers, showing either a long-sustained steady density or a rhythmic series of oscillations over time. Presumably in all such cases, regulation is by some feedback device: overcrowding, however perceived, depresses the birth rate or increases the death rate, or both, and so accomplishes its own corrective. But what is fed back to what, and how it is perceived, are questions requiring painstaking research, for regulatory devices are at least as numerous as are species. Under restrictive mathematical assumptions, or simplified experimental conditions, it is easy to simulate self-regulation, but the degree to which it applies in a given patch of wild nature is ordinarily open to doubt.

External Controls. In the grasslands of the Great Plains, four species of grass are prominent: big and little bluestem, characteristic of wetter areas, and blue grama and buffalo grass, in drier areas. The former tend to occur on the eastern plains and on low ground, while the latter are more abundant on the western plains and on high ground. During the severe drought of the 1930's, blue grama and buffalo grass expanded, moving down from high to low areas, and spreading eastward as much as 150 miles. In the several years of high rainfall that followed, the trend reversed: big and little bluestem moved upward, and also westward. Smaller changes in the same directions have followed the smaller variations in rainfall during the past twenty years. The case for external (climatic) control seems clear, but the reason for the linkage of the species is less certain. Do big and little bluestem respond independently to soil moisture, or does one follow the other for some other reason?

Daphnia, a freshwater crustacean, can maintain very dense populations on a constant food supply: the populations oscillate remarkably, but after a few generations they approach a constant level that is directly proportional to the supply of algal food. If even a modest rate of removal ("fishing") is applied, the density falls sharply, but not linearly; higher fishing rates have proportionately less effect. Even with removal rates as high as 30 percent per day, a small but vigorous population persists. The effect of fishing mainly for the young is quite different from that of fishing for adults only. The species has numerous mechanisms for adaptation to different levels of predation or food supply and, not surprisingly, exists in nature in a wide variety of conditions. To an unusual degree it displays that wonderful resilience that man exploits: if we rarefy a population, we increase its rate of growth, and a certain degree of rarefaction actually increases the steady yield of animals harvested. Resilience is a benefit that works both ways, of course; pest controllers are less enchanted to find that the more rats they kill, the more there are.

Predation alone can be sufficient to exclude an organism from an otherwise suitable environment. For many years a native silkmoth has been raised on wild cherry trees, each tree inclosed in a protective net. Survival from egg to adult can be as high as 80 percent under these conditions. Each year, some trees are left unprotected, and on these not one silkworm has yet survived through the larval stage. The moth exists at very low density in nearby woods, but among cherry trees in open fields it cannot survive.

Internal Controls. Outside the laboratory, the best-attested cases come from birds and mammals, where the ages and identities of the adults, and especially the number and survival of the young, can sometimes be kept under observation. With the alpine swift in Switzerland, for example, the size of successful clutches is fixed at two and three quarters, which seems an odd number of eggs for any bird to lay. But it turns out that in a population made up (genetically?) of twice as many three-egg layers as two-egg layers, broods of three are about twice as likely to starve to death in the nest; and in four-egg nests the advantage gained by an extra egg is overbalanced by the extra work needed to feed four nestlings, and the chances are two in five that the whole brood will be lost. If this seems a pretty subtle way for nature to achieve constancy, consider the fact that many songbirds lay more eggs in the northern part of their ranges; the European robin adds about a tenth (0.07) of an egg for each degree of latitude. More young can be fed in summer where the days are longer, as David Lack points out, but as robins maintain their numbers fairly constant over thirty-five degrees of latitude, it seems that more eggs is only half the story; more young must *have* to be fed each summer because fewer adults survive the winter where the nights are longer.

Snail Controls. In recent experiments on pond snails, groups of adults were maintained outdoors so that some pens had densities several times higher than the controls, others much lower. Food, as living and dead vegetation, seemed abundant in all pens, and showed only slight grazing. Adults survived equally well at all densities, showing no regulation by differential mortality. In reproduction, however, regulation was immediate and complete: all pens produced the same number of eggs, no matter how many adults were present. The inference that food *quality* (not just caloric quantity) was limiting is supported by the effect of adding dried spinach (a very nutritious food for snails) to other pens. In these, reproduction was increased twentyfold. Later a second regulatory mechanism was suggested: these high populations of very young snails suffered a greater loss through predation than was found in other pens.

The population biology of snails is not just an academic matter. Freshwater snails are intermediate hosts for schistosomes, or blood flukes, a serious human parasite. In Egypt the host snails inhabit the intricate systems of irrigation canals, and are very difficult to eradicate. Year-round eradication is expensive. A first choice for a single season of intense poisoning was summer, when large snails were most abundant and the rate of transfer of the parasite from snails to humans was maximal. Close study showed, however, that the true population maximum occurred in spring, when the snails were very small, and that this was the time of greatest transfer of the parasite from humans to snails. Eradication in late spring was found to be more effective than in the summer, even though the immediate effect of eradication (visible dead snails) was much less apparent at that time.

Red Tides and Phytoplankton. Red tides are sporadic algal blooms — population explosions of a single species, usually a dinoflagellate, that is normally too scarce to be noticed but is highly toxic to fish when present in high density. The favorable circumstances are rarely predictable, but seem often to begin with the formation of a pool or lens of nutrient-rich brackish water in an estuary, temporarily prevented from tidal flushing while the stream-borne nutrients, and the population, build up. When eventually flushed to sea, the toxic water-mass may maintain its integrity for several days before being dissipated. Such a phenomenon can be understood only in the larger context of the regular succession of phytoplankton in lakes and oceans. Research in this field is unusually exacting, because the nutrients for which planktonic algae compete — dissolved N, P, Fe, Si, and little-known organic compounds — occur and are used in amounts called "traces" or "impurities" by other chemists, and a few micrograms of some nutrient per cubic meter of water can make the difference between bloom and no bloom, between environmental health and disaster.

The Sargasso Sea, an oceanic near-desert, is instructive in its extreme depletion of nutrients. N and P vary little throughout the year, and Fe not at all; as there is a definite bloom of diatoms every spring, while the alga *Coccolithus huxleyi* is present the year around as a steady but sparse population, substances other than minerals were suspected to govern the seasonal succession. When the main species of spring diatoms and *C. huxleyi* were cultured bacteria-free, and their nutrition studied, it became clear that all the diatoms needed vitamin B_{12} (cobalamine), while *C. huxleyi* required only thiamine. To find out, in the field, whether cobalt or cobalamine varied seasonally, increasing in the winter and disappearing at the height of the diatom bloom, an exceptionally sensitive analytical method was required. One of the cobalamine-requiring Sargasso diatoms, *Cyclotella nana,* provided a suitable bioassay method, and the predicted seasonal cycle of cobalamine was established. Finally, enrichment experiments were undertaken, using Sargasso water taken at the end of the diatom bloom. No diatom growth occurred without the addition of iron, but sustained growth was obtained only when nitrogen, phosphorus, and iron were all added. *C. huxleyi,* however, can be grown for several transfers without added iron.

In richer waters, with many more species of algae normally present at some time of year, it is unlikely that full understanding of phytoplankton ecology will be obtained by culturing species singly, or by studying nutrients one at a time. Interactions among species, both stimulatory and inhibitory, are certain to affect nutrition and growth, so that single-species experiments may sometimes be misleading. The number of two-species combinations needed for n species, of course, is $n(n-1)/2$, which means that the amount of work rapidly becomes formidable. Fortunately, this is the kind of problem in which computer simulation can accelerate research.

Interactions Among Species

A very large share of the genetic information possessed by most wild species is devoted to accommodating to the presence of other species. Such genetic information, not easily revealed by studies of bristles or chromosome numbers, influences food palatability, defenses against diseases and predation, patterns of courtship and mating, appropriate body size, length of life, and reproductive potential. The number of possible interspecific interactions among a few million species is very large; systematic study of a few of them seems certain to reveal profitable ways of utilizing more of the earth's biota for man's benefit. Biological control of pests, and new drugs, repellants, and other products are among the simpler and more obvious potential applications. It is this largely untapped and unknown potential, and not sentimentalism or misanthropy, that makes ecologists avid protectors of threatened species and of dwindling habitats harboring unique combinations of species. It would be tragic if potentially easy and imaginative solutions to future major problems are lost through ignorance and indifference.

Competition and Predation. The direct observation of mortality due to competition between species has been documented in a careful study of barnacles. Of two species that often occur on the same shore, one is excluded from the higher part of the intertidal zone because it cannot

Figure 11-3. Alewives on a Chicago beach. (*Chicago Tribune* photograph)

survive so much sun, exposure, and rainwater. The other species, more tolerant of such conditions, is excluded from the lower zone through competition, being either overgrown or undercut by the lower species. When this second species is removed, the barnacle typical of the upper zone lives very well in the lower zone.

Indirect evidence of competition is found in the ways that closely related species, living together, adopt differing ways of life. A study was made of five species of warblers nesting in the same spruce forest, and very much alike in their habits. A quantitative study showed their ecologies to be surprisingly diverse. Although they all feed on the insects in the spruce trees, each species has a unique combination of behavior patterns, based on the proportion of time they spend hovering, whether they tend to feed on peripheral or central parts of the trees, how frequently they fly from one place to another, etc. Thus, they tend to be exposed to different items of food.

In the northern states the periodical cicada takes seventeen years to mature, while in the southern states it matures in thirteen years. Different broods exist in different areas, but in any one area all of the cicadas are synchronized. Thus, there are about thirty different broods of these insects in thirty different regions of the country. What is most remarkable is that nearly every one of these broods is a mixture of three distinct species, synchronized to emerge from the soil together. Other kinds of cicadas, with life cycles ranging from three to seven years, have some individuals appearing every year, as in most organisms. Why only one brood of the periodical cicadas exists in one place, and how three such species remain invariably synchronized, are problems whose solution may tell us much about mechanisms of population regulation. That competition occurs underground seems certain. But it is also likely that each of the three species "parasitizes" the ability of the other two to oversaturate the countryside with cicadas, confuse all the predators (few of whom will ever have seen a periodical cicada), and get the population back underground before the birds "catch on." If birds are the principal predators, as they seem to be, it is interesting to note that thirteen is the smallest prime number that exceeds the maximum natural life-span of any known songbird. Prime numbers must be important because they have no factors; twelve years, for instance, would allow three-or-four-year periodicities in adjacent regions, which would spoil the whole system.

In the laboratory, one of the most informative studies of predation uses praying mantises as predators and flies as prey. The process is a consequence of four major phases: searching, pursuing, eating, and digesting. Each of these is composed of a number of analyzable elements, affected differently by environmental conditions. Equations were constructed for each phase of the process. The availability of high-speed computers allows the resulting mathematical model to be compared with actual events. This study, and several others that are similar, promise to bring a new level of precision and realism to models of species interactions.

Grazing. The Klamath weed was accidentally introduced into the western United States about 1900 where it became a serious problem in livestock ranges of northern California. Not only does the plant replace valuable forage, it is poisonous, producing death or, in milder doses, a phototoxicity in light-skinned animals. In its native Europe a beetle was found that fed upon the plant. In 1947 the beetle was introduced into the affected areas, and within a few years mass destruction of the Klamath weed populations resulted over most of the affected area. Feeding on the foliage by larva and adult was so heavy the plant exhausted its food reserves and died. Along highways and under the shade of trees the beetle populations are ineffective in controlling the plant. As a result the beetle and the Klamath weed populations seem to have struck an equilibrium with very low weed infestation. The response of the range vegetation to the loss of the weeds is pronounced, with other species, mostly grasses, increasing.

Native plants also have their numbers and microdistributions determined in part by native insects. The cowwheat is a small green annual plant, the roots of which attach to roots of woody plants such as pines and oaks. In a jack pine forest cowwheat increased its numbers and became more evenly distributed when pesticides were applied to the forest floor for three years. Insects, primarily the brown-backed katydid, keep the plant's seed production down by feeding on branches and seeds, while a carabid beetle collects many of the dispersed seeds into dense patches. Drastic reductions in these insect populations were reflected in higher plant numbers and less clumping of the individuals.

Seedlings of the saguaro cactus in the Saguaro National Monument, Arizona, have been shown to require shade of other plants while they grow to a point where their water storage volume is large enough to withstand water losses from their leafless surfaces. Also, the nurse plants, which are spiny, protect young seedlings from predators such as rodents. Thus, environmental conditions such as grazing, and climatic changes that tend to reduce the number of nurse plants, also reduce the number of saguaros. The main reason why this national monument was set aside by Congress was to preserve and display unique species. For preservation to be effective, the area must include enough diversity of environment to provide refuge during normal climatic fluctuations, and enough protection from abnormal stresses such as grazing to enable the species to perpetuate itself.

Norman Rabbits. The European wild rabbit was introduced into Britain from France by Normans, probably between the time of the Domesday Book in 1086 and the beginning of the twelfth century. With it came a flea which, in turn, is the only known host in Britain for the myxoma virus and the disease myxomatosis. The myxoma virus is found in the native rabbit of South America, but is not pathogenic to this species; in European rabbits, however, it produces a rapidly debilitating and fatal disease. Following enormously successful introduction of the disease in Australian rabbits (which also are European), it was released in France in 1952, reached Kent, England, in 1953, and spread rapidly through Britain in the next two years. By 1955, rabbits were practically extinct over most of Britain.

Before the myxomatosis pandemic, ecologists were only vaguely aware of the importance of the rabbit in the web of ecological relationships, but the removal of rabbits has had a tremendous impact on terrestrial ecosystems throughout western Europe and Britain. In Norfolk, where the rabbits began dying in 1954 and appeared to be extinct by 1959, plant species that had previously been restricted in their distribution, under the influence of grazing by rabbits, flourished and spread. Areas that had previously supported a covering of low mosses and turf became covered with deep mats of grass and stands of heather. The open-ground habitats of low mosses and flowering plants that were so typical of many terrestrial communities disappeared with the rabbits. These dramatic changes in the species composition and structure of vegetation had profound effects on the animals, especially insects, associated with them, while predators depending on the rabbit for food were also affected in numbers and feeding behavior. Thus the removal of one link in the web has been felt throughout the whole ecosystem, and the compensatory reaction of the remaining members of the system has produced a "new" set of relationships.

Recent discoveries have shown that the key interaction in this dramatic sequence of events is sharply focused in space and time. In order for the ovaries of the female flea to mature and produce eggs, she must obtain a blood meal from a pregnant doe rabbit or a nestling rabbit less than a week old. When the flea larvae emerge from the eggs, they then develop in the breeding nest of the rabbit. Thus, events during a critical period in the underground breeding nest of the rabbit are the hub of the myxomatosis epidemic and its colossal impact on the whole ecosystem.

Symbiosis. Not all interactions between species are negative. Mutually beneficial interactions are called *mutualism* or *symbiosis.* Many examples are known. Among the more interesting are producer-consumer systems based upon the cooperation of a plant and an animal. Algae known as *zooxanthellae* live within the cells or tissues of many aquatic animals, including hydras, corals, flatworms, and the giant clam, *Tridacna.* Although all of these animals must feed to survive, they show efficiencies of production per unit of food eaten that may be double those of relatives lacking the zooxanthellae or of the same organisms when kept in the dark. The algae appear able to capture and use a portion of the metabolites of the animal host. In addition, they take up enough respiratory carbon dioxide to produce, through photosynthesis, an excess supply of carbohydrate that is shared with the host. This partial recycling of carbon within the animal results in less of the food eaten being used for respiration, and more for growth and survival.

Flow of Matter and Energy in Ecosystems

Ecology became a quantitative science when ecologists began to count organisms, but it entered its modern phase only when they also began to weigh. Because the chemical composition of organic matter (the proportion of carbohydrate, protein, fat, and ash) specifies amounts of fixed chemical energy, the flow of carbon and of chemical energy through living systems are nearly interchangeable concepts. Some dramatic discoveries followed almost as soon as living systems were thought of as engines for capture and conversion of solar energy. The pyramid of numbers (big animals rarer than little animals) was seen as a special case of a pyramid of productivities, with green plants (photosynthetic or primary producers) always more productive than herbivores, which are always more productive than carnivores, and it was then obvious that managing a lake for game fish is very much like farming Africa for lions. Moreover, as engines, living systems have measurable efficiencies, and when comparing systems on this basis, ecologists quickly learned to look beyond the standing crop, or biomass, and focus on its rate of production.

As a result, phytoplankton crops command enormous respect, even in comparison with the best forests. (Agricultural crops, in general, are relatively unproductive.) Some oceanic areas, notably regions of upwelling off the west coasts of continents, where nutrients are constantly renewed from deeper water, can produce as much as 1.5 to 2.0 grams of carbon per square meter per day as phytoplankton: in Peru and Southwest Africa these areas stand in the sharpest imaginable contrast to the nearly plantless deserts on shore. Nevertheless, though worldwide data are much too scanty, recent estimates show the terrestrial quarter of the globe to be about two to four times as productive of fixed carbon, area for area, as the oceanic three quarters. One reason, presumably, is that planktonic algae, the green plants of the sea, are very small; their ability to capture dissolved nutrients is thereby enhanced, but their small size entails a proportionately large loss in respiration. Primary producers dispersed over a more or less deep column of water also can make use only of that relatively small fraction of sunlight which is not absorbed by the aquatic medium. If the algae themselves can catch most of the radiation falling on the water surface, as is the case in algae cultures or fertilized ponds, their conversion of solar energy into chemically bound energy works with an efficiency of 10–20 percent, whereas the average efficiency of a cornfield in Iowa is only about 2 percent.

The energetic-efficiency approach to ecosystems has taught ecologists a great deal, but its early methods were those of the bludgeon rather than the scalpel: though much is gained, much precious information is sacrificed when "all herbivores" are lumped as one "crop," dried, burned, and weighed. Recent work takes more careful account of the internal diversity of ecosystems. In a detailed study of the energy transfer in the open water of Lake Erken, Sweden, it turned out that organic carbon fixed by algae was by no means sufficient to support the herbivorous zooplankton (water fleas). Although some minute zooplankters filter up to 10 ml of water each day to get their ration, they could not fill their guts if they did not include in their diet plant and animal debris as well as bacteria engaged in the destruction of this dead material. Thus the "herbivores" were shown to be not only grazers of fresh vegetation but mainly browsers on plant debris (representing dead organic carbon fixed outside the pelagic community and perhaps several years ago) and feeding, in part, like vultures on the decomposing carcasses of other herbivores. This result of quantitative ecology indicates that the familiar concept of a lake community as a trophic pyramid is oversimplified. To the extent that herbivores are "primary producers" for each other, a short-circuit modifies the classical concept of relationships in a lake. A similar generalization—that browsers as a class are more productive than grazers—is emerging in terrestrial and marine ecology as well.

Carbon is not the only substance of interest that moves through living systems. Beginning about 1950, much attention was drawn to the tendency of animal food chains to concentrate some pollutants (such as DDT) in their end members, while discriminating against others (such as strontium-90) at one or more steps. The uses of radioactive isotopes as tracers of the metabolism of whole ecosystems has increased enormously; sometimes the tracers are introduced deliberately, as in biochemistry, but more often they are released inadvertently, and ecologists make the best of a bad bargain. Probably it is the application of tracers, more than any other new technology, that opens the possibility of comprehending large terrestrial ecosystems; until recently, lakes, being much more nearly closed systems than forests are, provided all the best models of input-output dynamics.

A Model Lake. Carbon isotopes provide two sorts of labels. Carbon-14, radiocarbon, is familiar as a biochemical tracer, much used by ecologists (though with awareness of its limitations) to measure photosynthetic fixation by phytoplankton. It is also a natural product of cosmic rays, dispersed in trace amounts through all living things, and measuring the time since their death and fossilization. Carbon-13, nonradioactive, can be thought of as a geochemical tracer, as it is relatively abundant in carbonate rocks, the ocean, and the air, but scarce, relative to ordinary carbon-12, in organic matter, living and dead. In a lake, the sources of carbon are mixed: modern (carbon-14-rich, carbon-13-rich) carbon comes from the streams as bicarbonate and, more slowly, as atmospheric carbon dioxide; old (carbon-14-deficient, carbon-13-rich) carbon enters as ground water, percolated through ancient carbonate rock. In 1960, when a typical small lake was studied, using these relations, there was an additional label: "super-modern" carbon (artificially enriched in carbon-14, from nuclear weapons) was entering from the air as carbon dioxide.

The balance sheet worked out as follows: 25 milligrams of carbon per square centimeter of lake entered in a year from the inlets: 1 milligram came from the air; 2 milligrams came from ground water; 13 milligrams were fixed by plankton, but most of this reappeared in the water, except for the 3 milligrams (net) that were fossilized and buried as mud; the loss to sediments balanced the gain from air and ground water, the planktonic production was an internal, balanced cycle, and 25 milligrams left the lake by the outlet, apparently unchanged. As one unexpected dividend of the work, modern lake mud proved to be up to 3,000 years "old" on the carbon-14 scale (owing to use of ground-water carbon by organisms), and lake mud is therefore not suitable for radiocarbon dating in historical studies.

Marine Snow. Organic aggregates—the flaky or ropy "marine snow" seen from bathyscaphes, even in the deep ocean—have become an exciting, and controversial, subject in biological oceanography. In the ocean, as in lakes, the store of dissolved organic matter is several to many times more abundant (depending in part on the definition of "dissolved") than particulate organic matter, which is living and dead plankton. Its role in the economy of sea is now suspected to be more than that of an inert sort of humus, on the way to becoming bottom ooze. It can be attacked by some microorganisms, but not by many; the exciting possibility is that it may be aggregated into particles large enough, and nutritious enough, to be eaten by zooplankton. It is known that bubbles of air will aggregate dissolved organic matter, and that some laboratory animals can survive on a diet of synthetic aggregates, but proof is still lacking that this is the mode of formation of marine snow and that oceanic animals use it as food. It is true, according to the textbooks, that there are no herbivores in the deep ocean, above the bottom, that could be eating aggregates. But such herbivores would be very small, and nets fine enough to catch them have almost never been used below 2,000 meters. Naturally, no algae were expected at such depths, and it was assumed that all swimming deep-sea animals must be carnivores, eating other animals that depend ultimately on plants produced in the lighted upper waters. Whether or not that is so, the abyssal regions are populated by a far more diverse assembly of bottom-dwellers than was previously suspected, and organic aggregates may help to explain why.

Guano Islands. A fairly simple example of the problems inherent in managing an ecosystem is furnished by several small islands off the west coast of South America. The potentiality of the vast quantities of guano covering these islands as a source of agricultural fertilizer was first noted in 1804 by Alexander von Humboldt.

The relatively cold Humboldt Current flows northward along this coast; as it swings away from shore, deeper water wells up to replace it at the surface. This upwelling constantly brings chemical nutrients needed for plant growth into the surface waters, where sunlight penetrates. The resulting luxuriant growth of algae supports a high production of small crustaceans. These are eaten by anchovies, which are also highly productive when supplied with abundant food. Cormorants feed on the anchovies and nest in enormous numbers on the islands, where they deposit their excrement, saved up so that it can be used as nesting material. The excrement, a nitrogen-rich phosphate rock, is guano, which has long been one of Peru's important natural resources. But Peru now harvests anchovies for the production of fishmeal, and the Japanese are fishing the same waters. This reduces the production of guano and has a bearing on the price of fertilizer around the world.

Hence, the permissible level of the annual anchovy catch, established by the Peruvian government, determines the amount of fishmeal available as a supplement to human dietaries, as an ingredient of chicken feed, and as fertilizer, while also establishing the availability of guano and the price of fertilizer. While such judgments are currently rendered in terms of the political and economic structure of Peru, they have profound nutritional consequences elsewhere on our planet. Furthermore, the Humboldt Current is not completely dependable, but in occasional years swings farther away from the coast; then the upwelling of nutrient-rich water ceases, and the production of both anchovies and guano fails.

Forests. On land, water and material balances need to be studied in whole drainage basins; smaller systems are usually not sufficiently self-contained to be fully informative. The water, energy, and nutrient budgets of small forested ecosystems are being studied by a team of scientists at Hubbard Brook, New Hampshire. Each of six instrumented drainage basins can be considered as a separate system, or all can be treated as a unit. By combining measurements of the chemical content of rain with measurements of runoff it is possible to estimate chemical input in precipitation; chemical output in drainage waters; net annual chemical losses from the ecosystem; rates of geological weathering; and the chemical effects of manipulating the vegetation. Removal of the tree cover from a drainage basin increases the flow of water from the area, because the smaller volume of soil exploited by plant roots and the changed reflective and aerodynamic properties of the surface diminish losses by evaporation and transpiration. The precise nature of these changes and their role in regulating water loss are still only poorly known.

Mineral elements incorporated in living vegetation return to the soil in litter, as exudates from roots, and as salts leached from leaves by rainfall. Plant roots in turn take up the liberated elements in the course of absorbing water. Many of the important elements circulate rapidly within the community. At the Oak Ridge National Laboratory in Tennessee, it has been found that about one third of a cesium isotope present in the trees in June was transferred to the forest floor and soil by autumn; the rest moved back into the stems and roots. Sampling at the end of the growing season indicated that about half of the cesium in the soil had originated from root exudation and decay, and the rest from litter fall and leaching by rain.

Ordinarily, mineral elements discharged to the soil are quickly picked up again by plants. However, when spraying of herbicides prevented all regrowth on one of the cutover drainage basins at Hubbard Brook, the outflow of nutrients increased three- to fifteen-fold. Cations, such as calcium, and anions, such as sulfate, were exported in different amounts and were differently affected by cutting. The proportion of airborne mineral matter that a forest receives by "dry fallout," rather than by washout during rain, was especially surprising. In other regions, where the bedrock is not granite or when the rainfall is distributed differently, one would expect still other chemical consequences of clearing. Clear-cutting of forests has been widely practiced in eastern United States and elsewhere. Studies such as the one at Hubbard Brook will add to our understanding of how this practice influences the water, energy, and nutrient budgets of extensive landscapes.

Stability and Diversity in Ecosystems

Natural communities as small as a patch of meadow have hundreds or thousands of species living together. The total number in a field, or in a wood or pond, is not known; every handful of soil is likely to contain species that have never been identified. Nevertheless, the main properties of the ecosystem, which is all the living and nonliving components that interact in a defined area, can be understood without knowing all its species, in the same way that an organism can be known without knowing all of its cells. Understandably, in so complex a system, some interactions are stronger than others; strong interactions are usually the obvious ones, long known to classical natural history. Ecologists nowadays spend most of their time evaluating weak interactions, many of which turn out to be not so weak, while the totality of a set of weak interactions is almost invariably both strong and nonobvious. The flow of matter and energy, as discussed in the previous section, are functional aspects of ecosystems. In this section we consider some organizational aspects—though if one says that a reef flat has more organization than a pine woods, it should be evident that *organization* is being used in an abstract sense, closely akin to *information content* or *order*.

Pattern of Organization. The diversity of species in an ecosystem is a function of both the number of species and the number of individuals of each species. A system of ten equally abundant species is more diverse than one with one very common species and nine rare species. Several indices have been devised to quantify diversity, some purely empirical, others founded on extremely interesting mathematical models. For many practical purposes, comparisons of diversity among ecosystems yield much the same result no matter which index is used. This sobering fact has not damped the explosion of research on the subject or diminished its excitement, but it is clear that our mathematical models are not yet adequate for the complexity of natural systems. The most ingenious and promising ones are too abstruse to be discussed in this nontechnical account of the subject.

A complete description of the pattern of a particular ecosystem must embrace three types of organization: (1) the pattern of the food web (the network through which energy flows, for example from an eaten individual to the eater), (2) the distribution and arrangement of different species in space and time, and (3) the grouping of individuals of several species into higher taxonomic units, which have varying functional roles. This last, which is also the main concern of systematic and evolutionary biology, is particularly important in ecology when one reflects that organization represents a moment in history. Evolutionary history is not irrelevant where different organisms interact; taxonomic distinctness is the product of such interaction over the whole span of the organisms' histories. The nature as well as the number of the individuals governs, among other ecological properties, the probability that populations will fluctuate with small or large amplitude through time. The following generalizations exemplify the three types of organization:

1. In general, the greater the number of species at any trophic (food-chain) level in a community, the greater the community stability at that level, and at lower and higher levels as well. Amplitudes of fluctuation of herbivore populations are determined by the number of species of plants they eat and by the number of species of predators and parasites that attack them.

2. The areal density of food plants determines the extent to which herbivore populations fluctuate, and the size of the herbivore population in turn determines population fluctuation among predators. Further, the extent to which plants of different ages and species are interspersed affects the stability of the animal populations.

3. When, in a given area, a genus or higher taxon is represented by a large number of species, all with about equal abundance, the information content (degree of organization) of the genus is high. When a genus has only one or a few species, and the commonest is much more abundant

than the rest, the information content is low. The information content of some genera of parasitic insects, so measured over a large area such as a state, has been found to be inversely proportional to the number of host species and to their average population stability.

Diversity and Succession. Ecological succession is the process by which one assemblage replaces another in time at the same site, producing a series of identifiable systems of increasing complexity, and ending with a self-replicating climax stage. The mechanisms are various, and have drawn attention for a hundred years. The significant aspects of succession and climax must be systematic changes in the flux and storage of matter and energy, but these are far from being understood. What is clear is that diversity tends to increase with maturity of the system. In one investigation, land abandoned by agriculture in 1952 was studied through 1963. The early stages were successively more diverse, producing after eight years a grass community dominated by broomsedges. During the ensuing four years the broomsedge community became more diverse, showing both an increase of plant species and an increase in the number of dominant species from eight to twenty-three. Production and diversity are not related in a simple manner, however. Production was high initially, decreased rapidly through the early stages, rose in the grass community to levels above that of the first year, and then declined slowly.

Diversity and Stability. Diversity and ecosystem stability are related, but the form of the relation is obscure and has given rise to controversy. Part of the difficulty may be that the relations differ as between animal and plant communities, and ecologists have attempted to generalize prematurely. If one thinks about a food web, for example, it is easy to see that a species' efficiency in feeding is in partial conflict with the demands of the total system. Food specialization will maximize efficiency for a given animal, but if all animals become perfect specialists, they all risk extinction during small environmental perturbations – the animal diversity may be maximal, but the stability of the system declines. For terrestrial plants, however, animal diversity may often be an unimportant epiphenomenon. With soil nutrients and air evenly dispersed over an area, competition is for space in the sunlight. And the greater the success of some species in becoming large and tall, thus obtaining more sunlight, the more different kinds of room there will be in the interstices for species like herbs and vines that are adapted to shade. So both plant diversity and the stability of the system may increase, almost without limit, as they seem to have done in tropical rainforests.

Computer simulation is a promising technique for understanding such matters, but computer models need both adequate formulation, or programming, and high-quality data, and so far their application to large

terrestrial ecosystems has had only modest success. Such systems being obviously the product of their histories, high-quality historical data
are particularly important. A very large body of historical information
exists in Europe and North America, covering environments of the last
ten thousand years or so, or since the continental ice sheets disappeared.
(The restriction is explained by the fact that basins of deposition—lakes
and bogs—are mainly found in recently glaciated terrain.) Minor changes
of upland vegetation are recorded in lavish detail by the sequence of
pollen assemblages in lake mud and peat. Before radiocarbon dating became available, this sequence, used as a chronology, was the principal
method of dating archaeological sites, sea level changes, volcanic eruptions, and many other events. Where pollen changes were synchronous
over wide areas, regional climatic change is inferred; and although the
role of human disturbance has probably been underestimated, there is no
doubt that early postglacial changes (9000 to 7000 B.C.) were dramatic
but orderly responses to climatic warming. From about 7000 B.C. on-
ward, however, what is most impressive about this record is not the
changes, but the stability: somewhat to the surprise of older plant ecologists, *climaxes* seem to have endured for millennia, not just for centuries.
Unfortunately, the entire record is nonquantitative, in the sense that proportions of fossil pollen in mud have no definable relation to plant population density in any particular area. As radiocarbon dating (which also
calibrates the pollen chronology) brings sedimentation rates under control, this difficulty is gradually being overcome, and the potentialities
of a quantitative historical ecology can then be realized.

Diversity and Disturbance. Though stability may be hard to measure
satisfactorily, it is often easy to sense, after the fact, when disturbance,
the inverse of stability, has occurred. Experiments along these lines are
rarely designed; most are performed inadvertently, by advancing civilization. One that *was* designed studied the role of calcium in lakes. An hour-
glass-shaped bog lake was divided into two lakes by an earthen barrier
across the constriction. Calcium hydroxide (lime) was added to one twin,
raising the pH from 5.9 to 7.3. In the first year the transparency increased by 60 percent and by the second year the well-lighted zone had
thickened from 2.7 to 7.0 meters. The *Daphnia* population was found to
replace itself each 2.1 weeks in the lime-treated lake, compared to 4.6
weeks in the untreated twin; both the size of the population and its rate
of energy transfer were increased by liming. In addition, new species of
phytoplankton and of rooted aquatic plants appeared and began to
thrive (Fig. 11-4).

When field collecting is concentrated on particular taxonomic groups,
the relations of common and rare species are often found to be remark-

Figure 11-4. Peter-Paul Lakes in northern Michigan were divided by a dam to make twin experimental lakes. Peter Lake was treated with calcium hydroxide, while Paul Lake served as a control. (Courtesy of A. D. Hasler)

ably orderly: a constant ratio holds between abundances, from commonest to rarest, and much the same rank order recurs from place to place and from year to year. A group of very similar species, if of about the same size and competing for similar resources, meeting similar predators, and so on, might ideally be expected to sort itself out numerically in this way, but many more departures from an ideal relation would be expected than are actually observed. The phenomenon doubtless holds the key to many puzzling aspects of ecological order, but a satisfactory general explanation has not yet been found. What is clear so far is that specific diversity, measured in this way in *taxocenes* (natural assemblages that are related both ecologically and taxonomically, like the diatoms in a stream or the mites in an acre of soil), is a sensitive measure of disturbance, especially of pollution.

The reason, probably, is that certain narrow assumptions about "ecological niches" apply best when species that occur together are genuinely similar; the larger the taxon (the birds of Massachusetts, say), the less likely that its members are truly competing for the same resources, which is to say that such a taxon is not a true taxocene. In more natural communities, under careful observation, the first hint of something abnormal is often the discovery that some species has become abnormally common, while the rest of its relatives are abnormally rare. Diatoms, censused after settling on glass slides suspended in streams, have proved themselves to be an appropriate taxocene, in that their diversity changes in response to pollution. *Cladocera,* or water fleas, have also done so, especially the family *Chydoridae,* which are almost ubiquitous in weedy ponds and lakes. Both diatoms and chydorids have the further advantage that they fossilize readily, often quantitatively, so that quantitative historical data are easy to get. Human disturbance (slash-and-burn agriculture) in Guatemala and volcanic ashfalls in a Japanese lake have both been proved to deform the chydorid diversity systematically *and reversibly*: after each episode of disturbance, the original orderly relation is restored after a few years or decades.

Man and Nature

All organisms modify their ecosystems. Natural populations at high densities can alter the environment so drastically that their own continued existence is in jeopardy. Man, however, occupies a unique position. He is capable of more widespread and destructive modification of environment than is any other animal, but he is also able to forecast the results of his activities. He can even decide to improve rather than degrade an environment.

Biologists are well aware of man's growing ability to alter the face of the earth. They doubt, however, that alteration for the sake of alteration is either socially necessary or ecologically sound. Our ability to utilize the abundance of the world's life is limited, but it is improving. Our goal is presumably not the Pyrrhic one, to conquer the natural world, but to live in harmony with it. "To attain this goal," as a thoughtful scientist has said, "we must manage both the external environment and ourselves. Especially, we need to learn how to avoid irreversible change. If we do not, we deny future generations the opportunity to choose the kind of world in which they wish to live."

The Tsembaga, a Model Ecosystem. The Tsembaga are bush-fallowing horticulturists, 204 in number in 1963, who occupy 3.2 square miles on the south wall of the Simbai valley in New Guinea. They saw their first white man in 1954, and their first resident anthropologist in 1963; they have not yet seen a missionary. They have affinal kinsmen living in other tribal groups throughout a wide district, to whom they are bound by reciprocal ties and ceremonial duties, and for most—actually for all—of their lives they live in uneasy truce with adjoining tribes. By repeatedly clearing second-growth forest and planting root crops, they farm approximately 1,000 acres, only 30 to 50 of which (depending on the size of the pig herd) are under cultivation at any one time. Native game and other products are taken from the primeval forest on the mountainside, and all boars live there (because domestic male pigs are castrated at 3 months of age), but the primary forest is never cleared. Some 99 percent of the food intake is vegetable; protein is available mainly from pork. Pigs are eaten only when some ritual requires a sacrifice—when something bad has happened, like a row or a death in the family, or when the affinal kinsmen need to be paid off, at festivals before and after battles, for their dubious assistance in warfare. Ordinarily, root crops are extracted from the gardens, with the important assistance of the pigs in cultivating and weeding, with a caloric gain (ratio of harvest to labor, in calories) of 17 to 1 for taro-yam gardens and 16 to 1 for sweet potato gardens.

A small population of pigs is decidedly helpful, but a large herd is a social liability, as pigs are no respecters of property rights and often fail to distinguish their owner's weeds from his neighbor's yams. Nevertheless, as the pig herd grows, over the years, 50 percent of the sweet potato crop, and about the same proportion of female labor, can be devoted to feeding pigs. One main kind of emergency for which they are being saved, over the protests of the women, is the outbreak of war, which can begin shortly after a major pig festival, during which the kinsmen are prevailed on to help. Hostilities, then, can go on for weeks, but throughout them there are taboos on sexual intercourse, on taking native game, and on eating food prepared by women. On the day of a battle, warriors are fed heavily salted pig fat but may take no liquids on the field. Open hostilities end, surprisingly soon, in a sort of "truce of God." A sacred plant is planted, and it is said "as long as the *rumbin* is in the ground there shall be no fighting." There is wholesale slaughter of pigs, and the kinsmen and ancestral spirits who have helped in the battle are ceremonially paid off, but only partially. A debt has been incurred that can only be fully repaid when the pig herd grows large again, which will happen, as minor emergencies take their toll of the protein supply, only after several years of *rumbin* truce.

The anthropologist who made this insightful study, Roy Rappaport, assumed initially that he was interested in ritual—which, "by definition," has no influence on the external environment. He concluded as follows:

> In short, ritual among the Tsembaga may be regarded as a kind of servo-mechanism which maintains a number of variables in a system, or set of interlocking systems, within ranges of viability. Its operation helps to maintain an undegraded biotic environment, limits fighting to frequencies which do not endanger the existence of the supra-local

population, adjusts man-land ratios, mobilizes allies, facilitates trade, distributes local surpluses of pork throughout a supra-local population, and insures to people high-quality protein when they are most in need of it.

The model, naturally, has certain local and special properties that limit its applicability to the world at large, but if one substitutes "belief systems" for "ritual" in the foregoing quotation, its generality is startling.

Agriculture. The role of ecology in agriculture began with the first attempts at cultivation. There was long, initially unplanned selection of plants and animals, accompanied by planned and unplanned alteration of habitat and by totally unplanned alteration of man's social behavior. Since the end of the Neolithic, however, there has been no essential modification of ways of extracting food from cropland. Old World and New World crop plants were mixed in the sixteenth century, but since the ninteenth century a basically Old World (Mediterranean) system has been propagated around the globe. The cost of this procedure is not appreciated, even today; a modern midwestern farm may spend more calories in the form of fossil fuel than it gets in the form of harvest. When this happens, gasoline is simply converted to carbohydrate with fractional efficiency, and the process is catalyzed, not powered, by newly received solar energy.

As more intensive exploitation of the same crops has led to rigorous selection for greatest yield of product of the highest quality, a trend toward simpler agricultural systems has occurred. In some operations this approach will continue to be fruitful. The brewmaster and cheesemaker have found that the quality of the product is dependent on rigorous control. However, most of the rest of men's domesticated ecosystems cannot be operated in this way. Extensive systems are open systems dependent on inputs of nutrients and water, and therefore always subject to new invasions and genetic alteration of resident populations. Primitive man discovered empirically that high diversity is a good strategy. Various maneuvers that retain diversity — and in primitive agriculture their number is incredibly large — somehow paid off. Suddenly, Western agronomists can see that these maneuvers are more than superstition. One reason is the high stability, including resistance to pests, that diversity confers; highly artificial systems are esthetically pleasing to Westerners, but they may cost more than they are worth.

The practices of temperate-zone agriculture are simply not open to developing tropical countries. Attempts to force nature in these areas have consistently met with failure and have compounded local difficulties. Apparently highly productive rainforests can quickly give way to useless deserts if converted to maize cultivation, for example. Tropical agriculture faces far more complex problems of water and nutrient balance than are encountered in the temperate zone. There is that much more reason to exploit the local information pools—genetic and ecological information in the native biota, and agronomic information in the minds of primitive cultivators. Slash-and-burn practices were universally regarded with abhorrence in the Western world until recently; controlled, rotational clearing is better practice than uncontrolled clear-cutting, however, and may sometimes be the only effective way of managing rainforest without destroying it. Paradoxically, more is known scientifically of slash-and-burn agriculture as it was practiced in Denmark in the Bronze Age, and recorded by the fossil pollen record, than is known in the present-day tropics, where millions of lives depend on it. In temperate-zone forestry, too, fire is proving to be more a good servant than a bad master, if used intelligently. And evidence is accumulating for the view that fire, used for millennia by Indians as a means of driving game, has played a vital role in producing the deep fertile soils of our western grasslands.

Husbandry. The entire New World was opened to human habitation only at the end of the Pleistocene, more than 10,000 but less than 20,000 years ago. By 3000 B.C. most of the world as we know it was inhabited by much the same kind of people who live here today, though in smaller numbers, and most of the arable land was already under cultivation. Ecologists (though not many archaeologists, as yet) are becoming convinced that this wildfire spread of people, and not climatic change, was ultimately responsible for the extinction of the many large Pleistocene mammals and birds. A symposium on this subject was held in 1965; the following is quoted from the introduction to the resulting book:

> And the value of this kind of study is not purely theoretical. Noticing that most of the extinct mammals and birds were large herbivores living in savanna country, and that some of them, like ground sloth, water buffalo, Columbian mammoth, and giant wallaby, were powerful converters of carbohydrate to protein, we can also infer that they had a powerful influence on the makeup, as well as on the amount, of vegetation. (These quantitative inferences are among those that most need more research.) Plainly, their niches on all continents are currently filled, however badly, by domestic cattle and sheep. Any one-for-one replacement, like that of bison by Herefords on the western plains, might be ecologically sound, though the issue has always been prejudged, up to now, without much ecological inquiry. One can state categorically, with no inquiry, that no one or two domestic species can replace all the lost herbivores with equal success.
>
> The reason, of course, is to be found in the long evolution of ecological order, with a community of some twenty species of native African

ungulates providing a relevant example. Shouldering each other into separate niches, over the course of the Pleistocene or longer, they evolved into short-grass grazers, long-grass grazers, browsers with short and with long necks, species with narrow or wide ranges, species more or less tolerant of thirst and of tsetse flies, species with patrilineal and matrilineal social organizations, and so on and on. Such a diverse system, naturally, is considerably more resistant to disturbance, whether by locusts or by hunters, than the one-grazer-one-carnivore system favored in the Fertile Crescent, and propagated thence around the world. It is also inherently more efficient, when considered as a converter of solar energy to protein, as some African ranchers have been finding out.*

Population and Wastes. Although some very dense human populations, past and present, have been supported on a nonindustrial base, it appears to some ecologists that the present population, nearly 3.4 billion persons, is already greater than the earth can support indefinitely, on an adequate standard of living. Meanwhile, the death rate falls, births decline more slowly if at all, and the population continues to rise. At the outside, perhaps a factor-of-ten increase might be possible. Population growth in the animal kingdom is usually curtailed by built-in correctives, and there is reason to think that man is no exception. Continued fouling of the environment, all by itself, would be a built-in corrective for which there are many precedents. However the curtailment comes, it will not be easy, and a great deal of human misery will result.

Ecology is faced with its ultimate challenge in coping with the next phase of population increase. The acute problems today are those of waste disposal in water and air and of unrestricted suburban sprawl; the chronic problems are the old ones—food, water and disease. All such problems are hydra-headed, of course, simply because ecosystems are systems. The routine flushing of petroleum wastes by tankers in cold waters, seemingly harmless enough, threatens Cornish summer resorts and the North Sea fisheries, and a single disaster like that of the *Torrey Canyon* could wipe out Peru's guano industry. New sources of energy, atomic energy especially, may ease the pressure on fossil fuels but bring new problems of waste disposal and of public health, and tend to exacerbate the suburban sprawl. Medical men are uneasily aware that infective disease has not been conquered, but is kept at bay at a given level of human density; if the density becomes high enough, some of the mass killers of the Middle Ages—plague and typhus—can be expected to return. Ecologists are particularly concerned lest some ill-considered

* Martin, Paul S., and Herbert E. Wright, Jr., *Pleistocene Extinctions: The Search for a Cause,* Yale University Press, New Haven, 1967.

pollutant—a detergent, an insecticide, or a contraceptive drug—interfere with some crucial link in a cycle of microbial geochemistry, such as nitrogen fixation or sulfate reduction, and make the earth uninhabitable. Thermal pollution, some direct and some indirect, resulting from increase of carbon dioxide in the atmosphere, has already significantly changed climates, and dust and smog will continue to do so. The side effects of weather modification are exemplified, but not exhausted, by noting that silver and lead, used for cloud-seeding, are highly toxic to most organisms, but less so to many pests—which is one of the reasons they are pests.

What all this means, however, is that living in the biosphere will be difficult, but interesting, like all evolution. As is true for other organisms, the object of man's game with nature is not to win, but to keep on playing.

Future Trends

Ecology has been radically transformed in the past thirty years. New physical and chemical technologies have made it, as a field science, very different from the "car window botany" of a generation ago. Physiological ecology, including animal behavior and psychobiology, has profited from the vigor and sophistication of laboratory studies, and is now able to carry on work in the wilder parts of nature with almost equal vigor. New intellectual excitement has been generated by a variety of mathematical ideas, covering such matters as the flow of energy and information through ecosystems, the taxonomic diversity of communities, and the relations between populations of real organisms and experimentally analyzable populations of genes. As larger and more complex ecosystems are brought under study, they turn out to contain men and their artifacts; as a result, human disturbance—found annoying by an older generation of ecologists—provides a rich series of quasi-experimental "treatments" by which the stability of ecosystems can be intelligently assessed.

Some academic ecologists may be surprised to see how strongly, in appraising future trends, we emphasize applied ecology and its practical benefits. Indeed, we are a little surprised ourselves. Increased social responsibility is characteristic of all science nowadays, and we make no apology for indicating some of the contributions ecology can make to human welfare. But we do not mean this section to imply that immediate practical benefits must henceforth motivate all ecological research. Major discoveries are certain to be made that anyone will call "basic," and they will be made because ecology is interesting, not because some application is clearly in view. The trouble is, we have no idea what these basic discoveries will be, and therefore cannot forecast them as "future trends," whereas many applications of present-day ecology can be predicted with confidence.

Ecology of Species

Many species have long been known to be of value to man, and, of course, a number of noxious forms exist as well. Undoubtedly more species than anyone now realizes are essential for man's survival and welfare. For both beneficial and harmful types we need to know the physical and chemical conditions under which they survive and reproduce, the extent to which they can adjust to change, the optimum conditions for survival and reproduction, and how physiology and behavior can be changed. With such knowledge we could predict whether a valuable species can profitably be introduced into a new region, whether an introduced form is likely to be harmful, and whether it would be detrimental or beneficial for man to change environments in specified ways.

Environmental limits for growth and reproduction are not necessarily alike. Oysters will grow in water too cold for spawning, and sheep grow well on Andean meadows at an altitude where rams are sterile. Carp survive for some time at temperatures too cold for feeding. Valuable plants thrive in regions where they require special protection from frost or drought, or special modifications of soil chemistry, and where they may not reproduce but have to be propagated as scions, or by seeds brought from other regions.

Changes of behavior following environmental changes can have important consequences. A New Zealand parrot, the kea, changed from an insect-eater to a predator of sheep when sheep were introduced. The black rat (*R. rattus*), a carrier of human plague, is a house rat in Europe and North America but a sewer rat in India, while the brown rat (*R. norvegicus*) shows exactly the opposite pattern. The cereal plants rye and oats are believed to have originated as weeds of wheat and barley, and to have become better grains than their hosts as early agriculture moved northward in Europe. In a similar manner, various mustards have come to resemble flax.

In general, the most urgent need in physiological ecology—apart from high-grade support from systematic biology, needed for all kinds of ecology—is for reliable and versatile instrumental methods. The past few years have seen the advent of accurate and truly portable instruments that can be used in the field for measuring gases and ions. These instruments are suitable for continuous monitoring and automatic recording.

We anticipate a great increase in the use of unmanned data-gathering stations, with the information brought to the laboratory by telemetry and reduced and stored by on-line computers.

There is already explosive growth in the use of wireless telemetry for monitoring environments and physiologies and for tracking animals; we are at the point where some of these systems can be used in conjunction with satellites. Radar, sonar, microwave, and infrared sensing systems are already finding uses, and such uses will certainly increase. Closed-circuit television will play an increasing role, especially in studies of behavior (Fig. 11-5).

Ecologists are also using and will increasingly use sophisticated instruments that will probably never be portable. Mass spectrometers, gas chromatographs, amino acid analysers, and particle and radiation counters are becoming increasingly important, and bulky.

Increasing efforts are being made to understand biogeochemical cycles and to identify the organisms involved. The need is urgent because man's accelerating alteration of the world environment may threaten indispensable forms whose existence may be unsuspected. For example, the nitrogen cycle, which is essential for all higher plants and

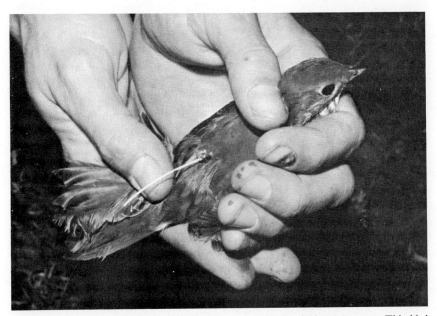

Figure 11-5. A radio-tagged thrush, carrying a transmitter weighing 2.2 grams. This bird was followed for 300 miles on a migratory flight. (Courtesy of the Illinois Natural History Survey. Photo by W. D. Zehr)

for the composition of the atmosphere, depends on several types of decomposer organisms for its continuance. Again, if anything should inhibit the organisms that possess the unusual ability to degrade them, inert organic materials such as lignin and chitin would accumulate.

Normally we will wish to encourage organisms that can degrade such substances as detergents and pesticides, but there will be situations in which we would like to encourage one chemical pathway and inhibit others. For example, aldrin usually breaks down to the more toxic dieldrin, and heptachlor goes to the much more toxic and persistent heptachlor epoxide. We need to find and encourage organisms that can degrade and/or recycle such substances harmlessly and quickly.

Probably many of the newly domesticated organisms of the future will be useful microorganisms. New antibiotics are constantly being sought, while searches are also being made for organisms performing particular fermentations or responding to traces of gaseous hydrocarbons. The latter would be useful in petroleum prospecting, at least, and might be turned to account in human nutrition. It is a striking fact that the only animals domesticated since the Neolithic are laboratory animals, like *Drosophila* and the hamster, or special-purpose species like the mink, and no new mammal capable of responding to man as a social partner has been exploited in modern times. The porpoises have real possibilities in this direction, but can scarcely be said to have been domesticated as yet.

Ecology of Populations

A population that is either large or small, relative to the carrying capacity of its environment, is less productive than a population of intermediate size. For populations valuable to man there must always be some optimum size that provides the maximum sustained yield. In practice the problem of optimum strategies for particular populations is formidable. We anticipate much more intensive research on problems of optimal yield. Greater attention can then be paid to the deleterious effects of underpopulation. The great blue whale, the largest and potentially one of the most useful animals that has ever lived, has been brought to so low a level of density as to make it uncertain that it can recover, even if all exploitation is halted.

As to control of overpopulation, all ecological experience suggests that the optimum strategy normally involves reduction of the carrying capacity of the environment. Much current practice, however, is based on a different assumption, that increasing deaths increases mortality *rates,* and that killing is therefore an optimum strategy.

Better ecological knowledge is being brought into some programs of pest control, and we anticipate further increase in this direction. There are surely undiscovered possibilities for rendering pests innocuous by relatively simple manipulations of microclimates. Changing time schedules for plowing, planting, or burning will often alter the pattern of development of weeds, insects, and rodents. The technique of introducing into a pest population either sterile or incompatible males takes advantage of the fact that any population has some critical minimum level of reproductive success below which it cannot persist. Such techniques are certain to be more widely used.

Parasites sometimes fail to control pests simply because the hosts become so rare at certain seasons that the parasite population itself falls too low. Some pests are actually worth rearing in the laboratory, to be released during seasons of shortage. Most species of blackflies and many mosquitoes will not bite man; perhaps environments can be subtly modified to encourage nonbiting species.

Another approach that shows promise is to introduce genetic diversity into crop plants so that a particular pest cannot sweep uninhibited through the entire crop. Cereals can be bred that are resistant to various strains of stem rusts, but the rusts eventually evolve strains that can attack them. By sowing a mixture of strains, spread of the pathogen is impaired. In 1966 in New York State, a new record for yield was set by a variety of oats that had been bred for variability in resistance to stem rust. It is noteworthy that in primitive agriculture today seeds of different strains are often mixed before planting—another "superstitious practice" that deserves more attention from scientific agronomy. Hedgerows of perennial plants separating adjacent fields can provide some of the same effect, on a coarser scale, and will also reduce evaporation, thus reducing damage from drought.

Human populations are subject to the same laws that govern populations in general. Overpopulation and underpopulation in particular situations are obvious enough to those who can be objective on the subject, but serious and competent attempts to define optimum population for man are almost nonexistent.

No population can continue to grow indefinitely, and disaster is inevitable for any species that seriously overshoots its limits. Man, as a species dependent on nonrenewable resources, has already done this, in a sense. Can he free himself of this dependence? If he can, can he maintain so large a population without progressive deterioration of the environment and loss of its carrying capacity?

Existing knowledge could be used to stabilize the human population, and Japan has shown that a determined people can, in less than one generation, bring the problem of excessive population growth under control. When a population has been stable long enough for its age structure to conform to a pattern of low birth and death rates, it can remain stable without vigorous applications of technology; records of a century in France, Iberia, Ireland, and Scandinavia confirm this. Unfortunately, a population that maintains itself near stability, even by exporting its surplus, is widely regarded as sick.

New Populations to Manage

It is improbable that conventional domestic animals can represent the best ways of producing protein in the tropics. In Africa there are many species of native ungulates, each of which plays a slightly different role in harvesting vegetation. The complex community of herbivores is more efficient than any one of its member species can be. Similarly, when vegetation is stratified into several layers adapted to different light intensities, solar radiation is utilized more efficiently, providing more food for more kinds of animals. Animal husbandry in Africa will almost certainly yield more protein if a mixture of species is used, but so far this idea has been tested more often by computer simulation than by ranching. Likewise, the saiga antelope (which used to live in Alaska) has proved more efficient than domestic sheep and goats at cropping the Siberian tundra; and on a Scottish island red deer also proved to be more efficient than sheep.

When forest is destroyed in the humid tropics, the nutrients held in the tissues are violently released and rapidly dispersed by leaching rains. Chemicals not captured by the subsequent burst of weeds are lost to the local system. Long-persisting destructive practices may so degrade the site as to prevent reestablishment of forest. Naturally, such degraded sites are of low agricultural potential. Clearly, very careful consideration of consequences should precede attempts to replace tropical vegetation by grass and domestic cattle.

The oceans and most bodies of fresh water are now very inefficiently used for food. The greatest mass of living matter is dispersed as plankton, and it will probably always be uneconomical for man to harvest plankton directly. There are a few species, other than fishes, that are large enough to invite serious consideration as grazers of aquatic plants. With characteristic lack of foresight, man threatens all of them with early extermination. The manatee, as a consumer of water hyacinth, itself one of the most productive of crops, looks particularly promising. One hopes that manatees, dugongs, green turtles, porpoises, and whales will be available for a while longer, while research proceeds. Theoretically, of course, man might obtain more food from the sea by eliminating predators and harvesting species that feed exclusively on plankton. However, the result would have disruptive consequences that cannot now be foreseen.

There is also a huge amount of nonliving organic matter dissolved in seawater. Though not particularly nutritious, it contains amino acids, sugars, and residues of plant pigments. Neither its origin nor its fate is adequately known, and any possibility of using it as food is far in the future. But its existence reminds us that most herbivores, calorie for calorie and gram for gram, are not grazers of green things, but browsers on dead organic matter; this is just as true in the sea as on land. If one of the major food animals of the future is the earthworm, as seems barely possible, another may well be a marine polychaet or sipunculid.

We have as yet barely started to consider the possibilities of breeding new types of animal to fill new niches in nature; animal husbandry is far behind horticulture in this respect. However, hybrid Pacific salmon have been produced that grow and mature more rapidly than their parents, and the increasingly widespread culture of the African cichlid fish *Tilapia* is beginning to use semidomesticated strains.

The Management of Ecosystems

A biotic community consists of populations of various species interacting in such a way as to make the system relatively self-sustaining, given inputs of energy and materials. The community with its nonliving environment constitutes the fundamental unit, the ecosystem.

Conceptually, it is convenient to consider ecosystems as analogous to organisms with distinctive patterns of development and physiology, and capable of undergoing morbid reactions as a result of imposed changes. For example, a lake and its drainage basin with all the life it contains can be considered as a unit. We can measure the annual energy input. We can learn how much of this goes to melt ice, to warm the water, or to drive photosynthesis. The heat budget would predict the consequences of additional heat, say, by using the water to cool a power plant. A chemical budget would enable us to predict the effects of a specified amount of raw or treated sewage, of phosphorus, nitrogen, or pesticides, or of specified industrial wastes.

Actually, as should be apparent, the general problem of ecosystem analysis is, with the exception of sociological problems that are also ecological, the most difficult problem ever posed by man. It is many times more difficult when we recognize such features as the vagaries of weather, which introduce very large uncertainties into any realistic analysis. Modern digital computers are not yet large or fast enough for truly realistic simulation of even simple ecosystems, but this is an area in which activity will increase tremendously as computers evolve. A related area, just in its infancy, is analogue simulation of ecosystems. We do not anticipate that older analytical methods will be superseded, but rather that the behavior of models will suggest new courses of analysis.

A few bodies of water have been studied intensively as ecosystems so that we probably know enough to make rather reliable predictions of the consequences of specific changes. A few relatively simple systems are under intensive study; these include small islands where all life is deliberately eliminated in order to observe reestablishment of an ecosystem — methodologically primitive, but a necessary first step. We are just at the beginning of such studies for terrestrial systems such as forests, and must still rely largely on history and recent experience for predictions. The early work on ecological succession was essentially descriptive, with manipulation minimal. The increasing sophistication that is being brought to bear on one- and two-species laboratory systems now permits succession to be approached as a multiple-species extension. Succession is currently being studied as a Markov process, or random walk, whereby the transition probabilities between successive species can be worked out and used in predictive models.

There will be an explosion of information on stable systems as well as experimental alteration of ecosystems. What happens when deliberate stress or disturbance is applied? What happens if you remove one of the living components? What factors are responsible for maintaining temporal stability? As the results of these studies accumulate, we will face increasing problems of data and literature retrieval; we are already at the point where some sort of national or international ecological data bank is urgently needed.

Movement of matter and energy in food chains — from sun, air, water, and soil, to producers, herbivores, predators, and decomposers — is under intensive study in many places. Efficiencies and rates of turnover are being studied. These studies are greatly aided by radioisotopes and other tracers, and we anticipate that new, rapid, and automatic methods of chemical analysis and calorimetry will lead to great advances.

An area of given size will support fewer species when it is isolated than when it is merely a sample of some larger area. This implies, among other things, that if man-made changes cause, say, Yellowstone Park to become an isolate rather than a sample of a greater Rocky Mountain biota, some species will become extinct there. Some of the African game preserves are probably not large enough to retain all the species they were designed to preserve. But ecologists do not really understand why small samples differ from large samples, and much work is being devoted to the problem.

Some of the most important questions about ecosystems involve their stability as related to their composition. We would like to be able to tell, for example, if something we are adding to soil or water is causing its microbiota to deteriorate or become unstable. Here we suffer taxonomic limitations because many soil organisms are undescribed and many others cannot readily be identified. This is a serious limitation because current theory holds that stability is best measured in terms of species diversity, and all such measurements are very sensitive to accuracy of taxonomy.

Soon, man will be assembling synthetic ecosystems, as life-support systems in spaceships and for use underwater, and also for improved production of food and other commodities. Much remains to be learned before we can assure the efficiency and reliability of such systems. Simple systems with few components, understandably, are favored by engineers. Ecological experience strongly suggests that simple life-support systems will prove highly unreliable. The biosphere as a whole, on the other hand, is definitely not simple, but it has been remarkably reliable up to now. The objective of applied ecology is to keep it so.

Chapter 12

HEREDITY AND EVOLUTION

This chapter is concerned with the rules and mechanisms by which hereditary information is transmitted from one generation to the next. Genetics was precipitately born in 1900 with the rediscovery of Mendel's laws of inheritance. The great accomplishment of this science has been to discover the physical basis of heredity and to show that the basic rules of inheritance are fundamentally the same throughout the living world. A practical consequence has been the development of scientific plant and animal breeding and an understanding of the biological basis of many human diseases.

Biological evolution first received wide attention with the publication of Charles Darwin's *Origin of Species* in 1859. Darwin argued that all living forms are related to life in the past, from which they have evolved by slow changes. The scientific world was gradually convinced not only of evolution as a historical fact but of natural selection as a mechanism. The missing element in Darwin's concept of evolution was a knowledge of the nature of heredity and variation; this was supplied by Mendelian genetics.

The exciting (or, to some, repugnant) discovery that man is a part of nature and shares a common ancestry with the corn plant, the earthworm, and—for some reason most shocking of all—the apes has totally altered man's view of himself and of his place in the world. On the one hand, the realization is humbling, as we see ourselves in relation to the whole of past and present life. On the other hand, it is challenging, since man is unique in understanding his past and, in consequence, may guide his own future. This is a tremendous responsibility, for the future evolution of countless species of animals and plants, and of man himself, will be greatly influenced by human decisions and actions. Man arose out of a process over which he had no control, but which he now understands and can begin to influence.

This chapter is an attempt to describe some of the accomplishments of genetic and evolutionary biology, some of the kinds of problems being studied, and some of the prospects and needs for future research.

Historical Review
1850–1950, A Century of Accelerating Progress

With the publication of Darwin's book in 1859, evolution immediately became a subject of public concern. Much of the emphasis during the latter part of the nineteenth and early part of the twentieth century was on the establishment of evolution as a historical fact. The strongest evidence came from the fossil record, but comparative study of anatomy, physiology, and development in diverse species contributed to the mass of evidence that was soon to become overwhelming. The study of systematic biology was given a deeper meaning as it was reoriented to reflect evolutionary relationships.

Darwin had argued not only for the historical occurrence of evolution but also for the basic mechanism—natural selection. He pointed out that if every species produces more young than can survive to reproduce, some types survive more often or are more fertile than others, and if the factors determining viability and fertility are to some extent heritable, then natural selection is a direct consequence. In its sweep and grandeur, in the way in which it brings relationship and meaning to a host of seemingly unrelated facts, the theory of evolution by natural selection must rank with the greatest contributions of the human intellect. Yet the idea is so simple and readily understood that it is something of a surprise that it had to wait until Darwin's time for any wide acceptance.

The big gap in the full understanding of evolution in Darwin's time was the ignorance of the nature of inheritance and variation. There was ample evidence that all sorts of traits were inherited, and biological variability was a matter of simple observation. Yet the essential nature of heredity and the mechanisms whereby variability is introduced into and maintained in the population completely eluded biologists of the nineteenth century. Darwin himself devoted much of his time to these questions and wrote extensively about them. Although many of his observations and collections of facts are still good today, he was unable to arrive at a basic understanding of the mechanisms involved.

There was one exception to nineteenth-century ignorance of heredity;

one man did have some of the answers. This was Gregor Mendel, whose experiments on garden peas had led him to formulate the rules of inheritance that we now call *Mendel's laws*. The prevailing view of the time was that the hereditary material is analogous to a fluid. Mendel showed that heredity is particulate in its nature, and the particles follow specific rules of transmission from parent to progeny. Unfortunately, Mendel's work made no impact on influential contemporary biologists. His paper was delivered in 1865, but it was not until 1900 that Mendel's principles were rediscovered and his place in biological history was recognized.

Mendel's characters or factors (which we now call genes) were deduced entirely from breeding experiments. He could explain his observations and predict the results of various matings by assuming the existence of these factors, and he described in detail the rules by which these were transmitted. Mendel had no idea of the size, composition, or location of these hypothetical entities; he wisely refrained from publishing any speculations.

The later years of the nineteenth century saw many improvements in the techniques of cell study. These techniques permitted detailed observations on the elongated, highly stainable bodies—the *chromosomes*—within the cell nucleus. In particular, cytologists were acquainted with the way in which chromosomes divide and separate during ordinary cell division (*mitosis*) and with the special divisions (*meiosis*) whereby the chromosome number is halved during the formation of sperm and egg cells.

As soon as Mendel's laws became widely known, the striking parallelism between the behavior of chromosomes, as seen through the microscope, and of Mendel's factors, as inferred from breeding experiments, immediately became apparent. Thus, the chromosomal theory of heredity had its origin shortly after the rediscovery of Mendelism in 1900.

The next step was to show how genes are arranged on the chromosomes. They were found to be in single file. The crucial experiments were done by T. H. Morgan and his students working with the fruit fly, *Drosophila melanogaster*. The experiments were remarkable for their ingenuity and for the simplicity of the experimental materials. To infer the positions of the genes, which could not be seen and whose nature was totally unknown, solely from the numbers of different kinds of progeny from different matings seems almost impossibly abstract; yet this group was able to construct chromosome "maps" giving the exact order and relative distances apart of the genes. At first the evidence was mainly the internal consistency of the chromosome maps and the accuracy of predictions made from them. Considerably later, after appropriate techniques had been developed, the gene order was confirmed by direct microscopic examination of broken chromosomes which showed the correspondence between a missing chromosome region and a missing or altered hereditary trait.

Similar experiments were done with other organisms and in many parts of the world. By 1915 the general rules of genes and chromosomes were beginning to be known. By 1940 the chromosomal mechanisms of genetic transmission were understood, and a big gap in the Darwinian theory had been filled.

The other big question that plagued Darwin was the origin of variability. The question was partly solved by the particulate nature of inheritance. With a fluid or blending theory of inheritance, variability is lost every time there is hybridization between individuals with contrasting characteristics, just as the mixing of red and white paint produces a uniform intermediate color and the original "variability" in color (red and white) is forever lost. With particulate inheritance the differences are conserved. A very slight input of new kinds of genes is sufficient to maintain a large amount of variability in the population.

This input is now known to come from mutation—a change in the gene or chromosome so that it produces a different effect. The phenomenon of mutation was reported early in the twentieth century soon after the rediscovery of Mendelism, but more techniques were needed before it could be understood. At the time of the development of the chromosome theory of inheritance and the localization of the genes on the chromosomes, geneticists showed that on rare occasions a gene spontaneously changed from one form to another. Furthermore, the new mutant gene was just as stable as was the original gene from which it arose. The rules of mutation were well understood by 1950—that the individual occurrence was essentially unpredictable although the average rate could be measured, that most mutants were harmful, that the rate of mutation could be increased by raising the temperature, by radiation and by some chemicals—but the physical or chemical nature of the mutation process was not understood, any more than the chemical nature of the gene.

This, then, was the state of genetic and evolutionary biology at the end of the first half of the twentieth century. Chromosome mechanics had been thoroughly analyzed and therefore the basic rules of hereditary transmission were well understood. Mutation, Mendelian inheritance, and natural selection provided the basis for a satisfactory theory of evolution.

Yet the essential nature of the gene remained a mystery. It was clear that the information most needed was a chemical understanding of the genetic material. In November, 1945, before the Royal Society of

London, H. J. Muller spoke prophetically of "the coming chemical attack on the gene." *

The attack was successful to a degree and with a speed that were beyond even the most optimistic expectations. The discovery of sex in bacteria and improved understanding of viruses made these organisms available for genetic experiments and tremendously increased the speed and precision of genetic analysis. This, together with sophisticated chemical methods, led to the first great triumph of molecular biology — the chemical understanding of the gene.

Population Genetics, an Extension of Mendelism

The close association of genetics and evolution in the years after the rediscovery of Mendel's laws led to the development of a new subject, population genetics. Its methods involve experiments and observations in the laboratory and in the field, along with mathematical theory. Its aims are a more detailed understanding of how mutation, selection, migration, population size, environmental conditions, and other factors influence the evolutionary process. Thus far, the available methods have permitted only the study of microevolutionary changes — changes within the species rather than the origin of higher categories such as genera and families.

Mathematical population genetics is a natural extension of Mendelism. Just as Mendel's rules predict the frequencies of different kinds of progeny from specified matings, the theory of population genetics gives the expected frequencies of different types in a population.

The first and simplest step was to determine the relationship between the proportions of genes in a population and the proportions of the various genetic types of individuals (genotypes) that arise by combining these genes at random. Thus, if p_1, p_2, p_3 . . . represent the proportions of alternative genes at a single chromosomal locus, the genotype frequencies are given by appropriate terms in the quadratic expression $(p_1 + p_2 + p_3 . . .)^2$. This simple principle was independently discovered in 1908 by the British mathematician Hardy and the German physician and geneticist Weinberg. The fact that these numerical relationships are attained in a single generation rather than gradually means that it is not necessary to know the previous history of a population. In practice it has turned out that many natural populations are sufficiently large and

---

* Much earlier, in 1922, Muller had written: "Must we geneticists become bacteriologists, physiological chemists and physicists, simultaneously with being zoologists and botanists? Let us hope so."

mating is sufficiently nearly random for a number of traits that the principle applies remarkably well. It has been a powerful tool, not only for analyzing natural populations but for determining the mode of inheritance of genetic traits in populations where experimental matings are not possible. For example, it has been known since their discovery in 1900 that the human A-B-O blood groups are inherited, but the exact manner was not proven until the 1920's when these principles were applied to the large bodies of data that had by then accumulated. Much of what is known about the inheritance of the newer blood groups and other traits has been gotten by combining population and pedigree analysis.

The number of potential genotypes in a population is much larger than the number of different genes, since it is determined by the number of *combinations* of genes; when the number of different genes is large, the number of possible genotypes becomes astronomical. An enormous simplification can be achieved by writing formulas for changes of gene frequencies rather than genotype frequencies. This entails loss of information, for knowledge of the gene frequencies is not sufficient to specify exactly the frequency of different genotypes. Nevertheless, these frequencies can usually be estimated to a satisfactory approximation with the Hardy-Weinberg principle, or a modification thereof if the population is not mating at random.

Furthermore, in a sexually reproducing population the genes are reassorted by the Mendelian shuffle that takes place every generation. The effects of such reassortment are largely transitory, since gene combinations are put together and taken apart every generation. Thus, the value of considering gene frequencies rather than genotype frequencies — in addition to the greater power achieved through simplicity — is that the genes perpetuate themselves as intact units, whereas the genotypes are reconstituted anew each generation from the pool of genes in the population.

On the other hand, the individual genes are not completely randomized every generation, so the knowledge of gene frequencies is not sufficient for a precise description of the population. This is especially true for genes that are close to one another on the same chromosome and which tend therefore to be linked together in inheritance. A full theory is very complicated and requires not only advanced mathematical methods but often the aid of high-speed computers.

The theory of inbreeding is the most completely developed branch of mathematical population genetics. Inbreeding has two interrelated consequences: one is a decrease in genic variability in the inbred strain; the other is an increase in homozygosity, i.e., in the number of loci where the two corresponding genes are identical.

Some genes are *recessive*; that is, they produce their effect only when present in duplicate. Many harmful genes are of this type, but produce no harmful effect in a genetically heterogeneous population because the effect is masked by the other member of the gene pair. Inbreeding, by making the gene pairs identical, brings out the effect of harmful genes that has previously been concealed. This provides an explanation of the weakening effects of inbreeding which had long puzzled many biologists, including Darwin. The theory of inbreeding has had great practical utility in quantitative plant and animal breeding and in the understanding of human hereditary diseases. It has also been of use in the analysis of hidden variability in natural populations of many species, thereby helping to quantify some of the evolutionary factors at work.

The main aim of mathematical population genetics has been to find prediction formulas for the distribution of gene and genotype frequencies in populations, taking into account mutation, various kinds of selection, mating patterns, migration, and the size and breeding structure of the population. Simple beginnings were made in the early 1920's by considering selection and mutation as deterministic forces acting on simple genetic systems. This "bean bag" genetics gave results that are useful as a first approximation in understanding how selection changes a population. One of its first uses was to see if the rate of changes actually occurring in evolution were compatible with reasonable amounts of selection. The first crude measurements indicated that observed intensities of natural selection are indeed sufficient for simple cases, but the answers were tentative. Much of the progress in recent years has been in dealing with more complicated and realistic situations, where gene interactions are complex and the genes are not inherited independently. The problems are much more complicated when the effects of chance are taken into account. Stochastic methods have been developed for the simpler cases. More complicated situations still resist meaningful analysis, and it is frequently necessary to resort to numerical solutions; this has now become feasible with the availability of high-speed computers. The present situation could perhaps be described by saying that population genetics has a mathematical theory that looks complex to the average biologist but might not appear so to a mathematical physicist.

Observational and experimental population genetics started with field studies of natural populations. Early workers documented the amount of variability in various species. Others demonstrated the occurrence of natural selection by observing differential mortality and fertility. Although most evolutionary changes are too slow to be witnessed in a human lifetime, some examples of unusually rapid evolution have been studied. One of the most famous is the evolution of "industrial melanism" in Great Britain and on the European continent. As smoke from factories gradually darkened the tree trunks in industrial areas, the light forms of several moths which rest on these trunks were replaced by a darker form. It was possible to calculate the intensity of selection required to cause such rapid evolution and, not surprisingly, this turned out to be very great. The actual working of natural selection was demonstrated experimentally by the release and recapture of marked insects, and by showing birds selectively catching light moths from the dark trunks in the industrial areas and dark moths from the light trunks in rural areas.

More recent and more important has been the rapid development of resistance to insecticides and antibiotics. This is an almost perfect paradigm of natural selection, giving man a chance to observe a major evolutionary change in a few years. The numerous examples have been excellent test cases for proving the efficiency of natural selection as an evolutionary mechanism and showing that, when conditions are right, evolution need not be the slow process that it ordinarily is. The wide-scale application of the poison kills the overwhelming majority of normally susceptible members of the insect population. The tiny minority that happen to have genes whose expression makes for resistance survive and, freed from the competition normally supplied by the rest of the population, multiply at a rapid rate. To the extent that the resistance is heritable, the next generation will be more resistant than the last. A few generations of this process, and we have the now-familiar phenomenon of large areas where flies and mosquitoes are resistant to the common insecticides. The insecticide either is useless or has to be applied in such high concentrations as to be potentially dangerous to other species, thereby upsetting other aspects of the ecology quite remote from the original problem and possibly of vital importance to mankind. Exactly the same thing happens with the development of drug and antibiotic resistance in microorganisms. Here the still larger numbers of individual organisms of varied genotype and rapid rates of reproduction make possible even more rapid selection of resistant mutants.

The traits studied need not be external characters. Much of plant population genetics has followed the effects of chromosome rearrangements, or has correlated the evolutionary pattern with the manner of reproduction. The giant salivary gland chromosomes of *Drosophila* have permitted the detailed study of changes in chromosome arrangements.

Laboratory experiments have been used in several ways. One of the greatest contributions of experimental population genetics has been to demonstrate the large amount of hidden genetic variability that is concealed in relatively constant natural populations. For example, recessive genes tend to accumulate to a relatively high frequency; this frequency is predictable from measurable parameters. One conclusion from laboratory analysis of *Drosophila* flies caught in nature has been that recessive lethal genes are too rare to be accounted for by observed mutation rates in a large population. There is either some selection against heterozygotes, or possibly a rather large amount of local inbreeding.

In general, then, population genetics is a science with various techniques — observations and experiments in the field and laboratory, and mathematical theory. From the field observations the distribution of variants can be observed; these may vary in space or in time. Laboratory experiments may be required to determine the importance of the different varying factors and how much of the variability is heritable. Within the framework of the Mendelian theory and the field observations, theoretical models are constructed. These permit certain predictions from parameters that can be measured. These theories are then tested by further observations on natural populations or in laboratory studies.

Cytogenetics

Soon after the discovery of the chromosomal basis of heredity, cytologists found that for normal development there must be exactly the right number of chromosomes in the fertilized egg. Most species are *diploid*; that is, they have two representatives of each chromosome in the fertilized egg and in the body cells derived from it by repeated divisions. When there are too many or too few chromosomes, or even if there is an excess or deficiency for only a part of a chromosome, the animal or plant has various abnormalities and sometimes cannot even survive.

Jimsonweeds. One of the classical studies involved the common jimsonweed, *Datura stramonium,* which normally has twelve pairs of chromosomes in each cell. If the plant has three representatives of a particular chromosome instead of the normal two, it is said to be *trisomic.* Each of the twelve trisomic types has a characteristic abnormal appearance so that an expert can easily recognize any one of them. Also, *monosomics,* with only a single representative of some chromosome, were discovered and they too had characteristic abnormalities, usually more severe than the corresponding trisomics.

These findings demonstrated the great importance of the correct balance among the genes on different chromosomes if the plant is to develop normally. Not only must the genes be normal, but there must be the correct numerical balance among the different genes. Such results have been corroborated in many other plants and in some animals.

Such unbalanced chromosome combinations can arise because of a mistake in the process of meiosis, such that an egg or sperm has too many or too few chromosomes. Such accidents are not common, but they are not exceedingly rare either. In every case where they have been searched for systematically, they have been found.

Wheat. Trisomic and monosomic types have been of great practical utility in plant genetics. By correlating the microscopic observation that a certain chromosome is trisomic with the characteristic inheritance pattern that occurs when a gene is present three times instead of two, the breeder can identify which chromosome carries a particular gene. Monosomics and more complicated chromosome anomalies can also be used. This type of analysis has been particularly useful in wheat, where it has greatly facilitated the transfer of useful genes, such as those for resistance to diseases or insects, or poor soil, from one variety to another. Furthermore, a gene for rust resistance has been transferred from a common weed, goat grass, into commercial wheat. A recent tour de force, using chromosome identifying methods, was the transfer of a gene from rye to wheat.

Controlled breeding through chromosome knowledge is one of the plant breeder's most powerful techniques. Many agriculturally valuable plant varieties are *polyploid,* having three, four, six, or more entire sets of chromosomes instead of two. Chromosome knowledge is often useful in getting fertile hybrids between widely different varieties, species, or even genera. One of the promising new cereal crops, *Triticale,* is an octoploid, having six sets of chromosomes from wheat (*Triticum*) and two from rye (*Secale*). Another type of chromosome engineering has made use of plants with only half the usual number of chromosomes in order to have better control of the genetic makeup. This has been particularly useful in potato breeding.

Human Cytogenetics. Human cytology lagged behind for many years. Human chromosomes are numerous and it was hard to study them in detail. In fact, even the correct number of chromosomes was determined only a little more than a decade ago. Rather surprisingly, the techniques needed to make human chromosomes easily visible — the use of the drug colchicine and other treatments to keep the chromosomes contracted and a hypotonic (low salt) solution to expand the cell and separate the chromosomes from each other — are not particularly sophisticated. They might well have been invented fifty years earlier.

Despite its slow start, human cytogenetics is now quite advanced, thanks to many rapid technical developments since the early 1950's, particularly in the field of cell culture. The techniques are simple, and

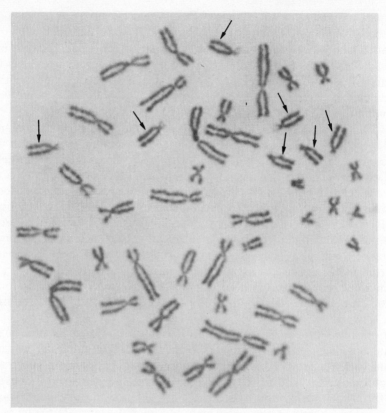

Figure 12-1. Human chromosomes from a white blood cell. This cell has 47 instead of the normal 46. The child from whom the cell was obtained had several severe abnormalities caused by the extra chromosome which is one of the seven chromosomes marked by arrows. There should be only six of this shape and size. (Courtesy Klaus Patau)

often a few drops of blood suffice for a chromosome analysis. Knowledge of human cytology is now comparable to that in the best-studied plants.

Once chromosome studies in man became feasible, the natural question was: to what extent are chromosome anomalies, such as had been studied in the jimsonweed and wheat, responsible for human disease, malformation, and early death? The answers began to appear very soon. The first trisomic disease was discovered in 1959 and turned out to be the already familiar "mongolism," or Down's syndrome (after the man who described it). The affected child has severe mental retardation and a number of characteristic physical abnormalities. Among these is a facial appearance that appeared to Down to resemble some of the mongoloid races — hence his unfortunate choice of a name for the condition (Fig. 12-1).

About 1 infant in 700 is born with mongolism, and such patients may constitute as much as a third of the population in institutions for the most severely retarded. Prior to the discovery of its chromosomal basis, the etiology of mongolism was quite mysterious. Many theories had been proposed (including the correct one), but the trisomic hypothesis became testable only after the development of human cytogenetic techniques.

One characteristic of mongolism is the number and variety of seemingly unrelated abnormalities. Now that the cause is known this is not surprising, for there must be many genes on the responsible chromosome, and any gene that produces an abnormal result when present three times rather than the normal two would produce its effect. This suggested an approach to finding other chromosomal diseases, and a search for patients with mental retardation and several other superficially unrelated abnormalities led almost immediately to the discovery of two other trisomic types, both new conditions previously unknown to clinical medicine. No others have been found in several years of study. Since the three known types of trisomy syndrome all involve quite small chromosomes, it appeared likely that trisomy for the other chromosomes was incompatible with the development of the embryo and fetus. Likewise, experience with experimental plants and animals has shown that monosomy is almost always more harmful than trisomy for the same chromosomes, so monosomics for any human chromosome might be expected to be lethal. This suggestion has been confirmed by a chromosome study of miscarried embryos. It now appears that a third or more of spontaneous abortions are caused by trisomy, monosomy, and more complicated chromosome anomalies.

An exception to the rule that chromosomes occur in pairs that are identical in appearance is found in the sex chromosomes, the X and Y. The human X chromosome is much larger than the Y. An individual with two X chromosomes is a female; one with an X and a Y is a male. The sex chromosomes are also an exception to the rule that monosomy and trisomy are lethal or severely harmful in higher animals. Monosomic individuals with a single X and no Y have the well known, but previously not understood, condition known as Turner's syndrome. Likewise, the trisomic XXY type turned out to be a known condition, Klinefelter's syndrome. Thus, chromosome study has provided understanding of two more syndromes, both of which had baffled earlier investigators trying to understand their causes.

In experimental plants and animals chromosome imbalance is also caused by broken chromosomes. In particular, chromosomes that have been rearranged through breakage and reattachment cause no immediate abnormality; but because of the rearrangement these chromosomes complicate the normal process of sperm and egg formation. This in turn leads to a greatly enhanced frequency of unbalanced chromosome combinations in the next generation. Hence a large proportion of children whose parents have rearranged chromosomes have physical anomalies almost invariably accompanied by mental retardation. Furthermore, the rearranged chromosomes are then inherited, so the tendency to produce abnormal children is passed on from generation to generation through otherwise normal persons. A skilled cytologist can perform an invaluable medical and social service by identifying those persons who, although being normal themselves, have chromosome rearrangements that predispose them to a large proportion of abnormal children and grandchildren.

The potential parent who has such a chromosome rearrangement faces a difficult decision. He or she has a high risk of having a miscarriage or a severely deformed and retarded child. Furthermore any normal children may themselves have abnormal children when they grow up. On the other hand, these people may be strongly desirous of having children, and some of the children may be normal.

There are now techniques for getting cells from the amniotic fluid of the embryo and growing them in culture. It is then possible to see whether the chromosomes are balanced or unbalanced and thereby predict whether the child will be normal or abnormal. If all abnormal pregnancies could be terminated, then the parents could be assured of having only normal children (or more precisely, of having only the same risks that any normal parent has, for of course there is no such thing as a pregnancy with no risk at all). Probably the techniques for detecting severe abnormalities in early embryos will improve so that many more conditions can be safely uncovered. Such a situation may lead to a direct conflict between humanitarian concerns for the child and its family and certain social and religious views on induced abortion. It is one more example of the often unexpected social impact of scientific and technological discoveries.

Polymorphism

Naturalists have long noted that some species of animals are *polymorphic*; that is to say, they exist in two or more quite distinct forms. A familiar example is the bear, where black and cinnamon types exist and are sometimes found in the same litter. Another example is found in the color phases of the red fox, made famous by feminine attraction to silver fox furs.

The theory of population genetics showed that for any gene locus, if the heterozygous individuals (say, A_1A_2) are somehow selectively advantageous in comparison with either homozygote (A_1A_1 or A_2A_2), then both genes, A_1 and A_2, persist in the population in a stable equilibrium determined by the relative fitnesses of the two homozygotes. There are other more complicated mechanisms, such as those involving several gene loci, selection based on the frequency of a gene, selection at different times in the life cycle, or a heterogeneous environment in which different genes are favored in various localities.

Some of the most conspicuous polymorphisms are found in butterflies. The stability of the frequencies of the various types could be determined from field observations. Breeding experiments showed that the differences were hereditary. Such polymorphisms are found throughout the animal and plant kingdoms.

Fruit Flies. By far the most extensive studies have been in various species of the fruit fly, *Drosophila*. Here the character most often studied has not been the external appearance of the fly but its chromosomes. Some species of *Drosophila* are characterized by a high frequency of the kind of chromosomal rearrangement whereby a piece of chromosome breaks out, turns 180 degrees, and is reinserted in reverse order. Such *inversions* lend themselves to microscopic analysis, and as a result this kind of study has been very widely pursued. The principal factor maintaining the multiplicity of chromosome rearrangements in the population is the greater average viability and fertility of a fly with two different arrangements in its homologous chromosomes—the simple mechanism first proposed by mathematical theorists.

A Human Polymorphism. In addition to chromosome rearrangements there are other traits that are not overt but which differ from one individual to another. The search for and study of such hidden polymorphisms in several organisms has revealed a large amount of variability whenever there has been a thorough search. Man is no exception and several new variants are found every year, most of them hidden and requiring special chemical tests in order to be demonstrated.

One of the most important of the human polymorphisms, both from the standpoint of human welfare and from the insights it has brought to fundamental research, has been the variety of hemoglobin types. It has been known for several decades that the disease sickle-cell anemia is very common in some parts of the world, especially Africa.

Sickle-cell anemia occurs only when the individual has two representatives of the abnormal gene; that is, the trait is recessive. This is a very severe anemia that, in the primitive African populations where the gene is found, must have in the past been almost invariably lethal. One would expect natural selection to have nearly eliminated the disease; yet, it is quite common in some areas. By analogy with known polymorphisms in insects and from the kinds of theoretical considerations previously referred to, many geneticists suspected that the gene, despite the severity of its effects in double dose, is somehow beneficial in single dose. As long ago as 1949, J. B. S. Haldane, noting the association of the disease with damp, hot climates, suggested that a single dose of the gene somehow confers resistance to malaria. This has since been abundantly confirmed, and it is now clear that the frequency of the gene is mainly determined by a balance between susceptibility to malaria in one homozygous type and severe anemia in the other.

The gene for sickle-cell anemia is important in the history of genetics for another reason. The abnormality is in the hemoglobin molecule. A series of finer and finer chemical analyses finally showed that the difference between normal and sickle-cell hemoglobin lies in a particular site in the molecule. In sickle-cell hemoglobin the glutamic acid normally in this position in the molecule is replaced by another amino acid, valine. This was the first of many similar examples that led the way to establishing the relationship between a gene mutation and an amino acid substitution. Thus, population and molecular biology have explained both the geographical distribution and the chemical basis of the disease. The same mechanism that maintains inverted chromosomes in *Drosophila* and unusual color patterns in butterflies is responsible for the maintenance of the sickle-cell gene.

Some Accomplishments of Classical and Population Genetics

In Understanding Life. The greatest accomplishment of genetics is in providing understanding of the fundamental mechanisms of heredity and evolution, the central problems of biology. The rules of transmission genetics are essentially understood; underlying an immense diversity of reproductive methods, of chromosome shapes and sizes, of external appearances, and of life cycles there is a hereditary mechanism common to all organisms.

Likewise, the known facts of mutation, Mendelian inheritance, and natural selection provide a sufficient basis for understanding the mechanisms of evolution. Furthermore, evolution has been brought into the realm of the experimental sciences. The detailed ways in which selection operates, the effect of population structure, and the values of various evolutionary strategies are now open to experimental investigation.

Mendelian genetics has provided an incisive answer to the old question of the biological value of sexual reproduction. Biparental reproduction and Mendelian assortment provide a means of shuffling the genes so that they can be tried out in various combinations. Then those that work best in the most combinations are retained by the population. In an asexual population, the only way that two favorable mutant genes can get into the same individual is if the second mutant gene occurs in the same individual or one of its descendants. In a sexual population mutant genes that arise in different individuals can be combined in the same one. In this way evolution can proceed much faster. The biological value of sexual reproduction, then, is that it greatly increases the speed of evolution. In this way the population has a far better chance of keeping up with a constantly changing environment.

We should not suppose that our understanding of evolution is applicable only over long geological times. Evolutionary processes of great importance are occurring on short time scales. We have a considerable understanding of these and as a result are able to make reasonable predictions. For example, genetic changes in man arising from the crossing of races, from the increasingly high correlation in intelligence of husband and wife, from changes in the mutation rate as a result of radioactivity, or from a possible law requiring the sterilization of persons with mental retardation can be predicted with reasonable accuracy because of our fundamental understanding of the way in which natural selection acts on genetic variation. Communities of plants and animals are undergoing rapid evolution as a result of short-term changes in the environment, such as is happening through the introduction of insecticides, pesticides, or new agricultural practices. Population genetics enables us to understand and predict the genetic changes likely to occur as a consequence. More and more, as man radically alters the conditions of existence for all other organisms on the earth, population genetics plays an essential role in understanding and predicting the effects of these changes.

In biology there are usually two kinds of explanations for any structure or process. One answers the questions: How does it work? What is the mechanical, chemical, or physical basis? The other asks: Why did it come about? What was its history? What advantage is it to the organisms possessing it? Understanding of genetics and evolution has unified biology in both ways. There is a common physical and chemical basis for heredity — and all living forms share a common evolutionary past.

In Practical Results. The most striking practical achievements based on genetic understanding have been in agriculture. The manipulation of chromosome numbers has permitted fertile hybrids between widely divergent plants. A famous early example is the radish-cabbage hybrid,

Raphanobrassica, made by the Russian geneticist Karpechenko. An example that offers great promise is the wheat-rye hybrid mentioned before. Almost all crop plants have disease problems, and the development of resistant varieties has been a major accomplishment of plant breeders. Sometimes resistant mutants have been found and selected. In most cases, genes for resistance have been brought in from other strains, often wild relatives of the domestic species, such as the rust resistance factor introduced into wheat from goat grass. Sometimes these crosses involve very sophisticated techniques of chromosome engineering, as was mentioned earlier in the transfer of genes from rye to wheat. In these ways varieties of crop plants, particularly cereal grains, have been produced that are high yielding and resistant to rusts, smuts, mildews, and insect pests, and to otherwise unfavorable climatic conditions.

Understanding of the effects of inbreeding and hybridization made possible one of the most important achievements of American agriculture—the development of hybrid corn. The efficiency of seed production has been greatly increased, and the cost of seed thereby lowered, by the development of extrachromosomal genetic factors which cause pollen sterility. By the appropriate combinations of these with ordinary genes that restore fertility the breeder can arrange things so that he can have fertility or sterility as he desires. Thus the costs and difficulties of "detasseling" the corn can be circumvented.

Another example of potentially great practical value was discovered through chemical analysis of the effects of mutant genes. Corn is deficient in some protein constituents that are important nutritionally. A mutant has been found that greatly increases the amount of the deficient amino acids lysine and tryptophan. The incorporation of this gene into commercial varieties, while carefully selecting to maintain the other optimum properties of the commercial strains, should produce corn of special value in improving the standards of nutrition in those parts of the world (e.g., Latin America) where the human population depends strongly on corn for nutrition. Had this corn been in common cultivation in this country at the turn of the century, we might never have known the scourge of pellagra.

Ordinarily, plants with odd numbers of chromosome sets are sterile. This is usually undesirable, of course. Yet there are times when sterility is very much wanted. Much of the desirability of bananas is that they are "seedless." They have three of each chromosome instead of two, with resulting complications during meiosis leading to sterility and tiny seeds. This suggests that in other circumstances where seedlessness is desirable, it may be accomplished by getting triploid strains. This was recently accomplished for watermelons by Japanese geneticists. There is the practical problem of how to maintain a sterile strain. This is solved by producing the strain with three chromosome sets anew each generation by crossing two fertile varieties, one with two sets and the other with four.

In breeding animals and plants for quantitative traits—in particular, performance or yield—the theory of population genetics has been particularly valuable. Selection for desired traits involves the same principles as natural selection, so much of the theory developed for the study of evolution can be carried over directly to give prediction equations for plant and animal breeding. One practical result of selection for body conformation and efficiency of growth in poultry has been that this form of meat is no longer a luxury item.

In medicine the most important practical result has been the deeper insights into disease-producing mechanisms that genetic study has brought about. As described in Chapter 16, there is an ever expanding list of heritable disorders of man. As more is learned about human genetics, genetic counseling becomes increasingly useful. The number of diseases whose heredity is known is now very great and, although most of them are relatively rare, collectively they add up to a great deal of human misery. Much of this can be prevented or anticipated and alleviated by genetic counseling.

In Man's View of Himself. Perhaps the most important result of the growth of evolutionary biology and an understanding of the mechanisms of heredity and evolution is a change in man's view of himself, of his place in the living world, and of his responsibility for its continuance.

Man used to regard himself as somehow apart from the animals and plants, following a set of rules that were different from those followed by the rest of nature. Then the study of comparative anatomy made him realize that he is similar in many structural ways to the other animals. The study of physiology showed similar mechanisms of blood circulation, of muscle contraction, of digestion, and of other body functions. Comparative biochemistry demonstrated the basic similarity of chemical mechanisms, reaction sequences, and metabolic patterns in all living organisms. The study of evolution revealed that all these similarities were the consequence of a common origin.

The interrelatedness of all life is now regarded as a part of the beauty and excitement of nature. We thereby understand ourselves better. The view has practical consequences in that we can learn a great deal about ourselves by studying other organisms. Man, knowing that he is a part of nature, realizes his dependence on the natural environment. We realize that we cannot change this radically from the environment in which man evolved without generating serious problems.

Man's knowledge of his long history gives him a different perspective about his future. He realizes that he has changed greatly in the past and that it is in his nature to continue to change. He now understands his history and the origin of human diversities and similarities. These diversities are not unnatural but are seen as part of a continuing process.

It is humbling to realize that man is, in this sense, only one part of nature, just as a consideration of the size of the universe makes him realize his own relative smallness. But evolutionary biology has also shown us the central role that man is destined to play in evolution from now on—unless, of course, he engineers his own extinction. Although man arose out of an evolutionary process that he didn't understand and over which he had no control, he must now realize that he is unique in the living world in the realization that the responsibility for continuance of this process is his. The future evolution of the orangutan and the whooping crane and of most other species will be determined by human decisions and hardly at all by anything done by the species themselves.

Thus the evolutionary view gives man not only a sense of humility but also a sense of responsibility. The question is not whether man is to influence evolution or not; he is already doing so and indeed changing things so that evolution is taking place more rapidly than at any time in recent history. He now has not only the opportunity to influence the other species, as he has done in the past with domestic plants and animals, but also the opportunity—perhaps the obligation—to influence his own future evolution. The capacity of biologists to develop ways by which man can determine his future evolution is undoubted. The more difficult question is whether he will choose to make such decisions, and with what wisdom.

Current Problems and Changing Approaches

The central problems of population biology are: How did the present kinds and numbers of plants and animals come about? What forces are acting on these populations to maintain or change them? What predictions can be made?

Population biology has already been helped greatly by techniques from other fields. The methods of molecular biology are already beginning to revolutionize the study of hidden variation, and as better methods for measuring nucleic acid and protein differences become available, these will be used for population studies. With the large, fast digital computer, entirely new areas of theory, previously too complex to handle, can now be studied. Computerized data acquisition and analysis, particularly information from human populations, will permit the large numbers needed for deeper understanding of population problems.

A basic limitation of classical genetic analysis is that it depends on breeding methods. A great deal has been learned about genetic differences between two strains of *Drosophila* because they can be crossed. But there is no way of assessing the genetic differences between elephants and mice. Cellular and molecular methods promise to make this possible in the foreseeable future. It is now possible to fuse, in cultures, cells derived from organisms as diverse as mammals and fish. This may lead to a way to analyze genetic differences between distant species. Comparison of proteins, such as hemoglobins, cytochrome C, and ribonucleases, where amino acid sequences are known, has made it possible to determine, for example, how many amino acid differences there are between man and horse in these proteins. From this one can make reasonably accurate estimates of the actual number of mutations required to change a horse gene to a human gene. For the first time geneticists can begin to get an idea of the extent of genetic differences between organisms too different to be crossed, and a fundamental limitation on genetic investigation has been removed. Such studies are in their infancy, but already immensely fruitful.

The same kinds of investigations give for the first time the opportunity to measure *rates* of evolution in absolute terms. It used to be possible to say that the size of the horse had changed by a certain percentage in a million years, but one had no idea what this meant in terms of the number of gene changes involved. It is now possible to discuss rates in the most fundamental units, in terms of the number of base replacements in DNA. Thus it is possible to say, for example, that the rate of evolution of hemoglobin in the recent mammalian past has been roughly one gene replacement per 10 million years.

A related question is this: What fraction of our genes distinguish one human from another, compared with the fraction that make us human? Or what fraction of the genes are the same for all mammals? Or all vertebrates? Or all animals? These kinds of questions can now be approached. The methods of DNA hybridization give a crude beginning. As more exact methods are developed, leading eventually to exact knowledge of large sequences of DNA, such questions — previously outside the realm of answerable problems — come within the range of experimental investigation.

A very similar question is one that has been asked by geneticists since early in the century, but which until recently was such that it had to be dismissed from consideration because of the impossibility of getting an answer. Is the "normal" gene in different individuals a single entity, or is it really a population of different types that differ from one another in ways such as to escape any ordinary means of observation? It has been

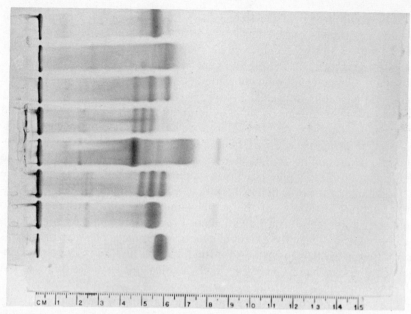

Figure 12-2. Photograph showing the electrophoresis on an acrylamide gel for several individual *Drosophila* flies. The position and appearance of the spot is characteristic of the protein (an enzyme) produced by a specific gene. The first and last are homozygotes, the others are all heterozygous for two different enzyme-producing genes. (Courtesy R. C. Lewontin and J. L. Hubby)

the history of research in genetics that, as each new technique making possible a detection of finer differences is used, such differences have been discovered. For example, among "normal" genes are found forms that are alike by any ordinary criterion but which can be shown to be different by some special technique; perhaps they have different mutation rates, or different expressions in some unusual environment, or have different effects on some other gene. So, differences do exist but there has been no systematic way to search for such genes, and no way to estimate whether they are typical or rare.

Biochemistry has provided the tool. The method of distinguishing enzymes and other proteins by gel electrophoresis has been applied to *Drosophila* populations, with the result that a great deal of variability has been demonstrated. Preliminary estimates suggest that at least one eighth of the gene loci in an individual *Drosophila* are heterozygous or, another way of stating almost the same thing, more than one third of the gene loci are polymorphic. The methods are not able to detect all differences, so these estimates may be substantially too small. Clearly, beneath the superficial uniformity hidden by the word "normal" is an enormous underlying variability (Fig. 12-2).

The question of evolutionary statics—what are the mechanisms by which genetic variability is maintained in the population?—has been the subject of much attention by population geneticists. Although there has been progress in many ways, there is still no quantitative apportionment of the variability among the various causes. In a way the problem is the opposite of what is often the stumbling block. Rather than not having any explanation, geneticists have thought of several mechanisms, any one of which would be sufficient to explain the existing variability. The basic reason was mentioned earlier: with a particulate inheritance only a very small input of new genes is required to maintain a large standing variation. Population genetics theory tells us how fast genetic variability is lost by random processes in a population of given size. New mutations are one source of genetic variability. Another is a stable gene frequency maintained by the fact that a gene is favorable in some combinations, but not in others; the simplest situation is selection in favor of the heterozygous type, as in the sickle-cell anemia case mentioned earlier. Another is selection based on the frequency of a gene; for example, it may be advantageous when rare, but disadvantageous when common, as are some self-sterility genes in plants. Yet another mechanism is a heterogeneous environment that favors one gene in some areas and another gene in others. Other possibilities that seem less promising, but may be of importance in some cases, are distortions of the normal Mendelian ratios by some meiotic peculiarity or selection between gametes, seasonal fluctuations in selection intensities, transitory variability because of a changing environment, and high mutation rate. But much work must be done before we know in any large number of cases how to apportion these various factors.

Another class of problems in which we can expect substantial progress in the near future is in the development of a more complete and flexible theory. Evolutionary genetics has profited by the fact that gifted mathematicians have chosen to work in this area. This will undoubtedly continue and, together with new computer techniques, almost insures an improved theory. Current theory is very powerful, as mathematical theories in biology go, largely because of the elegance and symmetry of Mendelian inheritance. The problems become much more difficult when genes are closely linked—that is, close together on the same chromosome and hence having a tendency to be inherited together—and when there are complex interactions between gene effects. This problem is now being studied both by mathematical methods and by computer. Only the simplest models have been studied as stochastic processes—i.e., with the effects of chance taken into account. As more general procedures for treating such models are developed, they will be useful in population genetics problems.

Human population genetics has commanded increased attention in recent years. One reason is the discovery of a large number of new polymorphisms detected by serological and chemical means. There is general realization that if we are to understand how natural selection has operated in the human evolutionary past, we had better study some populations that are still living under comparable conditions. For example, large, low-income, high-mortality, highly fertile populations in Brazil have been studied to find the way in which selection is acting on the major polymorphisms. So far, the data indicate that the intensity of selection on most of them is very small; but this conclusion needs verification in other populations.

The study of the formal genetics of man is complicated by small family size and the impossibility of experimental matings. Ingenious techniques for extracting meaningful information from this unpromising material have been worked out by statistical geneticists. The general paucity of good data can be partially overcome as more and more hospital and census records are computerized and linked with one another so that large pedigrees can be traced by mechanical means.

An area that has had relatively little emphasis in the past, but is becoming increasingly prominent and promises to be very fruitful in the future, is the border between population genetics and ecology. Population ecologists have many observations and theories regarding the population age structure, the changes in total numbers, the effects of cycles and of fluctuating environments, density-dependent factors, and the effects of other species. But ecological models lack the simple mechanistic basis that Mendelism provides for population genetics. On the other hand, population genetics has not paid sufficient attention to many ecological factors. The recent trend for ecologists and population geneticists to work together holds great promise for the future development of both fields.

Transmission genetics is no longer the most exciting or the central part of genetics. That role is now played by molecular, cellular, and developmental genetics. But there is continued need for study of "classical" genetics on a comparative basis. Despite the underlying similarity of the genetic system and the unifying base provided by the universality of DNA and the genetic code, there is great diversity at other levels. The science of comparative genetics could become as important a part of the study of evolution in the next fifty years as comparative anatomy was in the past. The peculiar sex-determining system in the honeybee, distortions of the regular Mendelian ratios in some strains of *Drosophila* and mice, the chromosome eliminating systems in the fly *Sciara,* and various sexual and asexual reproductive systems in plants show the wealth of diversity in genetic and evolutionary mechanisms. But the number of species studied in any detail is such an extremely small and nonrandom sample of all of nature that only a beginning has been made.

Mathematical and experimental studies of evolution have been concerned primarily with rather short time changes in rather simple systems. The theory deals primarily with competition between individuals. Yet, it seems likely that selection on other than an individual basis is also important in evolution. This must have been especially important in higher organisms with a social structure, and still more so in man's history. By helping his close relatives an individual is helping to preserve his own genetic heritage, because of shared genes. Thus natural selection will increase genes leading to such behavior. How important such "kin" selection has been in evolution is not known, but it is the most obvious way of explaining the development of cooperative and altruistic behavior by natural selection. The general question of the relative importance of selection at the individual and group level is in need of more study.

In another direction, we need to know more about the evolution of species. What are the necessary conditions for species formation? We know that new species can arise by geographical separation over long periods of time and by sudden changes in chromosome number. What are the genetic and ecological factors in general that lead to species formation? What other mechanisms are there?

Biological research includes both a search for generality and a search for variety. Molecular biology is seeking and finding biological facts that appear to be true for all living forms. At the other extreme, systematic biology emphasizes the diversity of life. Both aims are meaningful and important aspects of biological research, and population biology utilizes both approaches. The theory of evolution has great generality. But the detailed ways in which selection works are also of interest and often of great practical value. Out of the details will emerge the hierarchies of levels of generality that make biology so fascinating and will serve as a guide to the future.

Chapter 13

THE DIVERSITY OF LIFE

Wherever we study nature, be it the microscopic life in a drop of pond water, the flowers on an alpine meadow, the birds and trees in our woods, or the marine invertebrates in the intertidal zone, we are overwhelmed by the number of different kinds of organisms we find. When we go north, south, east, or west, we encounter new kinds of animals and plants, and if we go to another continent, South America, Africa, or Australia, the entire animal and plant life will be different.

Only he who studies it with great care can appreciate the magnitude of this organic diversity. Physicists deal with about fifty kinds of elementary particles. Three of these combine to form just over a hundred different elements, and the number of naturally occurring simple molecules is a matter of a few thousand. In contrast, biologists estimate that five to ten million different species of organisms exist today, each differing significantly from its closest relative. Within a single species most of the millions of members are genetically different from all the others. They are unique. And yet currently living species are only a small fraction (far less than one percent) of all the different kinds that have lived and died since life began on earth, some three or four billion years ago. The totality of biological diversity is almost incomprehensible to the human imagination.

The biological science that deals with this diversity is *systematics*. It deals with the elementary classification of animals and plants (taxonomy) and studies the evolutionary, ecological, and behavioral aspects of their diversity. In these broader concerns it joins with all other biological disciplines.

The study of diversity is important for many reasons. Organic diversity is one of the most conspicuous aspects of the world we live in. It is part of man's nature to be interested in more than purely utilitarian things, to concern himself with the stars in the heavens and with all his fellow creatures. As early as 1694, the great British botanist John Ray charmingly discussed "why the good Lord had created such a vast multitude of insects as the world is filled with; most of which seem to be useless, and some also noxious and pernicious to man." He gave a number of reasons. "One might be to exercise the contemplative faculty of man; which is in nothing so much pleased as in variety of objects; . . . new objects afford us great delight, especially if found out by our own industry." The modern biologist sees still other reasons.

Every species of organism is a unique genetic system, differing from all other species in structural, physiological, behavioral, and other characteristics. Every biologist must determine the identity of the organism with which he is working to make sure that his observations and experiments are meaningful. A classification of the diverse species is an indispensable information retrieval system. The name of an organism is like the index number of a file; it gives immediate access to all the information existing about it. The scientific name is the key to the entire literature that deals with a particular species or higher taxon. Evolutionary relationships among organisms, revealed by classification, represent an important source of information for every kind of biological study.

The high specificity of different kinds of organisms is also of great practical importance. When prickly pear was introduced into Australia by a cactus fancier, it spread unchecked and overran fifty million acres of valuable sheep pastures. Only after 145 organisms found feeding on prickly pear in North and South America were carefully studied was a small and inconspicuous moth finally located in Uruguay which flourished in the Australian climate, and whose larvae soon destroyed the prickly pear plants, restoring the pastures to their former value. Hundreds of similar examples can be cited from the biological control literature.

Water pollution is now rightly considered one of our foremost problems. There is no more accurate or quicker way to determine the degree and the nature of pollution of a given body of water than to study the algae and other microscopic plankton organisms found in the water. Each species has its own requirements for oxygen, nitrogen, and other organic and inorganic additives to the water, and their study permits a rapid and inexpensive monitoring service. Monitoring for pollution through numerical surveys for key species plays an increasing role in the study of soils and polluted waters. Other areas where a precise knowledge of organic diversity is of great importance will be discussed below.

Aspects of Diversity

Life appears to have originated on earth only once. The diversity of life now found is due to a continuous process of speciation, the process wherein one species yields several descendant species. Since each of the major groups of organisms—the seed plants, the insects, the birds, the mammals, the primates, the hominids, and so on—go back to one original founder species, speciation is the most important single event in evolution. How does it come about?

Darwin's great work was entitled *On the Origin of Species.* Yet, curiously, Darwin actually failed to solve the problem of the multiplication of species, the problem of how one species splits into several daughter species. He failed because he did not fully understand the nature of the biological species. Species of organisms cannot be defined by degree of difference or by their essences, as can "species" of inanimate objects or the species of the philosophers. A species of animals or plants is characterized by two properties: by representing a gene pool adapted to utilize a particular niche in nature, and more importantly by the possession of protective mechanisms that prevent mixing with other gene pools. The genetic mechanisms by which crossbreeding with other species is prevented are called *isolating mechanisms.* Each living species is a harmoniously adapted genetic system, and the isolating mechanisms operate to prevent the mixing of two incompatible genetic systems which could lead to the production of disharmonious and selectively inferior hybrids.

It is now possible to pose the problem of speciation more precisely. How do new gene pools originate protective isolating mechanisms that work efficiently? The most frequent process to achieve this is "geographical speciation," the temporary spatial separation of a population from the gene pool of the parental species and the gradual building up of isolating mechanisms in the geographically isolated population. After the isolating mechanisms have been reasonably perfected through steady process of mutational change, the extrinsic (mostly geographical) barrier can break down, and the daughter species can now coexist with the parental species, protected by its isolating mechanisms.

Another process of speciation is by chromosome doubling (polyploidy), a process to which about half of the plant species owe their origin, but which is very rare in sexually reproducing animals. As noted in the earlier discussion of the origin of new proteins, in an organism possessing a duplicate set of chromosomes, one set is free to mutate without threat to viability. If the products of the mutated genes afford selective advantage in a specific environment, an evolutionary step has been taken.

Although the process of speciation is now understood in its simplest outlines, there is still much uncertainty about the factors that control the rate of speciation in different organisms. What influence does the size of the gene pool have on this rate? There are indications that small "founder populations" speciate far more rapidly than large populations. Most of our knowledge is based on birds, a few other groups of vertebrates, as well as some insects, molluscs, and flowering plants; speciation in lower invertebrates and lower plants has hardly been explored. Most available data concern organisms that live in the middle latitudes of the Northern Hemisphere. Here it is evident that the climatic changes during the Pleistocene fragmented the ranges of many species, greatly accelerating the process of geographical speciation and that here, as well as on islands, are numerous instances of incipient species, many of them highly localized. Incipient species provide an invaluable opportunity for elucidating the rate of geographical speciation and the factors that contribute to it. It is imperative that such studies are carried out before man's misuse of the environment destroys this opportunity forever. The nature of the biotic environment and other ecological factors basic to speciation have been studied insufficiently. There are, as yet, no answers to such questions as:

1. How does the coexistence of populations of other, closely or distantly related, species affect the rate of speciation?
2. When several coexisting species have similar environmental requirements, does this facilitate shifts into other environmental niches?
3. Under what conditions does a limited amount of hybridization between sympatric species result in a gradual breaking down of the reproductive isolation between these species, or conversely lead to the perfection of the isolating mechanisms through the selective elimination of inferior hybrids? Do plants differ in this respect from animals?

Answers to these questions can be provided only in part by a perceptive study of nature's own experiments; it will surely also require some deliberate experimentation — that is, the manipulation of populations under essentially natural conditions. A particularly great need exists for expanding speciation research into the tropics. The tropics, for example, the Amazon Basin, are notable for their extraordinarily rich faunas and

floras. These areas are also remarkable for their highly stable environments, and the question arises to what extent is the high number of
tropical species due to a high rate of speciation and to what extent due to
an increased survival of species in the equitable tropical environment.
The richness of the tropical biota does not necessarily prove an elevated
rate of speciation. Sophisticated work on rates and mechanisms of
speciation in the tropics is remarkably scarce. Tropical ecosystems are
characterized by containing very many species, each with relatively few
individuals, in contrast to nontropical ecosystems containing many
individuals of relatively few species. Is there any relationship between
these differences in ecosystem structure and the rates and processes of
speciation?

There are indications that geographical isolation may be unnecessary
for speciation in certain ecological specialists, such as plant-feeding insects that are highly host-specific. After a population has become established on a new host plant, can selection pressures overcome the leveling
effects of gene flow between populations on the old and the new plant
hosts? How large a part of the genotype participates in the genetic basis
for host specificity and isolating mechanisms? These unanswered questions are wide-open areas for future experimental research.

We have every reason to assume that no qualitative difference exists
between speciation in marine organisms and the processes established
for terrestrial organisms. But we do not know what the geographical barriers in the oceans are, particularly for pelagic organisms. Many species
are restricted to certain water masses with well-defined physical-chemical
properties, and this preference may reinforce the geographical barriers.
As with freshwater organisms, the presence of particular species in a
given body of water is often as useful an indicator of the history and the
physical properties of this water mass as certain physical constants.

The shoreline, particularly the intertidal zone, presents some fascinating problems. The total width of the species range at a given locality may
be just a few meters, and yet may extend for five hundred or a thousand
miles. The essentially linear nature of the distribution of the rich intertidal
fauna and flora poses problems of climatic gradients, geographical variation of niche preference, and changes in the competitive interaction with
the changing biota of other localities. Many intertidal genera are rich in
sympatric sibling species, and their precise identification is a prerequisite
of ecological studies.

The determinants of the actual number of species found in a given
locality are still incompletely understood. Why is a tropical reef ten
times as rich in species as a rocky reef in cool waters? Why is a tropical

forest so rich in trees, insects, and birds? What are the respective contributions made by competition, predation, richness of resources, or mitigation of seasonal contrasts? We cannot begin to answer these questions until we have better factual information, based on improved census methods. The study of the causes for changes in species diversity is at present one of the most active areas of population ecology.

Geographical Variation

A species is represented at every locality by a single population, and it is this population that interacts with the coexisting populations of other species. Yet each species has a more or less extensive geographical range, and most consist of thousands or even millions of such local populations. Even though they share the isolating mechanisms and other physiological and developmental components of the genetic system of the species, they will, nevertheless, differ in minor genetic ways from one another, not only owing to chance phenomena (e.g., mutation, recombination, errors of sampling), but also because the population of each locality is exposed to a slightly different set of selection pressures. For example, where the environment changes abruptly, as may occur in soil color, the protectively colored coat of mice may change equally abruptly, while other attributes of these mice remain unchanged. Where the environment changes gradually from one end of the species range to the other, one generally finds only a gradual change in those characters that vary geographically.

Any feature of an organism that adapts it to its physical or biotic environment may vary geographically. This is as true for physiological and behavioral characters as for structural ones. Populations of a grass may flower in March along the Gulf Coast, while other populations of the species in Kansas may not flower until May or June. The breeding season of populations of a species of toad that lives in the Great Plains is regulated by rainfall, while in populations of the same species in the Great Basin, with permanent runoff water from the mountains available, the breeding season is regulated by temperature and/or photo period.

No matter how well populations respond to the demands of local environments, there is a line, the geographical species border, which is the limit of tolerance of the genetic system of a species. Insufficient research has been done to answer the tantalizing question of why the frontier populations of a species do not respond to the selection of new genotypes that would permit expanding the species border at a regular annual rate. To answer this question would require a far greater knowledge of the cohesive factors in the genetic systems of species than we have at present.

There are rather severe limits to the tolerance of a gene pool. A phyletic line can expand its utilization of the environment only by budding off new gene pools (speciating). Yet, the entering of new niches can be effected by a minor reconstruction of the genotype. Birds illustrate excellently how a type of organism can become adapted to a multitude of different environments without any basic change of its original morphology. No matter how diverse the niches of woodpeckers, penguins, hummingbirds, albatrosses, ducks, swifts, etc., are, these birds are nevertheless anatomically, physiologically, and in most aspects of their life histories remarkably similar.

Among plants we find that some families have become almost entirely adapted to certain special environmental situations, such as the cactus family to arid country and the water lily family to aquatic situations. Other families are much more flexible and flourish in many different kinds of environments without giving up their basic family identity. For example, the sunflower family runs almost the whole gamut of plant forms, ranging from annual and perennial herbs, including some of our most familiar weeds, to large woody trees and shrubs, herbaceous and woody climbing and twining vines, the strange plants of high mountains in Africa and South America that consist of a tall, thick stem with a crown of leaves at the top, and even to cactuslike succulents.

Evolutionary convergence, with similar selective pressures driving unrelated and rather different genotypes into similar ecological niches, is another exciting but inadequately investigated phenomenon. The "cactus" growth form has appeared in several distinct families of plants, and some of these succulents are so similar in appearance that a nonspecialist has difficulty in identifying the family. Old World tree frogs and New World tree frogs are so similar in adaptation to life in trees that it is necessary to examine the skeleton to determine which is which, yet they have originated as independent radiations within separate families. In Australia, where ordinary frogs (ranids) are virtually absent, a tree frog has evolved habits, body size, and even shape and appearance of our common leopard frog (a ranid). These and many other examples of convergence imply that there is a finite number of ways in which an organism of a given basic genotype can "make a living." However, the study of convergence is only now beginning to shift from a purely descriptive natural history phase to a sophisticated and statistical analysis. We do not know yet what part of the genotype responds to such highly specific selection pressures and how the harmony of the gene pool is maintained during the acquisition of the new adaptation.

Origin of Higher Groups

In addition to species, we distinguish broader assemblages in the diversity of nature, such as birds, beetles, ferns, and snails. How did they come about? Some students of evolution formerly favored large-scale mutations as the cause of the origin of new types. But all the available evidence indicates that higher groups of organisms arise through an extension of the same summation processes that give rise to species. The interpretation of the fossil record by paleontologists, combined with an understanding of the genetic and evolutionary mechanisms, permits the evolutionist to paint a convincing picture of how macroevolution occurs.

The first step is always the entrance of a population or species into a new niche or adaptive zone. It seems as if some individuals of such a population are genetically predisposed to make such a change. In other cases the mere formation of a new habit without an initial genetic change may be the first step. Once this step is taken, a new selection pressure will arise, favoring all those individuals which by their genetic constitution are superior in utilizing the new niche. This is apparently how the earliest ancestors of all terrestrial animals became amphibious and how the earliest ancestors of all flying animals began to glide. The probability is, of course, extremely low that any particular genotype has the potential to initiate a new major group, but with millions of species simultaneously in existence, this must have happened many times in the course of the more than three billion years of life on earth. Even where the first adaptations were behavioral, like air swallowing in an ancestor of the lungfishes, they set the stage for additional structural and functional adaptations which make the occupation of the new adaptive zone more effective.

How do entirely new organs or structures come into existence? Darwin knew that there are two answers to this question, even though much of the detail has been worked out only in recent years. Sometimes merely the intensification of the function of a previously existing organ is involved, such as when lungs developed as sinuses of the esophagus in air-gulping fishes living in stagnating swamps. The other answer is that a preexisting structure takes on a second function without interference with the original function until the new function becomes the primary one. The feathers in birds, for instance, are believed to have been acquired by the avian ancestors to facilitate maintenance of a constant body temperature and acquired only secondarily the new function as enlargements of the gliding surface of the wing. Evolution is quite opportunistic, selection making use of whatever variable structures are available. Floating in water is tremendously important in all pelagic animals. Yet each group has solved this problem in a somewhat different way: some by air-filled swim bladders, others by storing oil drops, and still others by enlarging the body surface (to increase friction) or by methods for active swimming. It is this very diversity by which evolution solves an adaptational challenge which indicates that the Darwinian interpretation, variability and selection, is indeed consistent with all the known facts.

The fossil record poses numerous challenges to the evolutionist. Why do certain groups remain virtually unchanged for hundreds of millions of years, while others simultaneously undergo radical changes, seemingly in the same environment? Why do certain groups undergo almost explosive diversification leading to a simultaneous invasion of all sorts of new adaptive zones—referred to as adaptive radiation—while others show no indications of branching and remain within the ancestral niche?

Some of these evolutionary happenings, long known to the paleontologist, seem to be going on right under our noses. Beautiful contemporary cases of adaptive radiation are known from tropical archipelagos. An example is Darwin's finches in the Galapagos Islands. Here a finch-like ancestor has given to rise to grosbeaks with enormous bills and to other forms that fill the ecological niches of warblers and woodpeckers. Even more extreme is the case of the Hawaiian honeycreepers (Drepanididae), in which just about every bill type has evolved that is known among songbirds, ranging from extreme grosbeak types to the most slender, long, curved sicklebills (adapted for nectar feeding). There is every reason to believe that cases of adaptive radiation are extremely widespread, but only a few have been thoroughly studied up to the present.

One of the most interesting challenges of evolutionary research is the reconstruction of the intermediate stages leading from one kind of organism to another one. The discovery of key fossils, so-called missing links, has been a great help, such as *Archaeopteryx* between reptiles and birds, the mammal-like reptiles (therapsids) between reptiles and mammals, and *Ichthyostega* between rhipidistian fishes and amphibians. Many other such transitions are still shrouded in complete mystery. The higher plants (angiosperms), now the dominant group of plants in most of the world, have not yet been clearly traced to an ancestral group among the lower plants. Some 25 major phyla are recognized for all the animals, and in virtually not a single case is there fossil evidence to demonstrate what the common ancestry of any two phyla looked like. Representatives of nearly all the animal phyla with preservable hard parts appear in definite form at the time of the Cambrian (or latest Precambrian), from 500 to 600 million years ago, when the first animals turn up in the fossil record. A more careful study of the earliest fossils, a study of the chemistry of the preceding strata to determine the reasons for the sudden occurrence of so many hard-shelled forms, a far more extensive search through late Precambrian deposits, are among the needs of further research. This has to be combined with a new look at the axioms of comparative anatomy. What structures of the primitive invertebrates are genuine indicators of relationship, and what others might have originated repeatedly as the most logical responses to functional demands? What is the meaning of the facts of embryology in relation to phylogeny? A large area of biology that seemed an exhausted mine is suddenly becoming productive again.

Processes of Extinction

Of all evolutionary phenomena, extinction, the termination of an evolutionary line without descendants, is perhaps the most poorly understood and yet one of the most remarkable. More than 99 percent of all evolutionary lines that once existed are now extinct. Considerable progress has been made in recent years in explaining the extinction of species owing to changes in the physical or biotic environment. Yet, all explanations for the decline and final extinction of entire major groups, as has occurred many times in the geological past, are still totally unsatisfactory.

At the close of the Cambrian period, of sixty trilobite families, the dominant group of animals in this era, nearly forty disappeared from the subsequent fossil record, and after another period of flowering in the Ordovician, the entire phylum disappeared before the end of the Paleozoic. Near the end of the Permian about twenty-four orders and half of the then known families of animals became extinct; and again, during the last part of the Cretaceous, one quarter of all the animal families were eliminated. Such periods of extinction have been equally devastating for dominant groups in the oceans, like the ammonites, and on land, like the dinosaurs. This great group of reptiles included relatively small species and gigantic ones, carnivores and herbivores, running species and sluggish, amphibious dwellers of swamps, and yet they all succumbed. Not one of the many theories advanced to explain this catastrophe is convincing. By contrast, plant extinctions have been more gradual; the important floristic changes have not coincided with the major extinctions of animal groups. Most major groups of plants persist for long periods, and many are seemingly immortal.

The Permian, Triassic, and Cretaceous extinctions involved both marine and terrestrial animal groups, many of them distributed throughout the world in a wide range of habitats. Competition from evolutionary newcomers, changes in climate, or modifications of breeding habits can hardly explain the disappearance of such dominant and widespread groups as the dinosaurs or the marked decline of the ammonites at the close of the Permian, during the Triassic, and their final extinction at the end of the Cretaceous; nor can these factors explain the extinction of the Devonian placoderm fishes and the abundant and diversified Mesozoic marine reptiles. With so many species in existence, one would have expected at least some of them to shift into new adaptive zones and thus escape the fate of their relatives. Why was natural selection so powerless to prevent these wholesale extinctions?

Competition is sometimes a factor, and the absence of it is undoubtedly a primary reason for the survival of *Sphenodon,* the last representative of the rhynchocephalian order of reptiles, on an island off New Zealand. The prosperity of marsupials in Australia and the Papuan region may well be due to the scarcity of placental mammals in these areas. It is much harder to believe that the diurnal terrestrial reptiles of the Mesozoic were actually competing with the presumably nocturnal Mesozoic mammals, although it is correct that the extinction of the Mesozoic reptiles vacated broad niches and habitats that were subsequently filled by the diversifying mammals.

A family, an order, a class, or a phylum does not become extinct at once. Instead, the most reasonable general explanation for extinction is to relate it to changes in the entire ecosystem. The rise of the angiosperm plants in the Cretaceous undoubtedly had an adverse effect on the previously ruling herbivore reptiles, and this in turn brought about the decline of the carnivorous types. The important point is that the entire biota at any one time is interrelated and interdependent in an extremely complicated manner. Whatever factor affects the primary producers in such a system will have a profound and selective effect on the primary and secondary consumers that may lead to partial and complete extinction and to the formation of new ecosystems.

The History of Life

Students of fossil life have succeeded to a remarkable extent in reconstructing the sequence in which various forms of life first turned up in the various geological ages. Establishing this chronology opens up many intriguing biological problems to investigation, particularly trends and rates of evolution, and the many questions raised by the origin of evolutionary novelties. Without a knowledge of the fossil record the evolutionist cannot begin to solve these problems; indeed, he would be unaware of some of the more fascinating phenomena of evolutionary biology. All more ambitious studies must start with the precise description and reliable classification of the fossil forms. To draw the proper inferences from the seriously incomplete fossil record is no easy task. How incomplete this record is, particularly for soft-bodied organisms, is indicated by the estimate that only 1 out of 5,000 to 10,000 formerly existing species is preserved in the known fossil record. Organisms with preservable hard parts have left a far better record. For example, the history of the vertebrates is now understood in its major outlines, even though there is still much uncertainty about the earliest history of the amphibians and the more primitive types of fishes. The origin of the major groups of plants is far more shrouded in mystery, well illustrated by the fact that we still search for the ancestor of the dominant group of modern plants, the angiosperms. The gaps in our knowledge are still enormous, but there is hope that some will be filled through further research.

Organic Diversity and the Conceptual Framework of Biology

The life sciences encompass a broader field than the totality of the physical sciences. Within this area, each branch of biology makes its particular contribution to the sum of biological understanding. Neglect of any part of biology leads to a weakening and an imbalance of biology as a whole. The continued well-being of systematic biology is of such great importance to biology as a whole because the study of diversity with its emphasis on evolution, the creativeness of the selective process, the history of genetic programs, the uniqueness of individuals and species, and the statistical properties of populations and taxa, places emphasis on perhaps the most strictly "biological" of all phenomena. At the molecular and cellular levels, the biologist is very close to chemistry and physics; indeed it is his avowed objective to reduce his findings to phenomena that can be expressed in terms of chemistry and physics. The evolutionist, on the other hand, is constantly aware that organisms are the products of individual genetic programs carefully adjusted by hundreds of millions of years of natural selection. All the components of these organic systems are explicable in terms of physics and chemistry, but each system as a whole, with its evolved genetic program and all of its homeostatic control mechanisms, is more complex by at least one order of magnitude than anything found in inorganic nature. Stated otherwise, granted our understanding of DNA, enzyme mechanisms, membranes and nervous conduction, these still do not permit prediction that there would be butterflies, orchids, or porpoises, much less man. Philosophy has not yet digested the biologist's way of looking at living nature, free of all vitalistic and finalistic ideas; but in the wake of the spectacular advances of chemical and evolutionary biology, one day there must emerge a new philosophy of science, based largely on the findings of biology rather than those of physics.

Systematics, including evolutionary biology, has produced fundamental generalizations of concern to every thinking human being. Perhaps the most important contribution after the theory of organic evolution is the development of "population thinking." The populationist stresses that all classes of objects and phenomena in the living world are composed of uniquely different individuals and that all statements concerning such populations of individuals must be taken in a statistical sense. Almost all statements which one makes in biology except at the molecular level are relative or statistical. One cannot understand the working of natural selection or the phenomenon of race or of fitness unless one fully understands the populational nature of biological phenomena. The gradual replacement of the ideology of essentialist philosophy, dominant from Plato and Aristotle to the Kantians, by population thinking during the past century has been one of the most important, even though hardly noticed, conceptual revolutions in the history of biology, a revolution originating in systematics and evolutionary biology.

These developments have decisive bearing on our understanding of man. Although man is unique, he is part of the evolutionary stream and cannot be understood if treated as an isolated phenomenon. He must be compared with the remainder of the organic world; systematic biology has supplied much of the information and the conceptual framework to make such a comparison feasible. This comparison has revealed in which respects man resembles other organisms as a consequence of his evolutionary heritage and in which respects he is indeed unique. *Evolutionary biology has succeeded in dealing with man objectively and scientifically, rather than as an object of ideology or dogma.*

The evolutionary process applies to man in the same manner as to all other organisms. Every problem faced by man, whether it be disease prevention, increasing the length of life, population control, ethical systems, the possibility of eugenics, etc., will be better understood as our comprehension increases of the evolutionary process by which man evolved and acquired his present characteristics. As man's knowledge increases, and as he acquires more and more control over his own fate and his planet, he takes on an increasing responsibility to predict the consequences of his actions farther and farther into the future and to adjust his actions accordingly. He can do this only by understanding the present in terms of the past. It would be a fatal mistake to consider man as something static. He is the product of evolution, and he is continuing to evolve as an inevitable consequence of genetic variability and differential reproduction. Evolutionary biology gives us major tools with which to conduct the studies that are necessary for a scientific approach to the future of man, and will contribute to creation of the badly needed bridge between biology and the social sciences.

Applications of the Study of Diversity

The study of diversity is of great practical importance to man. Perhaps the most important lesson we have learned is the high degree of specificity of every species in nature. It is not nature that produces drying oils, fibers, or drugs, but it is sheep that produce wool, cotton plants cotton, pigs bacon, cows milk, *Hevea* trees rubber, a specific mold penicillin, and so forth. The general laws of biology are important, and the study of the basic unit processes and macromolecules is fascinating and useful, but biology would remain one-sided and ineffective if it did not simultaneously develop a study of individual organisms on a broad scale.

Animals and Plants

Whether we focus on beneficial organisms or noxious ones, it is most impressive to consider the impact of certain species on man. Let us start with some noxious species. The cotton boll weevil requires the annual application of tens of millions of dollars worth of pesticides to prevent destruction of the cotton crop. *Complete control of one major pest, the rice stem borer of Asia, would immediately provide food for 120 million people, without additional effort or labor or updating of agricultural methods.* Consider the impact on the North American landscape and agriculture of the inadvertent introduction of such pests as the European corn borer, a multimillion dollar pest, or the gypsy moth, also from Europe, which has destroyed tens of thousands of acres of forest, or the notorious Japanese beetle, or the fungi responsible for the chestnut blight, or the Dutch elm disease! Past experience has shown that chemical controls of such pests have numerous drawbacks. They are expensive, usually result in the development of resistant strains, and tend to do much damage to the associated fauna and flora. This use of dangerous poisons must be eliminated, so far as possible. Biological control is far preferable, as demonstrated by the control of the prickly pear, the Klamath weed, various citrus scales, and the screwworm. Yet this requires an imaginative and painstaking analysis of the life cycle of the pest, its diseases, predators, and competitors, its wintering habits, etc. Control of the screwworm was not possible until it was shown that two sibling species were confused with each other, only one of which was noxious. Highly beneficial species can exist undiscovered right under our noses, with their ecological role unknown and unappreciated. For instance, attempts to grow figs in the United States failed repeatedly until a tiny wasp, previously not known to be necessary for pollination of the fig flowers, was imported.

It is obvious that permanent, effective control of some of the world's most destructive insects has not yet been achieved. In considerable measure, this reflects lack of a broad systematic and biological knowledge of the diverse potential parasites and predators that would carry out the job for us.

A thorough knowledge of the diversity of organisms is even more essential when we try to harness additional beneficial species for our purposes. The world's oceans have been called the last "great unexplored and unexploited frontier," and it has been suggested that the world's protein deficiency could be covered by the productivity of the sea. There has been a great increase in the harvesting of fish, particularly by automation, but the development of fundamental background knowledge has not kept up with purely commercial exploitation. All the fishing pressure at present is on comparatively few species. Undoubtedly, other species might be added to the pool of potentially exploitable species. How large are their geographical ranges, and when are their breeding seasons? What restrictions must be placed on fishing to maintain the breeding stocks? Decisions based on many kinds of biological information will surely have to be made. How to divide up the oceanic pool of fish derived from continental breeding stocks (such as salmon) has already become a question beset with ancillary economic and political complications. Fishing pressure cannot be regulated wisely until much more research has been carried out. For the Northern Pacific salmon populations it has become necessary to identify individuals and populations derived from individual breeding streams. In order to identify populations correctly, it has become necessary to apply immunological procedures, sophisticated morphometric analysis, and other modern systematic approaches. Even the parasites have been useful in difficult cases, and extensive lists of organisms associated with the salmon have been compiled for different geographical regions.

Crustaceans furnish rich yields of high-grade protein, but remarkably few species are so far exploited. A substantial proportion of the annual catch in the United States consists of one or two species of shrimp, even though hundreds of unexploited species of crustaceans of comparable size exist, as well as thousands of smaller species, which could be subjected to processing of some kind. Why should it not be possible to develop harvesting and processing methods for the krill (*Euphausia superba*), the whale food, which is obviously highly nutritious and occurs in rich abundance? Protein extracts from fish are now being produced routinely; crustaceans could be used just as well, and have an additional tremendous potential as producers of oils and of vitamins and their precursors. A small, ancient industry in southeast Asia produces "shrimp paste" from a variety of crustaceans, not only highly palatable and nutritious but also promising as a processing approach for a great variety of crustaceans now completely bypassed, yet in large part readily available the world over.

The possibility of direct harvesting of plankton has often been discussed. Here the problems are decidedly taxonomic, since repugnant and indeed toxic species exist in many plankton assemblages. The identification of directly usable plankton might eventually lead to the possibility of specialized culturing of such organisms. Pilot activities indicate the manifold problems that still have to be overcome, particularly an exhaustive study of the total requirements of the relevent species.

Aquatic farming for many kinds of organisms is rapidly expanding. Raising carp and carplike fishes is an ancient custom in Europe and Asia. Fish rearing in tropical lands has long passed its pioneer phase, but its full potential has nowhere been reached. Many additional species that might be suitable for freshwater farming have yet to be exploited.

The farming of marine organisms is even less developed. Its greatest success has been the farming of shellfish, such as clams and oysters, where an even richer protein source can be made available through further development of technology. At present only a few species are used the world over, but with the systematic knowledge now in hand, shellfish farming could unquestionably be vastly expanded through imaginative and ingenious exploration, unless prevented by the increasing pollution of our estuaries and coastlines. The production of pearls and the harvesting of many products of marine plants, as the alginates, agar, and other compounds, involve procedures basically similar to those of food harvests. Commercial pearl production has also expanded to previously unexploited species of molluscs because they produce products that are in special demand. Many further species of marine organisms with a wide diversity of applications could be successfully subjected to various farming procedures. In addition to their food value, they are undoubtedly an important potential source of drugs, antibiotics, and other complex products.

In the exploitation of wild plants for drugs and other natural products, the identity of the plants concerned, as well as their systematic relationships, becomes especially critical. For example, those species of *Cinchona* related to *C. calisaya* give a high yield of quinine and quinidine, and are the source of highly selected varieties long cultivated in Java and Sumatra. *Cinchona pubescens* and its relatives, however, as well as species of the related genera *Remijia* and *Ladenbergia,* produce primarily the alkaloids cinchonine and cinchonidine, which do not have nearly as high an antimalarial value. *Rauwolfia,* from which the first successful tranquilizer was obtained, has been well known in India for millennia. However, because the genus was relatively well known systematic botanists predicted immediately that certain related tropical American species would likewise be active — as proved to be true. Yet only three species are so far being exploited commercially, in spite of a hundred that need to be studied. Another relatively recently introduced drug is *curare,* whose source was a mystery well kept by South American Indians. Now, however, we know that the primary genera concerned are *Strychnos* and *Chondrodendron*; here, again, both the Indian who makes curare for hunting and the individual who collects these plants commercially for industrial purposes must be aware of the various species and which are the best ones for the purpose.

Not only individual species, but whole genera and even families have highly specific characteristics. For example, the Rubiaceae are rich in genera that produce alkaloids: in addition to *Cinchona,* we find coffee and ipecac, which was known to the South American Indians as a specific for amebic dysentery long before it was added to the European and American pharmacopoeia. The Asclepiadaceae and Apocynaceae, very large families especially well developed in the tropics, contain few members that are not toxic. Because of their abundant production of alkaloids — our common roadside weed of the temperate United States, *Apocynum cannabinum,* for good reason is called the "dogbane" — many tropical and subtropical ornamental plants, belonging to these families, are dangerously poisonous, including such familiar plants as the oleander. This knowledge of widespread properties is useful in many families of plants and give a very useful guideline for drug companies and others who are interested in natural plant products.

An excellent illustration of the utility of systematics is given by two closely related plant families, some of whose members are difficult to distinguish by the usual morphological methods: the Solanaceae (or nightshade family) and Scrophulariaceae (or snapdragon family). Most members of the first family, even the so-called Irish potato, are rich in alkaloids, many of them of medicinal importance, such as atropine, whereas the second family has no alkaloids at all, only saponins, some of which, like digitalis, are also of great medicinal value. By a survey of higher plants, then, one can identify certain families that have, through evolution, specialized in the production of certain useful materials. To find new sources and new products, one need only extend the study within a promising family. Already published systematic research has provided an extremely useful shortcut in such searches, whereas poorly known plant groups have had to be investigated laboriously for potentially useful products.

Other evidence of the economic value of systematics comes from a survey of the cultivated plants—and it is astonishing to see how few plant families provide so much of man's food and fiber. All our major cereals belong to the grass family, in the tropics as well as in temperate areas. The hundreds of kinds of peas and beans of the legume family found in every continent not only form a staple food of man but provide the greatest source of protein of any major plant family. The Rosaceae are the greatest producers of fruit cultivated by man or harvested in the wild, from strawberries through raspberries, blackberries, and their relatives, to stone fruits, as peaches, plums, and cherries, and apples, pears, and their relatives. Most of our root crops are produced by two families, the carrot family and the turnip family, both of them excellent examples with many related forms that immediately come to mind. The carrot family provides such edible leaf stalks as celery, fennel, and parsley, whereas the turnip family provides us with such edible stems, leaves, and flowers as cabbage, brussels sprouts, cauliflower, and many others. Other families of importance to man, especially for food, are the lily family (onions, garlic, and relatives), the squash family (including melons, cucumbers, pumpkins), the nightshade family, with many edible forms, such as potatoes, tomatoes, and peppers (as well as poisonous ones), the heather family with cranberries, blueberries, lingonberries, and many other kinds of berries—and so on. Some families are so important that whole cultures are based around them, for example, the palm cultures of tropical India and elsewhere, and the bamboo cultures of southeast Asia, where the plants provide not only basic food but also the primary source of shelter.

In summary, the families of higher plants that are rich in useful species can have their usefulness extended by further systematic study, and the many plant families that are now little used may well turn out to have unexpected and surprising products of great use to man if we have but the wisdom to seek them.

Fungi and Microorganisms

Yeasts, molds, and other fungi, bacteria, and other microorganisms form a vast and almost untapped reservoir of natural resources which cannot be fully utilized until their classification has been further advanced. Yet their economic potential is highly diverse:

1. As food sources for the future: Although only few species of mushrooms are used in commerce today for food, many thousands of species

are edible and untold further thousands are still undescribed. Yeast, known to be an excellent source of food protein and vitamins, can be produced very economically from waste products of many industries to supplement the nutrition of man, livestock, and poultry. The use of fungi as food needs further study, as man cannot afford to overlook any source of food for the future, in view of the population explosion. Bacteria that can be grown on petroleum have a high potential for tomorrow.

2. As sources of drugs: The discovery of antibiotics in fungi revolutionized the drug business, as well as public health activities and practice. In spite of the importance of antibiotics, it is possible that only a small beginning has yet been made. The recent discovery of tumor-inhibiting substances in puffballs has created an urgent need to collect, identify, and test this group. Other fungi, taken by primitive peoples for their hallucinogenic effects, are a rich source of alkaloids related to mescaline.

3. As sources of toxins: The poisonous products of nature are legion, from mushrooms that are deadly poisonous to the botulinus bacterium that occasionally makes canned and stored foods so extraordinarily toxic to humans. Although inimical to human life and welfare, some poisons may be beneficial in very small quantities.

4. As pathogenic organisms that affect man, other animals, and green plants: For this reason they are of the utmost importance to mankind and warrant intensive study. Extensive attention has been given to those organisms recognized as pathogenic for man, but much remains to be done. The biochemistry of parasitism poses some fundamental problems, since it sometimes determines how one organism interacts with another. The fascinating series of races of *Fusarium* wilt, for example, were perhaps the first group of "cryptic" taxa known. Although exactly alike morphologically, they differ in the particular host they harm. For example, the race of *Fusarium* specific for watermelons will rapidly kill watermelon plants, especially at the seedling state, while other crop plants, each with its own specialized *Fusarium* race, are resistant in varying degrees to the watermelon wilt. This is an area that deserves research as much for basic scientific as for economic reasons. The fungal diseases of the tropics are poorly understood. As vast areas are cleared for a one-crop agriculture, there is real danger of new diseases appearing, which could overnight make the whole enterprise uneconomical, as happened at one time to the banana industry.

5. As agents of deterioration: The tropical deterioration of electrical equipment, leather products, paper goods, optical equipment, and textiles, etc., caused great problems during and after World War II. As time goes on, we will become more and more aware of damage by highly specialized saprophytic fungi to materials that would have seemed com-

pletely resistant. Certain fungi and bacteria are able to ferment aliphatic hydrocarbons such as petroleum, thereby helping to keep highways clean.

6. Industrial uses: Through fermentation of solutions containing carbohydrates, such metabolic products of fungi and bacteria are produced commercially as alcohols, citric and other acids, glycerol, enzymes, steroids, fats, plastics, growth-promoting substances, vitamins, and other compounds of great importance. Curiously enough, few species have so far been tested, and even fewer are used industrially. There is probably no chemical transformation that cannot be carried out by some microorganism, under proper cultural circumstances, even though it might not be economically worthwhile at the moment. Some of the metabolic products are so complex and so biologically active that it seems almost impossible that they could be produced in plants—for example, the production by some mushrooms of polyacetylenes, which are actually explosive, and of other compounds so energy-rich they give off light. It is safe to predict that the industrial use of fungi in chemical transformations will increase as natural resources become less abundant.

7. Major transformations in nature: Without the destruction of organic wastes by bacteria and fungi, all life, and especially the higher forms, would soon disappear. These organisms are vital for the removal of organic debris, the concomitant return of carbon dioxide to the atmosphere, and humus formation, essential for the growth of plants. By the same process, of course, fungi cause wood to rot and food to spoil, to mention two among hundreds of detrimental phenomena. The fixation of nitrogen by bacteria, and many other transformations in our environment are given little recognition considering their great importance.

8. Mycorrhiza: The relationship between fungi and the roots of trees is poorly understood, even though this symbiotic relationship is vital to the development of many forests and for the growth of many cultivated plants, including food crops and the commercial production of orchids.

9. Biological control: Fungi are effective agents in the control of other organisms in nature; many fungi are parasitic on insects in nature, yet their potential for biological control has not yet even been touched, except for the use of bacteria for beetle larvae that damage lawns. It is possible that fungi can be used for the control of other fungi, especially pathogenic ones, as well as of nematodes and other organisms harmful to man's activities. The great potentiality of this kind of biological control depends largely on our systematic knowledge of the organism concerned. All in all, the study of the diversity of fungi and other microorganisms is eminently justified by the extraordinary range of activity of these organisms.

The Task Ahead

What are the most urgent tasks of the student of diversity? This question, which every scientist should ask himself occasionally, is not easy to answer. The sheer magnitude of organic diversity poses problems of research strategy not found in other areas of biology. The increase in our knowledge has been so rapid that the fraction of all kinds of organisms which a single individual can handle is steadily becoming smaller. During the 1700's, Linnaeus was able to treat both animal and plant kingdoms in their entirety. But he was the last person to do so. In 1818, the famous French naturalist Lamarck published an account of all invertebrate animals, again the last person to be able to do so. By now, two centuries since the great works of Linnaeus, systematists have discovered, described, and classified about a million and a half different species of organisms, and yet each year more than ten thousand previously unknown species are discovered and described. At that, the formal description of a species is only the very first step in the task of the systematist (to be discussed). How much of his research time shall he devote to it? How endless is the task ahead of him? Is it really worth doing? In order to answer these questions, we must give a short report on the current state of the inventory of the world's biota.

Inventory of the World's Animals

The inventory of the animal and plant life on earth has progressed very unevenly. This is evident from a cursory survey of our knowledge.

Vertebrates. Such large and conspicuous diurnal animals as the birds are relatively well known. The two main senses of birds, vision and hearing, are the same as in man, and all communication among birds is based on these senses (plumage coloration, displays, and songs). Not a single special technique is required for the recognition of all birds in a given district, merely the keen sense of observation characteristic of the naturalist. Consequently, only two or three new species from very remote regions are added annually to the 8,600 species of birds already known. Other less conspicuous or nocturnal vertebrates, even mammals, lizards, and snakes, are far less known. Fishes, in spite of their great potential for exploitation for food and the important role they play in aquatic ecosystems, remain the most poorly known group of vertebrates. By a conservative estimate, at least one third of the living species of fishes remain unknown to science. A leading authority stated in 1931 that there were probably 20,000 species of fish known at that time, "and one hundred or more new forms seem to be discovered every year." That the number of new forms described every year has not decreased during the nearly forty since this statement was made is indicative of the remaining task of inventorying the world's fishes. Many of the undescribed fishes are marine. The most spectacular illustration of our incomplete knowledge of diversity of life in the oceanic depths was the discovery in 1938 of the coelacanth fish, *Latimeria*, representative of a group thought to have been extinct since the days of the dinosaurs, more than 70 million years ago. The need for a continued exploration of the diversity of marine fishes is indicated by the fact that as recently as 1966 a new suborder (Megalomyceroidei), containing two new genera, was described from material collected off Bermuda. Poorly known continental areas probably equal the oceans in number of unknown fishes, as, for instance, the huge Amazon Basin. One specialist of Amazonian fishes has estimated that although well over 1,000 species of Amazonian fishes are already known, the figure will ultimately reach 2,000.

Invertebrates. Compared to the inventory of vertebrates, that of the invertebrate animals is much less complete; indeed, it is certain that far more species are still undescribed than those that have already been made known to science. To illustrate this by just one example: a group of soil ecologists at the University of Chile found it necessary to describe 700 new species during an examination of the first 10 percent of the soil samples collected during a transect of Chile.

Insects. Insects far outnumber all species of plants added together, known and unknown. There are three species of insects known for every other animal species of any kind. And yet, in spite of the 750,000 species already described, insects are among the most poorly known of all animal groups, and 6,000 or 7,000 previously unknown species are being discovered every year. Undiscovered species are by no means restricted to such out-of-the-way places as tropical jungles in underdeveloped countries. Only a few years ago an entomologist discovered a whole series of new species of fireflies within a few miles of the U.S. National Museum, which had previously been thought to be a single species. By analyzing cricket songs with the help of new sound-recording equipment, two other entomologists found that more than 40 percent of the 108 cricket species of the eastern United States had been unknown prior to their research. And yet crickets are highly conspicuous animals, and this is one of the most intensively studied regions of the world. Another entomologist estimates that of the approximately 500 species of ichneumon wasps collected in traps on his lawn in Michigan during the past few years, half are unknown species. Based on the proportions of undescribed species in collections that he has examined in various parts of the world, he estimates that three fourths of the ichneumon wasps, a group with over 15,000 described species, are still unknown. All of them are insect parasites, and many of great potential in the control of injurious insects. The rate of discovery of new species of insects is determined almost entirely by the number of investigators available for the search at any given time. For this reason, an estimate of the total number of insect species is extremely difficult. Guesses of experts have ranged as high as 10 million, and this may not be far off, although we can accept 2 or 3 million as more conservative estimates.

Mites. The rapid enlargement of the inventory of species of mites is illustrated by advances in the knowledge of the chiggers (Trombiculidae), a family of mites of great medical importance as vectors of scrub typhus and other rickettsial diseases: 3 species were known in 1900, 33 in 1912, 517 in 1952, and about 2,250 in 1966. Although thousands of species have been described in medically unimportant families of mites, it is estimated by specialists that less than 10 percent of the total number of species existing on the globe have been identified. What an enormous task is ahead for the specialist concerned!

What is true for insects and mites is equally true for many other kinds of invertebrates. For instance, the nematodes, a group of mostly small worms, some free-living, others parasitic, are still largely undescribed, in spite of their great importance in the ecosystem and for man's welfare.

Marine Invertebrates. The inventory of marine invertebrates is still in its early stages, and much of the world's oceans remains unexplored. Most of their shores have only been sampled, although intense studies have been carried out in Europe and along the coasts of the United States. The coastlines of the other continents of the world, largely unexplored, harbor countless species of marine organisms unknown to science. The exploration of new habitats and the development of novel collecting procedures will open whole new worlds of marine organisms that will provide a mass of new information.

Marine microorganisms, particularly bacteria and fungi, are poorly known, but procedures for obtaining them in sufficient quantity and in appropriate condition for taxonomic treatment are now being developed. We may be sure that microorganisms from plankton, benthos, and other communities and habitats will contribute much information and material for description.

Rather recently, an entire new fauna, called *psammon,* was discovered to live between the sand grains and mud particles within the substrate of beach and ocean floor. This fauna, at a size level well above that of microorganisms, contains many previously unknown types of organisms, including even new orders and classes. It will clearly add many new species to our inventory, belonging to many different classes of invertebrates. It is estimated that only about one percent of this fauna has so far been described, because the onshore forms, being highly sedentary, are very localized geographically. The portion of the psammon that lives below the tidal zone has been so little sampled that a one percent sampling figure is probably also true, even though this fauna may have a wider distribution.

Every deep-sea expedition has returned with an abundant harvest of new species. Even though the deep-sea fauna of all major oceans of the world has been studied, the difficulties of collecting suggest that less than half of the species have so far been described. Our biological knowledge of this fauna is virtually nil, and much work remains to fill in such essential information as the stages of the life cycle, place in the ecosystem, relative abundance, dispersal pattern, mode of speciation, reproductive pattern, structure of communities, and other biological information of vital importance for the biological oceanographer.

High-speed sampling is still yielding a high proportion of forms new to the systematist, and a vast area of the ocean still remains to be studied by this technique, so that the potential of further new forms of midwater fauna to be discovered and studied is great.

Although some 150,000 species of marine organisms (invertebrate and vertebrate) have now been described, fewer than 15,000 species parasitic upon them have been recognized. Since the parasitic population of a single fish can run to tens of species of assorted organisms, and many invertebrates have numerous known parasites, it is clear that a vast descriptive task still remains to be done in this area of systematic biology.

Inventory of the World's Plants

Even though the number of species of higher plants is considerably smaller than that of higher animals, our knowledge of them is still very incomplete, because many species are highly localized. Even so, the individuals of a single species may be highly scattered. In the tropical rainforest, for example, only one or two specimens of any one tree species generally occur in the same square mile, so that botanical collecting has had to be largely a kind of random sampling.

The Amazon Basin possesses an especially rich flora; it probably surpasses any other area of similar size in the world in the number of species of plants present. Richard Spruce, who spent from 1849 to 1860 in the Amazon Basin, wrote in 1858 that by moving one degree of latitude or longitude, he found approximately half the plants to be different. He calculated that there yet remained to be discovered in the great Amazonian forest, "from the cataracts of the Orinoco to the mountains of Mato Grosso," some 50,000 or even 80,000 new species. In the hundred years since Spruce left South America, many of these species have been discovered, but others remain undescribed. The magnificent forests of the Pacific coast of Ecuador and Colombia are little known and almost equally rich.

Approximately half a million higher plants are now known, but probably a quarter-million species remain undetected in remote tropical areas. Ferns, with perhaps 5,000 species, hepatics, with approximately 10,000 named species, mosses, with some 25,000 named species, represent primitive groups which are of special interest because they represent very ancient lines of evolution in the plants. Yet they are highly vulnerable to extinction when their habitat is changed through man's activities.

Another large group of plants that needs a more rapid tempo of investigation is the fungi. Although of great economic importance, systematic mycology lags far behind other areas of systematics. Our knowledge of fungi in vast areas of the world, particularly in the tropics, is virtually nil. Little is known about the ecology, genetics, physiology, chemistry, and behavior of the species that have already been described. Their total number will certainly reach at least half a million, even though only 100,000 species have so far been described. Considering that fungi can carry out almost any conceivable chemical transformation, it may be expected that many more will be used in laboratories and in industry as their synthetic capabilities are made evident by research.

Inventory of the World's Fossil Organisms

Paleobotany and paleontology, the sciences of fossil plants and animals, produce information of great importance for evolutionary biology, historical geology, and other branches of science. It has been estimated that of all the species that have existed, only 1 out of 5,000 to 10,000 fossil species have so far been discovered and described. Considering the fragmentary nature of the fossil record, it is remarkable how well paleontologists have succeeded in reconstructing the probable history of life. "Missing links" are now available to fill the gaps between many of the major types of vertebrates. Some of the gaps in our knowledge stem from inadequate exploration and sampling. It is urgent that these gaps be closed before man's further alteration of the landscape irretrievably destroys the record. Some groups of organisms, such as the early invertebrates, are poorly represented in the fossil record because they lacked hard parts, or because such parts are loosely associated or fragile.

However, our knowledge increases steadily through new discoveries and more thorough investigation of previously described forms. Modern techniques in collecting and preparation have made it possible to obtain and study many rare and poorly known groups. The development of acid etching and celloidin "peel" techniques for fossil plants has enabled the paleobotanist to study microscopic structure. Numerous large groups of invertebrate animals, as the corals, sponges, and radiolarians, and of lower plants, especially bryophytes, have so far been rather neglected by paleontologists. The exciting field of paleomicrobiology is on the verge of a flowering that could rival in excitement the discoveries of any branch of science.

We may safely predict that remarkable and startling discoveries about evolutionary history will be made through the study of fossil plants and animals. An example is the recent discovery of what may be the earliest evidence of life in the form of primitive algae and bacteria deposited in rocks that may well be over three billion years old. This work makes us realize more than ever before the drastic differences in rates of evolution in different organisms. Close relatives of some of the blue-green algae found in these early rocks are still in existence and have undergone astonishingly little morphological evolution in several billion years.

Is an Inventory of All Species Needed?

The magnitude of our ignorance about kinds of animals and plants is obvious. Should we really try to describe them all? If 5 million species of animals remain to be described, and if taxonomists throughout the world annually described 10,000 species, it would require another 500 years to complete the task of naming these animals and thus making them known to science. And yet, describing is only the first step: the scientist must also study the totality of properties of these organisms, arrange them in a meaningful classification, investigate their speciation and biological evolution, and so forth.

A single systematist can become expert on a group containing perhaps 1,000 to 3,000 species. The number of groups of organisms is so great that frequently one man during his lifetime is the only person investigating a particular group. Many groups (taxa) are at present entirely "orphaned": not a single specialist in the entire world is studying them. In large groups, such as most insects, the number of new species described at any time is limited almost entirely by the number of investigators searching for them during that period, in contrast to the situation in birds and mammals where the number of species that remain to be discovered is steadily diminishing.

Large groups of invertebrates remain undescribed because the techniques for their study are too demanding, and this along with practical considerations places those who work on these taxa at a disadvantage. Protozoa, for example, are so difficult to collect and preserve that it is impossible to establish adequate type collections or extensive museum reference collections, making their descriptive taxonomy a formidable task. The taxonomy of sponges (Porifera) requires the study of anatomical features that are only disclosed by special techniques of preservation and of microtechnical procedure. The various jellyfish types (Coelenterata and Ctenophora) present considerable problems in both collection and preservation, so that few satisfactory collections are available for study in museums. Sea anemones require such extensive and detailed microtechnical processing for a determination of the basic taxonomic characters that hardly a specialist for them is left in the whole world. Similar difficulties exist for virtually all soft-bodied invertebrates, including flatworms, nematodes, internal parasites, and such marine groups as Phoronida, Enteropneusta, Pterobranchia, Nemertea, Sipuncula, Echiura, and Priapuloidea. The result is a great shortage of specialists, even though many of these groups are important, as components of ecosystems, as parasites, or as a major food source of food fishes. For example, at most 10,000 species of nematodes are now known, even though competent authorities estimate that 100,000 free-living species still remain undescribed.

The investigator facing such problems is tempted to abandon all further work on an inventory of species and concentrate on what may appear to be more rewarding aspects of the study of diversity. In the face of this situation, it seems advisable that the taxonomist should continue to devote part of his research time to the description of species for some of the following reasons.

1. Every species has unique properties. Knowing all about the bluebird will not tell us all about the nightingale. Every species of organism is a unique genetic system. Each species represents a separate line of evolution, and each species is characterized by different biochemical specificities. The exact identity must be known for every organism that is used for experiments in genetics, physiology, behavior, or ecology; otherwise results cannot be compared and repeatability, the essence of science, is lost. The recognition and description of species is thus important for basic as well as applied biology. As one striking example, this kind of knowledge led to the development of a synthetic sex attractant that has proved efficacious in the trapping of the gypsy moth, a major insect pest, and may prove to be valuable in its control. In 1964 the highly injurious oriental fruit fly was eradicated from the Pacific island Rota with the use

of eugenol, an organic chemical highly attractive to males of the insect. Small pieces of fiberboard saturated with a combination of the attractant and an insecticide were uniformly scattered about the 33-square-mile island. In less than six months the entire fly population was destroyed. Similar knowledge of other species is yet to be acquired, and its acquisition constitutes a profitable field of investigation.

2. The characters of natural groups of organisms cannot be determined until a minimal number of species in these groups has been described. Every organism is a unique product of millions of years of selection in a complex and fluctuating physical and biological environment. Every property of every organism, whether structural, functional, chemical, or behavioral, is thus the result of its past history, and its study is basic for understanding the biotic world as a whole.

3. Our great ignorance about the properties of most organisms precludes determination of their usefulness for man. Who would have guessed the medical usefulness of molds until penicillin, streptomycin, and other antibiotics were discovered? Who knows the potential medical significance of the many organisms that have not yet been taxonomically described? Certainly, many species would be more suitable as biological material in laboratories and industry than the ones now employed. The relatively recent introduction of *Neurospora, E. coli,* hamsters, etc., is indicative of the untapped reservoir.

4. Understanding of ecosystems depends on a knowledge of the individual components of the system. Whenever new ecosystems need to be studied, whether in the temperate zone or tropics, on land or in water, an inventory-taking of the taxonomic components is essential.

How Urgent Is the Task? In a stable world, one might well recommend declaring a moratorium on the further describing of new species, in order to concentrate instead on a thorough study of those already known. Unfortunately man's technological progress has released forces that lead to an ever accelerating destruction of natural habitats. Dozens, perhaps hundreds of species are annihilated each year, species that required hundreds of thousands or millions of years to evolve. They cannot be replaced. Wherever man transforms the landscape for his own purposes, he destroys most of the native populations, usually causing their replacement by a few species that thrive in man-made environments. Highly localized species are most vulnerable, and this class includes an amazingly high percentage of all species. Cave species are destroyed by the exploitation and pollution of caves, as are stream endemics through pollution, silting, and the conversion of streams into water reservoirs. Estuaries, marshes, and swamps are being drained or polluted. The native vegetation is disappearing at a rapid rate in many parts of the world, especially in the tropics, as the result of the pressures of expanding populations and intensified agriculture. Many species of potential practical and scientific interest have undoubtedly already been exterminated. The existence of others is acutely threatened at this very moment, but it is only for a limited number of large mammals, birds, and reptiles that we have any information whatsoever concerning their vulnerability. The proverbial dodo, the mammoth, the New Zealand moas, and several hundred species of large mammals and birds have already become extinct since man became a hunter. The near extinction of David's deer, the Hawaiian goose, the whooping crane, the California condor, and the Arabian gazelle illustrate the ongoing process. Once a population is reduced below a certain level of size, its genetic variability and flexibility become so low that extinction is almost inevitable. Where an organism is rigidly specialized for a single habitat, it is doomed to extinction as soon as this habitat is threatened. Our knowledge of almost all groups of animals and plants is so limited that we cannot enumerate the species of which only few individuals still survive. The rate of extinction at the present time is greater in subtropical and tropical areas than in the temperate zone. Here, the population explosion is particularly rampant and the destruction of the native vegetation takes place at a threateningly rapid rate. Even in the vast Amazon Valley, large international corporations are planning to clear huge areas for the large-scale cultivation of single tree species (for pulp and veneer) with the inevitable destruction of the vast local fauna and flora.

Extinction has been going on through the geological ages, witness the dinosaurs and ammonites. The present range of the *Sequoia* ("big tree" and redwood) is only a small remnant of the range of this genus in the recent geological past, when it occurred widely in North America and across Asia into Europe. In Japan, China, and other parts of the Orient, some plants were so rare and unusual that they became objects of religious or superstitious attention, and we owe to this fact the survival of many species known today only in temple gardens in the Orient: they have become extinct in the wild. An outstanding example is the *Ginkgo,* a very primitive type of gymnosperm with motile sperm, which at one time had an extremely broad geographical distribution. Botanical gardens, in an analogous manner, have brought some particularly interesting species into cultivation. But what fraction of the estimated 750,000 species of higher plants can any botanic garden maintain, indeed all botanic gardens of the world together?

There is an urgent need for the conservation of as many types of original biota as is possible. Even though many areas still appear to be wild and untouched, they have remained so only because local population pressures have not yet reached the level to demand their exploitation. As yet we do not even have the information to determine where such sanctuaries should be and what proportion of the vanishing faunas and floras they would preserve. Where they cannot be preserved in the wild, at least an effort should be made to preserve samples of these unique representations of life in scientific collections. Once they are destroyed, they are irreversibly gone. We have an obligation to posterity to prevent this whenever possible.

Classification. The description of species, the inventory of the units of diversity in nature, is only the first task of systematics. Another task is the arranging of the chaotic mass of species into groups of related units, the so-called higher taxa. The 5,300 species of songbirds, for instance, are much easier to understand after they have been classified into thrushes, warblers, flycatchers, wrens, etc. Such classification is even more urgent for large groups, like the 750,000 species of insects or 25,000 species of fishes. The members of a higher taxon are descendants of a common ancestor, and each taxon is thus the product of evolution. The taxa fit into a hierarchy of larger and larger groupings of less and less closely related forms, with the kingdoms of animals, plants, and micro-organisms forming the most comprehensive groups. The nearest relative of a group of organisms is by no means always evident, and indeed the determination of relationships is one of the most challenging areas in taxonomy. The findings of comparative biochemistry, cytology, phys-iology, and behavior are used to shed light on relationships, each new finding requiring scrutiny and sometimes correction of the still inadequate existing classifications, largely based on a few morphological characters.

Conversely, the whole field of comparative biology depends on sound classification. A continuous reciprocal feedback between classification and other branches of biology must be cultivated for the health of biology as a whole. Every classification is a scientific theory. Its explanatory value is that each taxon is a phylogenetic unit (descendants from a common ancestor), and its predictive value is that it predicts most of the characters of newly discovered species as well as the taxonomic distribution of newly studied characteristics. Physiologists, cytologists, and biochemists not only contribute by their findings to the improvement of classifications but themselves make use of the zoological and botanical classifications in the planning of their comparative researches.

A classification is also an information retrieval system, and the superior taxonomist delimits his taxa to increase their value for this objective. The existence of millions of species, each with sexual, age, and other variability, each with information on biology, physiology, structure, and biochemistry, poses enormous problems of information storage and retrieval which even the largest computers cannot yet handle.

The Species as a Unit of Biology

The original description of a new species, often based by necessity on the morphological characters of a few specimens, represents only a meager beginning. Species are populations that coexist with one another in highly complex ecosystems, and have many other attributes far more important than the few obvious morphological characters. A species is not merely an item in an identification key, but a biological system. The student of diversity must determine and describe for every species all stages of the life cycle, differences between the sexes, internal anatomy, physiological characteristics, behavior and ecology, pathology and parasites, and the innumerable interactions with other inhabitants of its geographical range. There are only few species on which we have reasonably complete information of this kind. For well over 90 percent of the 1.5 million "known" species of animals and plants on this globe, nothing more is known than a name and a few diagnostic characters. This is why taxonomists increasingly study living animals and plants in their natural environment, and this is why new techniques for the study of new characters are being used, particularly all sorts of experimental approaches. Biochemical systematics, a rapidly expanding field of investigation based on the study of molecules, has provided a new set of tools for obtaining information on relationships. The new methods of analysis, such as chromatography, electrophoresis, gas chromatography, and amino acid analysis, have come into wide use in both plant and animal systematics.

Hybridization experiments provide still another important source of information. By attempting to hybridize species, the experimental taxonomist can determine whether or not species populations that occur together in nature, or that might possibly come together at some future time, are capable of influencing one another through the interchange of hereditary factors. Since all systems of an organism do not necessarily evolve at the same rate, failure of individuals to cross sometimes reveals them to belong to "cryptic" species with similar morphology but with reproductive incompatibility. The hybridization experiments thus aid in improving the classification at the species level. Since the degree of compatibility indicates the degree of genetic divergence, hybridization experiments also help in the reconstruction of evolutionary history. Cytological studies of chromosome number as well as of "marker" chromosomes that can be identified in various groups give important information about relationship. Chromosome numbers and patterns have been determined for only a small fraction of existing plant and animal species.

One of the most exciting areas of investigation of species is the study of the causation of reproductive isolation between coexisting (sympatric) species. Contrary to popular belief, this is, at least in animals, rarely a sterility barrier. Behavioral barriers that prevent mating are far more important than the genetic incompatibility which comes into operation after mating. It is obvious that an arrangement which prevents an unproductive mating between species is of greater selective advantage than one that permits the wastage of the gametes of the hybridizing pair through genetic incompatibility. Two main classes of premating isolating mechanisms are commonly involved in any particular instance. Signals, by which individuals attract and identify other individuals as being reproductively ready members of the opposite sex, are most effective, because they are misunderstood only rarely. In birds, frogs, and many insects, vocalizations are important as signals. The availability of high fidelity portable tape recorders and audiospectrographs permits accurate measurement of these signals and experimentation on the effectiveness of differences in vocalization as isolating mechanisms. This type of work has already revealed many cryptic species in all the vocalizing groups, and future work will certainly contribute to the more accurate recognition and classification of species.

In other kinds of animals, as mammals, salamanders, many insects, and other invertebrates, species-specific secretions (scents, odors, sex-stuffs, etc.) serve as means of communication among potential mates. Very few of these compounds have so far been identified, but present-day methods of analysis, as by gas chromatography, make this now feasible, and this particular area of research should much expand in the immediate future. In still other kinds of animals, such as insects, fishes, reptiles, birds, visual signals involving color patterns and ritualized displays and postures provide premating isolating mechanisms. Here again, a great deal of interesting and important research is to be done.

The second major class of premating isolating mechanism involves separation of the reproductive activities of sympatric species by space or time. They may reproduce at different times—as in one species of elm that flowers in spring and a sympatric species that flowers in late summer —or they may select slightly different breeding sites, as do two sympatric species of toads, one of which breeds in running water and the other in rain pools of the same small valley. Premating isolating mechanisms of this category are widespread both in plants, where they take the place of behavioral isolating mechanisms, and in animals, where they tend to augment them. Up to the present, however, only a minute fraction of the species of plants and animals are adequately known with respect to either of these classes of premating isolating mechanisms or with respect to their postmating mechanisms.

In short, the study of biological diversity, based on all properties of the living organism, has hardly begun. This work is necessary for the taxonomist himself, to eliminate errors in classification based strictly on morphology. More important, it is imperative that we know as much as possible about *all* the attributes of those species that significantly affect man and his resources.

Chapter 14

DIGITAL COMPUTERS AND
THE LIFE SCIENCES

An essay on the role of digital computers may seem odd in an exposition on the nature of the life sciences and their contribution to our society. No separate chapter is devoted to instrumentation or other supporting technologies, on which the life sciences are utterly dependent. Why is the case different with digital computers?

The answer lies both in the ubiquity of the computer and in the transformation of the style of life sciences research which it portends. Although barely begun, this transformation is sufficiently foreseeable and radical to generate a feeling that the picture of life sciences research offered in this volume may not adequately represent the future.

We wish first to present some basic facts about the computer and its underlying technology. This will make clear the grounds of its ubiquity and some of the driving forces, external to the life sciences, that all but guarantee the impact of the computer. None of these considerations are unique to the life sciences; they apply equally to other sciences and to other segments of our society. They are nonetheless relevant. If they are already familiar to the reader, the review is still appropriate to set the stage.

The central part of this chapter presents six illustrative examples in an attempt to convey the diversity of computer use in the life sciences. With this background, some highly probable features of the future of digital computation in the life sciences are then considered.

531

The Nature of the Computer

The digital computer is a device that processes a form of information bearing the same degree of generality as natural language. It is a universal machine. The "bits" that it deals with can be fashioned into arbitrary symbols — into patterns that denote things other than themselves. Expressions made up of these symbols can be processed in ways as diverse as our ways of using language.

It is an accident of economics and interest that the first "computers" were number factories. To think of them as converting everything into numbers on the inside, since "numbers are what the computer really understands," is to miss entirely their true nature. They are symbol manipulators or general information processors. What they really understand is a collection of simple instructions, some of which have to do with numbers, but most of which have to do with storing information, retrieving it, making decisions, and making contact between the various parts of the computer (e.g., the memory and the printer).

Numbers are important for the computer for the same reason they are important for the scientist, the engineer, the accountant, the economist, and the Internal Revenue Service. Numbers and the laws of arithmetic underlie a vast amount of symbolic processing normal to our society. To these ends, the computer must deal with numbers, and great effort is spent in making it do so efficiently. But it is a general device for taking instructions that is being bent to this task, and not a special-purpose, superfast, desk calculator.

Those immersed in the computer field do not themselves fully understand what it means to have a general-purpose symbol manipulator always available — one that can process pictures, text, signals from electronic instruments, circuit diagrams, genealogical trees, parts catalogues, patients' records, as well as numbers. The history of the computer is that of continued discovery of new schemes for processing new types of data. Much of the impact of the computer for the future of the life sciences arises from the nonnumerical processing the computer can do. Since science is a highly quantitative enterprise, this will occur frequently in conjunction with numerical processing. But the computer can also do the "getting ready," the "watching out," the "looking to see," and the "telling what's wrong" that surrounds all numerical processing.

These considerations do not mean that the limitless potentialities of the computer are instantly available. We are very much in the position of a tribe of savages that has just found an airplane: they could achieve incredible locomotion, if they only knew how to fly it. Only slowly and painfully will we assemble the knowledge and understanding to realize these potentialities. Indeed, the limiting factor could well be our own inventiveness and our ability to program computers, though other, more tangible limitations exist as well.

Although an exceedingly complex device, a computer system can be reasonably specified by knowing: (1) how many operations per second it can perform; (2) how much memory it has immediately available; (3) how much memory it has available in a file system; and (4) through what devices it communicates with the world. This simplicity comes about because of the universality and because other aspects, even though important, are lock-stepped with these in order to have a balanced computer. For instance, reliability must improve, since otherwise there would be no point in producing ever faster computer systems. Likewise, the instruction codes must all provide about the same array of processes.

Figures 14-1 and 14-2, adapted from work for the recent National Commission on Technology, Automation and Economic Progress, portray the almost unbelievable story with which we have been living for 15 years. Figure 14-1 shows what has been happening to computer speed. Note that the scale is logarithmic. Today, the fastest computers are running at almost 3,000,000 operations per second, and this is increasing about 60 percent per year. Figure 14-2 shows that the cost per operation is decreasing by a constant factor per year. Thus, today it only costs about a penny to buy a million operations and this figure is decreasing by 30 percent each

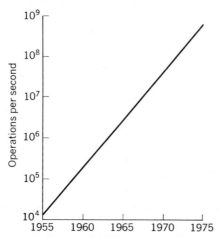

Figure 14-1. Computer speed. (From "Computer Aspects of Technological Change, Automation, and Economic Progress" by P. Armer in *The Outlook for Technological Change and Employment,* Appendix I of *Technology and the American Economy,* Nat'l Comm. on Employment, Automation & Econ. Progress, Feb. 1966, U.S. Printing Office)

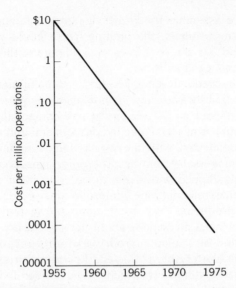

Figure 14-2. Cost of computation. (From "Computer Aspects of Technological Change, Automation, and Economic Progress" by P. Armer in *The Outlook for Technological Change and Employment,* Appendix I of *Technology and the American Economy,* Nat'l Comm. on Employment, Automation & Econ. Progress. Feb. 1966, U.S. Printing Office)

year. These figures relate only to the speed of operation, not the amount of immediately available memory. Computer memory is undergoing equally rapid change. In 1953, the amount of memory commercially available was a thousand words (each equivalent to a 12 digit number); today it is a million words; and it continues to grow. File systems — discs and tapes — have shown a more modest, but still substantial, increase in costs and performance, now permitting storage of 10^8 words within 0.3 second access.

This tremendous change in capacity at ever decreasing prices dominates the whole of computer usage. Each year the ground rules change under which computing is done. Procedures that were impossible last year must be reevaluated for next year. No rules of thumb about what is easy, difficult, or impossible have meaning for more than a few years.

The final aspect of a computer system is the collection of devices available to communicate with the outside world. Nothing has been more frustrating to life scientists who have sensed the potentialities of computers than the fact that information gets into them only through punched cards or paper tape, and emerges only via a printer. Although numerous specially built systems accept analogue information (the kind most life scientists have) or permit rapid interaction back and forth between computer and user, they have remained out of the ordinary until recently. Only a handful of experimental systems have gotten pictures directly into the machine.

Important though quality of access is, much more important is that the interface to the world is, so far, largely exempt from the tremendous performance improvements and cost reductions exhibited by the central processor and memory. These interfaces, by and large, remain on a human scale, involving mechanical motions. In any event, the cost of total computing systems will decrease much less rapidly than our two figures show. However, the amount of computer intelligence — measured in terms of memory and processing capacity — that can be devoted per task will still continue to rise dramatically.

We are about to present some concrete instances of the use of computers in fundamental and applied research in the life sciences. These are offered as tokens of the universality and power of the computer. But to see them in this symbolic role one must engage in two exercises of abstraction: first, to recognize that the same kinds of information processes are of use in widely separate parts of the life sciences; second, to understand that the diversity of processing can be built up from a few building blocks, so that a single device, the computer, is capable of accomplishing them all. The following preliminaries may help the reader with his "abstraction exercises."

Basic Principles of Digital Computers

Consider that the computer is a device with three generalized capabilities. First, it may work with any type of data structure, performing on it the operations that are proper to that data structure. We may call this the *any-data* principle. Second, it may operate any kind of device — any tool, instrument, or machine — performing the control operations that are proper to it. We may call this the *any-instrument* principle. Third, it may perform any sequence and combination of its data controlling operations in order to carry out a task. We may call this the *any-behavior* principle.

These three principles are operative at a very high level; they are not what engineers can build directly into a machine. The complexities inherent in the word "any" must be reduced to something definite. We will attempt this reduction shortly, but the reader will not be misled if he takes the foregoing phraseology seriously. He will not be misled if, under the influence of these principles, he approaches a problem of application by first asking:

—What are the data structures that *I* am interested in, and what are the operations and manipulations that are appropriate and natural to them?

—What are the instruments *I* am interested in controlling, and what are the operations that are used to control them?

Only then will he ask the direct question of application:

—What are the patterns of behavior (expressed, now, in terms of the operations defined above) that will accomplish the tasks I am interested in?

Generality of application can already be sensed from these three principles, even without examples. As long as you can specify some types of data—defined in terms of your problem—you can make use of the computer. They indicate a division of labor in applying the computer. One part provides the general facilities claimed in any-data and any-instrument principles; the second specifies the behavior for a particular application.

Again, the reader will not be misled if he views the development of computer technology in these terms (always remembering the base of increasing power and memory). Each apparently new type of application —list processing, natural language data processing, numerically controlled machine tools, process control—is essentially an exemplar of the division of labor just described. In each, clarification has finally emerged on the data structures of interest (or the devices to be used) and the operations proper thereto. Facilities for operating directly in terms of these data structures and instruments have been provided by the computer profession, packaged so that the user need only attend to the final step of specifying the behavior for his application in these natural, problem-oriented operations.

The foundation of the any-data principle is a variation on the theme of Gertrude Stein—a bit is a bit is a bit—for a common medium is used throughout all digital technology. All information is represented as a structure of bits—a pattern of binary states resident in some memory. It is the universal experience that any information that can be represented at all can be represented in patterns of bits (either directly if the information is already made up of discrete symbols, or by approximation if the information is continuous). Data structures can be represented in bit patterns; hence, all operations performed on data structures are ultimately operations on bit patterns. And this is what the computer engineer provides: basic operations for manipulating bit patterns. With only two distinguishable states (call them 0 and 1) and all patterns being sets of bits in different places, the operations that have to be provided are few and definite.

The foundation for the any-instrument principle is somewhat different. Machines and instruments tend to be constructed with only a small, discrete set of controls and sensors of the environment. Thus the stage is set for digital control. Whereas existing instruments are rarely adaptable, having been designed for human operation, new designs can almost always incorporate digital control. (The rate of incorporation is governed strongly by the cost of digital technology and by the designer's perception of whether digital control is required by users.) It is as necessary to sense the environment of an instrument as to be able to issue its commands, and as we shall note in a moment, the development of such data acquisition systems has become an important part of digital technology.

The any-behavior principle rests on the ability to interpret instructions and discriminate data. At any instant the computer has within its attention some few data structures, and has a choice of which operations to perform on them (from those appropriate to the data that have been made available). The sequence of choices will determine what total behavior will result, especially since these also determine what new data structures are brought within view. This choice is made by interpreting a data structure as an instruction of which one to do. The computer has one such data structure built into it, machine instructions. But by the any-data principle, the computer should be able to interpret any data structure that represents instructions about how to behave. The development of higher level programming languages, such as FORTRAN, ALGOL, and COBOL, reflects this.

So much for reduction. Before we turn to application, assuming our three principles, a cautionary note is in order. To say that any data structure is possible, does not automatically produce a new data structure of adequate sophistication when needed. To discover data structures (always with their proper operations) appropriate to new information processing tasks is an achievement whose creativity may be of the same order as fashioning a new theory in an area previously unformalized. Thus, just as in the case of the instruments, there is a growth through time of the collection of useful data structures. It is a prime task of computer science to carry on that development. Those who wish simply to apply computers, must take the current repertoire of data structures as given.

Calculations. Consider now the most familiar way of using a computer — to perform a calculation. It might be statistical, finding a regression line; or crystallographic, finding the coordinates of atoms from diffraction data; or chemical, determining reaction rates. The data structures for all these situations consist of numbers, and the proper operations are arithmetic. Actually, one doesn't want to deal just with a particular number, as in asking for $A + B$, but with arrays of numbers, as in performing $A(i) + B(i)$ for all values of the index i. The latter, familiar to any user of FORTRAN, already exemplifies the construction of an appropriate data structure with proper operations.

The essentials for performing a calculation are shown in Figure 14-3 — the input data, the program to instruct the computer what calculation should be done, and a place for the output. These are shown as boxes in a big box, the latter indicating the main memory of the computer. The calculation is performed by the central processor, shown as a circle. It is entirely surrounded by the main memory, indicating that the processor takes all its information from an internal representation (in bits), and all new information produced is likewise in some internal representation (in bits).

Figure 14-3 does not provide a true picture, if the calculation is performed for some user. We need the expanded system of Figure 14-4. The original data exist in an external representation — on paper or in his head. It must be *encoded* into the internal data structure. Similarly, on the output side, the answer must be *displayed* in some form the user can read, usually by printing it on paper. Finally, the calculation specified by the user requires a *translation*. In the figure the user wrote the program in FORTRAN, the translation producing machine code. Each new process has a little box above it to note that all processes are achieved by means of other programs that reside in the memory.

Why all the attention to things other than the "essential" additions and multiplications? Because the user wants these other services as badly as the central computation; they make the difference between a calculation that can be specified, communicated, and delivered in useful time, and one that requires so much effort to set up that it is only worthwhile for very extensive calculations. These additional tasks are at the heart of many of the new areas of application.

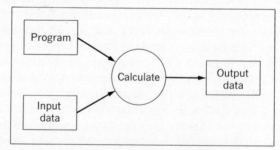

Figure 14-3. Essentials of calculation. (Courtesy Allen Newell)

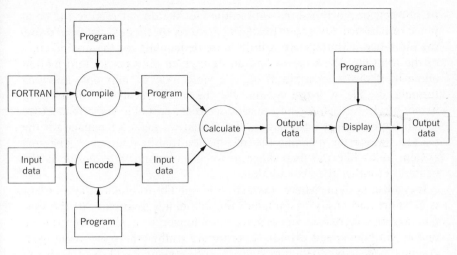

Figure 14-4. Complete calculation. (Courtesy Allen Newell)

Inquiry and Display. Consider next an inquiry and display system (Fig. 14-5). We have a large file of information. We wish to come to this file, ask it about some of the items, and have displayed the associated information in the file. First, what are the data structures? The items could be almost anything. They might be chemical formulas; very likely they include natural language text. The proper operations on the items are quite modest, since all we want to do is to display the information, and to read

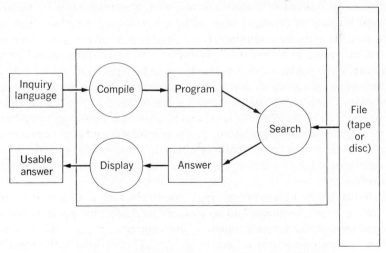

Figure 14-5. Inquiry and display. (Courtesy Allen Newell)

in, correct, or rearrange the data in the file. We do not require the computer to perform any sophisticated operations on the text, such as drawing inferences. Matters are a little more demanding for the organization of the total file. We wish to find an item given only partial information about it. If this were a file of organic molecules, we may only know its formula; if a file of drugs, we may only be able to recall some features of its action. Indeed, if our information were not partial in some respect we would have small use for such a file. Thus, we need a language for the user to state to the machine the information that he does have. The final system looks like the final diagram for calculation, with *search* as the central act rather than calculation.

In such a system, where a question is quickly formulated and an answer short and easily assimilated, the communicative parts of the system assume increased importance. No longer is a single centralized output via high-speed printers appropriate; rather there are many geographically distributed inquiry stations, either typewriterlike or televisionlike devices. Figure 14-6 shows this modified system. It has some genuinely new functions to perform, since it must handle multiple requests, which make conflicting demands on the central searching facility. There must be a way of discussing with the user the status of the computer and the prospects for his request, and of interrupting some tasks to do others of higher importance. These abilities are indicated by the additional device outside the processor, labeled *exchange*; and a program inside, labeled the *executive,* whose job it is to oversee everything else.

Image Processing. The data structures usually provided for input are linguistic — sequences of letters and digits. Often they have to be keypunched into cards or paper tape, although in inquiry systems they are typed directly into the computer. But consider next an *image-processing system,* as shown in Figure 14-7. We start with a two-dimensional image or picture, external to the computer. It might be a photograph, it might be a direct view of a scene via a television camera. To be able to process such images well would be of immense importance to the life sciences, where so much of the data is visual and requires the human eye and brain for its elementary interpretation. (This is true not only of microscopy but also of all access to the features of whole organisms.) We will devote one of our examples to discussing the need for image processing in neuromorphology.

To return to the image-processing system, the task is to give the computer access to this image and to process it. Again, the issue is one of first getting into the interior milieu of the computer, where all is bits and we can fashion operations proper to images. This is done in the most direct manner possible, by transforming the picture into an array of bits,

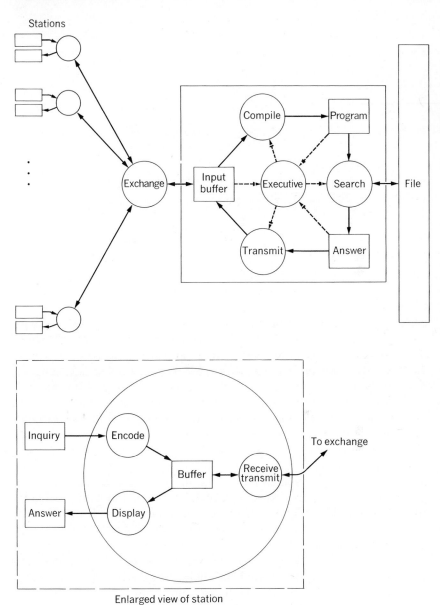

Figure 14-6. Multi-user inquiry & display. (Courtesy Allen Newell)

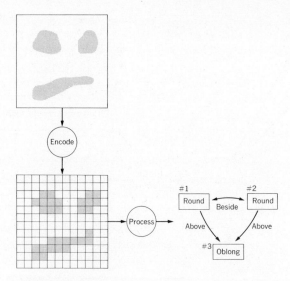

Figure 14-7. Image processing. (Courtesy Allen Newell)

each bit corresponding to a particular small area of the picture. Both degrees of grayness and color could be encoded; our simpler "black/white" illustrations show the principles as well. The image, as shown in Figure 14-7, could be brought into the memory all at once, as by a television scan; or could be picked off in small sections as needed, much as an eye scans and rescans its environment. In either case, this internal image has all the information in the original (degraded somewhat), but it is clearly not easily accessible. For example, we cannot easily count three objects in the scene or distinguish round from oblong. The technology of image processing is concerned, then, with transforming the image into a structure where such information is easily obtained. The figure shows this as nodes representing each object, with links between the nodes giving the relationships between objects. This, of course, is yet another representation (usually called list processing or graph processing) with its own set of proper operations.

The operations proper to image processing extract features from the image, modify the image to make such extraction easy, and recognize objects and relationships from features. Some of these are shown pictorially in Figure 14-8; they are accomplished, of course, by a series of instructions that match bit patterns together and that insert, delete, and detect bits in the image.

Data Acquisition. Figure 14-9 shows a *data acquisition* system employing *signal-processing,* such as might occur in taking continuous physi-

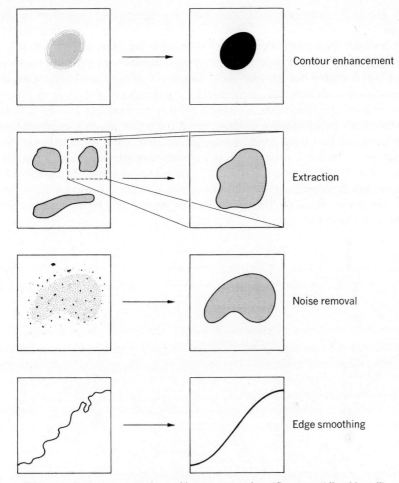

Figure 14-8. Proper operations of image processing. (Courtesy Allen Newell)

ological measurements from an organism. Externally, the data structure is a set of continuous time series. Internally, it becomes an array of numbers, possibly with a time index added for future reference. Only a small time segment of the series will be in the memory at any time, since the whole series is much too voluminous (even if one could wait to the end of the experiment to process the data). The part after the exchange in the figure is analogous to image processing. The sampling of the continuous input into a discrete set of numbers is analogous to the bit array. Operations for smoothing out the noise in the signal are analogous to those in image processing for smoothing up a line. Recognition processes (say for spike potentials) are analogous to recognizing an object in the image.

A broader look at the figure shows strong resemblances to the inquiry and display system. There are many simultaneous inputs, all of which must be attended to. Unlike most inquiry systems, which operate in human times of seconds or minutes, a physiological data acquisition system may operate in milliseconds. Sometimes matters can be a little simpler than in an inquiry system, since the information can be picked off the inputs in a rigid round-robin fashion, but if the measuring instruments perform local processing (e.g., when are there data to report?), then the resemblance to the inquiry system is very close. In addition to processing the input, a good data acquisition system provides a display of the incoming data, so that immediate judgments can be made about the quality of the data.

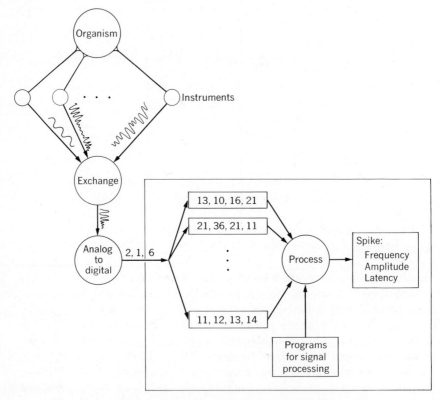

Figure 14-9. Data acquisition system. (Courtesy Allen Newell)

Simulation. As a last example, consider a system expected to perform a simulation—that is, to have a symbolic version of some aspect of a living system run through its paces symbolically. Again, the first step is to identify the data structures and operations appropriate thereto. For a biochemical system the objects are known chemical species; the data structures are numbers representing the concentrations of each species. For an ecosystem, the data structures represent the various organisms; each may contain a collection of items, giving species, age, location in the environment, male/female, stage of development—whatever features are relevant to the investigators' purposes.

With each such data structure are associated a set of operations: differential equations that express chemical reaction rates; translation operators that move organisms around in the ecosystem. These component actions operating on the set of data structures representing a current total situation transform it into a new current situation at some small time later. Thus the simulation program "walks through time," carrying along an ever changing situation that corresponds in some measure to the changes that would occur in the real system.

The system so far described is only the kernel of a useful simulation, just as Figure 14-3 gave only the kernel of a calculation. It must be easy to specify the nature of the simulation and the variables to be manipulated, to set up an initial situation, to measure and acquire data on the simulation, and to display these data. When all these are added we get a system not unlike Figure 14-4, except that "calculation" has been replaced by the processes that carry out the simulation.

These, then, are our "abstraction exercises." They should have left an impression that the same considerations show up repeatedly. This results, in part, from description that is a crude overview, concealing thereby technical issues. But the similarities are in fact real, especially when the data structures and their proper operations have been identified.

We now present six instances of the use of computers in the life sciences. They have been selected with an eye toward the lessons they are to teach: diversity and ubiquity. There are examples from research and from application, from the laboratory and the field. Some of the uses are routine, others are not. Some examples discuss existing applications; some discuss areas that are clearly ripe for advance, but where only preliminary progress has been made. All of the types of systems we have discussed in the abstract appear among the six cases.

Our aim is to make clear the basic lessons about computer use, not to present six spectaculars. The impact of the computer is both quieter and more profound than an attempt to dazzle would indicate.

Finally, let a great element of arbitrariness be noted in the selection of these examples. Quite other examples could have made the same points as well.

Specific Examples of Computer Use

Measurement Calculations in Molecular Biology and Biochemistry

Those who seek quantitative answers to biological questions have found the digital computer to be an extremely powerful and increasingly versatile research tool. This experience is particularly characteristic of investigators in molecular biology and biochemistry, where the primary goal is to explain the function of biological systems in molecular terms. It would not be difficult to generate an extensive list of applications of computer techniques in these areas: kinetic analyses, multienzyme system simulation, analysis of centrifugation studies, spectroscopic data processing, and quantum mechanical calculations. However, instead of recounting a series of relatively disjointed advances in automation, it seems more appropriate to focus upon a few specific areas of biochemical research which clearly have been revolutionized by the advent of computer technology. The areas of mass spectrometry and x-ray crystallography meet this criterion.

Fundamental to much of biology is understanding of the structures of the relevant molecular species. In the mass spectrometer, large organic molecules are fragmented into a host of lesser ionized pieces which are separated in terms of their absolute masses and the relative amounts of each sensed by an appropriate device. The resultant pattern of unit fragments is absolutely characteristic of the original molecule. Accordingly, by mass spectrometry one may either elucidate the structure of a newly recognized compound or identify and quantitatively estimate the relative abundances of several compounds in a mixture obtained from natural sources. With the development of high resolution mass spectrometers, the resulting data, obtained from larger organic compounds, became unmanageable. Computational requirements increased severely, particularly if the instrument was to be utilized in relatively routine fashion — and the digital computer became indispensable as an adjunct.

Conventional mass spectrometers can be used to analyze substances with masses up to 600 or even 1,500, and can resolve adjacent mass peaks differing by 1 mass unit at about mass 500. Such instruments are very powerful analytical tools. The development of double focusing mass spectrometers, with resolving powers of 1 part in 10^4 or better, and accuracies for a given mass of at least 1 in 10^5 virtually removed the molecular weight restriction implicit in the single focusing and time-of-flight instruments. This opened up new problem areas, and new difficulties were encountered as well, in dealing with the extraordinarily complex spectra that resulted and in learning to make optimum use of these expensive instruments. Two methods of recording high resolution mass spectra are available. One of these methods uses an instrument in which all the ions are collected simultaneously in one focal plane on a photoplate. Each plate can hold many spectra. The mass spectra are then read with the aid of an optical comparator, the data entered onto magnetic tape and the resultant digitized spectrum analyzed with a computer program to produce a map indicating the elementary composition of each ion fragment. Such a system is shown in Figure 14-10. New programs for computer-assisted analysis of these element maps are being developed constantly, and it is clear that the present semiautomatic data acquisition and interpretation systems will, with the aid of digital computers and skilled scientific research, become virtually foolproof and almost totally automated within the next few years.

The other recording system involves magnetic scanning of the ion fragments to yield a tracing of the spectrum that can be simultaneously recorded on magnetic tape. The tape is then processed on a computer, as in the photoplate system. Each of these systems has advantages in specific applications. It is quite feasible to record and process up to fifty or sixty spectra in a day using such systems, so the need and demand for automated aid to interpretation of this enormous volume of data are understandable. Spectra are not easily interpreted correctly, however, and computer programs designed to provide assistance in determining structures must combine logical elimination with knowledge about probable fragmentation patterns and permit interaction with the user's chemical intuition.

Recently a system has been described for the on-line monitoring of the effluent from a gas chromatograph with a scanning high resolution mass spectrometer. The implications of such a combination are great, since vapor phase chromatography is now routinely used in the separation and purification of sugars, steroids, hydrocarbons, lipids, and innumerable other complex mixtures. In this system, the effluent from a gas chromatograph is fed through an interface system to reduce the pressure and bleed off the eluent gas (usually helium) and thence into the mass spectrometer. Samples of 1 microgram or less provided mass spectra with a resolution of 1 part in 10,000. The resulting FM tapes are analyzed on a computer to provide an element map for study and interpretation. This system has successfully analyzed lipid mixtures of great

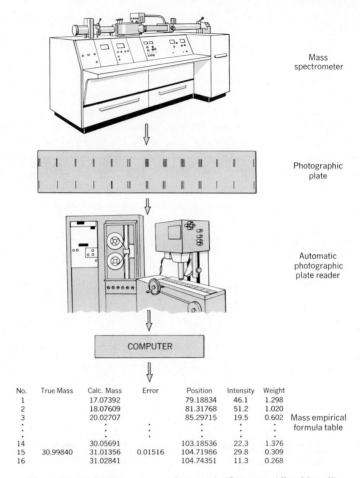

No.	True Mass	Calc. Mass	Error	Position	Intensity	Weight
1		17.07392		79.18834	46.1	1.298
2		18.07609		81.31768	51.2	1.020
3		20.02707		85.29715	19.5	0.602
⋮		⋮	⋮	⋮	⋮	⋮
14		30.05691		103.18536	22.3	1.376
15	30.99840	31.01356	0.01516	104.71986	29.8	0.309
16		31.02841		104.74351	11.3	0.268

Labels at right of diagram (top to bottom): Mass spectrometer; Photographic plate; Automatic photographic plate reader; COMPUTER; Mass empirical formula table.

Figure 14-10. Mass spectrograph system. (Courtesy Allen Newell)

complexity. The system is general enough to permit an extension to other instruments such as infrared spectrometers or nuclear magnetic resonance spectrometers.

Other examples of important advances in mass spectrometry are evident in the use of high resolution mass spectra to determine the amino acid sequences of oligopeptides. In these studies the N-terminal and C-terminal ends of a polypeptide are blocked (by acylation and esterification, respectively) to increase the vapor pressure, and the N-terminal residue is labeled, typically with a halogen or deuterium, to give a starting point. The mass spectrum is then recorded and analyzed. The computer programs output the peptide sequence with any ambiguities indicated. Since the size of the sample required is very small (micrograms) and the size of the peptides limited only by volatility and thermal stability, the mass spectrometric method seems likely to be routinely used to help derive the primary structures of proteins in the near future.

The use of computers in the empirical determination of protein conformations has been as extensive and impressive as that in mass spectrometry. The only technique now available for determining the molecular structures of proteins is x-ray crystallography. To locate the relative positions of the atoms in a protein crystal, it is necessary to measure the intensities of thousands of diffraction maxima which appear when the crystal is irradiated with x-rays. These data must be processed for the protein crystal and for several heavy metal derivatives of the parent protein. Next, a Fourier series must be summed using the resultant 10,000 to 20,000 intensities and derived phase angles (which provide the time relationship or phase lag among the diffraction maxima) to yield a map of the electron density in the crystal. This electron density distribution, typically sampled at about 500,000 points within the crystallographic unit cell, must then be interpreted in terms of the amino acids and other chemical entities known to be present in this particular protein. Here we have an immense amount of calculation in the service of measurement.

The importance of direct knowledge of the three-dimensional structure of proteins cannot be overemphasized. Only with such knowledge can scientists understand in depth the biochemical and biological behavior of these molecules. The structure of myoglobin was essentially available in 1960, yet even now we are just beginning to understand this protein. Hemoglobin, a much larger protein, is still being studied to provide a crystallographic electron density map at atomic resolution. Even so, the crude resolution studies taken in conjunction with the similarity of the hemoglobin subunits to myoglobin have provided valuable information on the normal and abnormal functioning of this essential protein. A group in London has determined the molecular structure of the enzyme lysozyme and this, in turn, has provided the most penetrating insight yet available of the mechanism of enzymic catalysis. In this country, similar studies have recently been completed for ribonuclease and work on triose phosphate dehydrogenase is well-nigh complete. In their sum, these studies constitute one of the great landmarks in the history of science. If computers were to contribute nothing else to biochemistry and molecular biology beyond allowing a view of protein structures in this detail, they would still well justify themselves.

Radius 1.95 Å   Radius 3.40 Å

Figure 14-11. Electron density diagram. (From R. W. Stacy and B. D. Waxman, eds., *Computers in Biomedical Research,* Vol. I. © 1965 by Academic Press, Inc.)

Both in mass spectrometry and in x-ray crystallography our interest has focused on the role of calculation. In both of these systems we should have noted the essential role of an appropriate display, such as the electron density diagrams in Figure 14-11. Such systems, once the essential couplings of information occur, evolve toward more complete systems providing additional useful functions. Automation has proved valuable for controlling the operation of the x-ray diffractometers which yield the primary data. The interpretation of the electron density maps calculated from such data by building of molecular models within the computer has also developed. One particularly exciting activity has used both energy and crystallographic information in the development of a molecular model building system which permits operator intervention and guidance throughout the process. This system is clearly a harbinger of things to come.

Models and Data Acquisition in Auditory Physiology

The ideal scientific "model" provides a coherent, economical, and elegant description of a natural system. It should be a simplified representation allowing the investigator to focus his attention on the most important attributes of the system under study. In addition, the ideal model should be more accessible to study than reality. Digital computer simulation, reflecting the any-behavior principle, often provides such accessibility, since any variable can be examined in detail and parameters can be manipulated at will.

The validity of a model must be tested by comparison of its behavior with that of the natural system under study. This comparison may require massive acquisition of data which, reflecting the any-instrument principle, can be accomplished with a digital computer.

Models of the auditory system to aid understanding of this complex and sensitive mechanism have long been the goal of auditory physiologists. A useful model of the entire system should, someday, aid the teacher, the otologist, the hearing-aid designer, the teacher of the deaf, and researchers in other fields such as those concerned with the development of speech typewriters.

Digital computers, unused in auditory physiology a decade ago, have become indispensable. The increase in their use has been dramatic in both the gathering of data and in the development of the models themselves. We can trace the variety of ways they have come to be used by reviewing the auditory system, starting with the external ear and moving toward the brain, as shown in Figure 14-12.

The external ear—the pinna, and the canal terminated by the eardrum—can be studied quite well using only the laws of acoustical physics. Conventional mathematical analysis served until about 1965, when improvement in the models of the rest of the auditory system forced a more detailed evaluation that is most easily accomplished on a large-scale digital computer.

The middle ear transforms vibrations in the air at the eardrum to vibration in the fluid of the inner ear by means of three small coupled bones called ossicles. Models of this system were based on techniques analogous to those used in electric circuit theory. Computers have aided study of the adequacy of this model and the accuracy of its parameters. Recently the nonlinear properties of the middle ear have begun to be included in these models.

The inner ear, or cochlea, is a bony organ about the size of a pea in man. Within the cochlea is a spiral tube divided longitudinally by a flexible partition, the basilar membrane. Along this membrane are ar-

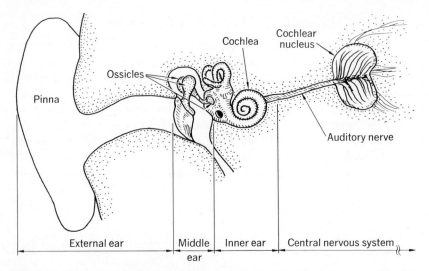

Figure 14-12. Sketch of the auditory system. (Courtesy Jerome R. Cox, Jr., adapted from Francis M. Weiner, "How We Hear," *Physics Today* 2:8, 1949. © American Physical Society)

ranged about 30,000 nerve endings that transmit to the auditory cortex information about the sound-induced motion of the basilar membrane. The complex patterns of motion of the basilar membrane are related to the frequency selectivity of the organ. Analytic techniques have not provided satisfactory explanations of these patterns, and computer models are now used in the search for a more complete understanding.

These models of the outer, middle, and inner ear have been primarily of two kinds, "empirical" and "structural." The purely empirical model fits the observed functional characteristics of the prototype with a convenient analytic function and uses the computer to minimize error and ease the calculation of intermediate values. The purely structural model starts from knowledge of the underlying anatomy and physiology and assembles a mathematical system in which all important variables, whether actually measurable or not, are identified and can be calculated. Often the mathematical system cannot be solved in closed form and computational techniques are required to compare the model with the prototype. Though more difficult to develop than empirical models, the structural models produce greater understanding of the mechanism under study and have stimulated critical experiments. Many practical models are neither purely empirical nor purely structural, but are a combination of the two.

The empirical models of the mechanical action of the cochlea have been based exclusively on the observations of Georg von Békésy. Structural models, developed without complete anatomical or physiological information, have, in general, confirmed Békésy's observations. Since the structural models are usually described by partial differential equations, standard digital computer techniques could be applied if accurate knowledge of all of the parameters were available. This is not the case, and graphic displays of results are important both for manipulation of the poorly known parameters and to aid in the understanding of the wondrously complex motion of the basilar membrane.

In both approaches, the role of the computer has been primarily calculational, although with this last step the display becomes important. As we pass to the process whereby mechanical motion is transduced into neural impulses, matters become very poorly understood indeed. No experimental technique has yet offered direct evidence concerning the mechanisms involved. With the aid of digital computers, statistical data describing the firings of primary fibers in the auditory nerve have raised questions about the validity of present models of the mechanism of the cochlea. Now the difficult task is to collect and analyze data describing the neural signals conducted along the auditory nerve toward the information processing center at the cochlear nucleus. Because this data could not have been collected and analyzed without digital computers, it is interesting to review the circumstances.

Signals obtained from electrodes implanted in an animal's auditory nerve or in the auditory system in general could produce a million bits of data in a few seconds. Digital processing systems were unaccustomed to the torrential data rate, and analogue processing schemes could not muster the logical complexity required to analyze the data. Irrelevant, unwanted signals confused the recordings; frequently it was necessary to obtain only indirect measurements of the physiological variables under study, and the sheer quantity of the data needed to draw reliable conclusions was overwhelming.

A way to surmount this pyramid of problems arose from the kind of chance collaboration often fostered on university campuses. In the late 1950's, two advanced digital computers were made available at MIT: TX-0, the first all-transistorized digital computer, and ARC, a specialized average response and histogram computer. ARC could provide a graphic display of summarized results while an experiment is in progress and a measure of control for the rapidly moving experiment itself. TX-0 provided flexible, off-line processing of the large mass of data generated by an experiment, along with good display of results. The combination of ARC and TX-0 formed the first data acquisition system for research in the life sciences in the sense sketched in Figure 14-9, where the full processing of a digital computer is available both during and after the data have been acquired.

These problems of gathering data helpful in gaining an understanding of the auditory system are like those experienced by many physiologists. However, only a few facilities like the TX-0 were available in 1961, and neither researchers nor computer manufacturers were then certain of the specifications of a reasonably priced, adequate system. Fortunately, a timely NIH- and NASA-supported collaboration between biologists and computer designers produced the Laboratory Instrument Computer (LINC), blending some of the most attractive characteristics of the ARC and TX-0 into a system extremely useful to the biologist, yet hardly more expensive than an electron microscope.

One of the most attractive qualities of the LINC is its ability to function "on-line"—to gather data, analyze them, and display the results while the experiment is under way. This ability to produce quick results has often been crucial in minimizing the loss of experimental time due to unsatisfactory biological preparations.

The widespread requirement of many biologists, particularly physiologists, for small, on-line computers, the emerging ability of computer technology to produce inexpensive systems, and the trail blazed by the LINC have led to the availability of a variety of computer systems capable of the data gathering and processing tasks needed to study complex physiological systems such as the auditory apparatus.

With the aid of these computers, models of the transduction mechanism in the cochlea, of neural transmission in the auditory nerve, and of neural processing in the cochlear nucleus are beginning to appear. A summary model of the entire auditory system from pinna to cochlear nucleus is now a reasonable goal. Such a model, when validated, will increase our understanding of the auditory system by an order of magnitude. The teacher of physiology can then present his material more elegantly and economically. The otologist's understanding of auditory disease will be enhanced by his ability to deduce. the consequences of specific malfunctions. The design of hearing aids for the deaf can then be systematic rather than empirical. The quantitative description of the peripheral auditory system will aid investigators interested in the production, transmission, and understanding of speech by identifying the important characteristics of the acoustic signal. And, inevitably, important steps toward the development of speech typewriters will result.

As we have moved through the auditory system we have encountered a wide range of computational systems: calculation, simulation, and data acquisition. We focused somewhat on the latter, since work in auditory physiology happened to be the site of important developments in data acquisition at one point in history. As important, however, is the variety of ways in which digital processing comes to be used even within a restricted locale of the life sciences.

Computers and Cows

The application of genetics and nutritional science to animal husbandry has generated an excellent example of widespread use of computers by a segment of the biological community who are not computer specialists.

The goal of applied genetic science is development of better or more specialized animals by control of their genetic structure. In its simplest forms, animals with desired characteristics are selected from the general population and bred. In more sophisticated endeavors, animals are crossbred to obtain particular combinations of genes. In all cases, genetic "control" is indirect; it is not possible to work with individual genes, so that whole animals which contain both wanted and unwanted genes must be accepted as a unit. Furthermore, genetic combinations may produce side effects which are difficult to predict, such as disease resistance or susceptibility. The quality and quantity of the American food supply is a tribute to previous genetic practice.

Knowledge of theoretical genetics and nutrition is insufficient to assure its application; extensive organized efforts are necessary to make this knowledge widely applicable and available. The current state of such applications can be illustrated by the National Cooperative Dairy Herd Improvement Program. It will be clear from the following description that great gains are achieved by the present program, and that there are great opportunities for further advances.

The program maintains a record file on about 2,000,000 dairy cows, or 20 percent of the total dairy cows in the country. The farmers in each area form an association which has a tester who visits each herd once a month. He measures the daily milk production, butterfat content, and size of each cow, records the amount of grain ingested, and notes whether she is pregnant or dry. He also records the total food consumed by the herd.

These data are sent to one of fourteen regional computing centers. Within four or five days, the center returns to the farmer a report that notes, for each cow, the value of her milk, the cost of her feed, the amount of grain she should receive, based on her size and milk production, and whether she should be bred or her current lactation terminated. These data are vital for the management of the individual cows. Summary comparative data are also provided for the last month and the last year. For the herd, the percentage of cows in milk and the ratio of feed consumed to milk produced constitute a measure of the overall competence of management.

At the end of each lactation period, a summary sheet brings to the farmer's attention the data needed to decide whether to keep each cow. The information is also sent to a national computation center to compute breeding data.

In addition to a barn name, all cows in the program have a number which provides unique identification in the countrywide program. This identification and the identifying numbers of the sire, dam, and the herd owner identify the lactation record at the national center. Such careful specification is essential because of the wide commerce in both cows and semen.

At the national center, lactation data are summarized for breeding purposes. A list of about 2,000 bulls is published three or four times a year, together with an estimate of their daughters' milk-producing ability which can be attributed to genetic factors. The daughters of a sire tend to be widely separated geographically; consequently, summaries of national data are necessary. Milk production depends strongly on nongenetic factors, such as the quality of the pasture and the time of calving. Hence, a valid estimate of genetic superiority requires a careful comparison against selected herd mates who have calved at the same time which can best be done with a large central computer. Genetic superiority estimates range as much as 2,000 pounds of milk more or less than the average production of about 12,000 pounds per lactation. This large effect can easily make the difference between profit and loss for a herd. Further, the cost of semen from a good bull is little more than that of an inferior bull. One bull can service over 50,000 cows per year. So an essential factor in herd improvement is the knowledge provided by the computer.

A similar estimate of genetic milk-producing factors is made for the top 2 percent of the cows. These data are used primarily to select dams for future sires.

The computation techniques involved are simple numerical calculation and large file maintenance and searching. It has many of the aspects of the inquiry system of Figure 14-6, except the interaction rate is very low, so that the system itself initiates the output messages to the users. The largest file contains the lactation data for several million cows. It must be sorted to locate the highest producing cows and to locate the daughters of a given sire.

The information in the bull and cow lists is a major result of the program which was formerly unavailable. Previously, breeding was almost a matter of chance; now, with this information, simple genetic selection can be performed. Providing even this simplest information requires a large computer program and a national data collection network.

Many extensions of the program are easy to envision, although they may be hard to achieve. Genetically controlled crossbreeding to develop an equivalent to hybrid plants is potentially possible if the enormous evaluation and data processing problems can be solved. It will require predicting the interactions of sire and dam genes, a much harder task than estimating their average effects separately.

More complex nutritional programs could be developed which would compute a detailed diet for each animal. (Manufacturers currently do extensive calculations to determine feed mixes, which, of course, are used by many animals.) The diet could depend on the price and composition of available foodstuffs, as well as on variables associated with the animal. Present nutritional estimates assume the common food for the herd is equitably divided. This may not be the case — some cows are more aggressive than others. Measuring the individual consumption of each cow in a herd would require an extensive data collection network. The technology for such a network exists; its practical usefulness would have to be established.

To summarize, this program constitutes an application of genetic and nutritional science that could not be effected without the use of computers. At present, only the simplest aspects of these sciences are applied. Even so, these programs contribute significantly to our gross national product. Eventual applications of more advanced principles will be of the utmost importance, and will require even more computation.

Image Processing in Neuromorphology

Research in neuroanatomy and neuropathology is beset with certain difficulties which are negligible in studies of other organ systems. Many of these difficulties are conditioned by the fact that even the most primitive vertebrate nervous system is characterized by an extremely high degree of localized variation and specialization. Not only do the constituent cells of the nervous system vary in size, shape, and density of distribution from region to region, but the interrelationships — spatial as well as physiological — can change very markedly and characteristically within distances of the order of millimeters or less. These regions are usually not delineated by bounding fiber bundles nor, in contrast to other organs, are there connective tissue boundaries to aid in identification. Probably no class of somatic cells exhibits a greater range of variation than the neuron, be it in regard to size, shape, "internal" structure, or other morphological properties.

The structural heterogeneity of the nervous system presents responsible neuromorphological research with problems of sampling and reproducibility of a very high order. These problems are increased manyfold when the required morphological analysis is to transcend simple diagnostic statements—i.e., to provide objective and reproducible measurements for the characterization of substructures which are the subject of physiological, biochemical, pharamacological, or anatomical research interest. Clearly the labor involved in the adequate study of a single brain is very great. In contrast to blood counts, neuron counting cannot be delegated to subprofessional personnel except under very special circumstances. Even if such delegation were possible, the heterogeneity previously noted implies that characterizing a brain specimen by mere cell count is relatively uninformative in the absence of positional information. Hence, because of the huge effort required, the detailed studies of interslide and interspecimen variation necessary as a basis for quantitative neuromorphology has gone unperformed. Such work is unglamorous: the travail involved does not have at its end a reasonable prospect for a "breakthrough." Yet, progress in understanding of brain function and structure requires such a quantitative basis. Innumerable physiological studies—e.g., the results of ablation, chronic stimulation, etc.—have been published without anatomical analysis of the local lesion, simply because of the physical impossibility of completing a morphological analysis worthy of the physiological experiment involved.

Obviously, then, the general area of neuromorphology is an outstanding example of the need for automated *assistance*. This is not to substitute a machine for the microscopist, but rather to free him from the overwhelming burden of precise shape description and measurement, a burden that has been rejected in desperate self-protection.

While the need for computer-assisted neuroanatomy is very great, the number of investigators who have been venturesome enough to employ computers in histological studies has been small. In contrast to the need and potentiality for automated neurohistological techniques, work to date has been the result of a mere handful of investigators and the efforts very preliminary. Accordingly, this section is not an account of a marked success, but a hopeful estimate of future prospects.

Image Processing. At a recent conference on the automated processing of biological images, a participant asked what is the potentiality that automatic processing can answer questions that could not be answered otherwise. In this field, the problem is not to answer questions better, faster, or more completely, but to obtain information not possible with existing equipment and technology. For example, there is experimental evidence to support the hypothesis that certain forms of brain dysfunction are equivalent to brain damage and to loss of neurons, and that there is a quantitative relationship between the size of the lesion and the magnitude of the functional deficit. And the proximate causes of mental retardation and of functional disorders such as schizophrenia may be related to brain dysfunction. The problem of ascertaining nerve cell losses is difficult; unless such losses are gross, obvious subjective impressions of neuronal diminution may be misleading. Until cell counts performed on a large series of normal subjects can be compared with many similar counts in psychotic individuals, statements of mild focal or diffuse nerve cell losses must be viewed with suspicion. Unfortunately, adequate anatomical and histological data will probably not be forthcoming until automatic image recognition and processing is a reality. Then, cell-counting procedures may reveal significant changes in the brains of mentally defective individuals.

The magnitude of effort involved can be appreciated by considering the gross statistics involved in quantitative estimations of the neurocytological content of brain tissue. For example, it has been estimated that there are 10,000 neurons per cubic millimeter of cortex and that about 100,000 fibers cross the boundary between white and gray matter in each square millimeter of visual cortex. In addition to the variation in number of cell bodies from layer to layer, there is a large variation in the distribution of cells within each layer. Therefore, a relatively large number of sections would have to be counted in order to characterize this distribution. The one-dimensional distributions of packing densities measured as a function of depth, from one layer to another, have some crude correlations with function, such as in the different distributions in the motor and visual cortex. Thus, it becomes apparent that the demands for quantification are such that conventional counting methods now in use are adequate neither for determining nor comfirming significantly what variation in the two-dimensional distributions occurs within layers from different cortical regions. Automatic processing will be necessary for making such determinations. Even though nerve fibers are probably distributed more homogeneously, no quantitative information is available about their distribution.

There is reason to believe that the anticipated sensitivity of a successful automated procedure would reveal significant changes which cannot be detected by conventional microscopy, since demonstration of suspected micropathology requires the examination of large numbers of sections. In addition, automatic procedures may make it possible to measure the two- and three-dimensional distribution of the various sizes of neurons when counting cell bodies and axons, respectively. Since there is, in general, a direct relationship between the size of the cell body and the diameter of the corresponding axon, it may be possible to correlate more quantitatively the functional significance of fiber diameter in peripheral and spinal cord nerves.

Any reasonable approach to correlating neuronal function with anatomical structure must include a study of connectivity as well as the mere presence or absence of cells and fibers. The totality of the neuroanatomical considerations serves to emphasize the formidable problems that will be encountered as well as the need for filling in this vacuum of information.

The preceding examples of needs for accurate descriptive neuromorphology have assumed scanning of the traditional tissue cross section. Optimally, innovative histological approaches would provide means whereby three-dimensional neuroanatomy would be reconstructed automatically from continuous, rather than serial, cross sections. Although such an approach would involve the development of a completely new technology, the value of the results obtained thereby may well warrant such dramatic changes in histological methodology. As a beginning, however, existing techniques for preparing brain tissue offer far more information than can be extracted, much less utilized. At this point, the need is for the development of suitable programs which can effectively assure the maximum utilization of existing histological techniques with operating computational facilities.

So far we have considered the shape of the task and the clear and present need. Figure 14-7 described the outlines of an image-processing system. Some such experimental systems do exist, although not designed for neuromorphology as discussed here. Figure 14-13 shows the data input and output, with one or two intermediate states, in a system for chromosome analysis developed at Argonne National Laboratories. The processing system follows closely the earlier abstract schema.

Substantial work by several investigators has been done on image analysis of chromosomes and we could have developed our essay in its terms. However, since the technology for processing images is still in its early phases, and since the ultimate payoffs appear to be so great, it seemed appropriate instead to focus on the problems rather than on accomplishments to date. Hopefully, the technology will soon develop to meet the needs.

Information Processing in Patient Care

Let us start with the dramatic — the use of computer technology to monitor critically ill patients in the intensive-care units of hospitals. In patients with coronary artery disease, for example, prompt treatment of

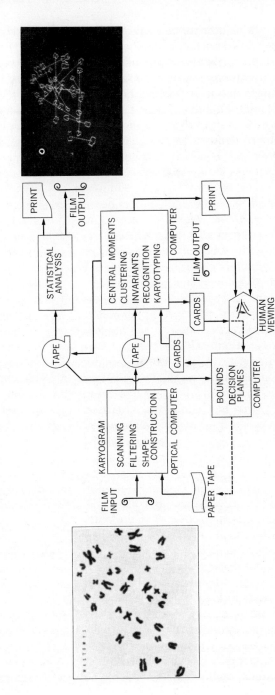

Figure 14-13. Automatic system for chromosome mapping. (From Argonne National Laboratory and J. W. Butler, *Developments in Industrial Microbiology* 8:370)

cardiac arrhythmias can often restore integrated cardiac activity and permit full recovery. To this end, patients with acute myocardial infarction are maintained in coronary care units, especially equipped and organized to treat arrhythmias, with special emphasis on resuscitation of patients experiencing potentially fatal arrhythmias. The essential components are electrocardiographic monitors for continuous surveillance of heart rhythm, an alarm system to alert the staff of changes in cardiac behavior, and vigilant, highly trained nurses who can intervene in the event of cardiac arrest. Such units have made it possible to reduce death resulting from arrhythmias in hospitalized patients with acute myocardial infarction.

Monitoring a single electrocardiogram does not require computer technology. But satisfactory surveillance of an acutely ill patient, in fact, involves a whole array of physiological measurements, which need to be controlled, stored, processed, and displayed in an integrated manner. Computer technology offers the means to achieve this, especially when such systems are still very new and much flexibility is required.

Now to the prosaic—our experiences, reader and life scientist alike, as individuals in hospitals. The typical sequence of events is: enter, wait, questions by admitting officer, wait, questions by nurse, wait, examination by doctor, wait, attainment of bed, rest, arrival of medicine, rest, and so on. In this role, the patient is on what analysts of large management systems call "a single thread." At the same time, the hospital experiences a skein of hundreds of threads, each at different stages, each intersecting a different set of facilities at any instant of time—impressing different loads at different times on the various facilities. The course a thread takes through this system requires decisions at every point, which in turn require the acquisition of the necessary data at the decision point at the right moment. Thus, an inherent part of a large system engaged in the flow of goods, services, and patients is an information system that must acquire, store, and monitor enough information to control the process.

Centuries of professional tradition and intimate involvement with individuals in a state of need, helplessness, and pain may suggest that discussions of medical practices are most appropriate in terms of person-to-person relations. To consider human beings as "threads" in a system is not, however, to deemphasize the personal aspects of patient care. Indeed, both the humanity and effectiveness of modern medical treatment depend on seeing the hospital as a large complex logistic and decision-making system, with stringent requirements for the information system that controls it.

The functions of the modern hospital bear little resemblance to those of fifty years ago. New techniques, new laboratory tests, and new therapeutic procedures, all based on increased understanding of the disease process, have modified the patterns of delivery of health service. The shift to an urban society and the general rise in expectations for medical care have also contributed to the change.

Optimally, the hospital should be a modern managed system: yet the hospital of this decade is, in fact, far from it. An encounter with the routines of a hospital of today bears this out. Most of the *information collection* is performed manually, frequently in illegible script on diverse forms. Most of the subsequent *information transmission* involves both the manual distribution of multiple pieces of paper to many different areas on the hospital and numerous telephone calls. Most of the *information retrieval* is a manual search of reports and the medical record—a relatively unorganized collection of professional observations, test result reports, and reports of therapeutic activities. Figure 14-14 gives an indication of the diverse and widespread components of the hospital that contribute to a patient's record. When multiplied by all those tangled threads, the complexity of the hospital information problem is revealed. Over 25 percent of the hospital budget goes into such information processing. In addition, a significant portion of the time of physicians, nurses, and technical staff—the resource in shortest supply—is expended in "bookkeeping" activities. Let us look at the dimensions of the problem.

The information processing activities of even the most modest hospital include three types of functions: (a) hotel, (b) diagnostic, and (c) therapeutic management. These activities are important for both admission and

Figure 14-14. Data base for treatment decision. (Courtesy Allen Newell)

continuing care of the patient. Figure 14-14 illustrates the data that form the base for diagnostic decisions and therapeutic management. Two aspects of this decision process are particularly pertinent to information processing.

First, a great diversity of information about the patient exists in many forms: numbers, pictures, words, and symbols. Each segment of information originates in some particular place and must travel to other places for processing before it eventually returns to the decision point, which may be at the patient's bedside, at a consultative conference, at a nursing station, or elsewhere. Furthermore, the items have been collected at different times prior to the decision terminus. This diversity and decentralization have been the major stimulus to development of automatic processing of patient care data.

Second, the team of medical and nursing personnel must have collective access, not only to the information on the particular patient, but also to a general data base of diagnostic and therapeutic information. Abortive or deficient decisions may result when the appropriate team and decision makers with the correct and sufficient data base are not assembled at the right point at the right time or cannot communicate in an effective and timely manner.

The task implied in Figure 14-14 depends upon the development of techniques and procedures adequate to capture information at each point of origin, as well as provide for an inquiry and display system. The multiuser system illustrated back in Figure 14-6 is an appropriate picture, provided that all of the diverse centers are reliable agents for generating and capturing the information. If the system is expected to file requests and monitor various activities, such as the entry of laboratory test results, a form of process control must be added. However, the effectors of such a system are more reminders than true effectors. Like most inquiry systems, the amount of processing and calculation is small and the system is devoted mostly to communication, updating of central files, searches, and production of effective displays.

The decision process itself and the potentialities of computer diagnosis have been much discussed. The use of computers in this decision-making process has much broader implications and potential than just the classification of a single diagnosis. However, good decisions cannot be made on an inaccurate or distorted data base, regardless of the intelligence of the decision maker, so that from this viewpoint, too, inadequacies of the presently used manual operation remain an important concern.

A treatment plan based on the decision process must include the assurance that the plan is effected reliably and without gross error. Reliability of extended treatment plans, sometimes over a period of months, requires a system with great stability. Diagnostic and prognostic reviews produce redesigns of the treatment plan throughout the treatment period. In this context, the diagnosis, prognosis, and treatment are all iterative processes and can hardly be separated.

The hotel function of the hospital, another communication-dependent component of the hospital, involves admitting the patient, finding and assigning a bed, knowing where he is at all times, ordering and serving meals, providing necessary supplies, calculating charges for services, discharging the patient, and totaling the bills. Such a system is partially dependent upon the more fundamental data collection, diagnosis, and treatment system just discussed, but in many respects it is simpler. The hotel functions are also easier to implement, since the data structures required and the operations to be performed are those of business data processing coupled with reservation systems, both of which are easily within the capabilities of current computer technology.

So far we have been discussing integrated functions, where the information is widespread and diverse. Many of the locales delineated in Figure 14-14 have independent needs for control and data handling. Thus, one can conceive of a series of independent modules, each developing in its own way, which will contribute substantially to the total hospital operation. An example is the outpatient department, where the challenge is to use the time of the physician and the physical resources efficiently while minimizing the waiting time for patients. Another example is the blood bank, where the challenge is to optimize the inventory of blood, given that several blood types must be stocked, but unused blood must be discarded after a specified period.

Another example is the clinical laboratory, which not only is a critically important hospital department, but one that is currently a very active candidate for automation. Use of hospital laboratories is expanding at a rate of 15 percent yearly. The average laboratory technician spends over 30 percent of his time performing redundant computations and transcriptions. Modern instrumentation technology makes it possible to automate most of the common chemical analyses used in diagnosis and treatment. Currently available computing systems have a clear potential for handling not only the control of the automated chemical analysis, but also the calculation of test data, the preparation of daily log sheets, laboratory summary and statistical reports, quality control reports and billing information, and finally the reporting of the test result to the patient's medical record.

While not necessarily the most important, the functions where the application has been the most emphasized, and frequently most productive, have been those associated with hotel reservation systems, inventory, and the individual departmental activities for which the data processing requirements are relatively circumscribed. Several hospitals utilize small computers to handle blood tests routinely, the computer accepting the output of the automatic chemical analyzer equipment and generating the test reports for the patient's medical record. Unfortunately matching the report to the patient's record remains a manual operation. Several hospitals also have computers that handle substantially all of the hotel functions. The next decade will undoubtedly see the introduction of large numbers of such systems.

Substantial research efforts have been addressed to the development of the overall hospital information system. Several primary obstacles limit the rate of implementation of these research efforts: shortage of competent and imaginative personnel to carry out the systematic problem analysis and engineering development required; fragmentation of the administrative structure; and the nonquantitative orientation of many hospital staffs. It is also difficult to innovate in a situation where continuity and reliability of operation are vitally important.

There are also obstacles of a different kind. Each new major area of application—and hospital information systems must certainly be so considered—makes special demands on computer technology. Special terminals, operable by nontechnical hospital personnel; high systems reliability; and very large files are some of the hardware demands. Appropriate programming languages and the ability to handle extremely errorful input data (e.g., misspelled words and nonmatching names) are some of the software demands.

Despite all these obstacles, and the long stretch between demonstration systems and systems for routine use, the forecast is basically optimistic. Substantial effort is already being devoted to information processing as related to patient care. Indeed, wherever applicable many hospitals are attempting to employ automation to meet increasing demands for better health care.

Finally, it should be mentioned that apart from the single hospital concept, there are also possibilities of multihospital or national health networks. The potential for sharing a common computer resource and a common data base among hospitals and other health facilities is enormous. Although this approach has been used only in limited areas, such as hospital accounting, there are indications that the concepts emerging from individual hospital information systems may extend to more comprehensive information networks. An equally exciting potential is the use of such health networks to assist the practicing physician in the community in the information processing activities concerned with the individual medical care he gives his patients. The vast bulk of medical care is given by individual practitioners. A health network could be of enormous value as a readily accessible source of diagnostic information, as a tool for the collection, storage, and retrieval of patient medical record information, and as a technique for making available the therapeutic planning which is available now only in a modern teaching hospital.

Simulation in Ecology

Much of the power and generality of the computer derives from its ability to simulate. This is, in effect, the converse aspect of the any-data and any-behavior principles. The usefulness of simulation itself rests on its being a general substitute for mathematical analysis as the systems under study become increasingly complex.

The essentials of simulation are few: building up in the computer a data structure that mirrors the real structure on the outside, and constructing programs corresponding to each of the actions in nature so that change in the internal symbolic structure mirrors change outside. With these essentials correctly done and working, the simulation may be started at some presumed state of nature and its evolution over time observed. The initial situation determines which programs are run to change the situation, these in turn determine the next programs, and so on through a continual sequence of changes that takes the simulation as far into the future as the investigator wishes to go. Thus, simulation is a way of investigating a particular future. If one wants to look at many possible futures that correspond to different happenings of some "random" aspect, such as the weather, the simulation must be run many different times.

It is clear why simulation substitutes for mathematical analysis. The symbolic structure, which represents the real situation, and the programs, which represent the laws of change, form a mathematical system. Generally, especially in biology and physics, they correspond to a set of equations that can be written down outside the machine. Instead of trying to analyze these equations mathematically, the simulation simply calculates one special case after another. This is less satisfactory than a general analysis; it is done only when the system is too complex to permit mathematical analysis. Furthermore, since it is useful primarily for complicated systems, the amounts of computation and bookkeeping are generally quite large. Thus, simulation has come into its own only with the availability of computers.

The literature of the life sciences now presents a plethora of instances of simulation: multienzyme systems, the growth of genetic populations, epidemics, arterial blood flow, the way the eyes track a moving object, and on and on. We choose one area, ecology, to represent them all.

Ecology is the study of populations of organisms, each of which depends on some of the others, so that in toto they make up an interdependent ongoing community. Thus, the kind of symbolic structure to be constructed in the machine for simulation consists of the numbers of each type of animal in the ecological community. In outline, what affects the number of organisms in a community is known. Organisms use each other for food: there is a *food chain* in which the grass feeds off the sunlight and the decayed remains of dead plants, the herbivores eat the plants, some carnivores eat the herbivores, and other carnivores eat the first carnivores. Organisms reproduce themselves and die of diverse causes. Other dependencies also occur, as in parasites and the use of plants for shelter and nesting. Reasonable assumptions often permit these effects to be stated precisely enough to make a simulation. Twice as many cows probably eat twice as much grass and have twice as many calves.

In the mid-twenties a mathematical theory describing such biological populations was developed by Lotka and Volterra. Although the mutual dependencies can be written down, one gets little from it. There are two difficulties. The first is obtaining enough good data to fill in the details, such as the relative abundance of species in a specific community, the probabilities of their encounters, of who escapes and who gets a meal. This difficulty is not our main concern here. The second difficulty is reasoning from the theory to the happenings in the real ecological community—working out the consequences of *all* the innumerable interactions. Here simulation on computers does provide an effective solution.

One of the most important aspects of ecological simulations is their close connection with the management of the environment and its resources. We have become increasingly aware of our dependency on our environment and that many long-term indirect effects can build up to near disastrous proportions. Air pollution, river pollution, the dust bowl (to pick one from our father's generation), the possibilities of a "silent spring"—all reflect our membership in ecological communities. Simulation is ultimately a necessary tool in trying to achieve such understanding and control.

The salmon fisheries of the Northwest provide an example. The confluence of scientific and economic interests has engendered extended efforts to understand the biology of the salmon. The general situation is depicted in Figure 14-15, which shows the life cycle of sockeye salmon, one of five commercially important species. It follows the history of 2,000 eggs which are laid in stream gravel in September. By the time the eggs have hatched into fry and the fry emerged from the gravel to move to the lakes, only 100 of the original 2,000 are left. The next year is spent in the lakes, with only 60 survivors. At the end of that second year, some migrate to the sea, some stay another year in the lakes. The fish stay at sea for two to three years and then return to the stream of origin to lay eggs and complete the cycle. The staircase effect at the right side of the curve is where each returning group passes through the fishing stations on the way upstream, yielding up its contribution to the fish harvest for that year.

The heart of the salmon problem is that they are the prey and we the predator, but we stay numerous and efficient even if the salmon decrease. If we mount too heavy a fishing effort, not enough salmon get back upstream to lay eggs. There is management of fishing, both in the type of fishing gear and in the days when fishing is allowed (e.g., not on weekends). But the complexities are many. Data are poor at the beginning of a season, better toward the end—but by then control measures have less effect. The effects of fishing in any one year are not seen until three to five years later. Yet fishing should not be reduced simply on general "safety" principles, for doubling the number of fish that escape upstream does not double the number of salmon in later years. Other fac-

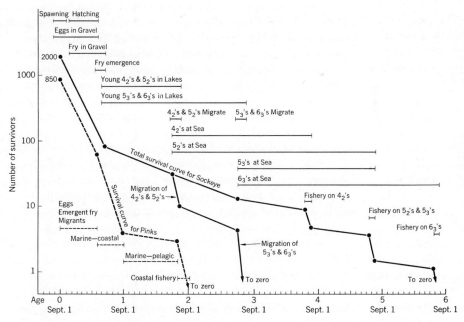

Figure 14-15. Salmon life history. (From K. E. Watt, ed., *Systems Analysis in Ecology.* © 1968 by Academic Press, Inc.)

tors, such as limited physical spawning grounds, will then take a larger toll.

Simulations have been constructed that take into account the life cycle of the salmon, the decisions and actions of the fisheries, and the strategies and options of the regulatory agencies. These simulations involve over a hundred variables with many hundreds of relations among them. They require large digital computers and utilize special programming languages which were developed, not for the life sciences, but for such areas as management science and engineering.

None of these simulations is, as yet, soldered into the day-to-day management of salmon fishing in the Northwest. Such application will only follow considerably more experience than has yet been accumulated; it will also be influenced by political and economic factors outside our present concern. And there may not yet be enough information about the life history of the salmon. But they foreshadow the kind of system that must come into being for most of our important biological resources if we are to avoid courses of economic action whose disastrous consequences are manifest only several years after ecological sin has been unwittingly committed.

The salmon fisheries portray well the close coupling between the study and management of ecological systems. They do not reveal the true dimensions of the complexity. Only two species seem involved, salmon and man, where each stage of the salmon's life cycle can be summarized by a factor showing percentage survival. But in fact, numerous other organisms and nonbiological agents enter into these "factors." Indeed, the system loops back on itself, since the salmon of one generation feed on the fingerlings of later ones.

To assess the size of systems with which ecology must eventually cope, we may note attempts to describe a total web of interrelationships. Figure 14-16 shows a field of cabbage (*B. oleracea,* at the center of the web) where an exhaustive account was made of all the other organisms that became ecologically involved with the plant. Some 210 species were identified, of which about 40 and their relationships to each other and the cabbage are shown in the figure. Even here, no organisms below ground were added to the account, nor any microorganisms. Furthermore, the area was kept carefully weeded, so that many other possible plant species were carefully kept out of the picture.

Fortunately, one cannot conclude from such a diagram that a significant simulation of the ecological community must include everyone. For many purposes large numbers of the organisms can be lumped together, just as, in the salmon case, all effects on the fry were lumped into a single "mortality factor." However, such diagrams do give an indication of the underlying complexity.

Salmon fisheries constitute a production situation where gradually, through years of scientific study, enough becomes known to build models that include the economically pertinent factors. Another use of simulation is to anticipate the normally unanticipated effects of ecological actions, such as pest control, extensive reforestation, new schemes of crop rotation, the addition of new pollutants to a stream, and so on. A massive action of some kind is proposed, which constitutes an immediate social good. The question is whether an ecological time bomb is also involved. To use simulation to examine the future for consequences does demand that we look at very large ecosystems, since we do not know in advance what parts are relevant. After the fact, sometimes, we may discover how many links lay between the action taken and the unanticipated effect that later came to light. Often these effects have occurred via only two or three links. Yet adequate management may well demand simulations that might have detected such an effect, in advance, even though it had to radiate outward some three links with some twenty to thirty branches at each step (if we take Figure 14-16 seriously).

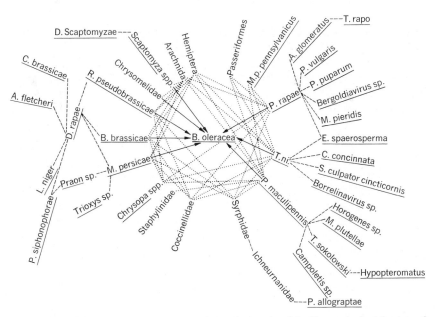

Figure 14-16. Ecological web. (From D. Pimentel, *Annals of the Entomological Society of America 54:*323, 1961)

The technology of simulation is already well developed from other fields, and efforts such as that for the salmon fisheries can import it rapidly. Extrapolation to very large simulations is not beyond the capability of computers with their rapidly increasing power.

Two factors will determine, more than anything else, how rapid will be the growth of ecological simulations. The first is the technical sophistication of the ecologists themselves. Ecology has been one of the less quantitative life sciences, even though we noted at least one live tradition of mathematical theory. The second is the availability of data in sufficient volume and precision to make simulation worthwhile. Indeed, these two are intimately related, since one of the strongest stimuli to obtaining adequate data is a theoretical apparatus that needs it.

Scientific motivation is not the whole story, however, since most effort in ecology goes into manual gathering of data. The technology for data acquisition in ecology must also undergo innovation to keep pace with the power of simulation that is already available. Image processing, which we considered with respect to neuromorphology, is as readily applicable to ecology, using infrared and ordinary photography as well as videotapes from airborne or satellite cameras.

The Present and Future Role of Computers in the Life Sciences

Our six examples have certainly not communicated the full heterogeneity of computer uses in the life sciences. Some are mundane—cows. Some have contributed to scientific spectaculars—solving the three-dimensional structure of organic molecules. Some, such as the crystallographic calculations or auditory data acquisition, require large amounts of computation; some, such as the patient care, require little. Some represent usage routinely performed today; some are just coming into being and are highly projective, such as image processing and patient care. Some uses simply make life easier (we tended not to illustrate these); some permit accomplishments not otherwise possible. The cows can illustrate the latter. The existence of the system itself finally makes possible, in a decentralized society, collection and utilization of comparative data not otherwise obtainable. The data structures in the six examples range widely: numbers, text, signals, images. Likewise, no particular area of the life sciences, nor any division between pure and applied or hard and soft, seems especially favored.

Thus, the great lesson is that no aspect of the life sciences will remain untouched by the computer. Science is an information processing activity, and that is precisely the forte of the computer.

The diversity of use, which we have tried to communicate by illustration, should not lead to the conclusion that the computer is now universally employed by every life scientist. Physics, chemistry, and the engineering disciplines are much farther along in the assimilation of the computer. The reasons for this are neither subtle nor especially deplorable. The generally greater quantitative aspect of physics and chemistry, coupled with the initial development of computers for numerical processing, is sufficient reason. If, by some quirk of history, image processing had been first developed to a fine degree, conceivably matters could have been otherwise.

Thus, most of the history of the use of computers in the life sciences is yet to be written, and most of the impact yet to be felt. Accordingly, it is appropriate not just to summarize the current uses, but to dwell on the future role of computers in this arena.

There are some peculiar difficulties in assessing this future role, and it is well to be clear about them. The development of computer technology has its share of failures. Failure, of course, is a relative notion, and rests on a history of prior prediction of success. The best known example is probably the hope of machine translation of other natural languages where extensive efforts, over a decade, have only revealed the problem to be much more difficult than anticipated during the first five years of hopeful pronouncements. And there have been others.

To focus on a newly budding area of application is to invite similar disaster or disbelief. An important example for us is image processing. This is indeed barely budding, especially when measured against the type of operation that would make it truly revolutionary for the life sciences: a routine aid to the examination, classification, and measurement of visual fields in pathology, neuromorphology, ecology, or wherever. Possibly, its development may come along nicely. Possibly, it may meander along for another half decade for lack of funds or substantial interest. Possibly, it may hit a barren plateau in which certain simple things can be done, but far short of the sophisticated applications previously envisioned, and where further progress seems very hard to attain. The most probable prediction is that image processing will develop into one of the major information technologies for the life sciences, but its eventual arrival will lag behind the predictions of success by several years.

The fundamental problem lies in the factors emphasized in the introduction: the immense increase of power at steadily decreasing cost, and our lack of understanding and imagination about how to instruct the computer. The first guarantees that revolutionary developments will take place; the second makes it almost impossible to predict which of many paths it will take.

The Computer Utility

As a vehicle for communicating the extent of probable changes, we will expand on a single aspect. This is a development now taking place in the computer field quite independently of the life sciences—the "computer utility." The analogy is to the power utility, which provides power automatically and reliably in whatever amounts are demanded by the consumer whenever and wherever he demands it. The analogy is seductive, valid to a point, and the reality that lies behind it sufficiently impressive to justify serious discussion and to make our point.

The history of the digital computer is not just that of accelerating growth of computational power concurrently with rapidly decreasing costs, though this overshadows much else. But, stage by stage, we are discovering what constitutes an adequate general-purpose information processing system. Before 1950, the vision of a computer was that of an automated statistical clerk with a desk calculator. The arithmetical organ loomed large. All else—memory, input/output, control—though necessary, was secondary. Then we learned, primarily from concern with business data processing, that the input/output had to be much more powerful and versatile. Next we learned about programming languages. Effective communication with the computer demanded the use of a different language from the one the engineers built into the machine. FORTRAN was the turning point; now there are hundreds of languages, adapted to many different uses. Still, a machine was viewed as truly single-minded. It finished one job; you then fed it another program with its data; it did that job, output the result, and was ready for the next. Then (circa 1960) we found that a computer needed to attend to many things. We learned to interrupt its computing from the outside, without spoiling work in process, so it could temporarily put its current job aside, attend to a new job for a moment, and then resume. Concurrently we learned to keep in the computer at all times a program (called the operating system, or executive) to keep track of the jobs to be done—to do the list of petty supervisory tasks familiar to any foreman in a job shop. The computer moved one step closer to being an agent with an independent view of the world and independent powers. No longer did the momentary user own the total machine.

The next step started before 1964 and is not yet complete. It is called time-sharing, and arises from the observation that since human rates of information processing are very slow (a few words per second at best) compared with computers (a million operations per second), one computer can communicate with many people simultaneously (from the people's point of view). If it switches rapidly from one person's program to the next, each can believe his own problem is being worked on. Multiuser computer systems do date back to the mid-fifties with the development of military command-and-control systems for air defense. Somewhat later, in even more special guise, came the airline reservation systems. However, it was not until 1964 that large time-sharing systems for general use came into operation (the most well known being Project MAC at MIT). These allowed some twenty to thirty people "on line"—that is, seated at a typewriter connected to the computer such that every time a person typed a message the computer immediately processed it, did any indicated computing, and typed a message back to the person.

We recount this history to indicate that the concept of a computing system has been undergoing large, almost revolutionary changes ever since its birth in the forties. Underlying all these changes are the continually increasing amounts of memory and power available per dollar, which keep changing the ground rules of the possible. But underlying these changes is also a process of discovery. Journalistic imagination can perhaps keep ahead of any explosion in technological capability—it only takes a sentence to give every man his own computer. But technical imagination must move at a more deliberate pace. Each possibility must be conceived, made real, and provide many minor lessons from its realization before the next leap can take place. Thus, in each half decade throughout the history of the computer we have learned another fundamental lesson, or two, so that "what a computer is" has become conceptually different.

The computer utility is the probable next stage in the evolution of our concept of a computing system: View it as a network of facilities—of memories and processors—into which one can tap at any point for whatever information processing one needs.

The concept grows out of existing time-sharing systems. First, there is no reason why the person communicating to the computer need be near the computer at all. He can be in his office, or in his study, or across the country. These various degrees of remoteness have operated with existing time-sharing systems, first as technical stunts, so to speak, then as routine modes of usage as they turned out to be convenient. Second, if many people are communicating with the same computer and have their programs and data records in the same large file, there is no reason not to borrow each other's programs, and communicate about them via the computer. By this means, each man has access to a much wider array of tools than before. To be sure, programming languages such as FORTRAN and ALGOL, and packages of subroutines, such as for standard statistical calculations, assure that extremely fruitful tool building already exists. Free interchange among all users, cooperatively and communicatively, will amplify these efforts. Some empirical indications already appear in existing time-sharing systems.

If men can communicate this way, so can computers. If one computer has too much to do, it can request another to do some of its work. If a small computer finds itself with a task requiring a large memory it can ship it to some other part of the network where such memory is available. The analogy with the distribution of electrical power is again appropriate. Within a large area of the country all the local power systems are tied together and automatically make demands upon each other for power, thus averaging the power load over the entire system and providing insurance against local failure. Ultimately many of the large computers in the country will be tied into each other, and special facilities anywhere in the country will be automatically available anywhere else upon demand.

Although the concept of the computer utility has grown out of time-sharing, it is a substantially more advanced system, both technically and socially. Indeed, in foreseeable development it passes beyond its metaphor, exceeding in scope any existing form of utility by a wide margin. Within itself it carries most of the functions of a total society: education, legislation, revenue, judicial, and law-enforcement. Where, for most other systems, these functions can be exercised externally by the standard mechanisms of society, the diversity and speed of happenings in a computer utility imply that all these functions will be incorporated into the system itself.

The total vision is dazzling, even before making explicit some of the consequences for life science research. However, one must take care again to distinguish journalistic imagination from technical imagination, and the latter from accomplished and operating fact. With a sentence we have tied all computers together; it is hardly accomplished so easily. Let us outline briefly some difficulties and limiting technical factors.

The first difficulty is our heritage of existing as isolated computer systems. Almost no current computers or programming systems are prepared to communicate freely with each other. The time-sharing systems are the first major attempt to meet the new conditions in a sufficiently general way. And let it be said that we are currently in a time of troubles with the new generation of large-scale, general-purpose, time-sharing systems. It will be some years yet before these systems emerge, well understood and a solid credit to the computing art.

Another concern is the vast amount of memory such networks will require. All experience with current systems shows that they can fill up more memory core space than anyone can provide. This difficulty, although real, is the least of the problems we will mention. Its solution will come from basic hardware advances, and we have reason to have faith in these.

Not so simple is the question of communication. In such a computer network the cost of communicating information from one place to another, in both dollars and time, becomes critical. A memory across the country is not as good as one nearby. More important than delay is the problem of providing communication systems that can take the high rates of data transmission required. This problem is perhaps as much a question of governmental policy as of technology, for this will probably be an expansion of the present telephone system. This has undergone vast expansion since the Second World War, with the introduction of television, the general increase of voice communication, and the already felt pressure of computer-to-computer communication. The growth of computer utilities will surely press against the bounds of our ability to enlarge the communication net. How the rate structure is adjusted to meet these new demands may have a limiting, and inappropriate, effect upon its adequacy.

We are not through with the problems. Mention earlier of the power grid analogy will have cued the reader to the great Northeast power failure of 1965 that put New York out of power for eleven hours. This power failure was a true "systems" problem — a cascade of failures starting with a small initial failure and spreading throughout the entire system because of the pattern of interlocking dependencies. It emphasizes how little we know about huge networks. Putting together a large nationwide computer utility is a matter of gaining much experience and exercising even greater caution. Thus, it will grow fitfully and in special ways at first, and some painful moments will no doubt occur when our ignorance permits substantial failures. One reason for citing earlier all the societal functions required in a computer utility was to emphasize the complexities involved.

So much for the difficulties. They are substantial and will limit the rate at which computer utilities come into being. However, modest time-shared computing is already being offered commercially by half a dozen firms to anyone anywhere in the country at costs reasonable enough to be competitive. Their existence indicates that we have already started along the way.

Computer utilities will come into being independently of the life sciences, and will affect other parts of society at least as greatly as the life sciences. Here we will keep our view narrowed to the life sciences. We will discuss four specific effects, taking these in the order in which they may well develop.

Small Theoretical and Data Analysis Calculations. A substantial part of quantitative activities in the life sciences involves small calculations of either a statistical or chemical nature. Most of the operating time-sharing systems (some commercial, some in universities and research organizations) are geared to this level, and it is, clearly, the capability that utility computing will first make widely available. Investigators in major universities will tap the systems that their universities acquire. Schools and organizations which are not computationally sophisticated can obtain services at modest (though nontrivial) costs from some outside utility. Most important, they can do this without themselves, as a department or laboratory subunit, getting into the computer business even in a small way. Let us emphasize again that, for the next few years, this kind of access holds only for small numerical computations.

What will be the effect on the life sciences? Certainly not the direct production of new "breakthroughs." However, the general quantitative sophistication of life sciences research should increase somewhat, with computational drudgery taking a smaller fraction of the scientist's total time. These effects may be greater the farther one moves away from existing centers of high competence and sophistication, since the great medical schools and biological laboratories have long found ways to get their computations performed.

Problem-Oriented Programming Systems: The Encapsulation of Art. Science proceeds by the accumulation of technique as well as by the accumulation of data and the construction of theories. Some technique reduces to pure cookbookness—how to use a chemical balance, or how to run an immunoassay. Many calculations associated with these techniques are appropriate to the computation facilities just discussed. But technique exists also at a higher level—the ability to study a complex proposed multienzyme system to see whether it is consistent with existing knowledge, or the ability to construct a simulation of an ecological system about which one has partial knowledge. Think of this as art, rather than technique, if the latter term has too cut-and-dried a ring. But it is an art that rests solidly on the ability to put symbolic systems together and explore their consequences, and it is punctuated with substantial amounts of numerical calculation. (There is also much laboratory art that is not of this kind.)

It has proved possible to construct programming systems that make it much easier to practice these arts. They are often called *problem-oriented programming languages.* They have already built into them terms that refer to important things in the subject matter, and processes for doing the manipulations one wants to do (the any-data and any-behavior principles again). For example, in an engineering problem-oriented language for the area of hydrology one is concerned with rainfall over a countryside. One can simply ask for the standard calculations of amount of runoff from a given distribution of rain. The programming system knows where to get the data, and how to calculate the quantities of interest. It knows this, of course, because some programmer-engineers spent much effort constructing the program to do it. But once this effort was invested, it remains available to subsequent usage by engineers without the same cost. A permanent addition to the conceptual tools available to the field has occurred.

Few problem-oriented programming systems exist in the life sciences as yet. There is an extensive system for biomedical statistics, a few for enzyme kinetics, and some others; such systems range from the trivial to the profound. From our vantage point, however, they form a major way in which technique can be encapsulated and made available to other scientists.

The computer utility with its emphasis on the intercommunication of programs and data, and the construction of programming systems which can sustain such interaction, enhance both the need and the payoff from problem-oriented programming systems. It will lead to basic developments that make it easy to construct such problem-oriented systems, rather more by computer scientists than life scientists. At the next level up, however, it will lead life scientists to engage in constructing a wide array of such systems. There will be systems for chemical calculation, ecological simulation, image analysis, genetic simulation, and on and on. It will be easier than at present for a scientist to obtain such systems and learn their use. Existing systems of program libraries work by mail, and are already of immense value. To be able to discover in short order whether a programming system exists somewhere in the utility and to obtain it automatically, ready to run, will be an additional substantial gain.

As important as the real gains will be a change of view in the life sciences, which will see the creation of such systems as a worthy professional endeavor. This will come about through the same intercommunication mechanism. Scientific colleagues will become aware of a contribution and utilize it, if it be useful. Hence, such a programming system becomes a professional contribution and not just a private tool.

In turn, this will raise the sophistication of the life sciences. The lone investigator at a small school can then have access to many more of the intellectual tools that his colleague in a large institution has been able to command.

There is substantial impetus in the development of problem-oriented programming systems for science and technology independently of the computer utility. The latter will simply enhance greatly both their usefulness and their attractiveness. However, some of the aforementioned benefits can grow only as fast as a rather substantial intercommunicating network grows. As mentioned earlier, this will clearly not happen overnight.

Sophisticated Laboratory Instruments. Of the four effects we shall mention, this seems to us the most exciting. This is the ability to bring into the laboratory measured amounts of automatic data processing and data communication. As now designed, laboratory instruments are "standalone" devices, each with its own interface with the outside, each with only those features in it that are economically viable for the total market. A laboratory soon becomes a system of instrumentation, patched together by the investigator from among the instruments available in various catalogues plus the special devices he fashions himself to interconnect them to do special jobs. Until now, almost all of the sophisticated processing of data available with digital techniques has been excluded from such systems.

This is not completely true. Small special-purpose computers for average response times have become available. Some laboratories have acquired small digital computers, although these are rarely integrated into the rest of the instrumentation system in any automatic way.

The computer utility plus the availability of small specialized digital processors could permit a rather radical transformation. A laboratory could have an outlet to computer power into which it can simply plug for whatever general processing needs it has. One of the handicaps to getting general-purpose digital processing into the laboratory has been the need for developing programming systems for the laboratory computers. With the computer utility, the small digital processors are simultaneously linked in with the large system. The programming systems used to program and debug the smaller devices may be done in the larger system, with its large memory and powerful languages. The small machine does not have to be adapted to performing these additional functions which add much to its cost and complexity; it need only perform the laboratory measurement and specialized processing functions plus having the ability to be plugged into the utility.

The other aspect of this transformation is the potential availability of a new class of instruments, based on digital technology, that can be easily hooked into a larger digital network. We now have a large investment in instruments not so adapted. However, one of the more certain effects of the increased speed and decreased cost of digital systems will be the development of digitally based laboratory devices, some simply digital in nature, some with digital interfaces, and many with specialized digital computers integrated into their design. All of these new laboratory devices will be adapted to making the most effective use of a computer utility.

Three features of the computer utility will determine the extent of the interaction with such digitally based laboratory instrumentation. The first of these is reliability. Although obviously necessary for all uses, reliability becomes particularly important in experimental work where, once an experimental session starts, failure aborts the whole. In much computing, failure is only an annoyance—the garbled line can be corrected, the last part of the task done over again. The loss is larger if one is doing real time monitoring of a patient or an experimental animal. Such situations may require local computational power sufficient to reduce the requirement for reliability of the utility.

A second feature that determines the extent of the utility's interaction with the laboratory is data rate (bandwidth in the jargon of the trade). Many life science experiments generate large amounts of data in a hurry during an experiment. Thus, concern is not only with average rate, but also with whether the utility system will be prepared to receive large amounts in small fractions of a second. There will be very stringent limits on this, and the amount of local buffering and specialized processing of data required will have to be adjusted through experience with each new situation.

The other determining feature besides reliability and bandwidth is "response time." Requirements in the laboratory for quick response may, in some cases, continue to force the use of considerable local processing. When the course of an experiment depends upon preliminary results calculated in fractions of a second, the computer utility will probably be ineffective. But subsequent processing to obtain final results could still best be conducted where programming is easy and memory size and arithmetic speed are not limited.

The role played by the "utility" in the laboratory need not depend on a far-flung intercommunicating network. Rather modest networks, even within a single university, already suffice to provide the wherewithal to encourage the development of such digitally based laboratory instrument systems.

Access to Large Data Bases. A final effect will be the accumulation of large files of information about areas of the life sciences that can be interrogated from anywhere in the country. The possibility of such data bases has already captured popular imagination in such forms as nationwide health information networks and scientific information retrieval systems. We mention such possibilities last, because they can come to fruition only at a rather advanced stage in the development of the computer utility. They depend on having the network well connected all over the country with a very large number of users on line. As we have noted, this will occur rather late, after a number of local networks have grown up, and many of the other advantages have accrued. Still, it will come.

Actually, the two examples cited are unfortunate for another reason. They must depend for their usefulness on a large number of inputs from a large number of sources; they must be distributed data acquisition systems as well as data retrieval systems. For management of the scientific literature, much work has gone into developing central acquisition systems, as in the literature-abstracting organizations. These are now part of the way down the road. The health data system is much farther off, as we noted earlier, since the gathering of health records and their standardization and reliability are still a tangle of local affairs.

The benefits from automatic access to large data bases will come first in areas where a data base can be put together by a small number of people, e.g., by an appropriate professional society. Thus, an identification service for large biological molecules from mass spectrometry data, or a compilation of the biological effects of diverse organic chemicals, is likely to be an early example of such systems. Likewise, special compilations of clinical data or of taxonomies of parts of the plant or animal kingdom are good possibilities.

Conclusion

Hopefully, the main themes of this essay are clear to the reader: an exploding technology; universality of means and diversity of ends; and a flavor of inevitability despite limitations of imagination, know-how, and overconfidence. Perhaps it is a little too clear, perhaps a trace over-familiar. For all this has been said before. The fundamentals on which we have drawn for our picture have been visible for almost two decades. The events of the past few years, which have provided our examples, have not demonstrated anything that was not clear earlier. Some mark points of application one step farther along the advance, thus providing confirmation, if such is needed, that advance is continuing. Even the two glimpses of the future we have emphasized, image processing and the computer utility, are merely illustrations of a technology in progress, and not final end points, no matter how relevant to the style of life sciences research as we see it now.

Yet the story must be told in these terms, for it is a peculiar feature of this "wave of the future" that it consists of a ground swell of success continually capped by a crest of failure and disappointment. The under-developed nations are not the only ones trapped by their own rising expectations. At all times most of the new computer developments that seem truly exciting are destined to disappoint their proponents—stretching out beyond the predicted moment of success, sometimes for years, until they seem to be just another backwash of technology. In fact, the wave metaphor is quite apt. Who has not, in watching the ocean waves, seen the white cap of a large wave and tried to follow its course, only to have it escape visual grasp as it subsided into the smooth curve of the wave itself. So it is with the leading edge of computer technology, which must always be those predicted applications that seem to stretch most toward the future. Their subsidence without apparent issue says little about the body of the wave.

Thus, the story must be retold in the familiar superlative terms or it will distort the more fundamental truth. More serious than the danger of exaggeration is the danger that the advance will seem inevitable and autonomous—that nothing need be done by life scientists except to await the development, say, of the computer utility and then simply plug in. There is, of course, a measure of truth in this, but only because other segments of society—the military, the business community, the nuclear physicists—are not awaiting developments. They are forcing them with both dollars and professional concern.

If the life sciences are to shape the developing computer technology to their own advancement, they must be prepared to invest in it the same professional concern and dollars. And this has already happened. The development of the LINC, already mentioned, stands as an example of the life sciences' influence on the development of computer hardware, not just for itself, but in the movement of the field toward the development of small computers. But there have been few others.

Often the attitude is taken that life scientists, concerned as they are with the substantive problems of their field, should not have to devote their lives to developing computer technology. If the experience of other fields is any indication, a number of them will, in fact, have to do so or the adaptation of computer technology to the life sciences will go comparatively slowly. Almost without exception throughout the entire history of computers, the art has been pushed and the technology given direction by massive developmental and "demonstration" efforts, invariably supported by federal funds. For instance, the current surge in time-sharing was brought about by such a demonstration effort, at a number of places simultaneously, but all supported by the Advanced Research Projects Agency, at a cost of upwards of $20 million for its initial thrust. The market alone has never operated to bring the new computer technologies into existence.

Emphasis on the rapidly decreasing cost per operation of computers should not obscure the fact that it is fundamentally a very expensive business. In part, our rising expectations always lead us to reach too far in conceiving new systems. But more important, the computer business is continuously developmental—the changing technology guarantees this. Development costs are notoriously high and difficult to predict.

In sum, to push hard on using the computer in the life sciences is to devote substantial amounts of funds and attention, and to join the ranks of frustrated system builders. It is also to gain the rewards of better science and more extensive application of that science to the needs of society.

Chapter 15

ON FEEDING MANKIND

The world's food supply, long known to be inadequate in quantity and quality, is becoming yet more inadequate. Malnutrition and starvation are common in many countries where food supplies are incommensurate with population growth. Prompt action is needed to meet this condition, yet even after achieving the resolution to do so, action is necessarily slow. The entire organization of governments and the slow evolution of societies are involved. In this seemingly hopeless circumstance, increased agricultural endeavor offers the greatest hope. Some immediate relief to the needy presently comes from the United States and a few other nations able to produce a surplus of food and willing to give it away. At best, however, we can hope to meet only a tiny fraction of the food requirements of other countries. An eventual balance is necessary between population growth and agricultural productivity of the entire planet.

In the intermediate term, we can help a nation in need to evolve a more productive agriculture. Some of our knowledge can be transferred, a few scarce materials can be supplied, and we can advise in planning and organization. But in the end, the conditions of food production are unique to each country. Introduction of new crop varieties, improvement of animal breeds, application of pest and disease control, and the prevention of after-harvest loss depend upon local conditions. Most of the needy nations are tropical, and our knowledge and experience with tropical agriculture are still limited. While growing seasons are long in the tropics and several crops might be raised in one year, fertility levels of the land are often very low, and pests are far more serious than in temperate climates where winters serve to control them. An adequate agriculture can be initiated only by research, and once increased production is under way, continued research is required for its maintenance and improvement.

Maintenance of the present levels of food supply in the world for the coming 15 years will require a 50 percent increase in production. The projection is minimal both for total caloric need and for the protein component. The annual increase in production was less than 2 percent during the past 5 years, which failed to match the population increase. An overall projection for the next 15 years is that the average food supply per person will decrease by more than 5 percent from the present already inadequate level. The decrease, moreover, is likely to occur in nations where the need for increase is greatest. While the situation is desperate, it is not hopeless. Application of biological knowledge as the principal ameliorating factor is imperative (Fig. 15-1).

The United States, fortunately, can produce more food, fiber, and manufactured products than its people consume. Pressure to meet requirements for bare necessities thus is absent. Emphasis instead can be turned to increased productivity of labor and continued improvement

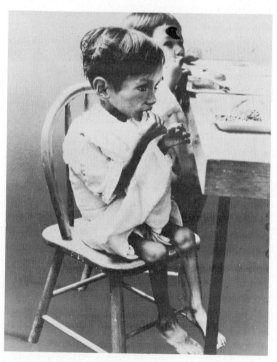

Figure 15-1. Malnourished children. (Courtesy Agricultural Science Review and Cooperative State Research Service, USDA)

of living standards. This condition is the result of many factors including, importantly, effective research. Because agriculture deals with living things, biological research is central to its well-being.

Biology has many roles in the production of food and fiber. Major contributions come from the genetics of plants and animals, the physiology of reproduction, principles of nutrition, knowledge of animal and plant disease control, the functioning of the normal individual, control of pests, and the interaction of the species and the environment.

A synthesis of diverse knowledge is attempted in this examination of the role of biology in the production of food and fiber. Full use is made of past and current examinations of the federal, state, and commercial establishments for research and development and of the land-grant universities and other schools concerned. Particular reference is made to "The World Food Problem," a report of the President's Science Advisory Committee, and to "A National Program of Research for Agriculture," sponsored by the Association of State Universities and Land-Grant Colleges and the U.S. Department of Agriculture.

Because of the diversity of life and of the arts of husbandry and harvest, it is necessary to consider crop and forest plants, domestic animals, and fish separately. Genetics, which is of pervading importance, is particularly emphasized. We start with the soil.

Biology of the Soil

Agriculture depends on the soil. This is perhaps a truism, but if so, its breadth is sometimes forgotten when the dependence of agriculture on knowledge of biology is being considered. The soil has not been a favored region for biological study. To examine the soil is often far more laborious than dealing with the air or with waters. The main biotic regions, however, are the air, the waters, and the soil.

The thin covering of soil over the land is a sort of intermediate zone between the earth and the air. It supplies water and nutrients through the roots to the tops of plants. The roots, to function, must also draw upon the soil for air.

The soil and plant relationship is an evolutionary one. Roots are adapted for life in the soil. Hormonal actions within the plants determine the downward growth of roots and the upward growth of shoots along the gravitational gradient in a way that is only vaguely understood.

The soil, moreover, not only is suited for growth of roots, but serves equally well for many other forms of life that interact with each other as well as with the roots. Agriculture is greatly involved with these interactions. A cubic inch of fertile soil can contain as many individual living organisms as there are people on the earth. The diversity among organisms is far greater than among the people. Most of them are microforms, chief among which are bacteria followed in order by actinomycetes, fungi, and algae. The animals, while fewer in number, are of equal magnitude in mass. Chief among these are nematodes, or roundworms, followed in decreasing order of numbers by mites and springtails. In order of mass, however, earthworms and potworms as well as ants and insect larvae are significant. Finally, there are the larger burrowing animals. Roots are only one living form in this microcosm.

As in the other areas of science, we can hardly deal with the whole of soil life and function, but rather must break it into parts. The parts can be disciplines, broadly, of soil flora and fauna. The diversity of form, however, requires more detailed subdivision into microbiology, or rather soil microbiology, mycology, nematology, acarology, and entomology. An alternative splitting can be into aspects of plant pathology and plant symbiosis where the emphasis is on a plant or production function. Still another way of division is into soil chemistry and physics, that is, into basic processes.

Examples of several specific biotic interactions will best serve to bring a realization of some of the working elements of the whole and of the need for knowledge in this area to serve agriculture.

Root rots affect many crop plants often to the point of complete loss as in the "take-all" disease of wheat, the root rot of cotton, and root diseases of tobacco. The causative organisms in cotton are chiefly fungi (*Ophiobolus graminis* and *Phymatotrichum omnivorum*), filaments of which grow through the soil and invade the roots to be followed in turn by other organisms. A first question, from a crop point of view, is to prevent or decrease the fungal attack. There are two chief hopes. One is to find a degree of resistance in the plant and to breed for its incorporation into commercial varieties. This has been successful with sugarcane and many other grasses for attacks of some fungi. But such endeavors require many years for success—and in time a mutation of the fungus will probably return to the attack. Accordingly, such programs require a continuing research and breeding program. No resistance, however, has been found for the root rot of cotton, which attacks a wide variety of plants. In such cases, the agricultural effort sometimes turns to attempted modification of the soil environment, as might be achieved by crop rotation or liming or other chemical treatment to reduce the numbers of pathogens or to let other forms get the upper hand. These efforts rest on a thorough knowledge of the causative organism, but on only a rudimentary knowledge of its soil ecology. Since this is equally true for many other plants, we cannot overemphasize the need for a broad program of study of soil ecology.

Crop rotation is one of the oldest forms of dealing with soil ecology in a broad and often successful, but poorly understood way. Crop rotation, while widely practiced, can be too costly on valuable land. Its beneficial use is shown with the "take-all" disease of wheat where rotation of wheat with nonsusceptible barley varieties can be used to decrease the saprophytic fungal population living in decaying wheat straw. Another example is in control of root rot of beans in areas of Michigan where beans following corn in a long rotation reduce the fungal invasion to a reasonable level. In general, rotation affords time for a soil to change from being suited to being unsuited for a particular organism.

Crop rotation has other uses, chief among which is maintenance of soil structure. The end result of good tilth has a biological cause in part. The first elements of the food chain in the soil are dead residues of plants. These and dead microorganisms provide food for bacteria, some of which produce gummy material (uronic acids) and polymerization products of lignin. These materials interact with the clays and minerals of soils to form aggregates which resist puddling. The soil is an assemblage of aggregates affording a loose system for root penetration and small spaces for retention of water with larger voids for air. This architecture is necessary for economic return from crops. It also affords the special nooks and crannies where the abundant soil life can best fend for itself. A "dead" soil soon degenerates.

Living organisms in the soil are never far removed from being food themselves. They do have protective mechanisms other than simply being the most numerous. One of these is the production of antibiotics by many fungi. While antibiotics undoubtedly play a part in the ecology of the soil, their operation may be difficult to detect, for while some organisms are suppressed, others thrive and destroy the antibiotics. Another form of protection is for the organism to pass into an inactive or inert form when conditions of survival are adverse. Thus, some bacteria and many fungi form resting spores and the animal forms produce eggs, cysts, or undergo diapause. An agriculturally important example of pathogenicity in this area is the golden nematode of the potato, the potato eelworm. As long as potatoes are grown in a particular field, some factor, which is still unknown, derived from the plant causes the cysts of the nematode to develop. The population of cysts can be exhausted only by withholding the infected area from use for potato culture for many years.

Interaction of the plant and soil organisms is by no means always adverse. Two examples of favorable interaction are symbiosis of bacteria (rhizobia) with the roots of legumes and of fungi with the roots of many plants (mycorrhizae). Legumes are not only an important food source because of their protein quality; they are also a primary instrumentality for obtaining necessary nitrogen for growth from the air. In this way, they serve as a main factor in the overall nitrogen balance for plant growth in the world. The rhizobia invade the roots through the root hairs and then form nodules in which the nitrogen fixation takes place in association with the bacterium. This process is of such practical importance that there is commercial production of the best strains of bacteria for use on various species and varieties of legumes.

The chemistry of nitrogen fixation by bacteria, such as *Azobacter vinelandii* has been intensively investigated. In this process the unreactive nitrogen molecule (N_2) is reduced to ammonia (NH_3). The entire process appears to occur, in consecutive steps, while the nitrogen is bound to the enzyme nitrogenase. No free intermediates are seen; N_2 approaches the active site of the enzyme and $2 NH_3$ depart. This requires attack on the N_2 by 6 electrons. The latter are furnished by the organic metabolism of the bacterium, mediated by an iron-protein called ferredoxin which, in photosynthetic organisms, serves as the immediate acceptor of electrons from activated chlorophyll. It is conceivable that a modification of this process may, one day, be employed for the large-scale fixation of nitrogen.

Fungi living in close association with roots, mycorrhizae of trees such as pines, apparently play an important part in the nutrition of the plants. This is a sort of symbiosis of much the same type as that of the lichens, where fungi and algae are associated. It is held that because of this symbiosis, pine roots can obtain a supply of phosphate and other minerals from poor soils, thus greatly increasing the land areas suitable for productive forestry.

The diverse soil population is also beneficial to agriculture by degrading the residues of crops and organic matter present in the soils. The very fertile lands of the Corn Belt depend on this process. They contain organic matter inherited from the long period as grassland prior to cultivation. This old organic matter, as well as fresh crop residues, serves as a food source for the soil population with the accompanying release of some excess nitrogen and phosphorus compounds required in plant growth. It is a sort of mining, by the microlife, of a heritage, the utilization of a resource that must be carefully conserved to avoid useless dissipation with loss of the associated soil structure.

Agricultural man usually accepts the ecology of the soil as he makes his choice of crops and farming methods. But sometimes his only chance for survival is open warfare. An example is the ravages of nematodes which, if ignored, can prevent economic production of celery, pine-apple, and many other crops in some areas. They considerably reduce plant growth in all areas; and to counter their attacks, in extreme cases, soils must be fumigated. Fumigation is costly and, in time, its effects are lost be reinvasion, but the cost is repaid if the crop is valuable. Similarly, greenhouse operators and others must sterilize soil to prevent fungal attacks on seedling plants as well as to destroy weed seed and insect larvae in collected soil. Methods applicable to field areas of low-value crops, like wheat or corn, are needed for reactivating and destroying life stages of many inimicable soil-borne organisms.

The soil population and the soil processes can degrade a wide variety of materials and compounds, although the process is slow for many met-als and some organic compounds. This degradative facility is useful in changing farm waste from animal lots to beneficial plant nutrients and in maintaining soil structure. The pesticide materials that the farmer uses, whether on plants or by addition to soil, finally confront the soil population. If these residues are inorganic compounds, such as some arsenates, the element itself cannot be destroyed and, when used to ex-cess, can be detrimental to the land. Virtually all organic compounds, however, are destroyed in the end. The rate is so slow in some cases as to allow the compound in question to be transferred to another area such as a neighboring lake where its toxicity is unwanted. The accepted answer to this difficulty is carefully to tailor the pesticide for biode-gradability as well as its primary activity. This will surely be accom-plished in the future, but at the moment, we are in a transition period where some of the most effective and economically useful materials are too persistent or too toxic to species other than that being controlled.

Biology of Plant Growth

Interest in the biology of plants used in agriculture starts with the farm-er's need for the germ plasm of his various crops, the seeds and the vegetative clones. Meeting this need is the function of plant breeding, as discussed later, which is based on knowledge of the distribution and evolution of plants of the world as well as methods of genetics. The vari-eties eventually selected by the breeder must be increased in the hands of seedmen and turned over to commercial channels.

Germination and rapid seedling growth are next in order of the farmer's concern. The crop must get a good start. Soil climate—the temperature and moisture content—as well as a correct seedbed preparation is im-portant. A few days' delay in emergence of the crop might result in change of yield by an appreciable fraction, particularly in northern regions or where winter crops are raised in the south. Losses from fungal attacks, or damping-off, must be lessened or avoided. Weed competition must be reduced where necessary by cultural practices and use of pre-emergent herbicides. In many dry regions, soil salinity might delay germination and early growth. Each of these concerns is a subject of biological research in seed behavior, with respect to temperature, salinity, light, seed age and vigor, dormancy factors, and structure.

Decisions are made at planting time about the number of plants desired per unit of area, how they are to be spaced, and how forced along in growth. The way in which fertilizer usage—or plant nutrition—is to be managed must be decided at planting. Increases in yield *now* come more from correct fertilizer usage than from any other factor in crop production, as shown in Table 1. Plants require large supplies of compounds of nitrogen, phosphorus, potassium, calcium, magnesium, and sulfur. The first three are the major nutrient elements, hence are the chief components of fertilizers. The other three are required in relatively moderate amounts. In addition, a number of minor nutrient elements must be supplied, particularly iron, manganese, zinc, copper, and boron. Plant growth depends not only upon the absolute level of supply of each nutrient, but also upon their interactions. Some minor nutrients, such as copper and boron, are toxic at excessive levels.

Table 1. Average Yield of Corn/Acre in the United States as Influenced by the Use of Hybrids and Fertilizer (for Illinois)

Year	Average Yield/Acre	Hybrids % Planted	Plant Nutrient Tons (Thousands)
1933	22.6	0.1	—
1943	32.2	52.4	28
1953	39.9	86.5	295
1963	67.6	95.0+	820

Source: Agricultural Statistics, U.S. Department of Agriculture 1966.

Biological interest first centered on examining the essentiality of the various elements for plant growth and their way of functioning as displayed by the appearance of plants. In this way, many poor practices were corrected, and regions and types of soils were recognized in which particular deficiencies were common. The cattle industry of the Southeast, particularly Florida, became possible when it was found that their soils were cobalt-deficient, and that cobalt, although not essential to the growth of grasses, is incorporated into growing grasses and then becomes available to the microorganisms of the bovine rumen for synthesis of vitamin B_{12}, which is vital to the welfare of cattle. Present interest lies in finding the manner of functioning of each nutrient and the way it enters the root and is translocated throughout the plant. The processes involved are dependent upon the transport systems of the membranes of both cells and subcellular organelles. Such understanding may improve the formulas for commercial fertilizers. Agricultural interest here fuses with cellular physiology.

The crop, from selected seed and past its seedling hazards, enters a period of rapid growth if water and nutrient supplies are adequate. Now the dependence is more on the sunlight and the air, required for photosynthesis. Rapid progress toward understanding photosynthesis has been made during the past twenty years. An outline of current understanding of this process is offered in Chapter 3. The essential features of carbon dioxide fixation are now known, but much remains to be learned about the event in which the energy of sunlight is coupled with this process.

Agriculture has long survived without human knowledge of photosynthesis, even as man has lived without knowing how his brain functions. Now, with understanding, more attention is being turned to ensuring adequacy of photosynthesis in crops. One way is to ensure an adequate supply of carbon dioxide. In glass houses, the carbon dioxide can be increased, over the low level in the air, with striking effects on plant growth. In the field, attention centered on the exchange with the crop of air above the field. This exchange depends on the wind velocity, the turbulence, and the roughness of the crop surface. Attention to the way in which sunlight gets into the crop canopy is rewarding in yield. It is essential for the crop to intercept a maximum of sunlight as early in crop growth as possible. For this reason, the number of plants per given area is being increased by as much as two- or three-fold over former practice. Plants are also being selected with upright growth so that the top leaves intercept sunlight during early and late hours without shading lower leaves. Attention is given also to orientation of rows consistent with field contours.

As knowledge of the photosynthetic process grows, hope rises in modifying it to prevent growth of some plants, weeds, or to vary the plant products, for instance, sugar formation in sugarcane, instead of new leaves. These hopes depend on knowledge of growth control as well as of photosynthesis.

The purpose of raising a crop is to obtain a product that might be herbage or a fruit. Control over the product can be exercised in various ways during growth. The most important of these is genetic and is exercised in the selection of germ plasm. Striking examples are afforded by selections for stiffness of straw in rice and wheat, for early maturity in barley and potatoes, for lack of flowering in sugarcane, and for seasonal adaptation in soybeans. The last of these, in which change from vegetative to reproductive growth is particularly involved, will illustrate some of the principles.

A variety of soybean suitable for Iowa would be a total loss in Arkansas. The cause lies in dependence of flowering on the day length of the region. The soybean used in Iowa flowers when the days are longer than needed for the varieties used in Arkansas. The soybean plant grows vegetatively during early summer and flowers only after the plants are quite large. A variety unsuited to the day length of a particular latitude might flower when quite small, while another would not mature before frost. This property of plants which widely enters into selection by breeding, and is a major underlying factor in plant adaptation through dormancies, is also under hormonal control acting in part through sunlight. A basis is being provided for working toward solution of such problems as frost damage to flowers of fruit trees, restrictions of soybean growth which still seriously affect yield, and obtaining more continuous summer growth of northern trees.

The interplay of biology with agriculture is not ended at harvest. Many of the products are still living. Fruits and grains still undergo change which can be affected by proper choice of moisture content, temperature, and atmosphere, of storage, as well as use of various agents such as ethylene. The living products are still susceptible to microbiological decay and enzyme action. Herbage and other dying products can be suitably handled to preserve their nutritive content. And here begins the transition from agriculture to the food and feed industries which are considered later in this chapter.

Heritability

Large populations of single botanical types are used in modern farming. These provide favorable environments for the growth and evolution of their many kinds of pests and parasites — viruses, bacteria, fungi, worms, insects, and other plants and animals. To be most effective, breeding must be based on knowledge of the total environment and the population dynamics of the various species concerned. The trend toward raising one variety may have to be replaced by greater use of genetic diversity to reduce the risk from disease.

It is useful to have a quantitative measure of the relative importance of heredity and environment in determining the expression of characteristics of plants and animals. The most widely used figure of merit is the *coefficient of heritability*. Since the concept of heritability involves the relative amount of variability due to genetic causes and to environment, the heritability coefficient takes the form of a ratio of variances. Specifically, it is the ratio of the *genic variance* ($\theta_G{}^2$) to the total variance.

$$H = \frac{\theta_G{}^2}{\theta_G{}^2 + \theta_E{}^2}$$

where $\theta_E{}^2$ is the environmental variance. Both $\theta_G{}^2$ and $\theta_E{}^2$ can be estimated through appropriate experiments, although adequate experiments are difficult. It is to be noted that the hereditary and environmental factors are separable and are taken as additive in the denominator.

Genetics Applied to Plant Production

The goal of most breeding is to improve yield and quality. Sometimes the approach has been direct, as in the breeding of sugar beets. Early attempts to produce sugar from beets were unsuccessful, largely because of sugar contents below 7 percent, but selection over a long period gave varieties capable of consistently producing 15 to 18 percent sugar. Examples of the breeding of higher-yielding varieties can be cited for practically any major crop species.

Increased yield has more often been approached by improvement of one or more specific components of yield. One method is to fit the growth cycle of a crop to the available growing season. An example of such fitting is the modification of grain sorghum. This species, a tropical grass, was originally confined to the warmer climates of the world. Development of earlier-maturing varieties extended the range in the United States to the Canadian border. Another indirect approach to yield improvement is through adjustment of various agronomic or horticultural properties. Again, the grain sorghums provide a good example. The types originally introduced into the United States grew higher than a man's head. The cost of hand-harvesting was prohibitive, and because of delay, the crop was often lost to rain, snow, or birds. Dwarf varieties, which grow only three or four feet tall, were developed to permit mechanical harvesting. Achievement by the grain sorghums of a place among the ten most important crops of the United States rests chiefly on this last factor.

It is now clear that all crop species have large stores of inadequately explored genic variability. This is particularly true for many crops suited to the warm climate of underdeveloped regions where food needs are great. Rice production in the Far East is an example. Many rice varieties now used are tall growing. They "lodge" seriously before harvest, particularly if adequate fertilizer is used to enhance the yield. The tall varieties do not allow the sun to penetrate deeply into the crop. Short, stiff-strawed varieties, which respond to fertilizer, have been developed at the Rice Research Institute in the Philippines. With these varieties, yields of more than 9,000 lb/acre have been obtained in large experimental plots whereas the average yield had been about 1,200 lb/acre. Seed of this strain has been placed under cultivation in a sufficient fraction of Philippine acreage to convert that nation from a net rice importer to a net rice exporter. As this strain is adapted for use in other southern Asiatic lands, it can prove to be the most important agricultural event of this century.

Corn improvement with respect to protein quality is another example of what can be gained. Corn grain is deficient in the nutritionally essential amino acid lysine, the content of which is controlled by a single gene. This gene is now being transferred to the major inbred lines of corn used in producing hybrids, with promise of greatly increasing the protein quality of those dietaries in which corn is the principal cereal. On a worldwide basis, the most critical deficiency in the diet quality is shortage of the sulfur-containing amino acids, cystine and methionine. As increase in the content of these amino acids in the protein of wheat, rice, and corn would go far toward reducing protein deficiencies in the food of adults in several underdeveloped countries.

An agricultural variety, however, depends not on the action of one gene or another, or on any one component of performance, but on the whole interacting set of genes and the interactions of many components. The hereditary constitution of the tall rice varieties is the product of a long process of evolution under conditions of low fertility, and suddenly this genic system, modified by a few genes for shortness, is placed in an environment of high fertility to which the plant is not adapted. Further progress requires new levels of knowledge of integration of genic systems.

Finally, the reader is reminded that there really are no genes for shortness, lodging, lysine content, etc. Genes control synthesis of specific proteins or regulate the operation of other genes that do so. It is the balance of the proteins synthesized, and their amino acid content, that make for the genetic traits of concern to the plant breeder. At this stage of knowledge, such breeding is conducted without definitive awareness of the true physiological function of those genes whose expression ultimately is revealed as one or another of the traits with which the plant breeder is, properly, concerned.

Plant Disease and Its Control by Breeding

The Irish famine in the middle of the last century was one of the great tragedies of modern times. Two circumstances were responsible for the famine. First, the people had become dependent on the potato as the major source of calories in their diet. Second, in two seasons, 1845 and

1846, the potato crop was almost totally destroyed by fungal attack, the "late blight." A million people starved and a third of the population emigrated to escape.

While modern knowledge is probably adequate to prevent another holocaust like the potato famine, it has not stopped the incursion of plant disease. Yearly losses in the United States amount to 15 to 20 percent of total production, valued at current prices, in excess of $3 billion. The cost for use of control measures is of the order of $300 million.

Clearly, discovery of methods that would effectively reduce these losses would be of enormous nutritional and economic benefit.

Fungal and Bacterial Diseases of Plants in the United States. Fungi and bacteria are responsible for most disease losses in cultivated plants. Among fungal pathogens of cereals are species of wilt fungi (*Fusarium*), rusts (*Puccinic*), leaf blotch (*Helminthosporium, Septoria*), smut fungi, powdery mildews, and scald. Fungal diseases of barley decrease the annual yield by 9 percent in the United States. Most other crops also suffered approximately 10 percent losses, caused by fungi and bacteria. For example, annual losses from fungal diseases of corn are estimated at 12 percent, of which fungus-caused stalk rots caused 3 percent, leaf blights (*Helminthosporium*) 2 percent, and smut, ear, and root rots, as well as brown spot (*Physoderma*) cause the remainder. Bacterial leaf blight accounts for 0.5 percent.

Among the many measures developed to control diseases of plants, the use of resistant varieties is not only the easiest and most economical but frequently the only effective approach. For certain crops, such as small grains, virtually the entire acreage of the United States is planted with varieties bred specifically to tolerate or resist a particular disease, or several different diseases. This is also true for alfalfa, corn, cotton, tobacco, and tomatoes. There can be no doubt that the breeding of resistant varieties has been a major factor contributing to the great increases in agricultural productivity during the past half-century.

Breeding of wheat varieties resistant to the bunt (stinking smut) disease is an outstanding example. Prior to the development of resistant varieties, this disease caused serious losses in the productivity of California wheat lands and even more serious problems by contamination of the harvested grain with the spores. The disease is now completely controlled.

In other cases, the adoption of resistant varieties has been followed shortly by shifts in the strains of the pathogen, and, in others, the control of one disease has been accompanied by outbreaks of another. When large-scale plantings were made of oats deriving their resistance to the crown rust disease from the variety Victoria, there was widespread devastation from a previously unknown disease which was, appropriately, called Victoria blight.

Beans suffer large losses from attacks by fungi (*Fusarium, Rhizoctonia, and Sclerotinia*). The losses have increased in recent years because the crop is planted in closer rows, which, though increasing yield, favors fungal infection by producing a suitable microclimate. Annual losses are estimated at 17 percent, of which 2 percent is from bacteria, 13 percent from fungi, and 2 percent from viruses.

Cotton also suffers greatly from fungal attack at all stages of growth. Seedlings are subject to *Verticillium* wilt, and older plants also succumb to *Fusarium* wilt. The roots are subject to a root rot (*Phymatotrichum*) and the bolls often rot. Minor diseases sometimes are severe in local areas, and sporadic epidemics cause serious losses. The average disease loss in cotton is estimated as 12 percent of the crop.

Plant breeders have been remarkably successful in translating the goal of the "best" or "optimum" genotype into practice, and it is now common for a single plant variety to be cultivated over hundreds of thousands or even millions of acres. This extensive monoculture can lead to explosive increases of pest species and is the basis for some of the devasting eruptions of pathogens. Information about the factors that govern the numbers of a species is only now being gained, as also is an understanding of the factors that determine the natural dispersal and migration of organisms. The mechanisms of parasite-host, predator-prey, and host-pathogen interactions at the population level are only vaguely understood. Mathematical models of the dynamics of communities have received little attention, and the possibilities of employing the techniques of systems analysis to predict populational changes have hardly been touched.

Viral Diseases. Lack of basic knowledge about viruses long restricted attention in agriculture to recognition of symptoms, breeding for resistance, exercise of quarantine, and control of vectors. Historically, tobacco mosaic virus was the first virus to be isolated in quantity; it served as source material for the basic studies that were to be so fruitful. Advances in molecular biology now make possible the recognition and isolation of many plant viruses, the presence of which, previously, could only be suspected. The markedly improved understanding of the nature of viruses and of their methods of invasion and multiplying raises hope of learning to restrict or resist their invasion. Agriculture stands hopefully at the threshold of a new era in dealing with viruses.

No organism is immune to all viruses, many of which have caused catastrophic damage to plants. At one time, curly top caused almost complete abandonment of the sugar beet as a crop in parts of the western

United States—the San Joaquin and Yakima Valleys. An intensive breeding program led to resistant varieties; this effort was coupled with efforts to control the distributing vector, the beet leafhopper. While curly top is not vanquished, farmers can plant new sugar beet varieties with confidence of obtaining reasonably high yields (Fig. 15-2).

The orange crop has been threatened since World War II by a disease known as "quick decline," or *tristeza,* a Brazilian word describing the poor appearance of the trees. This phenomenon has recently been shown to be a viral disease transmitted by aphids and transferred through the sour-orange rootstocks used for propagating the commercial orange varieties. A search was made for rootstocks resistant to the virus, demonstrated by testing with infected aphids. Several resistant stocks have been found and are now in wide use, including some Mandarin orange varieties and a South African rough lemon. The orange industry of southern California has been saved, but the margin of success was a narrow one.

Figure 15-2. Strains of corn, exhibiting differential susceptibility to maize dwarf mosaic virus. (Courtesy Agricultural Research Service, USDA)

Maize dwarf mosaic is now a serious and still unmet threat in the major areas of corn production. The viral infection has been found in widely separated areas. First steps are being made in the search for resistant varieties, but the situation is touch-and-go.

Forest and Range Research

Forestry uses knowledge of genetics, plant pathology, and plant growth in much the same way as does agriculture. Since forestry depends upon natural stands of wild species, some aspects of this subject are also discussed in the chapter on renewable resources. When the natural stand of timber is harvested and the forest is replanted with selected strains, the wild species is domesticated and timber becomes a crop.

The situation is similar for many forage species, especially those that provide feed on range or wild lands. While forage production on millions of acres of range lands is almost entirely from indigenous species, management is being practiced increasingly to encourage certain of these species and to discourage others. Also, plant breeders have begun to exploit the variability that exists in the more useful species by selecting desirable types to use in range improvement programs. Consequently, the domestication of range species has begun and range forage is being handled more and more as are agricultural products.

Managing and farming of forests is now common in western Europe and is increasing in the United States. Genetic studies are under way with the aim of developing better strains of timber species. Forests are being fertilized because of demonstrable gain from fertilizer use a few years before harvest. Removal of nonuseful trees — weed trees — enhances forest productivity. A sustained harvest from Canada to the southern United States varies from 0.5 to 4 cords/acre/year. An increase to 10 cords can be anticipated as knowledge advances and management is intensified. The necessary lead time and forward planning far exceed those in agriculture, for some forests must be started 60 to 80 years before they are to be cut.

Treatment of forest and range species as cultivated crops is too recent to have provided much backlog of experience and information. The species grown are long-lived, and many years are required for a community to reach maturity. Many species are involved, which dilutes the attention they receive in view of the low income per unit area. This is particularly true for the tropics, as in the Amazon Basin, where as many as 200 species of plants per acre have been identified. Finally, the harvests of forests have, as a rule, been cataclysmic events that have devastated the landscape, further complicating already complex ecological problems.

Fungi, which are so destructive to most cultivated crops, are occasionally beneficial or even necessary for growth of some trees. These are the fungi that form mycorrhizae and are closely associated with roots. They are particularly evident on most pines, spruces, and firs. Many experiments indicate that the mycorrhizae transfer nutrients from the soil to the tree in a manner as yet unexplained. Attempts to establish pines in drained peat bogs and in many tropical areas have failed time and time again. Dramatic results, however, have followed when the fungi are supplied by the addition of soil from established forests. This was the case when pines were introduced into Puerto Rico about 15 years ago. The introduced Honduras strain of Caribbean pine now grows as much as 10 feet per year.

But fungi are also very destructive in forests – perhaps second only to fire. The chestnut was totally destroyed as a timber tree in the United States by the fungus *Endothia parasitica*. American elms are similarly threatened by the Dutch elm disease caused by *Ceratocystis ulmi*. Serious losses of white pine result from blister rust, *Cronartium ribicola*. These and other fungal diseases have been very difficult to counteract. A major effort is devoted to plant quarantine between continents. In this way, a serious leaf fungus of rubber trees has been prevented from spreading from South America to Southeast Asia. Unfortunately, though, quarantine often fails as it did with "quick decline" of oranges, probably because of belated recognition of the problem. Forestry has become increasingly scientific, drawing ever more heavily on biological understanding, but it is evident that scientific forestry is in its infancy.

Plant Protection and Modification

To protect food and fiber supplies against pests, man not only uses genic modification and biological controls where these are feasible, but increasingly uses biologically effective chemicals. Rapid progress continues in the development of herbicides, fungicides, nematocides, and insecticides. Other chemicals are used for modification of plant growth, such as stem elongation and the time of fruiting. So armed, the whole pattern of agricultural management is being changed.

The use of these active chemicals engenders four major types of problem which demand adequate biological information: (1) effectiveness and nature of action on the pest; (2) effect on the host, either the crop or animal; (3) possible toxic effects of residues on man; and (4) persistence and transfer in the environment, i.e., pollution. The first requires a great amount of knowledge of the pest itself, in sum, therefore involving broad areas of microbiology, mycology, entomology, etc. There are probably 100,000 diseases of plants caused by fungi and bacteria and of the order of a million insect species! The second and third areas are particularly important in the use of growth modifying agents – viz., hormonally active compounds – on both plants and animals. All are areas of great ferment and foment for the producer, the consumer, and the protector of the environment. They have not only biological and agricultural significance but social and political import as well.

The magnitudes of losses occasioned by disease and pests are shown in Table 2. While the losses are not strictly additive, they total perhaps 25 percent of the U.S. annual production. Percentage losses in the less-developed tropical nations are often much higher. In India, for example, estimates are as high as 50 percent. Through pest control part of the loss is preventable at far less cost in money and effort than would be required to increase production by any other means.

Table 2. Crop Loss Due to Pests and Disease
Percent of Total Crop

Crop	Disease	Nematodes	Insects	Weeds
Corn	12	3	12	10
Rice	7	–	4	17
Wheat	14	–	6	12
Potatoes	19	4	14	3
Cotton	12	2	19	8

Source: "Scientific Aspects of Pest Control," NAS Pub. 1402.

Farmers long depended on cultural or mechanical techniques to control pests. Weeds were removed by cultivation or hoeing, and crop rotation was used to reduce disease and insect spread. Research and technology provide three other general methods of pest control: (a) chemical pesticides, (b) biological control measures, and (c) specialized techniques such as sterilization and chemical and physical attractants. Each method has great potential and advantages. Likewise, each presents serious problems.

Pesticides. The discovery of DDT (dichlorodiphenyltrichloroethane) in 1939 and its extended use in World War II against insects attacking man initiated a new era of insect and disease control. Likewise, the discovery of the herbicidal properties of 2,4-D (2,4 dichlorophenoxyacetic acid) in 1941, as the culmination of a systematic hunt based on the molecular structure of the naturally occurring plant hormone auxin, led to a revolution in weed-control practices. In each case, the initial discovery was important, not so much because of the effectiveness of the new chemical, as because of the future potentialities of chemicals for pest control.

Pesticide application has grown phenomenally during the past 25 years. In 1964, 94 percent of the farmers in the United States made some use of 250 available pesticides. In that year, farmers spent some $480 million for pesticides, 85 percent of which was for control of crop pests.

The rapid rise of pesticide use is due primarily to their relatively low cost and immediate effectiveness. Serious problems have arisen, however, which illustrate the weakness of total dependence upon pesticides as the primary defense against pests. Resistance has developed to some pesticides, especially by insects. And control is an annual operation with attendant annual costs in contrast to the use of plants resistant to certain fungi.

An important objection is the threat of some pesticides to man and nontarget organisms. This is especially true of the persistent chemicals such as the chlorinated hydrocarbons. Some of these as well as other pesticides are toxic to fish and wildlife. Several move into the soils and waters where they remain for years because of resistance to biological destruction. Furthermore, their concentrations build up in some cases as they move along the food chain. Most insecticides are equally toxic to desirable and undesirable insects; hence, there is constant threat to the pollinating and predatory insects.

Modern highly productive agriculture is impossible without these agents, but their use poses great problems and demands continual monitoring. Hopefully, pest control may ultimately be achieved by means that avoid or mitigate these problems.

Use of herbicides, in contrast, offers desirable agricultural effectiveness comparable to that of the recently developed insecticides without the drawbacks. Their toxicities are very high for many plants and exceedingly low for animals. To be effective, except for pentachlorophenol and a few others, their use always requires limited persistence. The development of herbicides with a high degree of plant specificity presents many biological challenges; success in this direction is well illustrated by control of dandelions and other broad-leaf weeds in fields and lawns. The goal is usually to destroy one type of plant, the weed, without damage to another, the crop. The striking successes, to date, have been achieved by use of screening procedures and by rational analysis of possible modes of action. Within a decade, ancient arts such as the frequency of plowing to control weeds and elimination of tares in grain have changed.

Biological Agents. Control of pests by biological means is not new. In fact, it is nature's way of determining the association of organisms in an environment. For more than 75 years, parasites and predators have been sought that affect insects. Of the 650 kinds of beneficial insects which have been introduced from overseas into this country for pest control, 100 have become established. They have been effective in controlling insects such as Japanese beetle (*Popillia japonica*), European corn borer (*Pyrausta nubilalis*), and several scale insects and mealybugs.

More recently, microbial agents and viruses that attack insects have been identified and their use developed. More than 1,000 viruses, bacteria, fungi, protozoans, rickettsiae, and nematodes have been found to parasitize insects. A few have proven effective for use in the field. For example, a bacterium, *Bacillus thuringiensis,* is recommended for the control of the cabbage looper (*Trichoplusia ni*) and the alfalfa caterpillar (*Colias eurytheme*). When used in combination with specific viruses, this bacterium is even more effective.

Biological agents have shown some potential for weed control. For example, insects have been used to control prickly pear (*Opuntia inermis*) in Australia, and the Klamath weed (*Hypericum perforatum*) in the western United States. Although the insects have not eradicated these weeds, an equilibrium control has been established. A recent example is control of the toxic range weed tansy ragwort. The ragwort seed fly (*Hylemya senciella*) was introduced in 1966 to bolster biological control efforts begun in 1959 with introduction of cinnabar moths into California. In such a case, hazard to other plants is carefully tested over a period of many years before purposeful release of the particular insect. While chemicals can be used to control tansy ragwort, areas of infestations are so large, and in many cases so inaccessible, that spraying is impractical.

The successful control of some pests by biological means illustrates the potential of nonchemical methods—a potential that remains to be exploited. At the same time, these attempts, along with many failures, emphasize the need for detailed, sophisticated scientific input well in excess of that of the past if biological methods are to replace, or work in harmony with, pesticides. Success will depend on basic studies of the life cycles, physiology, ecology, and genetics of pest species. Also, thorough investigation must be made of the total effects of new biological agents—just as is now required for the chemical agents. Biological methods will likely eventually be integrated with chemical cultural and special techniques. Moreover, one cannot look forward to an early static situation: as current pests are brought under control, other species will flourish in the newly established ecosystem, and must, in their turn, be brought under control, etc. (Fig. 15-3).

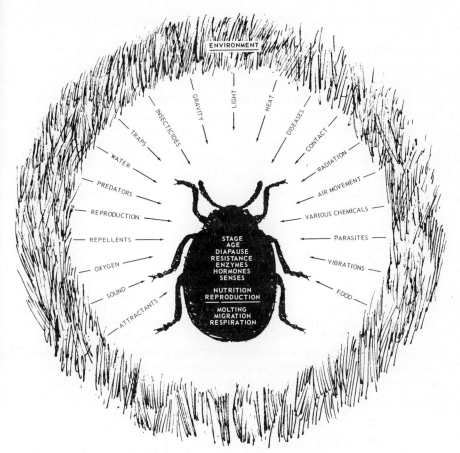

Figure 15-3. Factors affecting insect activity. (Courtesy Cooperative State Research Service, USDA)

Special Control Methods. The introduction of sterile insects into natural populations is an imaginative approach to pest control. Insects are reared artificially, sterilized by irradiation or chemosterilants, and then released into the natural population. The sterilized insects mate with the native population, but produce no offspring.

The most striking example of the success of this method has been eradication of the screwworm fly (*Cochliomyia hominivorax*) from the southeastern United States. The program, costing $7 million, made possible an annual estimated savings well in excess of this amount for cattle growers in the affected area — and with no release, into the environment, of potentially hazardous chemicals.

The use of specific chemical agents to sterilize insects in their natural environment is being investigated. Also, attempts are being made to develop inferior strains of insects which can be used to introduce inferior genes into the natural population, a sort of negative evolution with replacement of the fit by the unfit.

Chemical and physical attractants show promise as means of concentrating pests where they can be more easily controlled. For example, minute quantities of natural or synthetic sex attractants lure the male insects to traps or to localized concentrations of pesticide. This technique is especially helpful in detecting infestations of unwanted insects. It was used in eradicating the oriental fruit fly (*Dacus dorsalis*) from the island of Rota in the Pacific. Attractants for a number of our more serious pests have been isolated and in some cases identified and synthesized. The potential for achievement in this area is great indeed.

Light and sound are known to affect the behavior of certain insects. Traps equipped with different kinds of lamps, such as ultraviolet, have been used under field conditions. They were effective in reducing tobacco hornworm (*Protoparce sexta*) infestation in North Carolina and are being used to some extent for detection and quarantine purposes. Basic understanding is urgently needed of phototaxis and the response of economically significant insects to various light spectra. Photoflash light exposures during prolonged dark periods (night) have been shown under laboratory conditions to upset the life cycle of an insect. If this relation holds in the field, there is potential for using light itself as a basis for control.

Animal Production in Agriculture

There are about 180 million cattle, hogs, and sheep in the United States, or about one per person. Chickens number more than 360 million. The meat and animal products supply more than half of the protein consumed. Animals are the intermediate consumers of the corn crop; moreover herbivores can live on grass and other cellulose sources, which are abundant, but not utilizable by man.

Much of the zest of diets in the Western world comes from meat and animal products. Diets in Eastern countries, in contrast, consist mainly of primary plant foods—grain consumption in India is about 350 lb/capita/year, of which 320 are eaten directly. In the United States, it is 1,700 lb with only 200 directly consumed—12,000 calories from plants give a 3,000 calorie/day diet in contrast to India where 2,300 calories of plant product provide for 2,000 calories/day.

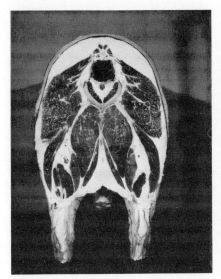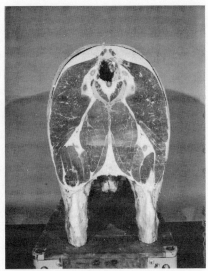

Figure 15-4. Selective breeding brought about improved meat quality of the round cross-section on the right. (Courtesy Iowa State Experiment Station)

The domestic animal of the Western world is a highly specialized result of careful breeding and selection. It is continuously being brought to higher and higher levels of performance. And again, biological understanding has been essential to achieving the desired end of high animal productivity (Fig. 15-4).

Animal Breeding and Genetics – Some Examples

Improvement of Poultry. No agricultural enterprise applies more science to the solution of breeding, nutrition, disease, and economic problems than the poultry industry. Several traits of the fowl are of utmost importance: among these are egg yield and quality, growth rate, body shape and meat quality, efficiency of feed use, fertility and hatchability, and viability. Of those traits, adult body weight has the highest heritability (H), 50–60 percent. Growth rate, age at sexual maturity, and annual egg production have H values between 20 and 35 percent, and genetic improvement is highly practicable. Fertility and hatchability of fertilized eggs have low H values, and the association of mortality with genetic makeup is also low.

Genetic improvement of poultry, while leading to the excellent present situation, has promise of an even larger future. There is no reason to believe that growth rate, efficiency of feed utilization, meat quality, and egg numbers and quality have reached the highest possible levels. The egg production and reproductive rates of meat-type chickens and turkeys leave much to be desired; in fact, the viability of all poultry types is one of the most important factors limiting efficient production. In spite of the progress made in disease control, nutrition, and management, the mortality of older fowl is often as high as 50 percent during the first laying year. Since they have a genic makeup to lay at a high rate for up to two years, the prevention of loss by death is of first importance.

Evaluation of genic makeup in terms of adaptation to the environment is only beginning. Some lines of poultry are adapted to the entire temperate zone; many perform well in other parts of the world—in subtropical and tropical areas, in both dry and humid climates, and at varying altitudes. However, day length, temperature, humidity, and altitude have profound effects. Poultry can yet be significantly improved by further understanding of individual gene action, genic interactions, systems of breeding, and the interrelationships of genetics, physiology, nutrition, the environment, and susceptibility to parasites and disease.

Improvement of Milk-Type Cattle. The most important factor in the breeding of dairy cattle in the United States is the level of milk production. When dependence on milk fat was greater than at present, most cattle breeders selected simultaneously for milk volume and percent of butterfat. The ready availability of other edible fats, the consciousness of the public with respect to caloric restriction, and emphasis on the protein quality and nonfat solids content of milk have affected the goals of dairy cattle breeders.

Breeds of dairy cattle may be selected for size, color, total milk volume, butterfat, milk protein, milk solids, general body conformation, conformation of the mammary gland, or even size and shape of horns; for self-evident reasons, most selection is in terms of milk volume and composition. The heritability of milk production is rather low, 20 to 30 percent, and that of butterfat production and of nonfat and total solids is in the same general range. These factors are controlled by many genes, and the genes for milk volume are not identical with those controlling the various aspects of milk composition. Simultaneous selection for a large number of characteristics slows progress unless the genetic correlation of the factors is high.

Fortunately, milk production can be accurately measured, and breeders have long been concerned with the identification of sires able to transmit this characteristic. The Dairy Herd Improvement Association's sire-proving program and similar programs of the breed associations have had a high impact in the United States (see Chapter 14, on computer use). The advent of artificial insemination and improved techniques of proved sire identification have done much to improve dairy cattle.

Among the most important factors limiting more efficient dairy cattle production are low fertility, reproductive diseases, and diseases of the mammary gland. Although some types of infertility have a genetic basis, the heritability of reproductive efficiency is quite low, and the problem must be attacked by other approaches.

Many attempts to transplant the highly productive dairy animals of the temperate zones to other climatic areas have failed. This is not surprising in view of the fact that H for milk production is only 20 to 30 percent. Environmental temperature affects both milk and butterfat production. The problem is further complicated by solar radiation in tropical or desert regions. Heat generated by the bacterial metabolism, in the rumen, of the large volume of feed required to support high milk production, and high temperatures and humidity increase the heat burden of the animal. Certain parasites and diseases are endemic to some regions, and the natural feedstuffs are often lacking in energy, protein quality, or other nutritional properties.

Livestock and poultry species vary greatly in adaptation to extremes of temperature. Thus, *Bos indicus,* a tropical cattle breed, thrives in the tropics, while *Bos taurus* from temperate zones does not. Genetic studies were conducted to combine the heat tolerance of *B. indicus* with the superior milk or meat productivity of dairy and beef breeds of *B. taurus.* It was found the *B. indicus* adjusts to high temperature by slowing down — eating, moving, growing, breeding. *B. taurus* attempts to accommodate by excessive water intake and output and rise in body temperature as well as reduced feed intake. Hybrid vigor in *B. indicus* × *B. taurus* offspring is substantial and results in heavier weaning weights in such calves than in the parental stocks. Crossbred females are superior to the parental stocks in maternal ability, and they wean heavier calves.

Lactation increases the burden of heat adaptation in proportion to quantity of milk produced. Recent Missouri studies indicate that increasing ambient temperature from 18°C to 31°C decreases milk production even when feed intake is forcibly maintained. Efficiency of feed conversion under these conditions is about the same at the two temperatures, since at the lower temperature energy is transferred mostly to milk, while at the higher temperature milk production is lower, but body tissue is added.

The facts that the average level of milk production of many commercial herds has risen to 12 to 14 thousand pounds per 305-day lactation, and that many individual cows have produced more than 30,000 pounds, indicate that limiting capabilities have not been reached. As the biologist learns more about regulation of intermediary metabolism, parts of this knowledge will be applied in dairy cattle selection.

Improvement of Swine. Swine breeders in the United States have been forced to react to changing consumer demands to a greater extent than any other animal breeding group. All types of swine, primitive and domestic, deposit large masses of rather pure fat beneath the skin and within the abdominal cavity. When lard was the principal edible fat, this was desirable and swine were selected for maximum and efficient fat deposition. The success of plant breeders in the development of oil seed crops such as cotton, peanuts, and soybeans, the consequent replacement of lard by vegetable shortenings, and the more recent avoidance of animal fats in the American diet made the lard-type hog obsolete in this country. In other parts of the world, the problem is less acute.

The present objectives of swine breeders include rapidity and efficiency of growth, maximum muscle mass, limited fat deposition, and large litter size. With the exception of litter size, these traits are rather highly heritable. Although the best expression of muscle mass has yet to be developed, traits such as carcass length, loin-eye area, thickness of backfat, percentage of loin and shoulder are highly heritable, 45 to 60 percent, and rate of gain and feed efficiency are heritable at about 30 percent. Testing stations have been established at many of the land-grant universities, and breed associations and individual swine producers have enthusiastically endorsed programs for the performance testing of boars, barrows, and gilts and for progeny testing.

Development and crossbreeding of inbred lines of swine, similar in principle to those of hybrid corn, have not been as successful as some geneticists had hoped. Practical breeders, however, do rely heavily on crossbreeding and the resultant hybrid vigor. While dairy and beef cattle breeders hold the view that crossbreeding leads to a progressive decline in the quality of livestock, swine producers have long practiced the technique of alternating boars of different breeds in their commercial herds. Geneticists have furnished the reasons for the success of the practice and have developed crossbreeding systems which have markedly improved the results. At one time, it was common to cross two breeds and to market all crossbred stock. The necessity of buying new female stock from time to time limited the practicability of this system and led to the three-breed rotational-crossing system which is common at present. This system is preferred when high-quality boars of several breeds are readily available and has the great advantage that crossbred sows are continuously used.

Animal Reproduction

Gametogenesis. The number of offspring of a species depends on the number of ova produced by the female. She usually produces ova in some type of cyclic pattern: 1 per lunar month in man, 10 to 20 per 21-day cycle in swine, 1 or 2 per cycle at specific times of the year in sheep, and at an annual rate of 250–300 in egg-type chickens. The male may produce sperm at some season of the year, but is more likely to form sperm in very large numbers in a continuous, although fluctuating pattern.

Spermatogenesis of the male is desired at the earliest practical time, in order to permit early matings for determining the animal's genetic worth. Once this is known, spermatogenesis at the highest possible rate is desired in order to produce a maximum number of offspring. The techniques of collecting, preserving, and inseminating sperm have provided animal breeders with a powerful tool for livestock improvement. Preservation of cattle sperm at very low temperatures has made it possible to utilize the genes of a superior male for several years after his death and for one sire to be mated with thousands or even hundreds of thousands of cows. The worldwide application of artificial insemination has done much to upgrade the quality of livestock, and its full potential has by no means been reached.

In the female, the practical objective is the production of ova capable of fertilization, normal development, and the birth and survival of normal young. Superovulation accompanied by fertilization is rather easily accomplished in rabbits, and the fertilized ova can be implanted in other rabbits for normal development. Although successful transfer of fertilized ova has also been made in cattle and sheep, it is by no means near practical application. The production of large numbers of viable ova from superior females, the increase in length of the reproductive period, the recovery of either viable or fertilized ova and their storage in a manner analogous to that now possible for sperm could have a profound effect on livestock production throughout the world.

Enhanced interest in population control has resulted in a substantial increase in research on all aspects of gametogenesis. Neuroendocrinology and neurobiology, which underlie reproduction, are attracting molecular biologists in increasing numbers. It is reasonable to expect that answers will be forthcoming to such classical problems as the nature and control of sex, controlled parthenogenesis, the detection and correction of genetic defects in the gametes, and, of course, regulation of the female reproductive cycle.

Fertilization and Gestation. The penetration of the ovum by a sperm and the union of the male and female pronuclei are extremely complex.

Interference with the process at any stage could form the basis for population control or explain a particular type of infertility. Both gametes have time restrictions which affect their fertilizing capacity. In most mammals, sperm retain their fertilizing capacity for 24–48 hours after entering the female tract, although bat sperm remain viable for up to 135 days. In chickens and turkeys, sperm may remain viable for 30 to 60 days, respectively.

Progress in storage of swine and poultry semen has been quite limited. If the viability or survival of sperm could be increased, following deposition within the female, it might be possible to inseminate the female at any stage of the estrual cycle. Practical application of large-scale artificial insemination in swine is being delayed both by inability to store boar sperm for prolonged periods and by lack of control of ovulation time.

Early embryonic death is probably of greater importance in both cattle and swine than failure of fertilization. It may be limited by genetic defects or by the uterine environment, which includes factors such as endocrine imbalances, circulation, nutrition, disease, and the physical spacing of the embryos. Transport of the fertilized ova to the implantation sites, attraction of some sites for implantation, mechanisms that prevent two or more blastocysts from simultaneously attaching at the same site, migration of blastocysts from one uterine horn to another, adjustment of the uterus to the increasing needs of the embryo and fetus, and the great differences in the placentae of different species are all awaiting further clarification.

Animal Nutrition

Biologists must accept the responsibility of studying the ingestion, digestion, absorption, utilization, and excretion of food. Research in nutrition has resulted in well-tested, precise estimates of requirements for protein, amino acids, energy, many vitamins, and minerals for growth, reproduction, and maintenance of the major livestock species and laboratory animals. Publications of the National Academy of Sciences–National Research Council now state scientifically established requirements and allowances for each species. Some of the most basic questions dealing with the composition and utilization of feedstuffs, however, remain unanswered. Among these are feed efficiency, optimal product composition in conjunction with the desired quality, interactions among nutrients, and the efficiency of conversion of feed nitrogen by livestock.

Feed Efficiency, Intake, and Nutrient Availability. Feed efficiency of young animals is about 35 percent for sucklings and for poultry of equivalent age, in terms of dry feed of about 80 percent digestibility converted to live animal weight. Gross efficiency of conversion of feed to flesh decreases as animals of a particular species increase in weight. Realized efficiency for slaughter animals, including maternal feed cost, is about 10 pounds per pound liveweight for beef, 14 pounds for lamb, 5 pounds for swine, and 3 pounds for broilers in terms of corn equivalent feed units. Each net increase of one percent in efficiency, per species, saves about $60 million annually: a 20 percent improvement in the next 20 years appears to be feasible by appropriate breeding.

Feed intake and productivity are highly interdependent. While animals tend to have a maximum dry-matter intake, silage made from partially dried herbage containing 35–40 percent dry matter may equal hay in intake. Ingestion of hay of high digestibility is greater than that of low digestibility. Neither ruminant nor nonruminant can digest cellulose and hemicelluloses, but their gut microbes do this to varying degrees. While plant stems and leaves have about the same energetic value on a dry-matter basis at all stages of maturity, digestibility diminishes as the plant becomes lignified while the energy available for use by the animal diminishes even more rapidly. Crop residues are a cheap and abundant potential feed source if means can be found to enable livestock to utilize them more efficiently.

Ruminants not only digest cellulose with reasonable efficiency, but also convert some nitrogen from the nonprotein materials to protein form by action of the rumen microflora. About one third of the nitrogen in a diet containing otherwise traditional materials can be supplied in this way as urea which is cheaply available on a large scale. Indeed, purified diets containing only NPN as a source of nitrogen and containing a high proportion of starch will support cattle through successive lactations and pregnancies. Work is in progress in many state and federal laboratories on the microbiology of the rumen and the lower gut.

Vitamins in Chicken Nutrition. An important part of research in nutrition was the determination of nutritive requirements for egg production and hatchability in the domestic fowl. The hen's egg is an unusually suitable subject for such research. The hen requires all of the nutrients, except vitamin C, known to be essential for any animal, including man, if her eggs are to produce strong and viable chicks.

Research in the 1920's defined the role of vitamin D, without which egg production and hatchability fall in temperate zone latitudes during winter. Studies of calcium and phosphorus requirements continue because hens still lay a substantial proportion of fragile eggs, especially as the duration of the laying period lengthens.

Vitamin A, and its carotene precursor, also received early research attention. While vitamin A is essential to hatchability, the liver reserves

Figure 15-5. The chick on the left has been fed a diet adequate in Vitamin B$_{12}$; that on the right a diet inadequate in it. (Courtesy Agricultural Research Service, USDA)

are adequate during short periods of vitamin A deficiency in the ration. Requirements of B vitamins and vitamin E have been established with unusual precision. Surprisingly, after two decades of intensive research, chickens were found to require a previously unrecognized factor. Eggs from hens housed in cages and limited to cereal and soy protein were found to be nonhatchable after a few weeks of such a ration, while their counterparts from hens living on "litter" continued to hatch at a fair rate. This finding led to a search for the "manure factor," which was finally demonstrated to be vitamin B$_{12}$, the vitamin required to prevent pernicious anemia in man. Chicken rations for commercial use now include this vitamin (Fig. 15-5).

Animal Nutrition to Meet Food Needs

The livestock industry can continue to supply the people of the United States with their current consumption of about 70 grams per day of animal protein for the foreseeable future. The peoples of the developing countries of the world will be hard put to maintain or modestly increase their meager supplies of animal protein. An accelerated program of research in animal nutrition and systematic application of available and new information, as it is obtained by research, are essential to these objectives.

In the advanced nations where feed grains are in good supply, where the economy will support a highly specialized poultry, meat, and egg industry, and where well-trained research workers are available, there is no doubt that the chicken will continue to be modified by applications of basic research in genetics, nutrition, pathology, and physiology. The problems in the developing nations are somewhat different. At the outset, systematic study of native sources of energy and protein suitable for poultry need to be determined. This will include knowledge of nutrient availability in locally available feedstuffs and practical means of overcoming deficiencies in vitamins, minerals, amino acids, or other essential substances. In many cases, the feedstuffs necessary for efficient poultry production may be those that are often used for human food. Judgments must be made as to how much corn, wheat, or pulses can be used for poultry without depleting human stores. At the same time, the possibilities of introducing crops which do not compete with human diets need to be investigated. In some cases, improved varieties and improved cultural practices for corn, wheat, barley, sorghums, soybeans, and other crops will permit the simultaneous improvement of human diets and the development of a more efficient livestock industry.

Swine have long been utilized to salvage materials having few alternative uses. These materials include the garbage of city and urban dwellers, skim milk and whey as by-products of the dairy industry, tankage and meat scraps as by-products of the packing industry, pasture crops of various types, native grasses and legumes, and highly specialized feed grains, such as corn when available at low cost. A diet consisting of a single grain, such as corn, is not sufficient. Such diets must be supplemented with vitamins including A, D, and the B complex, with minerals including calcium, phosphorus, iron, zinc, and copper, and with good quality protein. In more recent years, as the role of the amino acids has become better understood, it has been shown that corn is deficient in two important amino acids, lysine and tryptophan. In 1964, a single mutant gene was found to change the protein quality of corn, and in 1965 a second mutant gene was observed to affect the amino acid content of corn. It is now clear that the content of lysine and tryptophan (and other amino acids) can be significantly increased. The nutritional value of such corn is markedly improved for man and swine.

Swine are found in all of the developing nations and, with a few exceptions due to religious beliefs, are a preferred item in the diet. In some primitive societies, swine exist upon native grasses, roots, nuts, and human food wastes. Even under these conditions, some improvement in production can be made. Native forages and roots or feed grains can be improved and the human diet upgraded by the resultant improvement in swine feeding and husbandry.

The ruminant animals, especially cattle and sheep, may exist almost exclusively on native and improved forages that are unsuitable for direct human consumption. It has been estimated that nearly one fourth of the world's surface is suitable chiefly for animal grazing. There are many limitations in improving the animal utilization of these vast grazing areas. Some are extremely rough in surface and at high altitudes and can be grazed only by the most agile animals. Some are in desert or semiarid regions and can support only small grazing populations; many of these areas could be greatly improved by the drilling of wells or the use of irrigation. Some in tropical zones may be subject to periods of excess rainfall and of extreme drought. Some regions, heavily infested with parasites, are reservoirs of uncontrolled animal diseases. And in some regions, excessive domestic and wild animal populations cause serious damage to the land itself so that no animals are properly nourished.

Dairy cattle have tended to be located near population centers because of the perishability of the product; hence, they are fed in a more standardized way than are meat-type cattle. In spite of the greatly increased use of high-energy feed grains in milk-producing cattle, forages such as grass and legume hays, and corn or other types of silage, form the basis of the diet. Meat-type cattle, like swine, are often used to convert local crops or by-products to edible products. Such local special crops and by-products include alfalfa hay, corn silage, cottonseed hulls, beet pulp, corn cobs, and straw. Whatever the staple of the diet, it must be supplemented in such a way that the nutritional requirements of the animal are met.

Some Aspects of Human Nutrition

When food is adequate in both quantity and most aspects of quality, attention is turned to specific factors required for the well-being of the individual. There is concern both for sustaining the normal healthy person and for dealing with nutrition in relation to disease. Other considerations enter, however, when the quantity of food is marginal for an entire country. Then, if possible, ways must be found to extend and improve the available supply. Primary factors in quality are adequacy of vitamin and protein intake in relation to the level of carbohydrate supply. It may be necessary to provide supplements to meet these needs when the primary requirement of enough food is lacking.

Preliminary work in understanding human nutrition has traditionally employed rats and other laboratory animals as well as such livestock species as pigs and chickens. Refined studies closely patterned on human problems have become possible with the recently developed "mini pig" with adult weights of 100 pounds or less. Work with animals often opens the way to use new, seemingly exotic protein sources and amino acid supplements.

A most important endeavor is the continuing search for new sources of protein. Much of this effort is directed at ways of meeting inadequacies of amino acid composition of proteins in already available common foods. Algae, yeasts, and bacteria cultured on petroleum fractions are being tested on a significant scale with human populations. Synthetic and fermentatively produced lysine and methionine are currently being investigated. These are now sufficiently cheap that already they constitute the cheapest way to upgrade the nutritional properties of wheat. Much effort has been expended in the past twenty-five years on extraction of protein from leaves that could not otherwise be used for food. Animal sources of protein such as fish meal and treated offal are being developed. High-protein fish meal that is essentially colorless, odorless, and tasteless is now available, prepared from fish of species available on a large scale and otherwise inacceptable to man. Additions of this preparation to otherwise inadequate dietaries is a powerful weapon in the battle against malnutrition. Remaining to be solved are the problems of costs, means of distribution, and cultural acceptance by relatively primitive peoples.

An outstanding problem in human nutrition, especially in those developing countries where the diet comes chiefly from plants, is the role of vitamin B_{12}. This vitamin, essential to normal blood development and maintenance, to normal embryonic and fetal growth, and to neonatal survival, is produced by microbial metabolism, whether in fermentative processes in the rumen or gut or elsewhere or in biodegradation processes. It is not produced by animals or man. There has been no satisfactory assessment of the extent to which vegetarians are limited physiologically by the intake of vitamin B_{12} provided by such diets.

The association between obesity, high blood cholesterol, and atherosclerosis has stimulated interest in the nutritional role of fat. Much of this research has dealt with the quantity of fat intake and with the proportion of polyunsaturated to saturated fatty acids in the diet. The former tend to minimize cholesterol levels. Animal fats have lost favor because of a smaller proportionate content of polyunsaturated fatty acids than vegetable fats. These relationships first became evident in broad studies that sought to relate the incidence of atherosclerosis in many countries to local dietary practices. Despite a huge effort, this problem, of great significance in the United States and northern Europe, remains unresolved.

Basic research on the significance of intake of fats from different food sources as affected by other dietary components needs to be expanded to evaluate more fully the roles of hormones, environmental stress, and physiological functions. More information on the synthesis and metabolism of cholesterol and fat in the human body is necessary in order to evaluate differences in response to diet among individuals and changes in response and dietary needs during the life-span.

Control of Diseases of Livestock and Poultry

Infectious diseases and parasites are great hazards to the production of an adequate supply of animal protein. They are a constant threat to the livestock or poultry producer who can be wiped out of business by a catastrophic outbreak. The total losses to the public from animal diseases exceed $2 billion annually. Losses result from mortality, reduced productivity, cost of treatment or immunizations, cost of regulatory programs, and condemnations of meat at the slaughterhouse.

Many of the most prevalent and serious diseases of man have counterparts in animals, so that much research conducted with a prime interest in controlling diseases in animals also serves as experimental models for their counterparts in man. This has led to an expanding role of veterinary medicine in many areas of biomedical research. A large number of American universities, not only those that have schools of veterinary medicine but also those that have a department which may be designated as veterinary medicine or veterinary science are engaged in research on diseases of economic importance to the livestock and poultry industry. These include research on bovine rhinotracheitis, bovine virus dysentery, diseases of swine, airsacculitis, and infections of chickens, turkeys, and other species of farm animals with the minute pleuropneumonialike organisms.

Quarantine and sanitary measures to prevent the spread of animal diseases are practiced in many countries. The United States maintains an isolation laboratory at Plum Island, New York, where potentially hazardous exotic diseases are studied. These include foot-and-mouth disease, African swine fever, rinderpest, and several other very destructive diseases which are, unfortunately, common in underdeveloped countries. Foot-and-mouth disease of cattle, which is caused by a virus, leading to an increase in body temperature, lassitude, and slobbering, has not been found in the United States since an outbreak in 1929. It was stamped out in a serious outbreak in California in 1924–25 by preventive measures requiring the slaughter of about 100,000 domestic animals and more than 200,000 deer. In Mexico in 1948, where the disease was established before adequate eradication measures were started, extensive slaughter was necessary even though it threatened the Mexican economy; the total cost of protective measures was about $130 million, which the United States shared. Improved vaccines reduce the severity of the disease. Although almost eradicated in the United States, brucellosis and tuberculosis of cattle, several other domestic animals, and sometimes man still persist as foci of infection. Their final elimination remains a continuing objective.

Modern husbandry practices with concentration of large animal populations in limited areas favor the spread of disease and parasites. Sanitation is necessary at as high a level as economic practice will allow, but disease outbreaks cannot be prevented by sanitary practices alone. Among chickens, Newcastle's disease, bronchitis, infectious laryngotracheitis, and fowl pox are some of the highly infectious viral diseases. Losses from Newcastle's disease can be as high as 100 percent among young chickens. The average is about 30 percent when the disease is rampant, and surviving chicks are retarded in growth and utilize feed less efficiently. Vaccines are available for all four of these diseases; some vaccines can be administered through the drinking water, which greatly facilitates their use.

Use of chicken embryos, embryos of several mammalian animal species, tissue explants, and cell-line tissue cultures has allowed more extensive replication of experiments at greatly reduced expense and in greatly reduced time. The selection of pure cultures of animal and human pathogens, and a more competent evaluation of the infective agent, can now be made with confidence outside the animal. Disease prevention and control procedures underlie the production of experimental animals free of some common pathogens. Indeed, germ-free animals taken by cesarean section and reared under sterile conditions are available for experimental work and for establishing new colonies.

Commercial Fisheries

At least 40 million tons of fish are eaten by man each year. Harvesting of fish is essentially a hunting economy. Rates of harvest and sustainable yields are matters of continued concern about which much remains to be learned. Ocean fisheries, moreover, are mostly common property. Controls over these fisheries can be exerted only by international agreements. Greater use of the fishery resources of the world is now being pressed by several countries. This trend lends an urgency to the quest for greater knowledge, an essential part of which is biological.

Fishery products are excellent sources of good quality protein, valuable minerals, and essential B complex vitamins; hence, fish is a particularly desirable food for modern human diets. It is high in protein which contains all the essential amino acids, and the protein is easily digestible. The flesh is low in sodium. An average serving will supply about 10 percent of the required daily intake of thiamine, 15 percent of the riboflavin, and 50 percent of the niacin. The nutritional properties are approximately equal for all species. Very lean fishes, such as flounders, contain not more than 2 percent fat. The fat content of oily fishes like salmon or mackerel may be 20 to 25 percent of the total weight, but these fats are polyunsaturated, a characteristic that makes fish unique among sources of animal protein.

Roles of Biology in Fisheries

Aquiculture. Artificial rearing of fishes is older than fishery science. Until recently, methods have been empirical, with relatively little attention to the merits of various natural strains or the possibility of selective breeding. It is now known that the success of salmon and trout breeding, to increase yields or fishing success, depends heavily on selection of proper strains. Encouraging results have come from selective breeding and hybridization, but much more needs to be done before this art can become a science.

Breeding of marine organisms is less advanced. Seaweed culture has been practiced in Japan for many years, but this is largely manipulation of a wild crop. Accomplishments in selecting disease-resistant strains of oysters and in improving growth rates of clams by hybridization of Atlantic and Gulf of Mexico species of *Mercenaria* are promising. Techniques for rearing shrimp and other crustaceans from egg to adult have shown that successful shrimp farming is possible. In the United Kingdom it is believed that rearing and planting of plaice in large ponds are feasible. Recent success in laboratory rearing of pelagic fishes like Pacific mackerel and sardines from egg to advanced juvenile stages invites large-scale breeding of commercial marine animals. Many advantages can be gained by eliminating the adverse variations and effects of the natural environment, avoiding man-made effects such as pollution, and by improving growth and survival rates, flavor, texture, and other desirable characteristics. Remaining is the transformation of laboratory techniques to economical commercial scale operations.

Most aquatic organisms have a far greater reproductive potential than land animals. Females of many species produce millions of eggs.

If adequate protection could be offered, vast increases in yield could be obtained from spawning of relatively few adults. The critical stages for survival of fishery organisms occur very early in life. The potential is great for increasing fishery production and damping fluctuations in abundance by protecting young from hazards during this critical period.

The ecological consequences of introducing into the natural environment large numbers of certain kinds of animals with high-survival potential are not well understood. Freshwater fishery scientists understand these relationships far better than marine fishery biologists do, but there is a growing awareness that even in the sea the consequences of man-made changes in abundance can be far-reaching, and not always to man's benefit. Moreover, as long as wild, living aquatic resources remain common property, the economic advantages to be gained from tapping the great reproductive potential of aquatic organisms are applicable only to fish farming under some form of property rights or definitive, workable international agreements.

Development of methods to improve reproductive success of aquatic organisms requires a major increase in understanding of marine ecology. The serious decline in yield of Atlantic menhaden might be countered, and future fluctuations in abundance be buffered, by successful artificial enhancement of reproduction. The traditional concept of fishery management, which treats each species or stock as a unit independent of its interactions with the physical and biological environment, must give way to realistic ecological management models.

Various aspects of nutrition have been studied in the laboratory, but knowledge of nutrition in nature is largely restricted to examination of material in digestive tracts. To estimate the potential productivity of particular kinds of aquatic animals, beginning with carbon fixation by primary producers, nutritional studies in the natural environment have practical significance. An arbitrary value of 10 percent as the efficiency of conversion of energy from one trophic level to the next is usually adopted. Recent studies confirm this estimate for some important marine organisms, although there are variations with age, size, and species.

In considering ways of increasing world protein supply by developing fisheries, major attention is given to the ocean. This has drawn attention away from the potentiality of inland waters, especially artificial impoundments. With proper attention to nutritional requirements and disease control, fishery production from fresh waters in the United States could be increased enormously. For example, an acre of unimproved grassland converted to fish production can yield ten times as much fish as beef cattle. Yields greater than a ton of catfish per acre per year are common in Arkansas. Appropriate research should soon permit culture of shrimp in impoundments and large-scale culture of molluscs in offshore marine waters.

Control of Disease, Competition, and Pests. Diseases of fish and shellfish have been studied intensively for at least fifty years, especially in connection with artificial culture of salmonids and other freshwater fishes. The causes are varied, including viruses, protozoans, fungi, parasites such as copepods, flukes and tapeworms, and vitamin deficiencies of artificial diets. Fish and shellfish also are subject to tumors of various kinds, some hereditary and some produced by viruses or bacteria. Some highly infectious diseases can be transmitted by shipment of live, fresh, or frozen fish or by live fish eggs. The American Fisheries Society recently recommended that the Secretary of the Interior establish a Fish Disease Commission to eradicate and control fish diseases. Therapeutic measures have been developed to some extent for several diseases of freshwater fishes in hatcheries and ponds.

In the natural environment, direct methods of disease control are not now known. Indirect methods are possible, especially with sedentary animals like oysters, by taking advantage of ecological knowledge. The apparent absence or low incidence of oyster diseases like *Dermocystidium* and *Minchinia* in low salinity waters explains the success of natural oyster production and offers an indirect method of disease control.

Many examples of the value of limiting competition between fishery organisms can be cited. Removal of predators from a lake in which young red salmon are resident can increase their chances of return as adults from the sea. Selective fishing for sport fishes in a lake can foster competition and predation by rough fishes, sometimes with disastrous subsequent effects on sport fishing. Heavy commercial fishing of a marine species at a time when its own natural replacement is inhibited by environmental change can favor replacement by a competitor, as demonstrated by the collapse of the California sardine fishery and subsequent increase in abundance of the protected anchovy resource. Control of competition by using various physical devices is fairly easy in fish farming. In the natural environment, indirect methods are necessary; much more sophisticated ecological understanding is required to provide ways to frustrate competition.

Control of predators and pests of fishery organisms is feasible only if individual property rights to a resource have been established or government control has been instituted. Examples are fish farms and hatcheries, fish ponds, reservoirs, private or public lakes, and leased or public oyster grounds. Three general types of direct control are possible: physical barriers, chemical controls, and biological controls. Physical controls are inherent in hatchery and pond culture. An outstanding example of chemical control is the successful sea lamprey control program inaugurated in the Great Lakes. Promising chemical control also has been developed for such predators of oysters as oyster drills and sea stars. Biological controls have not yet come into common use in fishery science; instead there are, unfortunately, many examples of inadvertent biological changes detrimental to fishery resources.

Potential Yields. Of all fields of fishery research, environmental physiology has been the most neglected. Available energy at the surface of natural waters, in weight of carbon fixed per unit area per unit time (primary production), is much greater than present fishery production. It is extremely important to understand the links between primary production and fishery potential.

Some fishery scientists hold that ocean harvest cannot be increased by more than two or three times the present yield of about 40 million tons of all types of commercial fish. Others hold that a tenfold increase is quite feasible, and a hundredfold increase is conceivable. Even this optimistic estimate is far below primary production. Some gross yields from natural production in the ocean average 300 pounds or more per acre per year over rather large areas, but this rate of natural production could not be sustained over the entire ocean surface using present fishing methods.

Fishery scientists have been pioneers in population dynamics and have made many valuable contributions to this branch of ecology. Reactions of fish populations to increased predation, specifically fishing, may include changes in rates of growth and survival. Interactions with other animal populations create changes in competition, predation, feeding, and many other important phenomena. Greater attention is needed to interactions between individuals, stocks, and species — namely to population dynamics of entire communities. Freshwater fishery biologists are more knowledgeable than marine fishery biologists in this respect because they deal with simpler and more readily studied environmental situations. Fishery production can be increased substantially, but it cannot be maintained without increased knowledge of ecology and more effective regulation.

Domestic and industrial pollution is hazardous to fishery resources and to man. Many shellfish grounds are now closed because they are contaminated by coliform organisms or hepatitis virus. The flora and fauna of lakes, rivers, and the edges of the sea have been altered drastically by pollution. Controls are not uniformly adequate, and knowledge of the effects of various pollutants is incomplete. Research, monitoring, and control mechanisms need to be improved.

Preparation and Use of Product. Demand for fishery products centers on relatively few species. Twelve generic kinds of fish and shellfish make up more than 82 percent of the total catch; all 12 are marine, either partially or wholly anadromous. One of these, menhaden, is converted to meal, oil, and solubles, much of which is consumed eventually as chicken, pork, and other meats. The others are used directly as human food, which may be fresh, frozen, or canned. All except menhaden are relatively high-priced.

Fish is a highly perishable commodity with many possibilities for error in handling from fishing vessel to consumer. Relatively little of the edible fish consumed in the United States reaches the consumer in prime condition. Often its quality is sadly reduced in the distribution chain, in the retail store and, perhaps most regrettably, even in the kitchen. The Department of the Interior operates a voluntary inspection service which establishes and maintains standards of quality for processed fishery products and for plant sanitation. Only about 20 percent of domestic pro-

Figure 15-6. Juvenile oysters raised in tanks to determine suitability for commercial oyster farming. Selectively bred in hatcheries, they will produce progeny that can be planted on bay bottoms to grow to commercial size. (Courtesy Fish and Wildlife Service, U.S. Department of the Interior)

duction of edible fish comes under this system, however. Interest in mandatory inspection is growing, and bills to that effect have been introduced in Congress.

Recent approval by the Food and Drug Administration of a fish protein concentrate made from whole fish for human consumption opens the way to new uses of latent fishery resources. Estimates of the unused resources available for this purpose are not very precise, but domestic production could be easily doubled without extending the range of the fishing fleet beyond the continental shelf. Fish protein concentrate can be manufactured by methods other than the solvent extraction process presently approved, and other species than the hakelike fishes can be used. Preliminary experiments with radiation preservation of fish and shellfish show that shelf life of fresh fish can be increased substantially. Freeze-drying and other new techniques of preservation merit further investigation.

Maintenance of Potential for Meeting Food Needs. Being highly selective in its fish-eating habits, the United States has always been a leading exponent of maintaining the maximum sustainable yield species by species. Of the 12 major commercial kinds of fish and shellfish, a few are under effective management, and research is proceeding on others for this purpose. With few exceptions, the American fleets are limited in range and must return their catch to land-based processing plants. Thus, conservation of the resources within the range of the fishing fleets is particularly important.

Rapid development of foreign distant-water fisheries greatly increases the importance of having biological information. International fishery problems have been negotiated through international bilateral or multilateral fishery conventions, or through the Food and Agriculture Organization of the United Nations. If the resources around our shores are to be protected from uncontrolled exploitation, it is essential to measure the magnitude and geographical extent of these resources, their natural rates of renewal, and the effects of fishing upon them.

The Outlook for Fisheries. Several innovations in fisheries have been mentioned. Transplantation has been a popular method of increasing the variety of local fish fauna or of increasing the yield. Some deliberate transplantations have been successful and advantageous, such as the introduction of shad and striped bass from the Atlantic to the Pacific coast and the Marquesan sardine to waters around Hawaii. Others have failed, as illustrated by the strenuous efforts to eliminate carp from various waters into which they had been placed deliberately or inadvertently. The United States and Canada have spent millions of dollars to fight the disastrous sea lamprey invasion of the Great Lakes, and with encouraging results. The subsequent invasion of these waters by the anadromous alewife has wrought great changes in the fish fauna. On the Pacific coast, a destructive snail has been introduced with Japanese seed oysters, and a species of clam introduced in the same way is now widespread and abundant. Transplantation is a valuable technique for manipulating the ecology of a fishing region, but should be attempted only with the greatest caution.

The traditional concept of fishery management species by species is giving way rapidly to the ecological approach. Substantial reductions in numbers of one species affect the population dynamics of all other species in the same environment. Even in systems as large as the Great Lakes, fundamental changes in the fauna have been produced by fishing and by introduction of exotic species. In Lake Michigan, such forces have led to extinction of several native fish species and sweeping changes in the balance of species. Even in the relatively limitless ocean, the ecological balance can be shifted substantially and possibly irreversibly by selective fishing or by effects of local traditions and laws.

Fishery management is still largely a governmental responsibility, hampered by a wide variety of local traditions and other institutional barriers. Even when a considerable body of biological knowledge exists, application is difficult. The United States oyster industry is a good example. Adequate knowledge is available to reverse the steady downward trend of production which has been evident for eighty years, yet local traditions and laws prevent effective application in many places. Conflicts among segments of the commercial fishing industry, and between sport and commercial fishermen, further complicate the situation. Biological research is essential for management of fishery resources and for acceptance of scientific regulation by the public.

Summary

We have described a few of the many ways in which biological science has been utilized in the production of food. Much remains to be done in the further exploitation of such understanding, and the possibility of new research findings which can markedly affect production is promising indeed. The food supply of the United States is adequate and well protected, but cannot be increased without limit. The food supply of many other nations is dangerously tenuous; it can be improved, but only by a conscious effort in which knowledge of the underlying biology is an important component. The nutritional future of man is as promising or dark as we choose to make it.

Chapter 16

SCIENCE AND MEDICAL PRACTICE

The promise inherent in advances in biology and medicine, coupled with recognition that good health care should be a universal human right, has raised man's expectations for enhancement of the quality of life, maintenance of good health, and, when it occurs, the cure of disease. Successful progress toward these social objectives is made possible by fruitful interaction of the biological sciences and clinical medicine.

In a general way, examined in retrospect, this interaction has taken several forms: (1) unplanned contributions of basic scientific research to clinical medicine, (2) contributions of clinical investigation to medical practice, and (3) contributions of clinical observation and investigation to subsequent advances in the basic biological sciences. Each form of interaction will be illustrated by several examples, but it should be understood at once that this formal categorization is rather artifactual. Most advances in the prevention and treatment of disease have reflected the inextricable interdependence and mutual enrichment of the life sciences and clinical medicine. Even in recounting the historical vignettes of accomplishment, frustration and failure, here presented, decision as to which of the three categories just listed is appropriate is extremely arbitrary, and based on the viewpoint of the beholder. In fact, biology and clinical medicine have advanced in parallel, each continually enriching the other while accepting contributions from all other areas of science and human endeavor. The striking lesson of this history is that any narrowly conceived vision of medical research, independent of advancement along all the frontiers of science, would necessarily lead to an early arrival at an impasse after which man would be doomed to live with all the discomfort, pain, and disease with which he has, historically, been afflicted. The signal triumphs

627

of modern medicine, as we shall show, find their immediate roots in biological understanding. But any deeper probing reveals that these, in turn, were made possible by the development of chemistry, physics, engineering, and mathematics. The details of such activity will go largely ignored in this chapter. But ere we proceed further, let us acknowledge medicine's debt to Roentgen for his x-ray tube; to the nuclear physicists and chemists who gave us radioisotopes and the instruments to utilize them; to the imagination and skill of those who developed the synthetic organic chemistry which is a major source of all new drugs; to the pioneers of electronics, who made possible the wealth of instruments required by modern biomedical research and hospital practice; to John von Neumann, whose earliest description of the digital computer, based on McCulloch's analysis of the mode of action of a nerve cell, introduced a new era in managing human affairs, in the conduct of biomedical research, and in the management of the acutely ill; to the physicists and chemists who developed the ultracentrifuge, the measurement of nuclear magnetic resonance, and x-ray crystallography; to those who invented solid, gas, and liquid chromatography; and to the host of other scientists, outside biomedical research, proper, whose contributions, collectively, underlie the increasingly sophisticated enterprise that is modern biomedical research.

Understanding of disease and the ability to alleviate it have grown tremendously during the past twenty years. How has this growth been possible? In general, science progresses by organizing observations into concepts which, if sound, lead to additional observations that can fit on the conceptual framework and allow its further extension. Progress can be rapid when the conceptual framework is extensive and general enough in character to accommodate different kinds of observations, and when new observations can be made rapidly. Without such an intellectual framework, without the tools and methodology to make appropriate observations, knowledge grows slowly and only by accident. For medicine, the conceptual framework is that of biological science, and the major tools and methodology are those of biological science. The disruptions of disease can be understood and measured only as departures from normal. To be sure, medicine has achieved success by outright empiricism, but the returns have been relatively poor and the price high.

Since the mid-1940's biological science has made tremendous advances, based in turn on advances in chemistry, physics, and instrumentation. The phenomena of life are being understood to a degree that is truly revolutionary. But the complexity of life is enormous and the conceptual structure of biology, though impressive, is still quite fragmentary. Nevertheless, it is increasing our understanding of disease, and as the conceptual structure becomes more general and coherent, comprehension of disease will grow increasingly rapidly. New knowledge of the nature of disease does not necessarily result in immediate improvement in its management, but without such understanding there is no reason to hope for any progress at all.

The National Health—An Overview

Before undertaking a survey of some of the contributions of research to medical practice, let us gain some perspective by a brief examination of the national health, in the large. Such an examination should reveal those disorders that most acutely warrant investigation, and reveal what has been accomplished to date.

Mortality. The causes of mortality and morbidity in the population of the United States have changed considerably in the past fifty years. Fifty years ago, the major medical problems afflicting our population were similar to those now met in the developing nations. In our nation, the causes of illness and death, in both the young and aged, have progressively altered from those associated with acute disease to those that result from chronic, debilitating ailments. Diseases of infancy and childhood often predispose to disability and mortality in the older age groups.

Between 1 and 15 years of age, accidents, respiratory infections, congenital disorders, and cancer are the main causes of death. In later years heart disease, cancer, stroke, and accidents are the prime killers. The major causes of death in 1965 are presented in Table 1. Heart disease, cancer, and stroke head the list. Accidents are next in order. Motor vehicle accidents now account for over 40 percent of all accidental deaths. The death rate from motor vehicle accidents is about the same as it was in 1950, but the death rate from other accidents has fallen about 20 percent since that time.

Infant mortality, defined as deaths under 1 year of age, has been steadily declining but is still higher in the United States than in several other countries. It was 22.1 per 1,000 live births in 1967. Maternal mortality has shown a spectacular drop from 582.1 deaths per 100,000 live births in 1935 to 207.2 in 1945, 47.0 in 1955, and 33.8 in 1964.

Americans have been living progressively longer. Figure 16-1 shows how the overall death rate has gone down over the past few decades. In 1900, the death rate was 1,719.1 per 100,000 people. In 1965, it was 943.2. In 1900 the leading cause of death was "influenza and pneumonia," and "tuberculosis" came next. The combined death rate from these causes was greater than that from heart disease today. The death rate from tuberculosis alone was greater than that from cancer today. Diph-

Table 1. Death and Death Rates for the 15 Leading Causes of Death in the United States, 1965

Rank	Cause of Death	Number of Deaths, 1965	Rate per 100,000 Population
	All Causes	**1,828,136**	**943.2**
1	Diseases of the heart	712,087	367.4
2	Cancer and other malignant neoplasms	297,588	153.5
3	Cerebral hemorrhage and other vascular lesions affecting central nervous system	201,057	103.7
4	Accidents	108,004	55.7
5	Influenza and pneumonia, except pneumonia of newborn	61,903	31.9
6	Specific diseases of early infancy	55,398	28.6
7	General arteriosclerosis	38,102	19.7
8	Diabetes mellitus	33,174	17.1
9	Other diseases of circulatory system	27,279	14.1
10	Other bronchopulmonic diseases	26,518	13.7
11	Cirrhosis of the liver	24,715	12.8
12	Suicide	21,507	11.1
13	Congenital malformations	19,512	10.1
14	Other hypertensive disease	11,667	6.0
15	Homicide	10,712	5.5

Data from the National Center for Health Statistics, U.S. Public Health Service.

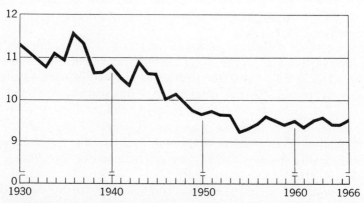

Figure 16-1. Death rates in the United States per 1,000 population 1930–1966. (Courtesy United States Public Health Service)

theria was the tenth ranking cause of death, and the death rate from diphtheria, 40.3 per 100,000 population, was about 70 percent higher than today's death rate from motor vehicle accidents. Quite evidently, many people who would have succumbed to infectious disease in an earlier day are now living to die, at a later age, of degenerative diseases and cancer.

The reduction in death rate since 1900 has been greatest for relatively young people. Nevertheless, all age brackets of the population have enjoyed an increased life expectancy. This progressive trend is shown in Table 2, which indicates the average *remaining* lifetime, for specified ages, at various intervals between 1900 and 1963.

Disability. The disabilities with which people must live are usually more important to their happiness than the ultimate cause of death. The activities of more than 22 million persons in the civilian, noninstitutionalized population were limited, to some degree, by chronic conditions during the period 1963–65. Table 3 presents the major disorders responsible for mild to severe disability. Arthritis and other disorders of the musculoskeletal apparatus, heart and circulatory disease are numerically the most important. Great disability is also caused by respiratory and

Table 2. Average Remaining Lifetime in Years at Specified Ages:
1900–1902 to 1963

Age	1900–1902	1919–21	1939–41	1949–51	1959–61	1963
0	49.24	56.40	63.62	68.07	69.9	69.9
1	55.20	59.94	65.76	69.16	70.7	70.7
5	54.98	57.99	62.49	65.54	67.0	67.0
10	51.14	53.79	57.82	60.74	62.2	62.1
15	46.81	49.37	53.10	55.91	57.3	57.2
20	42.79	45.30	48.54	51.20	52.6	52.5
25	39.12	41.47	44.09	46.56	47.9	47.8
30	35.51	37.68	39.67	41.91	43.2	43.1
35	31.92	33.89	35.30	37.31	38.5	38.4
40	28.34	30.08	31.03	32.81	33.9	33.9
45	24.77	26.25	26.90	28.49	29.5	29.4
50	21.26	22.50	22.98	24.40	25.3	25.2
55	17.88	18.90	19.31	20.57	21.4	21.3
60	14.76	15.54	15.91	17.04	17.7	17.7
65	11.86	12.47	12.80	13.83	14.4	14.3
70	9.30	9.74	10.00	10.92	11.4	11.4
75	7.08	7.49	7.62	8.40	8.7	8.8
80	5.30	–	5.73	6.34	6.4	6.4
85	3.96	–	4.31	4.69	4.6	4.5

For 1900–1902, data are for 10 states and the District of Columbia; for 1919–21, for 34 states and the District of Columbia. Beginning with 1939–41, data are for the United States. From USPHS Publication No. 600, "The Facts of Life and Death."

Table 3. Limitation in Activity by Selective Chronic Conditions. United States, July 1963–June 1965

	Average Number of Persons, in Thousands			
Selected Chronic Conditions	All Degrees of Activity Limitation	With Limitations But Not in Major Activity	Limited in Amount or Kind of Major Activity	Unable to Carry on Major Activity
All persons limited in activity	22,583	6,114	12,347	4,122
Heart conditions	3,619	652	1,941	1,026
Arthritis and rheumatism	3,481	725	2,076	680
Impairments (except paralysis) of back or spine	1,769	469	1,139	160
Mental and nervous conditions	1,767	429	923	415
Hypertension without heart involvement	1,369	314	836	219
Impairments (except paralysis and absence) of lower extremities and hips	1,325	384	704	237
Visual impairments	1,285	184	618	483
Asthma–hay fever	1,152	415	543	194
Conditions of genitourinary system	1,071	304	562	205
Other conditions of digestive system	958	206	534	218
Paralysis, complete or partial	923	118	361	444
Other diseases of muscles, bones, and joints	785	234	466	86
Other conditions of circulatory system	758	176	371	212
Chronic sinusitis and bronchitis	621	204	304	112
Diabetes	571	122	291	158
Hernia	556	91	363	102
Peptic ulcer	550	123	313	114
Varicose veins	535	161	313	61
Other conditions of respiratory system	501	87	233	181
Hearing impairments	461	97	219	145
Impairments (except paralysis and absence) of upper extremities and shoulders	401	92	258	51
Malignant neoplasms	260	35	111	114
Hemorrhoids	243	54	148	41
Benign and unspecified neoplasms	227	60	127	40
Tuberculosis, all forms	148	31	74	44

Major activity refers to ability to work, keep house, or engage in school or preschool activities.

From data of the National Health Survey, National Center for Health Statistics, U.S. Public Health Service.

gastrointestinal disease, defects of vision and hearing, and paralysis. Although mental conditions and neurological disorders have a high place on the list, it is believed that this cause of disability is actually underestimated.

In addition to those seriously limited in their activity during the 1963–65 period, perhaps 60 million persons experienced one or more chronic diseases or impairments that did not significantly limit activity.

The Quality of Life. Increased life expectancy, and the consequent rise in numbers of individuals in the age group over 65, has brought with it new problems which emphasize that merely increasing the duration of life is not, of itself, a sufficient goal. Prolonged life must both be rewarding to the individual and permit him to participate significantly in society. The quality of later life is, only in part, a medical problem. Amelioration of chronic degenerative diseases and the progressive disabilities associated with advancing age are, of course, of first importance. Understanding and control of these problems are essential if we are to reduce the impact of failing health in the later years of life. But each increment of medical success will increase the urgency of finding appropriate social solutions. The emergence of large numbers of healthy, elderly persons will necessitate creation of appropriate job opportunities, training for suitable avocations, and rewarding recreational activities if life is to be worth living. Financial security, alone, cannot achieve this. Just as the medical scientist is responsible for improving the prospects for good health in old age, the social scientist must turn his attention to assuring that prolonged life can be useful to society and rewarding to the individual.

Research and Medical Practice

The fact that the average patient in contact with the average physician has an excellent chance of benefiting by the encounter is the consequence of the transformation of medicine from a recondite art to a sophisticated, complex science. No aspect of medical practice has escaped scientific attention, and for virtually all the diseases of man there are improved modes of diagnosis and therapy which, at best, are specifically curative and, at least, are supportive and relieving. In the paragraphs to follow, we have endeavored to trace the historical origins of a selected group of significant modern developments. The choices made were a matter of taste and the personal interests of the authors; they are intended to be illustrative, with no attempt to be comprehensive.

Contributions of Fundamental Biological Research to Medicine

Infectious Disease. The impact of the combined biological investigation of infectious agents and clinical study of the diseases they cause can be seen in the sharp decline in the incidence of the major infectious diseases during this century. Thus, the control of typhoid fever, diphtheria, tuberculosis, and other bacterial diseases is attributable to the knowledge obtained of the bacteria involved and of their interaction with human populations. Mastoiditis and osteomyelitis are almost unknown to the present generation of medical students. This knowledge came from many different lines of attack—for example, studies of the biology of the organism with emphasis on the attributes responsible for its virulence, such as the production of toxins; understanding of immunity and the development of methods of immunization; the epidemiological pattern of disease and the basis for its spread through the population; and a systematic search for antibiotics. Thus, many levels of biological science were involved in these achievements.

Poliomyelitis—Conquest of a Viral Disease by Mass Immunization. The conquest of poliomyelitis represents one of the most recent and instructive examples of the role of biological research in the attainment of a practical goal. The general principle of immunization by the use of vaccines was established by the work of Jenner against smallpox in the last century, but much fundamental knowledge had to be acquired before the principle could be applied in poliomyelitis.

The modern era of viral research began in 1935 with the isolation of the virus that causes mosaic disease of tobacco. There followed two decades of research in which many laboratories learned how to isolate viruses in quantity, established their nature as either DNA or RNA with a protein coat, and sought optimal conditions for their mass culture. The latter problem remained complicated by the fact that, whereas bacteria replicate in simple media, viruses can only replicate in living cells of a susceptible host which provide all the necessary enzymic apparatus for the requisite biosyntheses and harnessing of metabolic energy. A great advance came with learning to grow some viruses in chick embryos, then in infected animals. The keys to success in the present instance were the development of improved techniques for growing mammalian tissues and cells in the test tube and recognition that there are three distinct types of infectious virus. Ultimately, a cell culture system was devised in which the poliomyelitis virus could be grown, and it was virus from this source that was used in the preparation of killed vaccines for the first programs of mass immunization. The subsequent development of live virus vaccines depended on an independent line of biological research, the isolation of mutant forms of each of the three viruses which had lost their disease-producing capacity without at the same time losing the ability to immunize. Significantly, the very possibility of such an approach, as well as its successful accomplishment, rested largely on the accumulated understanding and methodology of those engaged in the study of the genetics of bacteriophages, viruses specific for bacterial hosts.

The beneficial effects of the mass immunization program against poliomyelitis were dramatic. In 1950–54, the annual incidence of poliomyelitis in the United States was 14.6 cases per 100,000 population—i.e., more than 20,000 cases a year. In 1961, the rate had dropped to 1.8 per 100,000, and in 1965 there were only 61 cases reported in the entire country.

Immunization is only one of the methods of control that have been applied to the conquest of infectious disease. Others fall in the realm of environmental medicine, as illustrated by the central role of modern sanitation methods in the elimination of typhoid fever and the effectiveness of mosquito control in the prevention of malaria. In these cases, also, fundamental biological research was essential in providing the information on which the control procedures are based.

Antibiotics. A dramatic factor in the management of infectious diseases in recent decades has been the introduction of antibacterial and antibiotic drugs. It was the work of the German chemist Paul Ehrlich that established the foundation for antibacterial chemotherapy. Ehrlich realized as early as 1904 that infectious diseases could be conquered if toxic chemicals could be found that showed a greater affinity for parasite organisms than for host cells. Ehrlich did achieve some success toward his goal—the use of dyes against trypanosomes (African sleeping sickness) and arsenicals against spirochetes (syphilis). After the mass outbreak of typhus in World War I and loss of countless wounded due to secondary bacterial infection, followed by the great influenza pandemic of 1917–18, the medical world was poised for any discovery that might mitigate the often fatal and always debilitating infectious diseases. This fact is most strikingly illustrated by the intense interest in the discovery of bacteriophages (viruses that specifically attack and kill bacteria). In the years that followed their discovery it was hoped that they might provide a means of preventing and treating infectious diseases. Sinclair Lewis's novel *Arrowsmith* illustrates how this possibility had captured even the popular imagination. Unfortunately, for reasons that are now relatively well understood, bacteriophage therapy was never effective.

In 1935 Domagk found that the dye Prontosil was effective in treating streptococcal infections. Although this compound was without effect on bacteria, in vitro, it was soon demonstrated that patients treated with Prontosil excreted sulfanilamide, a degradation product of Prontosil which not only was effective in treating infections but also inhibited the growth of organisms in laboratory media. These observations gave rise to the class of chemotherapeutic agents known as sulfonamides and served to reaffirm Ehrlich's principle of direct attack on infective agents.

An immense effort in many laboratories, particularly in the pharmaceutical houses, rapidly yielded a series of sulfonamides greatly superior to sulfanilamide itself and tailored to the necessities of systemic, gastrointestinal, or urinary tract infections. Most important, historically, was the discovery that sulfonamides inhibit the growth of bacteria by preventing their biosynthesis of the vitamin folic acid. In this process, the compound p-aminobenzoic acid is incorporated into a much larger molecule. The close structural similarity of sulfanilamide and p-aminobenzoic acid permits the former to fit onto the active site of the enzyme which

Sulfanilamide   p-Aminobenzoic acid

normally utilizes p-aminobenzoic acid and attach so firmly that, despite the presence of the latter, it cannot be utilized. This revealed a paramount principle of drug design, the concept of "antimetabolites," compounds that structurally resemble some normal metabolite and interfere with whatever function is fulfilled by that normal material.

Microbiologists realized that antagonism among microbes exists in nature and that this phenomenon might provide the basis for a source of useful antimicrobial agents. The origin of the antibiotic era is often equated with the chance observation by Fleming in 1929 of the inhibitory properties of the fungus *Penicillium notatum,* which secretes penicillin into the surrounding medium. A deliberate approach to the problem is exemplified by the attempt to isolate substances from soil bacteria which would dissolve the capsule of the organism causing lobar pneumonia. This work culminated in the isolation of the antibiotic tyrothricin from the soil bacterium *Bacillus brevis,* which proved to be two distinct bacterial inhibitors, gramicidin and tyrocidin. Subsequent work on the bacteriology, pharmacology, chemistry, and clinical evaluation of these drugs established the systematics of antibiotic study and formed the scientific foundation of the antibiotic era. Although the principles established in these studies prevail even now, these events were somewhat obscured by the drama of the development of penicillin.

It was not until 1940–43 that penicillin was applied as a therapeutic agent. This substance, which was destined to become the most widely used antibiotic, was originally discounted as impractical because of its instability. However, a team of British scientists showed in 1940 that the substance was reasonably stable when partially purified and dried. Their preparations (which were only 50 percent pure) were shown to be non-toxic to man and to be very effective against susceptible microorganisms (one part of the drug in 30 million parts of culture medium was sufficient to inhibit staphylococci). Although the drug was very effective, its purification was tedious and the problems of mass production seemed insurmountable. The calamity of World War II prompted members of the group to come to the United States in the summer of 1941 to enlist the capabilities of American science and industry. Microbiological techniques were employed to develop media for increased production of the drug and for isolating better penicillin-producing strains of *Penicillium*. The magnitude of the achievement of mass production is exemplified by the fact that by September 1943 enough of the drug was being produced by the American pharmaceutical industry to satisfy the demands of all the Allied forces. However, many types of bacterial infections would not respond to penicillin therapy. One broad class of bacteria (gram-negative) was particularly insensitive, and so a search for a "broad-spectrum" antibiotic continued. In 1944 an effort involving the screening of thousands of soil samples led to the isolation of streptomycin, thus culminating a long and tedious search for an antibiotic effective against gram-negative bacteria. Streptomycin was shown to be effective against mycobacteria as well and, in conjunction with other chemotherapeutic agents, has proven very effective in treating tuberculosis.

The potency and usefulness of these first antibiotics prompted the establishment of programs of screening for still better antibiotics. A great deal of energy was expended both in the academic community and in the pharmaceutical industry, often with collaboration between the two. Among the results of these efforts are bacitracin, chloromycetin, aureomycin, and terramycin.

Once antibiotics were in wide use, it was soon obvious that they could not solve all of the problems of bacteria-mediated infectious diseases. Reports of bacterial strains resistant to antibiotics increased; this had been predicted by those investigators studying the physiology and genetics of bacteria. With the widespread use of antibiotics an artificial, selective genetic process had been introduced. Among a normal population of bacteria a few organisms will be present which have spontaneously mutated in such fashion as to be resistant to the bactericidal effect of a given drug; suppression of the growth of the normally abundant, sensitive organisms permits the resistant cells to outgrow the others, with the result that a resistant population is formed. This problem can be overcome to some degree by the simultaneous use of two unrelated antibiotics. However, under these circumstances, organisms have been isolated which have acquired simultaneous resistance to several antibiotics; notable among these are the enteric organisms that cause dysentery. Recent studies have shown that this type of resistance is due to the presence in the bacterium of an extrachromosomal portion of genetic material. This type of resistance is potentially very hazardous, since it can be passed among related microorganisms by an infectious process (transduction). However, the description of this process itself opens the way to solving this problem.

The need for new antibiotics continues, and efforts are being made both to discover new ones and also to modify those presently available. For example, a major effort has been put forth toward developing better penicillins. Although penicillin typifies the "miracle drugs," two problems soon accrued with its use: (1) Resistant organisms have appeared, notably strains of staphylococci that secrete an enzyme that destroys the drug. (2) Although penicillin is generally nontoxic, some patients develop hypersensitivity to the drug. For these reasons attempts have been made to modify the chemical structure of the drug so as to render it insensitive to enzymatic inactivation, to decrease its allergenic properties, and to increase its relatively narrow spectrum of activity. Structural analysis of the penicillin molecule revealed that the basic structure of this antibiotic could be duplicated only by synthetic procedures which are both tedious and expensive.

It is noteworthy that the structure of penicillin was established by the x-ray crystallographic studies of Dorothy Crowfoot, who later determined the structure of vitamin B_{12}, the most complex of all naturally occurring substances, and the specific agent in the treatment of pernicious anemia. Dr. Crowfoot's laboratory was the direct lineal intellectual descendant of Sir Lawrence Bragg. Clearly, had a narrower vision of research support, directed at medical goals, obtained, the complex and expensive art of x-ray crystallography could never have been brought to its present refinement and these accomplishments would have been impossible!

Fortunately, it was found that when the culture medium of the fungus is suitably modified, a precursor of penicillin rather than penicillin itself accumulates; the custom syntheses of a variety of new, substituted penicillins were then achieved using this precursor and relatively simple organic chemical synthetic techniques. Because of this, the number of possible "semisynthetic" penicillins is almost unlimited. Penicillins have been developed which have a broader antibiotic spectrum and which are effective against otherwise penicillin-resistant mutants. The allergy problem in the use of penicillin has not been solved. However, it is now known that the major allergen involved is not penicillin per se but one of its degradation products; with the production of more stable semisynthetic penicillins this problem will be solved.

The widening horizons of medicine will demand new and potent chemotherapeutic agents. For example, this need is presently being felt in attempts at organ transplantation. These procedures necessarily involve suppression of the immune mechanisms which are the body's primary line of defense against invading microorganisms; one of the principal means of replacing these defense mechanisms is antibiotics. During immunosuppression and other procedures, classes of organisms that are normally dormant in man have recently been described—viz., algal infections have recently been noted in severely debilitated cases. Reports of fungal infections are also increasing, perhaps only because of better diagnostic procedures; only amphotericin B and nystatin are available for their treatment.

Today the availability of antibiotic therapy is taken for granted. The impact that antibiotic therapy has had on the practice of medicine can be assessed by comparing present conditions with those before the era of antibiotics. Prior to 1940 a very large proportion of all hospital beds were occupied by patients suffering from infectious diseases, many of whom required isolation for long periods—e.g., those with typhoid fever and tuberculosis. Indeed, large sanatoriums were devoted exclusively to the treatment of tuberculosis. Today, very few hospital beds are required for primary infectious disease; antibiotics permit their care and treatment largely as outpatients.

The population explosion makes the availability of antibiotics even more significant. The sheer increase in number of persons overstrains our medical resources by demands for treatment of noninfectious diseases. If infectious diseases required the same effort as prior to antibiotics, our hospitals and their personnel would be overwhelmed. The benefits of antibiotics have been felt in many areas of medicine. In the field of public health mass treatment programs under the auspices of such agencies as the World Health Organization have allowed the eradication of endemic infectious diseases in certain areas of the world—viz., of yaws in Haiti. The morbidity rate associated with postoperative infections has been greatly reduced. And one needs only to remember the common sequence in which a child's streptococcal sore throat would develop into scarlet fever followed by rheumatic fever and serious heart damage; these sequelae have been eliminated by the early use of antibiotics. The impact of this cure is also felt later with a decrease in the number of younger adults with cardiac dysfunction.

Finally, it should be recognized that the classical task of microbiology — identification of the agents responsible for infectious disease — is far from complete. The viral etiology of cancer is a case in point. The number of such relationships, in man, is entirely obscure and must hold many surprises, such as the recent finding that the virus associated with Burkett's lymphoma, a disease once thought to be confined to central Africa, is the the causative agent in infectious mononucleosis, or, again, the finding that mycoplasma, related to the tuberculosis organism, occasion atypical primary pneumonia and may be a cause of rheumatic fever.

Cancer Chemotherapy. A variety of disorders are characterized by the uncontrolled growth of relatively undifferentiated cells. These may exist as a confined mass (a tumor), circulate freely in the circulation (leukemias), or diffusely invade many tissues and organs (cancer). There is no reason to assume that these arise from a single common cause. Of intense current interest is the finding that, in mice, a wide variety of tumors all represent the response to invasion by a single virus (the polyoma virus) which can be reisolated from the proliferating cells. Indeed, the viral origin of some growths was identified a generation ago — e.g., the skin papillomas of rabbits, the leukosis of chickens, and the tumors caused by the milk-borne virus of mice. But viruses have not yet been identified in human tumors or neoplasms, and there may well be other processes that remove the controls on cell growth operative in normal cells. In any case, the goal of cancer therapy is to reduce the rate of growth in such cells, and, because the lesion is heritable within the affected cell line, to obliterate all such offending cells. Since such cells, in virtually all respects, resemble the normal cells from which they arose, the challenge to specific chemotherapy will be apparent.

Patently, for solid tumors early surgical removal is the procedure of choice whenever possible. But distant metastases necessarily escape this procedure. Most other procedures now current rest on the fact that such a cell line engages more frequently in DNA synthesis than do normal cells. It is this process that renders them radiosensitive, the radiation causing chromosomal breaks, substitutions of bases in the DNA, and mechanical fusion of DNA chains so that normal replicative mechanisms are impaired. But such therapy necessarily damages the surrounding tissue; the beam can be narrow or broad but necessarily goes through healthy tissue, does not affect unsuspected metastases, and can be used only with difficulty in leukemia involving much or all of the bone marrow.

Accordingly, research in cancer chemotherapy has been diligently pursued for two decades. To date, only a few triumphs can be recorded, but the sense of hopelessness has been lifted and such efforts have acquired a new optimism. To the degree that such efforts have been successful, they stem entirely from new understanding of fundamental cellular metabolism.

Folic acid is a vitamin originally identified as an essential nutrient for monkeys, but also required in the human dietary; lack of it results in the disease sprue and in macrocytic anemias. In cellular metabolism, folic acid, in its tetrahydro form, serves as a coenzyme required for synthesis of the pyrimidine thymine, which is required for synthesis of DNA. Accordingly, it was argued, an antimetabolite of this vitamin should impair thymine synthesis, hence that of DNA, hence limit cell growth. Of a series of structural analogues of folic acid, one, methotrexate (amethopterin), has proved to be clinically useful. In early trials, partial remissions were found in childhood leukemias. When tested in choriocarcinoma, an all too frequent invariably fatal cancer of young women of child-bearing age, this compound effected cures in 50 percent of all patients. Actinomycin, the antibiotic that was previously noted to be bacteriostatic because it prevents RNA synthesis on DNA, also effects cures in about 50 percent of patients. When both drugs are used in sequence, the five-year cure rate appears to be about 80 percent, so that this combination is virtually specific therapy for this dreadful malady. The same combination has effected a 70 percent cure rate against Wilms's tumor, a malignancy of the kidney, and about a 25 percent cure rate in Burkett's lymphoma, a neoplasm of the lymph nodes first observed in children in central Africa but now known to be much more widespread, whose viral origin was noted previously.

Leukemias are the major cause of death in children. Their therapy has been attempted with a wide variety of agents. Methotrexate and other antifolic compounds have shown genuine promise, holding the disease in check for months or years. More recently, improved knowledge of nucleic acid metabolism has opened new approaches. An early clue was the observation that rat liver tumors exhibited a high rate of utilization of the pyrimidine uracil. This led Heidelberger to synthesize a series of fluorinated uracil derivatives, particularly 5-fluorouracil and its riboside, 5-fluorouridine. Both are converted to 5-fluorouridylic acid which then specifically inhibits the enzyme responsible for the final step in the normal biosynthesis of the thymine required to make new DNA.

These compounds have shown some striking successes in some leukogenous leukemias. In addition, they cause regression of lesions in perhaps 20 percent of all instances of carcinoma of the colon, rectum, breast, or liver. These limited successes prompted trial of yet another category of compound. Sponges of one species have been found to contain a class of nucleosides in which, instead of ribose, the pentose arabinose is incorporated. Of these, arabinocytosine, now available synthetically, has proved surprisingly effective in the hitherto utterly refractory myelogenous leukemia of children. Aggressive use of combinations of these drugs together with purine analogues such as 6-mercaptopurine offers the only present hope in these afflictions.

Interference with nucleic acid metabolism can also be useful in other clinical situations. Not all diseases that involve excessive growth of cells may be considered to be forms of cancer, and yet they can be severely debilitating. An example is to be found in psoriasis, characterized by essentially uncontrolled growth of portions of the skin. Although a variety of salves and ointments are of benefit to patients with minor forms of this disease, thousands of individuals are bedridden with advanced psoriasis. Again, from studies of potential antineoplastic agents, has come a successful treatment, but not cure, for this disease. The results obtained with methotrexate are impressive, but use of the drug requires care on the part of the physician to avoid toxicity. More recently, 6-azauridine has been found to be equally effective and to be much less toxic for normal human tissues. With these two agents, the majority of patients with advanced psoriasis can be cleared of disease or brought under control.

The classical hope of antitumor therapy was to take advantage of a metabolic difference between normal and neoplastic cells. But, until recently, the long and arduous search for such differences was unfruitful. The finding that certain forms of leukemic cells have an absolute nutritional requirement for asparagine, which is present in blood plasma, provided just such an opening. Almost all normal cells synthesize this amide for themselves. Accordingly, administration of the enzyme asparaginase, obtained by microbial fermentation, which catalyzes hydrolysis of the amide bond of asparagine, has proved to be remarkably effective in treating those specific leukemias involving asparagine-requiring cells, perhaps 5 or 10 percent of all leukemias.

The treatment of viral diseases by the use of drugs has been singularly unsuccessful; the only useful measure has been immunization prior to infection. Recently, it was discovered that the compound 5-iododeoxyuridine (iodoxuridine), an analogue of the thymine of DNA, inhibits the reproduction of DNA-containing viruses. When tested as an anticancer agent, it was discarded because of its undesirable effects on normal tissues. However, it has become the definitive treatment for a viral infection of the eye (herpes keratitis), previously a major cause of blindness in the United States, and can be administered with impunity as eye drops. This lead has encouraged trials of its action in other viral infections such as viral meningitis and smallpox. It may also be that such a compound could prevent the action of cancer-causing viruses in man, as has been demonstrated in experimental animals. This initial successful lead is being pursued in the synthesis and development of other analogues of nucleic acid constituents.

Cancer and viral disease remain scourges of mankind. But the limited successes achieved to date offer hope that a rational biochemical pharmacology, capitalizing on detailed knowledge of cellular metabolism, may one day lighten these human burdens.

Early diagnosis of solid tumors remains a serious problem. All present techniques rest on removal of some bit of tissue and subsequent microscopic examination. These techniques have improved little in fifty years, and there is urgent need for innovation in this area, such as the utilization of infrared thermography, the military "snooperscope" for the detection of breast cancer. The studies of histological changes in the vaginal epithelium during the estrous cycles of animals and the menstrual cycle of woman by Papanicolaou led to development of the cytological diagnostic test for cervical cancer. But this still requires inspection by a well-qualified cytologist, and this invaluable service cannot be utilized for mass screening until appropriate pattern scanning optical cytoanalyzers are perfected.

Homotransplantation of Tissues and Organs. It has been a long-standing dream of medicine to replace specific human organs when these have ceased to fulfill their normal functions. In early trials it was recognized that attempts to graft skin, to cover burned areas, failed unless the donor was the patient himself or his twin. These sufficed to discourage trials of homotransplantation of hearts, kidneys, adrenal glands, etc.

Early in the twentieth century, Carrel reported the technical feasibility of homografts of dog kidneys and other organs, but the grafts were destroyed after several days of good function. During the next four decades many scientists, studying transplantation of tumors and normal tissues in laboratory rodents, concluded that homograft rejection is an immunological reaction of the recipient against genetically determined antigens which are present in the donor tissue and absent in the recipient. This understanding was due, in large part, to the development of inbred strains of mice at the Jackson Memorial Laboratory in the 1920's. These strains are composed of mice with identical genotypes (in effect, all members of a strain are "twins"). Studies of tissue grafts between individuals of a given strain (isografts) and between members of different strains (homografts) elucidated the genetics of histocompatibility and established the feasibility of isologous grafts—e.g., between identical twins. Through the use of a number of measures it has become possible to a considerable degree to prevent immunological rejection of foreign tissues. Nevertheless, this continues to be the principal obstacle standing in the way of large-scale successful homotransplantation of organs in man. Many obvious clinical applications of homotransplantation await further resolution of this problem.

For a given recipient not all donors are equally foreign, i.e., not equally incompatible. One approach to the problem, therefore, is that which overcame the problem of blood transfusion reactions — namely, selection of compatible donors. An alternative approach is *immunosuppression,* which has been in use in conjunction with human kidney transplantation for about ten years, and has been recently employed with liver and heart transplants. Immunosuppression is reduction in the intensity of immunological reactions by any appropriate means. Immunosuppressant drugs are remarkably effective, but those presently available fall short of being a complete solution of the problem of rejection. Their use demands staying in the narrow zone between failure to achieve adequate immunosuppression, and lethal effects of overdosage. And, in the mid-range, there is grave danger of infection. The more compatible the selected donor, the less intense will be the rejection process for which immunosuppressants will be needed. Tissue compatibility testing and immunosuppression therefore are complementary approaches. Both approaches are broadly applicable to human homotransplantation generally, not just to a particular organ.

From animal studies and early experience with skin grafts, it was a reasonable hypothesis that kidney transplants between identical twins in man would not evoke rejection, but that transplants from other donors would. The first identical twin human kidney transplant was performed in 1954. This and several subsequent such operations were successful, with restoration of completely normal kidney function. On the other hand, in sporadically reported experiences with nontwin human kidney transplants, without the use of immunosuppression, from 1936 to 1957 none were observed to function longer than seven months, and most failed during the first month.

Nearly 1,200 human kidney transplantations were reported to the Kidney Transplant Registry by 1967, nearly all in patients who were treated with various immunosuppressants. Fifty-five percent of approximately 600 kidneys from related (mostly parental and sibling) donors, and 20 percent of approximately 600 kidneys from unrelated (mostly cadaveric) donors were functioning 12 months posttransplant. The survival rates were substantially higher in the latter years of this series. About 90 percent of transplants that were doing well 12 months posttransplant were still doing well at the end of the second year. Data on longer-term follow-up are fragmentary, but there are reports of patients with kidney transplants still functioning after seven years in cases of related, nontwin donors, and four years in cases of unrelated donors. Thus, without immunosuppression, kidney transplantation would be limited to the rare patient with an identical twin donor; but with the immunosuppressants now in clinical use, kidney transplantation provides significant therapeutic benefit to recipients of kidneys from other classes of donors; in many cases it has permitted return to robust health.

Total Body Irradiation. The effectiveness of total body irradiation as an immunosuppressant in experimental animals was well known when this means of immunosuppression was tested in conjunction with human kidney homotransplantation in 1959. These two patients were still alive seven years later. These early successes encouraged other experiences. Total body irradiation in many patients, either alone or in conjunction with other immunosuppressants, was used in numbers of patients, but because of difficulty in controlling dosage, attention turned to other agents.

Azathioprine. In 1959 a state of nonreactivity to foreign protein in rabbits was elicited by treatment with the drug 6-mercaptopurine, an antagonist of purine metabolism which had been synthesized and tested as an antitumor agent. A beneficial effect was observed when the influence of 6-mercaptopurine on canine kidney homografts was studied. Slightly better results were observed with a closely related compound, the imidazolyl derivative of 6-mercaptopurine, azathioprine (Imuran), which had also been developed as a purine antagonist for nucleic acid synthesis. This drug is now administered to kidney transplant recipients in nearly all centers engaged in this form of treatment. Because knowledge of the mechanism of graft rejection is incomplete in many respects, discussion of the mechanism whereby immunosuppressants inhibit the process must be speculative. It is known, however, that the immunological response to antigen entails a brief, intense proliferation of lymphoid cells. Perhaps this proliferation is prevented by the blockage of nucleic acid synthesis by these thiopurines.

Prednisone. Among the many effects of adrenal cortical steroids observed in the intensive study of these drugs experimentally and their use in man during the past twenty-five years has been a diminution in the intensity of inflammatory responses, including those associated with immunological reactions. Logically, therefore, these hormones were examined for their effect on homograft rejection. In 1964, clear evidence was obtained of prevention of rejection of dog kidney homografts by the use of prednisolone. Since then the administration of this hormone to patients with kidney homografts has been recognized as the most effective means of reversing an episode of threatened rejection. It is usually used with azathioprine. And again, the mechanism of action of steroids as immunosuppressants is not understood.

Antilymphocyte Serum. One more agent has recently been added to the armamentarium. Antiserum to lymphocytes was found, in rats, to reduce markedly the number of circulating lymphocytes, the source of the antibodies that react with the transplanted tissue to cause rejection. When given prior to skin grafting, this serum resulted in long-term survival where, ordinarily, sloughing would have occurred in a few days. However this occurs, trials are now under way of horse antiserum to human lymphocytes as an immunosuppressant adjunct to homotransplantation.

If, indeed, simple absence of lymphocytes would be an effective immunosuppressing technique, one approach would be their mechanical removal. In rats, this has been achieved by drainage of the lymph flow from the thoracic duct, and has remarkably diminished homograft rejection. As yet, this technique has not been utilized in human transplantation trials.

Tissue Compatibility Testing. The development of tissue compatibility testing in man was stimulated by a number of considerations: (1) large-scale human organ transplantation awaits further resolution of the problem of rejection; (2) immunosuppression has been only a partial solution of this problem; and (3) compatibility tests have been developed successfully in other systems. For example, highly reliable serological tests (blood typing) were developed to detect the factors responsible for blood transfusion reactions in man; blood donors now are selected with an incidence of untoward reaction which is a small fraction of one percent. In work with mice, initiated in 1937, serological tests were developed which greatly facilitated analysis of the complex genetic locus, H-2, which controls the principal antigens responsible for graft rejection in the mouse. The chemical nature of these tissue antigens remains to be ascertained.

The principal methods for testing tissue compatibility in man involve the use of white blood cells in a test analogous to the typing and matching of red blood cells for blood transfusion. The development of such typing has been in progress since 1958, when identification of a human white blood cell antigen called "Mac" was reported. Interpretation of the large body of information concerning white cell antigens, accumulated since 1958, has been facilitated and speeded by exchange of data, serological reagents, and ideas among the half-dozen investigators in Europe and the United States who have directed most of the work on white cell antigens. Although the number of white cell antigens is considerable, they are under the control of one genetic locus, designated as HL-A. From correlative observations with grafts of human skin and kidney it has been concluded, furthermore, that HL-A controls the principal antigens responsible for graft rejection in man. (HL-A therefore is comparable to H-2 in the mouse, and to the single locus that controls Rh antigens of red blood cells in man.) Thus, it is now possible to type a family with respect to HL-A and to identify those prospective donors who would provide the most compatible organ for a member of the family in need of a transplant. In recent experience with such donor selection, a much higher order of compatibility of human kidney transplants has been achieved than could have been achieved without such selection. Equally reliable selection of unrelated cadaveric donors is not now feasible but it is likely to become possible as more white cell antigens are identified and as known antigens are more precisely characterized than they are at present.

Other Considerations. The prevention of graft rejection in animals has been accomplished through the establishment, in the recipient, of states known variously as immunological enhancement, immunological paralysis, and specific immunological tolerance. For a number of reasons these approaches to the problem of graft rejection are impractical in man at present, but they do offer certain advantages, and clinical applications may be developed in the future.

Finally, it must be noted that, although graft rejection is the principal problem, it is not the only substantial problem deterring clinical organ transplantation. The limitations of presently available methods of organ preservation and storage are becoming increasingly evident; indeed improvement in these methods is lagging behind progress on the problem of graft rejection. As new clinical programs for transplantation of heart, liver, lung, pancreas, skin, bone, etc., are developed, problems peculiar to each organ type are likely to require resolution. For each organ, what are the indicators most useful in diagnosing threatened rejection? What, if any, are the functional shortcomings of the denervated heart and denervated lung? Should a liver transplant be in its natural location, or can it function well elsewhere in the abdomen or in the chest? Answers to these and similar questions will be needed simultaneously with resolution of the problem of graft rejection.

This discussion has been confined to the biological aspects of homotransplantation. It will be evident that the surgical manipulations that this process entails were brought to a high degree of perfection early in the history of this endeavor. Ultimate success, however, when it comes, will be the consequence of a long history of biological research – study of nucleic acid metabolism which made possible the thiopurine immunosuppressants, identification of the adrenal steroids and their biological effects, the emerging subdiscipline of immunogenetics, the long and involved history of attempts to understand the immune process, and, one day, recognition of the substances that serve as tissue antigens which are almost unique to each individual.

There can be no disputing that renal transplantation, in individuals for whom hemodialysis is an insufficient measure, is a lifesaving procedure. Similar considerations would apply, for example, in transplantation of an adrenal gland, or a thyroid gland, or even a liver. We shall not confront the tortuous ethical issues surrounding cardiac transplantation, nor deny that there are instances in which this procedure can be both lifesaving and appropriate. But as cardiac disease becomes the major killer of mankind, it will be evident that some alternate solution must be found. Clearly, for a variety of reasons, it will not become possible to perform 1,000 such operations per day in the United States, and it is imperative that other approaches, particularly preventive measures, be given the highest priority if this major health problem is to be managed successfully.

A Specific Drug for the Treatment of Gout. The history of the drug allopurinol, now the treatment of choice in gout, is an excellent example of the interactions and interdependencies of basic research and clinical investigation in leading to improved patient care. Gout is a disease that was known to Hippocrates to occur predominantly in the male and to be familial in its distribution. It is marked by attacks of unusually severe, acute arthritis and, in many patients, by the development of deposits of chalklike material that may lead to grotesque deformities and serious crippling. The chalklike material was named uric acid in 1798, when it was found in certain urinary stones. Gouty subjects were first discovered to have elevated levels of uric acid in the blood in about 1850. In 1898, Emil Fischer established the correct structure of uric acid and showed it to be a purine compound closely related to the purine bases found in nucleic acids.

In man, uric acid is the end product of the metabolism of the purine bases of nucleic acids, and of a large number of other purine-containing compounds that function as coenzymes. About two thirds of the uric acid formed each day is excreted through the kidney, and one third by way of the gastrointestinal tract. Because uric acid is so sparingly soluble, there is a tendency for uric acid crystals to form whenever its level becomes elevated in the bloodstream or urine. These crystals trigger the acute gouty paroxysm, and accumulations of crystals are responsible for the deformities and disability of gout. In addition, gouty subjects are prone to form kidney stones. The possibility of this affliction man shares only with the other primates. All other species possess the enzyme uricase, which oxidizes uric acid to form the much more soluble and readily excreted compound allantoin. Whether the presence in blood of uric acid is, in any way, related to the rapid evolution of the brain remains open for speculation.

The immediate reaction in which uric acid is formed is the oxidation of the purines hypoxanthine and xanthine, catalyzed by the liver enzyme xanthine oxidase. This enzyme has long been of great interest to biochemists studying the mechanisms of enzyme action, and much is known about it. Allopurinol differs from hypoxanthine only in the transposition of nitrogen-7 and carbon-8 of hypoxanthine into a carbon-7 and nitrogen-8 of allopurinol.

Hypoxanthine   Allopurinol

Allopurinol was first synthesized as a potential cancer chemotherapeutic agent, as part of a concerted search for analogues of natural compounds that might act as metabolic inhibitors to interfere with processes of rapid or abnormal growth. In this role allopurinol was completely ineffective. However, because of its analogy to hypoxanthine, allopurinol was subsequently tested and found to be a xanthine oxidase inhibitor. It was this property that led to its initial use in man as an adjunct agent in cancer chemotherapy.

The drug 6-mercaptopurine, commonly used in the treatment of certain types of leukemias, is oxidized by liver xanthine oxidase to 6-thiouric acid, which is inactive. It was reasoned that an inhibitor of xanthine oxidase might improve the chemotherapeutic effectiveness of 6-mercaptopurine by achieving a reduction in dosage, while providing more sustained blood levels of 6-mercaptopurine. When allopurinol was administered together with 6-mercaptopurine, it was indeed found to inhibit the degradation of 6-mercaptopurine and, thereby, to increase the sensitivity of the subject to this drug. In addition, it was found that the subjects so treated experienced a marked reduction in both serum and urinary levels of uric acid. This observation immediately suggested the possible usefulness of allopurinol in lowering the elevated uric acid levels of a subject with gout.

Several hundred patients were eventually treated with allopurinol under carefully controlled conditions. The drug was found to be predictably effective in controlling uric acid levels in both blood and urine and, by blocking the formation of uric acid, allowing the excretion of hypoxanthine and xanthine in place of uric acid. These substances are much less likely to accumulate in the body, because of a more efficient mechanism for their renal excretion. They are also more soluble than uric acid and have not caused formation of kidney stones. In fact, the use of allopurinol has remarkably reduced the tendency of gouty subjects to produce uric acid stones, and allopurinol has now also become standard therapy in treatment of patients who form uric acid stones, whether or not they have gout.

Genetic Basis for One Form of Gout. In virtually all gouty subjects who are given allopurinol, the increase in urinary excretion of hypoxanthine and xanthine amounts to only about two thirds of the concomitant decrease in urinary uric acid. Thus total purine production is reduced, and this result helps to counter the primary defect of gouty subjects— namely, an abnormality of metabolic control mechanisms leading to excessive uric acid production. It appears that the inhibition of xanthine oxidase leads, indirectly, to a greater reutilization of hypoxanthine for nucleotide and, thence, nucleic acid synthesis.

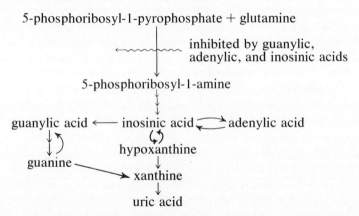

Synthesis and fate of purines and purine nucleotides

A rare type of gout is found in children with cerebral palsy, mental deficiency, and self-destructive biting. This syndrome is transmitted as a genetic recessive trait; the responsible gene is located on the X chromosome, and the disease occurs only in males. It was found that whereas allopurinol effectively inhibited their xanthine oxidase, there occurred no reduction in the total purine excretion, as in other gouty subjects. This result suggested that perhaps hypoxanthine could not be reconverted to more complex nucleotides in these subjects. Direct assay of the liver enzymes that normally catalyze this salvage reaction showed this postulate to be correct. Thus the use of allopurinol, plus careful clinical investigation of the treated patients, led to an understanding of the precise metabolic defect present in these children. It was further observed that certain gouty subjects with flamboyant overproduction of uric acid, particularly those in whom the disease began at an early age and who may exhibit some minor neurological abnormalities, may also show defects of the enzyme system responsible for reconversion of hypoxanthine and guanine to their respective nucleotides. This observation has considerable significance. Since this defect is present in only a limited number of gouty subjects, it establishes and confirms a long-suspected notion that "gout" is a heterogeneous disease resulting from several, perhaps many, different biochemical errors all of which cause hyperuricemia. It has led to the precise definition of at least one subtype of gout in biochemical terms. Finally, these studies illustrate the interdependence and inseparability of careful clinical observation, well-executed clinical investigations, and highly competent fundamental research, in leading both to a better understanding of disease and to practical results of improved patient care.

Allopurinol has now had extensive medical use over a period of four years. It is well tolerated by all but a few subjects. Gouty deformities can be prevented. Even severe deformities can at times be reversed, and after the initial phase of the treatment, acute gouty attacks are greatly reduced in number and severity. Proper use of allopurinol, together with other drugs available for the treatment of gout, makes it unnecessary for any patient to be crippled by this disease. Gout has been called "the disease of kings and the king of disease," but it appears to have yielded, at long last, to the unpredictable yet inexorable pressure of careful scientific investigation.

Vitamin K, Anticoagulation and Bleeding Disorders. The interrelationship between basic scientific research and the clinic is well illustrated by the development of knowledge of nutrition. Beginning with the experiments of Lunin, in 1880, which demonstrated that a synthetic diet, reconstituted from the materials thought to be present in milk, lacked an unknown factor needed for the growth of laboratory animals, knowledge concerning the components of food required by human beings has grown steadily. Elements of the diet necessary only in trace amounts, the vitamins, have been isolated and have been shown to repair and prevent specific disorders such as scurvy, beriberi, rickets, sprue, xerophthalmia, pernicious anemia, and pellagra; and each has been found to play a specific role in the metabolic processes of the organism. This new knowledge has been utilized not only in the treatment of deficiency diseases but in their prevention by supplementation of otherwise deficient foodstuffs.

The evolution of knowledge concerning vitamin K is particularly instructive concerning the interdependence of the laboratory and bedside medicine. The hemorrhagic states associated with liver disease and obstructive jaundice (in which the bile duct from the liver to the intestine is blocked) or in many newborn infants had long baffled physicians. In the early part of this century, George Whipple had demonstrated that such bleeding conditions might be associated with a deficiency of a specific clot-promoting fraction of plasma, prothrombin. This information was largely ignored, both because it was difficult to demonstrate the defect and because its recognition seemed of no practical value. The development of techniques for measuring the concentration of prothrombin in the 1930's revived interest in Whipple's observation, and led to the demonstration that this protein is synthesized in the liver.

Meanwhile, Henrik Dam, of the University of Copenhagen, began a series of fundamental studies in an apparently entirely unrelated field. Attempting to repeat earlier experiments on cholesterol metabolism, he fed chicks artificial diets from which sterols had been removed. To his surprise, after the chicks had been fed these diets for two or three weeks, they developed hemorrhages under the skin, in muscles, or in other organs. The nature of the bleeding tendency was not immediately apparent, but was believed to be related to a defect in blood coagulation. Soon, others found that the hemorrhagic disease of chicks could be prevented by feeding fresh cabbage. Dam undertook the isolation of the factor whose absence was responsible for bleeding, and obtained a fat-soluble substance from green leaves and hog liver, which he designated as vitamin K. Other laboratories showed that the defect in the hemorrhagic chicks was a deficiency of prothrombin. The newly discovered vitamin K was then linked to the bleeding tendencies found in obstructive jaundice, since the prothrombin deficiency in rats in which bile salts were excluded from the gut could be corrected by administration of vitamin K. Bile salts are needed for the intestinal absorption of this fat-soluble agent, and their absence from the gut in patients whose bile ducts were obstructed was responsible for a deficiency of vitamin K and the consequent bleeding tendency.

These laboratory observations were quickly translated to the clinic, with the demonstration by several investigators that the administration of vitamin K would rapidly reverse the prothrombin deficiency and bleeding tendency in patients with obstructive jaundice. Similarly, the prothrombin deficiency of hemorrhagic disease of the newborn was linked to deficiency of vitamin K, which proved both a curative and preventive agent.

Observations concerning vitamin K next took an unexpected turn. In the early 1920's, a financially devastating disease of cattle appeared in North Dakota and Alberta. Veterinarians demonstrated that the cause of the disorder was the ingestion of improperly cured sweet clover, which resulted in a severe prothrombin deficiency. Little came of this until 1933, when Ed Carlson, a Wisconsin farmer, drove up to the University of Wisconsin with a dead heifer, a milk can of incoagulable blood, and about 100 pounds of spoiled sweet clover, all that he could feed his cattle in those depression years. By chance he brought his cargo to a biochemist who had been interested in the nature of the sweet clover disease, and who promptly went to work to isolate the toxin in the spoiled feed. By 1939, he had isolated dicoumarol, the responsible agent from the sweet clover, and had found its action could be overcome by the administration of vitamin K.

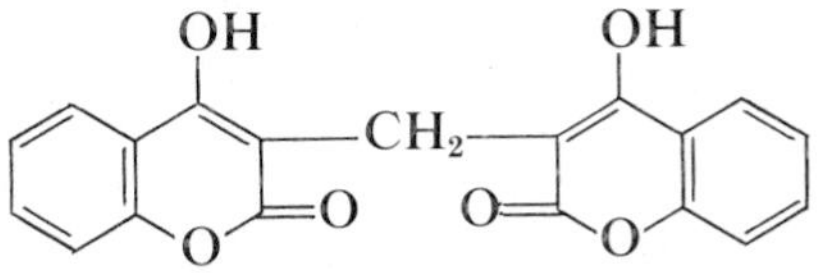

Dicoumarol

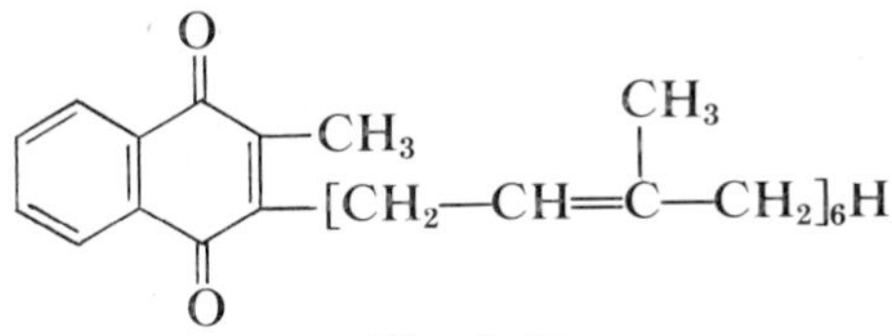

Vitamin K$_2$

The possibility that dicoumarol might be useful in the prevention and treatment of thrombotic disease, by deliberately retarding the blood-clotting process, was quickly realized. With the availability of synthetic dicoumarol, this possibility was soon tested, and the modern era of anti-coagulant treatment began. The value of dicoumarol was enhanced by ready analysis of its effects in man by the prothrombin time procedure and by the availability of vitamin K as an antidote in the event that over-dosage occurred.

One last application of knowledge concerning vitamin K and sweet clover disease must be mentioned. Dicoumarol is a tasteless and odorless compound. Link conceived the idea that its inclusion in baits would make it an ideal rodenticide, by inducing fatal bleeding. But dicoumarol proved too weak to achieve this purpose. He therefore proposed the use of a closely similar compound, warfarin. Warfarin has turned out to be a highly effective agent in the war between men and rats; literally hundreds of millions of pounds of bait containing warfarin have now been used. Unexpectedly, warfarin proved quite safe for human beings, and this drug has now partially replaced dicoumarol in clinical use.

Thus, our modern techniques for preventing and treating the bleeding tendency in obstructive jaundice and hemorrhagic disease of the newborn, and our use of anticoagulant drugs in the management of thrombosis, derive from a series of seemingly unconnected laboratory observations. Neither those who set out to study cholesterol metabolism in chicks, nor those who sought the agent responsible for farmer Carlson's troubles, knew where these studies would take them, nor the service they would do mankind.

Contributions of Clinical Observation to Fundamental Biological Understanding

In each of the instances presented in the previous section, the thread of the story commenced with an observation, made outside the clinic, which was subsequently translated into clinical practice—an agar plate with a bacteria-free area around a contaminating fungus, an inhibitor of nucleic acid metabolism or of purine metabolism, inbred strains of mice which would not accept skin transplants from other strains, bleeding chickens and heifers, mosaic spots on tobacco leaves. Little time was lost before the possibility of clinical exploitation was explored. In some measure, this reflects the structure of the American university and its medical school. The hospital-based medical school is constantly concerned with the human problems that present themselves daily. But the clinical faculty lives cheek by jowl with the medical sciences faculty, and they, in turn, are a bridge to the chemistry, physics, and biology departments of the campus. There need be no organizational barrier to progress from initial observation, to research, to development, and then to practice. Each member of the organization has access to the skills and knowledge of the others. In this sense, medical research may be unique in that fundamental research in virtually all other disciplines must leave the campus for its development, application, and field testing.

In this section, we shall note a few instances of the converse process, wherein clinical observation and research have illuminated basic understanding of fundamental biological processes. But again, it will be evident that this distinction is unreal, that just as the previous phenomena rapidly became clinical research, so here clinical observation almost immediately becomes fundamental research.

Immunity. All living things protect themselves as vigorously from invasion by smaller living things as they do from engulfment by larger ones, for it is as bad to rot from within as to be eaten from without; at least it is as decisive. Hence, the evolution of mechanisms for resisting infection began early in biological time and has been slowly continuing. The kind of resistance we now call specific immunity appeared first in early aquatic vertebrates like the eel, and is well-developed in the modern fishes and birds, as well as in mammals.

Specific immunity is a precise and elegant mechanism for the production of accurate antidotes to the poisons produced by the small bacteria that cause disease or to the organisms themselves. Since each invader is unique, its antidote must be like a sheath accurately fitted to cover its teeth and so to disarm it.

The antidote is called a specific antibody, and it literally fits over a portion of the offending molecule. The latter is called the antigen, and that part of it with which the antibody molecule reacts is called the "antigenic determinant."

Antibody Formation. Antigens must be substances not usually encountered by the antibody-forming cells, either because they are intruders from the outside or because they are sequestered and never enter the circulation, such as the protein of the lens of the eye. Antigens are not necessarily poisonous — they must merely be large molecules, protein or polysaccharide, and foreign to the host. So it is that parasites like the measles virus or the diphtheria bacillus, which cause human disease, also leave their surviving sufferers immune. Each organism, while present and releasing its toxic products, has not only made its host ill, but also stimulated his tissues to assemble antibody molecules which specifically neutralize the toxic molecule, thus preventing a second attack.

Immunization is familiar to all of us; it is a common experience of childhood. It was just such experience that first directed attention to the existence of immune mechanisms. Measles, mumps, chickenpox or (in an earlier era) smallpox and even plague were known to be suffered but once in a lifetime. Thereafter the survivor was immune. But the fact that each disease conferred its own immunity, without effect on susceptibility to other diseases, indicated the great specificity of the process. Such an exact reciprocal fit between antigen and antibody raises the question of how antibody production can be made responsive to specific antigenic stimulation. "What does the antigen do?" Before we can approach this question we must first describe briefly the cellular machinery known to be engaged in antibody formation, and then try to guess how the antigen could act, since no definitive answer is available.

The cell system responsible for immune phenomena was long in doubt, as indeed have been the functions of various cell types found in spleen, lymph nodes, and peripheral blood. Recently, it was found that the thymus, heretofore an organ of unknown function, is an important link in the development of active immunity. Removal of the thymus always interferes with the competence of the immune mechanism; the thymus functions as a source of some cells of immunological importance, and also as the site of synthesis of a hormonelike material which influences the development of other immunologically active cells. Much important work in this area is now under way, but the picture is muddy.

The first injection of antigen results in the production of a small amount of antibody, which slowly disappears from the blood plasma. The response may involve only a relatively few antibody-making cells, but it prepares the way for a much greater response if a second dose of antigen is given a month or more later. This second response is fifty to one hundred times as vigorous as the first, and many cells are engaged. The correlation between the number of cells found and the amount of antibody produced is good, suggesting that each cell is making a maximum, or a standard, amount of antibody. The peak of this second response is soon passed, the responsible cells quickly disappear, and the circulating antibody again falls to a low level. Another dose of antigen again produces a rapid response. The animal making such a recall or "anamnestic" response is clearly different from an inexperienced one; his tissues have "remembered" their previous experience. This memory is specific, and greatly fortifies resistance to a second attack of acute disease. (Indeed, infections that come and go suddenly are those in which the attack is successfully terminated by the antibody response. Chronic infections become so because the factors involved in specific resistance have failed.)

One of the outstanding questions in the study of the immune response is the nature of such immunological memory; in biochemical terms, in what kind of compound could the recognition of an antigenic determinant be stored? Most immunologists have concluded such storage must be in a protein—indeed, in some variety of antibody molecule, perhaps one that is fixed to the surface of a cell, such as a lymphocyte or a plasma cell precursor. The antigen then would be readily captured as it floated by in the plasma and thus be more likely to stimulate antibody formation on a second encounter than on a first when there was no antibody.

A recent discovery of great importance suggests that antibody formation begins by cooperation between two families of cells, the scavenger cells called macrophages, and the cells that synthesize antibody. It ap-

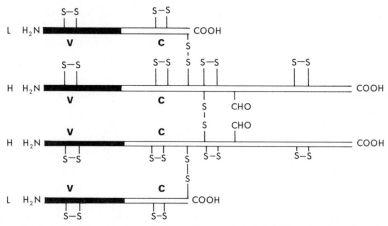

Figure 16-2. Schematic structure of plasma immunologlobulin. The structure given is that of the major antibody protein of the class IgG. L = light chains; H = heavy chains; CHO = carbohydrate unit. The variable and constant portions of the chains, with respect to amino acid sequences, are indicated by the labels V and C, respectively. It is not known whether V is the same length in H and L chains. (From White, Handler, and Smith)

pears that the macrophage may engulf and ingest the antigen and change it into a form that is a more active stimulus of antibody formation. Once formed, antibody is known to stick to the surface of macrophages; such antibody could assist in the engulfment of antigen by macrophages, somehow converting the antigen into some more active form. Such a mechanism could explain the puzzling features of immunological memory.

The techniques of protein chemistry have been applied to the structure of antibodies, which proved to be complex, indeed, yet simple in plan.

There are three major and several minor classes of antibody of which the class designated IgG is dominant, accounting for 80 percent of all plasma immunoglobulin. As will be seen from Figure 16-2, it is built by combining two short (light) chains (molecular weight 23,500) and two longer (heavy) chains (molecular weight 48,000) by —S—S— bridges. Only two subclasses of light and one subclass of heavy chains have been found. In a general way, all antibodies of the class IgG are identical in that portion of the molecule, on the right as drawn, which is unshaded. It is variation in the amino acid sequences of the shaded portion of both light and heavy chains which confers antibody specificity. This analysis of the structure of antibodies was simplified enormously by recognition of the fact that Bence Jones protein—a heat-insoluble protein first found in the urine of patients with multiple myeloma in 1848—is actually a mixture of the two forms of the light chains in IgG antibodies, overproduced by the malignantly transformed plasma cells.

Since it is the amino acid sequences of the polypeptide chains which confer immunochemical specificity for specific antigens, and since proteins are synthesized by the genetic apparatus, we are left with a major puzzle. How does the presence of antigen, as such or "transformed" by the macrophage, determine the amino acid sequences of the heavy and light chains as these are synthesized by the genetic apparatus? As yet, there is no clue to the answer to this puzzle.

Functions of Antibody. Once in combination with specific antigen, antibody molecules act in combination with cells or a substance called "complement," or both, to produce the various specific effects upon which specific resistance depends. An example has already been given of the simplest way in which antibody may function — the neutralization of a toxic molecule. Simple interaction of antibody with the protein coat of a viral particle may be enough to prevent its penetration into a susceptible cell, and hence account for the usual immunity produced by infection with viral disease and viral vaccines. But antibody reacting with surface molecules of some kinds of cells, and complement (see later), digests the cell wall, rupturing the cell. Or, antibody interacts with antigen, thereby activating some of the components of complement, producing a compound attractive to leukocytes, which swarm into the area and devour the entire complex.

"Complement," known for many years, is a factor present in normal serum, which becomes functional only after antigen-antibody interactions. From its behavior, "complement" must be a set of components, each of which activates the next like a row of standing dominoes. Some are known to be enzymes; probably all have enzymatic activity. They are just emerging as purified proteins and their function, as a group and individually, is only now beginning to be unraveled. Complement research is making rapid progress as new, effective methods of separation and analysis of these fragile, complex molecules are applied. It is possible that complement components, or deficiency of their naturally occurring inhibitors, may be found to play an important part in the development of some "autoimmune" diseases; one such deficiency has been found to be associated with the clinical condition known as angioneurotic edema.

Hypersensitivity. A number of important chronic diseases appear to be associated with aberrant functioning of the immune mechanisms. Familiar examples include allergies such as hay fever, precipitated by exposure to pollens or other biological dusts, and acute gastrointestinal illness after the ingestion of some protein in shellfish. The underlying basis of these conditions is not adequately understood, and their medical treatment is of marginal effectiveness. Even more obscure is the phenomenon of "delayed hypersensitivity" which occasionally occurs in connection with such chronic infections as tuberculosis. It consists of a specific, prolonged inflammatory reaction involving tissue cells, perhaps lymphocytes, but probably not antibody or complement. This phenomenon probably depends on antibodylike materials which can react specifically with antigen, but its essential features are obscure, as are the cells that mediate it.

Although some aspects of hypersensitivity, like hay fever, are associated with the presence of a specific variety of antibody demonstrable in the serum of the sufferer, this is not invariant. Thus, some forms of asthma seem to represent hypersensitivity, but no specific antibody has been demonstrated. It seems more likely that this failure reflects lack of an appropriate technique for detecting the antibody involved than that it is really absent.

Other abnormalities of the immune mechanism which result in human disease are failure to make antibodies and the making of antibodies against one's own tissue antigens. We will discuss these, in order.

In 1952, it was found that the serum of a boy of eight, who had had repeated infections, contained no demonstrable gamma globulin, the fraction of the blood serum associated with antibody. His serum was also deficient in the expected antibodies, including the "isoantibodies" of the ABO blood groups. This condition, hypogammaglobulinemia, has since been described in many parts of the world. Some cases are also associated with a deficiency of lymphocytes, and for these the outlook is poor. In rare cases, the disease is first detected in adult life, but most cases come to light in childhood, manifested by repeated infections, particularly of the respiratory tract and the middle ear. Treatment with antibiotics and systematic administration of gamma globulin has kept such individuals alive, preventing the repeated infections which otherwise terminate their lives. The disorder is familial, transmitted as a recessive trait. Hypogammaglobulinemia illustrates how genetic abnormalities elucidate basic biological mechanisms by showing the effect of selective loss of a normal function.

In complete contrast are the "autoimmune" diseases. These serious clinical disorders are the consequence of formation of antibodies in a given individual against the basement membrane of his own kidney, producing glomerulonephritis, an acute and chronic kidney disease; against the myocardial muscle fiber, resulting in rheumatic fever with acute heart failure and chronic damage to the heart valves; against the red blood cell, to yield hemolytic anemia; against the blood platelet, occasioning thrombocytopenic purpura, a severe tendency to internal bleeding; against the thyroglobulin stored in the thyroid gland, causing chronic thyroiditis, an inflammation of the thyroid gland; or against the nucleoprotein of the cell nucleus, resulting in lupus erythematosus, a serious illness with fever, arthritis, skin rashes, and other widespread manifestations.

Homograft Rejection. Earlier, we discussed in some detail the immunological rejection of homografts or organ transplants. At this point, we may ask what these rejection reactions are really for. Why should cells from other human beings be rejected — there is no obvious evolutionary selection pressure for such a mechanism. Can it be that such a mechanism has evolved and been maintained to eliminate mutant cells which are not under the normal controls of growth, viz., cancer cells? Is it conceivable that malignant transformation is a frequent event, but that such cells are instantly recognized as foreign, and eliminated like a foreign tissue graft? If so, cancer is a failure of the rejection reaction.

Practical Successes of Immunology. Immunization. By immunization, one takes advantage of the immune mechanism to induce specific antibody formation in advance of an infection, thereby preventing disease or greatly reducing its severity. Each case thus prevented reduces spread of contagion through the community. In the most favorable circumstances, the disease may be completely eradicated from large areas — e.g., smallpox in the United States. More recently, poliomyelitis has been all but eliminated from the United States, Canada, Europe, and the USSR by the widespread use of polio vaccine.

Vaccination is routinely used, and is uniformly successful, against smallpox, yellow fever, measles, diphtheria, tetanus, and typhus fever, although in epidemic typhus fever it may only moderate the disease. Vaccines against typhoid fever and cholera are only marginally effective; the resultant immunity protects against small but not large infecting doses of organisms. Thus, they probably protect against contaminated water, where the number of ingested organisms is usually small, but not against infected food, where the organisms multiply to produce a large infecting dose.

Other desired vaccines have, so far, resisted successful development. The most urgent, perhaps, is a vaccine against malaria, and more successful methods of vaccinating against tuberculosis and plague. Infectious hepatitis virus still defies isolation, thereby preventing the beginnings of vaccine development, since a supply of the proper antigen is the first step in the preparation of a vaccine.

Useful Serum Therapy. Administration of antibodies synthesized in another individual or in another species for the treatment or prevention of disease began shortly after the discovery of antibodies in 1890. The use of antitoxin prepared by immunizing horses was lifesaving in diphtheria and was instrumental in halting the growing clusters of youthful siblings in cemeteries throughout the Western world in the Victorian era. Antiserum was very effective in preventing tetanus in the wounded soldiers of World War I. This procedure, however, almost invariably results in formation of antibodies against the horse serum proteins and, two weeks or so later, development of "serum sickness." Such individuals should never be exposed to a second dose of horse serum. These diseases are now prevented by active immunization with tetanus and diphtheria toxoids (attenuated, noninfectious organism) in childhood. Collection and fractionation of human blood now permits the opportunity to use human antibodies, when necessary, in the treatment of these diseases, while avoiding serum sickness.

Other diseases for which antisera are still used include gas gangrene, the prevention of rabies, hepatitis (human gamma globulin), and rubella (German measles) after exposure during the first third of pregnancy.

The Uses of Immunology in Other Fields. Immunological specificity is so exquisite that it has found increasing use as a method for the identification of proteins in all fields of biological research. When properly conducted, immunological procedures can distinguish between two proteins which differ in their amino acids in only one or two positions in the entire molecule, a procedure that has been of great utility in tracing the evolution of specific proteins by comparative studies with many species. This furnishes yet another example of the cascade effect of science, each new advance accelerating several others.

Hereditary Diseases of Man. Metabolic Disorders. That some diseases tend to "run in families" was well established in many folklores. The reality of this seeming truth was first convincingly documented by A. E. Garrod, Physician to the British Royal Family, in 1908, not long after the rediscovery of Mendel's work. In a remarkable treatise, entitled "Inborn Errors of Metabolism" (when almost nothing was known about metabolism!), he demonstrated that cystinuria (urinary stones of the amino acid cystine), alkaptonuria (inky urine due to homogentisic acid, a degradative derivative of the amino acid tyrosine), porphyria (urinary excretion of porphyrins, related to the heme of hemoglobin), pentosuria (urinary excretion of the unusual sugar L-xylulose), albinism (failure to make melanin pigment from tyrosine), and congenital steatorrhea (fatty stools) were all transmitted as Mendelian recessive traits and were expressed only in the homozygous condition (both genes for the character in question are defective).

As knowledge of metabolism grew, an ever increasing list of such disorders has been compiled (Table 4). When examined further, each proved to be the consequence of either the absence of a specific protein, fre-

Table 4.
Some Hereditary Disorders in Man in Which the Specific Lacking or Modified Enzyme or Protein Has Been Identified

Affected Enzyme or Protein

Acanthocytosis	β-Lipoproteins (low density)
Acatalasia	Catalase
Afibrinogenemia	Fibrinogen
Agammaglobulinemia	γ-Globulin
Albinism	Tyrosinase
Alkaptonuria	Homogentisic acid oxidase
Analbuminemia	Serum albumin
Argininosuccinic acidemia	Argininosuccinase
Crigler-Najjar syndrome	Uridine diphosphate glucuronate transferase
Favism	Glucose-6-phosphate dehydrogenase
Fructose intolerance	Fructose-1-phosphate aldolase
Fructosuria	Fructokinase
Galactosemia	Galactose-1-phosphate uridyl transferase
Goiter (familial)	Iodotyrosine dehalogenase
Gout	Hypoxanthine guanine phosphoribosyl transferase
Hartnup's disease	Tryptophan pyrrolase
Hemoglobinopathies	Hemoglobins
Hemolytic anemia	Pyruvate kinase
Hemophilia A	Antihemophilic factor A
Hemophilia B	Antihemophilic factor B
Histidinemia	Histidase
Homocystinuria	Cystathionine synthetase
Hypophosphatasia	Alkaline phosphatase
Isovaleric acidemia	Isovaleryl CoA dehydrogenase
Maple syrup urine disease	Amino acid decarboxylase
Methemoglobinemia	Methemoglobin reductase
Orotic aciduria	Orotidine 5'-phosphate pyrophosphorylase
Parahemophilia	Accelerator globulin
Pentosuria	L-Xylulose dehydrogenase
Phenylketonuria	Phenylalanine hydroxylase
Sulfite oxidase deficiency	Sulfite oxidase
Wilson's disease	Ceruloplasmin
Xanthinuria	Xanthine oxidase

Table 4. *Continued*

**Some Hereditary Disorders in Which the Affected Protein
Has Not Been Identified**

Biochemical Manifestation

Congenital steatorrhea	Failure to digest and/or absorb lipid
Cystinuria	Excretion of cystine, lysine, arginine, and ornithine
Cystinosis	Inability to utilize amino acids, notably cystine; aberration of amino acid transport into cells
Fanconi's syndrome	Increased excretion of amino acids
Gargoylism (Hurler's syndrome)	Excessive excretion of chondroitin sulfate B
Gaucher's disease	Accumulation of cerebrosides in tissues
Niemann-Pick disease	Accumulation of sphingomyelin in tissues
Porphyria	Increased excretion of uroporphyrins
Tangier disease	Lack of plasma high density lipoproteins
Tay-Sachs disease	Accumulation of gangliosides in tissues

quently one that serves as an enzyme, or the presence of a defective, nonfunctioning enzyme. Before the nature of the genetic apparatus was clarified, knowledge of these mutant humans greatly fortified the conclusion, drawn from work with bacteria and molds, that a single gene controls the synthesis of a single enzyme. Indeed, it was exactly fifty years after publication of Garrod's treatise that there was provided a demonstration of the total absence of the enzyme homogentisic acid oxidase, from the liver of an alkaptonuric, both of whose parents' livers exhibited approximately half the normal level of this enzyme. And this reveals why these disorders appear to be "recessive" traits. With few exceptions, the normal complement of all enzymes is so far in excess of metabolic requirements that the presence of only half that complement in the heterozygous state goes undetected, since it suffices for normal life.

At the same time, each such metabolic block revealed a step in normal metabolism—e.g., since homogentisic acid accumulates in the urine of those so afflicted, and since its excretion is greatly enhanced by ingestion of tyrosine, there must be a normal metabolic reaction sequence which leads from tyrosine to homogentisic acid. The knowledge so gained, together with equivalent information gleaned from mutant microorganisms deliberately created by irradiation, was vital to the elaboration of the now almost complete "metabolic maps," flow sheets describing the multitudinous synthetic and degradative chemical reaction sequences which, collectively, are the metabolic activities of normal living cells (see Chapter 3).

So manifold are these aberrations of human metabolism that it is clear
that mutation occurs continually in man. When the metabolic disturbance
thus created affects a central reaction in the life of the cell—e.g., reactions
necessary to protein synthesis or the manufacture of ATP, the immediate
source of energy for all cell functions—the mutation must be lethal in the
homozygote and is never detected. When, however, the reaction is important but not absolutely vital, disease is manifest and the mutation is
observed. In retrospect, it seems that every such possibility probably
does exist in the human population. For example, six different enzymes
are required either to accomplish the synthesis of glycogen, the storage
polymer of glucose, in liver and muscle, or to achieve its degradation so
that the glucose may be utilized for metabolic purposes. As shown in
Table 5, humans defective in each of these six enzymes have been
identified; each results in a specific incapacitating disorder which, ultimately, proves fatal.

Hemoglobin Mutants. Further, the existence of mutant proteins in
humans afflicted with sickle cell anemia proved to be the critical key in the
elucidation of the nature of the genetic apparatus. This disease, which
afflicts 10 percent of the Negro population of the United States, was
initially described by Herrick in 1910. Almost forty years later, it was
shown that the hemoglobin of such cells (HbS) differed from that of
normal cells (HbA), since they could be distinguished by electrophoresis,
i.e., there is a difference in their net electrical charges. Clearly this must
be due to a difference in amino acid composition, and shortly thereafter
it was found that the difference is due entirely to the substitution of the
amino acid valine for the normal glutamic acid at position 6 in the β
chains. (A hemoglobin molecule is constructed of two α and two β chains,
strings of 141 and 146 amino acids, respectively.) This single change in
the immense molecule occasions a very serious disease! And, of great
significance, for the first time one could be sure of the intrinsic nature of
the simplest mutational event—change in the structure of the gene yields
an equivalent change in the amino acid sequence of the protein for which
it is responsible. Hence, the information in genes is the coded information
that determines the amino acid sequence of proteins.

In the years since, almost 50 other aberrant human hemoglobins have
been detected, each differing from normal hemoglobin by an amino acid
substitution at one of the 287 loci. The specific nature of these substitutions has constituted the best single check on the validity of the genetic
code; at the same time they have shown that this code in *Escherichia coli*
is identical with that in man.

Favism. A striking example of the influence of clinical observation on
the development of knowledge in the basic biological and medical

Table 5. Hereditary Disorders of Glycogen Metabolism

Type	Enzymic Defect	Glycogen Structure	Organ	Eponymic Name
1	Glucose-6-phosphatase	Normal	Liver, kidney, intestine(?)	von Gierke's disease
2	Amylo-α-1,4-glucosidase	Normal	Generalized	Pompe's disease
3	α-1,4 → 1,4-glucan transferase	Abnormal; outer chains missing or very short	Liver, heart, muscle, leukocytes	Forbes' disease
4	Amylo-(1,4 → 1,6)-trans-glucosylase	Abnormal; very long inner and outer unbranched chains	Liver, probably other organs	Andersen's disease
5	Muscle glycogen phosphorylase	Normal	Skeletal muscle	McArdle-Schmid-Pearson disease
6	Liver glycogen phosphorylase	Normal	Liver, leukocytes	Hers' disease

Source: Adapted from J. B. Stanbury, J. B. Wyngaarden, and D. S. Fredrickson, *The Metabolic Basis of Inherited Disease*, 2d ed., McGraw-Hill Book Company, New York, 1966.

sciences is afforded by the unraveling of the mystery of the hemolytic anemia associated with favism and with the ingestion of certain drugs. Favism, an ancient disease which has only recently begun to yield its secrets, has been known since the time of Pythagoras, the Greek philosopher of the sixth century B.C. who forbade his disciples to eat beans. The disease that Pythagoras was trying to avoid was favism, a hemolytic process induced in sensitive persons by ingestion of the fava bean. It has taken nearly 2,500 years to elucidate partially the basis for Pythagoras' prohibition. But now much is understood as the result of studies performed in the United States, Italy, and Israel during the past decade.

Studies of the hemolytic effect induced by the antimalarial drug primaquine demonstrated that the drug-induced hemolysis occurred principally in American Negroes and in some Orientals and that the defect appeared to be intrinsic to the red cell itself. This defect was correlated with an abnormally low content of the reduced form of glutathione. Glutathione is a tripeptide or string of three amino acids, linked much as in proteins, one of which bears a sulfhydryl, —SH, group. In the oxidized form, two such molecules unite by a disulfide bridge.

$$\left[2\ \text{G—SH} \underset{\text{H}_2}{\overset{\text{O}_2}{\rightleftharpoons}} \text{G—S—S—G} \right]$$

Reduction of glutathione is normally accomplished by the enzyme glutathione reductase; the actual reductant is its specific reduced coenzyme (triphosphopyridine nucleotide, or TPN).

$$\text{G—S—S—G} + \text{TPNH}_2 \rightarrow 2\ \text{GSH} + \text{TPN}$$

In the life of the red cell, TPNH_2 is generated by only two reactions, principally that catalyzed by glucose-6-phosphate dehydrogenase:

$$\text{glucose-6-phosphate} + \text{TPN} \rightarrow \text{6-phosphogluconic acid} + \text{TPNH}_2$$

Careful examination of primaquine-sensitive cells revealed that it was the latter enzyme which was present in seriously reduced concentration. Apparently, an erythrocyte with insufficient reduced glutathione, because of inability to generate the reducing power to reduce it, lives a precarious existence. The membrane is unstable and disintegrates when in contact with primaquine.

This demonstration prompted the search for incidence of this enzyme deficit in other populations. It was established very quickly that the hemolysis caused by the ingestion of fava beans, or by the inhalation of the pollen of the fava plant, is associated with the deficiency of the same enzyme in the red cells of the sensitive individuals. The hemolytic effects of many other compounds in common use appear to be associated with this enzymic deficiency. Among these are naphthalene, acetanilide, *p*-aminosalicylic acid, sulfanilimide, and acetophenetidine. Extensive studies have demonstrated this genetic defect in American Negroes, where it is present in roughly 11 percent of the population, in individuals of Italian or Greek origin, in Orientals and in Sephardic Jews. The defect is inherited as a sex-linked characteristic, and its manifestations are more prevalent in males than in females.

These examples of heritable disorders are but a few among many. More than 400 autosomal dominant and at least 175 autosomal recessive human disorders are known. Even so, mutations have been recognized in only a minute fraction of genetic loci. Many more remain to be found. Some disorders, such as diabetes, are clearly polygenic in character. How many more such there may be remains to be established.

Clinical Research

In this section are presented a few instances in which recognition of a major clinical problem resulted in intensive investigations, conducted, in the main, by investigator-physicians, usually in university medical centers. The information thus gained has contributed significantly to human health; secondarily, each has also illuminated an aspect of fundamental biology. As we have already seen, man may well be the best of all experimental animals. He can report his subjective reactions and voluntarily cooperate, without need for physical restraint. Moreover, the human population is so large and well-trained physician-observers sufficiently numerous, that the medical literature is a vast reporting system wherein are collected descriptions of nature's experiments, the sum of which constitutes a most impressive description of normal and abnormal human biology.

The Milieu Interieur. It was the distinguished French physiologist Claude Bernard, a century ago, who recognized that cells of the mammalian organism are bathed in a fluid of constant composition—the *milieu interieur*—which is safeguarded by an elaborate set of compensatory mechanisms. Almost all current understanding of this fluid, the blood plasma and the "extracellular fluid," as well as of such specialized media as the "aqueous humor" (a few drops in the anterior chamber of the eye) the cerebrospinal fluid, sweat, tears, and synovial fluid in the joint spaces of the skeletal system, and the secretions of the gastrointestinal tract derive from studies conducted with human subjects. In each instance, the primary stimulus arose from the necessity to control the behavior of this fluid in some disorder in which it is seriously disturbed. In sum, this constitutes one of the larger chapters in the history of medical research. Here we can but sample a few episodes.

Diabetes. Diabetes is a polygenic, genetic disorder characterized primarily by deficiency of insulin, the protein hormone secreted by the islet cells of the pancreas. Refined, supersensitive methods for its detection have now revealed that there are several forms of this disease, most notably (a) absolute deficiency in pancreatic insulin secretion, (b) overactivity of a tissue and blood plasma enzyme which hydrolytically destroys insulin, and (c) overactivity of the anterior hypophysis whose hormones negate, in part, the effects of insulin. In each case, the consequence is impaired ability of glucose to enter tissue cells; the liver continues to produce glucose which accumulates in the circulation and is excreted in the urine. At the extreme levels of glucose in the blood, it does enter muscle, even in the absence of insulin, and muscle metabolism is only slightly impaired. But the liver, which has discharged its glucose, then utilizes fatty acids almost exclusively as a source of energy. Under these circumstances, for a series of complex reasons, oxidation of fatty acids is incomplete and partial degradation forms, β-hydroxybutyric acid and acetoacetic acid, accumulate.

On entering plasma, these react with the bicarbonate ion

$$HAc \; + \; HCO_3^- \; \rightarrow \; Ac^- \; + \; H_2CO_3 \; \rightarrow \; H_2O \; + \; CO_2$$

with formation of carbon dioxide which is removed in expired air in the lungs, and the plasma becomes acidic. At the same time the kidney, which is forced to excrete unusual volumes of urine by the presence of the large quantity of glucose, attempts to conserve the composition of plasma, and the urine also contains ions of the offending acids, partly as such and partly in association with sodium or ammonium ion and, to a much lesser degree, potassium. These efforts ameliorate the situation — were there no bicarbonate in plasma, and if the kidney did not exercise its compensatory mechanism, the blood plasma would rapidly become fatally acidic. One other factor is operative. In response to the increase in plasma CO_2, recognized by the respiratory center in the brain, respiration is increased in both frequency and volume, so that the patient exhibits "air hunger." This effort removes much but not all of the excess CO_2.

If this process continues, without intervention, the patient becomes very seriously dehydrated (plasma and extracellular volumes are markedly reduced and the plasma sodium ion concentration is diminished), and because of the acidity of his plasma (acidosis) he may slip into coma. If untreated, either he will die of vascular collapse due to the dehydration, or the acidity may so damage the brain that the coma becomes irreversible. What then would be an appropriate therapeutic procedure? Patently insulin will terminate the events that gave rise to all this. Glucose, if provided, will reenter the liver which can then stop oxidizing so much fat — but neither can reverse the dehydration or acidosis and these are the acute threats to life.

Plasma volume and the neutrality of the blood (pH 7.4) can rapidly be restored by an infusion of a sufficient volume of a solution containing sodium chloride and sodium bicarbonate. But how much? This calculation requires a detailed knowledge of normal circumstances, and estimates of the deficit in plasma and extracellular fluid volume, the deficit in sodium, and the loss of bicarbonate. These are now made feasible by a series of readily performed determinations for plasma volume, sodium, chloride, bicarbonate, pH, and CO_2. The result is application of a rather precisely calculated infusion from a drip bottle of the kind now so familiar in hospital practice. There is now no excuse for death due to diabetic coma, once a major threat to life.

But in many instances, when normal circumstances had been restored, the patient, seemingly recovered, would suddenly develop a flaccid paralysis and die in cardiac failure. Closer inspection revealed that this was the consequence of the potassium loss which is aggravated by the fluid therapy. An estimate of plasma potassium and inclusion of this ion in the clysis now suffices to assure complete recovery but must be done with great care since an excess of potassium rapidly stops the heart in diastole. These procedures require the availability of a reliable, sophisticated clinical chemistry laboratory appropriately equipped; the materials to be administered are cheap and readily available.

Such episodes can be recounted many times over. Understanding of the underlying mechanisms, revealed by detailed study of plasma and tissue electrolytes, frequently using the radioisotopes of sodium and potassium, now provides the basis for rational diagnosis and therapy in such situations as acute diarrhea of infancy, pernicious vomiting, Addison's disease, hypoaldosteronism, diabetes insipidus, massive hemorrhage, various kidney diseases, and hysteric and meningitic alkalosis. Moreover, the intelligent application of these principles, in conjunction with antibiotics, and physiological monitoring techniques, has contributed enormously to the success of modern surgery, permitting the lengthy, complex maneuvers which occur daily in the operating rooms of every large hospital. And again, each of these experiments of nature has illuminated the mechanisms which normally maintain the constancy of the *milieu interieur*.

Cardiac Physiology. Assessment of Cardiac Hemodynamics. The primary problem of cardiac physiology is accurate estimation of blood

flow through the heart. In the decade 1920–30, Hamilton and his colleagues developed procedures whereby a burst of an indicator dye could
be injected upstream, blood samples taken for analysis at a distal point
and, from the exponential decay curve thus obtained, blood flow could
be calculated.

Twenty years later, it was demonstrated that thin, radiopaque catheters
could be introduced into the heart via peripheral blood vessels and
carefully positioned by fluoroscopy. With techniques for entering the
heart with safety and for assessing flow by the indicator dilution principle,
assessment of cardiac blood flow of man rapidly came into use in qualified
medical centers to obtain quantitative information concerning the functional status of the heart. The earlier analysis of vascular and intracardiac
pressure wave forms enhanced the clinical-physiological assessment of
patients undergoing laboratory procedures.

With the advent of techniques for direct surgical intervention for
repair of acquired and congenital anomalies of the heart, it became
imperative that there be made available to the surgeon, in advance,
precise information concerning specific functional and anatomical cardiac
abnormalities. The application of indicator dilution studies not only allowed assessment of cardiac output and stroke work per beat, but also,
detection of abnormal patterns produced by intracardiac defects with
intracardiac shunts. The systematic analysis of such data allowed the
detection of the site and magnitude of intracardiac shunts (blood flow
between the chambers of the heart through inappropriate channels)
and formed the initial basis for diagnostic and functional approaches to
congenital heart disease in patients considered for surgery. In acquired
heart disease, analysis of the details of the pressure wave form recorded
from various intracardiac chambers was essential in evaluating lesions
which produced obstruction or regurgitation at each of the operating sets
of valves.

During the past decade, these techniques have been extended to
provide direct evaluation of the functional characteristics and status of
cardiac muscle. Especially pertinent in the treatment of patients with
cardiac decompensation has been quantitative assessment of muscle function as regards its contractility. The work of A. V. Hill on skeletal
muscle, performed half a century earlier, provided the basis for the search
for a method to characterize heart muscle activity in terms of its force-
velocity-tension characteristics. Although there are considerable functional and ultrastructural differences between skeletal and cardiac
muscle, the development of conceptual and technical approaches to the
assessment of ventricular contractility in the human has become a major
quest in the evaluation of patients in cardiac failure.

Valuable information has recently been obtained describing the response of the heart to various types of abnormal mechanical overloads (obstruction and insufficiency of cardiac valves); this is especially useful in the selection of patients for cardiac surgery. This type of patient evaluation, requiring an elaborate laboratory facility, has demonstrated the importance of a quantitative physiological assessment which cannot be provided by purely "clinical" approaches. Thus, a major reorientation in patient management has occurred. Although it finds its origins in the physiology laboratory, most of the work has been performed with human subjects.

Recently, experimental laboratory models have been developed, in animals, to assess dimensional changes within the ventricles by direct transducer measurement techniques. This approach has been extended to clinical application with the advent of angiocardiography (x-ray visualization of the heart and associated vessels after injection of a radiopaque material). The demonstration of the existence of a family of ventricular function curves, depending upon the contractility of the heart, has been instrumental in the proper assessment of volume-pressure relationships in patients with a variety of lesions.

Neurogenic Influences on Cardiovascular System. The presence and functioning of the baroreceptors (pressure detectors) indicated the operation of important reflexogenic areas in the cardiovascular system. An important recently developed clinical application is the use of baroreceptor pacing as a means of reflex reduction of systemic blood pressure during episodes of angina pectoris.

Use of Electrical Stimuli to Alter Cardiac Function. Pacemakers, first used to control cardiac rate in animal physiological studies, have been employed in animal and human studies ever since it also was demonstrated that high-voltage DC shocks, delivered directly to the heart during episodes of ventricular or auricular fibrillation (rapid, irregular twitching of the fibrils of the heart muscles so that coordinated contraction, with pumping, cannot occur), produced reversion immediately to properly coordinated rhythms with return of normal cardiac function. It was further clarified, in animals, how long after the onset of chaotic rhythm restoration of normal function could still be expected. This work lay dormant for years. However, the information provided formed the basis for the development of techniques which now are commonplace as the first line attack in most serious cardiac arrhythmias.

In the 1950's Stokes-Adams attacks (syncope, loss of consciousness due to cerebral anemia) in patients with complete heart block came under intensive scrutiny of clinical cardiologists. Pacemakers were developed which operate by implantation of electrodes directly in the heart.

This has evolved as the optimal therapy for patients with heart block (muscular interconnection between auricle and ventricle is interrupted so that they beat independently of each other); permanent pacemaking prevents Stokes-Adams attacks, as well as cardiac failure due to extremely slow ventricular rates.

The use of high-voltage DC shock therapy has been extrapolated from early physiological studies in animals to the point that ventricular fibrillation, previously a universally lethal phenomenon, is now correctable in a high percentage of cases when diagnosed and treated promptly. An example of the extreme alteration in patient management made possible by this advance is evident in the experience of clinical cardiac catheterization laboratories. Prior to the development of high-voltage DC shock therapy for cardioversion (restoration of normal rhythm), ventricular fibrillation was the major lethal complication that could develop in such procedures. Currently, the appearance of ventricular fibrillation during cardiac catheterization is associated with practically no mortality and is no longer considered a major complication because of the efficacy of this mode of cardioversion.

Cardiac Electrophysiology. The basic nature of various cardiac arrhythmias and their genesis has been clarified markedly by the development of techniques for assessment of transmembrane action potentials in the beating heart. The functional refractory state of cardiac muscle as related to electrical repolarization has become a key area for evaluation of timing of local excitatory events for establishing abnormal arrhythmias from reentrant mechanisms. This information has been of marked importance in the clinical assessment of patients with myocardial infarction. The ischemic (bloodless) tissue around the infarct is associated with considerably slower than normal propagation of wave fronts detectable by electrocardiography. The ischemic muscle thus provides an important source for reentry of electrical wave fronts for the establishment of ventricular fibrillation, a common fatal arrhythmia following infarction. With this information, and the high-voltage DC shock therapy previously described, the mortality from myocardial infarction in the acute phase has been so reduced that with proper monitoring patients rarely die from arrhythmias now. Interestingly, with the establishment of cardiac care units, this important electrophysiological information and new method of treatment has limited the mortality from myocardial infarction almost solely to "power failure," rather than from arrhythmias.

Clinical electrocardiography has undergone a major reorientation. Techniques were developed for direct exploration of animal hearts to determine the mode of propagation of electrical impulses throughout the ventricles. The knowledge so provided established models for the electrical sequence of normal ventricular excitation as well as the sequence in several abnormal conditions, such as bundle branch block (interventricular block so that left and right ventricles beat independently). This has led to greatly improved diagnostic interpretation of clinical electrocardiograms with a firmer physiological base for interpretation. This information has also had a profound influence on the development of improved clinical electrocardiographic approaches. Studies of the total body surface potential distribution have demonstrated that electrical information is available on the body surface which represents selective intracardiac events. This has led to the development of techniques to view isopotential surface maps in humans. This recent development has already provided important information previously unobtainable. By this means, it is possible to detect myocardial infarcts, and the site of infarction, in isopotential surface maps, whereas such information is not available in routine electrocardiograms. This has marked importance for the detection and assessment of undiagnosed heart disease.

Antiarrhythmic Drugs. In view of the extreme clinical significance of arrhythmias, there has been long-standing interest in drugs that could reestablish normal cardiac rhythm. The first clinical trial of an effective antiarrhythmic agent was initiated by Wenckebach, in 1912, who found that quinine alkaloids were effective in controlling heart rate in a limited number of cases of atrial fibrillation. In 1918, Frey compared several cinchona alkaloids and found quinidine to be most effective. Over the next forty years there were many studies on the pharmacological basis for the action of quinidine and similar drugs and on the clinical use of quinidine. However, no equally effective drug was found until the introduction of procaine amide in 1951. Quinidine and procaine amide exert essentially similar pharmacological actions in animals and man. Both depress the contractility of the heart and similarly affect electrical activity, decreasing automaticity (impulse formation), conductivity, and excitability and prolonging refractoriness (time lag between beats). Both drugs thus have a similar range of clinical use and have similar toxic actions on the cardiovascular system. In excess, both produce conduction disturbances, including heart block, and serious arrhythmias, including ventricular fibrillation. Of the multitude of new drugs tested up to 1960, few were found to have limited clinical applicability; these again were similar to quinidine in their mode of action. Quinidine and procaine amide remain the most frequently used antiarrhythmic agents.

This failure of numerous attempts to develop more effective, more specific, or less toxic drugs for the control of cardiac rhythm resulted in large measure from the facts that the mechanisms responsible for many arrhythmias were unknown, and the effects of quinidinelike drugs on the electrical activity of the heart were imperfectly understood.

As we have noted, understanding of the electrical basis for impulse formation and conduction in the heart was given an important impetus when it became possible to record transmembrane potentials of single cardiac fibers through intracellular microelectrodes. By means of this technique, and the advantages it afforded to other studies, during the next ten years it was possible to characterize, in large part, the ionic basis for electrical activity of the heart and to identify the unique electrical properties of important specialized cells. Also, the ability to record directly from normal and ectopic cardiac pacemaker cells permitted an understanding of the electrical mechanisms responsible for the normal control of cardiac rate and rhythm by such factors as acetylcholine and norepinephrine, and variations, in extracellular ionic environment. These studies showed that a drug might cause a similar change in excitability, or threshold to electrical stimulation, by acting on independent variables such as the magnitude of the resting potential, the magnitude of the threshold potential or the availability of "sodium carriers."

As a result of these studies on cardiac cell transmembrane potentials it was possible to reevaluate classical studies of cardiac excitability made by use of extracellular electrodes and to define in terms of identifiable mechanisms such concepts as excitability, threshold, and refractoriness. The details of such studies are beyond the scope of this chapter. Suffice it to say that a highly detailed, albeit incomplete, picture has been developed describing each of the major clinical arrhythmias. Importantly, a beginning has been made in establishing the fundamental cellular mechanisms involved in the generation of transmembrane potentials — the basis for conduction of the impulse that triggers contraction — and the manner in which these are affected by available drugs.

A major advance resulted from a study of Weidmann which was concerned with the relationship between membrane potential and the inward sodium current caused by excitation, and the modification of this relationship by calcium, cocaine, and quinidine. The availability of sodium carrier, and thus the intensity of depolarizing current during the upstroke of the action potential, is related to the magnitude of membrane potential at the moment of excitation by an S-shaped curve. At potentials greater than -90 mV, inward current is maximal; at potentials less than -55 mV, inward current approaches zero. At intermediate values of membrane potential, inward current is reduced. A reduction in availability of Na^+ carrier, resulting from a membrane potential lower than -90 mV, causes a decrease in the inward sodium current during the upstroke of the action potential; usually, a decrease in the magnitude of the action potential would result in a decrease in conduction velocity and safety factor for propagation, and an increase in the likelihood of block or other conduction abnormalities.

This simple relationship explains, in part, such characteristics of cardiac fibers as absolute and effective refractoriness, changes in conduction velocity of premature responses, effects of changes in excitability on conduction (for alterations in excitability caused by a change in threshold potential or a change in resting potential), and several of the means by which the pattern of responsiveness of cardiac cells might be changed.

Evidence for the last point came from studies on the actions of calcium, cocaine, and quinidine. An increase in the concentration of extracellular Ca^{++} was shown to shift the curve en bloc to the left, to lower values of membrane potential. A decrease in Ca^{++} concentration had the opposite effect. High (toxic) concentrations of quinidine, on the other hand, not only shifted the curve to the right, to higher values of membrane potential, but also depressed the maximum inward current elicited at normal or increased resting potentials. These actions would cause an increase in effective refractoriness and a decrease in conduction velocity.

The results of these experiments permitted a new understanding both of the mechanisms responsible for changes in electrical activity and of actions of drugs modifying electrical activity; most of the recent important findings on the mode of action of antiarrhythmic drugs have resulted from the use of microelectrode techniques and Weidmann's presentation of the relationship between membrane potential and responsiveness. Thus, there is now available a rational, sensitive assay which should permit a screening program which, hopefully, may one day provide a battery of effective drugs, specific for the various cardiac arrhythmias.

Cardiac Surgery. The advent of cardiac surgery is one of the most dramatic episodes in the history of medicine. That it should have come so late must be attributed to the complexity of the many essentials necessary to support such surgery, essentials only recently discovered or developed and derived from a host of fields often seemingly quite remote from medicine. This is best illustrated by the instrument that has become the sine qua non of modern heart surgery: the heart-lung machine.

This machine takes over the function of the heart and lungs during the time of operation when the heart has been opened and a defect such as an abnormal, scarred, and immobile valve or a congenital hole between the two ventricles (pumping chambers) is being repaired by valve replacement or closure of the hole, or one of the major vessels is being repaired by removal of a severely damaged portion which is replaced by an appropriately designed plastic tube. In order to do this the blood from the upper and lower portions of the body is drained by plastic tubes into an oxygenator. In this chamber, venous blood from the body receives gaseous oxygen and gives off carbon dioxide. The blood then passes through a heat exchanger to maintain it at the desired temperature. The blood is then returned to the aorta, the major artery of the body, by a pulsatile pump. This apparatus was first used successfully in man in 1953, but years of apparently unrelated research in a variety of disciplines were required to make it possible.

William Harvey, discoverer of the circulation of the blood, was also first to recognize the true nature of the heart, which he likened to a water pump. The double-valve, one-way pump was developed in the fifteenth and early sixteenth centuries to draw water from deep mines. This "water bellows" appears to have provided an essential concept in Harvey's eventual discovery of the circulation.

In the nineteenth century, physiologists tried to duplicate the work of the heart by perfusion of various animal organs such as the kidney and liver, using a pump, in order better to understand the functions of these organs. In time, attempts were made to add oxygen and remove carbon dioxide from the blood used to perfuse the organ. These crude instruments were the forerunners of the modern heart-lung machine. They lacked, however, several important refinements. All parts were made of glass, rubber, or a metal such as brass. Since these experiments were short term and survival of the organ was not essential, damage to blood cells was not important. However, this is clearly vital to human application. Not until the development of the plastics industry could this problem be solved. Plastics such as the polyvinyls are nearly inert; their smooth, nonwetting surfaces cause minimal mechanical damage to blood cells. Similarly glass surfaces can today be coated with silicone compounds. Highly polished, inert stainless steel coated with silicone compounds also affects blood only minimally. If blood is oxygenated by passing the gaseous oxygen through it, the resultant foam offers a serious hazard to the patient and seriously damages both blood platelets and erythrocytes. Not until the development of silicone antifoaming agents was this vexing problem solved.

A most important prelude to the successful application of the heart-lung machine was the isolation and purification of heparin, a sulfated polysaccharide present in liver and lung which is highly effective in inhibiting blood clotting. With heparin, clotting, which is initiated when blood comes into contact with surfaces outside blood vessels, can be inhibited and blood passed through a complex apparatus for short periods. Normal clottability can again be induced by the administration of protamine at the end of the perfusion through the heart-lung machine.

In 1931, John Gibbon, a surgeon, watched a patient die from a blood clot that had become lodged in the pulmonary artery, the main artery to the lungs. Previous attempts to remove such clots usually had been fatal, since the entire output from the right side of the heart passes through this artery and there was no way of getting at the clot unless the heart and lungs could be bypassed. For the next two decades, Gibbon and others devoted themselves to the problem of heart-lung bypass. By drawing on the accumulated experience of physiologists, they developed a pulsatile pump that could return blood to the aorta without significantly damaging the red blood cells. The blood was oxygenated by allowing it to film over a series of vertical stainless steel screens surrounded by oxygen in a plastic box. By 1939, they could bypass the heart and lungs of a dog for rather long periods, with complete recovery.

Nevertheless, operations on human hearts were still remote. Cardiac surgery could not be attempted, even by the boldest surgeon, unless he was absolutely certain of the diagnosis and nature of the lesion he would encounter. This was provided by the intracardiac catheterization procedures described earlier. Independently, other surgeons had begun to operate on the heart and its great vessels, but they were limited to operating on the closed heart. Only by "blind" methods could such problems as scarred and closed heart valves be attacked. However, they initiated a new epoch, stimulating investigators in a variety of fields to help solve the problem of cardiac surgery. Advances in anesthesia, improved preoperative and postoperative care and blood bank techniques contributed much to these often dramatic results in an area where, previously, little hope could be offered.

In 1952, these developments were brought to a climax with the successful use of a cardiopulmonary bypass to perform an open-heart operation upon a young girl with a hole between the atria, the receiving chambers of the heart. This was the culmination of years of investigative work by physiologists, surgeons, physicians, engineers, and industrial chemists. Many refinements have since made the heart-lung machine safer and more readily available. Artificial heart valves, developed in collaboration with engineers, are in common use. Today, attempts to substitute the entire heart are in progress. But much still remains to be done. Oxygenators causing far less trauma than those currently in use will be required if heart-lung bypass is to be applied in a more prolonged manner than at present. The need for such techniques is evident in patients with serious but reversible lung diseases such as the respiratory distress syndrome (hyaline membrane disease) of the newborn. The use of artificial pumps either to partially or completely support the circulation in patients with a "heart attack" is a logical approach and has already been attempted. But this is far from a routine procedure and much investigative work is still required. Whether ultimately the entire heart will be replaced by a mechanical device cannot as yet be answered. Such problems as power source, regulation of pump output, and blood clotting on the foreign surfaces still vex those working on an artificial replacement of the heart.

If the idea of the pump oxygenator originated with the physiologist, he too has been greatly benefited by its sophistication in the hands of surgeons and engineers, for today the very same instrument used in the operating room forms a basic tool in the hands of the physiologist who still is learning more about the complex mechanisms of the heart and lungs. And, one day, the information so gathered will further aid physicians and surgeons in the battle against heart disease.

Hypertension. Arterial hypertension, or high blood pressure, is a disorder that illustrates the value of understanding based on physiological research. Although the causes of most hypertensive disease are unknown, enough is understood about the control of blood pressure to reduce it significantly, in most cases, with a favorable effect on the course of the disorder.

Sustained hypertension damages medium-sized and small arteries, causing impairment of the blood supply to affected body regions, particularly in the brain, heart, and kidneys. Large portions of these organs may be destroyed suddenly when a damaged artery of medium size is closed by a blood clot. Diffuse, gradually progressive destruction may be caused by small artery damage. Occasionally, bleeding occurs from a weakened vessel, especially in the brain. The heart may be overworked by pumping against high pressure until its delivery rate falls chronically below the minimum needed to maintain the health of other organs. Directly or indirectly, hypertension is a major cause of stroke, myocardial infarction, chronic heart failure, and uremia. These ill effects usually develop after many years of hypertension, but they can appear much more quickly in persons whose blood pressure is unusually high. This severe hypertension is said to be "accelerated" or "malignant." In about 15 percent of cases, high blood pressure is secondary to some well-recognized disorder such as decreased blood supply to a kidney, diffuse kidney disease of various kinds, or tumors of the cortex or medulla of the adrenal gland. In all other cases, the cause is unknown and the disease is then called "essential hypertension."

Approximately 10 percent of people become hypertensive. In 1965 some 66,000 deaths in the United States were reported as primarily caused by this disorder. Hypertension undoubtedly contributed to other deaths as well, especially in persons with arteriosclerotic cardiovascular or cerebral vascular disease.

Although many deaths are still caused by hypertension, there has been a striking change in recent years. From 1955 to 1965 the age-adjusted death rate from this cause has decreased by 45 percent. There is good evidence that this reflects a real change in the disease itself, not just a difference in the use of diagnostic terms. There are probably several reasons for the decreased death rate from hypertension, but the progressive development of methods to control blood pressure during the past fifteen years has certainly played a major part. The control of hypertension has not resulted from any single discovery, but rather has depended on a growing understanding of normal and abnormal circulatory function. The gains that have come from understanding can be appreciated by a brief survey of some of the pertinent research advances and the applications of this knowledge to the management of hypertension.

Arterial blood pressure, maintained by the pumping force of the heart, is regulated primarily by the degree of contraction or "tone" of the small resistance arteries, the arterioles. Arteriolar tone is controlled in part by the nervous system and in part by a variety of circulating substances.

As discovered by Claude Bernard and others over a hundred years ago, the nervous connections to blood vessels, the vasomotor nerves, are distributed primarily by way of the sympathetic nervous system, the paired chain of nerves and ganglia lying on either side of the vertebral column. It is connected, on the one hand, with the spinal cord and, on the other, with the various effector organs such as the small muscle fibers which regulate the size of blood vessels. The parasympathetic system is closely related. Together these constitute the autonomic nervous system; its relay stations or ganglia, central connections, and distribution of different kinds of peripheral nerve fibers, both vasoconstrictor and vasodilator, have been worked out. In the decades 1920–40 it was established that nervous impulses are transmitted through autonomic ganglia by the mediation of acetylcholine, which also transmits vasodilator impulses to vessel walls from the terminal fibers of both parasympathetic and sympathetic systems. Norepinephrine is the transmitter of sympathetic vasoconstrictor impulses from nerve fibers to vessels. Vasoconstriction raises blood pressure and vasodilation lowers it.

The sympathetic system normally maintains some vasoconstrictor tone. This tone is adjusted reflexly to resist changes in blood pressure which is sensed by "baroceptor" regions in the aorta and carotid arteries. It is also responsive to impulses from the central nervous system and to various blood-borne substances. Occasionally hypertension in man is caused by tumors of sympathetic origin which secrete the excitor substances epinephrine and norepinephrine.

The Renin-Hypertensin System. One of the better examples of the eventual direct application of information obtained in the physiology laboratory to the clinical care of patients is the link between the renin-angiotensin system and hypertension. In 1934, Goldblatt demonstrated conclusively that a form of hypertension similar to essential hypertension in humans could be produced by constricting the renal artery of dogs. It was quickly proposed that this was due to the release of a humoral agent. Over the course of thirty years, it was found that the affected kidney releases into the circulation a specific proteolytic enzyme, renin, which catalyzes the removal from a normal protein constituent of plasma, hypertensinogen, of a polypeptide with ten amino acid residues. This decapeptide, hypertensin I, has no physiological activity but, from it, there is cleaved by an enzyme present in normal plasma the terminal dipeptide histidyl leucine. The remaining octapeptide, hypertensin II, is the most powerful pressor agent known. Plasma from persons with essential hypertension contains hypertensin II in amounts sufficient to account for their hypertensive disease. This agent has a direct effect on the arterioles, resulting in their constriction. At the same time, it stimulates release of the hormone aldosterone by the adrenal cortex. This hormone mediates the retention of sodium by the kidney. The resulting increase in extracellular fluid volume, and the swelling of arteriolar walls, further increases the already elevated blood pressure.

All of this information was gleaned in animal studies. The next step was the development of a clinically applicable group of tests using this information to evaluate patients with renal vascular lesions and hypertension. It is now possible to determine with some certainty those patients whose hypertension would be cured by corrective vascular surgery on the renal arteries. Prior to the application of these techniques, there was no reliable means for making this distinction preoperatively; all too many patients were subjected to surgery without subsequent improvement in blood pressure. Recognition of the relationship of the renin-hypertensin system to the release of aldosterone has also made it possible to select those hypertensive patients whose elevated blood pressure is due to an aldosterone-secreting tumor of the adrenal gland. This has led to the early detection and subsequent cure of many patients with hypertension.

As predicted from these considerations, experimental hypertension has been produced by sectioning the nerve supply of the baroceptors, by restricting blood supply to the kidneys, and by combined administration of salt and aldosterone or desoxycorticosterone. The means by which sodium acts is not altogether clear, but in both human and experimental hypertension, sodium loading raises blood pressure and sodium deprivation lowers it.

Understanding of these mechanisms and development of appropriate diagnostic procedures permits identification and often surgical cure of those special varieties of human hypertension caused by functioning endocrine tumors and impairment of the blood flow to one kidney. In "essential" hypertension, blood pressure can frequently be controlled by drugs designed to reduce vascular tone through interference with the means by which tone is normally maintained. Some examples will be illustrative:

Agents such as hexamethonium and pentolinium reduce vascular tone and blood pressure by suppressing transmission of impulses through autonomic ganglia. Their action is often hard to control, however, and undesirable side effects are produced by blocking parasympathetic as well as sympathetic nerve impulses. They were used for a time with considerable success but have now been replaced by newer drugs.

Reserpine, a compound of plant origin, is a widely used antihypertensive drug. It decreases the content of norepinephrine and serotonin in the brain, has some tranquilizing action, but probably reduces vascular tone primarily by depleting norepinephrine stores in sympathetic nerve endings. This lowers vasoconstrictor tone.

Guanethidine is a potent antihypertensive agent which blocks the release of norepinephrine from sympathetic nerve endings. It does not affect the parasympathetic system and thus avoids some of the side effects of the general autonomic ganglion blockers. The drug is especially valuable in severe hypertension.

Some useful drugs were first identified as inhibitors of enzymes involved in norepinephrine biosynthesis and metabolism. One of these, α-methyldioxyphenylalanine, is an effective, widely employed antihypertensive agent. α-Methyltyrosine, which blocks norepinephrine synthesis in man, has found use in patients with inoperable norepinephrine-producing tumors. Inhibitors of the enzyme monoamine oxidase impair the normal degradation of epinephrine and norepinephrine and, paradoxically, have been found to reduce blood pressure and have also been employed in the treatment of hypertension.

The development of effective antihypertensive drugs has been made possible by the understanding of circulatory regulation provided by physiological and biochemical research. These drugs have prolonged many lives and prevented much disability; some forms of hypertension may now be cured. These significant advances in the management of clinical hypertension have depended on research in the general field of circulatory control, not necessarily specifically directed toward any disease. With continued broad-based research there is every reason to expect continued progress.

Diuretics. Diuretics interfere with the mechanisms by which kidneys retain salt, primarily, and water, secondarily. They are useful, often lifesaving drugs for the treatment of disorders in which dietary salt and water intake exceeds output. Dangerous accumulation of salt and water (edema) is most likely to occur in heart failure, in liver and renal disease, and in hypertension. Until 1950, the only effective diuretics were organic mercurials which, because of potential toxic reactions, could not be administered sufficiently frequently to maintain patients in water and salt balance. Clearly, there was a desperate need for an orally effective diuretic that could be taken as frequently as necessary. But at this juncture, no "crash program" of applied research could have met this need, for there was no theoretical background to guide the pharmaceutical chemist in his attempts to synthesize an effective drug. No one could have predicted that this background would be furnished by data obtained in the course of research that, initially, was unrelated to the function of the kidney or the development of diuretics.

Early in the history of the sulfonamides it was noted that persons so treated excreted an alkaline urine and developed a moderate acidosis. Keilin and Mann had just discovered that sulfanilamide is an inhibitor of the enzyme carbonic anhydrase, which catalyzes the simple hydration and dehydration of carbon dioxide,

$$CO_2 + H_2O \rightleftharpoons H_2CO_3$$

the rate of which, surprisingly, limits the escape of CO_2 from blood as it traverses the lungs. When this enzyme was also found to be present in quantity in the kidney, the basis for the effect of sulfanilamide became apparent. Knowing the basic requirements necessary for carbonic anhydrase inhibitory activity, chemists could now begin to fashion a molecule more effective than sulfanilamide. A new drug, acetazolamide (Diamox), became available in 1950 and was the first orally effective, potent diuretic. Happily, it also proved to be the first successful agent for treatment of glaucoma, hypersecretion of fluid in the anterior chamber of the eye.

This drug was not only useful clinically, it was also of great importance for two other reasons. First, it represented the beginning of a rational scientific approach to seeking and evaluating new diuretics, i.e., relating chemical structures to renal mechanisms. Second, it became extremely useful as a physiological tool in enabling renal physiologists to evaluate the role of carbonic anhydrase in renal transport processes. It was of prime importance in elucidating the renal mechanisms of bicarbonate reabsorption and hydrogen secretion; the concepts thus developed have been amply supported since by direct renal micropuncture experiments.

This development then had important influence on clinical care of patients, because the new understanding in physiology enabled a prediction of the specific electrolyte losses in the urine produced by drugs. Hence, derangements in acid-base and electrolyte metabolism of the body fluids could be anticipated, and marked life-threatening deviations from normal could be prevented by appropriate treatment with various acids, bases, and salts.

Although acetazolamide was safe, it could not be used continuously because it promoted retention of acid and, once acidosis had developed, was no longer effective. It was this particular difficulty that kept the search for better diuretics alive in the years from 1950 to 1955. The reward was chlorothiazide (Diuril), a compound constructed about the same active chemical moiety as acetazolamide. The discovery of chlorothiazide was one of the great achievements of modern pharmacology. Not only was it found to be an excellent diuretic which can be given to the ambulatory, nonhospitalized patient, but also it lowered blood pressure. So great was its impact that the number of prescriptions for diuretics in the United States increased sixfold in the five-year period following its introduction for general use in 1958. Withal, the actual basis for the effect on chloride excretion remains without explanation.

As physicians learned more about chlorothiazide, several drawbacks became apparent. Many patients who had severe congestive heart failure or various other diseases with massive edema could not be controlled with the drug. Moreover, urinary excretion of potassium was often so pronounced that serious cardiac disturbances and muscular weakness occurred. What was still needed was a diuretic that could be used in small doses to control salt and water balance of most patients, in large doses for patients with severe, refractory edema, and which in addition would not increase excretion of potassium.

At first chemists merely modified the chlorothiazide molecule. This resulted in the development of several potent diuretics whose effects occur at dose levels below those required with chlorothiazide, but no more efficacious drugs. And all increased excretion of potassium. Obviously, a new approach was needed. Pharmaceutical chemists then turned to aldosterone, the adrenal hormone that causes retention of sodium and loss of potassium from the body. Several compounds were synthesized which structurally resemble aldosterone so that they can displace the hormone from sites where it is normally bound in the kidney, yet are sufficiently different so that they do not possess the pharmacological actions of aldosterone. By thus occupying the effector sites of the natural hormone, they function as competitive inhibitors and thereby prevent excessive excretion of potassium. These new drugs did not entirely solve the potassium problem; there was still danger that the amount of potassium held in the body could increase above normal levels, but they did prove useful and, by 1965, diuretic therapy was better than ever.

As knowledge increased and problems of diuretic therapy became clearer, applied research became less empirical. No longer was it necessary to screen chemical compounds at random.

This led to a new drug, ethacrynic acid, which is so effective that physicians must use it with great caution. Patients who would never have responded to any previous diuretic are now being treated successfully with ethacrynic acid. Another new agent, however, furosemide, owes its existence to basic studies with chlorothiazide and related compounds. Both of these new drugs were discovered to be at least as potent as mercurials in man and possessed the advantage over the older drugs that they could be administered both orally and intravenously. With the addition of these two effective drugs, it is now possible to treat successfully abnormal fluid accumulation in almost all patients who have nondiseased kidneys and who are not in the terminal phases of their disease.

"Third Factor." Most recently there has been demonstrated, by a study in dogs, a new hormone, "third factor," which appears to play a significant role in the production of edema in clinical conditions such as heart failure, nephrotic syndrome, acute glomerulonephritis, and cirrhosis. Individuals with these disorders develop an inability to excrete sodium, with consequent edema. Recent observations suggest that in addition to the glomerular filtration rate in the kidney and aldosterone (factors I and II), there is a third factor which strongly influences the renal handling of sodium without effect on potassium. Normally, the effect of this hormone is to increase sodium excretion in response to overexpansion of the intravascular volume. Intensive work is currently under way to isolate, purify, and characterize this hormone. A sensitive bioassay has been developed now which can detect this substance in the plasma in both normal and sick patients. This problem is at a stage comparable to that of the renin-hypertensin system ten years ago and would appear to have great potential clinical usefulness in the management of disease states characterized by edema.

Coincidental with the testing of compounds in the laboratories of the drug companies were scientific investigations by physiologists and pharmacologists in the research laboratories of the universities, medical schools, and the National Institutes of Health. Evaluation of the mode of action of these drugs in the kidney was important both in predicting complications of diuretic therapy and in gaining new information about renal physiological mechanisms. The use of thiazides, ethacrynic acid, and furosemide as physiological tools has led to new insights into the renal mechanisms of urinary dilution and concentration. It has been shown that there are at least two sites of urinary dilution in the nephron, a thiazide-sensitive site and an ethacrynic acid-sensitive site. Furthermore, the fact that ethacrynic acid and furosemide, agents with major sites of action in the loop of Henle, are such powerful natruretic agents, stimulated a re-evaluation of the quantitative importance of the distal portion of the nephron with regard to sodium reabsorption and the regulation of sodium excretion. These new physiological discoveries directly improved understanding of the various renal sodium retaining mechanisms operative in congestive heart failure and other edematous states. They will certainly lead to more rational preventative approaches to edema as well as to improvements in therapy.

Contributions of Pulmonary Physiology to Medicine. The exchange of oxygen and carbon dioxide in the lungs and the carriage of these gases in the blood have fascinated physiologists for many years. Knowledge derived from study of these processes was used in the 1940's for equipping man for high-altitude flight, first with oxygen masks and then with pressurized aircraft cabins, and it is being used to prepare him for exploring outer space and the ocean floor. Some of the research basically supporting these efforts was stimulated by specific needs, but much of it was done simply to gain additional understanding of normal function.

Advances in respiratory physiology have also had important applications in clinical medicine. The understanding and techniques developed through the study of normal function have also allowed us to appreciate and to measure the functional abnormalities caused by disease, thereby enhancing the ability to diagnose lung disease correctly and to treat it effectively. Here we shall consider how some elements of respiratory physiology have been applied to the problems of medicine.

In resting normal man, about 4 liters of air and 5 liters of blood, per minute, pass through the gas-exchanging portions of the lungs. The great air passages of the lung, after many subdivisions, terminate in a great number of tiny air sacs, the alveoli, richly equipped with capillary blood vessels. Gas exchange occurs between alveolar air and capillaries, with the absorption of about 250 ml of oxygen and the discharge of about 200 ml of carbon dioxide per minute. Oxygen and carbon dioxide pass between alveolar gas and capillary blood by simple diffusion. This process is so effective, and ventilation is so well distributed in relation to blood perfusion over the lung, that the pressures of oxygen and carbon dioxide in the arterial blood are very close to their pressures in alveolar gas, about 100 mm Hg for oxygen and 40 mm Hg for carbon dioxide. With exercise, the rates of oxygen consumption and carbon dioxide production can be many times greater than at rest, but ventilation is normally so closely adjusted to the metabolic rate that the arterial blood gas tensions change very little.

The proper function of the respiratory system depends upon the co-ordinated function of several elements, each of which can be affected by disease. The central nervous system must adjust the ventilation rate to need. The muscular and bony structures of the chest cage must work as an effective bellows. The airway resistance of the lung and its elasticity must be so balanced that the inspired air is well distributed. The blood exchanging surfaces must be of adequate size and quality to handle the required diffusion rates. Modern clinical medicine makes use of a variety of tests to evaluate the function of these components separately and together. Although greatly refined by present-day technology, many of these tests are based on principles and concepts that had their origin in the physiology laboratories of an earlier day. Others are quite recent. Nearly all derive originally from studies of normal function.

Measurements of the oxygen, carbon dioxide, and hydrogen ion concentration, or pH, in arterial blood is helpful because they reflect the overall effectiveness of the effort to aerate the blood. These measurements, together with understanding of the means by which oxygen and carbon dioxide are carried in the blood, often shed much light on the nature of the lung disease present. For example, disease that lowers arterial blood oxygen but does not elevate carbon dioxide may be caused by either a diffuse disorder or one that involves only a part of the lungs. However, significant elevation of carbon dioxide with decrease in oxygen means very widespread impairment of alveolar ventilation. The ability thus to monitor and interpret blood gas changes allows the physician to take appropriate, remedial action which is often lifesaving. Tests of the various properties of the lung itself fall into several general categories such as measurements of lung volumes, ventilating ability, the mechanical properties of the lung, blood and gas distribution within the lung, and the pulmonary diffusing capacity. Measurement of these properties allows quantitation of lung disease and indicates something about the kind of disease present. Serial measurements allow one to follow the course of the disorder and evaluate the effect of treatment.

Lung volumes may be reduced, as in disease that scars the lungs, or increased, as in obstructive pulmonary emphysema, which leads to over-inflation of the lungs. Ventilatory function, the ability to move air in and out of the lungs with normal speed and ease, is often impaired by lung disease, and the impairment can be measured in a variety of ways. The mechanical properties of the lung, primarily airway resistance and pulmonary compliance (a function of lung elasticity), are markedly affected by diffuse lung disease and are being measured with increasing frequency. The measurement of airway resistance has recently been facilitated by the use of the body plethysmograph, which was introduced by pulmonary physiologists. This allows speedy and comfortable estimation of the resting lung volume and the airway resistance and provides a most convenient way of following the effects of treatment in chronic bronchitis and obstructive pulmonary emphysema.

There are many tests for detecting uneven mixing of blood and gas in the lungs, but they have had only limited clinical usefulness. Although they can quantitate defective mixing, they cannot localize the trouble. The recent development of radioisotopic scanning techniques is beginning to allow localization of lung regions in which mixing is especially defective; some of these conditions can be helped by surgery. Measurements of the pulmonary diffusing capacity for carbon monoxide permit an estimate of the effective gas-exchanging function of the lung. This has prognostic value in some common varieties of lung disease. In certain conditions the diffusing capacity may be definitely reduced while the lungs still appear normal by x-ray. Pulmonary function tests have added much to the diagnosis and management of chest disease and are now established as an essential part of the chest physician's armamentarium.

The development of breathing-assist devices and respirators is based on the specifications provided by pulmonary physiologists in the course of studying the mechanical properties of the lung and chest wall and the processes of gas exchange within the lungs. Work which had been accomplished many years before by Rohrer, Neergard, and others provided the substantial base for the advances made by pulmonary physiologists during World War II. In particular, Fenn and his associates clarified the performance requirements of pressure-cycled respirators and related apparatus. This fundamental work allowed rational, systematic approaches to the design of respirators for patients with various disorders, particularly those with high airway resistance. It has also been basic to the development of anesthesiology.

One of the most dramatic examples of the practical utility of respiratory physiology is provided by the recognition and management of severe respiratory insufficiency, especially when precipitated by the injudicious administration of oxygen. Persons with such disorders as chronic bronchitis and emphysema, which limit the ability to breathe freely, may become severely ill when their breathing capacity is still further reduced by an acute respiratory illness. The blood oxygen falls, the carbon dioxide rises, and the patient becomes weakened and somnolent. In certain of these cases the administration of high concentrations of oxygen has an untoward effect. Although the blood oxygen deficit is relieved, this also removes some of the stimulus to breathing, ventilation is still further reduced, and the carbon dioxide which is being continuously produced by metabolism accumulates dangerously. These patients become extremely acidotic and quickly lose consciousness. Unless ventilation is improved they will die in relatively short order. The condition can also occur without administration of oxygen. The diagnosis of critical respiratory insufficiency is made by appropriate measurements of the arterial blood, and the essential element of treatment is the improvement of ventilation, often by a respirator. This state, sometimes called "carbon dioxide narcosis," owes both its recognition and its treatment to the background provided by studies in respiratory physiology.

The interest of physiologists and clinicians in the coordinated processes of breathing and the circulation of blood through the lungs was one of the stimuli to the development of intracardiac catheterization as a technique suitable for use in human beings. With the catheters in place, the pressure cycle in different heart chambers can be recorded and samples of blood from various sites can be analyzed for their gas content. Radiopaque substances, injected through the catheters, allow x-ray visualization of the heart's interior. This technique has greatly increased understanding of the function of the heart and lungs in health and disease, indicating clearly whether inadequate aeration of the blood is the consequence of disordered pulmonary or cardiac function.

Atherosclerosis. Atherosclerosis is among the major medical problems of the economically developed nations. Characteristically, it commences with deposition of a mixture of lipids, among which cholesterol is prominent, on and in the walls of the great blood vessels. This may be followed by mineralization with calcium salts. The resulting structure becomes weak and brittle, susceptible to rupture by the repeated pounding of the "water hammer" action of the heart. In time, this results in such phenomena as aneurysm of one of the large vessels, formation of blood clots, occlusion or rupture of smaller vessels in the heart's own circulation (coronary arteries) or of lesser vessels in the brain (stroke). In our society the deposition may begin in early childhood; certainly it is established in adolescence. Few Americans have "clean" aortae. There is no reason to believe, however, that this process is a necessary concomitant of the passage of time.

In a general way, those so afflicted exhibit elevated concentrations of blood lipids, notably cholesterol. That this high level, of itself, contributes significantly to the atherosclerotic process has been evident from the very high incidence of hypertension and atherosclerotic disease in persons with poorly controlled diabetes, all of whom have very high serum lipids, and in those relatively rare individuals with "familial hypercholesterolemia"—viz., extremely elevated lipids despite a normal diet and no signs of other causative or associated disease. Moreover, epidemiological studies indicate relatively lower concentration of serum cholesterol in populations, such as that of the Mediterranean basin, who ingest large quantities of vegetable oils rather than animal fats, and among whom serious atherosclerotic disease is decidedly less frequent than in the United States, Denmark, Germany, or Great Britain. There seems little doubt that relatively high intake of fat of animal origin (saturated fat in the sense of the absence of double bonds in the aliphatic chains of the fatty acids) tends to raise cholesterol levels while unsaturated fat of plant origin has an opposing effect. As yet, long-term studies of the consequence of eating various mixtures of these fats have failed to reveal whether one can, thereby, deliberately avoid or reverse atherosclerosis.

In the hope of treating those with advanced atherosclerotic disease, or permitting others of us to enjoy our normal dietary regimens, much effort has been expended in the hunt for "hypolipidemic" agents. Such studies are now in train and it is too early to evaluate them. One can only indicate the approaches now employed.

The ultimate fate of cholesterol is oxidation of its side chains to the corresponding "bile acids." These normally are secreted in the bile and then, in large part, are reabsorbed in the small intestine, returning to the liver for another cycle. There is some evidence that the availability of the bile acids determines the rate at which cholesterol is to be oxidized. Accordingly, one approach is to feed relatively large quantities of an ion-exchange resin (an anion exchanger) which then binds the bile acids and passes through in the stool. The large quantities involved are not conducive to a lifetime of such treatment, but it is clear that this procedure can effect a dramatic reduction in serum cholesterol.

Presumably, the ideal procedure would be to inhibit cholesterol synthesis (daily synthesis by the liver far exceeds that ingested). That this is feasible, in theory, is indicated by the fact that if rats are fed cholesterol, the rate of de novo synthesis from its normal precursor is markedly depressed. It is assumed that this represents feedback inhibition of the reaction which is the committed step in the synthetic sequence. Although no drug is known which actually works in this manner, there are some promising leads. Atromid-S, a detergent, dramatically reduces blood cholesterol, by a mechanism that has not been discovered. (Ironically, this drug was discovered by accident. An English laboratory, testing the effect of a steroid as a possible depressant of blood cholesterol, obtained a gratifyingly positive effect. The steroid was dispersed in a solution of Atromid-S. But an identical effect was obtained when one group of hypercholesterolemic individuals was used as a control—and given only the dispersing solution without the proposed steroid!) Yet another lead is afforded by marked reduction of cholesterol in animals given one of the "polyene antibiotics." The reasons are obscure, and these compounds are sufficiently toxic to have restricted them to external toxic use. But if there be sufficient reason, these compounds can be modified in the hope of retaining the desired effect while the toxicity is lost.

Other candidates include nicotinic acid, a vitamin that must, in this case, be effective for other reasons; d-thyroxine (the unnatural isomer of the normal hormone); and modification of estrogenic hormones (women, before the menopause, have lower blood cholesterol levels than men).

The reward for success in this pursuit would be great indeed. The prospect of success cannot be evaluated at this time. One of the difficulties that beset the endeavor is the lack of a suitable experimental animal for assay purposes. Hypercholesterolemia can be induced in animals by various means. The closest approximation of human atherosclerosis is seen in the pyridoxine (vitamin B_6) deficient monkey. But none are truly analogous to the human situation, and unfortunately man himself must remain the appropriate assay object.

Conception and Contraception. Significant progress is being made today in coping with two ancient ills of mankind: childlessness and the unwanted pregnancy. Utilizing information first obtained in studies of the reproductive cycles of animals, it has been possible to formulate methods of treating sterility and of preventing conception that have been gratifyingly successful. The final solution of these problems, however, is not yet in sight: too few patients are suitable candidates for the presently available remedies, the hazards of using such remedies are not fully known, and there is general agreement that the optimal treatment probably has not yet been discovered.

Conception. Infertility arises from a variety of causes and can be either transient or persistent. The only type of infertility for which the use of drugs is indicated today is that resulting from a disordered pattern of pituitary gonadotropin hormone secretion, in which the output of gonadotropins is inadequate, timed incorrectly, or both.

For two decades, episodic attempts were made to treat this type of infertility with injections of gonadotropins. Favorable results were perplexingly few; only an occasional patient ovulated. The answer was supplied by a scientist working on quite another problem. A physiologist who had undertaken a study of the effects of pituitary growth hormone in the rhesus monkey was surprised to find that it had little effect. The potency of the preparation of growth hormone, obtained from the pituitary glands of slaughterhouse animals, had been demonstrated in rats.

When hormone was instead prepared from a large number of monkey pituitary glands, it proved to be highly effective in monkeys. Species specificity in the response of primates to pituitary hormones has since been demonstrated to hold true for all pituitary hormones, including human beings.

It was now evident that, to be effective, gonadotropins of primate origin would have to be used in the treatment of infertility. At first glance, this was a discouraging development. A preparation that mimicked lutein-stimulating hormone (LH), human chorionic gonadotropin (HCG), was available, but adequate amounts of human follicle-stimulating hormone (FSH) seemed unattainable. The quantity of human pituitary glands that could be obtained at autopsy clearly would not suffice. Some Italian chemists decided to exploit an earlier finding of Aschheim and Zondek and obtain FSH from the urine of menopausal women. Solving many problems related to the large-scale production of an acceptably purified hormone, they ultimately were able to market the preparation known as human menopausal gonadotropin (HMG).

The optimal doses and injection schedule of HMG and LH were established in 1962 by a Swedish clinician who induced ovulation in a high percentage of cases of female infertility apparently arising from disordered gonadotropin secretion. And a high percentage of these became pregnant. The sequential use of HMG and LH remains today the treatment of choice for many patients with this type of infertility.

The incidence of multiple births in patients receiving these hormones is considerably higher than in an untreated population; occasionally so many eggs are ovulated and become fertilized that pregnancy spontaneously terminates before extrauterine survival of the fetuses is possible. Injection of these hormones sometimes causes rapid enlargement of ovarian cysts; if pregnancy follows, abnormal abdominal distention may develop with the accumulation of ascitic fluid.

Despite the demonstrated effectiveness of the HMG-HCG regimen, investigators continued their search for new means of treating infertility. They hoped to obtain an agent that would be free of the untoward effects of the gonadotropins, be effective by mouth, and be useful in cases of infertility arising from other causes. Although many potential drugs have been tested, the combined gonadotropins remain the procedure of choice. The ability to produce ovulation by the administration of drugs represents a wholly new and important scientific achievement. The societal implications of this development are suggested by the fact that adoption agencies estimate that one couple in ten is childless or can have fewer children than they wish.

Contraception. Prior to the introduction of the oral contraceptive drugs, reasonably satisfactory methods of contraception of a mechanical or physiochemical type existed. The incidence of pregnancy is probably less than 10 percent with the proper use of a diaphragm or condom, and possibly that low with spermatocidal jellies, foams, and douches. It is human nature that has limited the success that could be achieved with these measures, for all too often it has become apparent that they have been used improperly or not at all.

It was thought that an orally active agent might be a more effective means of contraception, because, taken regularly each morning, no special thought need be given it. As a prelude to the search for such an agent, rigorous criteria were established. The agent must effect contraception in such a way as to cause no harm to the recipient, and its effects must be wholly and readily reversible. These stipulations effectively excluded all agents then known to be contraceptive via a direct action on the gonads. It seemed logical to search for a drug that prevents ovulation by altering the secretion pattern of pituitary gonadotropins. Findings in animals indicated that this could be accomplished by administration of estrogenic or progestational hormones. Subsequent clinical studies showed that estrogens are particularly potent in this respect. However, the estrogens proved to be effective for only a very few menstrual cycles. The pituitary gland appeared to "escape" from their disruptive actions and ovulation occurred. In addition, physicians were loath to administer estrogens chronically, fearing that they might produce excessive uterine endometrial proliferation and that they might be carcinogenic.

Progestational hormones had been demonstrated to prevent ovulation, but were weaker in this respect than the estrogens. Further investigation of their effects seemed, however, to be the most promising pathway open at the time. The naturally occurring hormone progesterone is not effective by mouth. The few orally active derivatives of progesterone available were expensive and not particularly potent inhibitors of ovulation. Medicinal chemists therefore set out to prepare new semisynthetic steroids with progestational properties. The new compounds were prepared by modifying existing steroid hormones. Many synthetic steroids produced in the early 1950's were studied first in rabbits and rats. Prominent among the investigators at this stage was the research team headed by a zoologist, Gregory Pincus. When several of the new compounds (of approximately 200 tested) seemed to be of exceptional promise, Pincus initiated collaborative research efforts with a group of clinical investigators. Large-scale clinical trials indicated that, of the new compounds evaluated, norethynodrel was the most effective.

The next discovery can probably be attributed to the chronic dissatisfaction of chemists with the purity of the compounds they synthesize. They found that the norethynodrel preparations that had been used in the clinical trials were contaminated by the presence of a small amount of an estrogenic steroid, "mestranol." When the mestranol was wholly removed, the ability of norethynodrel to effect contraception dropped to unacceptably low levels. Thus it was determined that, for optimal contraceptive effect, a mixture of an estrogen and a progestational steroid should be employed.

Clinical trials revealed that the norethynodrel-mestranol mixture (ultimately to be marketed as Enovid) seemingly was completely effective in all women who faithfully adhered to the prescribed schedule of usage. By all of the criteria employed (including visual inspection of the ovaries of subjects undergoing surgery for unrelated reasons), the mixture appeared to have blocked ovulation. It is presently assumed that the mixture prevents ovulation by altering the secretory pattern of pituitary gonadotropins; studies of the plasma concentrations and urinary output of FSH and LH during the ovarian cycle in women receiving the mixture indicate that gonadotropin secretion is definitely deranged.

Following cessation of use of the mixture, normal menstrual cycles were exhibited by most women in one to two months. A number of them subsequently became pregnant. The effects of the contraceptive steroids now appear reversible; whether this will remain true when they have been used steadily for more than just a few years remains to be determined.

Later clinical studies indicated that a number of other semisynthetic steroids could be used as contraceptive agents. At least five substitutes for norethynodrel are now so utilized, each in conjunction with an estrogen, either mestranol or ethinyl estradiol.

Because of certain untoward changes produced by the mixtures and because of concern about their possible long-term effects the dosage regimens for these agents have been modified in various ways. The relative amounts of the two steroids in the mixture have been varied, with the view of keeping the dose of each as low as possible without sacrificing contraceptive efficacy. Reductions in dosage have made the mixtures cheaper in price, have reduced the incidence of certain untoward effects, and may have made them safer for chronic administration. A second type of variation relates to the schedule of usage of each component of the mixture. The original Enovid schedule called for use of an unvarying mixture each day of the month that the drug was used. The subsequently developed "sequential" schedule prescribes an estrogen alone for most of the month; a combination of the semisynthetic progestational steroid and estrogen is taken only for approximately the last week of the dosage schedule. Advocates of the "sequential" approach feel that it more nearly mimics the natural schedule of hormonal secretion and therefore produces fewer untoward effects.

The acceptance of oral contraceptive drugs has been so great that large proportions (25 percent or more) of all women in their childbearing years are using them in many countries of the world. The fact that so many women are taking these drugs regularly makes all the more urgent the need to know all that is possible about them and the consequences of their prolonged use. Unfortunately, there is much that is not known about the contraceptive drugs; some of the troubling questions will be considered in the following paragraphs.

The mechanism of action of the contraceptive drugs has not yet been adequately explained. That these agents alter the secretory pattern of gonadotropins is not questioned. However, the various agents produce strikingly different alterations in gonadotropin output. Furthermore, it appears that they may not, each month, prevent ovulation, yet exert a contraceptive effect nonetheless. The latter finding has been explained in various ways. The appearance of the endometrium in women receiving contraceptive drugs is abnormal, and it may be incapable of a decidual response, even in the presence of a fertilized egg. Also, the progestational component of the mixture may stimulate the release of cervical secretions so viscous in nature that they effectively entrap spermatozoa.

Determination of the mechanism of action of contraceptive drugs, which may vary with the different steroids and schedules of administration, will not merely satisfy our curiosity. When the mechanism(s) of action of these agents is known, we will be in a much better position to determine if the optimal agents and regimens are being used to achieve contraception. It should also be possible to predict with greater confidence the possible risks associated with the long-term use of these drugs.

Most investigators are convinced that the optimal means of achieving contraception with drugs is not yet known. While their use provides a virtually complete contraceptive effect, the known and potential risks justifiably occasion reservations. New agents and new schedules of administration should be vigorously sought. Further basic information about reproductive processes must be obtained. The more that is known about reproduction, the stronger will be our position if difficulties with the presently available drugs should oblige us to seek new types of contraceptive agents.

The risks associated with the use of contraceptive drugs are imperfectly understood. This not only is true of the long-term risks, but holds as well for some short-term effects such as possible disturbances in clotting and visual damage. Investigation of all of the risks associated with use of oral contraceptive drugs must be pursued on a systematic basis. Too much is at stake to permit a casual approach to these problems. Meanwhile, it is clear that contraceptive drugs, the culmination of a half-century of research in endocrinology, reproductive physiology, and synthetic chemistry, are among the greatest boons science has yet provided to mankind.

Role of Microorganisms in Oral Diseases. Following his discovery of bacteria in the seventeenth century, Anton Van Leeuwenhoek observed that "there are more animals living in the scum of the teeth in a man's mouth than there are men in a whole kingdom." Today, it is known that one milliliter of normal saliva contains an average of 750 million microbes; at least 30 distinct species of microorganisms have been isolated from the oral cavity.

Dental Caries. The significance of oral microorganisms defied more definitive study until the past two decades, with the introduction of germ-free methods of research and advanced microbiological techniques. It has now clearly been demonstrated that dental caries is caused by the interaction of bacteria and carbohydrate foodstuffs. The decay-producing bacteria ferment dietary sugars, forming acids which dissolve the hard tooth structure.

One of the first clues came in 1946, when investigators at the National Institute of Dental Research showed that penicillin would prevent the occurrence of dental caries in rats fed a cariogenic diet. In 1954, it was observed that no caries could be produced in germ-free animals even when fed an otherwise caries-inducing diet high in carbohydrates.

Extensive research programs have greatly enlarged knowledge of the causative microorganisms. The transmissible, infectious character of dental caries was demonstrated by producing tooth decay in germ-free animals by inoculating their oral cavities with a pure strain of streptococci. Subsequently, the disease was shown to be basically similar in animals and man, with the finding that a strain of human streptococcus could produce caries in the albino hamster. Since then, several strains of human streptococci have been isolated that can produce caries experimentally in hamsters or rats.

Thus, today, the focus is on specific bacteria, as contrasted with the long-held view that dental caries results from the activity of a wide spectrum of acidogenic microorganisms in the oral cavity. Current research suggests that cariogenic organisms are normally found in the mouth and that changes such as a dietary increase of carbohydrates, which increase their numbers, lead to decay.

Lactobacilli, once viewed by some as the likeliest causative organisms, are now generally considered only one of the microbial factors respon-

sible for the disease. The weight of evidence implicates particular streptococci as playing a major role in caries production in experimental
animals and points to sucrose as the principal caries-conducive dietary
factor. However, dietary variations of protein as well as carbohydrate
have been found to affect the persistence in the oral cavity of cariogenic
streptococci.

Decay-causing microorganisms consistently synthesize much intracellular polysaccharide from a variety of sugars, while those known to be
noncariogenic vary in this ability. Cariogenic organisms can store the
polysaccharides so that later, when no carbohydrates are available in
the host's diet, they can ferment the stored substance. In this way, they
produce decay-causing acids over longer time periods.

Of greater significance in identifying cariogenic bacteria is the more
recent finding that such strains can synthesize large amounts of *extracellular* polysaccharides, specifically dextrans (a polymeric form of
glucose in 1,6 linkage), particularly in the presence of sucrose. This substance forms an insoluble matrix for the bacterial plaque that adheres to
the teeth. On smooth tooth surfaces, as contrasted with pits and fissures,
decay occurs only under these bacterial plaques. Particularly pertinent,
and of considerable promise, is the demonstration that occasional lavage
with a solution of dextranase (which hydrolyzes the mucilaginous polymer
to soluble sugars) affords a very high degree of protection against caries.

The finding that certain antibiotics can reduce plaque formation and
thus aid in the partial prevention of dental decay also provides an encouraging lead for both further laboratory research and clinical trials.
The possibility that agents of both classes may be used judiciously for the
control of rampant caries, especially in handicapped, retarded, and
chronically ill persons, has been under intensive study. Preliminary findings on young rheumatic fever patients who had received penicillin daily
are encouraging.

The role of fluoride in inhibiting caries is not quite as clear, but it appears to increase enamel resistance. There is some experimental evidence
suggesting that fluoride may also affect bacterial activity. Current clinical
trials with schoolchildren are assessing the effectiveness of a topically
applied fluoride gel in reducing tooth decay. Concurrent epidemiological
studies will be facilitated by the recent development of a practical technique for the detection and enumeration of caries-inducing streptococci in
clinical examinations in the field.

These and other microbiological developments of the past few years
have shortened the trail from the laboratory to the patient and hold increasingly firm hope for the ultimate eradication of dental caries in the
foreseeable future.

Periodontal Diseases. Since these are believed to represent a plurality of disorders, rather than one entity, research must be directed toward finding a specific etiological agent or agents for each type. Here, too, as in dental caries, there is a variety of interactions, with strong presumptive evidence of the causative role played by bacteria.

Among various approaches, the mechanism of plaque formation is being probed as the key to the possible control of some forms of periodontal disease. For example, it has been shown that certain plaque-forming streptococci induce extensive loss of alveolar bone in germ-free animals. As this plaque material undergoes progressive calcification into a tartar (calculus) deposit, it causes a mechanical irritant reaction, which tends to be a complicating factor in periodontal disorders.

In 1963 there was isolated from the plaque of hamsters with periodontal disease a specific filamentous bacterium which closely resembles certain forms found in the oral cavity of man. By inoculating disease-free animals with these microorganisms, it was possible to produce similar mouth lesions.

Another approach involves systematically testing the action, upon the periodontal tissues, of enzymes, toxins, and antigens produced by specific bacteria isolated from the gingival crevice. The isolation from diseased human gingival tissue of such enzymes as collagenase and hyaluronidase, which are of tissue as well as bacterial origin, suggests that they may be involved in periodontal disorders. Certain bacterial waste products, such as ammonia and hydrogen sulfide, have also been shown to have a destructive effect on tissues of experimental animals.

Among microbial factors in oral disease, hypersensitivity to microorganisms and their endotoxins probably contributes to an extent greater than realized. While allergic inflammation has long been suspected as a contributing factor in some forms of periodontal disease, this cause has never been adequately demonstrated. Recent studies have provided experimental support for the concept of sensitization and allergic response in periodontal diseases. Tissue-bound immunoglobulins are abundant in inflamed gingiva but not in normal human gingiva; gingival inflammation similar to that seen in humans can be produced in animals by local treatment with allergens.

While much more needs to be understood about causative and contributory factors as well as mechanisms of action in periodontal diseases, research findings, to date, provide a significant basis for future studies of immunological control measures.

Oral Ulcerations. Considerable research effort has centered on recurrent aphthous stomatitis (canker sores) and herpes simplex (cold or fever blisters), which afflict a large percentage of the population.

The herpes simplex virus is not involved in aphthous stomatitis reactions, as had long been believed. Fever blisters are caused by the herpes simplex virus. In recent years, there has been evidence that there are several distinct strains of this virus. Different strains of the same organism have even been isolated from the same individual in different disease attacks. The changed characteristics of the virus may help explain in part why antibody response to previous infections does not prevent recurrences. More recent data shed further light on this question; surprisingly, the herpes simplex antibody can combine with the virus without necessarily destroying its capacity to infect. These findings may be important in explaining the chronic nature of certain viral mouth infections.

Time's Arrow and Human Biology

Early Human Development

Human biological potential is established, in large measure, in its experiences in prenatal life and in the early postnatal years. This tender period is beset by a host of possible difficulties; unfavorable outcome, in many cases, can mean serious permanent limitation in both physical and mental health and potential. This phase of human life is receiving increasing scientific attention, yet there are few areas where clinical capabilities are so limited by fundamental understanding. An intensive investigative effort directed at elucidation of the events and mechanisms of normal conception, pregnancy, parturition, and postnatal development is of overriding importance.

Some of these problems have already been considered in Chapter 6. Clearly all information descriptive of development in other species is relevant to equivalent events in human development. Each month there appear reports of human disorders which find their origins in the events of early life. It is the changing patterns of mortality and morbidity, largely the consequence of the minimization of infectious disease, which have brought these health problems into new focus as primary hazards to health and happiness. A few examples of research in these areas will be considered, only as illustrations of the magnitude and complexity of the problem.

The Prenatal Period. The prenatal period begins with fertilization of the ovum, preceded by spermatogenesis and sperm migration, by oogenesis and ovulation. Some of the practical problems concerning relief of infertility and the control of conception have already been considered.

Development of the blastocyst, its passage through the fallopian tube, and its implantation on a prepared endometrium follow next in the chronology of reproduction. Among the practical problems here is the etiology of early spontaneous abortion. Research in this period of development, utilizing a variety of laboratory animals, is concerned with the factors affecting tubal motility, the stimulus for the cell divisions of the fertilized ovum, the endocrinological causes and the specific biochemistry of decidua and trophoblast formation. Application of concepts derived from animal experiments to the human must, of necessity, proceed cautiously. Knowledge has grown but clinical triumph is rare.

Studies of the later stages of pregnancy currently focus on the development of the fetus, the physiology of the placenta, and the interrelationship between the two. Gross defects in the newborn infant, other than those of genetic origin, appear to result particularly from external agents, such as viruses, x-rays, or certain drugs, operative during the first twelve weeks of gestation. Thereafter, such abnormal states as diabetes, toxemia in the mother, blood type incompatibilities between mother and infant, and some still unknown causes of deficiency of placental function may result in fetal death or the birth of a damaged infant. Research on these problems centers on the study of placental-fetal transfer mechanisms and placental metabolism. The physiology of the fetus, particularly the coordinated development of complex functions, remains a critical area of ignorance.

Finally there is the period of labor, delivery, and neonatal adjustment to extrauterine life. The stimulus that brings about labor is unknown; errors in this mechanism may result in prematurity, the commonest source of neonatal mortality, or less frequently, postmaturity with its attendant fetal hazards. The uterine contraction can now be studied with the use of strain gauges placed in the amniotic cavity; variations in the characteristics of the contraction are being related to observable changes in placental transfer and fetal circulation. Alterations in fetal oxygen and carbon dioxide and the development of fetal acidosis are being studied by obtaining samples of blood from the fetal scalp, accessible through the cervix during the latter part of labor. Mechanisms to assure the earliest possible establishment of extrauterine respiration in the first minutes of life are under even more intense investigation, because of the hypothesis that prolonged postnatal hypoxia may have a lasting, unfavorable effect on the individual in later life.

Studies of fetal development and new means for its observation in man are laying the foundation for what promises to be an important division of medical science. If, as seems likely, not only heredity but the intrauterine environment and the vicissitudes of labor bear significantly on the future biological excellence of the individual, no area of investigation can be of greater significance.

Techniques for Determining the Physiological Status of the Fetus.
Studies of fetal physiology have necessarily depended upon the history
of observations made on laboratory animals; some useful studies have
been conducted on humans at the time of therapeutic abortion or cesarean
section. The need for techniques for examination of the physiological
state of the human fetus, without interference with the pregnancy or
the course of labor, has long been apparent.

The obstetrician needs this information to know when to induce labor
in the face of a presumptive threat to the fetus or to alter the means
planned for delivery when the fetus is in danger during labor. Historically
only clinical impressions, estimation of the rate of growth of the fetus,
and counting of the fetal heart sounds with a conventional stethoscope
have been available. Several recent scientific developments promise
more precise and objective methods.

1. *Urinary Excretion of Estriol.* For some years it had been known that
the maternal blood levels and excretion of estrogens fall to low levels
in the presence of fetal death; the rate of estrogen excretion was regarded
as a crude measure of placental function. More recently it has been shown
that the amount of the estrogen estriol excreted in the maternal urine
reflects also fetal production, and further metabolism. Several reports
have indicated the utility of urinary estriol determinations as a guide
for the induction of labor in the presence of conditions threatening fetal
life, such as diabetes, toxemia, and postmaturity.

2. *Monitoring of the Fetal Heart.* Counting of the fetal heart rate with
a stethoscope has been a traditional obstetrical practice; rates greater
than 160 or persistently less than 100 often precede intrauterine fetal
death. Recent years have witnessed efforts to refine techniques to permit
more fundamental analysis of the characteristics of rate and rhythm of
the fetal heartbeat and to correlate observed changes with fetal outcome.
Electronic devices which now permit instantaneous evaluation of the
fetal heart rate and its recording throughout.labor verified the long recognized significance of persistently high or low rates. Special types of rate
change, such as "rapid fluctuations," "spikes," "transient ascents," and
"dips," have been classified but their practical utility has not been established.

The other approach to the monitoring of the fetal heart has been the
development of fetal electrocardiography. Technical problems of amplification and separation of the fetal complex from that of the maternal
electrocardiogram have been partly solved, and a variety of different
leads, including rectal, vaginal, abdominal, and fetal, have been tested.
The cataloguing of types of electrocardiographic disturbance, with their
clinical significance, is now in progress.

3. *Microanalysis of Fetal Blood Samples.* The development of a technique for obtaining, during labor, minute samples of fetal blood from the part presenting at the cervix has initiated a study concerned with fetal blood chemistry. Particularly valuable has been detection of low pH values as indicators of fetal acidosis, associated with anoxia. This technique is being extended into other metabolic areas, e.g., blood glucose levels, and there should be many opportunities for fruitful investigation.

These still crude methods now permit acquisition of some information concerning the more severe physiological disturbances affecting the fetus. Ultimately refined techniques should provide the obstetrician with information not only about major aberrations that threaten the life of the fetus but also about less acute disturbances that, nonetheless, may diminish the infant's potential for full physical and mental development.

Congenital Defects. The incidence, in man, of congenital abnormalities, as conventionally defined, is estimated to be about 7 percent. If reduced life-span, sensitivity to infectious disease, and propensity toward degenerative conditions are included as late manifestations of abnormal development, the incidence would, undoubtedly, increase appreciably. Accordingly, understanding of the developmental basis of human frailty and of outright congenital defects is one of the major concerns of preventive medicine. The awesome appearance of human beings with congenital defects has elicited attention from the time of the first known written record in Babylon, and the interpretation of these defects by religious or pseudomedical superstitions was frequently more extensive and more deeply ingrained in the popular mind than beliefs about other abnormal conditions of the body or mind.

Genetic and Environmental Factors in the Origin of Congenital Defects. The existence of an intrinsic genetic component in many congenital defects has been established by a large body of evidence. Studies with a variety of animals — viz., rats, mice, guinea pigs, and chicks — have shown that different genetic strains of the same species exhibit a different incidence of certain types of congenital defects and that such congenitally abnormal traits are transmitted in accordance with the formal laws of genetics. The familial incidence of human abnormalities has shown the genetic basis of congenital defects in man as well.

The importance of nongenetic, extrinsic factors as a cause of developmental disturbances is also borne out by extensive experimentation. In animal experiments a large number of conditions have been found which lead to a marked increase in the incidence of congenital defects. Chemicals, including drugs, deficiencies or excesses of oxygen, vitamins and amino acids, hormonal imbalance, radiation, and viral infections have been found to give rise, with different degrees of specificity, to a wide variety of defects in a large number of animal species as well as in man. Many of these agents produce defects that outwardly resemble otherwise genetically determined congenital abnormalities. For some time the significance of this parallelism was contested. The appearance of similar abnormalities caused by different external agents or genetic constitution was thought to be purely coincidental and due to the labile state of tissues at certain developmental periods. It was postulated that different tissues had characteristic sensitive developmental periods during which a variety of external as well as genetic factors would lead to tissue degeneration, and hence to similar congenital defects. However, more refined analysis showed some specificity in the response both to different external agents and to different genetic conditions. The incidence and the specific type of effects induced by experimental teratogens such as aminonicotinamide and nicotine have frequently been found to be dependent upon the genetic constitution of the test animals, which indicates operation of some mechanisms common to the intrinsic genetic disturbance and the extrinsically produced phenocopy.

Many investigators have anticipated that information obtained from studies of environmentally induced abnormal development will contribute to an understanding of the factors involved in gene-induced abnormalities, and that this, in turn, would lead to better understanding of the genetic control of development. Support for this expectation has been meager, but the potential utility of this approach has recently been illustrated. In rats, guinea pigs, and mice, maternal dietary deficiency of manganese results in the birth of progeny with ataxia due to defective morphogenesis of the vestibular portion of the inner ear. A somewhat similar ataxic condition is characteristic of mice homozygous for the "pallid" mutation. This condition can be prevented from developing among offspring of pallid mice if the maternal diet is supplemented with an unusual amount of manganese during pregnancy. Apparently manganese is important in the formation of the otoliths; the latter are involved in the maintenance of equilibrium and coordination of movements.

Developmental Biology of Congenital Defects. One of the main contributions of embryology is the discovery and experimental analysis of the role of tissue interactions in development. First described as the classical case of neural induction (see Chapter 6), tissue interactions have been found to control development of most organs. Isolation of the agents that mediate such tissue interactions is of great importance to understanding of normal development as well as to teratology (study of the formation of defective young), since deficiency or excess of such factors could be one of the causes of abnormal development. The search for such inducing substances remained unsuccessful for decades. Rather recently, some progress has been made in the isolation of tissue fractions (not pure substances) which induce mesodermal properties. Partial purification has been achieved of embryonic "hormones" which promote nerve growth and development of ectodermal cells at late stages of differentiation. The developmental role of the nerve growth factor was strikingly demonstrated by the rudimentary development of spinal and sensory ganglia after injection of antisera against the growth factor.

It is of interest that the metabolic loci of the neural and epidermal growth factor differ. The former activates gene transcription, whereas the epidermal growth factor was found to stimulate the translational step in the production of cell-specific proteins. A tissue fraction containing growth factors required for normal chondrogenesis (bone formation) has been obtained. Addition of this fraction to bone cultures with genetically retarded growth has been claimed to relieve this retardation. To what extent well-defined adult hormones, such as adrenal steroids or insulin, function in development and are responsible for some congenital abnormalities has not been established. Analysis of the mechanisms by which hormones may affect protein synthesis is under intensive scrutiny, and exciting, important advances may be anticipated.

It has generally been considered that congenital abnormalities arise either by insufficient growth and development of certain tissues or by abnormal cell degeneration. However, extensive tissue regressions are part of normal development, and inhibition of such normal degeneration leads to congenital abnormalities.

That cell death is part of normal development is evident from a tabulation, compiled in 1951, of 76 instances of cell degeneration at specific phases of development of a variety of embryonic tissues. These may be grouped as instances of (1) morphogenetic degeneration facilitating cell movement and concomitant change in form; (2) degenerations such as histolysis of muscle during metamorphosis or the regression of the genital ducts which lead to new tissue forms; or (3) phylogenetic degeneration such as the regression of larval organs. The extent of cell death during embryonic development can range from the rapid breakdown of the major portions of larval tissues during insect metamorphosis, to the regression of a few appendages in amphibian metamorphosis and mammalian ontogeny, or to the necrosis of small cell groups as in the spinal cord ganglia or the wing bud of the chick.

Such descriptive classifications are expected to lead to a search for the mechanisms of these various forms of developmental cell degenerations. The timing of such cell death must reflect some event external to the cell in question — viz., arrival of an embryonic hormone, such as ecdysone or a vertebrate equivalent, or a "tissue factor" from adjacent tissue. But there has been no clear evidence of such an event. Indeed, the opposite would appear to have been observed; transplantation of a prospective degenerative tissue—e.g., the posterior zone of the chick wing bud—to another environment does not prevent the expected degeneration. Thus the trigger for this process has not been elucidated. Nor is the operative mechanism entirely certain. Such cells early show chromosomal degeneration—viz., pycnosis with apparent dissociation of DNA from its normal envelope of basic protein.

Conceivably, the effects of excess vitamin A on rudimentary limb bud explants will prove to be a satisfactory model of normal embryonic cell death. This molecule appears to disturb the integrity of various, perhaps all, cell membranes. Of particular importance is rupture of the membrane of the lysosomes (Chapter 5) with release of their complement of hydrolytic enzymes which then destroy the normal cell macromolecules. This appears to explain the multiple lesions in the skeletons of rats fed excess vitamin A. Moreover, there is evidence that this vitamin is essential to normal development, since the offspring of vitamin A deficient animals exhibit such abnormalities as persistence of supernumerary aortic arches and incomplete regression of genital ducts with pseudohermaphroditism.

The Middle Years

The minimization of infectious disease as a serious health hazard for a major portion of the life-span has, in consequence, reduced mortality rates over the middle years to somewhat less than 1 per 1,000. In the advanced countries, mortality due to maternal deaths is now smaller than 1 per 100,000. Accordingly, even a stringent effort to reduce these yet further will have little effect on the gross mortality rate, which rises significantly only in the sixth decade of life. Many of the principal causes of death in the middle years reflect the problems of man in our society—accidents, suicide, homicide, peptic ulcer. Attempts at reduction of these events are worthy indeed, but not so much for the effect on mortality as on the quality of life of a much larger fraction of the population.

Accordingly, it is the effects of the environment, of our culture, on human biology which are of greatest interest as one views the middle years. Continuing progress can yet still further reduce mortality from the great killers, but more important will be those advances that reduce morbidity due to such disorders as rheumatoid arthritis, hypertension, and peptic ulcer.

Perhaps more important will be sharper understanding of events in childhood which determine later potential. Accumulated evidence suggests that early nutrition, stimulation, and loving care have profound effects on patterns of both physical and mental development. Suboptimal early nutrition, particularly with respect to protein deficiency, leads to later mental insufficiency and apathy. In contrast, stimulated, petted, loved youngsters attain a larger stature and greater intellectual capacity than do those who are relatively deprived. This concept has been demonstrated with experimental rats and mice. In independent cross-cultural samples, where heads or limbs are molded or stretched, where circumcision is practiced, or where appendages are pierced, the mean adult male stature is more than two inches greater than in comparable societies where these customs are not practiced. Only glimpses of such relations are now apparent, and they warrant extensive investigation in the future.

Secular Trends in Age at Menarche and Menopause. Biological maturity, in the sense of ability to reproduce, is being reached earlier and earlier. In western Europe and the United States since 1830, menarche has accelerated by about 4 months per decade, or 1 year in every 30. In the United States, menarche has been reached earlier than in Europe, at any period, by roughly 6 months to a year.

The problems of earlier biological than psychological or social maturity (or financial independence) in a culture that penalizes early reproduction and rewards restraint for education and training are all too apparent. They range from illegitimacy, venereal disease, educational dropouts, teenage marriage, and divorce, to the frustration of prolonged delay in family formation for professional persons. From the purely biological point of view, apart from ethics or morality, some of these problems could be greatly reduced by the wider practice of contraception, a product of basic biomedical research. Historical records strongly suggest that the progressive earlier age at menarche is a reversion to an earlier day. The onset of female adolescence and increased stature witnessed for the last century is not a genetic, evolutionary trend but probably a reflection of improved nutrition and childhood care, since there is much evidence for early maturation in European females before the industrial revolution.

The clinical consequences of accelerated rate of maturation are unknown; longevity has been increased in laboratory animals by underfeeding and thereby delaying growth and maturation. Very young mothers are less efficient obstetrically, and produce smaller children who have higher perinatal death rates, than older mothers. Cardiologists speculate that overenthusiastic feeding of children may contribute to increased incidence of coronary heart disease in modern times, and pediatricians now question the conventional wisdom that a fat child is a healthy child.

Longitudinal studies of sizable groups over a lifetime will be needed to settle such basic questions.

The age at natural menopause appears to be later now than formerly, though the evidence is scanty and the methodological problems great. A recent study based on the National Health Examination Survey in the United States, 1960–62, established the startling fact that a quarter of women 50–64 years of age reported that they had entered menopause as the result of an operation. The normal onset of menopause was described by a logistic curve with the 50-percent end point at 49.7 years. This is three to five years later than commonly accepted figures. Whether the latter were poorly documented underestimates or whether a real change has occurred is unclear. Age at menopause was unrelated to recalled age at menarche.

Stature. Height is increasing in all advanced countries, in Japan as well as in the West. The trend began at least 100 years ago and is still continuing in the United States for the whole population, as shown by the National Health Examination Survey, 1960–62. The height of American soldiers increased by 0.7 inches between the two World Wars and by a further 0.5 inches by 1957–58, a total gain since 1917 of 1.2 inches during a period of restricted immigration. Among a selected subgroup, Harvard students of old American descent, an increase of 1.3 inches between fathers and sons on entrance to the university occurred between 1840 and 1930. This can be taken as a measure of environmental effect among the economically favored. The total increase among all Harvard students between men born in 1846–55 and 1906–15 was 2.2 inches. Among a very different group, Italian-American factory workers born in the United States to parents themselves born near Naples, Italy, a startling increase of 2.1 inches has been recorded between fathers and sons. This indicates marked improvement in one American microenvironment and the marked growth potential or plasticity of the human genotype permitting a phenotypic response of this magnitude. Part of the secular increase in size results from accelerated growth, but only part. Full stature now seems to be reached around age 22 or 23, on a cross-sectional basis, whereas growth seems to have continued into the late 20's a century ago.

The prime basis for the worldwide increase in human stature must be environmental. Although it has been proposed that heterosis, a tendency of hybrids to exceed relatively inbred parents in size and vigor, consequent on geographic mobility and marriage outside one's native village, may be significant in this regard, there is little to substantiate this proposal.

The aspects of the environment that caused acceleration of rate of growth and a larger end-product are known only in general terms. Better nutrition and sanitation are generally credited, and with reason. Prevention of overt disease which could delay or stunt growth plays a minor role. If nutrition is the cause, it must be a change in the balance of the diet, the relative intake of certain essential factors, not an increase in caloric intake. Conceivably psychosocial factors such as urbanization, crowding, pace of life, or even stress of one kind or another play a part. The positive correlations, reported from a wide variety of primitive cultures, between early physical stress and ultimate stature, mentioned previously, may well be highly relevant.

The secular trend in the rate of growth and maturation and in body size, a major phenomenon of human biology, has profound implications for medicine, education, and human affairs generally. Some of the avenues of investigation have been outlined. The interplay of culture and genetics, and the interlocking web of causative factors (rather than the simple cause-and-effect models of the experimental sciences), are characteristic of human biology. Free-living, functioning human populations are the unit of study, not cells, tissues, organs, individual persons, or experimental animals. A different research design, different kinds of investigator, and a different supporting organization are required.

The Menopause. The course of the decline of reproductive function differs sharply between the two sexes. In the male it is gradual, not made evident by clear subjective or objective manifestations, nor consistently related to a narrowly circumscribed age period. In the female the menopause tends to be an event, rather sharply separating, in a physiological and perhaps psychological sense, two epochs of life.

The Decline of Fertility. Decline in female fertility begins early and imperceptibly, but is statistically detectable in the early 30's. From that time on the possibility of pregnancy diminishes slowly but steadily, is reduced to about 50 percent by the age of 40 and is essentially absent after 50. This loss in fertility, preceding the appearance of amenorrhea, is apparently due to failure or abnormalities in ovulation, in spite of the persistence for a time of regular menstrual bleeding.

The Event of the Menopause. The cessation of the periods themselves, occurring with striking consistency between the ages of 45 and 50, takes various forms: an abrupt, unheralded cessation, a year or two of periods at increasing intervals, a dimple diminution in the amount of the still regular flow, or excessively heavy, prolonged periods of bleeding. Sometimes well before these changes, but more often in relation to the first episode of amenorrhea, there develops the condition of vasomotor instability perceived as "hot flashes." At this time the ovary ceases to contain corpora lutea, ripening or even immature follicles. Pregnanediol

is absent from the urine, estrogen excretion is diminished, while gonado-
tropic hormone appears in larger quantities.

The Postclimacteric Years. After the menopause is established, atrophy
of the genital organs proceeds in different women at a variable rate, often
not reaching its ultimate stage for a decade or two. This atrophy affects
the entire tract, and predisposes to some pathological processes, notably
to numerous vaginal inflammations.

Research continues on the phases of a woman's reproductive life along
the following lines:

It has been accepted that all ova that will ever develop are present at
the time of the birth of the individual and that the menopause occurs when
the last of the ova have been "used up," either in ovulation or in follicular
atresia. Little is known, however, about the causative changes in hypothalamic function or about the interrelationships with the autonomic
nervous system, which underlie the "flashes." Other problems of this
period concern the causative factors and therapy of infertility due to the
premature appearance of the menopause.

A major practical problem is to identify conditions for which the menopause is a specific causative factor and distinguish these from diseases
that accompany the general aging process. Among these are various
psychiatric disorders, osteoporosis, and forms of vascular degeneration,
including perhaps coronary artery disease. Certain forms of cancer,
notably carcinoma of the corpus uteri, may have their origin in the hyper-
plasias of the endometrium developing during the years of abnormal
ovarian function in the late 40's.

The availability of natural and synthetic estrogens has led to their wide
use in clinical practice. There is a great need for a carefully planned
study of the effectiveness of estrogens in relation to claims that they
maintain youth, prevent osteoporosis and some vascular disorders, preserve sexuality, and reduce nervous tensions. Conversely the possibility
that cancer, particularly of the breast, may be favored by prolonged estrogen administration must be examined.

Decline of Reproductive Function in the Male. The relationship between spermatogenesis, androgen production, and sexual potency requires renewed study, and these should be related to variations in hypophyseal and hypothalamic function. The effect of changed hormone status
is probably a factor in some constitutional disease in men as well as in
women; although there is certainly a relationship of some sort between
hormonal changes and prostatic hypertrophy and carcinoma, the nature
of this relationship is obscure. Male reproductive function after 50 remains a largely uninvestigated subject and one extraordinarily in need
of scientific study.

Aging

After reaching maturity most living organisms exhibit unfavorable changes in structure and function which accentuate with time and are coupled with ultimate death of the organism. The total process by which senescent changes develop is what is meant by the term *aging*; the state in which the senescent changes are maximal or near maximal is *senility*, and the death of the organism as a result of these phenomena is referred to as *natural death*. Research on aging deals with three broad questions: (1) What processes are responsible for progressive decline in structure and function of the adult? (2) What are the characteristics of the senile state as distinguished from frank disease phenomena? (3) How does the progressive loss of structure and function become incompatible with continued life?

Research on aging is just beginning to emerge even though writing on the subject goes far back in history. During the past three decades, research attempting to find differences between young and old individuals has been undertaken in earnest. Two basic difficulties beset such studies. First, there appear not to be qualitative differences between young and old individuals; in old as in young organisms, the muscles contract, nerves conduct, secretion continues, etc. The changes that occur in aging must be of a subtlety consistent with maintenance of close to normal tissue function. To recognize such differences may require methods more precise or sensitive than have been employed in the past. On the other hand, comparisons of young and old can be meaningful only if the young are indeed young. If age changes have already been effected in the so-called young group, the difficulty in finding differences between this "slightly old" group and the senile group is significantly increased.

Ideally, for studies of aging, one requires a species with a short lifespan, standardized and optimized nutrition, freedom from infections and other external sources of insult, and genetic uniformity. An organism like the rotifer meets these requirements and also is favorable in that all of the cells in the body of the rotifer are of the same age. Unfortunately, biochemical studies of this species are difficult because of the small amount of material available in a single animal (about 1,000 cells), and one also must determine whether aging of the rotifer, an invertebrate, is equivalent to that of higher forms. If one demonstrates a change with age in mammals, how can this be distinguished from a change due to disease, nutritional variations, genetic heterozygosity, or ill-defined environmental insults? Moreover, the shortest-lived species of mammals live at least three years. Commercial suppliers, for very practical reasons, do not even keep animals this long. The investigator is faced with the task of rearing animals over their life-spans under conditions that reduce disease and infection to a minimum. This is costly in time, space, and money, and most laboratories are not in a position to meet these costs. The problem of availability of suitable animals for research on aging has been and continues to be a major deterrent to efforts in this field.

Against this backdrop of difficulty and uncertainty, one can take a positive view of aging. The suspicion that "aging" does not occur at the cellular level was initiated by the work of Carrell maintaining tissues in culture; recent studies to be discussed have dealt this belief a body blow. A number of carefully conducted studies of organ function, e.g., muscle strength, indicate that there is little or no difference between young and old except that the "reserve" of the latter is reduced largely due to cell death. Clearly what is needed now, for research on aging to progress effectively, is a series of chemical markers that will define old from young.

Genetics of Aging. Aging is a deteriorative process. It is characterized by a decrease in viability and an increase in vulnerability. There is probably no single cause of aging. One concept which could serve as a unifying theory is that aging reflects the instability of the genetic apparatus of cells. In ways that are not understood, the characteristic life-span of each species must also be under genetic control. Patently, the range of variation in the maximum life-span among different species is much greater than the range of individual life-spans within the species. One of the fundamental problems in relating genetic causes of aging is to separate the genetic basis for the normal changes that occur in developing tissues from possible genetic bases for the aging of these tissues.

In multicellular adult animals, there are cell populations that conveniently divide themselves into three types which are important to understanding of a possible underlying genetic mechanism for aging phenomena: (1) those that do not divide once they reach maturity, e.g., neurons and muscle cells; (2) slowly dividing cells typified by those found in the liver; (3) cells that divide rapidly, such as the primitive cells that give rise to fibroblasts and the cells composing the blood elements, skin epithelium, and intestinal lining.

Genetic instability as a cause of aging is not necessarily confined to those cells that divide rapidly, since the genetic instability of nondividing cells could be manifest in their decreased ability to function over a period of time. The instability of the genetic material could be a faulty copying of information. The genetic material is DNA, a self-duplicating molecule, and such a process is not necessarily perfect. As cells divide or as information is read in nondividing cells from the information-containing molecules, one can expect an accumulation of errors. This is very much like the kind of blurred image that we can expect after making photographic copies from a previous copy. Thus, a copy of a copy of a copy, etc., gets increasingly blurred as the reproduction of the information is carried out. This concept has often been referred to as the *error theory*. The errors involved are presumably changes in the chemical characteristics of DNA and are cumulative and heritable. To the extent that mutations occur in the somatic cells, this process must be exaggerated. It is also possible that some errors that accumulate are the result of *cross-linking*, binding of the DNA molecule with proteins that may occur over a period of time. This type of binding represses part of the information-containing DNA molecule.

Were this so, as errors accumulate, the resultant random cell death would be manifest as "aging." When two highly inbred strains of animals, for example, mice, are bred with each other, the progeny live significantly longer than either of the highly inbred parents. This *hybrid vigor* is obviously related to the genetic material of these animals and may provide some clue to the aging process. It is possible that in this situation repair of genetic errors that have accumulated in the parental strains occurs by blending the gene pools. Several studies in recent years have shown that there is a significant increase in the number of chromosome anomalies found in the blood cells of human beings as they age. Whether this phenomenon is a cause or effect of aging remains to be determined.

Studies of Aging in Tissue Culture. Until recently, it was thought that when animal cells are released from the regulatory mechanisms of the intact animal by cultivation in tissue culture, such cells can perpetuate themselves indefinitely. Classical experiments purporting to show the "immortality" of cells grown outside of the animal body have been reevaluated and reinterpreted. The earlier experiments cannot be repeated, and it is suspected that the nutrient fluids used periodically to feed the cultures introduced new living cells into the culture.

A series of well-controlled experiments in many different laboratories has conclusively demonstrated that normal animal and human cells grown in tissue culture divide for a finite number of generations and that cessation of division is not related to faulty culture techniques. Normal cells divide in tissue culture for periods of time not much greater than one year. In those rare instances where cells divide indefinitely, they are invariably found to be abnormal.

If it were true that normal human and animal cells can divide indefinitely in tissue culture, one conclusion of profound importance would be that aging is more likely to be explained as the interplay of events occurring at levels of complexity greater than that of the single cell— viz., cell groups, tissues, and organs. Since normal cells do have a limited division potential in tissue culture, one interpretation of this property may be relevant to senescence in the whole animal; i.e., senescence may result from events occurring within rather than among individual cells. The loss of proliferative or functional capacity of normal cells grown in tissue culture may provide clues to our understanding of the aging process. Normal human fetal cells divide approximately 50 times in tissue culture before dying, and adult human cells divide approximately 20 times before cessation of cell division. The difference in replicative capacity of normal and abnormal cells in tissue culture is also expressed in the animal itself. Thus, animal tumors can be transplanted from animal to animal apparently indefinitely. Similar kinds of abnormal cells when grown in tissue culture also will proliferate indefinitely. Conversely, when normal tissue is transplanted from animal to animal as each host grows older, the transplants eventually fail. In like manner, normal cells grown in tissue culture also have a finite capability to replicate.

Of related interest are asexually dividing unicellular organisms and some higher invertebrates in which, if exchange of genetic material is prevented, indefinite proliferation of the population is not possible. Thus, cell death not only is a consequence of multicellularity but occurs on a vast scale in unicellular organisms as well.

These considerations should not lead to a simplistic view of aging. It is not yet clear where the physiological chronometer lies. Loss of muscle strength and mental acuity occurs in tissues of the nondividing class; loss of cell duplicability would seem to be irrelevant. Much attention must be given to the continuing search for time-dependent, irreversible changes. Among such, for example, is the progressive cross-linking of collagen, the fibrous protein of connective tissue. With time, it becomes rigid and insoluble. Since it is the major component of intercellular space and of capillaries, this process, conceivably, could limit the nutrition of cells in affected regions and thus contribute to cell failure. Surely other such processes will be found and contribute to understanding of the complex process of the aging of a multicellular animal.

Aging: The Organism. What characteristics of the normal aging process should be studied? In view of the nearly total lack of knowledge based on longitudinal research, all organ systems require investigation. There is need to know the age at onset, the individual rates, and the variations in the decrements in height and weight, the increase in chest depth ("barrel chest"), and the changes in the amount and distribution of body components (fat, muscle, bone, body water, and the like), the speed, strength, and range-of-motion change with age. Such purely descriptive data are necessary for the proper design of equipment to be used by the elderly, which includes such items as housing, furniture, hospital supplies, and even automobiles. Similarly, careful description of changes in the special senses and in neurological functions is needed for such practical matters as automobile driver and aircraft pilot licensing and the educational, occupational, and rehabilitational capacities of the elderly. The first requirement of studies on aging, therefore, is description. Clearly all organ systems do not age at the same rate. Which measures provide the best indices of chronological or physiological age, or of the whole complex of functional decrement? Visual accommodation and dark adaptation have been proposed as such measures. What about graying of hair or elasticity of skin? Would a combination of several variables be better? If so, which? Are the intercorrelations among the various systems similar at different ages? This raises the question of multivariate analysis on a longitudinal basis, a statistical technique that has yet to be developed.

The third aim of longitudinal studies is *prediction*. Are there indices which relatively early in life will prognosticate who will age rapidly and who will retain his physiological capabilities?

The Advancing Front of Scientific Medicine

The preceding sections are neither comprehensive nor a catalogue. Hopefully they illustrate the manner in which scientific medicine advances. The trail of research in some instances commences in the laboratory, in some in the clinic. But thereafter the course is much the same. The distinction between clinical and fundamental research is utterly arbitrary; clinical research is fundamental research in which man is the species under investigation. In some instances, no other species will do; but when another species will serve, there can be no excuse for studies in man until the ground has been well prepared, using whatever species is most appropriate.

Experimental Animals. Were it not for the continual offensive against their use by well-meaning individuals, a description of the many services of experimental animals to man, or a defense of their use, would seem unnecessary, for these are within the experience of all. Without carefully designed, humanely conducted studies in animals, most of the advances in the prevention, diagnosis, and treatment of disease could never have been made. The only alternative, to perform the same studies in human subjects, would represent so great a breakdown in the moral structure of our society as to make early death from disease a blessing.

The earliest extensive use of experimental animals was in the discovery that large numbers of human disorders were due to infectious agents. Only the fact that diseases similar to those in man could be produced in experimental animals by microorganisms isolated from patients established their relationship to human disease. The immediate fruits were in the application of public health methods to prevent disease as in typhoid fever, in the discovery of prophylactic immunization as in diphtheria and tetanus, and in the preparation of antiserums useful in the treatment of infectious disease as in diphtheria, meningitis, and pneumonia. Later, the discovery that experimentally infected animals could be treated successfully with chemotherapeutic drugs and antibiotic agents led immediately to the use of these agents in human disease, with a remarkable change in the outlook for the afflicted patient.

The discovery that animals, injected with infectious agents, developed protective antibodies soon led in unexpected directions. Animals, it was found, produced antibodies, not against living organisms, but against their specific macromolecules. Our present concepts of diseases of disordered immunity, such as asthma, hay fever, serum sickness, and anaphylactic shock, stem directly from observations in animal models. An appreciation of the process of antibody production formed the basis of our knowledge that different human beings had different blood groups, leading first to the successful use of blood transfusion and later to an understanding of the cause and treatment of erythroblastosis fetalis, the disease of "Rh babies" which was a major cause of neonatal morbidity and mortality. Experiments down another avenue underlie current attempts to transplant tissues and organs from one human being to another. Understanding of such diseases as rheumatic fever and disseminated lupus erythematosus is largely derived from immunological theories developed in animals. To cite the most recent example, the nature of a hereditary angioneurotic edema, a rare but lethal illness, is based upon studies of complement, the mysterious complex of proteins that enhance immunity, first recognized because of its existence in guinea pig serum.

As far reaching in its implications has been the use of animals in determining the fundamental nature of such widespread plagues as beriberi, pellagra, and scurvy, the consequences of faulty nutrition. Studies of the effects of experimentally deficient diets, which have utilized the entire battery of laboratory animals, permitted the discovery of the vitamins and their importance in the prevention and treatment of disease. Every loaf of bread fortified with vitamins to ensure their adequate supply, every child treated for rickets, scurvy, or xerophthalmia around the globe, every jaundiced adult treated with vitamin K, every coronary disease patient on anticlotting therapy, testifies to the importance of the original research in animals. Eradication of pellagra, for three decades the leading cause of death in the American Southland, followed a few years after recognition that "black tongue" is its canine equivalent. Exploration of the effects of iron deficiency in dogs led, through a circuitous route, to the control of pernicious anemia, once a dreadful, lethal disease.

The entire science of endocrinology rests on animal experimentation which has revealed both the effects of extirpation of each of the endocrine glands and the effects of excessive hormone administration, simulating equivalent disease states. Other surgically produced animal models of disease were responsible for explanations of the circulatory failure resulting from congenital disease. Surgical methods of treatment, first worked out in dogs, brought about the revolution in the care of "blue babies" and in the management of a wide variety of cardiac, vascular, and even neurological diseases. The alternative, to perform the initial studies in man, is unthinkable.

Whenever possible, scientists have attempted to mimic human disease in animals. To catalogue them all would be an endless task, but mention should be made of the induction of leukemia and other tumors, arteriosclerosis, and thrombosis in experimental animals. Even our knowledge of the processes of the human mind has been advanced by such methods as the production of emotional frustration and deprivation in animals.

Clinical investigation has also been aided immeasurably by studies of the normal physiological mechanisms and responses of experimental animals and of organs isolated from them. Much of what we know about the physiology of the heart, lung, and kidney is derived from experiments in animals. The perfused, isolated heart-lung preparation, one time-honored method, has been responsible for the evolution of many concepts that have had usage at the bedside and the mechanical assistance imperative to all cardiac and pulmonary surgery. Similarly, suitable physiological studies of the nervous system of animals have provided the basis of modern neurology and neurosurgery.

The techniques developed to study the normal physiology of animals have become a sine qua non for the evolution of new therapeutic techniques. The past century has seen the discovery of a host of chemical agents useful in the treatment of disease and disability and the alleviation of pain. Their virtues have almost always first been demonstrated in experimental animals or in their isolated organs. Once their possible utility has been established, such drugs have been tested in animals to determine whether they may be given to human beings with safety. Indeed, federal law now requires that the safety of drugs shipped in interstate commerce be tested exhaustively in animals before clinical trials are allowed to proceed.

Sometimes physiological studies in animals have had widespread clinical implications not anticipated by the investigator. The diagnosis of disorders of the gastrointestinal tract such as peptic ulcer depends in large measure upon x-ray studies performed after the patient has ingested radiopaque materials. This everyday "GI series" is the clinical extension of early experiments upon the motility of the gastrointestinal tract in animals, performed to learn about normal physiology and without any diagnostic implication in mind.

Animals have helped man to understand disease in yet another way. They, too, have diseases, and in some cases these closely resemble those of man. Careful observation of natural disease in animals has provided a way to learn about such pathological processes under conditions that would be inappropriate in human subjects. Three examples will suffice. Dogs, like humans, may be afflicted with hemophilia. The availability of such dogs has made possible studies of the genetics of hemophilia and of the nature of the bleeding tendency (its principal symptom) which would be impossible to perform in human subjects. The peculiar defect in metabolism of the Gunn strain of rats has brought about major advances in our understanding of the processes that result in jaundice in man. And a number of animal species have naturally occurring forms of leukemia or cancer which seem sufficiently similar to human tumors to be useful in the search for improved methods of treatment.

Sometimes it is not their diseases, but the remarkable adaptation of some animals to difficult environments that has advanced knowledge about man. The desert rat, which manages to survive without drinking water, and the toad fish, which can elaborate urine despite an absence of glomeruli (the blood filtration apparatus in mammalian kidneys), are typical examples. The alertness of biologists and veterinarians to the possible significance of these adaptations of animals has been responsible for many advances in our knowledge of human disease.

What is animal experimentation and what is not is a difficult philosophic question. The improvement of animal stocks by careful breeding is a science at least as old as recorded history; Genesis describes Jacob's experiments in some detail. With the development of modern genetic theory, the hereditary process has come to be investigated in a wide variety of species. Because of their rapid maturation, fruit flies have been particularly helpful as a tool to examine both the natural processes of selection and the effect of such agents as x-rays upon heredity. Careful inbreeding of rabbits has provided clues to the differing susceptibilities of human races to tuberculosis. Similar studies, performed in many species, have had wide application in unraveling the way in which human disease is inherited. Yet to be explored are the possible virtues of carefully inbreeding strains of dogs to provide a relatively uniform subject for experimental studies.

The various uses of experimental animals in helping the clinical investigator can be measured at the bedside, in the diabetic receiving insulin, the child whose congenital heart defect has been repaired, or the pernicious anemia patient who can now live out a normal life-span. But the implications for society have been much wider. Our need for an ever-growing food supply has been met to a large degree by improvements in animal husbandry derived from observations in which the investigator had human disease in mind. And, most ironically, when one considers the motivation of the antivivisectionist, the health of domestic animals and pets has profited dramatically from the knowledge gained in such experiments. It is a reasonable assumption that man and beast alike will continue to benefit from the use of animals for the study of fundamental biological processes and as models for the management of human disease.

Biomedical Engineering

The well-being of the community is the joint concern of all its members. Although a number of particular responsibilities are conventionally delegated to professional fields, such as medicine and the life sciences, engineering and the physical sciences, psychology and the social sciences, economics and the management sciences, etc., care of the community is not the sole and unique responsibility of any one of these; society is served by the synergism of all pertinent knowledge and skills. A contemporary example is the emerging area called "biomedical engineering." Biomedical engineering has been characterized as "The application of the methodology and technology of the physical sciences and engineering to problems in the context of the living system with emphasis on the diagnosis, treatment, and prevention of disorder in man."

Biomedical engineering is not a coherent discipline with a systematic philosophy or body of knowledge. It is growing rapidly but haphazardly and opportunistically and is involved with almost the entire spectrum of biology and medicine. Like engineering itself it is addressed both to building — development of instrumentation and data processing systems — and to analysis of complex biological mechanisms by application of engineering science.

Implicit in this statement of scope is the recognition that neither the engineer nor the physician nor biologist can contribute effectively in isolation from other disciplines. In almost every case he must function as a member of an appropriate team of specialists. This does not imply that the engineer or his counterpart from the life sciences is an expert in all pertinent disciplines. It does imply that he is an expert in his field who is willing to learn how to communicate with, understand, and respect serious workers from other fields. Although this statement may seem a familiar platitude, it does contain the essence of what currently is a somewhat troublesome obstacle to progress.

Any attempt to provide a listing of all of the examples where engineer and life scientist teamwork has provided significant contributions to humanity would be presumptuous and boring. Unfortunately, the actual field is so diverse that no sample actually conveys its broad nature. Nevertheless, it must suffice for the purposes of this chapter to consider only a few examples where engineering has provided substantive contributions to the diagnosis and treatment of certain serious disorders.

Scanning for Brain Tumors. Radioisotope scanning for the location of brain tumors is a valuable technique only recently made feasible for routine purposes. It is based upon the selective absorption from the blood, by tumorous tissue, of certain radioactively tagged dyes. A new device, the "Tetrascanner," illustrated in Figure 16-3, is a four-probe, electromechanical, gamma-ray detection and mapping system. Simultaneous production of four planar projection maps of radioactivity distribution in the front, back, left, and right sides of the head provides a definitive location for the site of a tumor. This is accomplished in approximately fifteen minutes.

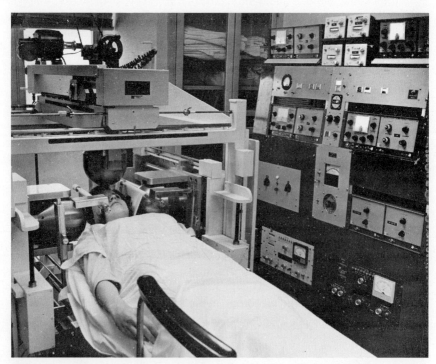

Figure 16-3. The Tetrascanner, a device used for intracranial location of brain tumors. (Courtesy National Institutes of Health)

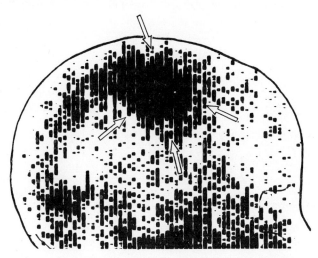

Figure 16-4. Lateral scanning map. A scan, in one plane of the head with an individual with a brain lesion. Human serum albumin, tagged with Technetium[99], was administered intravenously. Note concentration by the tumor of the tagged material. (From G. DiChiro, W. L. Ashburn, and A. S. Grove, Jr., Neurology *18*:225–36, 1968. © Lancet Publications, Inc.)

Figure 16-4 shows a single plane record from an actual scan. Arrows indicate the region of a suspected tumor site. The widespread area of high concentration in the lower portion is due to the normal extensive vascularization of the upper neck and mouth. Smaller, more localized lesions are also readily defined and mapped with little difficulty. Should such diagnosis call for surgery, the patient may enter a neurosurgical operating suite where the floor layout is specially arranged for optimum traffic and work flow patterns and attempts to make the best possible use of modern instrumentation and communication designs.

This facility incorporates comprehensive physiological monitoring and display systems with remotely operated x-ray unit, as well as closed-circuit color television. The surgeon has direct voice communication with the members of the surgical team and observers in the gallery. A 25-channel digital data acquisition system is available, as are facilities for multichannel magnetic tape, videotape, EEG and EKG recordings, oscilloscope displays, and means for monitoring and recording a host of other vital parameters. Table 6 suggests some of the variables that may be simultaneously monitored.

Neurosurgery. Surgery for parkinsonism involves making a tiny lesion in the thalamus of the brain. This can be done by simple cutting, freezing, electrocoagulation, injection of chemicals, or ultrasound. An

Table 6. Physiological Functions Measured by Instrumentation Systems in Cardiac and Neurological Operating Rooms

What	*Where*	*How*	*Why*
Temp #1	Esophagus	Thermistor probe	Patient temperature for hypothermia control
Temp #2	Rectum	Thermistor probe	
Temp #3	Internal	Thermistor needle	
Temp #4	Heart-lung machine inlet	Thermistor probe	Blood temperature for hypothermia control
Temp #5	Heart-lung machine outlet	Thermistor probe	
Pressure #1	Arterial system	Catheter or needle and strain gauge	Measure patient blood pressure and pulse wave forms at various points in the circulatory system
Pressure #2	Arterial system	Catheter or needle and strain gauge	
Pressure #3	Arterial system	Catheter or needle and strain gauge	
Pressure #4	Arterial system	Catheter or needle and strain gauge	
Pressure #5	Venous system	Catheter or needle and strain gauge	
pO_2 #1	Heart-lung machine inlet	Clarke electrode	Effectiveness of oxygenator
pO_2 #2	Heart-lung machine outlet	Clarke electrode	
Blood flow	Heart-lung machine	Electromagnetic flow probe	Determine flow of oxygenated blood to patient
Dye curve	Arterial system	Dye perfused into vein	Diagnose circulatory defects
EKG #1	STD leads	Plate and needle electrodes	Electrical activity of the heart
EKG #2	STD leads	Plate and needle electrodes	
EEG #1	Scalp	Flat or needle electrodes	Determine level of activity of brain for depth of anesthesia indication
EEG #2	Scalp	Flat or needle electrodes	
PPL	Finger	Photoplethysmograph	Indication of pulse pressure
Heart rate		EKG, Pressure, PPL	Cardiac function
CARDIAC ONLY			
Min. volume	Endotracheal tube	Flow screen and differential pressure gauge	Accurate measure of respired gas volume
Blood loss	Collection bottle	Force transducer weighs bottle	Precise and convenient indication of blood loss
NEUROLOGICAL ONLY			
GSR	Palm of hand	Resistance probes	To gauge psychophysiological reaction
Stimulus current	Brain	Direct electrode probe	Determine threshold stimulus
Respiration rate	Chest	Expansion transducer	General patient condition

720

extremely precise instrument for treatment by electrocautery is shown in Figure 16-5 (two views).

The stereotaxic device holds the patient's head firmly in place and allows the surgeon to pinpoint the brain lesion.

Preliminary examinations and x-rays show the general area where surgery is necessary. The device is then mounted on the skull with three permanently implanted screws. After determining the position of the target area, an incision is made and the electrodes are passed through the skull, deep into the brain, guided by the stereotaxic device. Multiple electrical recordings of brain wave potentials are taken as the electrode is advanced. The appearance of a distinct pattern signifies the exact region of disturbance.

A small segment of brain tissue is destroyed by heating the electrode. The three screws remain implanted in the patient's skull so that, should there be a recurrence, the preliminary steps for surgery would not have to be repeated.

Biomedical engineers and mathematicians, well trained in signal theory and systems analysis, are now hard at work with expert neurophysiologists attempting to define the precursors of conditions such as parkinsonism and epilepsy. Their studies are based on the hypothesis that incipient disorder is implied by particular patterns in the electroencephalograph. If they are successful, it may be feasible to do away with the drastic measures now required.

Other Applications. The engineer bears almost complete responsibility for the reliability of the equipment he designs and builds. For example, during open-heart surgery a heart-lung bypass machine is used. Only one is provided. Should the system fail during operation, there is not sufficient time to replace it with another unit. Thus, backup machines are not feasible and the instrument must be perfect.

The state of the art in materials is probably the chief current stumbling block to progress in some areas of medical instrumentation, especially in the field of prosthetics. Technology is woefully inadequate in knowledge of the physical and chemical properties of inert materials for long-term implantation within the body. But there is also a profound lack of information on the properties of living materials, such as bone, tissue, and body fluids. Satisfactory devices for renal or cardiovascular replacements cannot be delivered by engineers until the short- and long-term detrimental interactions of inert and living media can be controlled. Pertinent problems that remain to be resolved include corrosion, infection, thrombogenesis, protein denaturation, and toxicology. All are being studied vigorously, and subsequent positive developments can be anticipated with confidence. There is strong justification for a concentrated program of research, development, and testing in the area of materials

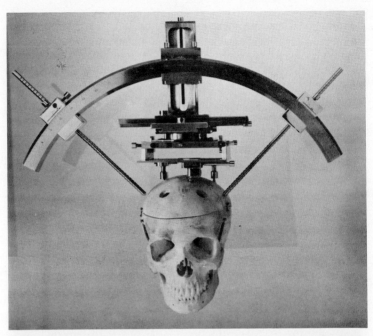

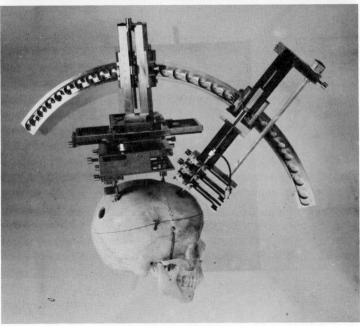

Figure 16-5. Demonstration of stereotaxic device for treatment of Parkinsonism. (From J. M. Van Buren, *Electroencephalography and Clinical Neurophysiology 19*:398–403, 1965. © Elsevier Publishing Company)

performed by collaboration of the best talents from the fields of the physical and life sciences together with their peers from medicine and engineering.

We can here only indicate some other applications of bioengineering, most of which are presently in a rudimentary state. These include application of the systems approach, or cybernetic analysis, to neurological function; models of the circulation including analysis of blood flow and dissipation of the work of the heart; models of the respiratory system; application of the principles of mechanics to understanding the properties of vessel walls, the capsule of the lens, skeletal joints; examination of heat flow through the human organism; and detailed analysis of the propagation and spread of the potentials in an electrocardiogram. The use of computers will soon revolutionize biology as it has the physical sciences. Many instances have been given throughout this book. Here we need only note also the use of computers for pattern recognition which elucidates the manner in which this is accomplished in the human brain; the use of computers, summarizing the totality of available diagnostic data, to screen a population for possible disease; and the use of computers and scanning band-pass filters to provide a highly sensitive, discriminating "stethoscope." Of great current interest also are design of ever smaller and more reliable cardiac pacemakers, ultrafine beam lasers as surgical tools, diagnostic use of ultrasound to visualize soft parts of the body and by "echosonography" detect tumors of the breast, liver, etc., the entire development of the man/machine complex for space travel, and the "flying spot" electron microscope. In addition, bioengineering has provided the entire array of instrumentation characteristic of the modern biomedical laboratory and hospital and the computer systems that must soon take over the entire system of record keeping for the hospital.

Recent popular literature has painted impressive pictures of some remarkable accomplishments achieved via technology and medicine. Special attention has been given to artificial organs, automation, and medical applications of exotic forms of energy. Serious workers in the field acknowledge the relatively crude nature of what has been accomplished. The very best of the new devices must be considered as temporary, stopgap measures, to be viewed with caution and suppressed enthusiasm. However, although the current position may be rather primitive, the trend is highly encouraging, and the future appears limitless.

Expected Trends in Clinical Research

The subject of clinical research is people with disease. But the changes made by disease can only be understood by reference to the normal state.

Only by understanding the phenomena of life as deeply as possible can we hope to understand the nature of disease. Clearly, there is no way of telling what is abnormal unless one knows the normal. When a bone is broken in a fall, it is clear how things went wrong and why the victim is disabled. The understanding that a particular kind of illness in a child is caused by deficiency of an enzyme needed to complete the making of an adrenal hormone and knowing how to restore health could never be gained just by the examination of sick and well people. Behind it must lie the enormous task of unraveling the biosynthesis and mode of action of that hormone.

Clinical research is disease-oriented, but the trail rapidly leads far from the bedside into country charted by fundamental life scientists. Clinical investigators have done some charting of their own in many such regions, but they are rarely equipped to be pioneers. Because of the mutual interdependence of medical progress and biological science, a discussion of activities in clinical research quickly becomes involved with more basic biological science. Since the field is vast, attention must be limited to a few of the major present-day areas of interest.

Whatever the progress of medical science has been, the fact that half of the individuals born today can expect to die before their seventieth birthday measures the distance still to go. The gravest risk still lies within the first year of life. The next decades will doubtless see increasing efforts to predict and anticipate those situations providing the greatest danger to mother and child and to develop more effective diagnostic and therapeutic methods of management. Indicative of the direction in which information will be gained is the evolving art of detecting the asymptomatic carriers of hereditary disease, the development of ways to diagnose potentially hazardous disease before or at the time of birth, and the elaboration of new techniques to prevent erythroblastosis fetalis, still a major cause of neonatal morbidity. At the same time, increasing knowledge of contraceptive techniques, developed for a variety of needs, will find application in the knowledgeable, deliberate prevention of hereditary disease.

Perhaps the greatest advances made in medicine have been in the prevention and treatment of infectious diseases, particularly those of bacterial origin. The therapy of viral disorders is still primitive. In these diseases, the patient's cells are invaded by agents containing deoxyribonucleoprotein (DNA) or ribonucleoprotein (RNA). Because of the central role of DNA and RNA in the biology of all organisms, including man, a major portion of modern experimental medicine is devoted to their study. Hope that effective means of neutralizing the effects of viruses will be found rests today on deeper understanding of the metabolism of these substances.

The hereditary information which passes from generation to generation via the chromosomes of the ovum and sperm is carried within the DNA, which serves as a code from which are developed templates upon which the body's enzymes and other proteins are synthesized. The particular DNA one inherits determines the individual characteristics of each of us, the healthy and those afflicted with hereditary disorders. As information concerning the nature of this material accumulates, there are those who dream of attempts to supplement the defective DNA of patients with certain hereditary disorders with DNA from normal individuals; in this way, an individual who cannot synthesize some essential enzyme would be made to do so by utilizing the DNA of transplanted cells from normal individuals. In view of the widespread distribution of defective genes, and increasing success in keeping their bearers alive to reproductive age, research so directed should be encouraged even if the goal remains over the horizon for the indefinite future. The inadequacies of our present methods of organ transplantation are due, in large measure, to an imperfect understanding of the means of suppressing the normal immunological mechanisms which serve to destroy any tissue foreign to the body. Such studies can be expected to continue until a solution is found.

The expanding understanding of the participation of DNA in the development of all cells and of the body as a whole will probably have its greatest effect in prevention and treatment of tumors. Whatever the "causes" of cancer, tumors are characterized by unbridled growth. Information must be obtained which will tell us how the size of each normal organ and tissue is controlled normally, so that each cell assumes its relative place. Why does the regenerating liver cease growing when it attains a "normal" cell mass? Such knowledge may lead to understanding of the nature of the disordered growth of tumor tissue and its control.

Once the hazards of childhood have passed, the greatest risk to life resides in disorders of the heart and blood vessels. The major cause of death from these diseases is the development of arteriosclerosis and thrombosis — that is, hardening of the arteries and clots within blood vessels. Several lines of attack currently being pursued can be expected to continue. The relationship between heredity and such environmental factors as diet and smoking will continue to be studied by epidemiological means, attempting to alter the habits of selected, closely observed populations. Animal models of arteriosclerotic disease, not presently available, will be of great importance in determining the effects of various potentially deleterious or therapeutic agents. But the greatest advances may be anticipated from studies of the intimate details of the metabolism of vascular tissues, particularly in relation to lipids. Prevention rather than cure must be the goal of such programs.

The process of thrombosis has remained a mystery despite a massive effort. To date, the bulk of our understanding has come from studies of its mirror image, conditions such as hemophilia in which patients bleed excessively. Further development of experimental methods of inducing thrombosis may provide the tools needed to prevent and treat this pathological process. A closer liaison between physicists, interested in fluid mechanics, and clinical investigators, puzzled by the development of thrombosis when blood flow is retarded, may lead to progress in this area. The treatment of heart disease will progress, too, from the continued invention of surgical methods of repair, a field in which trials in animals must certainly precede application to the human patient.

Yet another major cause of death and disability is accident. The application of modern computer techniques to a moment-by-moment study of the bodily changes associated with shock, now in its infancy, should bring us closer to a solution to this baffling problem. Improved methods of storage and transfusion of blood, its components, and synthetic substitutes are needed to restore normal physiological conditions in severely injured or burned patients. And continued inventiveness by surgeons and orthopedists may help to minimize the crippling aftermath of accident. But the greatest need is an increase in our understanding of the psychological processes which lead individuals to put themselves at undue risk. We are only at a beginning, too, in learning how to construct the environment so as to minimize the danger of accident – in the construction of automobiles, in the choice of chemicals to be used in the home, in the supervision of athletics. Although these fields seem far from those usually pursued by the clinical investigator, his skill is needed by engineers, chemists, and others more intimately concerned with such problems.

If the disorders reviewed thus far are potentially lethal, those such as rheumatism, diseases of the nervous system, and psychiatric disturbances may make life hardly worth the living. Fundamental advances in elucidating the nature of diseases of joints are being sought in two major areas. Headway is being made in an appreciation of the role of immune mechanisms in the development of such diseases as rheumatoid arthritis. The increasing efforts to understand the chemical events responsible for the inflammatory and destructive changes that take place in diseased joints may lead to more immediate benefit. Here, rapid advances in knowledge concerning chemical mediators of inflammation can be expected and, concomitantly, perhaps the development of more effective therapeutic agents.

No aspect of biomedical research is of greater importance than investigations of the aging process. How much disease and incapacitation is the unavoidable consequence of the passage of time? Can the deleterious effects of aging be postponed – as in Shangri-La – even without an increase in the mean life-span? What could be a greater boon to humanity? Only a beginning has been made concerning the fundamental nature of the many crippling neurological diseases. As general knowledge of biochemistry and genetics increases, their application to those disorders may furnish new insights with prophylactic and therapeutic application. Thus, the recognition of phenylketonuria as a cause of mental retardation has led to the development of prophylactic, diagnostic, and therapeutic methods; and an intimate understanding of the chemistry of Wilson's disease (accumulation of copper in the brain due to lack of a normal copper-carrying protein of plasma) has brought about new techniques for retarding and reversing this process. Bold surgical measures, based upon a growing knowledge of the physiology of the nervous system, have led to the alleviation of the tremors of patients afflicted with parkinsonism. And from studies of amino acid metabolism came a seemingly specific drug for this unpleasant malady. Presumably, as time goes on, other disorders will become amenable to treatment. The great distance yet to go can be exemplified by that form of mental retardation known as mongolism (Down's syndrome). The application of cytological techniques developed by geneticists has led to the discovery of gross abnormalities in the chromosomes of afflicted individuals, but no therapeutic measures are yet within reach.

An equally pessimistic view must be taken concerning the immediate future of studies of psychiatric disease. Of course, myriad psychiatric disturbances exist, and no single approach will serve as a key to all. In some instances, biochemical studies may be the first significant steps, as in the recent elucidation of one form of destructive behavior in children. In others, a more complete understanding of the relationship between the individual and his environment, hopefully unfettered by the cliches of the past, may be rewarding. Although these various methods are being utilized increasingly, a new giant step, comparable to the development of psychoanalytic theory, is needed before much progress can be expected.

This brief summary has only brushed at the approaches to clinical research that may be anticipated in the next decade. Predictions of the future direction of clinical investigation, like those of other human affairs, are hazardous, but on the record, the greatest benefit will accrue from the slow accumulation of basic knowledge concerning the nature of normal physiological and chemical processes. One cannot apply knowledge to the prevention and treatment of disease until the knowledge exists.

Clinical research, after a millennium, has come of age. In the intensively managed, highly instrumented "clinical research units" of our great hospitals, clinical investigation has become a legitimate science. Human biology is being explored with unprecedented vigor and sophistication, and the information net of the biomedical community assures that scientific discovery, in all disciplines, is applied to human disease with wondrous alacrity.

This endeavor, the focal activity of university medical centers, is less than two decades old. How, then, shall one measure its success? Not alone by the large and small insights into the nature of life or the pathogenesis of disease, nor by the pain alleviated or the lives saved. We are all too aware of the woeful limitations of medicine, of the anguish of suffering, tortured humanity, including those who are left behind. The true measure of success of this research enterprise is to be found in the hopeful, confident spirit of the biomedical research community as it faces the future, armed with an increasing wealth of information and insight, and with ever more powerful tools with which to undertake its noble task.

Chapter 17

RENEWABLE RESOURCES

Both the biological and physical elements of the earth are vital to man. Land (soil), water, air, and populations of plants and animals can, under certain conditions, be used over and over again. These are man's renewable resources, and their sound management has become a prime concern to man for both his well-being and, perhaps, his survival on this planet. The greatest single threat to environmental resources and to man himself is his own "population explosion," with the rising pressure on food, land, and water needs. Only by understanding the function and interaction among biological and physical elements of the environment and applying that understanding to the management of resources can man control his numbers and keep his environment livable.

Man is an integral part of the vast natural system that surrounds him. Although the major portion of man's food comes from only about 100 species of plants and animals, many thousands of species including microorganisms interact to provide the environment required by these major food sources. It has been estimated that at least 150,000 plant and animal species in the United States are involved in the collection and transfer of the sun's energy for the maintenance of life. In addition, some of these species are decomposers serving to break down waste products and dead organic material to make such essentials as carbon, nitrogen, and other elements available to plants for reuse and transmission to animals through the food chains of the biotic system. Beyond these material needs, living organisms are important in fulfilling esthetic and recreational needs.

Living systems have evolved for many millions of years to become a part of the environment as we know it today. Adaptation through selection and genetic change has required many generations. Although civilization has developed throughout history at the expense of natural resources, population growth and technological achievements in the twentieth century have produced a disruptive assault on the environment on a scale greater than ever before. Contamination emanating from these technological developments and urban concentrations has altered the chemical and physical characteristics of our seas, lakes, rivers, soils, and air. While simplified food chains have been exploited on some land to satisfy civilization's requirements for food and fiber, other vast land and aquatic areas have been developed for uses not associated with biological production. Economists project that within the next 20 years some 28 million acres (an area larger than Ohio) will be converted into urban areas and highways in the United States; four fifths of this land will come from croplands, pastures, and forests. Poor management in the past has resulted in loss of a third of the topsoil in the United States, with consequent lowered potential productivity.

It is difficult to return land to cultivation once it has been built upon. The quality of some of our surface and ground waters can be restored, but the results of pollution are costly to reverse with the knowledge currently available to us. For example, even if the introduction of fertilizing nutrients is terminated, and if the waters of a historically heavily polluted lake can be completely exchanged over a period of time, the enormous amount of harmful matter bound in the bottom mud may continually replenish the pollutant materials.

How much can we abuse our renewable resources—how much area can we remove from production, how many species can we destroy—before our resources will be unable to support man in a quality environment? These crucial questions need answers now before renewable resources deteriorate to an irreversible level. We must maintain a continuous assessment of our renewable resources—land, water, air, and living things—because their status constantly changes. Only with such information can we find new and better ways to ensure their continuing availability.

The purpose of this chapter is to review the important biological relationships of natural resources and man. Particular emphasis will be placed on the application of ecological knowledge to agriculture, forestry, fisheries, wildlife, recreation, health, and community and industrial development. We will concentrate on the important role ecological knowledge has played in managing our renewable resources for maximum use and improved environmental quality.

Role of Science in the Management
of Renewable Resources

Life has been subjected to continuous environmental influences since it appeared on this planet. Even the earliest conscious efforts of primitive man to cope with or take advantage of environmental factors to enhance his survival required recognition of these factors and attempts to understand them. Although man has continually sought to improve his understanding of his environment, his efforts to manage it have fallen short of preventing the deterioration and depletion of resources.

The observations of early naturalists made important contributions to these efforts to understand the environment. More recently, studies by pioneering systematists, geneticists, physiologists, evolutionists, and morphologists provided much information of value to problem-solving ecology, although the significance of their contributions was not recognized for many years. For example, it was systematists who demonstrated there are two species, with different ecologies, in the screwworm fly group, which greatly simplified subsequent control operations directed against the screwworm fly devastation of cattle.

During the past half century or so, ecologists have searched for the principles underlying the organization and functioning of living things and their environment. Gradually they have come to recognize the complexity of these systems and have categorized the influences on them as physical, biological, and, in some instances, social or cultural. Modern concepts of this dynamic relationship recognize the constant interaction among all factors that make up the ecosystem.

Ecology

Ecology deals with the interrelationships of living organisms themselves and their environment. Modern ecology evolved from natural history. Today four major methods of study can be recognized, each representing an advance in synthesis over the preceding one.

Species Studies. The most direct kind of ecological study is the study of the distribution and requirements of species. Some of this work has taken its origin in pest, disease, or crop production problems. Here the life history of the species and the various environmental influences, including environmental stress, are studied. The dominant approach of this type of ecology, frequently called autecology, is to focus on a species and to regard everything else as "environmental factors," including the effect of other plants and animals. It finds its expression in recent literature as "ecological life history."

Population Studies. Many natural phenomena cannot be adequately explained by research on the properties of individuals and environment alone. Therefore, the properties of groups of individuals, or populations, need to be considered. Indeed, populations have properties not shown by individuals. An individual dies but once, but a population has a death rate that varies with its environment and age composition of the population. In addition, the population has a birth rate that varies also according to environment and age. These two are combined to produce the rate of population growth and productivity, and these properties are involved in the management of renewable resources and in understanding fluctuations in natural populations.

Community Studies. Biotic communities consist of species populations, and therefore the focus in community studies is the interrelationship and interaction of populations. For example, the growth and development of an active population of insects may affect the condition of its host species population, which may, in turn, influence the development of populations of insects. Thus, for a given type of location one can develop the idea of the biological community in which the various species perform particular kinds of functions and are related to one another in a complex but definable way. The development of ecological concepts of primary production, consumption, and decomposition led to studies of the production of organisms and organic materials, and the transfer of these materials through the interacting parts in the community. The concept of the community as an organized system with some degree of self-regulation has proven valuable in understanding the control of population size, natality, mortality, and productivity.

Ecosystem Studies. In general the ecosystem is the community plus the nonbiological parts of the environment—that is to say, the inorganic chemical components of the environment and such physical factors as temperature and light. Here again, the community strongly affects the character of the environment in which it lives. In a lake, the development of a crop of algae reduces the concentration of scarce nutrient elements, affects the penetration of light into the lake, and thereby affects the temperature of the upper water. Thus, a detailed study of the chemical and temperature conditions of the lake cannot be made without some measurement of the biological conditions also present. An essential point to understand here is that the whole system responds. A direct effect of an environmental change on one part may feed back to cause other parts of the system to make readjustments in activity or abundance.

Natural Selection and Ecology

Detailed studies of ecosystems or communities provide impressive demonstrations of mutual adaptation of species to one another and to their physical conditions. Host and parasite, prey and predator, and herbivore and plant are integrated in their life histories and requirements. These conditions can be understood in the light of modern evolutionary theory which is based on genetic variability and natural selection and provides a satisfactory framework for understanding the diverse characteristics of the biological world. The result is the sum total action-reaction of population, genetic variability, and environment. In this area understanding of population properties is most critically needed. With the process of evolution considered as changes in gene frequencies in populations, it is essential to understand environmental selection that affects the genes in future generations and the ways population properties are influenced by the genetic makeup of the individuals.

An understanding of the principles of natural selection is required for the intelligent management of renewable resources. Management almost always involves manipulation of populations by methods that depend heavily on artificial selection of genetic traits governing such group properties as productivity, longevity, and reproduction rates. Ability to predict results will increase as more is learned about the mechanisms involved, both in the individual and in the interaction of populations.

Physical Sciences and Engineering

Living organisms depend upon and are influenced by the physical and chemical environment in which they exist. At the same time they perform certain functions that are requisite to the structure and behavior of the physical environment—e.g., production of oxygen by plants in the process of photosynthesis. Thus, the proper understanding of the biosphere requires information about the physical nature of the environment (geology and soil science), the transport systems that move substances to and away from living things (meteorology and hydrology), the transformations that take place in the nonliving parts of the environment (physics and chemistry), and the means of modifying the environment (engineering, including weather modification).

One example of the interrelated interests of the scientific and technological community is the so-called greenhouse effect of carbon dioxide. Carbon dioxide is nearly transparent to visible light, but is a strong absorber and back radiator of infrared; consequently an increase of atmospheric CO_2 could act, depending on water vapor and cloud cover, much like the glass in a greenhouse, to raise the temperature of the lower air. This is clearly of concern to the meteorologist studying the heat balance of the earth. The biologist is concerned both because any change in the temperature regime will affect ecological systems, and because plants in turn are important in removing CO_2 from the atmosphere. Other parts of the CO_2 in the atmosphere are taken up by the oceans by physical processes and converted to carbonates by chemical processes.

Similar interrelations of environmental biology and physical sciences and engineering occur in virtually all other biogeochemical cycles (such as the nitrogen cycle, hydrological cycle, etc.). Geochemical prospecting involves application of knowledge of these cycles to the discovery of minerals. Still other examples are the elucidation of physical processes carried out in living organisms, such as reverse osmosis.

Principles of Management

In any rational plan to manage an environment either intensively (as in agriculture) or less intensively (as with wildlife), it must be recognized that each area has a certain set of characteristics, that each living organism has a certain range of physical conditions that it can tolerate, and that for each condition there is some point or zone within the range which is near optimum. Organisms are aggregated into communities, the members of which are determined equally by their common ability to tolerate the physical conditions of the site and by their interactions with the other members of the community. The relationship is not passive, for the organisms in turn interact with and may change the site. Their tolerance levels are not necessarily identical, but they overlap in the range of conditions present on a site. As conditions change, new forms, with tolerances that fall within the new ranges, may become a part of the community; some of those originally present may be eliminated. The less rigorous the conditions of the site, the greater will be the variety of niches and inhabitants.

The members of the community influence, and in turn are influenced by, the other organisms present. They may compete for common resources such as water or oxygen, or trace elements, or even living space; and they may eat or be eaten. Green plants are the only important means of capturing and storing energy from the sun. Other organisms feed on these primary producers and may in turn be fed upon. Still others return the complex organic molecules of dead things into mineral elements which will again be cycled through the community. In the aggregate these com-

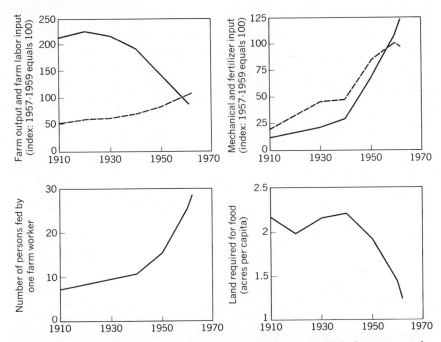

Figure 17-1. Vast improvement of agricultural production in the U.S. demonstrates the value of modern techniques. At top left, index of farm-labor input (black curve) declined from 212 in 1910 to 85 in 1962, while the farm output index (broken curve) rose from 51 to 108. The change was due in great part to increased use of machinery (top right, broken curve) and fertilizers and liming materials (black curve). The number of persons supplied by one farm worker in 1820 was 4.12. By 1910 it had risen to 7.07 (bottom left) and in 1962 it had jumped to 28.57. The number of acres needed to feed one person declined from 2.17 in 1910 to 1.23 in 1962 (bottom right). (From "Food" by Nevin S. Scrimshaw © 1963 by Scientific American, Inc. All rights reserved.)

munity members perform a range of functions indispensable to the well-being of man.

Two basic courses are open to us in using our surroundings: we can adapt our needs and demands to the capabilities of each area, or we can modify an area to change its capabilities. Urban and regional development, waste disposal without overloading the water or the air, and some recreational pursuits are examples of the former.

In changing areas, we can manage with different intensities. Beginning with the most intensive management, we can control the species present and the physical features of the environment. This is what is done in agriculture (Fig. 17-1), pond fish culture, and some plantation forestry. On a somewhat less intensive basis we modify the environment to favor selected species already present on the site, as is usually done in wildlife management or extensive forestry. Lastly, we can harvest from what is present, adapting our harvest to the capability of the population to produce, as is done in most high seas fisheries, wild rubber harvest, etc. With all three levels of intensity, we may also influence or control the biological interactions such as competition, predation, and disease. Generally speaking, the more intense the management, the farther conditions will be from "natural" and the greater the input in energy required to maintain conditions in the desired state.

Environmental Management

Agriculture

Agriculture has evolved beyond crop culture to become an environmental technology with its prime focus on the management of land, water, air, and biological resources for the production of food and fiber and for the preservation of natural resources. The farm or ranch is, in fact, a managed ecosystem, and to be successful it must be a well-regulated ecosystem where the renewable resources are effectively conserved. More than ever before in man's history it is imperative that intensive research be utilized to develop the technology by which agricultural practices can more effectively conserve our vast land, water and biological resources.

Through sound management, agriculturalists have been successful in making permanent use of renewable resources, especially land. In many places, the quality of the resources has been improved by careful use and management, with resulting increases in production and income. For example, in studies of individual farms in Illinois, yearly investments of about $35 per acre in conservation practices for soil and water returned about $41 per acre per year. Similarly land that had yielded an average, per acre, of 15 bushels of corn yielded 304 bushels per acre after six years of effective rotation and cropping practices. This kind of management makes possible the continuous and efficient use of the same natural resources year after year. In coming decades with expanding world populations, this aspect of conservation will become even more vital.

In sharp contrast the unsound use of renewable resources has led to disasters of the magnitude of the Dust Bowl. Previous to the settlements in the 1870's and 1880's, the Great Plains had been protected against erosion during periods of drought by the natural cover of the short grasses. The first white settlers cultivated the land for wheat and in doing so destroyed the protective, natural sod. Then bare soil was exposed to wind and other eroding forces until the soil structure was broken down.

Thus, when severe droughts came in 1910 and 1931, soil conditions were ripe for devastation such as never had occurred before in the Great Plains areas. The Dust Bowl, involving 100 million acres, was a costly lesson to American agriculture, and as a result, the Soil Conservation Service was formed in 1935 to devise and encourage sound land management techniques.

For maximum economic production, all factors involved in the growth and reproduction of plants and animals must be managed as an integrated unit or system. Soil, water, nutrients, and weather make up the physical environment. Crop plants, the basic producers, provide food for man directly, or indirectly through his livestock. Insects, diseases, weeds, and other organisms constitute the predators, parasites, and competitors in this system. The efficient transfer of stored light energy from crop plants to livestock and, finally, to man involves the field of energetics. Adapting plants and animals to the farm and ranch habitat involves evolution through selection. These are some of the more important factors in the farm ecosystem that the agricultural scientist must manipulate to achieve maximum sustained productivity.

Soil conservation practices (contour farming, strip cropping, rotation) illustrate effective use of applied ecology to maintain, even improve, soil resources. Other ecological principles have been employed to increase crop and animal production but often have not been extended far enough to protect our renewable resources. For example, pest control by pesticides continues to increase, with pesticides consequently becoming important pollutants both on and off the farm.

Water will always be a precious resource, and its pure quality and supply must be maintained. In agriculture, much ground and surface water is lost or polluted by current practices. Manure, silts, and pesticides are some of the most serious pollutants. It is estimated that a fourth of all water stored for irrigation is lost by evaporation before use; yet water use in agriculture is increasing (Fig. 17-2). Research has begun but more is needed to find ways to reduce evaporation of water in storage; some new chemical films offer considerable promise under special conditions.

Research is also under way on weather modification with an emphasis on "rain-making." The most immediate likelihood of effective increases in precipitation is an increased snowpack in the mountainous watersheds of the West. There are also experiments in "seeding" of summer clouds to increase precipitation in both the Southwest and the Dakotas. Eventually there will be increased efforts to modify precipitation patterns in the East. The degree of increase in precipitation anticipated is on the order of 10–20 percent. Increases of this magnitude may well revolution-

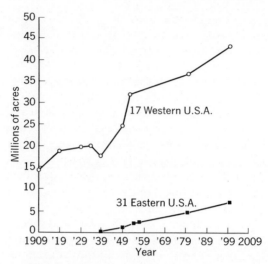

Figure 17-2. Recent and projected trends in the acres of farm land in the 31 Eastern and 17 Western states of the United States. (From Senate Committee on National Water Resources, Print No. 12, 86th Congress)

ize crop and animal production in some parts of the United States; they may also profoundly affect natural plant and animal communities. Programs leading toward management of the weather must also be accompanied by programs to understand the biological and legal consequences. We must be clear that when such programs are undertaken on a large scale, the net changes produced will be beneficial. Some concern has been expressed about the potential biological effects of silver iodide, which is used in cloud seeding; however, it seems unlikely that such effects will be evident because of the extremely small amounts of this compound needed to form the precipitation nuclei.

Control of transpiration by plant hormones also offers a real opportunity to conserve water. This is well illustrated when it is recognized that of the 500,000 gallons of water absorbed by an acre of corn in Illinois, in one season, 498,750 gallons of water are lost by transpiration to the atmosphere.

We know the gross requirements of most crop species for soil, nutrients, and water and recognize that the specific requirements may be altered by breeding. A delicate balance exists for the plant in its environment, and more detailed studies are needed on the nutrient and water budgets of plants. Plant density per acre is important in production; hence, plant competition and the influence of plant spatial patterns need further investigation. With more complete information about environmental requirements of plants for increased production, it may be possible to use less fertilizer and water.

To support increased production, agriculturalists must intensify their studies on genetic aspects of plant and animal adaptation. When crop plants and livestock have been brought from the wild they have been selected and bred to improve certain characteristics. Heretofore, selection in crops has been primarily directed at better yield, storage, and shipping qualities. These breeding procedures have frequently resulted in the loss, for example, of insect and disease resistance. Research in the future should focus on adapting plants to the total farm ecosystem. This would include selecting and breeding plants not only for the usual characteristics but for additional characters—e.g., insect and disease resistance, effective growth using less nutrients and water, plus improved nutritional and flavor quality. To include all these characters might reduce yields slightly, but this would be more than compensated for by reduced production costs for insect and disease protection in addition to reduced costs for fertilizer and water. In total, therefore, crop production would be significantly more economical, while at the same time reducing pollution hazards and conserving our resources.

Greater effort should be made to integrate the work of the various specialists in agriculture. For example, pest control specialists should be part of the team contributing to the "farm system" approach, because both plants and animals must be protected against pest attack if maximum yield is to be realized. Pesticides are essential in today's food and fiber production and the protection of health of our livestock. Along with their beneficial qualities, however, pesticides are costly, are causing pollution of the natural environment, are destroying beneficial organisms, and are even creating new pest problems. Reduction in pest control problems can be achieved by research focused on the development of well-coordinated diversified control programs. The strategy of control should be centered on the management of pest populations as a part of the farm or ranch ecosystem. Once a pest's ecology is understood, it may be possible to modify the crop system to control a pest.

In crop protection several major avenues of research and development can be followed to reduce pollution hazards without sacrifice of agricultural productivity. Breeding of pest-resistant crop plants and animals should be intensified. Control of the Hessian fly by breeding resistant wheat demonstrates the effectiveness of this procedure. Research on the uses of parasites, predators, and pathogens in pest control should also be intensified. The possibility of controlling pests through genetic manipulation deserves much more attention. Hormones, pheromones, and other chemicals that influence the behavior and ecology of pests or their hosts should be investigated more intensively. Environmental manipulation practices, such as plant spacing, water management, sanitation, soil preparation, crop rotation and fertilization, and mixed-plant-culture in crops and forests, may seriously affect pest populations. These practices should be studied with a view to understanding how to manipulate the crop environment so as to minimize pest populations.

Much remains to be learned about improving the effectiveness of pesticide use. There is urgent need for investigations seeking pesticides with greater specificity for the target organisms as well as new methods of applying these agents directly to the pest.

One of the most important needs in pest control is knowledge of the ecology of the pest species. Once the habits and factors influencing the survival of a pest species are understood, ways are more easily devised for its control. Too often poisons are employed with little knowledge about either the pest or any of the other species present in the biotic community, and as a result the environment may be radically and perhaps unnecessarily changed. For example, organic insecticides had been used for about fifteen years against cabbage pests before any attempt was made either to identify the parasites and predators attacking the pest insects or to measure the effects of the insecticides on the parasite and predator populations. After more than one fifth of a century of use of the newer insecticides against pest species, little or nothing is known about their impact upon the majority of species that make up the biotic communities for most crops grown in the United States.

Combinations of species of plants and animals growing in mixed associations offer possibilities not only for pest control but also for increasing productivity. Instead of a monoculture of one plant or one animal, for example, it should be possible in cultivated pasture management to increase the numbers of plant species and at the same time have several animal species grazing the plant complex; increased protein production has already been attained in this way using native ungulates in some areas of East Africa.

Agricultural wastes, both manure and crop residues, have become a major environmental pollutant. For example, a cow generates as much manure as sixteen humans. Farm animals in the United States also produce ten times as much plant waste as does the human population. A similar problem exists with piles of crop residues (straw, stalks, stems, bulbs, cobs, nut shells, and fruit pits). Some of these wastes are finding their way into streams, ponds, and other vital water resources. Not only do these wastes produce unpleasant odors and otherwise pollute the air and water, they also afford a breeding place for insects. Ideally, these wastes should be recycled in the farm and ranch ecosystem. Currently animal wastes are being surface-buried to speed the return of the nutrients to the soil and to avoid unpleasant odors and insect breeding. Research on the biological, physical, and chemical properties of agricultural wastes is basic to the development of new ways to make effective use of them in agricultural production.

In some intensive agricultural operations, such as the battery raising of poultry, it is no longer possible to recycle manure wastes on the farm or ranch itself. Ways will have to be found to move the wastes from these farms and to reuse them. These wastes have a high nutrient content, and through research new products might be developed, similar to that of the processed poultry manure which is presently being fed to cattle as an additional protein source.

By processing crop residues to extract proteins, fats, and vitamins we have been able to make some use of them. Some of the dried residues have been used whole for animal bedding, mulching, building materials, and some, like nut shells, have been used as dust carriers for various chemicals. Residues have also been dried and ground and used as livestock food supplements. By-products today make up more than one third of the poultry rations and about one seventh of the ration for growing and fattening swine. They are also important in feeding beef and dairy cattle.

Intensified research should lead us to other effective means of making use of agricultural wastes. Perhaps the establishment of new food chains on farms and ranches will provide one answer to the problem of disposing of these wastes.

Forestry

Forestry deals with the management of wooded lands for various goods and services. The term *wooded lands* is liberally construed to mean forest landscapes including areas of alpine rockland, native grass, brush, and swamps. Such areas often influence management of adjacent lands. Wood production is the principal objective of most large corporate ownerships, but water yield, watershed protection, recreation, grazing, wildlife production, and protection of scenic values have explicit recognition on many private lands and are primary aims in the management of most public holdings.

The obvious economic value of wood has generated a curious tendency among many conservation writers—including some foresters—to largely equate forestry with timber production. In fact, a century and a half of historical development, as well as present-day practice over large areas, has emphasized game production, stream flora, steep land protection, and nontimber products. This emphasis finds its modern expression in the "multiple use" doctrine which Congress has now declared to be the guiding principle for some 180 million acres of National Forest. It is likewise espoused in varying degree by many other public and private forest landholders. For example, revenues from hunting club leases approximately offset land taxes on some industrial forest holdings. Thus, forestry substantially overlaps the wildlife, recreation, and range management topics discussed elsewhere in this chapter.

In forestry practice, biology is the major, but by no means the exclusive, background discipline. What may be called the earth sciences generally (geology, physiography, hydrology, climatology, and soil science), engineering, and a large economic, social, and managerial component often dictate the framework for biological applications. Moreover, protection from accidental fires has been the sine qua non of forest management through much of North America and necessarily absorbs a substantial part of the resources and technical effort devoted to forest land.

Nevertheless, the protection, manipulation, and use of vegetation are the dominant aim of most forestry activities. Hence, an understanding of the dynamics of this vegetation and its associated populations of animals interacting with the physical environment is the foresters' primary tool.

The applications of biology to forest land management are more readily understood when account is taken of the very different levels of management currently practiced. These have already been referred to under "Principles of Management." The most extensive management for wood products is simply exploitation of useful trees, usually with protection against severe fire and pests, with the hope of natural renewal. The input of biological skill is minimal and the results range from excellent, as in many of the eastern Canadian spruce-fir pulpwood cuttings, to the destruction of the resource. As intensity of management increases, measures such as restricted harvesting, timing of operations, prescribed fire, and thinning are employed to favor reproduction and growth of desired species and reduce competition with less valuable species. Such measures may be insufficient to perpetuate recalcitrant species, such as the American bald cypress or the New Zealand podocarps, whose regeneration requirements are neither met nor understood. At the highest intensities of management, desired species or genotypes are planted or otherwise made dominant, and density and structure as well as composition of the forest are closely controlled. The environment is modified by reduction of competition and pests, and sometimes by soil treatments.

At the lowest intensity of management the reliance upon natural processes is complete; detailed understanding may be minimal. At intermediate intensities, great dependence is placed on understanding the requirements of individual species, their competitive position, and the nature of successional trends which may be either reinforced or combated. This concern diminishes at the highest intensities as regeneration, composition, and density are brought under control, usually with marked reduction in age and species diversity. Attention then shifts to altering genotypes, additional manipulation of soil and plant features, and specific measures against injurious insects and diseases.

One may compare selected management compartments from a paper company holding in the Southeast and a remote district of a National Forest in the Rocky Mountains. The former may consist largely of selected strains of loblolly or slash pine planted on soil prepared by clearing and draining as needed; the wood will be mechanically harvested as raw material for a nearby paper mill in two to three decades. In contrast, the National Forest in the West consists of several age classes of ponderosa pine resulting from natural regeneration after fire or cutting. The climate is such that trees do not reach marketable dimensions in less than a century; low-intensity recreational use, water yield, or grazing may have equal or greater attention as management objectives. The needs for specific biological information and the feasibility of its applications obviously differ vastly between the two situations. The Southeast forester will be concerned with the effect of genotype on fiber quality, the influence of stand density on dry matter production, and nutrient availability in drained soil. The Western forester may place first attention on measures to ensure natural regeneration in the face of adverse climate and grazing pressure, and on the probable alterations in ground vegetation as age and density of the canopy change.

The adequacy of present knowledge can be regarded in terms of species, populations, communities, and ecosystems. For example, the gross morphology of forest trees ordinarily would be considered adequately known, and one might have thought that further study would be unproductive. Yet the nature and widespread extent of the root suckering habit in aspens and sweet gum have only recently been described, and the implications of the resulting network in population structure for the ecology and management of these important species are still being examined. Again, the extent of root grafting among individuals of the same species and its significance in sustaining weaker trees and in distributing diseases and introduced poisons is not yet fully appreciated. In fact, only a handful of commercially important species have been studied sufficiently to be certain that no surprises in structure and function await us. Still less is known about the genetic variability and detailed physiology of most species.

Knowledge of populations of injurious insects and of vertebrates may be more advanced than that available for plants, where communities rather than populations of single species more often have been the objects of study. Many individual components of forest tree "life tables" have been examined intensively for some species—e.g., seed production and dispersion, germination and establishment losses, stocking, mortality, and stand structure. Rarely, however, has a sufficient number of such studies been combined for a single species, quantified, and extended over time to indicate the feasibility of this framework for organizing knowledge about long-lived trees. The simple cases of spaced plantations of single species are ordinarily studied only in respect to gross numbers, mortality, and size; nevertheless observation with radiata pine plantations (that trees destined to die usually could be predicted from changes in growth rate seven to nine years in advance of death) demonstrated that much could be learned about the dynamics of intraspecies competition.

Studies at the community level constitute the bulk of classical plant ecology and include description, classification, and dynamics of forest vegetation. Most of present understanding of forest succession and much of low-intensity management is derived from such studies. Forestry and range management has achieved statistical competence, and sampling capabilities and technological change have diverted much of the ecological interest of foresters to individual species or interactions with the physical environment. As a result, foresters' efforts at classifying and analyzing vegetation are likely to go under the name of ecosystem studies, combining only moderate innovations in categorizing vegetation with considerable attention to climate, geomorphic and soil relationships.

The term *ecosystem studies* is sometimes preempted for the gross aspects of carbon fixation or energy and nutrient flow within simple communities. Thus far, sampling problems imposed by the physical dimension and life-span limit the studies of most forest systems. In the main, the goal of comprehending whole forest ecosystems has been more praised in the abstract than taken as feasible research strategy.

The existing ecological information appears moderately well utilized if account is taken of the limits imposed by economic feasibility.

Fisheries

By fisheries, we mean the use of living aquatic resources by man. True aquiculture, with man's complete control over all phases of a tended organism's life cycle, including a well-regulated harvest, has only regional importance (e.g., carp in the Far East and Israel; trout in North

America and Europe). Nonconsumptive use of aquatic resources, such as fish watching in underwater parks, is also meaningful.

Fishery resources range from marine algae to whales and from the brook trout of alpine streams to benthic crustaceans at 200 fathoms in the sea. With few exceptions, fisheries are restricted to the lighted zone of the waters.

The resources are used primarily for human nutrition, globally making up between 15 and 20 percent of man's protein diet. They also have industrial uses such as the alginates of the cloth and cosmetics trades or the fish oils in paint and related manufacturing processes. Rendered fish products like meal and liquid concentrates are used as fertilizers and animal feeds.

In the Western world some fish species are pursued primarily for sport (e.g., bass), while others are sought for both sport and commercial ends (e.g., lake trout, salmon, billfish), and still others, mostly harvested in bulk, provide food staples and industrial products (e.g., herring, menhaden, anchovies).

Considering the gamut of aquatic plants and animals, the important species harvested are but relatively few in numbers—about 200 among the over 20,000 kinds of fishes—and far fewer are algae, molluscs, crustaceans, or aquatic mammals. Only 12 of these constitute 80 percent of the total catch. This limited number of species used reflects both our willingness to use a particular species and our ability to harvest it. For example, small rock-boring invertebrates or the fauna of a kelp forest, though their biomass may be large per unit area of substrate, are so difficult to harvest that they are not worth the effort required to extract them.

Management for sustained yield is based on several factors, including (a) information (knowledge of age, growth, fecundity, longevity, and mortalities due to natural causes and to exploitation) about the stocks or populations and subpopulations which are often the effective breeding units; (b) information about the taxonomy, life histories, and behavior of the species under natural conditions and when confronted with capturing tools (included here are foods, food habits, sensory capacities, territorial or schooling behavior, knowledge of the actions and selectivity of the capturing gear); (c) information about the environment and the influences on the stocks of such variables as temperature, salinity, currents, and pollutants.

This knowledge, while needed, is available in only a few cases. It is more easily obtained in the freshwater environment than in the open sea. In most places, studies of the hydrosphere have not been conducted long or intensively enough. Among exceptions are the North Sea, parts of the Mediterranean, and certain temperate zone lakes and rivers (e.g., Lake

Mendota in Wisconsin, Horokiwi Stream in New Zealand, the Danube, and the Volga Delta). Although information on population characteristics, including environment and behavior, is lacking for most species of the open sea and tropical fresh waters, there is considerable potential for an increased harvest in these areas. A beginning is being made for the high seas environment, for instance, in the Central Pacific.

The deficiency in information needed for the adequate management of aquatic organisms can be ascribed to (a) lack of planning and failure of political boundaries to correspond to biological boundaries, (b) the short duration of studies in relation to the time span over which natural forces act and in which natural fluctuations take place, and (c) lack of funds, personnel, and interest.

Research on management of renewable natural resources is traditionally the concern of local, national, and international bodies. The level of management-oriented fisheries research is usually determined by the importance of aquatic resources in the nation's economy.

The intensity of management measures applied to living aquatic resources decreases as the population dispersion and area occupied increase. Carp and trout, with their tolerance of confined freshwater areas, can be bred and tended intensively like domesticated animals with good control over their environment, while we can do little or nothing in the vast marine areas required by tuna or herring. With fishes of the latter type, management must now depend upon prediction of population levels and controlled harvest. In the case of tuna in the Pacific, enough is now known about the relationship between tuna distribution and environmental conditions that satisfactory forecasts of distribution of tuna stocks can be made several weeks in advance for the benefit of fishing fleets. Recent advances in tracing the life history of salmon at sea coupled with detailed simulation models of the fishery, including the freshwater phase, provide an improved basis for prediction. Manipulation of spawning areas certainly provides opportunity for genuine management.

Management possibilities and the impact of man differ in the various regions of the hydrosphere. Fish and mammal stocks in the high seas can be managed only if characteristics of population and environment are known. Research on the high seas should be international in scope. Regional fisheries councils facilitate pelagic fisheries research. Agreements on apportionment of harvest through exclusive or joint exploitation are feasible. However, the common property nature of high seas resources makes enforcement of harvest limitations difficult (e.g., only about 1,000 blue whales exist today). Furthermore, catch limits can be quickly filled with modern mechanized gear, and this leads to difficulties in keeping vessels and manpower profitably occupied (e.g., tuna stocks of the Western Pacific).

Offshore fish resources are the most important from the point of view of bulk and dollar value. Such fishes as herrings, sardines, anchovies, and ground fishes (flat fishes) occur in abundance in various inland seas (North Sea, Caspian Sea, etc.) and on the west coasts of certain continents where currents and winds stimulate the upwelling and mixing of nutrients. Geographically, the region coincides with the continental shelf and overlying waters. Management here, like that of the high seas stocks, must rely on regulation of gear and times of capture. More intensive methods of management are not presently feasible. There exist here common property resource problems which can be solved by bilateral agreements (e.g., Canada and the United States, in the halibut fisheries). More and better agreements of this kind are needed; some may require new legal concepts because of the impending exploitation of this zone for other resources (minerals).

Near or inshore resources are often concentrated in shallow waters, near deltas and estuaries, or are associated with coral reefs. They are exploited by operators of small craft who, throughout history, have made up the bulk of the world's fishermen. Of the ocean environments, the inshore resources are most amenable to overexploitation and to environmental deterioration caused by man. Along both coasts estuaries are being filled with wastes at an alarming rate by industrial and housing developments. In addition streams and rivers dump pollutants, collected from their drainage basins, into the estuaries. All this has already altered the ecology of these regions. Now many of these inshore resources will be subjected to further change by the addition of heated effluents from both nuclear and fossil fuel power plants along our coasts. These plants require enormous quantities of water for cooling, and the low-grade waste heat carried by this water will also be enormous. If, for example, sufficient combined nuclear power and desalting plants were constructed on the West Coast to meet the needs for both fresh water and electric power, the rise in temperature of inshore waters might be as much as 4°F. Such a change in temperature would certainly alter the kinds, distribution, and abundance of animals inhabiting this area. We need to be mindful of the opportunities to modify parts of this environment beneficially with this vast resource of low-grade heat which could, with careless use, become a destructive pollutant.

The range of phyla from which man harvests is greater in the inshore regions than in other regions of the hydrosphere; the range of species captured is also considerable and is comparable to that yielded by tropical lakes and rivers. The ecology of the inshore environment is varied in the temperate zone. Inshore regions offer opportunities for intensive resource management (e.g., oysters and other molluscs). At present, some species are intensively managed but no facilities exist for increasing reproductive rates (milkfish, mullet, shrimp), although experimentation is in progress.

The inshore marine environment, together with fresh waters, support the sport fisheries, which are of particular importance in the United States. These regions, marine and fresh water, suffer most from man's activities. Ecological imbalances resulting from events on the land are often difficult to correct, mainly because of traditional divisions in jurisdiction and management of land and water. Authorities entrusted by society with the management of inshore and fresh waters have few or no organizational ties with those who determine land use, location and operation of industrial enterprises, and urban development.

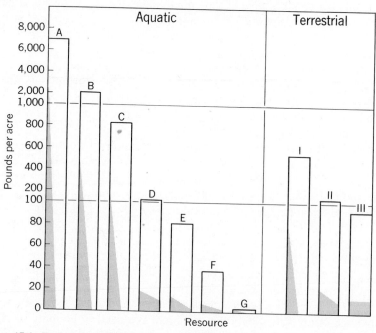

Figure 17-3. Estimated potential yields of fish and meats from various aquatic and terrestrial systems. Peak of shaded area indicates pounds of protein per acre; area of shading indicates proportion of protein relative to total weight of catch. A. Fish ponds, fertilized; B. Tropical lakes; C. Fish ponds, tropical; D. Eutrophic lakes, temperate; E. Fish ponds, unfertilized; F. Atlantic off Iceland; G. Oligotrophic lakes, temperate; I. Hogs; II. Beef, pasture; III. Beef, range. (From G. Borgstrom, ed., *Fish as Food*, II. © 1962 by Academic Press, Inc. And from E. Heen and R. Kreuzer, *Fish in Nutrition*, for the International Conference in Nutrition. © 1962 Fishing News (Books) Ltd.)

The contribution of fresh water to the world protein supply is proportionately greater than would be predicted on the basis of area. High yields from fresh waters (Fig. 17-3) are due to their great primary productivity (sometimes augmented by fertilization) and, in part, to the ease with which they can be exploited. Tropical fresh waters (reservoirs and ponds) seem destined to contribute prominently to human nutrition. The management of these artificial bodies of water in the tropics offers some real challenges, for we know too little of their food chains, nutrient cycles, and thermal regimes. Some, at least, are more resilient under heavy exploitation than those in other areas, and, in fact, underharvest may be our most difficult problem.

Sport fishery in inland waters, especially in the United States, is strongly selective of certain predaceous members (e.g., bass and pike) near the top of the food chain. These make up a very small fraction of the total fish population available for harvest. Commercial fishermen, with their economic needs, stop fishing when it is no longer profitable. Anglers continue fishing for these large fish even though the numbers of fish decline and they have small chance of success.

Anglers are interested in trophies while commercial fishermen depend upon volume of catch. It is seldom expedient to manage natural fish populations for large size of individual fish. Planting of large fish is not the answer. Attempts at management for the production of trophy fish may offer higher quality recreation though perhaps for fewer anglers. Regional customs and provincial attitudes may determine hierarchies in values. Trout fishing is more desirable to some portions of the American angling population than perch or carp fishing, although there is a dwindling supply of trout streams. Similar considerations apply to various other species, such as smallmouth bass or striped bass and bluefish, which tolerate little deviation from their optimum environmental requirements. Their supply is limited while the demand for them increases. It may be possible, perhaps even easier, to modify the life habits of their predators, the anglers, than to conserve the fish and their environment, though this is not a plea for giving up such endeavors. Sport fish management should consider the fishermen as well as the fish.

Wildlife

Wildlife may be defined as wild plants and animals in their natural environment. Wildlife management is the art of producing desired populations of wildlife (though often only animals are considered, and here we consider mainly birds and mammals). The objectives of wildlife management include (a) production and harvest of game species; (b) the maintenance of nongame species; and (c) control of damage by wildlife to crops, forests, range, livestock, or human life. The techniques of wildlife management have developed in a historical sequence which began with restrictions on time or methods of taking game, later included predator control and refuges, and still later moved to artificial replenishment and finally incorporated environmental manipulation.

Even though our knowledge of habitat manipulation is considerable, we still rely on season and bag limit restrictions as the principal management measure for game species. While artificial game propagation attracts much public interest, most wildlife biologists have come to regard this practice as better suited to private, intensively managed or commercial shooting preserves than to public hunting areas.

In its broadest sense, wildlife management includes social, economic, and geographic dimensions; however, its principal concepts are ecological in origin, and wildlife management is clearly an aspect of applied ecology. A recent survey of pertinent literature underscores the importance of ecology in wildlife research. Approximately one third of the papers were concerned with the development or utilization of measurement techniques for population parameters. Another group of papers, making up nearly a second third of the total, were concerned with general ecology and life history studies. One sixth of the total were concerned with mortality or natality, and the last group formed a heterogeneous mixture of ethology, habitat manipulation, miscellaneous techniques and control of wildlife populations.

The distribution of subject matter in these papers reveals a central concern of the wildlife ecologist with population dynamics. A great deal of the effort of fish and game agencies is directed toward gathering information on mortality, natality, and welfare factors which will be integrated to form the basis of the annual announcements concerning time and limits of harvest. Judgment gained from decades of trial and error still weighs heavily in the interpretation of field data; however, increasingly sophisticated techniques are being employed. For example, in big game management, many states have an annual surveillance of sex-age distribution in the population as well as productivity estimates from fawn/adult ratios and other population indices. Additional information is gained at hunter checking stations on ovulation rate, placental scars, and weight and condition of carcasses. On many big game ranges, annual surveys of forage are included as part of the information needed to establish the recommended harvest.

Similarly, information on large segments of species populations (flyways) of migratory game birds such as doves and waterfowl is obtained by an elaborate sampling system designed to estimate the sex and age ratios in the annual kill. The estimates are integrated with an estimate of current productivity to arrive at a projection of an allowable harvest in the upcoming season.

Most wildlife ecologists would agree that habitat manipulation is potentially a far more responsive tool for managing areas intensively than is the regulation of restriction of harvest. Unfortunately, the manipulation of habitats is not feasible on some public and private lands where other uses have high priority. However, on some lands practices such as prescribed burning to maintain jack-pine warbler nesting habitat in Michigan and fire, herbicides, mowing, and grazing to maintain remnants of prairie grouse habitats are used. The most successful widespread use of habitat manipulation came as a result of investigations in the fire ecology of the Southeast pinelands. Here, scientists have developed a high degree of skill in the use of fire to manipulate forest communities for maximum wildlife production combined with timber or pulpwood production.

Among wild terrestrial vertebrates, particularly birds and mammals, much of the descriptive work at the species level has been accomplished. Yet, despite the fact that there are few species that have not been described, many species occupying important niches over large areas are still not well known. For example, until the appearance of a recent monograph, the mountain gorilla was largely a creature of mystery and misunderstanding. Similarly, the Wilson's snipe is an important migratory game bird in the United States which was largely unknown to us until a thorough field study of this species was completed recently. There are also gaps in knowledge of some of the dominant members of the widespread communities in North America. There is, for example, little knowledge of the actual effects of weather on deer, field voles, cottontail rabbits, or upland game birds. Nor do we understand the physiological and behavioral adaptations of these species. The interactions among closely related species also need much more work. For example, the effect of an expanding starling population upon other cavity-nesting species and its role as a vector of domestic animal diseases should be more thoroughly studied.

On the community level, we have few examples to point to as models of understanding. Perhaps we have a better comprehension of grassland and tundra communities than any other. We know little about complex woodland communities, and we need to know how seral stages compare in productivity and utilization. Moving to the ecosystem level, our list of accomplishments diminishes correspondingly.

The use of electronics, telemetry, and photography in remote sensing offer opportunities for real gains in dealing with wildlife problems. Research is under way using some of these capabilities, but progress is considerably short of what seems possible. The space research program may in the near future launch a satellite with some components suitable for use by wildlife ecologists; however, many more applications are immediately feasible. For example, there are now microtransmitters with sufficient lifetime to permit following waterfowl or seabirds through an entire pattern of seasonal migration. With receivers which could be mounted in present satellite packages, continuous surveillance could be maintained on a sample of migrants fitted with microtransmitters. The same technique seems promising for marine mammals, large terrestrial predators, and wide-ranging ungulates.

Perhaps one of the greatest shortcomings in application of existing knowledge lies in the harvest of deer and other large ungulates. Satisfactory inventory techniques have been developed, but the public seems unconvinced of the high productivity of healthy deer in favorable habitats and fails to realize the resilience of a thriving deer population. Hunters, especially in the Northeast and Lake States, cling to their ideal of "bucks only" and frequently refuse to support a more flexible policy. The resulting underharvest of big game herds has resulted in semipermanent damage to millions of acres of overutilized range (Fig. 17-4).

Another area of confusion in applying research findings is in the control of pest animals. Numerous investigations have questioned the wisdom of pursuing traditional statewide predator control programs with little evaluation of either the need for the program or the effectiveness of the control effort.

The manipulation of vegetation along the rights-of-way of county, state, and federal highways is a vast area wherein cooperative efforts between highway maintenance supervisors and wildlife managers would be mutually profitable. Wildlife managers have developed a wide variety of habitat manipulation techniques which, on one hand, could enhance the natural beauty of major roadways and, moreover, might bring about a significant reduction in accidents due to collision with wildlife.

At the species level, there is need for a great deal more knowledge about habitat affinities, physiological limits, behavioral mechanisms, and effects of weather on natality and mortality. We also need better quantitative techniques for measuring the parameters of a wildlife population. Age and sex criteria as well as census methods are much needed. We need to continue to explore the mechanisms whereby the natural regulation of wild populations is effected. The incidence and ecological importance of parasites and disease in wildlife populations would be part of this work.

Overpopulations of deer and elk are a nagging problem in national parks and on large military reservations where hunting cannot be used

Figure 17-4. A deer browsing on trees. Note that trees and shrubs are damaged as high as a deer can reach. (Courtesy Michigan Department of Conservation)

to achieve population reduction. In these situations the use of chemosterilants offers promise of being a highly effectual technique. Considerable
experimental research has already been done using these compounds on
feral pigeons, gulls, and carnivores. This pattern of applied research
should be extended to ungulates. Furthermore, increased effort in reproductive physiology would greatly fortify our understanding of the effectiveness of antifertility compounds.

The effects of environmental pollution on wildlife is a subject of immense importance. While the task of measuring direct effects of new
spray materials is a demanding one, the subtle and pervasive phenomenon
of bioaccumulation is of far greater importance and is also much more
difficult to evaluate. The first step is to work out the pathways of pesticide
residue transfer and accumulation. The uptake, metabolism, and storage
of pesticides are obvious physiological studies which would support
this effort. The ultimate fate of pesticide residues would be much better
understood if concepts of major watersheds as ecosystems were more
clearly defined and described. The practical problem of monitoring pollution loads would be greatly aided by advances in analyzing ecological
systems.

Also, one could wish for greater understanding of the mechanisms of
ecological succession (natural replacement of one group of species by
another group of species in a biotic community). The successional concept has been one of the cornerstones of ecology, yet there has been
and still is a great divergence of opinion as to the nature of this phenomenon. Since species succession is the pattern upon which much of
habitat manipulation is based, an increased understanding of the effects
of stress on various successional stages would be most helpful. Finally,
the subject of habitat manipulation would be greatly strengthened by
further studies in community organization and function from the standpoint of production of living matter, population stability, and diversity
of species.

Recreation

Provision of adequate opportunities for outdoor recreation* requires
an understanding of the needs and desires of the potential participants,
the kind and location of environment that will meet these needs, and the
effects of use on these environments. Until one can better understand

---

* We consider outdoor recreation to include that activity or planned inactivity undertaken outdoors because the individual wants to do it. However, for purposes of this report
we have restricted our discussion of these activities to those in which renewable natural
resources play a role. These actions include most but not all of those recognized in a report
of 1962 to the President and to the Congress by the Outdoor Recreation Resources Review
Commission.

(1) why people seek outdoor recreation and (2) the motivation that determines their recreation choices, and until management can communicate to these individuals the impacts of their recreational activities upon the natural scene, much of our effort will be of the stopgap variety. Such superficial treatment of the symptoms does not identify and rectify the cause; thorough knowledge of the physical and biological components of the recreation environment is imperative to the solution. Equally necessary, however, is a deeper understanding of human behavior.

Although recreation use is expected to double and, in some areas, redouble in the next few years, management is still trying, unsuccessfully, to cope with problems of the present. Each year more campers, skiers, fishermen, and seekers of outdoor recreation use our magnificent out-of-doors. Ever increasing effort is made to accommodate this demand, and, as a result, the impact upon the resources increases. For instance, Big Meadow Swamp was an extraordinary park feature in Shenandoah National Park containing many plant species of unusual distribution and interest. The flora of this area has been under investigation for more than twenty-five years. In trying to cope with demands of increasing visitor pressure, the Park Service extended the neighboring campgrounds into the swamp area. It has been reported that the results include reduction in the water level by drainage, serious damage to the flora in the construction and use of the new campsite, and permanent alteration to the ecology of the area. Of course, there are numerous examples in the National Park and National Forest systems where appropriate advance planning with greater consideration for the fragility of certain areas has resulted in deliberate efforts to keep visitor pressures well within those which the resources can tolerate.

With better understanding and concern for the frailties the natural resource may possess, recreation visitors would show necessary restraint in their activities. One needs but consider the deterioration that has accrued to readily accessible coral reefs in the Florida Keys and the Bahamas to appreciate the impact of increased visitor pressure and unrestrained "souvenir" hunting. Even in our National Park system, consisting of areas the Congress has specifically set aside for preservation, the National Park Service must sometimes take drastic measures to halt careless, indeed sometimes willful, destruction of resources by certain of the visiting public. Examples include the necessity for protective rail barriers around the bases of the larger sequoias in some of the western National Parks and the construction of a chain fence at Ash Meadows in Death Valley National Monument to prevent further destruction by visitors of the spring-fed pool which is the only remaining habitat of a fish species believed to be a relic of the Pleistocene. Management tries to compensate but each year falls farther behind rather than achieving a position wherein it can routinely anticipate such visitor-related problems and prevent their occurrence.

In many instances, biologists and other resource managers have not considered the visitor and the resource to be part of the same ecological situation. Possibly this has resulted from a feeling that man's role in a wildland setting is that of an outsider. The use of the term *visitor,* in this case, may be unfortunate because man must be considered part of the ecosystem. Nonetheless, at a time when perpetuation of the resource depends in part upon the visitor's understanding and cooperation, he and his fellow citizens, many of them urbanites, seem uninformed and careless about soils, plants, animals, and their interrelationships.

The recreation visitor and his activities have an influence on the immediate site being occupied as well as on the adjacent areas that form the scenic backdrop. His presence may generate problems above and beyond those which already exist. Wilderness Areas and National Parks represent good examples in which visitor-recreation problems extend beyond the immediate site being occupied. Although many such areas are more than several hundred thousand acres in size, the direct physical contact of visitors is concentrated on a very few acres. Within these small areas of intensive use, vegetation is trampled, soils are compacted and eroded, and water supplies are subjected to pollution. Overuse and abuse, albeit unintentional, prevail. Further, these sites of intensive use are often in esthetically pleasing but fragile areas least capable, biologically and physically, of withstanding great visitor pressure. To a certain degree, the selection of such sites is a result of uninformed management or poor planning in terms of land use. There is some evidence, however, that these are the kinds of areas that many visitors—the recreation public—prefer. To be sure, some persons wish to camp in relatively isolated sites in more stabilized vegetation systems irrespective of the lack of modern conveniences. However, recreation campers most often prefer to congregate tenement-fashion in high-density campgrounds where modern conveniences of electricity, sanitary facilities, hot and cold water, cooking accommodations, etc., are available and where the existing vegetation is in a highly vulnerable, unstable stage of development.

A number of visitors come to the wilderness, allegedly, to experience or view one or more of several situations—untrammeled scenic grandeur, game, the forest primeval, and/or solitude. Many such recreationists are staunch advocates of "keeping it natural," and they look upon the landscape as being more or less a static community which should be preserved inviolate in its present state. Despite repeated assertions to that effect, however, there is some doubt that they really want nature to take its course, for the two concepts of maintaining the status quo and of maintaining a natural situation are somewhat incompatible.

While recognizing the remarkable and continuing rapid rate of increase in numbers of individuals who engage in outdoor recreation activities, we must take a serious look at the facilities available for their accommodation. There can be little doubt that in periods of peak activity, present ability to handle the masses of outdoor recreation enthusiasts is rapidly becoming quite inadequate. There seems little reason to believe that outdoor recreation as an individual and family activity will not continue to increase in popularity. If the number of visitors to our National Parks and National Recreation Areas is any criterion, we are faced with a real dilemma (Fig. 17-5)! The visitor load in these public areas has increased nearly 6 times in 20 years, and in 1968 it reached 151 million. The number of parks has increased, of course, but at a much slower pace (Fig. 17-6). Indeed, the number of units in our National Park system including National Parks, Monuments, Seashores, Historic Sites, etc., has increased only 50 percent in this period. Moreover, potential sites for additional large-scale and magnificent recreation outlets are not unlimited. If visitor pressure on national forests, other wilderness areas, and state or local recreation facilities has followed the general pattern experienced in the National Parks, and if there are not substantial changes in the concepts of visitor management, we are clearly in danger of running out of space for certain types of recreational activities.

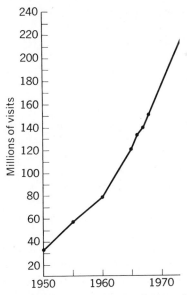

Figure 17-5. Total visits to National Parks and related areas 1950–1968, and projected visits to 1975. (From *Statistical Abstract of the United States, 1969*, Statistical Information Division, U.S. Department of Commerce)

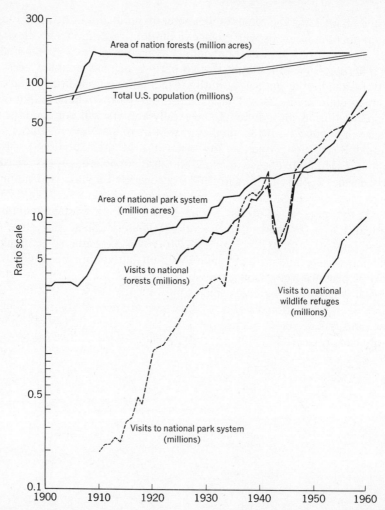

Figure 17-6. Growth in visits to national parks system, national forests, and national wildlife refuges, compared with growth in acreage and in national population, 1900–1960. (From M. Clawson and J. L. Knetsch, *Economics of Outdoor Recreation*, Johns Hopkins University Press)

The scope and amount of research needed to correct the deficiencies in our knowledge of the problems in the relationships between outdoor recreation and natural resources are rather substantial. These needs apply equally to the participant and to the environment in which he pursues his recreation activities. There is little definitive information concerning the motivations that stimulate individuals to seek particular kinds of outdoor experience, the kinds of recreation outlets people would utilize if availability and custom weren't governing factors, the true mental and physical benefits of recreation experiences, the relative demands for different kinds of recreation facilities, the factors other than personal preference which determine the choice of recreation outlet, the relation of age group to the kind of recreation sought, the degree of satisfactory experience achieved in recreation ventures under conditions which currently exist in outdoor areas, or the nature of the public's desire with respect to the state of the outdoor setting in which recreation experiences are most often sought. In short, we do not really know a great deal about recreation participants, their wishes, needs, or fulfillment.

The deficiencies in information necessary for manipulation of living resources to accommodate recreational activities is reasonably well known, but is too great to discuss in detail here. However, in many instances, maximum use is not now being made of sound information which already exists. For example, although the potential value of controlled fire as a management tool under certain conditions has been amply demonstrated, this technique has not yet achieved full acceptance in our National Parks where fire has long been viewed as a deadly enemy. Reproduction of sequoias is severely restricted in certain areas of Sequoia National Park by the competition from other more rapidly growing tree species and probably by an accumulation of excessive duff on the forest floor. There is substantial evidence that natural fires invaded these areas periodically during their earlier history. The judicious use of controlled fire would serve to decrease the heavy layer of duff, hold in check the invasion of competitor trees, and reduce the potential danger of catastrophic wild fire fed by fuel which is continuing to accumulate in the forest debris. Fortunately, the National Park Service has now initiated limited experiments to determine the usefulness of this management tool. Carefully monitored burning has been implemented in Everglades National Park to preserve the natural conditions of certain pine-dominated communities. Consideration should be given to the use of controlled fire under proper moisture conditions as a means of restoring the vigor of the vast sawgrass prairies of the park as well. These are not criticisms of the National Park Service but rather are examples of reluctance to implement new management procedures in the face of long-established custom and policy until serious threat provides the motivation. Indeed, the state of knowledge relative to the use of controlled fire and the nature of public opinion are justification for reasonable caution by the Park Service in these instances.

While many resource problems associated with outdoor recreation are generally recognized, others are not so well known. On wild lands managed for several purposes, the need for both a more thorough ecological understanding of the landscape as well as greater insight into the physical requirements of an attractive landscape is coming into sharp focus. The public seems often more concerned about the "visual resource" than the physical resource. The outdoor-oriented American public evidently does not wish to become reconciled to the recognition that land use, and indeed natural processes, must sometimes be accompanied by temporary ugliness. Resource managers have become well aware that good silviculture practices, controlled burning to permit regeneration of more desirable trees, burning to maintain a plant community characteristic of a true prairie, reduction in an elk herd to forestall starvation of the animals and destruction of their range, or introduction of native predators to assist in the control of big game or other animal populations, often contribute to poor public relations despite the fact that they do simulate natural events and are necessary as good, long-range management procedures.

There are gaps in knowledge concerning management of natural resources and understanding of the recreationist's requirements, and obviously a substantial amount of research is required. Significant contributions to the solution of these problems will be made, however, if we can (1) develop greater understanding and communication among the several scientific disciplines which have roles in the outdoor recreation complex, (2) establish much better understanding and communication between the recreation user and the managers of outdoor recreation resources, and (3) establish outdoor recreation management as a legitimate discipline in our academic and research programs.

Each of the several fields of study concerned already has a substantial amount of important and usable knowledge on hand. The effective application of this knowledge, however, calls for the combined effort and understanding of each discipline. For example, the successfully maintained landscape requires the services of the ecologist, landscape architect, silviculturist, wildlife biologist, animal husbandryman, sociologist, engineer, and the economist. In addition, the pathologist, entomologist, hydrologist, geneticist, geologist, and others will have contributions to make. Although good communication exists between some of these specialties, all must be appropriately utilized to satisfy the requirements of recreation.

Where do we meet these needs? Certainly a substantial effort must be made at recreational sites in the field, but the problem is sufficiently complex that it needs to be treated as well at other levels involving the recreationist. Since the largest proportion of recreation devotees live in cities, better understanding of the problem should begin there. Conservation training or education programs should be accelerated and amplified. Many new approaches such as the establishment of nature trails and other means of familiarizing people with their natural environment in urban areas must be developed and tested. Research in communications should be added to the list of research requirements, for we need better methods by which the resource manager can communicate with those who use the resource, and by which we can bring together in close harmony a great many scientific disciplines focusing upon one major topic — the people and their understanding, enjoyment, and use of natural resources.

Health

Ideally, health should be regarded not only as absence of disease, but as a positive attribute, enabling man to take advantage of all his physiological capabilities and mental potentialities. Such a state of "positive" health is, of course, utopian. It cannot become reality because man never achieves a perfect and stable state of adaptiveness to his physical and social surroundings. Since the environment and man's ways are forever changing, survival demands a continuous adaptive response — on the part of man, an adaptive effort that is commonly associated with struggles and sufferings. In practice, health and disease are expressions of the relative degrees of success or failure experienced by the organism in its efforts to respond adaptively to environmental challenges. Although the ideal of perfect positive health may not be reached, it constitutes a creative force nevertheless because it sets goals for biomedical sciences and helps them to chart a course toward a better adaptation of man to his environment.

The fact that health and disease are so profoundly conditioned by the consequences of the adaptive interplay between man and his environment points to the importance of ecological concepts in biomedical sciences. In this regard, it is of interest to note how frequently the phrase *environmental health* has come to be used during the present decade in the vocabulary of medicine and public health. Admittedly, some have recently expressed dismay at the thought that society should be more concerned with the health of man's environment than with the health of man in his environment. But such concern is unwarranted. Biologically, mentally, socially, as well as economically, man is not only part of the environment, he is in fact shaped by it. The quality of human life reflects the characteristics of the technological and urban environment in which modern man now functions. Indeed, man becomes what he is in the very process of creating his environment; genetically and phenotypically he eventually becomes transformed by the ways of life he creates.

The ecological approach to biomedical problems has a long tradition. Indeed, it reached a highly sophisticated form 2,500 years ago in the Hippocratic treatise "Airs, Waters, and Places." This treatise did more than relate the types and frequency of diseases to environmental conditions. It boldly suggested that climate, topography, soil, food, and water affect not only the state of health, physical stature, and behavioral patterns of different populations, but also their military prowess and political institutions. Recent experiments with animals and observations of children have established beyond doubt that early environmental influences do indeed affect the whole of human life—even more profoundly and lastingly than Hippocrates had anticipated.

Concern for the quality of the environment first reached its most conscious, rational, and coherent form probably during the second half of the nineteenth century. In western Europe, and then in the United States, the first phase of the industrial revolution had resulted in crowding, misery, accumulation of filth, appalling living and working conditions, high rates of morbidity and mortality, and incredible ugliness in all the mushrooming industrial cities. Within a few decades it became apparent that the physical and mental degeneration of the working classes was intolerable for social conscience, and furthermore constituted a threat to industrial development.

The social protest against the misery of the nineteenth-century proletariat took many forms, one of the most vigorous and original being a systematic effort to correct the evils of the physical environment caused by urbanization and industrialization. "Pure water, pure air, pure food" was the motto around which the campaign for environmental reform was initially organized. More interestingly perhaps, the reform movement went farther than these words implied. Efforts were made not only to sanitize the environment and improve water, food, and dwellings, but also to reintroduce into city life some of the the amenities and values that had been destroyed by industrialization. Country lanes and waterways, parks, boulevards adorned with trees and flowers, were almost as much in the mind of the nineteenth-century reformers as was the maintenance of sanitary conditions.

The programs for urban planning and the specifications for dwellings formulated by several outstanding early workers were immensely influential in improving the health of city dwellers during the past century. Yet the message of these early workers is now of only historical interest. Not that their contributions lost their validity, but the aspects of urban and industrial civilization that were emphasized are very different from those that are responsible for today's problems. In the United States, the nineteenth century was concerned with malnutrition, overwork, filth, and microbial contamination. In contrast, many of the diseases most characteristic of our times find their origins in economic affluence and chemical pollution (Fig. 17-7). Many medical problems are still largely environmental in origin, but they have different ecological determinants.

The average expectancy of life has increased all over the world, especially in prosperous countries, as a result of the control of early deaths that used to be caused by acute infections and malnutrition. But, life expectancy past the age of 45 has increased only slightly even in the social groups that can afford the most elaborate medical care. Vascular diseases, certain types of cancers, chronic ailments of the respiratory tract, are among the many conditions that appear to be increasing among adults in affluent societies. The increase in incidence of these chronic and degenerative diseases is due in part to the fact that a higher proportion of the population survives other causes of death and thus is at risk, and in some part to the environmental and behavioral changes that have occurred in industrialized societies.

It is widely felt that many medical problems today are the results of man's failure to respond successfully to the stresses of the environment generated by his own civilization. Although various aspects of modern life have been proposed as underlying causes for diseases of adult life in prosperous countries, as yet the evidence is only circumstantial. If, indeed, this hypothesis is valid, the mechanisms relating the environment and man's way of life to the increased incidence of chronic and degenerative diseases characteristic of modern civilization remain to be demonstrated.

Granted the deficiencies in etiological understanding, nevertheless man feels threatened by the constant and unavoidable exposure to the stimuli of urban and industrial civilization, by the varied aspects of environmental pollution, by physiological disturbances associated with sudden changes in the ways of life, by his estrangement from the conditions under which human evolution took place, by the emotional trauma and the paradoxical solitude in congested cities, by the monotony, the boredom, and even the compulsory leisure ensuing from automated work. These influences, which are presumed to play some role in the origin of medical problems in affluent societies, affect all human beings, irrespective of genetic constitution. They are not inherent in man's nature but are the products of the interplay between him and the new world created by his social and technological innovations. And in some measure, the disorders of the body and the mind in adult life are expressions of inadequate responses to environmental influences.

When considered from an ecological point of view, the increase in the prevalence of chronic, degenerative, and mental diseases in our societies

Figure 17-7. Smog over New York City. (Aero Service Division, Litton Industries)

can thus be interpreted as a failure of man's evolution and adaptation to the modern environment and ways of life. It must be emphasized, however, that the concepts of adaptation developed by biologists are not entirely suitable to the analysis of such problems of modern human life.

The general biologist usually defines the word *adaptation* in Darwinian terms. For him, the word implies a state of fitness to a given environment, enabling the species to multiply and to invade new territories. In this light, man is remarkably adapted to life in highly urbanized and industrialized societies, as shown by the fact that his populations continuously increase and that he spreads urbanization and industrialization to more and more of the earth. It is obvious, on the other hand, that further population increase has become objectionable, and may soon become catastrophic. Social man is at a stage where his biological problems can no longer be defined simply in terms of Darwinian fitness.

For physiologists and psychologists, a response is "adaptive" when it enables the person to maintain homeostasis through metabolic, hormonal, or mental processes that tend to correct the disturbing effects that environmental forces exert on the body and the mind. Such adaptive responses contribute to the welfare of the organism at the time they occur, but unfortunately, particularly if the stress and response occur repeatedly, they often have secondary effects that are deleterious at a later date. When evaluated over man's whole life-span, homeostatic mechanisms which allow man to tolerate a wide variety of environmental extremes, as they occur, may carry with them a serious penalty. It can readily be shown that many, if not most, chronic disorders are the secondary, delayed consequences of adaptive responses that serve one well at the time they occur, but are expensive in the long run.

The responses to environmental stimuli made by the organism in the very early phases of development, including intrauterine life, deserve special emphasis here because they exert profound and lasting effects on the physical, physiological, and behavioral characteristics of the adult. Observations in man and experiments in animals leave no doubt about this, and often such effects appear irreversible.

Most observers believe that, irrespective of genetic endowment, a child who grows up in a city slum will differ as an adult from one who has spent his early life within the sheltering cocoon of a modern apartment house, or who participated in the chores of a family farm. Admittedly, there is little scientific documentation for this allegation. But the prospect for such studies is not hopeless. Experiments have revealed that, also in other animals, early influences condition growth, longevity, behavior, resistance to stress, and learning ability. The effects exerted on human life by early influences can, therefore, be studied through the use of experimental models, much as is done for other types of biological problems. The knowledge thus acquired will certainly help in a better understanding of the interplay between man and his total environment.

Science has been most productive when concerned with isolated phenomena which can successfully be studied out of context and examined by altering one variable at a time. But it has been far less successful in dealing with complex natural phenomena, in situ, involving multitudes of organisms. In order to deal with problems of organized complexity, in which several interrelated systems function in an integrated manner, multifactorial investigations are necessary which will demand new conceptual and experimental methods.

Needless to say, there does exist some scientific knowledge of man's response to his environment. But it is highly episodic, derived in a somewhat haphazard way from attempts to solve a few practical problems. For example, research in organismic and environmental biology has been stimulated by the need to investigate the training of combat forces for operation in the tropics or in the arctic, the preparation of human beings for space travel, or the effects of solitary confinement. But there is not a body of systematic, scientific knowledge of man as a living entity in his environment comparable to what has been acquired for the isolated constituents of the body machine.

It is apparent that such studies, involving higher organisms, will demand research facilities nonexistent at the present time. Highly evolved organisms, maintained under well-controlled conditions, are required in order to study the response and adaptation to environmental stimuli and insults, especially if the findings are to be applied to man.

Fortunately experience has shown that for many of the problems of human life, it is possible to find in animal life models that represent close analogies to the human situation. This is true not only for physical and physiological characteristics, but also for pathological states, behavioral patterns, and social organization. By taking advantage of this fact, it should be possible to create a new scientific discipline that will provide an ecological basis for environmental biomedicine. Ecological biomedical science might investigate such problems as:

1. Lasting effects of early influences, i.e., the effects exerted by the total environment on the organism during the formative stages of its development
2. Effects of relative degrees of isolation or crowding on hormonal activities and behavioral patterns
3. Effects of housing conditions and environmental stimuli on the development of sense organs and of various physiological processes

4. Delayed and indirect effects of biologically active substances, such as drugs and environmental pollutants
5. Long-term consequences of toleration of injurious agents
6. Adaptive potentialities

The phrase *adaptive potentialities* has been introduced here to convey the view that the ecological approach to the study of human life need not be limited to the study of pathological phenomena. Man has a wide range of potentialities that become expressed only to the extent that he is given a chance to respond to the proper stimuli. Man makes himself in the very process of shaping his environment and of responding adaptively to the ways of life he is thus creating. Although a discussion of the formative, creative effects of adaptive responses would be out of place here, they probably constitute the most important aspect of human ecology.

As already mentioned, the development and exploitation of experimental models for the study of the ecological problems of human life will require facilities and institutional organizations very different from those found suitable for investigations, for example, in cellular and molecular biology. Among the facilities that will be required are:

1. Experimental animals of known genetic structure and of controlled experimental past
2. Quarters for maintaining animals under wide ranges of conditions throughout their whole life-span and indeed for several generations
3. Quarters for maintaining populations of various sizes and densities, exposed to different types of environmental stimuli
4. Equipment (especially telemetry) for measuring the responses of intact, undisturbed organisms
5. Equipment for recording, retrieving, and analyzing the complex data derived from long-term studies of complex populations.

The mere listing of these facilities points to the need for new types of institutions with a special organization of highly integrated personnel.

Few research institutes or universities will find it possible to finance, administer, and maintain the large and complex facilities envisioned here. Large, collective research facilities, analogous to the existing primate centers, operated on a regional basis would appear to be more appropriate. Here there could be developed a new scientific philosophy and methodology suited to the ecological problems of human life. The ecological aspects of biomedicine are today in a primitive stage analogous to that of physicochemical biology fifty years ago. In view of the scale of effort required, they will remain undeveloped unless they are deliberately fostered and adequate facilities provided for their exploration.

Urban and Rural Development

The problems of environmental management treated in the preceding sections fall into two major categories: first, those activities directed at meeting man's needs for food, fiber, outdoor recreation, and esthetic gratification; and second, the management necessary to prevent or minimize damage to the health of man. In this section, our concern is with the effects of man on his environment — with fitting man and his works into the landscape with a minimum of disruption to the functions and processes of the environment and with minimum upset to competing environmental uses such as agriculture, forestry, or grazing.

Man needs dwelling places, stores, industries, schools, museums, places of worship; he needs arteries for transport by rail or motor vehicles; he needs airports, canals, harbors, and dams. All these take space, and once the land is committed to these uses the commitment is essentially irreversible. Man's activities in these places change raw materials and natural products into new forms and often result in "waste" products that must somehow be disposed of or recycled. When these waste products reach the air or water or land in forms or concentrations that are detrimental, we call them pollutants. Unacceptable means of "waste disposal" is one of the major impacts of man on his environment.

With increasing numbers of people, our needs for food, fiber, industry, and transport, in fact for all kinds of goods and services, go up. Expansion of our cities converts more than a million acres of land a year to paved, biologically unproductive areas. At the same time, command of enormous and still increasing amounts of energy available for excavation, construction, and earth moving gives ever greater freedom of choice in where to locate cities and what changes to make in the landscape; but the changes we make are, all too often, unplanned and unthinking and result in changes that are unwanted. The big changes — the canals and dams and perhaps even interstate highways — are considered with some care and the more obvious costs and benefits publicly weighed. The results are not always those biologically best; but they are democratically acceptable. The more pervasive and uncontrollable changes result from incremental changes, as in creeping suburbia and filled-in wetlands. No single acre in these latter categories elicits much public defense, with the result that the aggregate loss exceeds what we should be willing to accept.

Cities are where they are as a result of history. At first men gathered where they could defend themselves or where they could raise food. Later, transportation needs caused coastal cities to be built on good harbors and inland settlements to stretch and crawl along water courses which formed easy access to the interior of the continents. These fresh-water rivers and streams served also as sources of power and water needed for factories. Raw materials such as iron ore deposits close to coal and readily available transportation dictated the location of some large industrial complexes. Today's cities have arisen by accretion to existing nuclei and sometimes by agglomeration of whole cities in the larger metropolitan sprawls. Historically, biology had little relevance to city location, except for avoidance of marshes in recognition of the danger of malaria and yellow fever.

Today we have new possibilities in the location of our cities. For urban renewal or any kind of modification of existing metropolitan areas, the problem is to make the "best" use of the area. Zoning may be one of the best tools to this end. Heavy, dirty industry can be positioned in relation to dwellings, open space, and other living parts of our cities so that air pollutants are carried away, noise does not reach the dwellings, and offensive odors and the grime of industry are out of range of the sense of most inhabitants. To beautify cities, there are trees, shrubs, and other plants that will tolerate even existing conditions. Transportation and communications systems can be planned so as to minimize the conflicts among the diverse demands of metropolitan life.

The imminent location and construction of whole new cities affords a superb opportunity and difficult challenge. As has been pointed out, before the turn of the century this nation will need to provide housing for an additional population equivalent to the sum of 500 Restons, 100 Columbias, 50 Atlantas, 5 Philadelphias, and 5 New Yorks, Either we can allow these to sprawl and congest the surroundings of existing cities, or we can start afresh. This time there need be much less concern with the needs for transportation and communications or nearness to resources. Locations can be based upon the amenities people might choose, and then water and raw materials can be brought to them, as well as over-land and air transportation, as these are required (Fig. 17-8).

Whether present cities are expanded or entire new ones built, it is imperative to consider the effect these will have on the environment. We ought to avoid the paving of ground water recharge areas. We ought not scalp steep slopes. Septic tanks can not and need not be placed in impermeable soil. Waste treatment facilities can improve rather than damage their surroundings. By establishing criteria in advance, it will not be unbearably costly to avoid such problems. Planners, architects, and engineers will be largely responsible for appropriate use of the environment. Development of understanding of land-use capabilities and a reciprocal interaction between the desired design and these capability criteria will permit optimum use of the environment (Fig. 17-9).

Figure 17-8. South of San Francisco, the construction of close-packed, look-alike houses is reshaping the Golden Gate landscape. (Courtesy Rondal Partridge)

Outside of the cities man's structures are often extensive, and here, too, biological understanding should be applied in the process of decision making. For example, a sea-level canal linking the Atlantic and Pacific between the Americas would result in the mixing of two biotas separated for eons, and cooling of the Caribbean, breeding ground of countless species. Before the decision is made, regardless of the means of excavation, biological evaluation of the significance of mixing these two bodies and their faunas is utterly essential. Imagine the equivalent of a sea lamprey invasion of the Great Lakes taking place in a whole ocean! But, at this writing, there are insufficient data to predict the outcome of the complex events.

Another example is the exploration and subsequent extraction of minerals from the continental shelf, where the chances of affecting living resources are very real. Each decision to explore or exploit should include biological considerations, particularly acquisition of the information needed to avoid or minimize potential dangers.

There are serious inadequacies in present knowledge about appropriate or optimum use of the environment, but there is an even greater failure to apply existing knowledge. Perhaps the most evident need for new knowledge is in environmental toxicology — the determination of allowable levels of contaminants or the allowable level of change in other environmental factors such as heat, light, noise, and space. Present knowledge is usually restricted to one or a few compounds and factors and to a relatively few species. The real and pressing questions of the moment are posed, for example, as, "How much estuarine or coastal marsh, and of what sort, must be retained in which locations to assure some desirable, prescribed level of marine organism production?" "How high a concentration of automotive exhausts (as emitted and as chemically or photochemically changed in the atmosphere) can occur in various environments without unacceptable effects on plants, animals, physical structures, or man himself?" "What burden of exotic chemicals can a given body of water tolerate without disrupting the processes of decomposition, mineral cycling and photosynthesis that are necessary to permit other uses of the water such as swimming or water skiing, or fishing?"

In spite of inadequacies of current understanding, much is known that is not put to use. A social or political invention is required to assure that

Figure 17-9. On Ventura Boulevard in Los Angeles, a telephoto lens catches one impression of the overgrowth of advertising signs. (Photograph Courtesy *Los Angeles Times*)

available knowledge is fitted into essentially all decisions that affect our environment. As noted earlier, such mechanisms exist for "big" decisions such as the location of a dam, agreements on atmospheric testing of nuclear weapons, or an interoceanic canal. But equivalent mechanisms are rare for such considerations in regard to the relatively small but widespread changes that result from urban and suburban expansion, estuarine filling, or dredging, etc., where decisions are usually made by smaller units of government. Two concepts are usually involved: multiple use, which is too often used to imply that a given acre may be used for any purpose, and zoning, which may establish an exclusive use. The widely scattered foci for these decisions have prevented effective consideration of biological effects. A flexible advisory procedure, easily available to local authorities, could be most helpful.

Opportunities

Opportunities for the applied ecologist to design strategies for the effective management of our renewable resources are unlimited. The complex environmental problems of the day will require the talents of imaginative ecologists well trained in both biological and physical sciences. The ecologist in resource biology has a unique opportunity to investigate socially significant problems while contributing to the formulation of new biological concepts.

Information is needed concerning all aspects of the ecology of most species. Much of the work already done has involved only economically important domesticated or wild plants or animals. Because we do not know how the population numbers of any single species are controlled in nature, fundamental studies are needed to advance understanding of population dynamics. Knowledge of the regulation of animal numbers will help in manipulating and controlling the numbers of economically important species.

Just as, in the past, many of the concepts and principles of population behavior and interspecific interaction were developed as a part of management programs for wildlife, fish, and insect populations, so today much can be learned from ecological studies of environments such as the farm or the estuary, or areas where wildlife and other species live in close association with man.

Little is known concerning the biological tolerance of populations under harvest pressure. Not only is this response related to sound fishery and wildlife management, but it is also fundamental to understanding of the survival of populations in nature. Density, growth, age structure, and harvest pressure are all interrelated, and the interactions and relationships have yet to be delineated in terms that have predictive value. Once understood, they will afford important insights into the productivity of populations and thus contribute to effective management of fish, wildlife, and insect populations.

Improved population sampling techniques must be developed to make reliable and effective estimates of population abundance, for many ecological data are based on such information. Teams of ecologists and statisticians, working together, could establish sampling techniques that would greatly simplify the monitoring of populations.

Cycles in populations remain a biological mystery. Since cycles can be investigated only in the field, resource biology offers a unique chance to help solve this mystery. Similarly, little is understood concerning the dispersal and migration of organisms. These areas should be fully studied, and answers will be of special use to both fisheries and wildlife management.

Parasite-host dynamics remain vague not only experimentally but also theoretically. Parasite-host, predator-prey, and interspecific competitors have been used to construct theoretical models demonstrating interactions of these species, but there are no effective models describing the functioning of these population systems in communities. The possibility of employing systems analysis and computers to describe population events in ecological communities awaits wider use and application, as in the biological control of pests.

A most rewarding area of research is investigation of the structure and function of both natural and man-made ecosystems. Not only would the knowledge of these ecosystems add to our basic understanding of ecology, they would also be most valuable in attacking the important environment problem of recycling wastes in homes, industries, and farms.

Further biological models with the aid of computers could be a helpful tool in studies of the basic principles underlying the function of communities and ecosystems and, of course, would be extremely valuable in all fields that depend upon resource management, including environmental health, recreation, and urban and rural development.

Research involving ecology and environmental management requires both instrumentation for measuring environment problems and long-term investigations. Investigations of populations, communities, and ecosystems require the measurement of numerous parameters over several years' time to sort out the roles of the various environmental factors.

Summary

As a matter of public policy in the use of renewable resources, local governmental and federal agencies should recognize that the public has a right to live in an environment of quality. The true costs of any program in the management of renewable resources, be it in industry, agriculture, recreation, health, forestry, fisheries, or urban development, should be evaluated and decisions made not by groups of specialists but by representatives of society as a whole, seeking what is best for our local, continental, and planetary ecosystems. Only by penetrating understanding of the function and interaction of the biological and physical elements of the environment and application of this knowledge in sound management programs can man expect to conserve the natural resources which are his great heritage.

Chapter 18

BIOLOGY AND INDUSTRIAL TECHNOLOGY

The Food Industry

The food industry is the largest industry in the United States. Employing approximately one seventh of the working population, it grew from $33 billion in 1945 to more than $90 billion in 1966. By accomplishing food preservation, transportation, and distribution it brings foods from the land and the sea throughout the year to communities large and small.

The biologist contributes importantly to this effort. He is concerned with all the living processes relating to growth and reproduction of food plants and animals, the biological aspects of preservation, the relation of foods to human intake, and the welfare of the food consumer. The basic research biologist determines "how" and "why" certain phenomena happen; the applied research biologist establishes "what" happens in actual practice. Integration of the efforts of these two groups has profoundly influenced the development of the foods we eat. More has been accomplished in the past fifty years of the food industry than in all preceding history.

The whole life of early man was devoted to seeking food and shelter and to protecting his family. He was forced to rely on food indigenous to the immediate area in which he lived. His eating habits were dictated by his environment, be it temperate, arctic, or tropical, and his supply was subject to the vagaries of the elements.

In time man slowly learned to have some control over his food supply. By 1800 there was some recognition of the importance of the scientific breeding of plants and animals. In this same year (1800) 94 percent of the United States population lived on small farms, but by 1966 this had fallen to 5.8 percent.

Concomitant with this trend from rural to urban living was the marked increase in the use of processed foods. Over 70 percent of the food we eat today has been subjected to some form of processing. Today the housewife can choose from 7,000 to 8,000 items in her supermarket as compared with about 3,000 items twenty years ago. Because of the year-round availability of food, our purchasing habits have changed markedly. In 1900, 40 percent of a family's disposable income was used for food, whereas the fraction so utilized in 1966 was only 18 percent.

The role of biological understanding in catalyzing the agricultural revolution has already been considered in some detail (Chapter 15). But biologists were equally essential to the development of modern methods for food preservation, storage, and transportation.

What *has* been accomplished? Man, the foraging biologist, discovered and put into practice the means by which meat, fowl, fish, vegetables, grains, and fruits could be utilized as food in all parts of the world. He learned to cope with seasonal commodities so that fresh foods are available throughout the year. He developed an array of preservation techniques that have extended the storage life of foods from days to months and years. He created new means of packaging for the protection of food in raw and bulk forms as well as for consumer use. The biologist learned how to combat harmful food microorganisms and utilize others advantageously. And he recognized certain adverse effects of food procedures on the physicochemical and nutritional properties of some foods. Steps are being taken to rectify these.

Food Development and Storage

In many cases the production of agricultural commodities is seasonal and requires special handling before the item is processed or consumed. Storage of raw products for days or months has confronted biologists with a variety of problems. Raw product storage has great economic advantages. It permits the out-of-season processing of food items, the out-of-season use of an ingredient in a formulated food, and the out-of-season consumption of fresh commodities. Fresh foods vary in perishability. Biologists have participated in developing the storage procedures, and are essential to assay the physical and nutritional changes that occur during storage. This has entailed monitoring, also, for the presence of yeast, molds, and bacteria as well as moisture and nutrient content.

The modern food industry then brings to the home, at all seasons, a rich diversity of fresh fruits and vegetables, meats, baked goods, fresh frozen vegetables, and a bewildering assortment of prepared foods which may be frozen, chilled, canned, or dry packaged. Never have so many been so well fed.

These accomplishments have been made possible by development of large-scale fast freezing procedures, cheap freezers for the home and store, rapid transportation, and means for storage in bulk of seasonal crops to be used year-round. In the main, therefore, they reflect triumphs of (a) agriculture and its continued development of increased productivity of diverse foods at lower cost, (b) engineering, and (c) an expanding economy which generates increased numbers of consumers with income to buy a wider variety of foods. But imperative to this endeavor, at each level, has been biological know-how. Biologists devised the assay procedures which tested and then monitored the nutritional quality of each of these products. They established the optimal conditions for bulk storage of each major foodstuff, and these proved to be highly specific with respect to temperature and moisture. Biologists monitor each process for contamination by yeasts, molds, and algae as well as insects and larger forms, assess the consequences to the nutritional and physical properties of each foodstuff of chemicals used as preservatives such as ethylene oxide, sulfur dioxide, and nitrogen gas as well as the consequences of drying procedures (vacuum, spray, drum, fluid bed, or freeze drying); they monitor processes in which preservation is achieved by fermentation (sauerkraut, buttermilk, pickles, cottage cheese), by heat, by large-scale osmotic effects (sugar syrup on fruits), by sterile filtration (beer, wine, fruit juices), and by irradiation.

For example, it was understanding of the oxidative processes that contribute to the darkening and deterioration of leafy vegetables, fresh fruit, and flowers which led to the growing practice of shipment in large trailers which are sealed and their atmospheres replaced by nitrogen at ordinary barometric pressures. They and their chemical colleagues have sought chemical preservatives and additives which improve texture or bulk (modified starch, glycerides, alginates, artificial flavors). And they have contributed to design of the ultimate packaging procedures.

By establishing the nutritional qualities of major foodstuffs (wheat, corn, etc.), they have also provided the basic knowledge underlying the fortification of these cereals with B vitamins and certain minerals and most recently with certain amino acids, particularly lysine.

Most recent has been the development of specialized foods. None represents large sales volume—as reckoned in this enormous market—yet several are of great significance to specific groups. For example, there are commercially available products free of sugar, yet sweet; minimal in sodium content, yet adequately salty; very low in phenylalanine, yet otherwise nutritionally adequate; or containing medium-chain triglycerides rather than normal long-chain fatty acids. These products are a boon to the individual seeking to control his weight, the patient with cardiac, hypertensive, or renal disease, the child with hereditary phenyl-ketonuria, and the patient with regional ileitis, sprue, or other intestinal disorder, respectively. These and other "specialty" foods are devised and monitored by the nutritionist and food technologist.

The triumph of the modern food industry is nowhere better seen than in the supermarkets of America. This triumph has been created not by a few great scientific coups, but by the continued efforts of thousands who have applied their knowledge of nutrition, biochemistry, microbiology, chemistry, and engineering to every step from harvesting to marketing of every major and minor foodstuff. The extent of this triumph is measured by the confidence of the homemaker as she shops, secure in the knowledge that the products she will bring home are nutritious, consistent, and uncontaminated.

The Pharmaceutical Industry

Much of the success of modern medicine derives from its ever expanding armamentarium of drugs. These agents are provided very largely by the research programs of the pharmaceutical industry, conducted by scientists trained in a wide variety of the subdisciplines of the life and physical sciences, organized in collaborative teams.

Prior to World War I, most synthetic drugs and chemicals used in the United States were discovered and produced in Europe. Curtailment of supplies, by the war, provided the impetus for establishment of a domestic chemical and pharmaceutical industry. In the years since, this industry has assumed a position of world leadership through its discovery and development of a host of new drugs of ever increasing specificity and usefulness.

The agents thus provided have been a major factor in the spectacular advances in clinical medicine in the past half-century. Life expectancy at birth has increased from 54.1 years in 1920 to 70.2 years in 1964 in this country. Perhaps less emphasis has been given to the improved quality of life that has evolved from the fact that man can expect to spend less of his adult life in illness or in pain and to the favorable economic impact of the introduction of important new drugs. It has been estimated that the decline in death rate between 1944 and 1964 meant the saving of 3,250,000 lives (this many more people, most of them children, would have died if the 1944 death rate had prevailed through 1964). Of this group, an estimated 1,200,000 wage earners produced over $8 billion in income in 1964 alone, on which about $1.35 billion in income and excise taxes was paid to the Federal Treasury. Comparable data are not available to estimate the economic consequence of reduction in time spent away from work due to transitory illnesses, but this must be substantial.

Discovery and development of the sulfonamides, antibiotics, and other antiinfective agents have dramatically reduced the death rates from a number of infectious diseases. Historically, a large proportion of the deaths from these diseases have occurred prior to adulthood. Mortality tables published in *Vital Statistics of the United States, 1961*, Volume II, show the impact of these drugs over a twenty-year span (Table 1).

Between 1944 and 1963, antibiotic therapy brought about a 90 percent decline in the death rate from acute rheumatic fever and reduced almost to extinction the incidence of rheumatic fever following streptococcal infection. Furthermore, the use of antimicrobial agents following hemolytic streptococcal infection has reduced the rate of recurrence of rheumatic fever from 50 percent to 2 percent.

Table 1. Effects of Antibiotics on Mortality Rate from Infectious Diseases

	1941	*1961*
Deaths from All Causes	**1,397,642**	**1,701,522**
Tuberculosis	59,251	9,938
Diseases due to spirochetes	18,011	2,863
Diseases due to bacteria	10,241	3,526
Diseases due to fungi	324	423
Total	87,827	16,750

Remarkable changes have taken place in the incidence, early diagnosis, and treatment of tuberculosis, and have caused a tremendous drop in mortality. Drugs must be given an important part of the credit. The mortality rate per 100,000 of population dropped from about 200 in 1900 to 4.2 in 1966. With the use of streptomycin, a 49 percent decline in death rate was attained, and within a year after the introduction of isoniazid, the death rate had declined by 86 percent. Today, most tuberculosis patients are treated out of the hospital, and many tuberculosis hospitals have been closed. Occupied tuberculosis beds in hospitals in the United States and its territories decreased from 99,251 in 1954 to 43,086 in 1963.

A number of classes of drugs have marked effects on the quality of life without significantly affecting longevity. Nonaddictive compounds that control pain are strikingly illustrative. The development of reliable oral contraceptive therapy has made intelligent family planning possible. Tranquilizers and other drugs that influence the central nervous system have made an important contribution to the control of mental diseases and the restoration of mental patients to normal activities. The resident patient population in public psychiatric hospitals increased annually until 1955, when it reached a high of 616,000. Thereafter, it dropped steadily. According to statistics compiled by the National Institute of Mental Health, it was 452,000 in 1966, whereas if the hospital population had continued to grow at the pre-1955 rate, it is estimated that there would have been 702,000 such patients in 1966. Hospital stays have been shortened for patients with some types of mental disorders, and a more favorable prognosis has developed for mental patients as a group. Currently, seven out of every ten such patients in first-rate hospitals can look forward to total or partial recovery.

These are offered as dramatic examples of the impact of new drugs. Other important specific examples of the impact of drugs on health and longevity, albeit involving lesser numbers of patients, might well have been cited. Where do new drugs come from? Much of the credit must be accorded to the research programs of the pharmaceutical industry. Rarely are new drugs — viz., new chemical entities with specific, desirable biological effects — discovered in academic or federal laboratories, although very frequently the fundamental research there conducted provides the clues, insights, and hence the opportunities to embark on programs that do lead to new drugs in industrial laboratories. Of the 627 new chemical entities introduced as drugs in the United States in the period 1941–64, the U.S. pharmaceutical industry originated 342 and shared credit with other U.S. or with foreign originators for discovery and development of a number of additional drugs. Most of the remainder were imported, as such, from European companies.

In 1965, drug companies sponsoring research allocated 10.5 percent of their sales revenue to research and development activities directed toward the discovery and development of new pharmaceuticals and biologicals for use in human and veterinary medicine. The drug industry finances almost all (98.5 percent) of its research and development with its own funds: no other industry spends as high a percentage of R and D funds for basic (15.8 percent) and applied (53 percent) research. Research in the pharmaceutical industry has grown from $12 million in 1940 to about $450 million in 1967; this now represents about 20 percent of the total funds allocated within the nation for medical and health-related research and has been growing at the rate of about 6 percent per year. Scientists and supporting personnel in this industrial research and developmental activity totaled about 2,000 in 1940 as compared with over 16,400 in 1965. Since sales of drugs in use before 1945 are now almost trivial, these efforts have provided the basis for a steadily growing ethical pharmaceutical market that was in excess of $3 billion in 1966. Table 2 present a summary, by major drug categories, of the 1965 U.S. drug shipments for human use.

Table 2. 1967 U.S. Drug Shipments in Major Categories
(*$ in Millions*)

Total		**$4,143.0**
Internal analgesics		488.7
Antibiotics		468.3
Hormones		413.5
Oral contraceptives	103.5	
Corticoids	141.7	
Others	168.3	
Drugs that affect the respiratory tract		366.6
Tranquilizers		321.5
Dermatological preparations		236.9
Vitamins		204.1
Drugs that affect the cardiovascular system		204.0
Antacids		137.3
Diuretics		94.7
Central nervous system stimulants		80.5
Laxatives		79.0
Hematinics		58.5
Antidiarrheal agents		41.3
Narcotics		40.3
Preparations for treatment of hemorrhoids		27.6
Barbiturates		25.4

Source: U.S. Department of Commerce, Bureau of Census, *Current Industrial Reports,* "Pharmaceutical Preparations, Except Biologicals—1967" Dec. 4, 1968.

Research in the Pharmaceutical Industry

An Industrial Approach to Biological Research. The classical pharmacopoeia consisted entirely of natural products, largely plant extracts. Numbers of these continue in use—digitalis, morphine, reserpine are excellent examples. Most, however, either have been discarded because they were ineffective where carefully scrutinized or have been replaced by more effective synthetic materials. The latter phenomenon is well illustrated by synthetic sex hormones used for contraceptive and other purposes, fluorinated steroids which are more specific and active in lower dosage than the natural products of the adrenal cortex, and the semisynthetic penicillins.

Each pharmaceutical house so engaged directs research toward securing new chemical entities with specific biological effects which would be useful in specific clinical situations. The effort is usually undertaken only when there is some clue that gives direction to the search—an existing drug that is not sufficient but is somewhat effective, knowledge of an enzyme to be inhibited, an effector or target structure, an animal or organ system which can effectively serve as a counterpart or model for a defined human disease, a metabolic pathway, etc. Although such approaches have provided the basis for discovery of most new drugs, despite vast effort, these rational approaches have only rarely proved successful when they are forced to start from first principles. Among the most striking of these have been the development of allopurinol and the new diuretics described in Chapter 16.

Chance, however, properly exploited has been the major factor in several of the greater successes. The sulfonamide series was discovered by accident and then remarkably sharpened by synthesis of hundreds of analogues culminating in such compounds as sulfadiazine and sulfamethoxazole. Antibiotics are still discovered by screening extracts of yeasts, molds, and fungi. Penicillin, streptomycin, aureomycin, and the polyene antibiotics were all found in this manner. Only long after their discovery was insight gained into their modus operandi. The most frequently employed tranquilizers similarly are the results of studies in which the right experiment was performed for the wrong reason. And, even now, there is no insight into the mode of action of many classic, well-established drugs—e.g., aspirin, morphine, and digitalis.

Withal, this is no cause for despair. There are leads, in abundance, to the possibility of new drugs. And it is only well-staffed laboratories engaged in a rational course of endeavor, adequately equipped and organized, which can capitalize on the unexpected and, thus, bring a new useful drug to the market.

The academic community has played a vital role in the development of new drugs and will undoubtedly continue in this function. Its role includes initial clinical evaluation of new drugs, development of new methodology for drug evaluation, development of biochemical or physiological rationales which prompt new drug design, and training of biological scientists for industry.

Most importantly, it is the totality of the effort in fundamental research that sets the stage for the research endeavors of those in industry who seek new drugs. It is the enhanced understanding of biochemical and physiological functioning, the newer insights into the nature of disease states, their etiology and pathogenesis, and the techniques elaborated by those so engaged that provides the absolutely essential broad underpinning of the entire enterprise.

Observations of clinicians have occasionally led to the discovery of new uses for drugs. Chlorpromazine, originally synthesized for testing as an antihistamine drug, was found to be extremely useful as a tranquilizer. The clinical use of this and related compounds has resulted in a marked reduction in the number of the mentally ill needing hospitalization, as previously discussed. Because clinical studies, as well as in vitro and animal test systems, are more detailed and better designed today than ever before, one can expect the development of more selective drugs for the treatment and cure of disease.

The development of new drugs and biologicals is increasingly complex. This is due to the desire for more specific knowledge of their mode of action, the demand for greater selectivity of action, and the need for better predictability of their effects in man. This trend is resulting in increased research aimed by industry at developing biochemical and physiological correlates of human disease states in animal models. For example, as techniques for the study of disease, comparisons are being made of the Egyptian sand rat, which develops diabetes when fed standard laboratory rat food, the K-K mouse, which develops a genetically derived diabetes, and the alloxan-induced diabetic rat.

A trend is evident toward increased emphasis on basic research, the understanding of the causes of diseases, the actions of drugs on enzyme systems, and the actions of drugs at the cellular level. Molecular biologists and biochemists, in industry, are increasingly concerned with the structure and function of enzymes and genes. The motivation for this increased emphasis on basic research is the need for more selective drugs and, wherever possible, for drugs that treat the *causes* of diseases rather than the *symptoms*.

Biochemists in the industry are becoming more concerned with the search for biomedical rationale to guide the synthetic medicinal chemists in the design of drugs more selective for specific aspects of disease. Accordingly, increased emphasis is being placed on studies of enzymatic processes such as those related to the biosynthesis of cholesterol, fatty acids, and triglycerides. Admittedly, there have as yet been few major rewards for such endeavors.

The classical pharmacological methods are being replaced by more automated and more biochemically oriented methods. The elevation or depression of tissue or blood levels of such important metabolic substances as acetylcholine, histamine, and catecholamines is used as a guide for drug studies. Psychopharmacology, a growing field, has introduced highly automated methodology which permits observation of behavioral changes in diverse laboratory animals. Neurophysiological techniques, biochemical measurements, and recorded behavioral responses are used jointly in the study of drugs that influence the nervous system.

Nutritionists are employed by the industry in increasing numbers as pharmaceutical companies diversify to include foods and food additives. Research on vitamins and cofactors continues, with new cofactors still being found and the modes of action of older vitamins and cofactors becoming better understood through more detailed studies.

Reproductive physiology is of new interest because of the increasing demand for drugs to regulate fertility and the concern about the effect of drugs on the fetus. Many species of laboratory animals, including subhuman primates, are being used for all of these studies.

Veterinarians employed by pharmaceutical companies are responsible for maintaining healthy animal colonies and developing new strains as models for the study of human disease.

The magnitude of this effort is revealed in Table 3, summarizing the use of animals by the pharmaceutical industry in 1965.

Table 3. Animal Usage in the Pharmaceutical Industry in 1965

Mice	23,200,000
Rats	9,900,000
Hamsters	900,000
Guinea pigs	350,000
Rabbits	250,000
Dogs	93,000
Monkeys	60,000
Cats	33,000

From a survey made by the Institute of Laboratory Animal Resources, National Research Council.

Biologists and engineers work together to develop instrumentation for diagnosis or treatment. Automated biochemical analyzers, heart monitoring devices, and electrical anesthesia inducers have been developed. Research is being conducted to develop biopolymers which can be substituted for natural body parts and organs—e.g., heart valves, artificial kidneys, arteries.

Virologists and microbiologists are concerned with the nature of viruses, fungi, bacteria, and protozoa that are pathogenic to man and animals. Tissue culture techniques have made it possible to produce viruses in large quantities for vaccine manufacture. This method of culture, which has resulted in the polio and measles vaccines, is now being brought to bear on the study of other viral problems.

The Process of Drug Development. New drugs are derived from two principal sources: (a) naturally occurring materials and (b) synthetic compounds. In the former class are the antibiotics (penicillin, streptomycin, etc.), the alkaloids (morphine, reserpine, quinine, etc.), the cardiac glycosides such as digitoxin, protein hormones such as insulin, and many others. The latter class comprises an extremely wide variety of synthetic compounds, some of which are patterned after naturally occurring drugs.

The isolation of naturally occurring drugs from plants is a continuing effort which requires the participation of trained botanists. New plant sources must be identified and their geographical distribution determined. Studies may be undertaken to determine the importance of the subspecies or strain, the soil, climate, and geographical habitat. Efforts to cultivate the plant may be required.

Experienced microbiologists culture the microorganisms which are the sources of new antibiotics and assay the activity of new antibiotics against a variety of yeasts, molds, and bacteria. A combination of microbiological and chemical methods permits new antibiotics to be distinguished from the host of older ones which have already been discarded for one reason or another. The microbiologist also must develop and perform microbiological assays in order for the biochemist to follow the course of isolation procedures.

Synthetic compounds are prepared because, from their structures, it was reasoned they might have certain activities. Alternatively, new classes of synthetic compounds may be screened broadly in an attempt to discover new activities. The incidence of successful prediction has been reasonably high for a few classes — e.g., local anesthetics and antihistaminics — but very low for most others. The pharmacologist helps in the discovery of drugs by devising "screens," batteries of biological assays, to determine the relative biological activities, if any, of a series of compounds. Normally, a large pharmaceutical company has numerous projects going on simultaneously, and a corresponding number of screens must be available which may require the services of endocrinologists, pharmacologists, parasitologists, biochemists, microbiologists, physiologists, or psychologists.

Representative samples of a series of compounds are usually screened broadly; in this way, a number of excellent new drugs have been discovered. For instance, a university chemist synthesized one compound with the thought that it might be a local anesthetic, but a pharmaceutical company later developed it as an antihistamine. Another pharmaceutical firm synthesized the same compound, but as a potential antispasmodic, and later marketed it as an antinauseant!

From this process of screening synthetic organic compounds, or from the successful isolation of a natural product, a new candidate drug may emerge. The next task is to determine its mode of action, toxicity, and side effects. A considerable scientific effort is needed to explore the pharmacological mechanism of action of a candidate drug. To be useful, the drug must result in elimination of infection or modification of physiological function in such fashion that useful therapeutic effect is exerted without undue deleterious influences on normal processes. Knowledge is then required of acute and chronic toxicity in a variety of laboratory animals, at several dosage levels, and over periods of time ranging up to two years. During the test period, animals must be observed carefully for adverse symptoms. At the end of this period, and occasionally during its progress, animals are sacrificed and their tissues are studied in the gross and microscopically by pathologists.

It is rare to find a potent new drug free of undesirable side effects. The pharmacologist must predict an effective human dose which hopefully will produce a minimum of side effects. He must also be able to warn the physician who first uses the drug in a human patient what forms of toxicity might appear, what abnormal conditions in the patient would contraindicate use of the drug, and how other drugs, administered simultaneously, might affect the recommended dosage schedule.

If the drug seems useful and devoid of serious side effects in animals, it is then necessary to learn about its absorption, distribution in tissues, metabolism, and mode of excretion. A necessary preliminary to this research is the development of adequately precise and sensitive methods for measurement of the drug in urine, blood, and other body fluids or tissues.

Two more steps must be accomplished before clinical trial. The pharmaceutical chemist must put the drug in a suitable stable dosage form (tablet, elixir, injectable solution, etc.) and see that the proper safety tests are performed. The second task at this stage is to file an Investigational New Drug Application (IND) with the Food and Drug Administration (FDA), a document that gives a full description of the new drug, where and how it is manufactured, all quality control information and standards, stability, analytical methods, pharmacology, toxicology, documentation of efficacy in animals, the physicians (and their qualifications) who will be doing the clinical studies, and complete protocols of the experiments to be performed. Only after this approval is granted may the drug be used, for investigation only, in man.

The first trial of a drug in man is done with great caution and on a very limited basis. Phase one is devoted to ascertaining the limits of safety in the human. When these have been established and are found acceptable, the drug is made available to a larger number of practicing physicians for phase two, the determination of efficacy. If, after phase two, the drug still looks promising, it is distributed more widely to selected practicing physicians for phase three, to secure data on as many patients as possible, to determine the incidence of untoward side effects, particularly uncommon effects which can be detected only when very large numbers of patients are studied, and to determine the optimal conditions for use of the drug to obtain the desired therapeutic effects.

Finally, before the new drug can be marketed, a New Drug Application (NDA) must be filed with the FDA and approval obtained. The NDA contains most of the information included in the IND, which has been revised and updated, as well as all the results of the clinical studies. Typically, such an application, today, consists of two to two hundred volumes. It is only after FDA approval of the NDA, an action taken only after detailed study by critical experts, that distribution and marketing of the new drug can begin.

It is evident that the development of new pharmaceuticals requires a large array of biological specialists, including bacteriologists, mycologists, virologists, pharmacologists, physiologists, endocrinologists, veterinarians, pathologists, toxicologists, immunologists, botanists, biochemists, pharmacists, and medical practitioners. Each plays a unique role in the process, and together with the organic, physical, and analytical chemists, the teams are constituted which, in concert, strive to find new, useful drugs and bring these to the market.

The magnitude of this effort is shown in the fact that, in 1965, 16,440 individuals were so employed, of whom 23 percent had doctoral degrees. The areas of scientific competence of the latter are indicated in Table 4.

New Areas of Challenge

Although the advances in medicine due to discovery and development of new agents have been so spectacular that the term *miracle drugs* has come into common usage, the needs and opportunities for additional advancement are vast. In the past, a large percentage of new drugs has emerged from empirical testing of compounds by biological procedures that bear some relationship to the disease to be treated. This combination of empiricism and methodology will continue to be of importance.

Table 4. Fields of Scientific Specialization of Scientists in the Pharmaceutical Industry in 1965

Field	%	Field	%
Chemistry	31	Research administration	5
Biochemistry	10	Pathology	3
Microbiology	10	Engineering	3
Pharmacology	10	Veterinary medicine	2
Pharmacy and		All other biosciences	9
medicinal chemistry	10	Other physical sciences	1
Clinical medicine	7	All other	1

From *Prescription Drug Industry Fact Book*, Pharmaceutical Manufacturers Association, Feb. 1966.

However, greater fundamental knowledge of the living state and of disease mechanisms is needed to provide a more scientific basis for discovering cures.

Molecular Bases of Diseases. The increasing sophistication of biological research assures that an understanding of the molecular bases of diseases will emerge (Fig. 18-1).

Much of the research of the past two decades was strongly influenced by the concept of competitive inhibitors, or antimetabolites. In a general way, drugs were sought which could interfere with the metabolism of a given compound, e.g., cholesterol, by virtue of their physical resemblance. With recognition that the "committed step" in most synthetic pathways is subject to feedback inhibition by a compound (the pathway product) that bears little resemblance to the substrate of the enzyme in question, this field is about to take on a new vigor. Knowledge of the molecular bases of diseases will strongly influence both the methodology of testing new drugs and the choice or design of compounds to be tested. Targets, or receptor locations, where drugs will act will be recognized and, hopefully, may be isolated and characterized. This information will be useful in acquiring new knowledge of the interaction between drugs and their receptor sites and in understanding the requirements for specific spatial orientation of essential structural features of drugs.

In this regard, drug synthesis should be enormously aided by the growing understanding of conformation of organic compounds such as carbohydrates and steroids. In the last analysis, to be active, a drug must lodge and bind to some molecular receptor site by virtue of its own steric structure. The rapid growth of conformational analysis of organic compounds should significantly enhance the capability of organic chemists to prepare appropriately tailored molecules. An excellent historical ex-

Figure 18-1. Germ-free mouse colony. The operators are working with the animals by placing their hands into the sealed gloves that extend into the cage. (Courtesy Eli Lilly & Co.)

ample is the group of semisynthetic penicillins; in retrospect, only those proved effective which retain the steric arrangements of the parent native penicillin. Future attempts in this regard will not overlook this fact and be misguided by the classical, shorthand structures by which such compounds are conventionally designated on paper. Drug design will also make provision for those characteristics that will assure absorption, transport to the receptor site, and harmless elimination of the therapeutic agent.

A more quantitative approach to normal and pathological processes and the effects of therapy will require greater utilization of mathematical models of the system in question in a form manageable in a computer. For example, the interrelationships between glucose and insulin levels in blood during administration of glucose to normal and diabetic subjects have been described in an analogue computer model. The model provides quantitative information on the effect of insulin on glucose uptake into tissues, and on the effect of blood glucose levels on the release of insulin from the pancreas.

Information about the control of metabolic processes is emerging from many laboratories. With understanding of the mechanisms by which hormones regulate life processes, and the influences of aging and disease on such activity, it may become possible to design agents which can exercise effective control of metabolism during disease and aging. If successful, some degenerative processes might be ameliorated, resulting in a longer span of useful life.

Hypertension and Atherosclerosis. In the light of these general considerations, advancements can be anticipated in control of a number of disease states. During recent years, the importance of high blood levels of cholesterol and certain other lipids in experimental and clinical atherosclerosis has focused attention on drugs that may inhibit metabolic synthesis and/or accelerate disposition of these substances. A number of such agents are even now under test. Perhaps the most interesting lead is provided by the unexpected observation that candidicin, a polyene antibiotic, rather dramatically lowers serum cholesterol levels, an observation that remains to be explained and evaluated. Many years of study will be required before it is possible to demonstrate whether such drugs prevent or ameliorate the problems of hardening of the arteries.

The acute problems associated with atherosclerosis are caused by formation of thrombi. Two approaches are being directed to this problem. (1) Platelet agglutination, the first step in the formation of a clot, is now being intensively studied. Some factors that stimulate agglutination have been recognized, and drugs are being sought to counteract this influence.

(2) Studies are also in progress seeking agents, such as enzymes, that will hasten the dissolution of a clot that has recently been formed.

In the past few years several compounds have been made available which effectively lower the blood pressure of hypertensive patients by affecting the nervous control of arteriolar pressure. Evidence is accumulating that these compounds, along with diuretics, are helpful in maintaining the health and prolonging the lives of such patients, but additional useful compounds are needed. Basic studies in the etiology of hypertension, and more meaningful animal models of the human disease, will be influential in solving these important medical problems of hypertension, and stroke.

Cancer. The prevention, control, and cure of cancer remain as goals that have not been achieved. Advances in chemotherapy remain modest, but older anticancer drugs are being used more effectively; and from time to time, new classes of compounds are found that contribute to and strengthen the hope for even more significant advances. Other avenues of research also show promise. New immunological and biochemical procedures have revealed the possible viral causation of some forms of cancer. If this work is successful, and the initiating viruses are determined, vaccines may be developed that could prevent some forms of cancer. The existence of tumor-specific antigens in both virally and chemically induced tumors, as well as new evidence for host reactions to the tumor, increases the possibility of useful immunological approaches to cancer.

Much additional work is needed to define the disease more specifically in biological and biochemical parameters and to provide the basis for a better rate of prevention and cure. Cancer appears to be a variety of diseases; undoubtedly several different approaches will probably be required to control it. A number of questions may be posed: Can normal differentiation be restored? What is the metabolic basis for the unbridled cell multiplication? Is the metabolism of cancer cells significantly different from normal cells to provide a basis for chemotherapy?

Viral Diseases. Development of procedures for propagation and counting of viruses in tissue culture has led to more precise procedures of testing compounds for antiviral activity. Recent research findings in which some biochemical sequences involved in viral multiplication have been determined provide insight into several possibilities for drug interference. These include:

1. Interference with viral attachment or penetration of the cell
2. Interference with viral-induced enzymes responsible for replication of viral nucleic acid

3. Interference with assembly of viral components
4. Induction of faulty coding

An increasing number of antiviral compounds are being discovered. For example, 5-fluorodeoxyuridine is effective in treating herpes of the eye, and isatin thiosemicarbazone has been used against vaccinia. These are small but meaningful triumphs. A lead that is being pursued is offered by a material called *interferon* which is elaborated by a mammalian cell infected with a virus. In sufficient quantity, it then prevents virus reproduction. Current efforts are directed at finding means to elicit interferon synthesis, on a sufficient scale to be harvestable, by cells in tissue culture. The current cupboard of antiviral drugs is unimpressive, but understanding of the nature of viruses and their reproduction is growing rapidly. Hopefully, this will provide a key to their control.

Mental Health. Reference has already been made to important advances in mental diseases brought about by tranquilizing compounds and other agents affecting the central nervous system. A new emphasis has been given to the importance of physiological and metabolic factors in mental processes. Empirical testing of compounds that influence learning, memory, and other mental processes in animals may be expected to provide the basis for additional progress in this important area.

Infectious Diseases. Starting with the sulfonamides and continuing with new antibiotics and synthetic agents, the antibacterial drugs have contributed to major advances in the treatment and control of bacterial and other microbial diseases. However, problems of drug resistance and patient sensitivity provide impetus for continued research. For example, a new problem in drug resistance involves the emergence of a transferable and infectious resistance factor. This factor can be transmitted to nonresistant organisms of different strains or species under natural conditions. Although evidence presently available indicates that this factor is not of major importance in the spread of resistance to antibiotic substances, additional research is needed. Agents that prevent the emergence of the factor or that prevent its infective properties may be sought, or future research may be directed toward agents that enhance host resistance. In a small but significant percentage of infections, the disease recurs in a manner that suggests a reservoir of live organisms. Some recent studies seem to indicate that certain morphological variants of bacteria may persist within some tissues. Perhaps a new type of drug or combinations of available drugs would eradicate these forms.

Tropical Diseases. The increasing penchant of Americans for overseas travel, and the stationing of Americans in many foreign lands, have heightened concern over the widespread importance of such tropical diseases as malaria, schistosomiasis, and parasitic infections. Experience in Vietnam has emphasized the existence of atabrine-quinine resistant malarial organisms. No drugs at present are completely effective in schistosomiasis, and even now culture of the schistosome in vitro is not possible. But both systems are under attack. Seemingly adequate "screens" are available and the problems are approached empirically.

Autoimmune Diseases and Organ Transplantations. Recent research has focused attention on various aspects of immunity other than those concerned with the use of prophylactic vaccines. A number of important diseases such as arthritis and multiple sclerosis appear to be manifestations of autoimmune phenomena. Antibodies appear to be formed to body constituents; these antibodies then combine with the tissue containing the antigen and cause degeneration. For these diseases, suppression of immune phenomena or induction of immune tolerance may be of great importance. The early generation of immunosuppressive agents has already made possible such success as has been obtained in organ transplantation. The search for better agents will continue, particularly for agents which, when withdrawn, permit full recovery of the immune mechanisms.

Hormonal Factors. Attempts are now under way to isolate new hormones, such as the releasing factors from the hypothalamus and certain gastrointestinal hormones. Their synthesis or, hopefully, the synthesis of an active fragment will be achieved. With the greater availability of these agents, more detailed studies of their function will be possible, and it seems likely that some of them will find a place in controlling important metabolic processes.

Reproductive Control. Control of reproduction represents an important area of continuing research. Although the presently available combination and sequential oral contraceptive agents composed of estrogens and progestins represent a major advance, new approaches to prevention of pregnancy are being sought. Basic physiological and biochemical processes of reproduction are being studied, in both industrial and other laboratories. These studies may be expected to provide the basis for new screening procedures in the present search for cheap, safe, convenient, and effective agents.

Other Diseases. Compounds are being sought that will more closely mimic the action of insulin in diabetics or ameliorate some of the long-term physical disabilities which they experience. More potent nonaddictive analgesic agents, sedatives that do not cause drug tolerance, better antiinflammatory agents, antiulcer drugs, and compounds that prevent or control osteoporosis are among the objectives of current research programs.

Comparative Pharmacology. More sophisticated techniques for study of metabolism have been brought to bear on the comparative effects of drugs in various animals and man. Frequently, the metabolism and therapeutic effects of drugs vary from species to species. Such variability can be the basis for differences in toxicity as well as differences in efficacy. For these reasons, increasing emphasis is being given to studies of comparative metabolism in man and animals. If a species of laboratory animal that handles a drug in a manner similar to man can be identified, one can have greater confidence that extensive testing will throw light on clinical efficacy, safety, side effects, etc.

Future Trends. As we have seen, the empirical approach will continue to be of great importance in the discovery of new drugs. But increasing contributions should come from fundamental studies that will characterize the molecular bases for health and disease and will provide the foundation for improved test systems and better projection of desirable drug structures. Unless American society chooses to erect some new research structures, research in the pharmaceutical industry will continue to provide most of the initiative in discovery and development of drugs. This effort can be successful only if academic and government laboratories will continue to make major contributions to our understanding of structure and function in health and disease.

Veterinary Medicine

Veterinary medicine is concerned with the health problems of household pets, with animal diseases that may be transmitted to man (rabies, ornithosis, brucellosis, salmonellosis, cat scratch fever, parasitic infections, etc.), and, most importantly, with adequate and nutritious food supplies for human use, the principal health problem of the world.

In underdeveloped nations, more than three times as many people die from malnutrition as from the five most important causes of death in the United States (heart disease, vascular lesions, cancer, respiratory diseases, and accidents). The food supply of the United States and American know-how are of critical importance in helping to meet these problems in a world whose population is projected to more than double by the year 2050, even with increasing use of birth control practices. To feed this burgeoning population necessitates emphasis on increased food production. Development and application of chemical and biological products to control animal diseases and to improve the production of meat, poultry, milk, and eggs represent one important approach to the problem.

Patently, many pharmaceuticals useful in man may find application to the problems of animal health. However, in this instance, economic factors are of overriding importance: the cost of treatment may exceed the economic value of the animals treated. Health of poultry and other animals must be maintained in order to obtain good growth and feed utilization, to give high egg production, and to assure wholesome meat for market. Emphasis on rapid growth and good feed utilization has also led to development of agents that are of special importance because of their ability to improve the utilization of feed. In some cases, animal disease problems require special agents. For example, most viral diseases affecting animals differ from those in humans and require separate vaccines. Parasite infestation is much more prevalent in animals.

These needs, with their similarities and dissimilarities to human disease problems, have stimulated research in animal health in the pharmaceutical companies. Some agents developed for human use have been tested and adapted for animal health problems. Procedures developed for screening compounds or for vaccine production for human therapeutic needs can be modified for the specific veterinary problems. However, provision must be made for special problems not encountered in human medicine.

In recent years, numerous applications have been found for the new drugs that have been developed by the pharmaceutical industry. Some drugs are used to control disease; others have increased growth and feed efficiency. For instance, feeding diethylstilbestrol to cattle has increased final weight by 13 percent while improving feed efficiency by 10 percent. Continuous feeding of low levels of selected antibiotics has increased growth and feed efficiency in several species. Higher doses of these same antibiotics control diseases which have been the cause of great loss through morbidity or mortality.

Anthelminthics now permit sufficient control of parasites so that land can be reused time after time, even though contaminated by parasitic ova. The development of effective coccidiostats has been an important factor in making possible large-scale production of poultry, thereby contributing to the 21 percent drop in the retail price of poultry between 1950 and 1966, despite inflation.

Many pharmacological agents used in human medicine also find their place in veterinary medicine—for example, antiinflammatory agents, hormones, diuretics, antitussives, and even tranquilizers. Anthelminthic screens with infected laboratory animals serve both human and veterinary medicine. The continuing search for hypoglycemic compounds useful in human diabetes is watchful for hyperglycemic compounds to treat bovine ketosis.

The antibacterial spectrum desired of an antibiotic for use in animals may be quite similar to one sought for human medicine. However, a few organisms such as pleuropneumonialike organisms, erysipelas, and pasteurella are of special importance in animals. Thus, screening searches for antibiotics regard both human and animal medicine as objectives.

New areas of opportunity are evident. Biological products to produce immunity to parasitic infections would offer significant advantages in providing continuous protection. This is especially important because most chemotherapeutics at the present time offer only temporary treatment and do not prevent reinfection of animals maintained in contaminated environments. Improvement in reproductive efficiency of animals offers tremendous opportunities affecting a large percentage of the animal population. Synchronizing estrus in beef cows as an expedient for artificial insemination is approaching practicality. Twinning of some species would double reproductive output. Prevention of the current loss of one third of the fetuses in swine would have considerable economic significance. Sheep, which are seasonally anestrus, might be induced to produce two additional lamb crops every three years. Beef cows, which offer a maximum potential of 100 percent conception, now conceive at a level of only 60 percent under the best of conditions. As land becomes more restricted and animals are maintained in smaller space, respiratory diseases and enteric problems will increase. In poultry, leukosis represents the most important unsolved disease problem. This viral disease, as well as others, offers significant opportunities for effective antiviral compounds.

Instances of inappropriate use of drugs and unexpected toxicities have engendered a conservative viewpoint and, in some instances, a fear of chemicals that has invited an emotional outlook on the part of some consumers. This apprehension has arisen primarily from the problem of persistence of some pesticides. Better toxicological data concerning residues are certainly needed. Protection of the consumer is of paramount importance. At the same time, one need be careful that regulations to assure safety of veterinary products do not act as deterrents to real progress.

The continued administration of antibiotics to animals, as well as their extensive use in human medicine, has raised the potential problem of transferable drug resistance. The significance and implications of such resistance are not adequately understood and warrant careful investigation. A second area of concern is that residues of antibiotics given to animals may remain in meat or milk when these products are prepared as food too soon after administration of the antibiotic. There is serious need for continuing education of the manufacturer and distributor of antibiotics, as well as the veterinarian and the food producer, with respect to this potential hazard. Enforcement of regulations that assure good practice is imperative.

The Industry

The pharmaceutical industry is a highly specialized instrumentality of American society where biological science, chemistry, and engineering are combined to discover new, useful drugs and make these available to the physician and his patient. Undergirding this applied research is the entire world research effort in fundamental biology, medicine, and organic chemistry. Withal, the economics of this industry are hazardous. Out of concern for the welfare of the consumer, this endeavor has been subjected to close regulation and supervision by the Food and Drug Administration which, properly in our view, demands that new drugs may be marketed only if they have been proved to be both reasonably safe and efficacious. Quite apart from the question of reasonable prices, and from the current discussion of generic equivalence of a given chemical entity independent of the manufacturer, our society must find a suitable solution to the underlying economic problem.

A variety of estimates indicate that, from the moment the decision is made to undertake a given line of research, to the ultimate marketing of the drug that results, an investment totaling $5 to $10 million is required. If the drug is applicable to a widespread disorder, and is truly useful, there is little problem in securing an adequate return on this investment. But if the drug finds a place as the drug of choice in a relatively rare disease, or if it is merely competitive in a market where other useful drugs already exist, the company is in a parlous position. And this cannot be known until most of the investment has been made. Indeed, these very circumstances discourage research directed at agents that can have only limited use in rare, albeit fatal, diseases and are eroding the initiative of many pharmaceutical houses with respect to the search for new drugs generally.

Since the research arms of the pharmaceutical houses are the primary source of new drugs, and since there remains a serious unfilled need in many areas, some appropriate solution is required to this dilemma.

Fermentation and Related Industries

Wine and leavened bread date back to antiquity, but only within the past 100 years has the nature of these processes become understood and the term *fermentation* clearly defined. A fermentation is a process whereby chemical changes are produced in an organic substance through the action of enzymes formed by microorganisms. Microbiologists, chemists, and engineers have combined their knowledge and skills to develop efficient, controlled industrial procedures whereby microorganisms and their enzymes can be employed to manufacture a variety of useful products. Yeasts, bacteria, streptomyces, molds, algae, and enzymes from some of these forms are either being employed, or have potential industrial uses, to produce pure chemical compounds or biological products. In other cases, fermentative processes are utilized in the preparation of foods (cheese, sauerkraut, pickles, olives, tea, cocoa, etc.), in the curing of tobacco, and in other transformations that occur in nature.

Future biological research may need to be directed toward using microbial fermentations to manufacture important substances that are currently too complex to be synthesized by ordinary chemical means, to prepare nitrogenous foods from substrates such as petroleum fractions, and to help maintain the ecological balance on the planet by destroying waste products of our complicated civilization. By the use of genetically selected microorganisms and new types of substrates (such as high-energy hydrocarbons and ammonia), it should be possible to manufacture protein foods and other unique substances on a profitable commercial scale.

In sum, the disparate fermentation industry constitutes a major national resource. Each of the major companies so engaged retains a staff of microbiologists, biochemists, chemists, and engineers. Together, they are responsible for the continuing monitoring control of the fermentations with which they are concerned. The microbiologists continually search, by the conventional techniques of bacterial genetics, for new strains of microorganisms which will more efficiently or more rapidly conduct the fermentation in question. Rarely do these groups, as such, discover new fermentations yielding new products of value. Most have been encountered earlier in the course of systematic microbiology, and the industrial research team develops the procedures whereby a laboratory observation is scaled up to the requisite industrial magnitude. An important exception has been the systematic hunt for new antibiotics by the drug houses as well as the deliberate use of bacterial fermentation for certain chemical transformations of steroids which were too difficult by the techniques of synthetic chemistry.

Because in its totality this represents a practical exploitation of the synthetic prowess of microorganisms which has not had wide recognition, we present below a summary of the industrial utilization of microbial fermentations, each of which represents the current exploitation of previous biological research.

Yeast Products

Yeasts are employed extensively in industry to produce some of the most important substances used by mankind.

Baker's, Food, and Fodder Yeasts. The dry and compressed-yeast industry began about one hundred years ago as a modified brewing operation; since then, many modifications have improved the process. In 1940, about 110,000 tons of baker's yeast were produced in this country; this amount increased to approximately 180,000 tons in 1967 with a value of almost $45 million. Food and fodder yeasts are manufactured under essentially similar conditions, although the propagation of yeast for human consumption is more refined. Special strains of yeasts are frequently used depending upon the raw material employed as a substrate and the desired end product. Many carbohydrate-rich materials that are cheap and readily available can be used as a substrate on a commercial scale—viz., sulfite liquors from pulp mills, molasses, and wood sugars, as well as such diversified substrates as fruit juices and hydrolyzed grain and olive residues.

Accurate production figures on food and fodder yeast are unavailable; estimates are several thousand tons annually and the industry is expanding. About 7,500 tons of dry beer yeast are produced each year in the United States; two thirds of this amount is sold as animal feed, and about one third is debittered and used directly in human foods (baby foods, etc.) or hydrolyzed to make yeast extracts for soup and flavors. In addition to baker's and beer yeast, over 5,000 tons of torulae are produced and sold for yeast supplements in animal feed and for human foods.

Industrial Alcohol. The use of ethyl alcohol in industrial processes today is so great that, with the exception of water, it may be regarded as our most important accessory chemical substance. Many products depend upon ethanol for their manufacture, from synthetic rubber to perfumes, antifreeze, and varnish. In response to industrial demands in the United States, the production of ethyl alcohol by yeast increased from approximately 19 million gallons in 1920 to almost 685 million gallons in 1945. Since then, the amount of ethanol produced by fermentation has decreased considerably, owing to the discovery of synthetic methods using petroleum products that are cheaper and easier to control. Only about 10 percent of industrial alcohol is currently being produced by fermentation. Federal food and drug laws require that the ethanol used in fortifying beverages and for medicinal uses must be made by fermentation.

Malt Beverages. The brewing of beer, ale, and other malt beverages that do not undergo distillation constitutes a large industry. In 1946, approximately 500 breweries produced about 85 million barrels (31 gallons per barrel) of malt beverages annually. By 1966 production had increased to approximately 110 million barrels. To brew this quantity of beverage required nearly 5,000 million pounds of malt, corn, rice, wheat, sugar and syrup, hops, and other raw materials.

Wines. Wine is made by yeast fermentation of grape juice and, at times, other fruit juices. Many types of wine are known, but to illustrate the magnitude of the industry and how it is growing, a few production figures may be cited for four different years:

| | *Millions of Wine Gallons Produced in* | | | |
	1944	*1964*	*1965*	*1966*
Still wines	108.8	193.3	197.2	234.5
Effervescent wines	1.5	5.8	6.3	8.2

Distilled Spirits. The manufacture of whiskey from fermented grain mashes, brandy from fermented fruits (grapes, apples, apricots, prunes, cherries, etc.), rum from fermented sugarcane molasses, and gin, cordials, and liqueurs requires large commercial organizations. In 1944 the production of distilled spirits in this country was about 69.5 million tax gallons; by 1965 this figure had risen to over 185 million gallons. In addition, in 1965, distilling materials produced at wineries for fortification constituted a volume of 468.6 million wine gallons.

Miscellaneous Yeast Products. Various species of yeast are a rich source of vitamins, enzymes, glutathione, nucleic acids, nucleotides, fats, and several other organic substances. Some of these materials are produced commercially, and others could be so obtained if other sources became scarce.

Riboflavin is produced industrially by certain yeastlike microbes. Annual production for human and animal consumption is about 1 million pounds, with a value of over $6 million.

Some yeasts readily convert sugars to fat, with up to 63 percent of the dry weight of the cells consisting of fat. Large quantities of protein can be synthesized from a variety of substrates including petroleum fractions by yeasts. These proteins may serve as a useful supplement in animal feeds in the near future, since several industrial companies are building plants for the production of yeast proteins from gas-oil.

Bacterial Products

Bacteria can be used in the manufacture of a variety of organic compounds, such as acetone, butanol and other solvents, lactic acid, 2,3-butanediol, dextrans and blood-plasma extenders, sorbose, certain antibiotics, vitamins, and amino acids. Also pure cultures of bacteria are employed commercially in the production of enzymes, vaccines, and toxoids, and for legume inoculants. Microbiologists must retain rigid laboratory control over these manufacturing processes so high yields of the desired products can be obtained, and so that contaminating organisms do not alter the chemical reactions. Constant search is under way to find new or more desirable genetic strains of bacteria that may be useful in industry.

Butanol and Acetone. Certain bacteria form acetone and butanol, along with other products, during their fermentation of carbohydrates (low-grade corn, molasses, etc.). At one time these important industrial chemicals were largely produced by fermentation. But now little, if any, of the total production (1,114.2 million pounds in 1965) of acetone comes from fermentation. Some years ago, about 80,000 tons of butanol were produced annually in this country by fermentation, but again, current production by microbial fermentation is negligible. Synthetic procedures have largely replaced fermentative methods for the manufacture of both butanol and acetone, because the processes are more rapid, easier to control, and the substrates do not have to be sterilized.

Lactic Acid. Since 1881 lactic acid has been produced periodically by fermentative means. The process has been much improved so that one plant has a capacity of over 10,000 pounds per day of 22 percent lactic acid. Annual production is now over 2,500 tons from various substrates, including starch hydrolysates, molasses, and whey. Various grades and derivatives of lactic acid are used extensively in food industries, in pharmaceutical preparations, in leather and textile industries, and in the manufacture of plastics and lacquers.

Vinegar. Manufacture of vinegar depends upon the acetic fermentation of dilute alcoholic liquids (wine, cider, beer, etc.) by so-called vinegar bacteria (*Acetobacter*). This ancient process is continually improved by selecting new strains of bacteria.

The production of 4 percent cider vinegar and 100-grain white distilled vinegar exceeds 130 million gallons annually in the United States, with a value of about $50 million. Additional quantities of wine and other unspecified types of vinegar are manufactured, having a value of about $5 million.

Dextrans and Other Polysaccharides. Certain bacteria (*Leuconostoc*) synthesize and secrete large quantities of dextrans (polymers of glucose in 1,6 linkage) when grown in media containing sucrose or other sugars. For many years the production of these substances caused much trouble in sugar mills and refineries because they obstructed the flow of juices and syrups through pipes or interfered with sugar crystallization.

Advantage is now taken of the synthetic ability of these bacteria to make these carbohydrates to develop industrial products. The usefulness of the dextrans and their derivatives depends upon their distinctive characteristics (molecular weight, structural distribution of component units, viscosity, solubility, etc.), which differ from other polysaccharides of commerce. One such dextran is superior to other common colloidal agents when used in oil-well drilling muds or for secondary recovery of petroleum; these applications provide an estimated potential market for 200,000 tons of polysaccharide per year. Dextrans are employed for protective coatings on seeds, as deflocculants for production of fine paper, as masking agents in engraving, and in photographic emulsions, to stabilize syrups, confections, ice cream and sherbets, and in the cosmetics industry.

The most important medical use of dextrans is as a blood plasma substitute. In the United States most of the standard clinical dextran (molecular weight 75,000 $\pm$ 25,000) is stockpiled by the government, but it is estimated that about 150,000 units (500 ml of 6 percent dextran in saline) are used for emergency medical and veterinary purposes in isolated areas. In other countries in the world where blood transfusion is not readily available, clinical dextran is in current use. Dextrans are used as a filler or emollient in several pharmaceutical preparations, and in the laboratory as an analytical molecular sieve to separate or fractionate proteins, nucleic acids, and other substances.

Sorbose. The industrial production of L-sorbose from D-sorbitol by bacterial fermentation annually yields about 5 million pounds, most of which is employed in the synthesis of ascorbic acid (vitamin C).

Amino Acids. Only L-glutamic acid and L-lysine are currently being manufactured industrially by bacterial processes. But it is possible to produce other L-amino acids (valine, tyrosine, phenylalanine, tryptophan, etc.) should need arise.

About 50 million pounds of monosodium glutamate, annually, valued at $25 million, is manufactured by a bacterial process in the United States. Larger quantities are produced in Japan and Taiwan. It is used primarily as a flavor enhancer. Perhaps 100,000 pounds of glutamic acid are employed in pharmaceutical preparations.

A large-scale process for production of L-lysine has been yielding about one million pounds annually. Should plans for supplementation of cereal grains, particularly wheat, with lysine in underdeveloped countries go forward, this process would become far more important.

Legume Inoculants. Bacteria such as *Azotobacter* in association with leguminous plants utilize atmospheric nitrogen and "fix" it, making it available to the plant. The usual practice is to grow the bacteria on industrial scale, and then spread them on the seeds of legumes just prior to planting. The manufacture of such legume "inoculants" requires careful selection of strains of bacteria in the laboratory, extensive field trials with plants on experimental plots before large-scale culture and continuous control of the industrial process.

In 1963 the seed inoculants produced by several companies in the United States amounted to 24,766,561 bushel units (amount required to inoculate one bushel of seed); their value was placed at about $7.5 million. Experience has amply demonstrated that the use of inoculants will greatly improve crop yields of leguminous crops on many types of soils. Thus, this practice serves to increase the world's food supply.

Insecticides. Certain bacteria are known to cause disease in over 120 insects, but are harmless to higher forms of life. Advantage is being taken of this fact to produce "bioinsecticides," using primarily *Bacillus thuringiensis.* Commercial preparations are manufactured as dusts, as wettable powders, and as liquid materials for spraying. These are not contact poisons; they must be consumed by the larvae of insects such as the cabbage looper, tobacco and tomato hornworm, alfalfa caterpillar, cankerworms, grubworms, etc. If appropriate agents can be found, bioinsecticides will become increasingly useful; no harmful residual chemicals remain, and they are potent in as small amounts as many of the better chemical pesticides. Many biological products are being tested. In this regard, we may note that the mold product griseofulvin shows some promise because it interferes with the synthesis of chitin, the major component of the exoskeleton of insects.

Miscellaneous Bacterial Products. Besides the substances previously mentioned, bacteria produce a number of organic acids (glycollic, propionic, tartaric), and other metabolic products can be harvested. Many such materials have potential industrial uses, but only a few are being produced commercially today.

The United States production of vitamin B_{12} for animal and human consumption, by fermentation, is currently over 2,000 pounds per year, with a value of about $8 million. Incorporation of 10 to 15 mg per ton of feed greatly increases the utilization of vegetable proteins by pigs and improves the hatching qualities of poultry eggs. Other vitamins, especially riboflavin, have been produced commercially using certain bacteria.

Streptolysin O is a microbial product that is now manufactured by at least five large companies in this country; the value is over $500,000 per year. It is required in the immunological assay of the sera of human patients with streptococcal infections.

A few bacteria are capable of utilizing petroleum products as a carbon source; if various technical problems could be solved, they possess a potential for producing substances (proteins, amino acids, and vitamins) that may be of value as food substitutes for domestic animals and man. Such plants are now on stream in France. Recent estimates indicate that it is technically possible to produce all the proteins required for feeding man and animals by using 15 to 20 percent of the world's production of petroleum. The protein food produced by such a process would be somewhat more expensive than present sources, and would not readily be acceptable as a major food by most people. But if research on increasing yields, improving nutritive qualities, and acceptability can be accomplished, certain microbial foods may have practical value, in countries that otherwise must subsist on low-protein diets.

Mold and Streptomyces Products

Various molds and streptomyces produce many metabolic substances of great economic importance, such as antibiotics, organic acids, vitamins, and intermediate compounds that are useful in the manufacture of steroids. New mold products are continually being found which are of practical value. For example, the gibberellins, which were discovered less than twenty years ago, today are produced commercially as plant-growth stimulants. Certain fungal toxins (aflatoxins), are potent carcinogens in experimental animals; they may be helpful in solving various aspects of the cancer problem.

Antibiotics. One of the greatest achievements of all time by man has been the discovery, practical manufacture, and use of antibiotics. The production of antibiotics constitutes the major fermentation industry of this country. Current annual manufacturing values are approximately 5 million pounds of antibiotics for human and veterinary uses, and 4 million pounds for feed supplements, food preservation, and sprays for protection of crops, sold in the aggregate for about $500 million.

Commercial production of antibiotics began during World War II when eight companies cooperated to develop a practical fermentation method for penicillin. Since then over 1,000 antibiotics have been described from molds, streptomyces, and bacteria; 53 of these have been produced on a commercial scale by various companies in the world. In recent years the following more important antibiotics have been manufactured in the United States by fermentation:

actinomycin	neomycin	7-chloro-6-dimethyltetra-cycline
aterrimin	novobiocin	5-hydroxytetracycline
amphotericin B	nystatin	tetracycline
bacitracin	oleandomycin	thiostrepton
cycloheximide	paromomycin	tyrocidine
cycloserine	penicillin G	tyrothricin
erythromycin	penicillin V	tylosin
fumagillin	polymyxin	vancomycin
gramacidin	ristocetin	viomycin
hygromycin	streptomycin	
kanamycin	7-chlorotetracycline	

Chloramphenicol (Chloromycetin), once made by fermentation, is now prepared solely by chemical synthesis.

Of the antibiotics listed above, most are used for human therapy except aterrimin, cycloheximide, hygromycin, thiostrepton, and tylosin. Aterrimin is added to chicken feed to stimulate growth of the birds; cycloheximide (Acti-dione) is employed to control certain plant pathogens; hygromycin is used as an anthelmintic in hog feed; thiostrepton is beneficial in treating bovine mastitis; and tylosin has certain agricultural uses. Bacitracin and streptomycin are also used in some animal feeds or for other agricultural purposes.

Several antibiotics are modified chemically to produce new medicinal agents. Examples are the formation of dihydrostreptomycin from streptomycin and methicillin from 6-amino penicillic acid.

Citric Acid. Under controlled conditions certain molds convert sugar to citric acid, which can be recovered in a pure state. Production in 1950 was estimated at 17,500 tons, in 1960 at 35,000 tons, and in 1966 at over 50,000 tons valued at $30 million.

Over half of the citric acid manufactured is used in foods or beverages as a flavor-enhancer, a preservative, an antioxidant, and as a pH regulator in jellies, candies, and soft drinks. Large amounts are also employed in pharmaceutical products (citrates, effervescent salts). Smaller quantities have diverse industrial uses, such as a sequestering agent in oil-well acidizing, in electroplating and engraving, in metal cleaning, in dyeing fabrics, in leather tanning, in the manufacture of cigarette papers, and as a component in floor cements, linoleum, and ink removers.

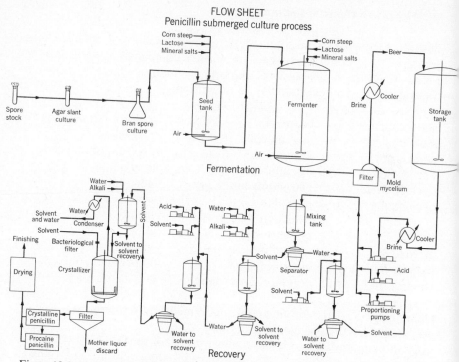

FLOW SHEET
Penicillin submerged culture process

Figure 18-2. Flow sheet of penicillin submerged-culture process. (From *Industrial Fermentations 2:*243. © 1954 by the Chemical Publishing Co., New York)

Gluconic Acid, Gibberellic Acid, and Other Organic Acids. Various molds ferment glucose and other sugars, forming a great variety (over 50) of organic acids. Some of these products are manufactured commercially and have wide uses. In 1966 about 12 million pounds of gluconic acid (and its salts) were produced, representing a value of $3.5 million. The substance is used primarily in the pharmaceutical and food industries.

A mold is now being used commerically to produce several hundred pounds of gibberellic acids (gibberellins) a year. These interesting substances stimulate the germination of seeds, improve the growth of young forest trees, increase the flowering of plants, "set" tomato fruit clusters, and break the dormancy of potatoes. To an increasing extent, gibberellin is used for improving the production of grapes, navel oranges, and lemons. In malting, gibberellin increases amylase production during the germination of barley.

Steroids. Of the various steroids of medical importance several are prepared by a combination of chemical and microbiological methods (cortisone, hydroxycortisone, methylprednisolones, prednisolone, and triamcinolone). More than 25 types of conversions of steroids may be brought about by selected strains of molds, streptomyces, and bacteria. The types of reactions usually involve the addition or removal of a hydroxyl radical, hydrogen, or oxygen to a steroid nucleus. For example, the formation of hydroxyprogesterone from progesterone is accomplished by hydroxylation at a certain position in the molecule. But microbial reactions that rupture the ring structure and that oxidize or reduce side chains of the steroids are also known. Several companies employ such processes for selected steps in manufacturing steroids, but information as to the quantities transformed by microbial means is not readily available.

Algal Products and Uses

Certain algae are collected from the oceans and processed to produce useful products for industrial and laboratory purposes, particularly the alginates. An important way that algae may be of great economic value is in the utilization of various waste products of civilization. In one foreign country, for example, an algae-growing sewage disposal plant is in operation. The plant has a designed capacity of 55 pounds per day of dried *Chlorella,* based on average weather and artificial light. At the same time the plant will produce 6,000 to 12,000 gallons of purified water. The *Chlorella* are rich in amino acids, vitamins, fats, carbohydrates, and minerals, and are of potential value as an animal feed supplement.

Agar and Irish Moss. The substance known as agar is made from certain red algae. It is widely used for making microbiological media, but it also has other uses, such as a thickening agent in various commercial food products. Another important substance manufactured from red algae is Irish moss, from which extracts are used in curing of leather, sizing of cloth, preparation of some foods, and as an ingredient in certain cosmetics, hand lotions, and shaving soaps.

Enzymes

Enzymes from various biological sources are now available commercially, and are in wide use (Table 5). Commercial bakers use certain proteases to speed up and control the breakdown of the gluten in the flour dough, so bread baking on a large scale can be accomplished. Chilling of beer causes it to cloud owing to the appearance of a fine haze of precipitated protein. By adding a protein-destroying enzyme the beer can be "chill-proofed" and the clear amber brilliance restored. Proteases are also the main ingredient in meat-tenderizing preparations. A recent expanding use of enzymes is in combination with detergents for the removal of stains.

Before weaving many cotton textiles, the fibers are coated (sized) with starch to protect them from abrasion and to give them a smooth finish. Since dyes will not penetrate such fabrics, they must be desized before being dyed; amylase is used for this purpose. The viscosity of chocolate syrup may be controlled by invertase and amylase, and that of liquid coffee concentrates by cellulase. Certain pharmaceutical preparations are used in medicine for cleaning (debriding) wounds without harming healthy tissues, and other products are employed for preventing indigestion.

Research in enzyme technology is at a high level, and anticipations are that many more practical uses will become available soon. The amylases, cellulases, pectinases, and proteases are now manufactured in ton quantities, whereas some of the other enzymes are specialty items and are produced in small amounts. In 1960 the commercial value of the enzymes employed in industry was over $26 million; in 1967 this figure was two or three times larger. Thus, it appears that the full commercial potential of enzymes has not been realized.

Cultured Tissues and Cells

For several years it has been possible to grow animal and plant tissues or cells in the laboratory as so-called tissue cultures. This has contributed greatly to the isolation of numerous viruses and an understanding

Table 5. Some Commercial Enzymes and Their Uses

Enzyme	Source	Industry and Application
Amylase	Animal (pancreas)	Pharmaceutical: digestive aids
		Textile: desizing agent
	Plant (barley malt)	Baking: flour supplement
		Brewing, distilling, and industrial alcohol: mashing
		Food: precooked baby foods
		Pharmaceutical: digestive aids
		Textile: desizing agent
	Fungi (*Aspergillus niger A. oryzae*)	Baking: flour supplement
		Brewing, distilling, and industrial alcohol: mashing
		Food: precooked baby foods, syrup manufacture
		Pharmaceutical: digestive aids
	Bacteria (*Bacillus subtilis*)	Paper: starch coatings
		Starch: cold-swelling laundry starch
		Laundry: stain removal
Bromelain	Plant (pineapple)	Food: meat tenderizer
		Pharmaceutical: debriding agent
Cellulase and hemicellulase	Fungi (*Asperigillus niger*)	Food: preparation of liquid coffee concentrates

Table 5. *Continued*

Enzyme	*Source*	*Industry and Application*
Dextransucrase	Bacteria (*Leuconostoe mesenteroides*)	Pharmaceutical: preparation of blood plasma extenders, and dextran for other uses
Ficin	Plant (fig latex)	Pharmaceutical: debriding agent
Glucose oxidase (plus catalase or peroxidase)	Fungi (*Aspergillus niger*)	Pharmaceutical: test paper for diabetes Food: glucose removal from egg solids
Invertase	Yeast (*Saccharomyces cerevisiae*)	Candy: prevents granulation of sugars in soft-center candies Food: artificial honey
Lactase	Yeast (*Saccharomyces fragilis*)	Dairy: prevents crystallization of lactose in ice cream and concentrated milk
Lipase	Fungi (*Aspergillus niger*)	Dairy: flavor production in cheese
Papain	Plant (papaya)	Brewing: stabilizes chill-proof beer Food: meat tenderizer
Pectinase	Fungi (*Aspergillus niger*)	Wine and fruit juice: clarification
Penicillinase	Bacteria (*Bacillus cereus*)	Medicine: treatment of allergic reactions to penicillin; diagnostic agent
Pepsin	Animal (hog stomach)	Food: animal feed supplement
Protease	Animal (pancreas)	Dairy: prevents oxidized flavor Food: protein hydrolysates Leather: bating Pharmaceutical: digestive aids Textile: desizing
	Animal (pepsin) Animal (resin) Animal (trypsin) Fungi (*Aspergillus oryzae*)	Brewing: beer stabilizer Dairy: cheese Pharmaceutical: wound debridement Baking: bread Food: meat tenderizer
	Bacteria (*Bacillus subtilis*)	Baking: modification of cracker dough Brewing: clarifier Laundry: stain removal
Streptodornase	Bacteria (*Streptococcus pyogenes*)	Pharmaceutical: wound debridement

of their characteristics, to the preparation of vaccines, and to a general understanding of the nutrition and metabolism of cells.

To obtain dispersed cells for culture from various animal organs, the connective tissue substances are first digested aseptically with enzymes such as trypsin. The cells may then be cultured by placing them in test tubes, flasks, or bottles containing nutrients consisting of serum, vitamins, amino acids, carbohydrates, and mineral salts. The cells may adhere to the glass, multiply in clumps, and eventually form a complete monolayer sheet over the surface. Or the cells may be cultivated in suspension, where they usually occur as single cells or as pairs. Growth is rapid, with a doubling of the cell population in 20 to 40 hours. Population densities in monolayer cultures sometimes reach maximums of 100,000 cells per cm², and in suspension cultures the population may reach 2,000,000 cells per ml. Several industrial companies are now engaged in marketing various cell lines for research purposes and for vaccine production, with an annual market value of $25 million.

With intensified research and technical developments during the past decade, it is now possible to grow animal cells in large industrial equipment similar to that employed for growing microorganisms that produce antibiotics or other fermentative products. In the future, such cultured cells may be used industrially to grow viruses for vaccines or to produce hormones and other important cellular components. Among the problems requiring further research before these processes can become successful are improvements in the culture media employed, prevention of contamination of cell cultures, selection of proper gas mixtures for aeration of cultures, a better understanding of environmental conditions for growth and proliferation of the cells, and sufficient understanding to prevent dedifferentiation of the desired, specialized cell line to an undifferentiated form.

Instrumentation in Industrial Biology

Instrumentation, the science and technology of measurement and control, is vitally important in the expanding field of biology. From the earliest stage of research to the ultimate delivery of a biological product to the user, instruments play key roles. Without them, antibiotics, pain-relieving drugs, and innumerable other blessings that we take for granted would not be possible.

Man's Natural Instrumentation

Man himself is endowed with a remarkable system of "instrumentation." His five senses enable him, quickly and effortlessly, to make measurements of a widely diverse nature. Without conscious attention, the eye, for example, with its associated built-in "computer" registers light intensity, the color, size and shapes of objects, their distance and location; it discerns motion and focuses on details with an extraordinarily high resolving power. Coupled with various control mechanisms of the body, it is part of an instrumentation *system* that exceeds in complexity and performance the best of man-made systems.

Consider an automobile driver approaching an intersection. If the signal light suddenly turns orange, his eye notes the change in color; the significance of the change is interpreted almost instantly; and a complex control system involving decision-making computers and complicated muscle mechanisms is activated. Should he go through the intersection or come to a stop? The eye gathers all sorts of essential input data, especially the positions and speeds of other vehicles, and perhaps the presence or absence of a traffic policeman. From his memory data bank, pertinent information is retrieved, such as earlier experiences, traffic citations, etc. In a split second the extensive data are evaluated and the decision is made. If it is GO, he hurries through the intersection, with his eyes functioning like radar units to guard his safety. If it is STOP, his built-in muscle-control system applies the brakes in precisely the proper way to bring the vehicle smoothly and surely to rest at a predetermined position. During this process, the eye supplies a constant stream of input data so that performance of the system is constantly monitored and checked against desired goals. Man's internal instrumentation system is marvelous indeed.

The Need for Instrumentation

Although the eye is a superb sensing device, it has limitations and falls short of meeting the requirements of modern science and technology. Its sensing range is limited to a narrow region of the electromagnetic spectrum, from deep violet to dark red. The eye is insensitive to the short wavelengths of ultraviolet and x-rays, also to the long wavelengths of infrared and microwaves. For measurements in these very important spectral regions, instruments must be used.

The eye is limited in its ability to see small objects. Microorganisms, key factors in industrial biology, could not be observed until the invention of the microscope by Leeuwenhoek in the seventeenth century. The compound microscope is an indispensable tool for today's biologist, yet even its resolving power is limited by the wavelength of the light used for illumination. The electron microscope has made it possible to observe particles as small as viruses or even large molecules. And this resolution will be increased by another factor of three- to six-fold by the "flying spot" electron microscope now under development.

Man has many technical limitations as a measuring tool. Physiological and subjective errors may readily arise. Some are color blind. Fatigue can cause perceptive errors and reduce sensitivity. Instruments can provide the objectivity and reliability so essential to research and control.

In addition to expanding the scope and sensitivity of man's senses, instruments reveal phenomena and forces to which the body is completely insensitive, such as magnetism and electric charge. Man's five senses are thereby multiplied several-fold.

Because of increasing sophistication and complexity of modern instrumentation, as well as more extensive use to enhance the effectiveness of trained manpower, instrumentation costs, expressed as a percentage of the budget for research or for plant equipment, are increasing. This trend seems likely to continue.

How Instruments Are Born

Most instruments of importance to biologists come into being as a result of a determined effort to meet a recognized need. Biologists make use of instruments developed for other fields, of course, especially chemistry and physics, but such use merely emphasizes the mutual interdependence of various scientific disciplines.

A research laboratory is usually the birthplace of a new instrument. Basic research particularly generates needs for new types of measurements, often measurements of phenomena or properties previously unknown or of little interest. Or it may be that a higher order of precision or speed of measurement becomes imperative. Whatever the need, it is usually recognized first in the research laboratory.

In the past, the researcher often found it necessary to build his own instruments. Special equipment not available in the market often was needed to make the physical, chemical, or biological measurements necessary for the researcher's programs. Today there is a vast array of commercially available and essential components, especially sensors, amplifiers, and readout devices that usually enable the researcher to assemble readily an instrumentation system to fit his particular needs.

Instruments designed to take advantage of a new phenomenon or physical effect usually are developed first by a researcher. If homemade apparatus appears to have utility for other researchers, the development and engineering required to produce a reliable and usable instrument are usually provided by the instrument manufacturer. Many researchers have neither the skill nor the time to build the same instrumentation themselves. The instrument manufacturer plays an important role in making instrumentation developed by researchers widely and rapidly available in reliable, well-engineered form and in constantly improving such instrumentation over the original device.

Competition among leading instrument manufacturers is the stimulus that promotes a never-ending stream of better instruments. Major instrument manufacturers maintain research laboratories devoted exclusively to the development and improvement of instruments, and it is to these laboratories that most credit must be given for the great variety of instruments available to biologists today. Investment in research and development by instrument manufacturers, typically 8 to 10 percent of sales income, is higher than for most other manufacturing industries, and is one of the reasons why the United States leads the world in the development of instruments of high performance and sophistication.

The development and design of a new instrument usually can be done best by a team of specialists. Many simple instruments seem to involve merely a little mechanical ingenuity, but even these must be designed by experts if they are to be manufactured economically. Most instruments are not simple, and an optimal design involves the complex interaction of many factors—not merely scientific elements such as optics, electronics, mechanics, or chemistry, but also practical factors such as size, weight, ruggedness, reliability, ease of maintenance, speed of response, compatibility with associated instrumentation, and, of course, cost. Every instrument is a compromise, for design elements often are unavoidably mutually antagonistic. Size must be balanced against convenience and portability, ruggedness against weight, speed of response, accuracy and performance generally against cost, etc. Time required for development and testing is an important factor, and decisions must be made as to whether to release a newly developed instrument at an early stage, thereby enabling users to reap early benefits from it, or to delay release for extensive field testing with the possibility of developing improvements.

As previously stated, needs for new or improved instruments are usually recognized first in basic research, but not always, particularly in industrial instrumentation. Here economics plays a major role in determining the extent and nature of instrumentation. The industrial biologist, like any other industrialist, is acutely conscious of costs. He is primarily interested in instruments, not from the standpoint of advancing the boundaries of human knowledge, but from the standpoint of lowering costs of production, enhancing and assuring quality, meeting legal requirements with respect to purity or pollution standards, etc.

The Biologist and the Instrument Manufacturer

It is obvious that a close relationship must be maintained between the biologist, whether in research or industry, and the instrument manufacturer. Each is dependent upon the other. Little progress can be made in the life sciences without instrumentation, and, in fact, without a continuing stream of new instruments that make available to the biological researcher and industrial biologist the benefits of new techniques for measurement, control, and data interpretation. The instrument manufacturer has interfaces with many diverse fields of technology. It is his task to relate developments in one field to another. Thus, he can make available to the biologist the benefits of integrated circuitry or lasers, for example, with no requirement that the biologist be skilled in these new technological advances. Conversely, the biologist can aid the instrument maker by informing him of the need for new instrumentation or for improvements in existing instruments.

Thus, a mutually beneficial symbiotic relationship exists. Better instruments enable the biologist to do his work better, whether it be the researcher exploring scientific frontiers or the industrial biologist seeking to make a better product at lower cost. The expanding use of instrumentation, on the other hand, means more business for the instrument maker. The ever-changing needs present challenges that stimulate his research staff and give to the instrument industry its characteristic growth and vigor.

Space limitations preclude listing all of the types of instruments or their special contributions to biological research and industry. Table 6 lists some instruments that are widely used and have special significance for modern biology. The investment in instrumentation for biology is difficult to determine because available statistical data on domestic production and imports of instruments list them by types and not by end use. The most recent information available from the U.S. Department of Commerce indicates that annual sales of instruments of interest to biologists are well in excess of a billion dollars. Comparative figures for 1964 and 1965, presented in Table 7, show the growth of the instrument industry.

Industrial Instrumentation

The term *industrial instrumentation* connotes in the minds of some a robot complexity that automatically performs tasks of measurement and control that otherwise would be performed manually. To a large extent this concept is correct, but manual operators also require instruments. Automation in instrumentation is primarily a matter of economics. Today a typical industrial plant relies heavily on automated instrumentation for precision of process control, reduced labor costs, and greater reliability. Other advantages may include greater safety, earlier detection of significant trends in process variables and, as a consequence of increasing use of computers, the ability to correlate many variables quickly and automatically for optimum process performance.

Striking changes are still occurring in industrial instrumentation. Not long ago, industrial process control was accomplished chiefly with the aid of instruments that measured only physical parameters, temperature, pressure, flow rate, etc. Today, such procedures as spectrophotometry, chromatography, and pH control make possible the continuing identification and measurement of individual molecular species with an extraordinary degree of specificity.

Instrumentation for biological industries is similar in many respects to that for chemical and petrochemical industries. Occasionally, there

Table 6. Some Instruments in Common Use in Biological Research

Microscopes 　Optical 　Phase contrast 　Electron	pH meter Radioactivity measurement 　Scintillation counter 　β-ray spectrometer
Colorimeter	Monitors 　Whole body counter
Spectrophotometer 　Visual range 　Ultraviolet 　Infrared	X-ray apparatus 　Irradiator 　Crystal analysis
Fluorimeter	Nuclear magnetic resonance spectrometer
Emission spectrometer	Electron paramagnetic resonance spectrometer
Atomic absorption spectrometer	Circular dichroism analyzer
Chromatograph 　Gas 　Liquid 　Paper	Multichannel recorder Automatic chemical analyzer
Electrophoresis	Oscilloscopes
Centrifuge 　Refrigerated 　Analytical ultracentrifuge 　Preparative ultracentrifuge 　Respirometer 　Oxygen electrode	Stopped flow analyzer Osmometer Mass spectrometer Pulse height analyzer
Amino acid analyzer	Operant conditioning apparatus

Table 7. Some Major Categories of U.S. Instrument
Industry Sales *†

(thousands of dollars)

	1965	1964
Primary laboratory and scientific instruments	216,392	186,101
Industrial and other process instruments	629,383	467,014
Other mechanical and controlling instruments, including nuclear radiation detecting and monitoring instruments	155,100	115,408
Optical and analytical instruments	270,590	235,655

* U.S. Bureau of the Census and Business and Defense Services Administration, Current Industrial Reports, Selected Instruments and Related Products: 1965 Series MA-38B(65)-1, Washington, D.C., 1967.

† Substantial quantities of foreign-made instruments are imported into the United States. U.S. Department of Commerce publication FT-9301(1967) shows that imports for the category "Scientific, Medical, Optical, Photographic, Measuring and Controlling Instruments" were $214.6 million in 1966 and $178.0 million in 1965.

are special requirements, however, such as the necessity for sterilization; the need for sterilization of sensors often imposes severe limitations upon their design and performance.

One interesting example of development of a special instrument for biological research involved the measurement of retention time of a new hormone. It had been proved that the hormone would effect the desired biological changes if retained for a certain number of hours. The major task was to prove that the hormone would be retained under a wide variety of conditions.

An instrument was then built by a commercial designer to measure the metabolism time of the hormone extracts. The radioactively tagged hormone was injected into small animals, and measurements were made of radioactive carbon in the expired breath. Measurements of the animal's respiration flow, oxygen, total CO_2, and radioactive CO_2 were fed into a small analogue computing system that continuously displayed and recorded the rate of O_2 consumption, total and radioactive CO_2 expiration, the respiration quotient (ratio of the oxygen consumed to the CO_2 expired), and the specific activity (ratio of the radioactive CO_2 to the total CO_2). The computer also integrated readings and printed on a tape at preselected intervals the total volume of O_2 consumed and CO_2 expired, and the picocuries of radioactive CO_2 expired. From these data the retention time of the hormone extract was determined. As a result, the time required for proving this aspect of the efficacy of the hormone extract was reduced from months to a few days.

Disposal of waste products is frequently a headache for industrial biology. National attention has been sharply focused in recent months on air and water pollution, and stringent new laws have been enacted in an attempt to control pollution. This has led to increased use of instruments to monitor air and water pollution. In most cases, instruments of high sensitivity must be used, as the concentrations of contaminants are often at the level of parts per million or billion. One recent example involved a large fish kill in the Mississippi River. Insecticides or pesticides were suspected. With the aid of the gas chromatograph, it was possible not only to detect the contaminating agent in the river but to trace it upstream and identify the plant from which it came.

Instrumentation of the Future

Research in the life sciences creates a never-ending demand for better instruments, instruments with greater sensitivity, wider range, faster speed of response, etc. Such requirements are a constant challenge to the instrument maker and stimulate him to produce successive new generations of instruments with better performance characteristics than their predecessors.

Sometimes instrument performance is limited by the properties of materials available for use in construction. The ultracentrifuge is an example. Centrifugal forces as high as 400,000 g are obtainable, using forged titanium rotors. Higher forces await the development of rotor materials of greater tensile strength. In the fields of filtration and dialysis, there is need of fundamental research on materials for filtration that have a sharp or well-defined boundary of filtered particle size.

Some instruments that currently are in early stages of development and that ultimately may be useful to biologists appear to be of special interest. One recent development that will have significant impact on biology is automatic degradation of complex polymeric molecules with attendant analysis to determine the nature of the fractions, carefully and precisely disconnected from the complex molecule. Another significant development is the automated synthesis of peptides.

A third device of potential value is the electron probe. Originally developed for microspatial chemical analysis of metallurgical specimens, its use has been expanded during the past few years into biology. The electron probe microanalyzer permits relatively complete chemical analyses to be performed in situ on the microstructures observed in the tissues of thin sections prepared by standard histological methods. All of the elements of atomic numbers greater than 4 (beryllium) can be detected with sensitivities of the order of 10^{-13} to 10^{-15} grams. This sensitivity should prove of considerable value in tracing elemental materials in drugs, foods, plants, etc. It permits the determination of chemical variability of individual microstructures and of localized association of different elements. A great deal of work remains to be done, however, particularly in the interpretation of diffraction pattern data, before the electron probe becomes a useful device for routine measurements. Data enhancement through computer processing probably will be very useful.

The atomic absorption spectrometer has been gaining favor in industrial biology and clinical analysis because of its speed, simplicity and high sensitivity for elemental analysis. Its wide range of industrial applications already includes determination of trace metals in foods, vegetable oils and fats, industrial waste waters, and wines and whiskeys, as well as measurement of minor nutrients in fertilizers that affect the growth rate of plants.

Of growing significance is the automation of procedures in clinical chemical analysis. Where formerly each analysis was performed by hand by a trained technician at high cost and low accuracy, today an unskilled individual need merely record the order in which blood samples are poured into an instrumental arrangement which makes precise measurements of a battery of constituents (pH, sodium, chloride, bicarbonate, urea, glucose, cholesterol, protein, etc.), the results of which are fed to a computer which performs the necessary calculations and records the meaningful data on the patient's chart. This has improved precision, reduced delay, lightened the financial burden, and hence has removed from the physician the inhibition against requesting such screening data where he was unsure of the diagnosis. Undoubtedly such instrumentation will be markedly improved and its scope expanded in the years to come.

A revolutionary factor affecting instrumentation is the burgeoning use of computers. The widespread use of electronic data processing imposes new requirements on instrument design. Most instruments today are of the analogue type—i.e., readings are made from the position of a pointer on a dial or from a graph on a recorder chart. To an ever increasing extent, users are demanding that instrument readings be in digital form, suitable for direct input into EDP equipment. In the new generations of instruments, direct digital readouts are becoming common. The ultimate objective is a completely automated instrumentation system. Analyses will be made automatically, the necessary mathematical functions performed—i.e., integration, normalization, error corrections, etc.—and the answer presented in the desired form and units.

Digital-type display undoubtedly will be accentuated in the future, with associated capability for direct real-time computer input. Such equipment is relatively rare at this time, but will become common as we progress farther into the computer age.

In a general way, the more sophisticated the instrument, the higher the cost. But each new instrument, indeed each new generation of an old instrument, provides the scientist with a new capability available in no other form. Each brings new insights and understanding, and the pioneer instrument of today becomes the routine instrument of tomorrow as knowledge, understanding, and their applications become ever more intense.

Pesticides

Because of widespread interest in the "pesticide problem" and the hazard it may pose to human health and the balance of nature, it seems appropriate to review how the pesticide industry came into being and the justification for its continued existence. For the present purpose the term *pesticides* will be limited to physical, chemical, and biological agents that are used to control insects, animals, fungi, and weeds which are detrimental to man by either their direct or indirect action.

The urban and suburban dweller thinks of pesticides largely in terms of the articles used in house and garden to control flies, mosquitoes, gnats, ants, fleas, roaches, lice, bedbugs, clothing moths, the destructive insects found on vegetables, flowering plants, trees, and shrubbery, and the weeds he does not want, such as crabgrass, plantain, dandelions, poison ivy. To the farmer, pesticides are agents that increase the yield of crops, and hence his income, by limiting the destructive effects of the various pests on the plants he grows. The third important use of pesticides is their application in the field of public health to control disease-bearing pests.

Some important diseases are endemic in insect and rodent populations and are carried by them to man. These diseases may constantly affect human populations in those parts of the world where the disease-carrying pests reside, or they may appear in massive epidemics, like the great pandemics of plague, when infected pests in large numbers move into populated areas for one reason or another. Plague, malaria, typhus, Rocky Mountain spotted fever, tularemia, and African sleeping sickness are examples of such pest-borne diseases.

While effective *treatments* now exist for these diseases, they are most effectively *controlled* by controlling the pest vector that brings them to man, and it has been largely through the use of chemical pesticides that plague, malaria and typhus have been brought under control in most areas of the world. The availability of DDT during World War II removed, for the first time in military history, the threat that major campaigns would be settled by disease rather than weapons. Civilian populations were, likewise, protected by the same pesticide against the epidemics of typhus which had formerly afflicted them in times of war.

The latter half of the nineteenth century witnessed the birth of the pesticide industry. Several important fungicides were discovered, including sulfur, lime-sulfur, and copper combinations which gave substantial protection against a number of economically important mildews and blights. Lead arsenate, calcium arsenate, nicotine, rotenone, and the pyrethrins were found to control a number of destructive insects. Most widely used of these were the inorganic chemicals, because of cost and availability in quantity, and they dominated the agricultural pesticide field for roughly a hundred years.

Modern Pesticides

The early 1940's witnessed the birth of a new era in chemical pesticides with the discovery of DDT, *d*ichloro-*d*iphenyl-*t*richloroethane. Its first applications were in the control of pest-borne diseases by the military, and its effectiveness was so startling that it was held for a time under military security similar to that applied to new weapons developments. The success of DDT spurred the search for other chlorinated hydrocarbons with insecticidal activity, and was rewarded by the discovery of BHC (benzene hexachloride), a mixture of isomers one of which, lindane or Y-BHC, turned out to be the most active. These two chlorinated hydrocarbon pesticides became available for public use after World War II and stimulated the growth and development of the modern pesticide industry.

The chlorinated hydrocarbon pesticides were not the outgrowth of chemical warfare research, but because of their actual and potential military utility, they were studied intensively during World War II under military sponsorship. Since DDT and BHC were primarily used for public health purposes involving application directly to man, it was imperative to know what risks to health might result from the insecticides themselves. Hence toxicity studies were carried out on laboratory animals, and it was concluded from them that DDT and BHC were of low enough toxicity for warm-blooded animals that they could accomplish their intended purpose of pest and disease control. It developed from these early studies that the chlorinated hydrocarbon insecticides killed by overstimulating the central nervous system, somewhat in the manner of strychnine.

Meanwhile, research carried out independently in Germany and in England was disclosing another class of potential insecticides which operated by inactivating cholinesterase, an essential enzyme for both insects and mammals, which participates in the activity of the autonomic nervous system. These were usually esters of substituted phosphoric acids. Since some members of the class were sufficiently toxic to have potential as chemical warfare agents, neither German nor British military authorities permitted disclosure or use of the less toxic insecticide candidates until the end of the war. When released for civilian use, they became known as the organophosphorus insecticides, but the subsequent discovery of anticholinesterase insecticides, which are esters of carbamic rather than phosphoric acid, makes the broader term *anticholinesterase insecticides* preferable.

The success of the new organic insecticides stimulated a search for new organic fungicides, herbicides, and seed disinfectants, and resulted in the appearance of new members of each class. The limited arsenal of pesticidal chemicals available before World War II had now been augmented by an array of new and powerful weapons. The success achieved may be illustrated by the number of cases of malaria reported in many areas of the world, including the United States, before and after the advent of DDT and BHC. Figures cited by Zhadnov (*Epidemiology*, Foreign Languages Publishing House, Moscow, undated) for the U.S.S.R. are merely illustrative:

Malaria Morbidity in the U.S.S.R.

Year	No. of Patients Registered
1946	3,364,502
1950	721,239
1955	35,704
1959	<1,500
1960	"finally eradicated"

No more dramatic instance can be cited than the near eradication of malaria in Ceylon, where, before World War II, almost 70 percent of the population was so afflicted.

Current Use of Pesticides in the United States

In the two decades since the advent of DDT and BHC, the total amount of pesticides produced and used annually has increased steadily, and the number of new synthetic organic pesticides and combinations thereof now number in the hundreds.

DDT production has remained relatively constant; the total increase is attributable to newer pesticides. The U.S. Tariff Commission preliminary report on U.S. Production of Pesticides and Related Products (March, 1967) gives a grand total of 1,012,598,000 pounds for 1966 production of synthetic organic pesticides and related products.

The rapid increase in use occurred because new pesticides have been developed which control hitherto uncontrolled pests, and broader use of pesticides in large-scale agriculture has increased crop yields significantly. Current trends in crop production involving large acreages, greater use of fertilizers, and intensive mechanized cultivation and harvesting offer particularly favorable opportunities for insect pests, and would result in large crop losses to these pests unless control measures were applied.

The increased number of new pesticides in part reflects a second generation of pesticides with more appropriate persistence for *economic* control of specific pests, more complete control of the pest, less hazard for the applicator, or leaving less hazardous residues on the crop. An additional impetus to the development of new pesticides comes from the fact that many insect pests have developed resistance to the older pesticides. The development of pest resistance does not necessarily entail the development of more dangerous pesticides. It need only be chemically different to overcome the pest resistance. The continuing search for new and more ideal pesticides requires the joint effort of research teams composed of organic chemists, biochemists, pharmacologists, physiologists, entomologists, and botanists. How and where insecticides are being used today is summarized in Tables 8 and 9, which are taken from Tables I and II of Appendix IV to Part I, Report No. 1379 of the 89th Congress, "Pesticides and Public Policy," issued July 21, 1966 (Part I, Appendix IV, pp. 983, 984).

These tables indicate that about 73 percent of the total insecticide usage is in agriculture, and about 25 percent is used in urban areas by homeowners, industry, the military and municipal authorities. The remaining 2 percent is applied to forest lands, grassland pasture, and on salt and fresh water for mosquito control. Over 50 percent of the insecticides used in agriculture is applied to cotton acreage alone.

When insect control measures are *not* used in agriculture, insect pests take 10 to 50 percent of the crop, depending on local conditions. Losses of this magnitude are not readily tolerated in the face of a rapidly increasing population with a concomitant decrease in agricultural acreage in the United States. In this sense, the use of insecticides might be deemed essential *at this time* for the production and protection of an adequate food supply and an adequate supply of staple fiber. While alternative

Table 8. Where Insecticides Are Applied

Major Uses of Land	Acres in Category	Acreage Upon Which Insecticides Are Applied	Acreage Upon Which Insecticides Are Not Applied	Percentage of Acres in Category Upon Which Insecticides Are Applied
Total acreage, United States (48 States)	1,934,572,000 [1]	89,500,000	1,845,072,000	4.62
Forest lands (Includes forested grazing lands, or range, including Federal range used by permit, reserved forest land in parks, wildlife refuges, and national defense areas)	640,000,000	1,800,000 [2]	638,200,000	.28
Grassland pasture (Open permanent pasture and range, private, State, and Federal grassland range used for grazing excludes cropland pasture)	630,000,000	1,600,000 [2]	628,400,000	.25
Other nonforested special use areas (Nonforested parks and wildlife refuges, duck reserves, and national defense sites)	45,000,000	–	45,000,000	–
Miscellaneous other land (Deserts, sand dunes, wildlands, open salt and fresh water swamps)	77,000,000	2,500,000 [3,4]	74,500,000	3.24
Water areas (Includes reservoirs, ponds, and lakes of over 40 acres in size and streams and canals of ⅛ mile or more in width)	32,572,000	–	32,572,000	–
Total of categories 2, 3, 4, 5, and 6	1,424,572,000	5,900,000	1,418,672,000	.41
Urban and other built-up areas (Cities, towns, industrial sites, Armed Forces installations, airports, railroad and highway rights-of-way, etc.)	53,000,000	15,000,000 [3,5]	38,000,000	28.30
Cropland and cropland pasture	457,000,000	68,600,000 [3]	388,400,000	15.0
Total of categories 7 and 8	510,000,000	83,600,000	426,400,000	16.39

[1] Includes 6,925,000 acres in ponds and lakes of less than 40 acres in size and streams and canals of less than ⅛ mile in dth not treated with insecticides.

[2] Actual 5-year average.

[3] Estimated 5-year average.

[4] Includes all public and private mosquito control on all salt- and fresh-water swamps and marshes.

[5] Includes private home, lawn, garden insect and termite control, industrial insect control, municipal fly and mosquito, reet tree and park planting insect control and public insect control on highway rights-of-way.

methods of pest control are under investigation and development, they are not yet ready to displace completely the chemical pesticides, and it appears that a pesticide industry will be required for some years to come.

Unwanted plants (weeds) are also classified as pests. They may be unwanted because of appearance (crabgrass in the lawn) or because they impose economic penalties (reductions in crop yield). They can be controlled by physical removal, by fire, by chemical herbicides, and by biological predators.

Until relatively recent times the main weapon in weed control was physical removal (cultivation). Some chemicals, like common salt, copper sulfate/sulfuric acid, arsenates, and heavy petroleum oils, kill all plant life and have been used for many years to produce temporary soil sterility. Fire has long been used to burn off weeds and other plants prior to replanting or along right-of-ways. Of these measures, only cultivation is selective.

The situation changed in 1944 with the discovery of the selective organic herbicide 2,4-dichlorophenoxyacetic acid, (2,4-D), based on the structure of natural plant hormones, the auxins. The success of this compound in controlling certain weeds while not harming certain desirable plants led to further research and the development of other selective herbicides such as substituted triazines and ureas in the laboratories of the chemical industry. This hunt has utilized teams of chemists, plant pathologists, and toxicologists. Herbicides, properly, are subject to the same legal controls as other pesticides and hence require toxicological evaluation to establish safety in use. As a practical matter, the herbicides currently in large-scale use have not posed serious problems of toxicity for man, domestic animals, or wildlife.

Table 9. Use of Insecticides on U.S. Croplands

Crop	Acreage	Acres Insecticides Applied on	Acres Insecticides Not Applied on	Average Number Pounds Applied Per Acre	Percent Categor Insectici Applied
Grains (includes corn, feed sorghum and rice)	216,590,000	32,482,500	184,107,500	1.0	15
Vegetables (includes potatoes)	4,141,000	2,070,500	2,070,500	3.0	50
Fruits and nuts	2,822,600	2,258,000	564,600	7.0	80
Cotton	15,816,000	11,862,000	3,954,000	7.5	75
All other (includes hay, seed crops, sugar beets and cane, flax, soybeans, peanuts, and all other crops not identified above)	217,630,400	19,927,000	197,703,400	.5	9
Total	457,000,000	68,000,000	388,400,000	—	15

Development and Testing of a Pesticide

Pesticide development requires the cooperation of the chemist and the biologist. The chemist creates modifications of existing pesticide molecules and synthesizes totally new compounds which might or might not have pesticidal activity. There has been little success in predicting, from the structure of a compound, that it will be effective against any particular pest. Accordingly, candidate compounds are screened against a variety of insect pests, fungi, and weeds by entomologists, mycologists, and plant pathologists.

If a compound shows promise in the laboratory or greenhouse screening tests, it must be further tested under field conditions in various parts of the country to determine effects of climate, temperature, rainfall, and other environmental conditions on its performance. Concurrently, the toxicology team—composed of toxicologists, biochemists, physiologists, and pathologists—will have begun to explore its acute toxicity in laboratory animals and to determine how it acts in the body, what organs are affected, and whether it tends to accumulate in the body. These toxicity tests might reveal potential rodenticides, but most often serve as a basis for preliminary judgment that the candidate would or would not be too toxic for its intended use. The plant pathologist will also study its toxic effects on the plants to which it is applied as well as on those which are to be preserved.

The few compounds that survive both the pesticidal and toxicity screens are subjected to more extensive field testing in various parts of the country, as well as to more thorough toxicological investigation. If the pesticide is not to be used on food crops, the toxicity testing would be directed primarily to the safety of the applicator and would include effects on eyes and skin as well as an estimate of chronic toxicity—i.e., the effects of repeated daily exposure to small doses of the pesticide.

Pesticides intended for use on food crops, however, require a much more extensive investigation. Analytical chemists determine what residues are left on the raw agricultural product at time of harvesting, and how much, whether the residue is the unchanged pesticide, or whether the pesticide has been transformed into other products. This requires methods to determine these residues to less than 0.1 part per million.

After the amount of residue of the pesticide left on the raw agricultural product is known, rats and dogs are fed diets containing several levels of the residue for a period of two years to ascertain adverse effects of long-term ingestion. The animals are examined periodically, and the metabolic fate of the residue as well as any changes it might produce in body tissues is established. Simultaneously, rats on various dietary levels are selected for breeding, and reproduction studies are carried out through three generations to determine possible adverse effects on the reproductive function. All animals dying during the test and the survivors that are sacrificed at the end of the test are subjected to gross and microscopic pathological examination. Occasionally tests on human volunteers are conducted in parallel to make sure that the rat, dog, and man metabolize the material in the same way. This is not yet universal practice because of the difficulties attendant on the use of human volunteers for this type of investigation. Frequently, observations on industrial employees occupationally exposed during the preparation and testing of the candidate pesticide have proved particularly helpful.

In addition, investigations will have been carried out on the possible adverse effects of the pesticides on fish and wildlife by feeding it to selected species of birds, mammals, and fish. An important phase of the investigation is to determine the extent to which the pesticide becomes incorporated into food chains, and whether it builds up in concentration as it passes from one link in the chain to the next.

Only when these data are in hand can the manufacturer petition the U.S. Food and Drug Administration for a "residue tolerance," which is to be granted only if the U.S. Department of Agriculture certifies the utility of and necessity for the pesticide, and the U.S. Public Health Service and U.S. Fish and Wildlife Service interpose no objections.

The toxicity studies just outlined would cost between $250,000 and $500,000 out of a total research and development cost of $2 to $3 million. The investment, therefore, is of the order common to the pharmaceutical industry for development of a new drug. The time required for the development of a new pesticide from initial screening to the granting of a legal "residue tolerance" is four to five years.

The Future of Pesticides

Pesticides have been tremendously effective, but individual pesticides, like sulfa drugs and antibiotics, tend to lose their effectiveness as species resistance to them develops. Hence, there will be a continual search for new pesticides as long as pesticides are considered to be required by the economy and public health. This search will require the continuing use of able biologists. As with drugs, new pesticides should be selectively toxic for specific pests, rather than broadly toxic against a wide variety of pests with serious side effects on nonpest species. Broad-spectrum pesticides affect an essential enzyme or system common to a wide variety of pests. A selective pesticide, on the other hand, either should affect an essential enzyme or system peculiar to a particular pest, or should be applied in such a way that only the particular pest gains access to it. An interesting example of a selective pesticide is the rodenticide norbormide [5-(α-hydroxy-α-2-pyridylbenzyl)-7-(α-2-pyridylbenzylidine)-5-norbornene-2,3-dicarboximide]. Norbormide is highly toxic for rats, particularly for the Norway rat. By contrast, the acute oral toxicity of norbormide for other species is much lower, the lethal dose for a great variety of birds and mammals, per kilogram body weight, being more than 100 times greater. The mechanism of the selective toxic action of norbormide for the rat is not yet elucidated.

The first approach requires a sophisticated knowledge of the anatomical, physiological, or biochemical peculiarities of the target pest as compared with other pests or vulnerable nonpests, and then the development of a suitable selective pesticide to take advantage of the peculiarities. This is obviously not easy to accomplish, and norbormide may prove to be unique for many years.

An example of the second approach would be introduction of a systemic pesticide into the host or food of the target pest. Other pests or nonpests would not contact the pesticide unless they shared the same host or food supply. As an example, a suitable pesticide may be applied to the soil and imbibed by the root system of a plant on which the pest feeds. The pest feeding on the plant then receives a toxic dose. The application of attractants or repellents (for nontarget species) would increase the selectivity of the systemic pesticide. The use of systemic pesticides on plants used for food by humans or domestic animals poses an obvious residue problem.

There has been a strong public reaction against the continued use of pesticides on the grounds that such use poses a potential threat to the public health, as well as a hazard to wildlife. Careful investigations have, *so far,* failed to establish the reality of the threat to the public health; i.e., as yet there are not clear-cut instances of humans who have suffered injury clearly related to exposure to pesticides which have been used in the prescribed manner. Report No. 1379 of the 89th Congress (July 21, 1966), for example, concludes: "The testimony balanced the great benefits of disease control and food production against the risks of acute poisoning to applicators, occasional accidental food contamination, and disruption of fish and wildlife. The conclusion is that no significant human health hazard exists today.

"The fact that no significant hazard has been detected to date does not constitute adequate proof that hazards will not be encountered in the future. No final answer is possible now, but we must proceed to get the answer." (Italics ours.)

Failure to establish such hazard does not mean that it does not exist. There are no living animals that do not bear a body burden of some DDT, including those in the Antarctic. Large fish kills have been demonstrated. The large-scale use of these agents has been practiced for less than two decades and use increases annually. Whereas the anticholinesterase compounds, which have high acute toxicity, are readily and rapidly degraded in nature, the halogenated hydrocarbons are not. With time, their concentration in the soil and in the drainage basins, lakes, and ponds and even the oceans must continue to increase, thereby assuring their buildup in plant and animal tissues. Over a sufficient time period, this is potentially disastrous. And should such a time come, the situation could not be reversed, except by waiting for a century or more. Because of the large economic benefit to the farmer, it is pointless to abjure him to be sparing; he will make his judgment in purely personal economic terms. Moreover, mankind badly needs the incremented food made possible by usage of effective pesticides; and the enormous benefit to public health by greatly reducing the population of insects that are disease vectors is a boon to humanity. Accordingly, it is imperative that alternative approaches to pest control be developed with all possible dispatch.

Alternative Approaches to Pest Control

Another conclusion of the above report was: "Future pest control must be accomplished with many alternative weapons, applied strategically in an integrated manner."

Perhaps the oldest of the alternative methods is biological control. This involves finding a natural predator of the pest to be controlled, and introducing it into the infested area. If successful, this technique results in an equilibrium between pest and predator in which neither becomes an insupportable economic or public health burden. In some instances, this method has achieved satisfactory control; in others, however, the predator has developed a preference for other diets and has, itself, become a pest. The selection of a suitable predator, therefore, requires rather sophisticated biological judgment.

A fairly successful example of biological control is the use of milky spore disease (*B. popillae*) for control of the Japanese beetle. When the grub of the Japanese beetle is infected by these bacteria, the blood becomes milky white in appearance and the grubs die. The spores of the bacteria, however, remain in the soil after the grubs decompose and are available to infect succeeding generations of beetle grubs. Thus when an effective colony of the bacteria are established in the soil, they remain effective almost indefinitely.

Extensive regrading of the infected soil may bury the spores so deeply that they no longer can infect the grubs, and in such cases the milky spore disease must be deliberately reintroduced. Three to five years may then elapse before the bacteria have spread enough to provide effective area control. Even under the best of circumstances, the control is not 100 percent complete, and this is characteristic of all biological control measures, but it may well provide satisfactory control for practical purposes.

Another alternative approach involves attractants and repellents. The use of repellents is self-evident and involves all of the steps and talents required for the development of a pesticide. Attractants, on the other hand, are designed to lure the pest to destruction by other means — e.g., by poison, electrocution, or trapping. The most potent attractants are related to sexual odors of the pest, and their identification and synthesis have required sophisticated biochemical and chemical techniques. Where feasible, attractants offer great possibilities of pest control without significant hazard to human health. It seems unlikely that pest resistance would develop to sex attractants. Industry might well play a role in the synthesis and production of attractants and repellents. The identification of attractants and their effect on the behavioral characteristics of the target pest demand an extremely sophisticated sort of biological research.

The sterilization of male screwworm flies by radiation, followed by their subsequent release, has effectively controlled the screwworm in the southeastern United States. Chemicals that induce sterility in the male pest can be used in place of radiation. These chemosterilants might well be developed by industry, and would require the usual array of biological talents. However, the sterile male method of pest control is practical only when the pest population density is relatively low. Hence it is applied most effectively on selected pests of low population density or on other pests after their numbers have been reduced by pesticides or from natural causes, such as unusual climatic conditions. It may not be effective for all species of insect pests, for the treated male must be not only sterile but viable enough to mate normally. Industrial laboratories might well address themselves to the development and production of chemosterilants.

One of the oldest alternatives to pesticides has been the search for pest-resistant varieties of the host. This method has yielded both spectacular successes and spectacular failures. In the past, industry has had little involvement with this method.

A recent development in insect pest control has been the possible use of juvenile hormone. This hormone, normally produced by insects and essential for their progress through the larval stages, must be absent from the insect eggs if the eggs are to undergo normal maturation. If juvenile hormone is applied to the eggs, it can either prevent hatching or result in the birth of immature and sterile offspring. There is evidence to suggest that juvenile hormone is much the same in different species of insects, and analogues have been prepared which are effective in killing many species of insects, both beneficial and destructive. There would, therefore, be great danger of upsetting the ecological balance if juvenile hormone were applied on a large scale.

What is needed, then, is development of chemical modifications of juvenile hormone that would act like juvenile hormone for specific pests but not for other insects. For example, a preparation from balsam fir has been identified which appears to be such an analogue and is effective against a family of bugs that attack the cotton plant, but not against other species. If it proves possible to synthesize similar analogues specific for other pests, a new type of pesticide may emerge. If so, it will be extremely important to explore possible side effects on other insect species and on warm-blooded animals before introduction of yet a new hazard into the biosphere.

Pest control will always be necessary, since man is always competing with other species for survival. Pest control is being accomplished today largely through the use of chemical pesticides, and the benefits to public health and to food and fiber production are apparent. We cannot rest with existing pesticides, however, because of evolving pest resistance to specific compounds and the serious long-term threat posed by the halogenated hydrocarbons. While the search for new, reasonably safe pesticides continues, it is imperative that other avenues be explored. And it is apparent that this will be effective only if, simultaneously, there is ever increasing understanding of the metabolism and physiology of the unwanted organisms and of their roles in the precious ecosystems in which they and we dwell.

CHAPTER 19

ENVIRONMENTAL HEALTH

Environmental health deals with the characterization and control of environmental factors that are deleterious to man's health and well-being. Its origins spring from efforts to control infectious agents transmitted through food and water and from efforts to eliminate occupational disease arising from biological, chemical, and physical agents. Although these activities are still of concern, a number of factors demand a major broadening of the scope of environmental health.

First, technology is increasing at an exponential rate; technological innovations frequently bring with them potential health hazards. Table 1 illustrates trends in power sources; two of these pose significant environmental health problems. Combustion of fossil fuels poses severe chemical air pollution problems. Nuclear sources bring manageable but challenging problems in the control of ionizing radiation.

Table 1. Projection of Source of Electric Power *
(megawatts)

Year	Hydro-electric	Fossil	Nuclear
1960	33,000	150,000	1,000
1980	70,000	220,000	150,000
2000	90,000	850,000	750,000

* U.S. Atomic Energy Commission, Civilian Nuclear Power – A Report to the President, 1962. The data for the generating capacities from fossil and nuclear sources have been updated by reference to several studies in late 1967 as summarized in *Nuclear Industry*, December 1967.

Table 2. Production of Synthetic Organic Chemicals *
(millions of lb. per year)

	1938	1958	1966
Plastics	130	4,500	13,585
Synthetic rubber	5	2,200	3,929
Surface active agents	—	1,355	3,321
Insecticides and agri-			
cultural chemicals †	8	540	1,013

* U.S. Tariff Commission Reports.
† Not including fertilizers.

Table 2 shows the growth in the production of synthetic chemicals in this country. One aspect of this exuberance is illustrated in the circumstance that there are now more than 45,000 pesticide formulations registered with the Department of Agriculture. The FDA, which by law is required to certify the safety of pesticides and food additives, receives, on the average, roughly a new petition for every working day in the year.

Second, with the growth of this technology, population patterns are also changing. In 1900, more than half of the population of the United States lived in rural areas. In the last census, 80 percent lived in metropolitan areas. Not only is a larger portion of the population moving to the city, but total population is increasing at a rate that is placing a severe strain on many facets of society. The increasing concentration of people in urban areas increases both pollution and number exposed.

Third, there have been marked changes of disease patterns in highly industrialized societies. The lengthening of life-span through improvements in nutrition and the mastery of many infectious diseases, achieved through advances in medical sciences and community sanitation, has brought large segments of our population into age groups where slowly acting environmental factors, of which carcinogens are only one example, become of increasing importance and where the contribution of environmental agents to the degenerative and aging processes becomes of greater significance.

A fourth factor which adds to the significance of environmental health today is an insistence on higher standards of health, which has been stimulated by the prosperity and abundance that an improved technology has given us. We can now afford to be concerned with health threats that at one time were of lesser consequence in relation to much more threatening and graver diseases.

The activities involved in the control of environmental health hazards focus on three factors: (1) the agent, chemical, physical or biological;

(2) the mode or medium of transmission, e.g., air, water, food, soil or animal vectors; and (3) the response of the exposed human being.

Optimally, those responsible for environmental health programs should be sufficiently skilled so that they can reliably detect and specify the presence, extent, and source of possible adverse effects, and generate the knowledge to control such occurrence and thus avoid adverse health effects. An alternative and often more realistic objective is to define the costs in health and otherwise, to society, of various alternatives in order to permit a rational choice among them. For example, such an analysis indicates that power production from coal is more costly in lives of those engaged in its production as well as in the health of urban populations than power produced from nuclear sources. The cost in dollars is now about at the crossover point.

Environmental health is thus a problem-oriented field with concerns that call on a variety of special skills for their resolution. These include the basic sciences of physics, chemistry, biology, and mathematics, the whole range of medical sciences, social sciences, and often, and heavily, the engineering disciplines. Obviously, not all of these talents are required in every instance; the specific need is defined by each problem. These multidisciplinary requirements pose a severe but not insurmountable problem in the development of training for work in the field.

In a broad sense, the goals of environmental health are to optimize man's life not only by the prevention of disease and accidental injury but by the elimination of conditions that interfere with normal growth and development or hasten senescence.

Man's physical structure reflects the evolutionary development of myriad adaptive mechanisms which permit him to cope with environmental stress. Disease or accelerated bodily deterioration occurs when these compensatory responses either fail or are only partially effective.

Man's brain is a uniquely developed adaptive tool which responds to external stress by modifying the local environment. These environmental modifications have produced a series of new stresses in the form of altered living conditions, habits, and the presence of potentially deleterious physical and chemical agents.

Technological advances succeed because of their immediate competitive advantage, without regard to their unforeseen and not necessarily desirable long-term consequences. Faced with a rapidly changing environment, man is compelled for his own welfare to establish effective means of coping with the impact of such changes.

The challenge to environmental health is formidable. New techniques in the biological sciences must be developed to detect the delayed and subtle damage produced by low-level chronic exposures to hazardous materials. Great advances are necessary in the social sciences to translate such findings into effective remedial action. Witness our failure to control the cigarette smoking hazard. We now see that man-made environmental changes have become decisive factors in health and well-being. Knowledge of the nature and magnitude of the biological effects of environmental hazards and the technological methods needed for their control are major components of the integrated social effort required to minimize the harmful consequences of technological progress.

Environmental health has become a recognized field of considerable consequence. National recognition of this importance has taken several forms. Thus, the United States Department of Health, Education, and Welfare is reorganizing its resources to move adequately to meet national responsibilities in this field. In line with this, a new Institute of Environmental Health Sciences has been added to the National Institutes of Health.

A series of national study groups have devoted themselves to these urgent problems, leading to recommendations that have played important roles in guiding national efforts. These include the report of the Surgeon General's Advisory Committee on Environmental Health in 1962; the report of the Environmental Pollution Panel of the President's Science Advisory Committee, "Restoring the Quality of Our Environment," in 1965; the National Academy of Sciences report, "Waste Management and Control," in 1966; "A Strategy for a Livable Environment," submitted by the Linton Committee to the Secretary of Health, Education, and Welfare in 1967; and others. At the level of local government there has been considerable enhancement in activity, particularly in the field of air pollution control. An increasing number of universities are establishing research and training programs in the field.

It is clear that there is a dual effect of a number of environmental factors because they constitute hazards not only to health but to the livability of the environment. Both aspects are affected in a beneficial sense by the institution of control measures regardless of which was the source of primary concern.

The scope of environmental health has been variously defined by different groups and in differing contexts. Obviously, the immediate ramifications are many, and the field in some degree has an impact on virtually all of man's activities. For the present purposes, this chapter confines itself primarily to those environmental factors related directly to human health.

In the sections to follow, an attempt will be made to illustrate the nature and problems of some of the diverse aspects of environmental health. In no sense is the range or scope of the presentations intended to be comprehensive. One of the factors that has been omitted may deserve special comment. That the bustle and tensions of modern life may lead to more frequent psychoses and mental disease has been widely considered as at least a possibility. Obviously, environmental factors, e.g., noise, may well represent significant components of these stresses.

It will be seen that some of our knowledge of the health hazards from low-level chronic exposures of large populations to agents such as chemical air pollutants and radioactive materials is based on studies of the effects of higher-level exposures to similar agents in industry. It will also be noted that epidemiology and laboratory investigations are the two interdependent research tools of environmental health, and that the understanding of health hazards depends heavily on basic research in the life sciences.

The complexity of the problems of environmental health precludes any easy or complete pattern of presentation. Some of the following sections group a number of diverse problems on the basis of a common mode of transmission—e.g., air and water pollution. Other sections deal with specific hazards (e.g., radiation) or the problems of a specific social group (occupations), or the etiological role of environmental factors in major health problems such as cancer.

Air Pollution and Human Health

In a broad sense, air pollution is an unfavorable alteration of the atmosphere, at or near ground level, brought about largely or wholly by human activities. The alteration may be physical, as in diminished visibility; chemical, due to effluents from combustion or chemical processes; or biological, due to the presence of pollens, microorganisms, or other biological products. These alterations vary widely in time and place, being closely related to population density, rates of energy consumption, meteorological factors, and levels of control imposed by man.

There is, of course, a natural background of pollution, from evaporation and wind action, forest fires and volcanic emissions, pollen release, and other sources. Little is quantitatively known about the natural background on any part of the earth's surface, of either trace chemical substances or the range of microorganisms, plant and animal products, and inanimate particulates. One reason for this is the absence, until very recently, of adequate methods of sampling, identification, and analysis of substances present in small amounts in the atmosphere. Even now, there are many gaps and inadequacies of method; for example, there are no reliable measurements of pesticidal chemicals in the atmosphere.

Some dramatic examples of increased morbidity and mortality have focused attention on the potentially serious health effects of air pollution, and a substantial start has been made in characterizing the atmosphere, at least in the most heavily populated areas. Beginnings have also been made in the more difficult task of relating air pollution to possible effects on health and disease.

A perspective of public awareness should perhaps be introduced at this point, even though it may not be involved in the applications of biology to human health and welfare. The public is now demanding cleaner air, through its elected officials and through communications media, and seems willing to ignore the inadequacy of scientific evidence for human health effects. The intensities of most chemical and particulate pollutants in American cities are probably not higher today than they were twenty-five years ago (excepting a few areas like Los Angeles). Larger areas and more communities are involved, but the most significant change is that people expect and demand a higher level of quality in the environment. Fear of disease is part of this motivation, but much wider considerations are involved.

Because of this high level of current interest, the effects of chemical pollution will be taken up first, followed by sections on aeroallergens and airborne transmission of pathogenic microorganisms.

Urban Air Pollution

Urban air pollution is significant to human health for several reasons: a clearly demonstrated relationship in episodes of increased morbidity and mortality, the potential for serious consequences of long-term, low levels of exposure, and indirect effects from economic losses and damage to the environment.

Two factors combining to increase the potential for harm are the continuing urbanization of our population and the tremendous increase in energy demanded by our changing living patterns. At present, 70 percent of our population occupies only 1 percent of the land, largely in major metropolitan areas. Projection of the population shifts of the past 50 years indicates that the great majority of Americans in the next generation will be born, live, and die as part of a megalopolis.

Concurrently with this population shift, a sharp rise in living standards has created a geometric increase in energy demands in our homes, in industry, and in transportation. These demands have been met largely by burning of fossil fuels in urban areas, resulting in the exposure of larger numbers of people to air pollution.

Paralleling the increased energy demand has been the universal acceptance of the gasoline-powered automobile as a means of personal

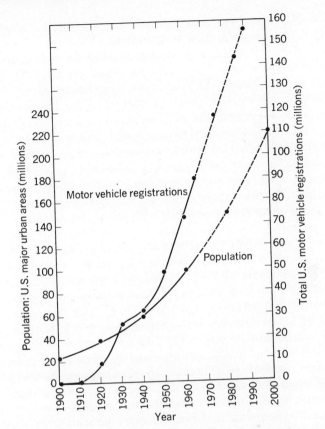

Figure 19-1. U.S. urban population and total motor vehicle registrations, 1900–2000. (Urban population: Reprinted by permission from J. P. Pickard, *Dimensions of Metropolitanism*, ULI Technical Bulletin 14. Copyright © 1967 by ULI—the Urban Land Institute; Motor Vehicle Registrations: From 1967 Automobile Facts and Figures by Automobile Mfrs. Assoc., Detroit, and U.S. Bureau of Roads, Department of Commerce.)

transport. Automobile registrations have increased even more rapidly than city populations and now approach (or in some areas exceed) a ratio of one car for every two persons (Fig. 19-1).

Another source of potentially hazardous air pollution is the rapid expansion and diversification of industry, with the development of hundreds of new synthetic compounds yearly. Many of these (pesticides, plastics, complex hydrocarbons) are present in detectable amounts in urban atmospheres.

A disturbing aspect of urban air pollution is the involuntary nature of the exposure. In the case of water, food, or industrial exposure, when suspect supplies are offered, they can be replaced by supplies transported from uncontaminated areas or by sources properly decontaminated or sterilized. Air offers no such choice. The city dweller must breathe whatever is present in his area at the moment.

In view of the increasing exposure of much of our population to urban air pollution, one would expect adverse effects on health to be readily observed. In fact, however, a consistent effect has been very difficult to document. Some of this difficulty is inherent in the nature of urban air pollution. It is an ever-present phenomenon in modern cities and towns; it varies only within relatively narrow limits; and it is intimately related to meteorological variables which in themselves have effects on health.

Observations of plant and animal exposures have proved to be of limited value in predicting effects on man. A large body of information exists on the effects of many single air pollutants on susceptible plants. Most of these effects occur at levels well below those that can be shown to affect animals.

Exposures of animals to specific air pollutants demonstrate marked variation among different species, leaving their relevance to human health in considerable doubt. Physiological effects on animals, moreover, usually require exposure to levels well above those reached in any usual urban atmosphere.

Studies of healthy human volunteers exposed to known constituents of urban air pollution (SO_2, CO, NO_2, O_3, etc.) reveal appreciable and consistent subjective symptoms, and in some cases demonstrable physiological changes. In almost all cases, however, the levels of each substance required to produce either symptoms or physiological change are well above those present in normal urban atmospheres.

The so-called acute air pollution episodes are usually associated with atmospheric inversions and/or other meteorological conditions, such as persistent fog or low wind speed. These conditions prevent dissipation of the regularly emitted urban pollutants, and permit buildup of pollution levels to varying degrees. Occasionally, under unusual meteorological conditions, extremely high levels of pollution may be reached, and these may persist for several days. It is during these dramatic, but fortunately rare, acute air pollution episodes that effects on human health are most readily demonstrated. Although episodes during which previously well people became ill are rare, the increasing urbanization of our population suggests that the possibility of such disasters must always be kept in mind. The episode at Donora, Pennsylvania, was striking in that almost half the population subsequently reported symptoms during the episode, and this number must have included many who were previously well. More commonly noted during episodes of increased pollution is a serious effect on persons with chronic cardiac or pulmonary disease. London has had recurrent episodes when persistent fog and low wind speeds associated with anticyclonic high-pressure air masses have permitted accumulation of air pollutants to several times normal levels. Regularly, each such episode is accompanied by a wave of excess deaths of persons with chronic bronchitis or heart disease. Thousands of others with these conditions are made worse during each episode.

Although the notorious London fog advertises the presence of such episodes, it is not an essential component of an episode of increased pollution; and it is probable that many large cities experience a toll of excess deaths during periods of increased pollution. Although such episodes have probably occurred considerably more often than has been recognized, persons so far shown to have been affected are those with pre-existing cardiorespiratory disease. Although this segment of our population needs protection from the added stress of high levels of air pollution, a more serious question is whether air pollution at generally occurring urban levels can affect the health of the average relatively healthy city dweller.

Most of the evidence for harmful effects of air pollution at ordinary community levels has come from associations of disease with geographic place of residence. Thus, because men of 45–59 years of age living in the United Kingdom have several times the death rate from nonspecific respiratory disease and twice the lung cancer death rate of their American counterparts, this has been attributed to the higher levels of air pollution in Great Britain. Other factors, however, could account for these differences: cigarette smoking habits vary with geography, and as a factor strongly associated with lung cancer, this could account for a geographic difference in lung cancer. Age, occupation, and social class are other etiologically important characteristics that vary with geography.

Other factors further complicate attempts to correlate disease rates with air pollution data:

1. There are two main types of air pollution—the *reducing* type characterized by the presence of sulfur oxides and carbonaceous particles from combustion of sulfur-containing coal and fuel oils, and the *oxidizing* type characterized by the presence of hydrocarbons, oxides of nitrogen, and photochemical reaction products including ozone and other oxidants. London, New York, and the majority of temperate zone cities have the sulfur-smoke type, and the atmospheric pollution of Los Angeles typifies photochemical smog. The atmospheric chemistry is sufficiently different that one cannot extrapolate health effects from one type to the other.

2. Monitoring of specific pollutants has been haphazard until recently; trends have not been established because of changes of methods and inadequate sampling. It is still not certain what ought to be measured to relate to possible health effects (with some exceptions, such as carbon monoxide).

3. Pollution levels within a community usually vary with the location of industry, housing density, and other factors. Areas of high pollution are often, therefore, areas of overcrowding and poor housing; these factors may affect health as much or more than pollution does.

4. When people become ill with respiratory disease, they tend to move from areas of high pollution, leaving the less-affected population behind. A similar self-selection occurs in response to occupational exposure; a worker with low tolerance to noxious agents in the air will be transferred or seek a different type of employment.

5. A factor of greatest importance in attempts to measure the health effects of community air pollution is the common personal habit of exposing oneself to the highly concentrated air pollution of tobacco smoking. The health effects observed in cigarette smokers are so pronounced that they almost overwhelm the effects of other pollution in a population under study. Because of its importance to the air pollution problem, the effects of cigarette smoking will be described in some detail.

The average annual consumption of cigarettes per person over 15 years of age in the United States, from 1900 to 1962, rose from 49 to 3,958 cigarettes. To a considerable extent, cigarettes supplanted other forms of tobacco, since the overall tobacco consumption per adult during the same period rose only by a factor of 1.7.

Attention was first drawn to cigarettes as a health hazard by the spectacular rise in the incidence of lung cancer at a time when occurrence of some other cancers was declining. The number of deaths per year in the United States from lung cancer rose from 3,000 in 1930 to 18,000 in 1950 and then to 27,000 and 41,000 in 1955 and 1962, respectively. Currently, the annual mortality exceeds 50,000.

From tentative beginnings in 1930, the association between cigarette smoking and lung cancer has been demonstrated by an avalanche of epidemiological studies of unparalleled scope and quality. Cigarette smokers after only a few years of exposure have substantially higher rates for disability and death than their nonsmoking counterparts in the population, caused primarily by higher incidences of lung and other cancers, chronic bronchopulmonary disease, and cardiovascular disease. Women, in general, have lower rates than men, probably because of lower levels and shorter duration of exposure. The earlier the onset of smoking, the greater the increase in death rate and disability. The cessation of smoking reverses the untoward effects to a considerable extent. Cigarette smoking is much more important than air pollution as a cause for high mortality rates from chronic bronchitis and pulmonary emphysema. There is also an association between cigarettes and cancer of the buccal cavity, pharynx, esophagus, bladder, as well as death and disability from peptic ulcer.

The carcinogenic action of cigarette smoke has been confirmed experimentally. Tobacco smoke condensates have been shown to produce skin cancer in mice, but exposure of animals to cigarette smoke has not caused lung cancer. Some of the carcinogenic hydrocarbons, e.g., benzpyrene, are present in cigarette tar, but the tumorigenic potency of these tars exceeds the content of the known carcinogens. Current studies are examining the possibility that cigarette smoke contains agents that are not capable in themselves of inducing tumors, but which promote the formation of tumors by otherwise inadequate doses of carcinogens.

Experimental studies on possible mechanisms of the cardiovascular effects of cigarette smoke have demonstrated that nicotine increases the oxygen requirements of the heart while carbon monoxide from the smoke tends to reduce the available oxygen supply. Moreover, smoking accelerates the rate of blood clotting, which may be a contributing factor to coronary thrombosis.

There is an association between long-term cigarette smoking and morphological damage of the bronchial tree. Components of cigarette smoke have an inhibiting action on mucociliary function which would tend to promote nonspecific injury of the lung by impairing its ability to clear itself of inhaled pollutants.

In summary, cigarette smoking, on the basis of epidemiological and other evidence, is clearly a highly detrimental form of air pollution. However, there is only rudimentary information on the mechanism of its adverse effects. The control of this hazard is difficult, first because of the economic importance of the cigarette industry and also because the use of cigarettes undoubtedly represents, to some extent, a compensatory response to social stress.

A few attempts have been made to separate the effects of cigarette smoking from those of community air pollution. Data on lung cancer in males, shown in Table 3, illustrate typical findings.

Community surveys of respiratory disease have likewise shown a much stronger association between cigarette smoking and disease than between community pollution and disease. British studies have also shown that when respiratory disease prevalence is corrected for smoking habits, there remains an "urban factor," presumably due to air pollution. City-dwelling males over 50 have somewhat less than twice as much respiratory disease as do rural males. Cigarette smoking, by contrast, produces a four- to seven-fold increase of prevalence.

Health Effects of Specific Pollutants. Detrimental effects of acute

Table 3. Lung Cancer Mortality in Relation to Smoking
History and Size of Community
(Rates per 100,000 in males aged 50–69 *)

Residence	Non-Smokers	Smokers	Difference Attributable to Smoking
Cities over 50,000	14.7	85.2	70.5
Cities 10,000–50,000	9.3	70.9	61.6
Suburban or town	4.7	71.7	67.0
Rural	0	65.2	65.2

* From Wynder and Hammond and Hammond and Horn.

episodes of air pollution have thus far been observed only in the reducing type of smog, in which there is an increase of smoke, SO_2, other sulfur-containing reaction products, such as sulfuric acid droplets and sulfates, and a host of other air pollutants. SO_2 and particulates are often used as indices of this type of pollution. SO_2 is normally well under 0.1 parts per million, but in periods of stagnation may increase to concentrations of 0.5 ppm or more. Even such concentrations are of no significance to a healthy person, although in the atmospheric complex associated with stagnation they could be harmful to the more susceptible members of a community.

To say that none of the constituents of common urban pollution has been definitely incriminated as a health hazard is not to say that individual components are not of concern. Some are of great concern, for example, beryllium, which is known to have produced disease downwind of processing plants. Further, some major pollutants of well-established biological significance are being added to the environment in ever-increasing amounts, and we have to be concerned whether they are increasing in concentration in the environment or in the human population. Two such pollutants are carbon monoxide and lead, both coming almost exclusively from automotive exhaust (92 percent in the case of carbon monoxide).

The environmental concentrations of carbon monoxide are potentially significant in two ways: (1) the highly variable local concentrations that occur during traffic rush hours and at busy intersections, and (2) the more widely distributed buildup of concentrations which represents a net gain of total production in an area over the convective processes which tend to lower the concentration in the area. Temporary local concentrations of over 100 ppm have been measured along freeways in Los Angeles and in the heart of London. The general buildup is illustrated by the observance of values above 30 ppm for at least 8 hours on 22 days at certain sampling stations in Los Angeles during 1966. Values of 10–15 ppm are common in American cities.

Although we know much about the rate of uptake of this gas and of its effects on the body, we know little about its possible effect on those few individuals in a city who may be vulnerable to hypoxia because of pre-existing disease. For most people, the high concentrations along freeways are of little concern because they are not exposed long enough to breathe in much carbon monoxide. This may not be true during rush hour tie-ups and for traffic policemen at busy intersections when there may be enough uptake to affect performance.

Lead is another pollutant disseminated widely by the automobile and present in the atmosphere to the extent that urban residents have higher blood levels than similar persons living in the country. The levels observed in city dwellers not occupationally exposed to lead are not known to affect health, but more study is needed to determine the margin of safety for lead. In a recent study, blood levels were reported for 2,342 persons in three American cities. Although no measurements were made of ingested lead, it was assumed that the alimentary intakes were constant, and the population groups were chosen on the basis of anticipated variation of exposure to atmospheric lead. The results showed a gradient from about 0.01 mg/100 g for nonsmoking rural residents to about 0.035 mg/100 g for traffic police and parking lot attendants. Garage mechanics and others with occupational exposure were higher; eleven were above 0.06 mg/100 g. Values for males were generally higher than for females, and smokers had higher blood lead than nonsmokers. Since toxicity is known to occur above 0.08 mg/100 g, the occupationally exposed groups appear to be uncomfortably close to an unsafe level.

Health Effects of Biological Components of the Atmosphere. Pollen and other spores play an important role in producing illness in sensitive people. Hay fever is a common allergic response of the eyes and upper respiratory system to wind-borne pollen or fungi. The seasonal incidence corresponds to whether the victim is sensitive to tree pollens (spring), grass pollens or fungus spores (summer), or ragweed pollens (fall). Aero-allergens also induce asthmatic attacks in sensitive individuals, as observed in students and others who are sensitive to the grain dusts from milling and storing operations in the Twin Cities.

In some farming areas, molds have been incriminated in the etiology of an occupational disease known as "farmer's lung." The organism *Thermopolyspora polyspora* occurs in moldy hay.

Airborne dusts containing spores of *Histoplasma capsulatum* from the feces of birds have been incriminated in outbreaks of human disease, and aerosols from infected soil can probably cause coccidioidomycosis.

Airborne Transmission of Common Infectious Agents

Although it is more than 100 years since Pasteur demonstrated the presence of invisible organisms in the air, the epidemiological significance of airborne transmission in relation to respiratory contagion is only now beginning to be widely recognized. Following Pasteur's evidence that airborne organisms existed, there was a flurry of excitement about their potential importance until it became apparent that the organisms cultured from the air were not the pathogens causing widespread disease. In the reaction that followed, airborne transmission was demoted to a position of negligible importance except possibly in the case of tuberculosis.

In the 1930's, pioneer studies were done on the size and source of airborne particles. The term *droplet nucleus* was coined for the tiny dried residues remaining after evaporation of respiratory droplets. Droplet nuclei remained airborne indefinitely in the presence of normal air movement, were removed from enclosed atmospheres by ventilation, and, being derived in nature from respiratory secretions, were assumed to contain pathogenic organisms if the human source was infected. The pathogenic organisms themselves could not be recovered from the air, but by analogy with contaminated water supplies, it was assumed that they were present in very dilute concentration. The point was proved by epidemiological studies. A remarkable reduction in the spread of measles in schoolchildren was accomplished by disinfecting the air of the schools with ultraviolet radiation. This classic work was necessarily preceded by studies, very important in themselves, which demonstrated the lethal effect of ultraviolet radiation on airborne organisms.

In the field of virology, rapid advances have taken place since World War II in defining the behavior of airborne particles, the factors affecting the viability of airborne organisms, and the development of sampling techniques for airborne bacteria and viruses. The ability to detect airborne viruses and to produce aerosols of known particle size and with known concentrations of virus has opened for quantitative study the whole area of acute respiratory contagion. At the same time, problems such as staphylococcal infections in hospitals, respiratory infections associated with industrial or agricultural processes, and the care of tuberculous patients in general hospitals have directed attention to these matters.

The sources of hospital-acquired staphylococcal infections have proved peculiarly difficult to sort out because, with the ubiquitous staphylococcus, it is probable that spread of infection may occur to a significant extent by direct contact and also by the dust-borne and droplet-nucleus-borne pathways. Experience has shown that careful attention to sterile technique, dust-borne organisms, and nose and throat carriers of infection reduces the likelihood of outbreaks of staphylococcal infections.

In view of the fact that acute respiratory infections are the chief cause of time lost from work in this country, studies of the transmission of respiratory viruses are particularly exciting. In an effort to evaluate the relative importance of contact infection as opposed to small-particle aerosol infection, quantitative comparisons have been made of infection in volunteers following intranasal instillation of virus in some subjects and inhalation of artificially generated aerosols containing virus in others. It was found that different parts of the respiratory tract differ in their susceptibility to a given infectious agent. For viruses that had a predilection for the lower respiratory tract, fewer viral particles were required to infect when administered by aerosol because the small-particle aerosol could reach the lungs while particles instilled into the nose could not. The number of particles required to infect by the two different techniques was more nearly equal in the case of viruses which had a predilection for the nose and throat. It would seem that intranasal instillation of virus, which was considered analogous to direct contact, would in fact be more likely to infect the upper respiratory tract than contamination reaching the mouth or nose by naturally occurring contact. In any case, the small-particle aerosol mechanism proved highly efficient at infecting any part of the respiratory tract. Success was also reported in detecting virus in the air of an army barracks during an outbreak of viral infection. A newly developed high-volume sampler was used which made possible the detection of very low concentrations of virus. This direct demonstration of naturally occurring airborne virus was a major triumph, complementing Wells's indirect evidence of airborne measles virus. The epidemiological importance of airborne virus was further supported by the demonstration of natural airborne transmission of viral infection between people occupying the same enclosed atmosphere but separated so as to eliminate the possibility of direct contact.

If, as seems increasingly likely, the small-particle aerosol (or droplet nucleus) mechanism is of predominant importance in spreading the viruses responsible for epidemic respiratory contagion, the use of air disinfection as a public health measure deserves renewed consideration. Because of the large number of different enclosed atmospheres in which the general public exchanges respiratory organisms, a very complex epidemiological situation exists which needs study in order to identify the places where airborne transmission is most likely to occur. On theoretical grounds, it should not be necessary to disinfect the air of all shared atmospheres in order to control epidemics of airborne contagion. While environmental control on a communitywide basis may prove less feasible than some form of immunological control, the difficulties of both approaches are formidable and both should be tackled. Epidemic respiratory contagion is a top priority public health matter and is currently completely uncontrolled. In addition to its enormous importance in terms of economics and human discomfort, it may play a role in the rising prevalence of chronic bronchitis and emphysema.

There is a solid basis for applying environmental control measures in the case of tuberculosis. It has proved possible to demonstrate the presence of tubercle bacilli in the air of a tuberculosis ward by exposing a large colony of guinea pigs to air exhausted from the ward. The quantitative aspects of the study suggested that airborne transmission alone was adequate to account for the spread of tuberculosis in a community. This inference is supported by the fact that the primary lesion of tuberculosis occurs in the lungs, a site that is directly accessible only to organisms associated with small airborne particles. The predominant importance of airborne transmission is now widely accepted in the case of tuberculosis, and the use of air disinfection as an arm in the control program seems indicated. Since most tuberculous patients receiving antituberculosis chemotherapy rapidly become noninfectious, the hazard to personnel caring for tuberculous patients has declined greatly, as shown by the records of the Veterans Administration in comparison with earlier records from the Bellevue Hospital Chest Service. The National Tuberculosis Association has accordingly changed its traditional policy and is recommending that general hospitals accept patients with tuberculosis. The greatest hazard to hospital personnel is considered to arise from active cases not yet receiving chemotherapy and from unsuspected and undiagnosed patients. Ultraviolet disinfection of the air is recommended in appropriate areas to minimize these hazards.

As if to underscore the fact that tuberculosis is airborne, that the unsuspected case is the major hazard, and that the hazard of infection is related to ventilation, an almost unbelievable outbreak of tuberculosis occurred aboard the USS *Richard E. Byrd*. Nearly 50 percent of 308 enlisted personnel were infected as a result of one missed case. The ship had closed-circuit ventilation which eliminated the normal removal of airborne organisms by exhaust air. Many individuals with little or no contact were infected because the ventilating systems of their compartments were interconnected. This disastrous episode confirmed, with human subjects, the guinea pig exposure studies previously mentioned and leaves no doubt that control measures must be directed primarily against airborne organisms to interrupt the spread of tuberculosis.

In this review of the current status of work and ideas relating to airborne transmission of infection, virtually no mention has been made of important technical advances, careful studies of specific microorganisms, fundamental studies of the behavior of particles in the air and in the respiratory tract, physicochemical factors determining survival of organisms in air, interrelations between air pollution and resistance to infection, immunization by breathing small numbers of attenuated organisms, and doubtless many other significant contributions. The understanding of airborne transmission rests upon these basic studies. They have provided a foundation which makes possible a consideration of public health implications and environmental control measures.

Water Pollution

That water, in addition to being a refreshing sustainer of life and health, is a medium in which human disease can be transmitted has been known in a qualitative way throughout recorded history. Yet, specific knowledge of its role in disease transmission goes back only to the past century, beginning with the classic investigations of John Snow on the spread of cholera by water (1849) and those of William Budd on waterborne epidemics of typhoid fever.

Cooperative work by engineers, biologists, chemists, and physicians on the organisms responsible for such diseases and in development of methods for their control was so successful over the next half-century that diseases such as cholera and typhoid fever have been almost eradicated from countries where adequate treatment and sanitary control of water supplies is maintained. Annual mortality rates from typhoid fever, for example, have dropped in the United States, since 1900, from about one per hundred to less than one in ten million. The occasional outbreaks of waterborne bacterial diseases today are attributable almost always to failure in application of known control measures rather than to lack of needed knowledge.

Defenses against waterborne microbial diseases fall into three classes: (1) protection of water sources against initial contamination, (2) removal of pathogenic organisms from the supplies by filtration, adsorption, or similar mechanisms, and (3) chemical killing or inactivation of the microorganisms by processes of disinfection. All three of these approaches have been put under continually greater stress by constantly increasing population density and demand for water. Relatively uncontaminated sources of water are becoming more difficult to find as demand grows and as the extent of contamination from human wastes increases and spreads. As a result, physical and chemical treatment of water supplies must be constantly improved to maintain hygienic quality. At the same time, better efficiency and economy of water treatment are required for processing the large volumes of water which are utilized by our industrialized society.

Recently, there has been a resurgence of interest in research on methods of water treatment, sparked by a need for better understanding of the factors that affect survival of waterborne pathogenic organisms in the environment, their mechanisms of penetration and spread through soils into ground water, and their sensitivity to methods of water treatment. Such research is needed to provide the sanitary engineer with a rational rather than empirical basis for design of facilities for collection, treatment, and distribution of water. Intensification of this research, in which cooperative efforts of biologists, chemists, and engineers are needed, is required to ensure continued safety of our water supplies.

Microbial Agents. Traditionally methods of water purification were directed against the enteric bacteria such as those responsible for cholera, typhoid fever, and dysentery. It has become apparent in recent years that these procedures may not be adequate for the control of certain viral diseases which may be waterborne under certain conditions.

Thus, epidemics of infectious hepatitis are now known to have been caused by water contamination. A most dramatic example was the epidemic in Delhi, India, in 1956, when nearly 30,000 cases of the disease resulted from a temporarily contaminated water supply. There are now about 50 documented instances of similar, although much smaller, waterborne outbreaks of this disease, some in this country. Evaluation and control of the agent is difficult at present, for the virus has not been isolated and no animal sensitive to the virus, other than man, has been discovered. One set of experiments with human volunteers during World War II and some field experiences during the Korean War have given indication that the virus of infectious hepatitis may be considerably more resistant to disinfection by chlorine or hypochlorite than the enteric bacteria are. Confirmation is very difficult, however, until a suitable test animal or tissue is discovered.

Other viruses are known to be waterborne but have not been shown definitely to transmit disease by this route. With the possible exception of the polio virus, confirming epidemiological patterns have not been found. There is, however, some basis for belief that sporadic outbreaks of mild diarrheas and respiratory disorders may arise from viral agents.

New techniques of investigation that will give definite information about the health significance of these waterborne viruses must be developed.

Toxic Chemical Agents. Although water may carry highly toxic metallic compounds and other similar inorganic materials to man, control of most of these substances is achieved readily by preventing initial access to the water. Thus, lead poisoning from water supplies, which was fairly common in the nineteenth century as a result of the use of lead for piping and jointing, has been controlled by prohibiting such use or by treating the water so that it does not act as a solvent for lead. Most chemical agents of known toxic effect can be brought under control in similar ways.

However, as a result of the enormous growth of industry, particularly in the chemical field, two types of potential hazard have arisen that cannot be dealt with as readily. Increasing numbers of new chemical substances about which little or no toxicological information is available are finding their way into water courses in domestic or industrial water discharges. Even the true chemical makeup of some of these materials is not known, so that estimates of long-term physiological action cannot be made at present, nor has the feasibility of their removal from water supplies been determined. The widespread use today of insecticides, herbicides, fungicides, and other pest control agents makes it virtually impossible to prevent their subsequent entrance into water supplies, either through runoff from the soil or through precipitation of airborne material in rain.

Several areas of research need to be developed and expanded if suitable control of the chemical hygienic quality of drinking water is to be secured. Long-term studies on the physiological effects of low concentrations of a wide variety of chemical substances are urgently required to establish permissible levels in water supplies. More studies are needed on the persistence and transformations in the aquatic environment of potentially hazardous substances, particularly of pesticides and waste chemicals that seem capable of producing cumulative, carcinogenic or mutagenic effects. Because the substances of concern occur in water in very low concentrations, there is particular need for microanalytical methods for their detection and measurement. There must also be active development of effective and economical methods for the removal of such substances from water supplies.

It must not be assumed that adequate toxicological knowledge is available even for many familiar chemical substances that may occur in water supplies. It is only about twenty-five years since an excess of nitrate, a very common constituent of water supplies, was shown to alter hemoglobin (to methemoglobin) so as to impair the oxygen-carrying capacity of the blood in infants. Recognition that cadmium in low water concentrations may have adverse physiological effects and that some water supplies do on occasion contain appreciable quantities of this element is even more recent. A Public Health Service Standard for an allowable limit of cadmium in water was set only in 1962.

In contrast to these problems from chemical contamination of water, a beneficial effect may come from the deliberate addition of a chemical. The outstanding example is fluoridation for the prevention of dental caries as seen in tooth decay. Fluorine in water in excessive amounts produces body injury but, fortunately, the water concentration needed for the prevention of caries is within limits well tolerated by man.

Recreational Use of Water. Increasing recreational use of water, especially for water-contact activities such as swimming and water skiing, coupled with increasing water pollution has created a growing concern for possible associated health hazards. Curiously, although one would expect many types of disease, including respiratory viral infections and enteric diseases, to be spread as a result of accidental ingestion of polluted water during such activities, no firm correlations have been established between the degree of contamination of water as measured by the standard coliform index (concentration of enteric bacteria) and the incidence of disease among bathers. The incidence of respiratory disease is often higher among swimmers or bathers as compared with nonusers of swimming pools, but the excess is not in proportion to the degree of bacterial contamination. Thus, the present bacterial standards for bathers and recreational waters must be regarded as having been based primarily on aesthetic rather than hygienic considerations. Despite this, there is considerable conviction that health hazards do accompany the use of polluted waters for bathing. The difficulty may lie in the investigational methods used. It may well be, for example, that for this purpose the standard coliform index is not a proper measure of hygienic hazard, or the cases of resulting disease may be so sporadic that they are overwhelmed by other ailments. Whatever the difficulty, it is important that intensive and extensive studies be continued to provide reliable bases for hygienic evaluation of recreational waters.

It is well known that schistosomiasis (infestation with liver and bladder flukes) and leptospirosis (infectious jaundice) may be acquired by contact with waters containing the causative organisms of these diseases; fortunately, these organisms are not characteristic of pollution with ordinary sewage or waste waters. Schistosomiasis is, however, a significant disease in tropical areas such as Puerto Rico. Adequate methods for control of this disease are still lacking.

Water Uses in Food Production. Shellfish, notably oysters and clams, will concentrate viable bacteria and viruses. Diseases produced by these microbial forms may then be acquired by ingestion of the shellfish, either raw or insufficiently cooked. Outbreaks of infectious hepatitis as well as numerous cases of the enteric bacterial diseases have been traced to this source. As the contamination of our estuarine waters has increased, this shellfish hazard has grown correspondingly; in consequence, many productive areas have had to be withdrawn from shellfish harvesting.

Although it is possible to decontaminate harvested oysters and, to some extent, clams from bacterial agents by subsequent immersion in chlorinated seawater, such treatment is not known to be effective against viral contamination. Here, as in the treatment of drinking water, expansion and intensification of research on waterborne viruses are vitally important.

Knowledge concerning the duration and conditions of survival of viruses in estuarine and saline waters is greatly needed to decide what circumstances will permit shellfish harvesting and use without significant hygienic hazard.

Use of treated sewage for irrigation has value as a method for multiple utilization of water. At the same time, it can create a potential health hazard because of transfer of viable pathogenic organisms to the surfaces of growing crops. Although some information is available to provide a basis for fixing rational conditions and limitations on this use of waste water, more detailed studies are needed to insure full safety.

In the past, it was possible to define the necessary conditions of water purity to ensure safe water supplies and to provide for control within these limits on the basis of rather simple, direct procedures. With the present density of population and industrial development in the United States, however, these earlier approaches are no longer adequate. Although a critical breakdown in our capability for maintaining the hygienic purity of water supplies may not be imminent, we are, nevertheless, faced with a gradual decline in quality unless scientifically improved methods of treatment and control are devised.

Food and Agriculture

Knowledge that food can damage health is age-old. The Old Testament prohibition against pork was probably based on health considerations. In the Middle Ages, the spice trade grew out of the need to prevent spoilage of meats. Ergot poisoning by a fungal contamination of flour caused large epidemics known as St. Anthony's fire. In the 1700's it was discovered that the lead in the vats used to make apple cider in Derbyshire, England, caused their seasonal epidemics of a highly fatal form of colic. A century ago, pasteurization was developed to control the bacterial contamination of milk.

The food supply was considered very early as a potential environmental health hazard. The need for safeguards led to the creation of a federal regulatory agency, the Food and Drug Administration, established in the early 1900's. This agency, earlier chiefly concerned with nontoxic adulterants and microbial contamination, is currently, with the increasing use of food additives and chemical pesticides, giving even closer scrutiny to our food supplies. In very recent times it has concerned itself with the problem of nutritional quality of food materials as well as excess of nutrients (e.g., excess vitamins or minerals).

Microbial Contamination. Of the agents transmittable by food, perhaps botulinus-produced toxin is the most dramatic. Although largely eliminated by improved processing techniques, recent outbreaks of *Clostridium botulinum* (type E) poisoning have again brought the problem to the fore. Particularly in marine products the possibility of the development of the toxin must be reconsidered. New packing techniques which render food materials anaerobic through the use of gas-tight films may be of considerable concern. The total number of cases of botulism poisoning would make such episodes almost insignificant if it were not for their high fatality.

At present the United States probably enjoys the safest food supply, microbiologically, in the world, although due to the massive expansion of this food supply, and possibly as a consequence of significantly better reporting, the problem of enteric organisms has again become of importance. *Salmonella typhimurium* has been implicated in a number of outbreaks of food intoxication. The majority of these have involved food products of animal origin, such as eggs, milk powder, and some herbs and colorants. Similar to the problem of *Salmonella* is that of *Staphylococcus aureus*, which has been found in some frozen foods that have been contaminated at their origin or allowed to defrost due to malfunction of the distribution system.

A difficult and poorly understood area is the transmission of viral infections to man through the food chain. A number of enteric viruses are not easily destroyed in the water supply. The increasing utilization of reclaimed water on food crops would suggest that this may be a problem on a much larger scale in the future.

Food Processing. There is extensive use of additives in the processing of foods in the United States, as well as the rest of the world. Some of these have been traditional for as long as recorded history, while others are of substantially modern usage. At the present time approximately 1,700 intentional food additives are in use in the United States, although 3,500 additives are approved, if one includes feed additives and packaging materials. While there has been no worldwide agreement as to the usage of additives, the usage in the United States has been under the regulation of the Food and Drug Administration for many years. The present permissible additives in the United States improve the quality and acceptability of food, through enhancement of keeping qualities, flavor, or texture. Screening of new food additives is rigorous and is under continuing review for improvement. It may be noted that there has been a gradual elimination of the aniline-based colorants.

Of food additives, perhaps the problems that may be of most concern in the future are those that may occur either in home preparation or as an effect of commercial preparation. These potential problems have existed as long as man has prepared foods, and are distinct from the processes employed by modern industry to enhance particular attributes of the food. The use of cooking procedures involving high temperature of fats constitutes an area in which little work has been done; the compounds produced and their toxicity are not known. The detailed analysis of many of our natural flavoring materials has revealed compounds existing in small quantities in common foodstuffs which are potentially of physiological interest. Safrol, the flavoring matter of root beer (a product which has been consumed for many years), was found some years ago to be a potential carcinogen and was removed from commercial sale. It is possible that similar discoveries will force from the public marketplace other products in routine consumption.

The application of polyphenols to food materials for their preservation, as practiced in smoking techniques, is a possibly hazardous processing operation which, although traditional, needs examination as to possible contribution to the hazards of the food supply.

Natural Toxins. The problem of naturally occurring toxic materials in the food chain must also be considered. Microtoxins came to light owing to the poisoning of poultry in Great Britain in the early 1960's by Nigerian peanut meal, which was shown to contain a toxin. The growth of the organism *Aspergillus flavus* upon grains produces an aflatoxin, an agent of significant toxicity in poultry. The toxin is a very potent carcinogen in experimental animals. The chemical identification of the toxin, and the ability to detect it, has indicated that a large number of the feed grains and meal cakes are potentially hazardous. Although there are no reported intoxications of humans, there are reports of poisoning of domestic and farm animals. Another material, cycasin (present in the cycad nut), is suspected as a possible liver carcinogen. Besides these, there are the accumulator species of plants, of which only some have been thoroughly investigated. For example, the selenium-accumulating ability of the sesame has been of concern in Venezuela, where it was proposed to use the extracted meal for human food.

Pesticides. Pests involved directly or indirectly in food production can be controlled by a number of means, including biological or chemical methods, with, of course, very different implications for human health from residual contamination. The alternative advantages and disadvantages with respect to considerations other than health, e.g., food production and wildlife, are discussed elsewhere. At present, the main attack upon pests is through the utilization of chemical pesticides.

The chlorinated hydrocarbon insecticides, such as DDT, dieldrin, and endrin, persist in the soil, while the organophosphates are dissipated more rapidly. For example, the treatment of a field with 5 pounds per acre of aldrin for 5 years resulted in residue levels of 4.6 pounds per acre at the end of the 5-year period, approximately 18 percent of the total applied dose. In other experiments, the concentration of malathion decreased to 3 percent of the applied dose in 8 days. The loss in soils is governed by soil type, moisture content, soil temperature, cultivation, mode of application, microorganism content, and type of crops grown. These circumstances have obvious implications for the contamination of foods. Thus, heptachlor (used to control alfalfa weevil in the United States) has been found in milk. The material was absorbed into the plants from soil and transported into the shoots, which were then eaten by the cows and the insecticide excreted in the milk. The use of this insecticide was discontinued in 1964.

The organophosphates and carbamates, which are being more widely used, do not normally cause soil residue problems even with continuous use. There appears to be a trend toward increasing use of systemic insecticides, i.e., insecticides which, by incorporation into the plant, make it toxic to insects. Surface washing will have little or no effect on the residue, so that these agents can present special consumer problems.

The herbicides are being increasingly used for control measures. The persistence of these, however, is not at the same level as the chlorinated hydrocarbons. These too, however, can be transmitted through the food chain to man if used in large quantities.

The general concern with the persistence of pesticides in the human food supply, as well as in our environment, led the Food and Drug Administration to conduct a series of examinations of the diets typically consumed in the United States. Total diet samples representing the intake of males between the ages of 16 and 19 years have been examined since 1964. The samples consist of 82 items of food and drink in an amount sufficient to provide a 14-day intake by the largest consumer of food in the population, e.g., the 16- to 19-year-old male. These were collected in 25 different cities periodically between 1964 and 1966. Initially, three geographic areas were considered, but in the subsequent periods this was increased to five areas. The diets were examined by procedures capable of detecting 50 of the common pesticide chemicals. The diets were classified into 11 general types of food materials and the compounds classified as to chlorinated hydrocarbons, organophosphates, herbicides, and carbamates. Table 4 indicates the results of the examination.

It is to be noted the chlorinated compounds are found in all diet samples and all food plant samples, except the beverages, and represent a daily intake of 0.0014 mg per kilogram of body weight. The protein foods, such as meat, fish, and poultry, were the major sources of pesticide residues and, when these are combined with dairy products, account for more than half of the total intake of the chlorinated compounds. DDT accounts for one third of the total pesticides found. There was no change over the period studied in the amount of the chlorinated pesticides which were found; hence, no significant trends in pesticide residues were established.

The conclusion that may be drawn from this study is that the residues of the pesticides which might be consumed by the U.S. population are very much below the limits set for acceptable daily intakes established for food.

An interesting sidelight of this study is the comparison of chlorinated pesticides found in human milk with those of cow's milk. The permitted total of chlorinated pesticides calculated as DDT in cow's milk was 1.25 ppm in fat (most samples were well below this), whereas in human milk the fat levels of DDT were in excess of this concentration.

With the widespread use of synthetic pesticides, the human population of the world has accumulated in its body tissues considerable stores of chlorinated hydrocarbons, in areas where there is essentially no use of pesticides, as well as in areas where there is extremely heavy use. Table 5 shows the ranges of DDT found in the body fat of humans. No ill effects of these concentrations were reported, including the formulators, whose fat had values as high as 1,100 ppm equivalent DDT. The human accumulates the chlorinated hydrocarbons in relation to dose rates. Loss of body fat or decrease in total dietary intake of the hydrocarbons results in a loss of accumulated stores. Although it has been speculated that under starvation conditions the mobilization of body fat containing high concentration of chlorinated hydrocarbons could cause acute toxicity, no such case has as yet been reported.

In general, it appears that the body burden of the chlorinated hydro-

Table 4. Examples of Pesticide Residues in Food in the United States

Chemical Detected	Dairy Products	Meat, Fish & Poultry	Grain & Cereals	Potatoes	Leafy Vegetables	Legume Vegetables	Root Vegetables	Garden Fruits	Fruits	Oils, Fats & Shortening	Sugars & Adjuncts
CHLORINATED CHEMICALS											
DDT	0.002	0.011	0.004	T	0.001	0.002	0.001	0.006	0.002	0.001	0.001
DDE	0.004	0.012	T	T	0.001	T	0.001	T	T	T	T
TDE	0.001	0.005	0.001		0.002	0.001		0.002	T	0.001	T
Dieldrin	0.001	0.002	T					0.001	T	0.001	
Lindane	T	T	0.003					0.001	T		
Heptachlor epoxide	0.001	0.001			T					T	T
BHC	0.001	0.001			T					T	T
Aldrin		T	T		T		T	T			T
Endrin			T				T		0.001		
Chlorbenside				T							
Heptachlor		T	T		T			T		T	
TCNB			0.002							T	
Tedion											
Kelthane									0.001		
Chlordane								T	0.003		
Perthane									T		
PCNB									T		

Table 4. *Continued*

Chemical Detected	Dairy Products	Meat, Fish & Poultry	Grain & Cereals	Pota- toes	Leafy Vege- tables	Legume Vege- tables	Root Vege- tables	Garden Fruits	Fruits	Oils, Fats & Short- ening	Sugars & Adjuncts
					HERBICIDES						
2,4-D										0.001	0.004
PCP		T	T								
MCP			0.002								
TBA										T	
					INORGANIC RESIDUES						
Bromides *			4.20	0.19					0.12	1.19	0.33
Arsenic (AS₂O₃)		T	0.002	0.063		0.001	0.001		0.002		
					CARBAMATES						
Carbaryl			0.021	0.003	0.004		0.001	0.002	0.008		0.005
Dithiocarbamates			0.012		0.014						

Daily intake of pesticide residues, listed by food class (18 composites in each class) and expressed in milligrams per day from June 1964 to April 1965. T signifies trace (less than 0.001 mg). The average pesticide intake from beverages was 0.104 mg of carbaryl per day. Percentage of fat content was 8 to 13 in dairy products; 17 to 23 in meat, fish, and poultry; and 83 to 88 in oils, fats, and shortening.

* Values reported are those in excess of 25 parts per million.

From Duggan, R. E., and Weatherwax, J. R., *Science 157*, No. 3793, p. 1006 (Sept. 1, 1967).

carbons is approaching an equilibrium value in the United States. The majority of intake can be accounted for from fat in food, although a measurable percentage is accumulated through water and a smaller but still measurable percentage is accumulated from the air.

At the present time somewhat over 45,000 formulations representing approximately 900 chemical agents have been registered for use in the United States as pesticides. DDT is the one most commonly used and represents something of the order of 10 to 12 percent of the total sales of pesticides. Applications for new pesticides have decreased considerably. Most new petitions for pesticides are reregistration of old pesticides to meet the new federal laws of 1968. In the year starting July, 1966, 106 pesticide petitions were filed with the FDA. In the same year 151 petitions for food additives were filed.

Table 5. Concentration of DDT-Derived Material in Body Fat of People in the United States with Special Exposure (Environmental, Occupation, or Dietary) to DDT

Exposure	Year	No. of Samples	Total DDT-Derived Material (DDE & DDT) [a] (ppm)
Died before DDT	<1942	10	Not detected
Environmental [b]	1954–1956	110	15.6
Environmental [b]	1961–1962	28	12.9
Applicators	1954–1956	30	35.1
Applicators	1961–1962	14	34.8
Formulator	1951	1	263.0
Formulator	1954	1	1131.0
Meat abstainers	1955–1956	16	5.9
Eskimos [c]	1960	20	3.0
Volunteers given 3.5 mg/day orally [d]	1953–1954	2	34.0
Volunteers given 3.5 mg/day orally [e]	1957–1958	6	71.0
Volunteers given 35 mg/day orally [d]	1953–1954	6	258.0
Volunteers given 35 mg/day orally [e]	1957–1958	6	321.0

[a] DDE is partially metabolized DDT.

[b] Residents of the Wenatchee, Washington, area living within 500 ft of agricultural application.

[c] Alaskan eskimos who ate predominantly a native diet shown to contain little or no DDT.

[d] Based on samples taken after 11 months or more of dosage.

[e] Based on samples taken after 21.5 months of dosage.

Adapted from Hayes, Wayland J., Jr. "Monitoring Food and People for Pesticide Content," p. 324, in *Scientific Aspects of Pest Control,* National Academy of Sciences, National Research Council, Publication 1402 NAS-NRC, Washington, D.C. (1966).

Radionuclides. Some foods accumulate radionuclides and the possibility exists that these are incorporated into the food chain. This issue is covered in the section of this chapter on radiation.

Occupational Health

For many centuries occupational disease has resulted from the absorption of toxic chemicals in the work-related environment. As chemistry advanced, industrial technology found increasing uses for a variety of compounds, and the number and diversity of intoxicants multiplied.

The earliest medical interest, in dealing with occupational disease, emphasized the qualitative factors associated with the definition of such diseases as "lead poisoning," "mercury poisoning," and "miner's phthisis," first as symptom complexes and later as disease entities. When particular substances and work conditions were recognized as causing disease, efforts were made to reduce the exposure. If at the reduced level, additional cases of illness were observed, a further reduction was made, and so by trial and error, work conditions were progressively improved, in some instances, to the point where no further overt cases of disease were seen.

Notable successes were achieved with many occupational hazards: lead poisoning was reduced significantly, for example, in the printing industry, in potteries, and in paint manufacture; some primitive efforts toward dust control reduced the silicosis risk in mining, stone cutting, and the ceramics industry. An outstanding example of such stepwise progress is seen in the early record of silicosis control in the South African gold mines where marked reduction in disease followed the introduction of a succession of basic dust-control measures.

This very practical approach was not enough, however, to ensure full success in all situations. Even when dust and fumes from hazardous processes were reduced below visible levels, cases of lead poisoning and silicosis continued to develop. With other hazards, such as carbon monoxide gas, which is odorless and invisible, no such sensory guide was available to apply even to the earliest control efforts. On the medical side, early success was limited because of lack of refined diagnostic techniques with which the degree as well as kind of illness could be determined, ranging from gross illness to the beginning signs of disease. Thus, many cases escaped early attention, and a false sense of security persisted until these cases had developed to demonstrable stages, frequently beyond medical aid.

Such difficulties were overcome by advances in analytical chemistry and methods of air analysis which described the magnitudes as well as quality of exposures in various work situations. Similar advances came about in the techniques of medical diagnosis which gave useful estimates of the degree of illness for purposes of correlation with the kind and degree of exposure. With these quantitative tools, it became possible to determine systematic dose-response relationships between measured work conditions and consequent disease. Actual accomplishments from improvements in work conditions could be measured and their consequence in terms of better health of the worker were demonstrated. It also became possible to discover and evaluate the degree of probable hazard associated with certain work situations before illness developed; and corrective steps could be taken in advance of troubles.

These advances called into being a new professional, the industrial hygienist, drawn from the physical sciences and engineering, who worked together with the medical scientist and industrial physician in the discovery and correction of hazardous work conditions in our major industries and occupations. Among the outstanding investigations carried on in this joint fashion have been the series of epidemiological studies by the United States Public Health Service on the health of workers in the dusty trades, mercury poisoning in felt hat manufacture, the lead hazard in the electric storage battery industry, and others.

Undoubtedly, one of the most valuable contributions that has emerged from these systematic quantitative studies is the concept of a "maximum allowable concentration" or "threshold limit value"—i.e., that there are acceptable levels of exposure to toxic chemicals and physical stresses below which no disability or demonstrable illness is likely to occur over a working lifetime. In its application to industry, this concept has contributed greatly to the protection of the workers' health in the face of tremendous expansion of the manufacture and use of chemicals. Threshold limit values have been developed by the American Conference of Governmental Industrial Hygienists for more than 250 substances, and these limits are now widely employed as guides and even as legal requirements in the prevention of occupational diseases by governmental agencies, by industrial insurance companies, and by industries themselves.

A complementary effort has been made in the toxicological exploration of the effects of hazardous agents on various animal species. A methodology and a body of knowledge were developed which permitted limited extrapolation of toxic effects from one compound to related materials, and from lower animal species to man. These procedures are now regularly employed in toxicological laboratories operated by several large manufacturers, by the Public Health Service, by universities, and by private organizations. These laboratories provide the basic information with which to establish and maintain safe conditions for the production and use of industrial products. Although the experience with such toxicological predictions has been very good, there are sufficient examples of its limitations to require the application of an effective and continuing health surveillance of the workers to ensure that reasonably safe and healthful work conditions have been attained. The chronic occupational disease due to beryllium, berylliosis, is a classic example of the failure of the usual laboratory techniques, utilizing customary animal models, to predict or to reproduce the human disease.

Applications from Industrial Experience to Study of Community Problems. Knowledge gained from industrial hygiene experience has provided the basis for our understanding of many environmental hazards in the community and will play a continuing role in the solution of these growing environmental health problems outside of industry. The resolution of effects from a small amount of a chemical or physical agent spread over a large population becomes increasingly difficult, largely owing to the fact that these effects are not necessarily specific, and because there are many coexisting potentially hazardous influences. Information gained from the evaluation of occupational exposure frequently can provide important guidance. The correlation of occupational health experience with reliably measured environmental data provides an extremely useful background for the development of criteria of safety for many substances. Correction factors are necessary to equate the differences between industrial groups and the general population, but it is increasingly apparent that the "hard" data which can be developed from occupational exposures sometimes offer greater substance than epidemiological investigations of general populations, which inevitably experience multiple minimal insults.

Future Developments in Industrial Hygiene. In consequence of the largely successful attack upon the specific chemical and physical hazards of industry, the well-known occupational diseases of the past have largely disappeared. Too many cases of, for example, frank lead poisoning and silicosis do occur today, but these illnesses result from failure to apply existing and effective methods of prevention.

Professional interest, especially research efforts, must now increasingly turn to other areas of concern where work conditions may also contribute to ill health. There are two categories of problems: (1) the possible effects of long-continued exposure to physical and chemical agents in low concentration (below presently accepted tolerance levels) in raising the susceptibility to the common illnesses of an adult and aging population, and (2) the physiological and psychological ill effects which may be associated with mechanization and automation.

In the first case, the etiological relationships are complex, and a suspected factor in the work situation will be only one of many that operate together to determine the total risk. The pursuit of these relationships will also bring many opportunities for industry to contribute significantly to the control of chronic diseases in the whole community.

In the second category, many questions arise concerning the man-machine relationships in which the human operator functions at a quite different level than in more elementary work situations. Design of production machines and automated processes without employing systematic knowledge of the anatomical, physiological, and psychological capabilities and limitations of man has resulted in improper man-machine relationships, with consequent breakdown of the system. The active application of industrial physiology, psychology, and human factors engineering (all part of an area known as ergonomics) is needed to avoid future problems resulting from our rapid extension of industrial mechanization and automation.

The Sources and Significance to Environmental Health of Chemicals in the Environment

Man has had a long experience with the effects of toxic chemicals in his environment, such as the vegetable poisons, irritants, stimulants, narcotics, and snake and insect venoms. The novelty in man's exposures, in our present chemical civilization, lies in the greatly increased number and variety of new chemicals. The enormity of the health problem from these as yet largely unexplored chemical exposures lies in the fact that 500,000 to 600,000 chemicals (a list growing at a rate of 500 annually) are produced and used in this country. Their ultimate distribution and fate can hardly be guessed. What each compound or what several or many compounds acting together are doing to man and especially to the complex interacting balance of life about us and including us is almost a complete mystery. How can the significance of these exposures be assessed? Even if attention is restricted to events that directly affect man, the magnitude of the problem is staggering.

Sources of Human Exposures. Today's civilized man meets an almost unending series of new molecules in every part of his life. Listing some of the sources will point up the complexity.

1. Occupational exposures are of special interest because without precautions large concentrations of active chemicals may be encountered, sufficient sometimes to poison or kill. While toxic exposures are usually confined to the factory area, residents of the surrounding neighborhood may be affected. For example, several tragic deaths from beryllium

poisoning arose unexpectedly from the dissemination of trace amounts of beryllium into the community air; at least one death occurred at a distance of a mile from a plant processing beryllium compounds.

2. Although in general, the principal atmospheric pollutants have been identified, a haunting uneasiness remains because of total community involvement and because new hazards may be waiting for identification. Are certain illnesses worsened by traces of pollutants? Definitive, exhaustive microanalytical examinations of the atmosphere of our cities are needed to give the baselines for the epidemiology of tomorrow.

3. Water pollution adds to the environment a variety of wastes, such as the odoriferous effluvia of the paper mill, the complex waste of synthetic chemical industries, the discharge of raw sewage.

4. Soils bear not only traces of fallout from atomic bomb tests but also residues of synthetic fertilizers and of a long list of agricultural chemicals (e.g., pesticides, herbicides, defoliants, fumigants), some of which are stable and will long remain as a potential hazard. The lead-laden soils of the South, contaminated by lead arsenate used as an insecticide in the tobacco industry, serve as an example.

5. Food additives (e.g., the noncaloric sweeteners), intentionally placed in our diets for the preservation, coloring, flavoring, processing, stabilizing, and packaging of our "daily bread," constitute a little of the price we pay for abundance of food. Unintentional additives, e.g., the pesticides in raw agricultural products, or the agents protecting food as it is processed, transported to market and brought to the table make another extensive list.

6. Surrounding civilized man are additional chemicals: in his clothing, in the astounding number and diversity of products under his kitchen sink, in his bathroom or garage. Hobbyists have special preparations; recreation may bring exposures to unusual molecules.

7. Few groups of chemicals have received as much public attention as our new drugs. Their lifesaving, health-restoring properties are acclaimed and respected. Almost as widely heralded are their adverse reactions, some life-endangering, many seriously damaging. Such illnesses are common; perhaps one in ten hospital admissions has an iatrogenic drug-induced disease as a part of the clinical problem.

Effects. The amount of chemical reaching the body often is the controlling factor in the response, ranging from prompt illness or death to no measurable effect. The most difficult problems are found in the "subliminal" toxicology—i.e., the effects of materials entering the organism in trace amounts over prolonged periods as in the case of food additives, pesticides in our foods, or water supplies, or air contaminants inhaled day after day. Multitudes of molecular species enter the body in such minute traces that no illness has been detected and, except for propitious circumstances, none can be detected with present techniques of evaluation. Most environmental chemical exposures fall in this category. The absence of presently detectable effects cannot indefinitely be accepted as proof of the innocuous nature of each compound. Sooner or later, evidence must be sought to ensure, to a reasonable degree, the safety of the exposure. An epidemiological surveillance approach may eventually be able to correlate exposures with medical histories to such purpose that exposures can be identified which leave their mark in reduced life-span, increased morbidity, reduced efficiency, or diminished comfort.

Interaction of Chemicals. Furthermore, it is not sufficient to examine the effects of each type of molecule individually. Within the body, chemicals may interact but to what effect, particularly when only traces are taken into the body, is largely unknown. Which chemicals may be antagonists and offset each other's effects, which may be synergists and reinforce each other's effects cannot be predicted. Interactions are by no means uniformly disadvantageous; some molecules are known to enhance the natural protective mechanisms of the body.

Two examples of biological interaction will illustrate how a comprehension of biochemical mechanisms can clarify toxicological problems.

A few years ago it was discovered in the laboratories of the Food and Drug Administration that when malathion and EPN, both organophosphate insecticides, were fed together to experimental animals, the toxic effects were considerably greater than would be expected were they merely additive—i.e., there was a true potentiation. As a result of this finding, the FDA instituted a new regulation requiring that each new organophosphate insecticide be tested jointly with every organophosphate already accepted. The pyramiding of tests as new insecticides were submitted can be easily conceived. Investigation of the underlying biological mechanisms has now clarified the basis for this potentiation and provided a simpler means for predicting this kind of interaction. The mechanism is as follows: both compounds produce their primary toxicity through their inhibition of cholinesterase, an enzyme essential to continued functioning of the neuromuscular system. Malathion is inactivated by another group of enzymes, the aliesterases; these, however, are inhibited by EPN. Thus, EPN interferes with the normal destruction of malathion by aliesterase, thereby permitting larger amounts of malathion to persist and produce an enhancement of its injurious effect on the essential enzyme, cholinesterase. An understanding of the underlying basis thus permits the direct measurement of the effect of new pesticides using enzymes in test tube experiments without resorting to elaborate and indirect animal tests.

Another example: certain foreign chemicals lead to an increased activity of a normal protective enzyme, hydroxylase, a liver enzyme that destroys or detoxifies some foreign chemicals. Such stimulation of enzyme activity is produced by many chemicals, including carcinogenic hydrocarbons such as benzpyrine, pesticides such as DDT, and many drugs. An experiment in which rats were fed a diet containing DDT illustrates such effects. DDT, through its stimulatory action on hydroxylase, altered two very different responses: (1) it decreased the effectiveness of phenobarbital as a sedative (sleeping time with the same dose dropped to 30 percent of the control value after one month on the DDT diet) and (2) it increased the rate at which the test animals detoxified a foreign chemical, aniline (an increase of 70 percent in one month). The former response, necessitating an increased drug dosage to secure the desired therapeutic effect, can, in some instances, represent a disadvantageous adaptation; the latter, by accelerating the rate of detoxification of a harmful chemical, represents a beneficial effect. The most important implication lies in the subtle ways in which foreign chemicals, be they from environmental sources or drugs, may interact. The levels of DDT fed in this experiment were extremely high, 500 ppm in the diet, so that the experiment in this sense is far removed from a "normal" situation. Whether there is any significant alteration in hydroxylase activity from current body burdens of hydrocarbon insecticides is unknown.

These examples serve to show the complex and sometimes unexpected interactions of chemicals and, most importantly, the ability of biological research to clarify and make comprehensible these interactions.

Because toxicology has been and will continue to be a major contributor to the solution of environmental health problems, an examination of this field will be rewarding.

Toxicology and Safety Testing. Toxicology, one of the oldest of the arts, is emerging as one of the newest of the sciences. A brief statement of the missions of toxicology will indicate how it can contribute to environmental health. The toxicologist is concerned with the effects of chemicals on living systems, in particular the adverse, disadvantageous, injurious effects, with the objective of predicting reliably how much of a chemical can be tolerated without untoward results. Two main areas of toxicological study can be identified; these are of strongly contrasting purposes:

1. Toxicologists search for molecules possessing greater, more selective toxicity. Such compounds are used, for example, in the control

of pests, as herbicides, or fumigants. Agents are sought which have surpassing but selective lethality or incapacitating ability against the target organism.

2. Preventive toxicology seeks to prevent injury. To this end, one can visualize that in the future the toxicologist must pretest all relevant new chemicals before they are put to general use and specify under what conditions they may be used safely.

The Data of Toxicology. What information must the preventive toxicologist have to assess the hazards of an environmental exposure? Several key kinds of information are useful.

1. The dose-response relationships. With increasing doses, intensity of effect usually increases. The response may occur in all exposed persons as, for example, increasing blood levels of carboxyhemoglobin with increasing air concentrations of carbon monoxide, or in a group, e.g., skin cancers occurring with increasing frequency in occupational groups having higher exposures to hydrocarbon carcinogens.

2. The time course of the response. How rapidly does the effect appear and how protracted is it? Is it nearly instantaneous, like the lethal effects of nicotine, or is it gradual and prolonged, like the onset of chronic lead poisoning?

3. Repeated dose effects. Is there evidence of cumulative effect either (a) in an actual accumulation of the compound or of its metabolites, or (b) in a partly irreversible injury? Does a tolerance develop so that larger doses are required to obtain the effect? Does the animal or the tissue alter its living processes in such a way that with continued exposure the organism depends on the presence of the compound for normal function and behaves abnormally when the compound is withdrawn?

4. Structure-activity relations. What changes in response accompany small or large modifications in the molecular structure? Although trends in response can frequently be traced in families of compounds, even minor structural modifications can drastically alter the character of the response. A single methyl group in a large polycyclic hydrocarbon molecule can convert a carcinogenic molecule into an innocuous one.

5. Metabolism. The fate of the molecule in the body, its transformations, and its disposition are important. If on entry into the body a compound is altered, the response may be to the newly formed metabolite rather than to the molecule administered.

6. Site. The site of action can sometimes be located primarily in one organ, e.g., the lung in ozone poisoning, but attempts to discriminate in greater detail are often futile.

7. Mechanism of toxic effect. The first mechanism of toxic action of any substance ever discovered was the demonstration by Voegtlin in

1923 that arsenic combines with sulfur (SH) groups in the poisoned cell. Knowledge of mechanism can be the basis for controlling toxicity. Thus, Voegtlin's theory was extended and put to use by Peters and his group at Oxford during World War II when they developed an antidote for arsenic poisoning (also useful for mercury), the well-known BAL (British Anti-Lewisite). For only a few compounds is a molecular mechanism known. Methyl nitrosamine injures liver cells by methylating guanine, thereby altering the nucleic acids of the cell perhaps sufficiently to account for the development of cancer. Uranium and mercury block membrane transport of essential nutritional substrates and thereby kill cells.

"Bench Marks": The Toxic Level and the No-Effect Level. Observations on animals must establish the conditions under which the compound exerts identifiable and characteristic toxic effects.

A major reason for conservatism in applying the results of animal studies to man is the variation among different species in response to chemicals. For example, β-naphthylamine produces bladder cancer in man and the dog but in virtually no other species. One study comparing the reactions to six drugs administered to the rat, dog, and man showed many important similarities, but of the 86 effects recorded, 33 occurred only in man. Man shows certain reactions, e.g., hypersensitization in the allergic sense, and blood dyscrasias not found in experimental animals, as well as symptoms, e.g., headache or numbness, difficult or impossible to detect in experimental animals.

In accepting a "tolerance" level or setting a standard, one component is a scientific judgment based on the margin between the no-effect level observed in animals and the maximal predicted human exposure. For man, a "no-effect" level is usually conservatively selected such that there is a low probability of occurrence of any effect in any, even a highly susceptible, individual. Several other factors are always considered and may be decisive: the seriousness of the toxic response, the need for the agent (Is there no effective substitute? What benefit will accrue from its use?), and nutritional, economic, and other factors. Ultimately the risk judged to be acceptable is balanced against the expected benefit. The standard thus established serves as a guide for those responsible for protecting the health of the exposed population.

In the earlier era, disability or death were sometimes accepted as unavoidably linked to certain occupational exposures. This day is long past and, in the future, concern must increasingly be with more subtle impairments (Fig. 19-2). Such disturbances must be detected and related to the stresses of the job. The degree of impairment must be kept well within the limits of compensation for stress illustrated in the figure.

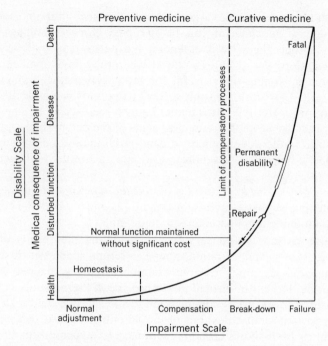

Figure 19-2. Impairment increases with aging, as a residual of illness and/or from excessive environmental stress. (From T. Hatch, *American Industrial Hygiene Association Journal 23:5,* 1962)

Limitations. Thus the objectives of toxicological assessments fall into several categories. Early in the development of a new chemical product the chief aim may be to aid in the selection of the most favorable compound among a number of alternative candidates—that is, one that will secure the desired technological effect with least hazard. In other instances, or at later stages, toxicology will attempt to define acceptable levels for air contaminants, for residues of pesticides in food crops, and so on. Unfortunately, our tools for such determinations are not as sharp and effective as one would like. This brings two penalties. The first is a nagging doubt that the predictions of safety are sound. The second stems from this concern and leads to elaborate, extensive, cumbersome, and probably often redundant test procedures and perhaps, in some cases, to overly conservative margins of safety. These difficulties arise uniformly from an inadequate ability to extrapolate to man the information gained in the often crude, albeit extensive animal studies currently used. If the only costs to society involve unnecessary elaboration of tests or the occasional rejection of useful materials, and safety has not been compromised, our present position is defensible but inefficient. By and large, this seems to be the case. With some glaring exceptions, e.g., thalidomide, we seem to have successfully skirted, not only disaster, but overt difficulty. The qualification must, however, be inserted that only in a very few instances—a possible but not reassuring example is DDT —have follow-up studies been made which would permit a firm judgment as to no ill-effects from the use of chemicals.

The alternative to the uncertainty from the overuse of cumbersome and crude procedures lies in the quantitative understanding of effect and mode of action on *man*. This does not mean the sole or even a major dependence on human studies, although carefully controlled investigations under circumstances that will assure safety are required at an appropriate stage in the investigation of chemicals. Rather, the direct path to more reliable and more efficient procedures for toxicological assessments is an improved understanding of the biological modes of action in animals and in man. Modern developments in the biological sciences provide powerful and discriminating tools for ensuring human safety.

The present long-term studies of animal groups can be expected to continue. In selected instances even more protracted and larger-scale studies may be required. Even more important, however, is a selective and shrewd exploitation of the entire range of the biological sciences. In this framework, toxicological studies will employ animal tests, isolated enzyme and cell systems, and sometimes, carefully controlled human studies, as well as epidemiological studies under conditions of actual exposure. The last is a major area of neglect; how rarely has a follow-up of human usage been made to determine whether "allowed" exposures were indeed safe for all individuals (taking into account age, sex, social class, biological variability, hypersusceptibility, etc.).

Chemical Mutagens and Teratogens. As noted earlier in this section, many kinds of biological effects are produced by chemicals; an awareness of these potentialities has generally guided toxicological examinations. Two effects of high importance, however, have received inadequate attention; these are genetic mutations, and injuries to the embryo during pregnancy. Chemicals producing the latter effect, known as "teratogens" or "monster-producing agents," are exemplified by thalidomide. The disastrous consequences of the release of this drug without adequate testing have alerted the scientific community. In consequence, procedures for testing teratogenic potentialities are now being actively but belatedly developed. The basic work which defined the biological mechanisms of this pattern of fetal injury—which occurs during organogenesis, a well-defined period in gestation—had been done more than two decades before the thalidomide tragedy.

The hazard posed by the mutagenic capabilities of chemicals has not yet been explored. Although much attention, both scientific and public, has been given to the possibility of inherited defects from ionizing radiation, virtually none has been directed to the same hazard from chemicals, which may be as great as from radiation. It is now well known that certain chemicals can produce both major chromosomal damage, likely to yield early defects in offspring, and point mutations, minor defects not detectable microscopically in chromosomes but which, if present widely in the population, can yield undesirable consequences in succeeding generations. With the wider distribution of chemical pollutants and increased usage of food additives, means must be found to ensure that significant sources of inherited defects from chemical mutagens are not produced.

The problem is complicated by the difficulties in testing. A complete assay for mutagenic potentialities in mammals such as mice or rats is extremely elaborate, usually requiring many thousands of animals. Well-developed and very sensitive procedures are available for detecting mutations produced by chemicals in microbial systems such as phage, bacteria, and fungi. These systems, however, suffer from the defect that they do not have the same capabilities as does man for altering the test chemicals metabolically. Conceivably, man may metabolize a chemical that is mutagenic for bacteria in a way that would make it inactive for man, or conversely, man may convert a nonmutagenic chemical into a mutagen. Microbial systems can, however, as a minimum be used for screening purposes, and when used with an understanding of the metabolic alteration of the test chemicals by man, could provide useful guidance. Similarly, the study of changes in chromosome structure in simple test schemes may be valuable. Finally, it will be important to establish national surveillance systems which can detect inherited defects resulting from environmental chemicals.

Physical Factors

Physical factors with which man must cope include changes of barometric pressure and electromagnetic radiations in their entire spectrum from radiowaves through visible and ultraviolet to x-rays. Allied to these are strong electrical and magnetic fields.

The effects of weight and weightlessness are, in this space age, emerging as of special concern. Man's tolerance to the forces of acceleration and deceleration has been studied extensively, giving indispensable information for spacecraft engineering. Weightlessness is now receiving attention as a possibly serious impediment to lengthy space missions. Changes in circulatory functions and in mineral metabolism (loss of bone calcium) in such flight may require the development of adaptive measures, e.g., scheduled exercise, pulsed pressure stockings, etc., to permit completion of extended space explorations.

Studies of the physiological effects of extremes of air pressure have engaged many scientists. Low air pressures were of intense concern in the earlier periods of aviation medicine. High-pressure effects including the "bends" are now reasonably well understood. The earlier development and application of this knowledge in tunneling operations has contributed to the successful operation of underwater research laboratories at elevated atmospheric pressures for extended periods.

The effects of extremes of temperature have been and are still the object of considerable investigation. Man is "warm-blooded," that is, he is capable of regulating his body temperature to a narrow temperature range very precisely. This development brings with it certain vulnerability. Failure of the heat exchange mechanisms, through external extremes of temperature or internal failure of the regulatory system, will bring collapse and, in extreme instances, death. The intricate regulatory mechanism which thus characterizes man and other mammals is still not fully understood. It is a field where the integrated skills of physiology and the mathematics of feedback mechanisms have made substantial contributions. It is to be noted, of course, that man's ingenuity in the development of "microclimates" (clothing, shelter, air conditioning) can almost indefinitely extend the range of thermal environments that are livable.

Mechanical vibration is a severe environmental hazard, as in the association of the vascular disorders of Raynaud's disease with air hammer usage. Noise has been responsible for occupational impairment of hearing and, as new major sources of community noise develop, may be of consequence to the general public. Currently, the hazards of laser beams and microwaves are under active study.

Of all these physical factors only two examples have been chosen for more detailed discussion: ionizing radiation and noise.

Environmental Radiations

Electromagnetic radiations, ranging from cosmic ray photons having frequencies of the order of 10^{23} cycles per second to the sluggish fields existing near 60 cycle alternating current generators, are capable of a variety of biological effects. The high-energy radiations, including cosmic rays, gamma rays and x-rays, are capable of disrupting molecular structure by ionization, as are the alpha particles and beta particles from radioactive disintegrations. These radiations are collectively termed *ionizing radiations* to differentiate them from others such as ultraviolet and visible light that cause biological effects by excitation of molecular orbital electrons and infrared or microwave radiations that produce heating effects by molecular excitation.

Only ionizing radiations are considered in detail in this section, although some of the other forms of radiation are important environmental hazards. For example, ultraviolet light from the sun is the major cause of skin cancer, the most common form of human cancer.

Man has always been subjected to ionizing radiation from natural sources. Externally, he has been bathed in gamma radiation from cosmic rays and radioactive nuclides in earth's crust; in addition radioactive substances leached or absorbed from the soil and ingested with food or water have irradiated man from within. The average dose of ionizing radiation on a worldwide basis is about 100 millirems per year, the usual total variation being less than a factor of two. There are, however, local anomalies. Certain villages in Brazil and India receive doses of natural radiations ten to twenty times higher than the worldwide average. The Joachimsthal Mines in Czechoslovakia, which have been worked for centuries, and our own uranium mines on the Colorado Plateau have sufficiently high atmospheric concentrations of radioactive substances to have produced a very high incidence of lung cancer among the miners.

With the discoveries of x-rays and radioactivity near the end of the nineteenth century and the subsequent development of technologies based on them, an enormous increase in potential exposure to radiation and its hazardous effects was created. Within three months of the chance discovery of x-rays by Roentgen, the development of medical radiography was under way in many countries. In another few months the skin burns and loss of hair produced by early radiographs prompted the exploitation of x-rays for treatment of cancer. Similarly, the isolation of radium from pitchblende was followed by the growth of uranium mining to provide radium for medical applications as well as luminous paints.

Deaths of at least one hundred x-ray workers by the 1920's from leukemia and other cancers prompted the first radiation control measures. About the same time, attention was directed to the hazards of internally deposited radioactive materials because of deaths among luminous dial painters, first from aplastic anemia and later from bone cancer.

During the same period, research into the biological effects of ionizing radiation demonstrated its lethal effects on whole organisms in addition to individual cells and showed that ionizing radiation can produce cancer as well as being useful in its control. About this time ionizing radiation was found to be a potent mutagenic agent. This discovery provided a valuable tool for genetic research but raised the specter of an entirely new kind of health hazard, that of injury to future generations.

With the discovery of nuclear fission, and the development of sources of nuclear energy, the number of persons occupationally exposed to ionizing radiations increased from a few thousand to several hundred thousand. Moreover, the potential for exposure of the general population to damaging radiation levels was enormously expanded. The early development of an energetic radiological health protection program in atomic energy installations, based on standards derived from the fundamental observations of the previous quarter century, has been markedly successful in preventing repetition of the long, painful history of occupational disease, characteristic of most industries. There have been only 9 deaths in 25 years, all from accidents resulting in massive external exposure to ionizing radiation. No injuries from internal emitters and no known delayed injuries from chronic external exposure have occurred. However, the diseases that would be expected to result from overexposure, such as leukemia and lung cancer, occur normally in the unexposed population. It is possible that a few cases attributable to radiation exposure could have occurred without appreciably increasing the expected number for cancer in the normal population.

Unfortunately this excellent record in research and industry has not been matched in the mining of uranium. The earliest atmospheric limits were based on concentrations estimated to be present in the Joachimsthal and Schneeburg mines, where workers had about 50 percent incidence of lung cancer. These recommended limits were not used, and there has been a dramatic rise in the incidence of lung cancer among domestic miners in recent years. The upward trend continues, and it appears that the proportion of afflicted miners may eventually reach that which occurred in the old European uranium mines. The need for revision of permitted exposure levels is clear, and efforts in this direction are in progress.

General Population Exposure. At our present stage of technological development there are three main sources for exposure of the general population to ionizing radiation other than the normal environmental background: medical uses of x-rays, fallout from nuclear explosions, and radioactive wastes from nuclear installations. These sources all are potential contributors to the two major environmental risks from ionizing radiation—increased incidence of cancer and leukemia, and genetic effects.

Studies on fruit flies have shown that the genetic effects of ionizing radiation increase in direct proportion to the dose received, and there is no threshold dose below which genetic effects are not produced. That is to say, each ionizing particle or quantum has a chance to touch off the events which lead to a mutation equal to that of any other particle of the same kind, unconditioned by previous radiation history. Recent studies with mice have shown that genetic damage in females is highly dependent on dose rate, but this has not been shown for irradiated males.

A conservative approach, based on the concept of no threshold for genetic injury, has been used in the establishment of doses permitted for the general population. The Federal Radiation Council has proposed that the per capita dose should be maintained at less than one-sixth rad per year over normal background, an increment that is comparable to the natural dose in many parts of the United States. Higher doses (5 rads per year) are permitted in occupational groups because the nature of the genetic effect is such that the consequences of irradiation depend on the dose to the total gene pool of the breeding population and the occupational radiation workers are a small fraction of the total population.

Quantitative evidence for the effects of ionizing radiation in inducing leukemia and other cancers comes from the experimental laboratory, from epidemiological studies on the survivors of Hiroshima and Nagasaki, from individuals who received therapeutic irradiation for ankylosing spondylitis, and from children irradiated in utero. The evidence suggests that there is a threshold for these effects. On the basis of conservative assumptions that there is no dose-threshold for the induction of cancer and that there is a linear relationship between radiation dose and the yield of cancer, it is currently estimated that leukemia and other cancers will be induced at a rate of one case per rad per year per million exposed people.

Precautions against excess exposure to ionizing radiation have been sufficiently effective thus far to keep average doses to the general population well below the recommended limits. The largest increment to the approximate 0.1 rem per year from naturally occurring radiation is the 0.025 to 0.050 rem from diagnostic use of x-rays. Recent large-scale studies have demonstrated, however, that up to 75 percent reduction in dosage can be achieved by greater efforts to limit exposed areas of the body and by the use of high-speed x-ray film. The next most important source has been fallout from nuclear weapons tests, which at its peak resulted in a 20 percent increase in the dose usually received by the skeleton. Industrial sources of ionizing radiation, including the burgeoning nuclear power industry, have not yet produced appreciable exposure of the general population.

Certain radioisotopes, which may be released to the environment from sources of nuclear energy, are of special concern because of their ability to concentrate in important organs or remain in the body for long periods of time. Iodine-131, which is concentrated in the thyroid gland, is particularly important. Human exposures occur mainly through the consumption of milk, and the greatest radiation exposure therefore occurs in infants. Maximum exposures during 1962 and 1963 produced doses in infants about twice natural background levels. Considerably higher doses, although of undetermined magnitude, were sufficient to produce pathological changes in the thyroid glands of some children in areas near weapons tests.

Strontium-90 and cesium-137 are other isotopes which enter the food chain and are accumulated by man. Strontium-90 localizes mainly in the skeleton, and cesium-137 is found principally in the musculature. The mean cumulative dose from strontium-90 by the year 2000 from weapons tests ending in 1965 will be equivalent to 2.5 years of natural radiation to cells lining the bone surfaces and 1.5 years to the bone marrow. The current dose from cesium-137 to the soft tissues is about 15 percent of natural radiation. However, Laplanders and Eskimos who eat caribou meat suffer exposures as much as a hundredfold greater because caribou consume lichens, which have an unusually high affinity for cesium.

Future Prospects and Problems. Although current knowledge of the biological effects of ionizing radiation is adequate to protect people under present circumstances, expansion of present nuclear applications and introduction of new uses for nuclear energy will introduce problems for which continued investigation and additional controls will be needed.

One prospective source of public exposure is from the peaceful uses of nuclear explosives. Copious production of activation products may be expected from the fusion processes that are proposed for projects in the *Plowshare* program. For example, tritium seems certain to be a major contaminant; yet its biological effects are not now understood fully. The extent of concentration in biological systems is not known, nor is the possible degree of enhancement of its mutagenic effects as a result of its ability to be incorporated into DNA.

The use of atomic energy or radioisotopes in spacecraft will also introduce hazards. For example, one satellite that used the decay heat of radionuclides for power entered the upper atmosphere abortively in 1963 and, in the course of burnup, introduced 17,000 curies of plutonium-238 into the upper atmosphere.

Space flight itself presents new types of problems from ionizing radiation. In outer space, high-energy, heavy ions whose effects have not been adequately characterized will irradiate spaceships and astronauts. The biological effects of these particles must be better understood if we are to ensure the safety of space flight.

Environmental Noise

The ubiquity of noise and its generally obvious nuisance effect have caused many people to be apprehensive about its possible adverse effects on public health.

The ambient noise level of the environment has risen both with increasing population density and with increasing use of machinery as a substitute for human or animal muscle-power. The increase is felt in private as well as public and occupational settings (Fig. 19-3).

In the home, greater use is made of noise-generating equipment, such as air-conditioners, fans, household appliances, and entertainment devices (e.g., radio, television, and phonographs). In the public sector, there are noises from motor vehicles, aircraft, and construction activities involving bulldozers, compressors, air hammers or drills, riveters and the like. In the occupational sector, there is a trend toward the use of high-speed mechanical processes which generate more noise than the older equipment.

Occupational noise levels generally exceed those of the public and private environments, and it is in the occupational environment that the effects of noise on man have been most thoroughly investigated. These investigations have established that exposure to excess noise levels over a long period results in a permanent reduction of hearing acuity and interference with the perception of speech.

Occupational Noise-Induced Hearing Loss. As early as 1914 in this country, it was noted that hearing loss caused by prolonged exposure to noise of high pitch was common among loom tenders, spinners, and railway engineers, and might also occur in telegraphers. The reverberating noise experienced by boilermakers and structural riveters had resulted in the syndrome named, by the workers themselves, "boilermaker's deafness." It was recognized that the cause of this kind of hearing loss was damage to the nerve conduction mechanism in the inner ear, and the loss was more pronounced for high than for low tones. High-pitched rather than low-pitched noises were most often responsible for hearing loss. Finally, hearing loss immediately after exposure to the noise was greater than after a period of rest away from the noise.

In recent decades, the number of noisy occupations has increased and the number of people exposed to potentially damaging noise levels has expanded with the growth of industry. In addition, there has been an evolution of social attitudes, and we now hold that workers need not ac-

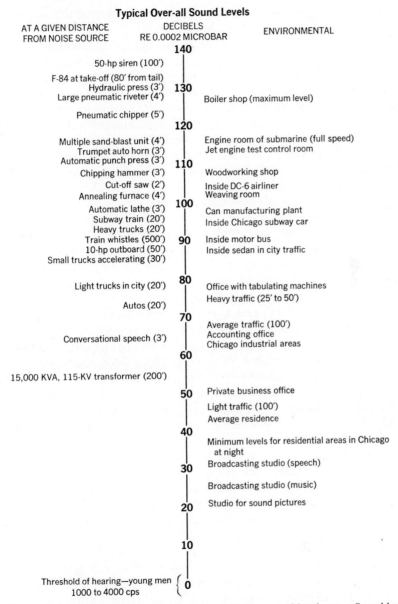

Typical Over-all Sound Levels

AT A GIVEN DISTANCE FROM NOISE SOURCE	DECIBELS RE 0.0002 MICROBAR	ENVIRONMENTAL
	140	
50-hp siren (100')		
F-84 at take-off (80' from tail)		
Hydraulic press (3')	**130**	
Large pneumatic riveter (4')		Boiler shop (maximum level)
Pneumatic chipper (5')		
	120	
Multiple sand-blast unit (4')		Engine room of submarine (full speed)
Trumpet auto horn (3')		Jet engine test control room
Automatic punch press (3')	**110**	
Chipping hammer (3')		Woodworking shop
Cut-off saw (2')		Inside DC-6 airliner
Annealing furnace (4')		Weaving room
	100	
Automatic lathe (3')		Can manufacturing plant
Subway train (20')		Inside Chicago subway car
Heavy trucks (20')		
Train whistles (500')	**90**	Inside motor bus
10-hp outboard (50')		Inside sedan in city traffic
Small trucks accelerating (30')		
	80	
Light trucks in city (20')		Office with tabulating machines
		Heavy traffic (25' to 50')
Autos (20')		
	70	
		Average traffic (100')
		Accounting office
Conversational speech (3')		Chicago industrial areas
	60	
15,000 KVA, 115-KV transformer (200')		
	50	Private business office
		Light traffic (100')
		Average residence
	40	
		Minimum levels for residential areas in Chicago at night
	30	Broadcasting studio (speech)
		Broadcasting studio (music)
	20	Studio for sound pictures
	10	
Threshold of hearing—young men 1000 to 4000 cps	**0**	

Figure 19-3. Typical over-all sound levels measured with a sound-level meter. Sound-level measurements give only part of the information usually necessary to handle noise problems and are often supplemented by analysis of the noise spectra and by oscillographic studies. These values are taken from the literature. (From *Handbook of Noise Measurement,* 5th ed. © 1963 by General Radio Company, West Concord, Mass.)

cept the consequences of a damaging work environment without receiving compensation even if the damage does not interfere with gainful activity. These developments have led to extensive investigations into the cause and prevention of occupational noise-induced hearing loss.

In order effectively to control noise hazards, it is necessary to determine how the intensity and duration of exposure, as well as the character of the noise (intensity, pitch, intermittency, etc.), interrelate to produce permanent reduction of hearing acuity. Moreover, it is necessary to relate hearing impairment to functional disability.

These relationships have not been thoroughly clarified, but a fairly consistent picture is emerging.

It is possible to make a graph of a person's hearing acuity by exposing each ear to pure tones of variable intensity, by determining the minimum intensity at which each tone can be detected, and by plotting minimum detected intensity against tone frequency. The record of such a test is called a pure tone audiogram. It can be compared with a "normal" audiogram of persons of the same age, or it can be compared with the same person's previous audiograms, to determine whether a deterioration in hearing acuity is taking place.

Sound consists of repeated alternate compressions and expansions of air. The pitch of the sound is determined by the number of vibrations per second (i.e., the frequency), and the intensity of the sound (related to its loudness) is determined by the amplitude of the vibrations. Pure tones are vibrations of a single frequency, e.g., 1,000 cycles/second or 1,000 Hz. Most ordinary sounds are mixtures of tones of many frequencies. The frequencies of greatest importance on the audiogram are 500, 1,000, and 2,000 Hz because the sounds of human speech occur in this range.

It is fortunate that the *first* indication of occupational noise-induced hearing loss is usually a decrease in hearing acuity for the 4,000 Hz tone. This tone is not significantly involved in speech tones, and hence the loss is not subjectively detectable, but its occurrence on the audiogram gives warning of impending future losses in the speech range if preventive measures are not taken.

The problem for industrial preventive medicine is, therefore, to prevent loss of hearing acuity for the 500, 1,000, and 2,000 Hz tones. Noises that are most effective in causing hearing loss occur relatively close to the frequency range of speech, i.e., from 500 to 2,000 Hz. If analyzed by appropriate instruments, noise can be separated into "octaves"—i.e., bands over which the frequency doubles from the minimum to the maximum frequency in the band. The octave bands 300–600 Hz, 600–1,200 Hz, and 1,200–2,400 Hz are considered to be the most important for potential damage to hearing acuity for speech.

A significant fraction of persons exposed for six or more hours a day to continuous sound exceeding 85 decibels intensity in any of the octave bands 300–600, 600–1,200, or 1,200–2,400 will develop significant permanent loss for the hearing of speech after a period of years. If the sound in any octave band has the bulk of its energy in one third or less of the octave, it is regarded as a "pure tone" noise. The allowable level for such tones has been set 5 decibels lower than for noise composed of a broad band of frequencies of nearly the same intensity.

If exposure during the working day is intermittent rather than continuous, the tolerable noise level is increased.

Tolerable noise levels cannot be defined with precision because of the individual variation in susceptibility to noise-induced hearing loss. Current opinion on noise levels that are tolerable is based to a large extent on extrapolation from temporary hearing loss, rather than on valid data from long-term occupational exposures.

It has long been known that there is more hearing loss immediately after exposure to severe noise than following a period of rest away from the noise. This phenomenon is known as temporary threshold shift (TTS). There is some evidence to suggest that the TTS induced by initial exposure to noise may be of the same order of magnitude as the permanent loss—i.e., "noise-induced permanent threshold shift" (NIPTS)—that would be experienced by the same person after five to ten years of continuous occupational exposure to the same noise. Decisive evidence of such a relationship has not been obtained.

There are several indicators that a given noise environment *might* induce NIPTS if exposure is for as much as 6 hours/day. These are (1) an overall noise level exceeding 92 decibels measured on the A scale of a sound meter (dBA); (2) noise levels exceeding 85 decibels in any of the octave bands 300–600, 600–1,200, or 1,200–2,400 Hz (80 decibels if "pure tone"); (3) a TTS of 15 decibels or more following an initial exposure to noise of closely related frequency and intensity; or (4) a decrease in hearing acuity for the 4,000 Hz tone as exposure progresses (regardless of exposure time and intensity).

Any of these indicators should be a signal for inauguration of a conservation of hearing program. Such a program consists of (1) attempts to reduce the environmental noise level below the 85 decibel (or 80 decibel) criteria by engineering methods; (2) the provision of personal ear protective devices for the employee if (1) fails; and (3) the taking of audiograms at regular intervals to determine whether hearing acuity is or is not decreasing.

In interpreting decreases in hearing acuity, account must be taken of hearing loss due to aging. Thus, in calculating the amount of hearing loss presumably due to occupational noise exposure, one usually deducts ½ decibel per year for each year over 40 from the average hearing loss for 500, 1,000, and 2,000 Hz tones. It is likely that some of the hearing loss attributed to aging is caused by the noise level of the community environment. It is generally agreed that hearing losses of 15 decibels or less compared with "normal" are no practical handicap.

The program for the conservation of hearing described above is limited to conservation of hearing for speech. It could be expanded, with more difficulty, to conservation of hearing for tones outside the speech range.

Effects of Noise in Community Exposure. There is little evidence that ambient noise levels in the private and public sectors of the environment generally are sufficiently intense to cause measurable loss of hearing acuity, although they probably contribute to hearing loss associated with age. We are, therefore, concerned mainly with the nonauditory effects of noise, realizing that these effects can also be experienced in the occupational environment.

Noise may affect physiological processes other than hearing. Loud, sudden noises may startle one to the point that an acceleration of heart rate is actually perceptible to the individual. This effect is, however, transient and can hardly be construed as adverse, since its presumed function is to prepare the individual to act quickly to evade danger.

Sustained moderately high levels of noise can be irritating, particularly if the noise is high-pitched. The irritation is a subjective feeling of annoyance or discomfort and may result in a decrease in efficiency if one is trying to concentrate, or frustration if one is trying to hear meaningful sound, such as a conversation or music. This kind of irritation is worse if the noise is intermittent than if it is steady, because adaptation to ambient noise occurs fairly rapidly and the initial discomfort disappears. In fact, the absence of accustomed noise may be as psychologically disturbing as the appearance of unaccustomed noise. There is no evidence that annoying levels of ambient noise produce any adverse long-term effects on physical health or any increase in diagnosable mental illness.

On the other hand, there is no question that sonic booms and the noises from traffic, aircraft, and other community sources are serious detractors from the quality of the environment. Where there is a community consensus that these noises are a public nuisance, there are grounds to seek its abatement even though health effects have not been clearly established, except possibly for a gradual loss of hearing acuity.

Some of the hearing loss attributed to aging may be caused by the noise level of the community environment. One study has shown a much lower hearing loss with age in a sample of primitive African males (Sudan) than in American males studied at the Wisconsin State Fair (1954), but a similar study of another primitive African group (Guinea) failed to reveal a marked difference. Genetic and other factors may, therefore, be of major importance in hearing loss with aging.

As with other environmental hazards, further studies will be needed to better characterize quality and quantity of community noise exposure, particularly as it relates to hearing loss and other effects of noise on the exposed population.

Accidents

Although space limitations prevent a detailed presentation, attention needs to be drawn to accidents as an important contributor to injury, death, and economic loss. The seriousness of the national problem of accidental death and injury is related to the huge numbers of risk situations to which the population is exposed. Even at low rates of occurrence, accidents result in staggering losses in terms of morbidity, mortality, and economic cost. Some indicators of the scope of the national problem are: *

Fatal accidents are the fourth leading cause of death (all ages)
Fatal accidents are the leading cause of death among persons aged 1–34

Annual Number of Deaths	
All accidents	112,000
Motor vehicle	53,000
Annual Number of Injured Persons	
All accidents	52,000,000
Moving motor vehicles	3,600,000
Hospital bed days for treatment	22,000,000
Estimated Annual Cost of Injuries	$12,000,000,000

Further, it is estimated that 1 of every 17 persons in the United States bears permanent physical impairments resulting from accidental injury.

Another index of the magnitude of the problem is that between the ages of 1 and 15 more deaths result from accidents than from the next four most fatal diseases combined.

The central urgency is the development of adequate preventive measures. Very substantial progress has been made in industry, where there is an excellent record of accomplishment; in many instances the employee

* Source: Injury Control Program, U.S. Public Health Service, Cincinnati, Ohio, 1967 (Unpublished).

accident rate is lower in the plant than off the job. Similar attention needs to be focused on nonoccupational accidents. Countermeasures are aimed at (1) preventing the accident and (2) minimizing the severity of injury if the accident does occur.

Although in some instances the action dictated by these objectives is obvious, in many cases it is obscure. The difficulties arise from the complex interplay of human factors and those intrinsic in the situation or device. Of the various research talents required to make headway in this area, two are outstandingly needed, those talents required for epidemiological inquiry into causes, and those for the bioengineering development of accident-proof equipment and procedures. Neither has been adequately used or available in the past.

Environmental Cancer

In 1775, a prominent English surgeon, Percivall Pott, described cancer of the scrotum in chimney sweeps, which he attributed to exposure to soot. This was the first clear description of an occupational cancer due to an environmental carcinogen. Better hygienic measures, stimulated by appropriate legislation, dramatically reduced the problem. The actual identification of the chemicals causing these cancers was achieved by Kennaway over 150 years later.

More recently, it has been established that cigarette smoking causes cancer of the lung, as well as cancer of the oral cavity, larynx, esophagus, and the urinary bladder, and increases mortality from coronary heart disease. Identification of tobacco smoking as a serious public health problem ranks in importance with century-old discoveries that polluted water supplies caused cholera and typhoid epidemics. The resolution of the problem requires legislative and sociological action, as well as further medical research. The potential benefit in reducing deaths from lung cancer alone, which is now the most lethal form of cancer in men, would represent the saving of at least 30,000 lives per year.

The identification of the chemical and physical agents in the environment which cause cancer has been the most effective method of preventing the disease. The epidemiological study of human and animal populations exposed to suspected carcinogenic agents has been the main method for determining the nature and magnitude of the cancer hazard. Laboratory studies are important in establishing the carcinogenic activity in animals and the chemical and physical characteristics of the carcinogen in the environment.

The interplay of epidemiological and laboratory investigations has led to the clarification of the cause and prevention of a significant number of neoplastic diseases. Among these are:

1. Cancer of the skin, in its relationship to occupational exposure to distillation and fractionation products of coal, oil shale, lignite and petroleum, and to excessive exposures to sunlight by light-skinned people.

2. Cancer of the lung, in its relationship to occupational inhalation of radioactive or chromate chemicals and asbestos, as well as the more general exposure to tobacco smoke and possibly urban air pollutants.

3. Cancer of the urinary bladder, in its relationship to occupational exposure to β-naphthylamine and related chemicals in aniline dye manufacture, as well as to tobacco smoking, and heavy infestation with the bladder fluke, *Schistosoma haematobium*.

4. Cancer of the uterine cervix, in its relationship to chronic infection and to male noncircumcision.

5. Cancer of the penis, in its relationship to noncircumcision and poor hygiene.

6. Cancer of the nasal sinuses, in its relationship to occupational exposure in nickel refining.

7. Osteogenic sarcoma, in its relationship to the intake of radium compounds.

8. Myelocytic leukemia, in its relationship to occupational, diagnostic, or other ionizing radiation, and to mongolism.

This partial list is being constantly expanded. There are now several hundred known chemical agents, as well as ionizing and solar radiation, and an ever growing list of viruses, that have been demonstrated to produce cancers of many types in rodents and other animals. Among the chemicals are several that are used extensively by man in the form of drugs; others contaminate the environment. The importance of many of these agents in human cancer is in most instances undefined and will require careful epidemiological study.

Under natural conditions, few people are exposed to pure chemicals. Exposures usually involve crude products that contain a variety of agents. The characterization of the carcinogenic potency of a material on the basis of the isolation of one or more chemicals that produce cancers in animals is often complicated by the presence of other chemicals in the mixture that can enhance or retard the carcinogenic reaction. The role of these cocarcinogens and anticarcinogens in tobacco smoke, for example, may be as important as that of the half-dozen carcinogens that are known to be present in minute quantities.

Cancer-producing chemicals are by no means limited to industrial processes or sources. Increasing attention is being focused on carcinogens from natural sources, such as plants and fungi. The alkaloids of

Senecio jacobaea, an edible plant of Africa, induce liver cancers in rats. Meal from *Cycas circinalis* contains a chemical, methylazomethanol glycoside, which produces cancer of the liver in rats and guinea pigs, as well as kidney tumors in rats. Bracken fern, *Pteridium aquilina,* when ingested by cows leads to hematuria and cancer of the bladder.

Aspergillus flavus, a common mold which grows readily under warm, humid conditions on protein food such as peanuts or corn, elaborates a lactone, aflatoxin, which is a virulent hepatotoxin and produces liver cancer in rats and rainbow trout. It may have a causative role in the high incidence of human liver cancer among primitive peoples, particularly in Africa. Several other fungal products, including griseofulvin, which is useful in the treatment of ringworm, also show carcinogenic activity in animals.

It is abundantly clear that human and animal populations are surrounded by chemical, physical, and biological agents that can produce cancer under certain conditions. Not only must these agents be identified, but the conditions under which they exert neoplastic activity must be specified. Moreover, the interactions amongst carcinogenic agents must be further elucidated, since it is already clear that such interactions do occur between viruses and chemical and physical agents. For example, thymic lymphoma is produced in mice by ionizing radiation and urethane. However, the development of this type of cancer is associated with the appearance of a virus which is capable of transmitting the disease to nontreated animals, suggesting close analogy to the behavior of "temperate" lysogenic bacterial viruses. Similar interactions undoubtedly occur in man, although they remain to be demonstrated. Other complex interactions are suggested by studies that involve the metabolism of the intestinal bacteria. The carcinogen from cycad meal, for example, must be hydrolyzed to the aglycone form in order to be absorbed from the intestine, a reaction that does not occur in germ-free animals. Production of the hepatocarcinogen, ethionine by *E. coli* occurs only when sulfate ion and methionine are available as nutrients.

Carcinogenesis, as with all biological reactions, is influenced by both the nature and form of the stimulus, and by the nature and status of the host exposed to such a stimulus. Of the hundreds of chemical carcinogens now described, some act at the site of contact with tissue, apparently without metabolic conversion. These are the "direct" carcinogens, exemplified by the polycyclic hydrocarbons. Aromatic amines and azo dyes require enzymatic conversion in the liver to N-hydroxylation products for activity. These have been designated as "procarcinogens." Carcinogenic activity is influenced not only by the chemical structure, but by the dose, the vehicle or the physical state, and the route and schedule of administration.

Carcinogenic reactions also depend on the genetic and environmental characteristics of the host. The rat develops liver cancers from azo dyes because the necessary hydroxylation enzymes are induced in its liver. The guinea pig, lacking these enzymes, is resistant to the parent substance yet susceptible to the synthetic hydroxylated derivative. Even the relatively small differences within genetic constitution of various strains affect the response to carcinogens.

Carcinogenic responses can be profoundly influenced by the sex, age, and nutritional status of the host. When rats of certain strains are given single oral administrations of 7,12-dimethylbenz(a)anthracene, the carcinogen is present in every tissue in the body within six hours. Yet in mature female rats, cancer of the breast is the main neoplastic response, in contrast to the cancers of the skin and sebaceous glands which develop in the mature male rat; leukemia occurs as a late-developing tumor in both sexes while in very young rats the main form of cancer is the subcutaneous sarcoma.

Because of the widespread and rapid distribution of chemical carcinogens in the body, it is surprising that tumors do not form in a greater variety of tissues. The study of nonreactive tissues deserves the same intense attention that has been directed toward those tissues in which the neoplastic reaction does occur.

It is clear that carcinogenesis is a complex process, and there are very important areas for research that need greater emphasis. More rapid, simpler assay systems need to be developed, since none has been found as an acceptable alternative to the time-consuming and expensive induction of neoplasms in animals. The use of newborn animals is a promising method which has good sensitivity and requires relatively short periods of observation. A wider exploration of species other than rodents may be fruitful. Certainly, comparative oncology is a field that should be stimulated, particularly in epidemiological and laboratory areas.

The goals of elucidating the causes of cancers, and means of preventing them, are worthy of a major continuing effort. Research in carcinogenesis can be approached meaningfully only on a team basis, in which many physical and biological disciplines, as well as statistical and clinical specialties, are represented. Carcinogenesis is but one of many chronic toxic reactions of an organism and must be considered in the context of other reactions, just as the occurrence of carcinogens in the environment must be defined in terms of the total ecology and not as an isolated occurrence.

Epidemiology on an international scale is not a luxury but is an essential method for obtaining information on populations living under different conditions of exposure. It, therefore, represents a method of obtaining knowledge that can be applied to our own population. For example, application of knowledge of the role of aflatoxin in liver cancer in Uganda might aid in preventing some occurrences of liver cancer in the United States. Breast cancer, the most prevalent type of cancer among our women, is one-fifth as prevalent among Japanese women. The explanation for this difference (and there are already promising leads to explore) could play an important role in the reduction of breast cancer in this country.

The complex, frustrating problem of neoplastic disease is giving way, but slowly and grudgingly to research. But it *is* giving way, and the outlook remains bright toward reaching through research the goal of prevention of many neoplastic diseases in man.

Conclusion

This chapter has touched on some of the high points in the relation between environmental factors and health. It is clear that these factors are important to our health, are diverse, and are rapidly changing. These considerations have strong implications for a strategy to guide the further development of this field. The challenges of environmental health arise primarily from technology and can be expected to change as technology changes. The field must accordingly have a flexibility and liveliness that matches man's inventiveness. Thus, an effective preventive program must be in close touch with the current trends in industry, and with the science from which the industrial innovations emerge, and at the same time be thoroughly alert to advances in engineering, in the physical, biological, and the social sciences, so that their tools can be exploited in developing an efficient machine for the attainment of the full promise which the ingenuity of our society places before us.

Environmental health has thus two equal, pressing and conflicting responsibilities. First, the nature and extent of our present environmental health problems must be defined in such a way that they can be dealt with and controlled within a framework of sound priorities. Second, while we are "catching up" with the problems now with us, it is of vital importance to predict which new technological process, agent or device may present hazards, and thus obviate difficulties before they arise. Sound, preventive procedures must be devised in parallel with technological advancement.

The task of restoring and then maintaining the quality of our environment, of identifying and tracing the origins of all the potentially hazardous factors, of discovering their capacity for injury, of stipulating noninjurious amounts, of preventing injury in an increasingly complex technology, may seem to be impossible. There are, however, reassuringly sound bases for optimism, and we can in fact accept a healthful environment as a realizable objective. With the imaginative collaboration of dedicated scientists drawn from many disciplines, with the support of industry, with the understanding assistance of legislators, a wholesome environment can be achieved. Medical scientists and practitioners, engineers, sociologists, ecologists, and technologists from many branches of industry are essential to this effort.

It is well within our ability to create a "livable environment" provided two primary needs are met. The first is *recognition* of the importance of the problem by the public, by industry, by governmental agencies, by the universities, and by the scientific profession. Once recognition has been achieved, it can be anticipated that the second requirement will be forthcoming in an orderly manner. This is the *resource* required to meet the challenge. The resource includes program support and trained scientists and practitioners. Happily, real advances in both categories have been made. Nevertheless, at this time, accomplishment is unequal to the need.

Chapter 20

BIOLOGY AND THE FUTURE OF MAN

The Nature of Man

The forces shaping the short-term future of man, perhaps to the turn of this century, are apparent and the events are in train. The shape of the world in the year 2000 and man's place therein will be determined by the manner in which organized humanity confronts several major challenges. If sufficiently successful, and mankind escapes the dark abysses of its own making, then truly will the future belong to man, the only product of biological evolution capable of controlling its own further destiny.

Social organizations, through their political leaders, will determine on peace or war, on the use of conventional or nuclear weapons, on the encouragement or discouragement of measures to limit the growth of populations, on the degree of increase in food production and on the conservation of a healthy environment or its continuing degradation.

These and lesser decisions will affect the composition of the human species. Some major population groups will grow in numbers, others will decline, relatively or absolutely. Thus, in the seventeenth century Europeans and their descendants on other continents made up approximately 20 percent of the world's population; in 1940 they represented nearly 40 percent of all people. A relative increase of Asian and African peoples has developed more recently. Each trend was the result of such complex circumstances as the opening of sparsely inhabited continents to immigration, the industrial revolution, the introduction of contraceptive devices, improvements in medical knowledge, and introduction of public health measures.

Man, a highly social being, is an animal as well. In form and function, development and growth, reproduction, aging, and death he is a biological entity who shares the attributes of physical life with the millions of plant and animal species to whom he is related. This relationship, known since prescientific times, became part of established science long before the theory of evolution was proposed. It is the reason why studies of fungi and mice, flies and rabbits, weeds, cats, and many other types of organisms have contributed to understanding man and to improving his health and biological well-being, and why future studies with experimental organisms will bear on man's own future.

Man's mental attributes form a superstructure which does not exist independent of his organismal construction. Human thought is based on the human brain; the brain—and, hence, the mind, the "self"—of each person is one of the derived, developed expressions of the genes which he inherited from his parents. Man's capacities are, thus, inextricably linked to his genes whose molecular nature is now understood to a very high degree, but which presently lie outside his control. The social creations of man—language, knowledge, culture, philosophy, society—have an existence of their own and are transmitted by social inheritance from generation to generation. But they depend for both their persistence and change on the genetic endowments of the biological human beings who are subjected to them while, at the same time, making them possible.

In these considerations, "man" should be taken as inclusive of all human beings on our planet. The brotherhood of all men is not only an ethical imperative, it is based on our common descent and on the magnitude of the shared genetic heritage. Mankind is divided into "nations"—geographic, political, economic, military, and cultural units—which insist on their sovereign status. The short-range future of man will differ among these sovereign groups, particularly between the "developed" and the "underdeveloped" nations. This discussion, written within the context of a developed nation, is particularly concerned with prospects in the developed countries.

The Great Hazards

War

The considerations of the future of man that follow presuppose that mankind will not be subjected to a nuclear holocaust. If such an event were to occur, the problems of retaining or re-establishing social organization, the breakdown of health services including the production and distribution of life-saving drugs, and the ensuing threat of worldwide epidemics would take precedence over all other aspects of human affairs. Modern technology is sufficiently powerful to make complete extermination of man a possibility. To accomplish such a deed would require overwhelming use of nuclear weapons over large areas of the globe and a deliberate effort to distribute lethal levels of fallout over all inhabited regions. Barring such extreme measures, some of mankind would probably survive a nuclear war. The acute dose of irradiation required to kill human beings in a single, brief exposure is relatively low. Accordingly, direct radiation from nuclear explosives would take an immense toll—but the survivors would probably be able to repopulate the earth.

Those who survived the immediate impact of nuclear explosions would be subjected to chronic irradiation from fallout which would lead to a variety of deleterious effects. In addition to the damage to their own bodies, the survivors would produce egg or sperm cells which would contain many new mutations leading to abnormal offspring. Nevertheless, the radiation dose which the survivors would have received from the initial exposure and subsequent fallout might often be low enough to permit them also to produce normal appearing and functioning children—provided the survivors would still want to create a new generation. Ironically, it is precisely under these circumstances that social inhibitions against control of human genetics would dissolve most rapidly; post-nuclear war man would almost certainly utilize available genetic understanding and biological technology to guide the evolution of his species.

Should *Homo sapiens,* as such, survive nuclear war, there can be no guarantee that he could reconstruct his civilization. Our technologically developed society rests on a complex web of production which could be rebuilt only with extraordinary difficulty. Meanwhile, this would probably occur in a world significantly altered. The ecological consequences of worldwide fallout and long-term rise in radioactivity are virtually impossible to predict. But plant and animal species vary remarkably in their radiosensitivity, and surely current food chains would be disrupted with such profound ecological consequences that it is not clear that man could continue to find sustenance, warmth and shelter.

Similar considerations may well apply to the possibility of widespread use of biological warfare. The constructive understanding of life which Biology provides can also be used for wholesale destruction of life. Once undertaken, war, in the future as in the past, is liable to grow beyond control, whether it be conducted with physical, chemical or biological means. A future for man can be assured only when the ultimate danger of modern war is fully recognized and mankind abandons warfare.

Man and His Environment

For thousands of years, since first he became a farmer, man has changed his general environment. Some such actions were favorable; for example, during a previous era the rainfall in the American plains was limited, enabling the Indians to annually burn the prairies to drive the buffalo. The resulting debris created our great grasslands and helped generate the deepest and grandest soils on this continent. But, deforestation and primitive methods of agriculture have denuded vast areas and exposed their soil to erosion. It was just such practice which silted the Tigris and Euphrates rivers, thus ending the great Sumerian civilization. With continuing loss, precious soil is essentially irretrievable. Return of the "dust bowl" of the south-central United States to productive agriculture will require years of expensive and intensive effort which will be economically rational only when national requirements are desperate. Hundreds of thousands of acres of forest were despoliated without provision for reforestation. Large areas of South American forest have been cleared for agriculture, despite the fact that, within a year or two, the rich forest is replaced by a concrete-like laterite soil; until research provides the technology to prevent this, such forest should remain in the native state. But when such knowledge is in hand, vast areas could be opened for productive agriculture. Excessive hunting of some animals for food, and of the large predatory animals, either for sport or in self-defense, has wiped out many species either wholly or in many regions. Witness the slaughter of the giant, flightless Moa by the Maori after they found New Zealand (about 1200 A.D.) and the decreasing numbers of virtually all of the great birds of our own country. When Europeans first came to this country, it harbored 5 billion passenger pigeons and 50 million bison. The former are gone and only 6000 of the latter remain. Less than 3 percent of the original acreage of redwoods now stands and there is no record of the disappearance of great numbers of species from our prairies, lakes and forests. And mankind is the poorer. The prospect of a planet populated exclusively by man and the few animal species he has domesticated is bleak indeed. How grim to think of a world without tigers, whales, condors, or redwoods!

The rise in population density, the operations of modern industry, and the diverse products of modern technology have led to pollution of air, water, and soil by a wide variety of chemical compounds and even to undesirable proliferation of certain living forms, notably algae, while defiling the landscape and minimizing the exposure of urbanites and suburbanites to natural surroundings. Large-scale use of pesticides can start a chain in which these substances concentrate in plant and animal tissues and, when ingested, accumulate in the adipose tissue of the human body. To illustrate this process, consider the record of Clear Lake, in California where DDD (a breakdown product of DDT) entered the lake at 0.02 parts per million (ppm). A year later, its concentration was 10 ppm in the plankton, 900 ppm in fish that eat the plankton, and 2700 ppm in fish that eat fish that eat plankton. No data are available for men who ate such fish. Similarly, the routine addition of antibiotics to the feed of domestic animals may lead to their ingestion by man and, by fostering growth of resistant organisms, may decrease the effectiveness of these drugs to fight infections.

The effects of these changes in the environment on man himself are not known. Although it is possible that some of the agents to which man is now inadvertently exposed will cause serious disease, shortening of the life span, decreased fertility, or deleterious mutational changes in genes, none of these has as yet actually been demonstrated to have occurred. This, however, does not imply that dangers do not exist. Such possible effects may be numerous, yet difficult to discover. It has taken decades to establish the statistical relation between cigarette smoking and lung cancer; the same may also hold true for the relation between new factors in our environment and other diseases.

Unlike the effects of acute, heavy doses of deleterious substances which rapidly lead to severe illness, pollutants are taken up in small amounts over long periods. Their effects, therefore, may be delayed for years or decades. Moreover, different individuals probably react differently to the same low level of exposure to a foreign substance. Some may excrete more of a given compound than others, thereby avoiding accumulation. Some may decompose the agent in their tissues while others leave it unchanged. Some may be more resistant to its effects. If, as an arbitrary figure, one in 1000 individuals will suffer ill effects from a specific agent, causal relationships can be revealed only by very large-scale studies of whole population groups. Yet if one incident in 1000 seems a small effect, consider that in a population of 200 million as many as 200,000 individuals would experience damage. Conceivably, the incidence of heart attacks may have been increased to this extent by the carbon monoxide of automobile exhausts, in regions where smog formation is heavy, but this has yet to be demonstrated. Appropriate studies would have to make use of large cohorts of people who are followed in their pattern of diseases, fertility, and life span over very long periods—perhaps longer than the professional life-span of a single generation of investigators. There is precedent for such studies in the research on the relation of smoking to lung cancer, but the scale of such studies must be greatly expanded.

Until reliable evidence thus obtained becomes available, public health measures designed to minimize exposure to such pollutants are patently advisable. But surely a rule of reason should prevail. To only a few chemicals does man owe as great a debt as to DDT. It has contributed to the great increase in agricultural productivity while sparing countless humanity from a host of diseases, most notably perhaps, scrub typhus and malaria. Indeed, it is estimated that, in little more than two decades, DDT has prevented 500 million deaths due to malaria which would otherwise have been inevitable. Abandonment of this valuable insecticide should be undertaken only at such time and in such places as it is evident that the prospective gain to humanity exceeds the consequent losses. At this writing, all available substitutes for DDT are both more expensive per crop/year and decidedly more hazardous to those who manufacture and utilize them in crop treatment or for other more general purposes.

The health problems engendered by undesirable contaminants of the environment may also be raised by substances which are intentionally ingested. Only large-scale, long-term epidemiological research will reveal whether the contraceptive pills, pain killers, sleeping pills, sweeteners, and tranquilizers, now consumed on so great a scale, have any untoward long-range effects on their consumers. The Federal record systems, particularly those of the Veterans Administration and the Department of Defense, are already available for epidemiological follow-up studies among veterans. They could be made still more useful by utilizing record linkages, i.e., linking together the many independent records of births, illnesses, deaths, etc., in the Defense and Social Security agencies, and many others. While this entails the possibility of intrusion into the privacy of individuals, it should be possible to erect safeguards against misuse. Such safeguards will be effective if the prevailing climate of opinion welcomes the attainment of useful information and forbids authoritarian attempts at improper exploitation of linked data. Man's biological future depends on knowledge of his experiences, good and bad, and record linkage is an important means of acquiring such knowledge.

Even more subtle than the effects of pollutants and of specific agents on man may be the effects of changes in his general pattern of living. Urban aggregation has removed many men from natural surroundings. The increased level of environmental noise, caused by industrial procedures and automobile and airplane engines, has added a new dimension to sensory exposure. Crowding together in overpopulated regions has greatly changed the interrelations among people who, only a few thousand years ago, lived in small bands with minor contact with one another.

Development of the science of animal behavior is beginning to give some insight into the interrelations between genetically-founded behavioral attributes, the effects of early training and of the immediate environment on overt behavior. We are prone to think of hostility, crime, and other anti-social behavior as conditioned by social circumstances. And there is indeed ample evidence to support this belief. We do not know, however, how much personal unhappiness and social distress is a consequence of man's basic biological nature in conflict with an unnatural, essentially nonhuman environment. The stereotyped movements of caged polar bears, viz., the reaction of bears to a non-bearlike environment, may well have analogies in mentally ill patients. Undesirable modes of behavior as well as various "psychosomatic" illnesses may frequently be extreme expressions of maladjustments of the human animal. Hopefully, research in behavioral biology will furnish deeper insights into man's nature and application of these insights may lead in the not-too-distant future to fundamentally new parameters for environmental engineering. These will endeavor to fit the environment to man instead of leaving man unfit for the environments which he created. Important to such studies are the nonhuman primates—apes and monkeys; every effort should be made to assure the survival of as many such species as possible.

Scientific advancement enabled man to triumph over his environment. With technological skills and machinery we are able to move, change, and control natural resources for our agriculture, forestry, fisheries, recreation, and urban and industrial development. The wasteful, injurious practices of yesterday have largely been abandoned. Forests are replanted as they are timbered; soils are fertilized so as to compensate for the minerals removed by the plant harvest; saline soils are restored to the useful tillage by large scale leaching; a beginning has been made at reversal of thoughtless practices which could result in the almost irreversible death of large lakes. Although Lake Erie is in serious trouble, Lake Washington is being recovered and Lake Tahoe may yet be saved. Civilization depends and will continue to depend upon the renewable resources of the environment—land, water, air, and populations of plants and animals, both wild and cultivated. Fortunately, the public and its representatives are increasingly anxious about the status of these resources and the vital role they play in our survival and general well-being.

Environmental pollution becomes of increasing concern as the human population congregates in cities and occupies more of the landscape. The public is pressing for greater understanding of the function and interaction of the biological and physical elements of the environment and for application of this understanding to the management of the renewable resources which supply man's food, clothing, recreation, and shelter. This sense of urgency, arising originally from the desire simply to assure the viability of life on our planet, is heightened by growing public appreciation of the importance of beauty, natural and man-made, in our surroundings for the improvement of the quality of life.

Many reports have directed attention to the more obvious, gross problems of managing the environment, problems which derive from a combination of population growth, advancing technology, and increased technological productivity. Concern has been expressed with respect to: rising atmospheric CO_2; increasing particulate content of the atmosphere; buildup of radioactivity; accumulation of diverse chemicals in lakes, streams, rivers,

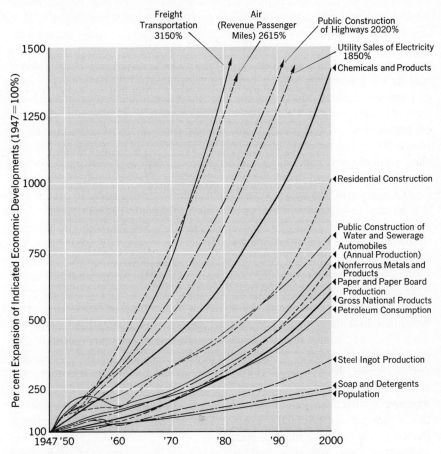

Figure 20-1. Projections of Expansion of Certain Industries Which Have an Influence on Pollution. Years 1947 to 2000.

Source: "Resources in America's Future," Landsborg, Fishman & Fisher. Resources for the Future, Inc., Washington, D.C., 1963 (medium level projections 1970-2000).

coastal waters and the ocean itself; soil erosion and destruction; replacement of fertile green farm and woodland by highways and towns; rising noise levels; and "thermal pollution." Figure 20-1 displays the record and projection of various endeavors of our society, each of which must necessarily adversely affect the environment. If these projections are even approximately correct, and if each of these enterprises grows without appropriate monitoring for its ecological consequences, the totality could constitute the saddest, most brutal and most disastrous act of vandalism in history.

Economic growth, in so far as it leads to higher standards of living, better health, and national security is clearly to be desired and fostered. But that life should be worth living—and this generation should assure that it can transmit to posterity a land whose beauty and resources have been safeguarded, embellished, and protected. To do so, demands a level of regional and national planning, with due regard for ecological understanding, without historic parallel. Moreover, we must assume the burden of transmitting such understanding and planning capability to the developing nations, most of which still retain the native qualities of their environments and are in danger of galloping destruction of their resources as they race to develop their technological capabilities and to achieve economic independence and a reasonable standard of living.

Biologists and engineers should work jointly to design cities of quality and beauty. Dwellings and industrial structures should be surrounded by at least minimal lawns and plantings of ornamental trees, shrubs, and flowers. There can be no relaxation of efforts to assure "clean" air and water, although useful operational criteria for these remain to be established. The burden of responsibility must be made to lie with those whose activities introduce contaminants into the environment. Even now, there are technological means for dealing with most pollutants at the source. A rational society will insist that these means be utilized and that new, cheap, and efficient means be continually sought. Where none exist, it becomes essential that the advantages afforded by polluting activities—nondegradable detergents and pesticides, heavy use of fertilizer, the exhaust of internal combustion engines, the sonic boom and high contrails of a supersonic transport—be weighed against their cumulative effects on mankind. It is doubtful that, at this writing, there exists the evidence on which to rest such judgments. Patently, this evidence must be sought.

Through care, planning, and utilization of the sciences of agriculture and forestry, the landscape of the country can be conserved, returning it to its simple charm with neither billboards nor automobile graveyards. Moreover, a great and complex effort, based on ecological understanding will be required to cope with those pressures which, annually result in conversion of one million acres of farm and wildland to highways and building sites. Certain areas representative of nature—seashore, mountains, desert, forest—should be preserved forever wild for recreation and on a scale adequate to preserve the natural biota. Ecologists and environmental biologists, together with other scientists, should combine to develop a strategy for the wise use of our renewable resources while at the same time attaining an attractive environment. The attainment of these goals does not depend alone on the technical skills of biologists and other scientists and engineers; people generally must desire to live in harmonious, healthful environments.

Without broad social motivation supporting their use, the knowledge and the skills of the specialists will lie fallow.

The Size of Human Populations

The upsurge in the growth of human populations constitutes the major problem for the immediate future of man. Accordingly, it is difficult to exaggerate the urgency of deepening our biological knowledge of man and his environment. There is every reason to expect that, by the end of the century, a brief thirty years from now, the world will have twice its present population. Unless forestalled by a worldwide holocaust, in the year 2000 the world population will surely be not fewer than six billion people, and may well exceed seven billion. See Figure 20-2. Since the means for improved control of disease are already at hand, if the food supply keeps pace,

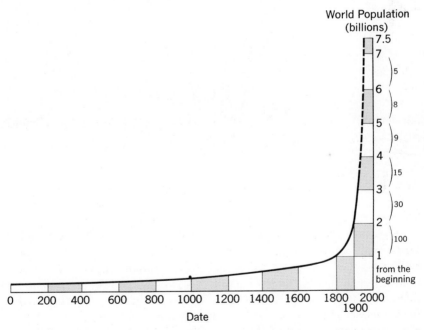

Figure 20-2. World Population Growth (Projected with assumption of constant fertility levels and declining mortality).

* Small numbers outside parentheses indicate the rapidly decreasing number of years required to increase world population by a billion people.

Source: *World Population: A Challenge to the United Nations and Its System of Agencies.* UNA-USA National Policy Panel on World Population, May 1969.

a world population of seven billion will be reached even if present birth rates are considerably reduced. Population growth is occurring most rapidly in the newly developing nations where abject poverty is widespread, the mass of the population is uneducated, and the industrial sectors of their economies are poorly developed. See Figure 20-3.

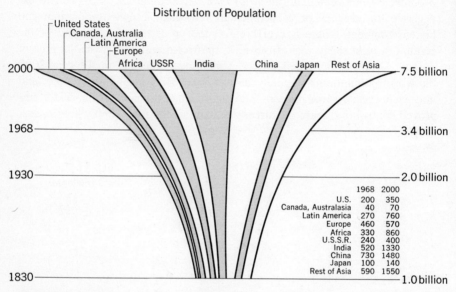

Figure 20-3. Projected Population of Developed and Underdeveloped Nations in the Year 2000.

Source: *World Population: A Challenge to the United Nations and Its System of Agencies.* UNA-USA National Policy Panel on World Population, May 1969.

Moreover, future demands on the biosphere are not to be measured by simple extrapolation from the present. Much of the present population is badly nourished while, because of improved communications and appreciation of the living standards of developed nations, popular aspirations for improved living conditions are high in almost all nations. Even a doubling of per capita consumption of protein, clothing, and shelter would leave present aspirations unfulfilled. If the projected doubling of the world's population is realized, and if political order is to be maintained, it is not unreasonable to expect that the demands on the biosphere by the end of the century will be from three or four times those of the present! The problem of achieving such increases becomes staggering when we realize that the end of the century is so close that this year's infants will then be in the heart of their childbearing period. Moreover, regard for the human heritage requires that these needs be met without despoiling either the quality of man or the material base from which he draws life.

Clearly a catalog of needed knowledge is a catalog of all of natural and social science—the nature of man and his modes of change, the extra-human biosphere, and its interaction with man and with the physical environment. This is just another way of saying that man's destiny turns on his knowledge of himself and of his total environment—inanimate, biological, and social. In the face of a desperate situation, almost nothing becomes irrelevant in the entire spectrum of basic and applied science.

It is clear that, in the long run: (1) population growth cannot continue indefinitely; and (2) if the major populations can be brought to an adequate level of education and technical achievement, the ultimate constraints to population growth will not appear until populations become significantly larger than they are now. Such a world would probably find it desirable, on humane and esthetic grounds, to check its growth far short of the numbers that could be supported by a world economy that continues to develop and apply scientific knowledge. To such a world, knowledge of the human gene pool, and of its potentialities for change, should be of paramount importance because, in the last analysis, man's destiny lies in his nature.

But today's most urgent problems are not yet those of a world of highly educated and prosperous populations. They are the problems of moving from worldwide poverty, hunger, and illiteracy to worldwide education and prosperity. To do so, we must survive the coming crisis of population growth with sufficient political and social coherence to permit the sensible application of our developing science. Unfortunately, crises divert attention from matters of the future to those of immediate relevance. Patently, many of the immediate problems are social, economic, or political, but it is to the biological aspects of the emergency that attention is here directed.

It is only necessary to note that: (1) much of the world is undernourished; (2) populations in the Americas south of the U.S., in Asia, and in Africa are growing at between 2.3 and 4 percent per year, i.e., they are doubling in from 17 to 30 years; and (3) agricultural production in some large areas is falling behind population growth. Production per acre has been increasing rapidly in the highly developed areas of the world, but in most underdeveloped nations gains in production have come primarily from the extension of cultivated acreage rather than from increased production per acre. Moreover, the constraints to the extension of acreage are becoming all too visible in many of the most densely settled parts of the world.

Food Production: The Short-term Problem. These facts suggest that: (1) there may be mass starvation on a tragic scale within this century unless there is a prompt and major rise in production; and therefore (2) there is urgent need for the application of already existing knowledge. Indeed, effective practical application of present scientific understanding could certainly suffice to manage the problems of food supply during the present century. Basic theory does not result in increased production without a great deal of scientific work on local soil and water, crop management, development of seed strains, animal husbandry, pest control, and, most importantly, fertilizer usage. Basic science gives us the principles and tells us how to go about learning to apply them, but it still does not indicate in precise local terms how to do the multitude of things that must be done. The emergency need in agriculture is for great increases in local applied work and in training for such work. The recent successes of the Rice Institute in the Philippines and in wheat production in Mexico are noble demonstrations that such efforts are both feasible and rewarding. Introduction of the new strains of rice and wheat they have developed has resulted in a startling increase in production in Pakistan, India, the Philippines, and Mexico—an increase which appears to have brought several years of surcease from the threat of famine in these countries. But this effort alone will not suffice without a concomitant endeavor to supply credit, manufacture fertilizer, ensure a water supply, build roads, and arrange for food and other commodity distribution. And none of the latter are meaningful unless the scientific basis for intensive local agriculture has been established.

Meanwhile it should not be thought that basic science has contributed all it can to food production. It will suffice to note that no new species of animal or plant has been adapted for human consumption as a major foodstuff in recorded history. We still have urgent need to provide fundamental designs for extremely intensive, very high-yield agriculture, to learn how indeed to take advantage of offshore opportunities for intensive "agriculture" of molluscs and, perhaps, of higher marine organisms, to breed wheat of more useful protein content, to find suitable alternatives to the dependence of man, globally, on just a few staple crops—rice, wheat, and corn. This dependence on only three cereal types offers the terrifying prospect of a worldwide pandemic of a virus to which no strain of one of these species might be resistant.

The fact that much of basic science is a product of a few nations and civilizations does not mean that the basic sciences cannot be learned, developed, and applied by other populations. Even though we have no means at present of comparing the intrinsic genetic endowments of different ethnic groups, it is clear that great reservoirs of trainable human genotypes exist in all of them. The shortage of brain power, in the world at large, that can be applied to the immediate problems of agricultural production is not due to biological limitations of genetic endowments in different human groups, but to the limitations of their education. Each area is potentially able to produce the numerous trained persons needed to explore and solve the specific problems which the region poses. Obviously, these problems are not restricted to agriculture. A corps of local scientific and engineering specialists is equally needed so that each population may share in the beneficial results of industrial and scientific technology, and American technical assistance should give high priority to assisting in the endeavor to train such specialists.

The immediate demands on the biosphere have been generated and exacerbated by rapid population growth which, particularly in the developing nations, is the consequence of the almost abrupt inauguration of public health and sanitation measures with drastic reduction of the death rate while the birth rate remained unchecked. Because no imaginable program of population control could restrain population growth significantly in the next decade, the emergency problem is to attain, as rapidly as possible, adequate levels of education and significant local programs in agriculture and related science and technology for the vast numbers of the human race. We are not optimistic that this can be achieved in time to avert disaster in the 1970's, but the attempt must be made. It is all too evident that the surplus agricultural productivity of a few developed nations—Canada, Australia, the United States—even if used to the full, can have little impact in this worsening situation. Moreover, population growth in these nations will, in time, require domestic utilization of their own production.

If this estimate of the situation is correct, the acute problem is not that of population size itself but of the speed of modernization and the extent to which the gains so realized are offset by the speed of population growth. The speed of modernization turns on many factors, on national and international allocation of resources for space, war, schools, and factories, *inter alia.* But basically it also depends, even at quite local levels, on the extent to which the growth of agricultural production can be made to exceed that of population. Investment in development can be made only after the current costs of growth have been met.

Population Control: The Long-term Problem. The long-term prospects for a truly human civilization depend in very large measure on whether humanity can, in time, succeed in moderating its fecundity. Only if this effort is successful and early can our progeny be offered the opportunity to relish the gift of life and to maximize their own human potential. The dimensions of the problem are dramatically evident in the remarkable diminution in the time required for doubling of the world population, as seen in Table 20-1.

This remarkable accelerated growth, largely the result of decreasing death rates due to simple public health and hygienic measures accompanied by

Table 20-1. Time Required to Double World Population.

World Population	Year	Time Required
250,000,000	1	
		1649
500,000,000	1650	
		200
1,000,000,000	1850	
		80
2,000,000,000	1930	
		45*
4,000,000,000	1975*	
		30*
8,000,000,000	2005*	

* Estimate.

commensurate increases in agricultural productivity, occurred first in Europe and the United States and is now operative also in many of the developing nations with startling consequences. Witness Brazil with a population of 52 million in 1950, 71 million in 1960, 83 million in 1966, and an estimated 240 million by 2000 or a 14-fold increase within the twentieth century!

Yet concern for population growth is not new. In *Politics,* Aristotle warned that ". . . neglect of an effective birth control policy is a never-failing source of poverty which, in turn, is the parent of revolution and crime" and he advocated that parents with excessive children practice abortion. He went unheeded through the following centuries as the Romans encouraged large families to man their wide-flung armies, the Judaeo-Christian ethic considered children as gifts of God, and St. Augustine stated the purpose of Christian marriage to be procreation, a view unmodified by the Reformation. Much earlier, Tertullian noted that "the scourges of pestilence, famine, wars and earthquake have come to be regarded as a blessing to crowded nations since they served to prune away the luxuriant growth of the human race." From time to time, advocates of population control appeared, most particularly Malthus who stated that, otherwise, population would always rise to the limits of food production capacity so that, necessarily there would always be hunger and poverty. (Ironically, Malthus rested his case on the history of eighteenth-century United States.) Unfortunately, his teaching was rejected both by the Christian ethic and by Marxism, which taught that overpopulation is merely a capitalist notion invented to justify the poverty of working-class peoples and is rectifiable by enhanced production and improved distribution rather than by birth control.

Malthusian predictions have largely been justified, although he foresaw neither the consequences of the introduction of agricultural technology nor the demographic consequences of simple hygienic measures. Today, these problems must be considered separately in global and local contexts. The food crisis of some developing nations, considered earlier, is patently urgent. Yet, worldwide, since about 1950 agricultural productivity has grown by about 3 percent annually while population increase has averaged less than 2 percent. Indeed, it is estimated that if worldwide per capita food consumption had held constant at 1955 levels, despite the population increase by 1975 there would have been a world surplus of 40 million tons of wheat and 75 million tons of rice. This will not occur because of both rising per capita food consumption and the controlled productivity practiced, in varying degree and kind, in the United States, Australia, New Zealand, Canada, France, and the Argentine. Meanwhile, the developing nations, caught up in the worldwide revolution of rising expectations, find themselves short of food and of capital for development.

Income for development can be generated by increased production and by decreased reproduction. Clearly, both are needed. Some inherently undesirable means to decrease the rate of population growth, e.g., war, famine, pestilence are all too evident. On the other hand, populations that have learned to reduce their fertility to the point where they enjoy good health and the longevity characteristic of the more developed nations, and whose growth amounts to only one percent per year should encounter no substantial difficulty in reaching a stationary position if that is clearly desirable. Only as that occurs can increased production of agriculture, extractive, and manufacturing industries be utilized for development and increase in the general standard of living. It may well be asked, however, how many countries can be expected to do this soon enough. Markedly increased agricultural productivity accompanied by population growth inevitably leads to rapid urbanization, frequently at a rate in excess of any prospect of gainful employment of the translocated individuals. Yet this process, at a moderate rate is imperative if a developing agrarian society is to acquire a sufficient urban population to sustain its growing industry, educational system, etc.

As we have indicated, if the oncoming food shortage crisis can be averted, known technology, if put into practice, can readily so enhance food production as to defer the world food problem almost indefinitely. It is the combination of new strains and application of fertilizer which has so remarkably increased agricultural yields in Europe, Japan, and the United States. In a general way, application of a ton of fertilizer nitrogen yields an increment in crop production equal to the basic yield of a 14-acre plot. Stated differently, there are about 3.5 billion acres of land presently under cultivation; application of $10 worth of fertilizer per acre would increase production by about 50 percent, i.e., for $35 billion per year or $10 per capita worldwide, world food production would rise by the equivalent of 1.7 billion acres of average land and a 50 percent increase in available food, per capita. Moreover, it has been calculated that if all land now in tillage were cultivated as in Holland, the world could support 60 billion people on a typical Dutch diet; if it were managed as in Japan, it could support about 90 billion people on a typical Japanese diet. And all of this apart from the realizable expectation of yet another agricultural revolution based on improved control of agriculture, growth of food yeast, bacteria, and algae, or synthetic foodstuffs based on petrochemicals. Approximately one acre is required to feed one man by efficient current agriculture—yet a one square yard tank growing algae can produce all of his caloric, protein, and vitamin needs! All of which is to say that measures to upgrade agricultural practice in the developing nations could forestall a Malthusian crisis for more than a half-century even at current rates of population growth. But with what consequences?

The problem of population growth involves much more than merely increasing agricultural production. The constraints to population size are all too visible even in the traditional self-sufficient agrarian society. Such societies have rarely been able to combine high population density with good health and relative freedom from poverty. But it is hard to specify the limits to the density of population that can be supported in health and prosperity by a highly educated population making sophisticated use of energy and raw materials, and continuing to develop both its basic science and technology.

There is reason to believe that, given the time and effort required to increase all forms of production sufficiently, this planet can sustain in relative abundance a total population considerably greater than the present. Although no data are available to establish what the maximum might be, it is patently very much larger than at present. Importantly, however, one can argue that the maximum possible is decidedly greater than the optimum. Clearly, even the present population suffices to populate the planet, at all times, with the diversified human talent required to contribute to progress on all human fronts—science, the arts, industry, government, etc. At some point, industry must forgo population growth as the underlying basis for economic expansion. Meanwhile, many of the most tragic ills of human existence find their origin in population growth. Hunger, pollution, crime, despoliation of the natural beauty of the planet, irreversible extermination of countless species of plants and animals, overlarge, dirty, overcrowded cities with their paradoxical loneliness, continual erosion of limited natural resources, and the seething unrest which creates the political instability that leads to international conflict and war, all derive from the unbridled growth of human populations. The fortunate nations are those which have, spontaneously rather than as a matter of national policy, achieved a low level of population growth or an exact equilibrium of the birth and death rates.

Accordingly, another set of important emergency problems of a biological nature are those relevant to a reduction of human fertility. In the long run birth rates must come down if death rates are to stay low, and in the short run, lower fertility would speed the process of modernization by widening the difference between the growth rates of population and of production. Reductions of the birth rate in the underdeveloped countries have an additional advantage. High birth rates produce high proportions of young people. In virtually every country with a birth rate of 40 or more per 1000 population, more than 40 percent of the total population is under age 15. Under these circumstances it becomes almost impossible for such a society to increase its working capital, to generate enough wealth to be used for school construction, higher education, improved housing, or industrial plants. In consequence, for example, the illiteracy rate must surely rise despite national determination to do otherwise.

In advanced countries with low birth rates, between 25 and 30 percent of the total population is under age 15. A reduction in birth rates brings down rates of growth and reduces the proportion in the ages of childhood dependence. Correspondingly, it increases the proportion of the population in the productive years of life.

Indeed, very high birth rates speed population growth in two ways: (1) they swell the entering stream of life; and (2) by creating young populations they cut the rate of depletion through death. Today, the lowest crude death rates (i.e., annual deaths per 1000 population uncorrected for age) are not found in the most highly developed countries. The world's lowest crude death rates are found in such places as Taiwan, Singapore, Puerto Rico, and Chile, where health protection is relatively good and a history of high birth rates has left a young population. In the long run, reductions in birth rates reduce growth both directly and indirectly by increasing the average age and, other things being equal, the death rate. Clearly, the possibilities of modernization would be greatly enhanced, globally, if rates of growth could be cut in 15 years from 3 percent to, say, 1 percent by reductions in birth rates. This would mean that populations now growing at rates that double their size in 23 years would come to a rate that would give them 69 years in which to absorb the increase, viz., the burden of natural increase in the newly developing countries would then be about that experienced by the United States in recent years.

Most societies and individuals desire to limit the size of families, but they are usually not content with a family size corresponding to zero growth of the population. Although, at the present stage of population growth, any reduction in family size is important, ultimately the mean family size will have to be limited to a replacement number. "Family planning" is not equivalent to population control. Family planning is the rational and deliberate spacing of children in the number desired by the parents. But that number is determined by cultural considerations, family income, and ego satisfaction in the developed nations, and by the economic utility of children in the underdeveloped nations. Accordingly, large families are the norm among the affluent and among the ignorant poor. Population control demands that families be limited to the replacement rate.

Nothing can do more to help obtain reductions of fertility than the development of more efficient, cheap, safe, reversible and acceptable methods of contraception. People will use even the best of methods only when they want to have fewer children. Historically, whereas strongly motivated couples have even utilized inadequate methods of contraception and resorted to abortion, weakly motivated populations must be enticed to use even the best possible methods. Today, readiness to accept contraception is widespread. More than half the population of the developing nations live under governments that have decided, as a matter of national policy, to foster the spread of family planning and limitation. The list includes most of the countries of Asia and a goodly number in Africa and Latin America. Most of these countries are developing educational programs to interest and inform their people, and service programs to give them supplies. Careful surveys of attitudes toward reproduction have been made in more than 20 countries. Virtually everywhere, the majority of women desire to limit their childbearing. This does not mean that they want only two or three children, but it does mean that they want to stop before their families get truly large. Moreover, where services and supplies are made available, women are beginning to seek them in large numbers. Taiwan, South Korea, Hong Kong, and Singapore have clearly reduced their birth rates through their family planning programs.

Today, in the developed nations, contraception has changed rapidly from use of the older, conventional methods to the combination steroid pill. In under-developed countries, new contraceptors are mainly using the plastic intrauterine device. Neither method is perfect, but both are spectacularly effective and successful compared with the conventional contraceptives, "rhythm" methods, etc. The availability of the cheap intrauterine device has encouraged governments of underdeveloped nations to build the organizations they require to spread family planning practices. With such organizations in being and operative, the next technological innovation can be introduced much more rapidly. It is because they have effective methods, hope for better ones, and the organizations to make use of them, that such countries as South Korea, Taiwan, India, and Pakistan now hope to halve their birth rates in 15 years. If they could do so, their long-run problems of modernization and economic development would be greatly simplified.

The world needs better methods than are now available. The pill and the intrauterine device represent major innovations because, temporally, they separate contraception from coitus. The intrauterine device is probably at a very early stage of development. An unacceptable fraction of all users spontaneously eject it, bleed, or suffer discomfort. On the other hand, apparently the majority of those who accept it, wear it without awareness and with very high effectiveness. Two to three years after acceptance, 50 percent or more of women continue to wear their devices. It is likely that better procedures, better materials, and better shapes will lead to a greatly improved experience. Clearly, it is imperative that appropriate, vigorous investigation be undertaken to solve the riddle of the mode of action of these devices and to ameliorate their occasional side effects.

Similarly, work is needed to reduce the side effects of steroid pills, to minimize their effects on lactation and on thromboembolic phenomena, to reduce their costs and to establish systematically and in sustained fashion the actual experience of those who take them, to reduce the frequency of subsequent multiple births, and, most importantly, to establish the biological consequences of long-term use with complete certainty. Work is going forward in a number of places with doses of progestins so small that their effects seem to be limited to the uterine level. Similarly, an effort to find means of replacing the oral route of administration with a depot injection, viz., an injection allowing a steadier rate of absorption and hence, smaller and longer-lasting doses, would be well repaid.

Meanwhile, as this research proceeds, we deplore statements decrying use of steroid pills on the ground of their manifest occasional untoward side effects. Since the death rate from such usage is clearly well below the death rate from pregnancy itself, these pills not only afford millions of families the opportunity for a richer, fuller life while checking the demographic explosion, on balance they also spare the lives of a significant number of mothers who would otherwise die of the complications of pregnancy.

It would be highly desirable, of course, to have a method that is, in effect, permanent until positive measures are taken to counteract the contraceptive. Children are often conceived as a consequence of careless contraceptive practice. Doubtless, birth rates would drop faster if there were a method in which carelessness meant failure to counteract a contraceptive. Clearly, however, such a development could pose serious problems of personal freedom unless the counteracting agent were freely available.

Only a beginning has been made in relevant basic research. Among other things, we need to know a great deal more about tubal events, including gamete transport, fertilization, and zygote physiology. The fields of neuro-endocrinology, immunological suppression of reproduction, blastocyst nidation, gonadotropin chemistry, and the mechanisms of sex hormone action urgently need development. An intensive program of basic research might produce important results which could facilitate population control. The fundamental knowledge, the techniques, and the requisite base of professional skill for such an effort are now beginning to appear.

In the long run, all practical results depend on basic research. But in the long run, unless birth rates are lowered rapidly, populations will become multiples of what they are today—unless death rates rise. In the past decade, applied research based on many preceding years of basic research made possible the contraceptive pills, the intrauterine devices, and, consequently, the beginnings of a birth rate decline in some developing areas as well as in developed nations. Further basic research is greatly needed to prepare for yet further advances, and it is the only pathway to completely new approaches in population control. Meanwhile, intensification and enlargement of applied research is an urgent necessity.

The United States and other developed nations find themselves in the embarrassing position of advocating that *other* nations increase their efforts at population control. Granted the validity of this position, viz., that it really does address itself to the self-interest of the affected nations, such a posture is not readily acceptable when the advice comes from a nation which has not itself adopted comparable internal policies. Since this country is in the fortunate position of enjoying a high economic level and a relatively low population growth rate, and while our total population is not yet excessive for our natural resources but is on the way to becoming so, the moment is opportune to examine our internal policies and alter these as seems appropriate.

Clearly, our relatively low rate of population increase reflects the fact that American parents have not been behaving in the manner seemingly encouraged by the national mores and laws. Is it not appropriate to reconsider laws which discourage abortion, forbid or make difficult distribution of birth control information and devices, which encourage large families by income tax forgiveness and by a rising scale of welfare payments? These derive from an earlier ethos when an expanding population was required to develop the national frontiers. They seem entirely inappropriate today.

Nor is the United States immune from the population explosion. Until recently our population growth has been dominated by the extremely low birth experience of the depression years and the subsequent war. But the children of the "baby boom" are just entering the child-bearing population. Thus, our female population in the age range 16-44 was 32 million in 1940, 34 million in 1950, and 36 million in 1960 but it will be 43 million in 1970 and 54 million in 1980. The potential for an extraordinary burst in population, unless checked, is evident in the very fact of the existence of this breeding population. The current rate of population growth, i.e., the excess of births over deaths, is about 2 million per year, yet it is estimated that about

500,000 babies per year are "unwanted." Surely, provision to the mothers of these unwanted babies of information, contraceptive materials or legal abortions would make for a happier society while reducing the societal burdens of population growth.

Moreover, it should be understood that the penalties for population expansion are far greater in an affluent society than in a marginal economy. This is already painfully evident in the United States. Rising per capita real income places decreasingly tolerable burdens upon the environment: vastly increased solid waste, nondegradable detergents, pesticides, containers and trash, more automobiles, thicker traffic, increased CO and CO_2 production, more smog, rapid erosion of fields for airports, highways, parking spaces, and suburbia, rapidly increased water usage for anything but drinking, viz., airconditioning, swimming pools, metal fabrication, and paper production plants, etc., while the same processes accelerate the depletion of all of our nonrenewable resources, e.g., oil, iron ore, copper ore, etc. Indeed, this is the lesson of Figure 20-1. Further, consider the seemingly impossible burden of coping with the demand for college education: college enrollments which were 6 million in 1965, will be 8 million in 1970, 10 million in 1975, and 12 million in 1980. The effort required to meet all of the expectations of this burgeoning population will be enormous—and will utilize yet more of our precious land and irreplacable resources. This is in clear contrast to the burden upon the environment generated by adding to the population of a developing nation more individuals whose mean income is but a few hundred dollars a year. Clearly, the national interest, and our individual interests would be well served by all measures which would damp the demographic explosion at home as well as abroad.

There is, however, one aspect in which population control and the health of the population are at odds. Population control would be furthered by encouraging late marriage, a principal factor for the low birthrate in Ireland. But the incidence of such congenital defects as Down's syndrome and cleft palate as well as of twinning rises with the age of the parents. Hence, the optimal situation would be that in which marriage occurs at a young age and a family of two or three children follows shortly thereafter. Success in such a program then requires the full cooperation of society and 20 to 25 years of uninterrupted, successful contraception. Without sterilization, statistically, this seems an unlikely prospect unless research can provide much simpler and more effective contraceptive methods than those presently available.

Guarding the Genetic Quality of Man

The human gene pool is the primary resource of mankind, today and tomorrow. The present gene pool is the culmination of 3 billion years of evolution and natural selection. The physical vigor, long life, and intellectual capacity of most humans reflect the fact that, historically, natural selection has minimized the incidence of genes which, when expressed in the homozygous phenotype (an individual with 2 identical genes for the trait in question) would result in serious physical or mental incapacity. However, advances in medicine in the last few decades have dramatically altered this situation. The "engineering" of human development so as to permit survival despite the handicap of such genetic endowment is called "euphenics" ("eu" = well, "phen" = appearance). By ensuring survival and, thus, permitting the reproduction of such homozygotes, medical practice has relaxed the selection against such genes.

For example, formerly the intellectual deficit of most phenylketonuric children was such that they were unable to reproduce; when raised from birth on a suitable phenylalanine-poor diet they will now, presumably, marry and have offspring. Instead of "extinction" of the genes responsible for the disease in the nonreproductive homozygote, this should lead to an increase in the frequency of these genes in future generations and consequently an increase in phenylketonurics. A similar situation obtains for all other genetic afflictions which can now be neutralized by various treatments. Consider pyloric stenosis, an abnormal constriction at the junction of the stomach and intestine which is a relatively common hereditary disease of the newborn, occurring in about 5 out of 1000 live male births and in 1 out of 1000 live female births. Formerly, most such infants died in very early life, but 50 years ago a surgical procedure was instituted which permits survival and normal health. The survival and later reproduction of these surgically treated children has resulted in the perpetuation of this genotype; among their offspring the frequency of infants with pyloric stenosis is about 50 times higher than in the general population. And these children, having been operated upon, will again later produce a surplus of their own affected kind. Thus, a continuous increase of the disease must be expected in successive generations. Similar considerations apply to galactosemia and fulminating juvenile diabetes, and the list must grow as clinical medicine learns to circumvent the consequences of many other genetic disorders. The extent of this problem is evident from the fact that, even now, 6 percent of all infants have detectable genetic defects of greater or lesser seriousness and all humans must be heterozygous (possessing two nonidentical genes, one from each parent, for a given trait) for at least a dozen or more disadvantageous genes.

The speed of accumulation of unfavorable genes in the population depends on many factors. Generally, it is a very slow process which, for centuries, will have no easily recognizable effects. Many a "bad" gene whose effects are overcome euphenically may be said to have lost its "badness," wholly or to a large degree, so that its accumulation no longer represents a serious biological load even though it may represent a considerable economic load.

Such accumulation may be contained by genetic counseling which leads some carriers of such genes to limit their families or even to refrain from having children. Genetic counseling can often assure worried persons that their fears of defective offspring are unjustified or exaggerated, but in some instances the predicted likelihood of severely abnormal offspring is high. Knowledge of the inheritance and the variability in expression of the numerous kinds of human defects accumulates steadily, and the outlook for improved foundations for counseling is favorable. It will be enormously enhanced as procedures are developed which might make possible positive recognition of those who are asymptomatic heterozygotes for specified undesirable genes. As medical euphenics becomes increasingly successful, it will become increasingly important that genetic counseling be universally practiced. Otherwise, in a few generations, the ethic which guides medical practice will have seriously damaged the heritage of countless previous generations. Having thwarted the historical process of natural selection against such disadvantageous genes, civilization must provide an acceptable substitute.

The possibility has been discussed that the great insights of molecular biology may make it possible, in the future, to replace specific undesirable genes in a person's cells with desirable ones brought in from the outside. However, many biologists think that the prospects for such "genetic surgery" are doubtful in the foreseeable future. Even if successful, this would probably simply be a more sophisticated euphenic technique. While there is some possibility that appropriate, desirable genes might be introduced into body cells, it seems unlikely that the new genes could be so inserted into appreciable numbers of germ cells.

The Opportunities

Biology and Medicine

It is in improved medical practice that advances in biological understanding make their most immediate impact on most people. As we have seen, biological and medical research are intimately intertwined; the fundamental discoveries which have found useful clinical application have been of such general character that they are best termed "biological," regardless of the institutional setting in which they are made. In our society, the benefits of such studies are to be found in innumerable individual events in medical practice from prenatal care through infancy, childhood, and adulthood to old age.

The prolongation of life expectancy at birth is one of the impressive over-all measures of the success of medicine. However, even in affluent societies this prolongation has primarily been due to a dramatic reduction, if not a near abolition, of infant mortality. Increases in life expectancy past the age of 45 have remained smaller although by no means negligible. Even medi-cally advanced countries still experience different life expectancies and in-fant mortalities, and it is likely that at least a major share of the differences is the result of social differentials. It is regrettable that infant mortality in the United States still exceeds that in more than a dozen other advanced nations. The major single contribution to our infant mortality is to be found among the economically and socially disadvantaged segments of our society, al-though it is also unacceptably high even in middle class families. The prob-lem then is not lack of knowledge but to provide prenatal and early pediatric care of the quality available to the rest of the population. See Table 20-2.

Table 20-2. Countries Reporting Twenty Lowest Infant Mortality Rates per 1000 Live Births, 1967

Rank	Country	Infant Mortality	Rank	Country	Infant Mortality
1	Gibraltar	11.8	11	Australia	18.2
2	Sweden	12.6	12	United Kingdom	18.8
3	Japan	13.3	13	Luxemburg	20.4
4	Iceland	13.7	14	East Germany	21.2
5	Netherlands	14.7	15	United States	22.1
6	Finland	15.0	16	Canada	23.1
7	Norway	16.8	17	West Germany	23.5
8	Denmark	16.9	18	Belgium	23.7
9	France	17.1	19	Czechoslovakia	23.7
10	New Zealand	17.7	20	Ireland	24.4
			21	Israel	25.3

Sources: United Nations, *Monthly Bulletin of Statistics* (October 1968), *Population and Vital Statistics Report* (July 1, 1968), *Demographic Yearbook* (1967).

Molecular Diseases. Future advances in the control of disease will come from better epidemiological knowledge, improved control of the environment, and deeper understanding of the regulation of life processes. Many of these advances will be based on applications of the fundamental information provided in recent years by molecular biology. With sufficient understanding will come a more powerful armamentarium for chemotherapy of endocrine disorders and cancer, treatment of autoimmune diseases, prevention of the degenerative disorders of the circulatory system, and therapy for metabolic disorders. There seems to be no reason why deposition of lipids in the great blood vessels, atherosclerosis, should be a necessary concomitant of human life. Research directed at rational prevention of this process by simple means should markedly reduce or delay the incidence of coronary artery disease, aneurysms of the great vessels, and stroke. Death will still come to all, but the quality of adult life should be markedly enhanced as the onset of debilitating disease is delayed into the latter years of a prolonged life. Life should not only be longer, but ever more enjoyable and free of the ravages of ill health, in consequence of increasingly effective preventive and therapeutic measures.

It is yet too soon to engage in speculation concerning future progress in prevention of or therapy for the major psychoses. Only the success of tranquilizers and mood-elevating drugs offers any basis for hope. Until the underlying basis for schizophrenia and the other psychoses is understood, it will not be clear whether there are fruitful chemical or surgical approaches to therapy. This should not be true of peripheral neurologic diseases. Even now, there are hopeful bits of progress in understanding the demyelinating disorders and there has just appeared a drug which seems quite specific for relief of Parkinson's disease. Insofar as diseases have specific molecular etiology, there is hope for specific molecular therapy or prevention.

Infectious diseases. Yet another major problem, concerning which assessment remains difficult, is the panorama of virus disease. Man lives in equilibrium with large numbers of each of what appears to be an ever increasing number of different viruses. Our chief protection against them remains our own intrinsic biology, particularly our immune mechanisms. The strategy appropriate to assisting the defense against an established infection is unclear. A truly effective synthetic substitute for the naturally occurring "interferon" would probably be a most useful drug. Hope in this direction is afforded by the demonstration that synthetic, double-stranded RNA is an effective stimulus to interferon release and can protect mice against otherwise lethal inoculations of the virus that causes hoof-and-mouth disease. Most drugs which interfere with replication of viral DNA or RNA must also seriously affect our own duplicating cells, as do most chemicals which interfere with protein synthesis. However, this approach is not necessarily hopeless because synthesis of viral nucleic acids within the host cell is accomplished by enzymes synthesized by the host cell machinery under the control of the infecting viral nucleic acid; not by the original host cell enzymes. A few antibiotics have already been found to block one or another of these virally induced processes without damage to the host cell. Increased understanding of the genetic machinery and exploration of drugs which interfere with its operation or create a temporary diversion, is our greatest hope of finding a rational basis for antiviral therapy, although there is, as yet, nothing to assure the prospect of success.

The most promising avenues of approach to the problem of cancer derive from the fact that a variety of neoplastic lesions, in experimental animals, are definitely associated with the presence in affected tissues of specific viruses. Only suggestive evidence presently links any tumor of man with similar viruses. It is thus apparent that there is more than one "cause" of cancer, but, to the extent that human neoplasia may have a viral etiology, the route to successful cancer chemotherapy may prove to have much in common with the search for antiviral therapy generally. Indeed, it is conceivable that current procedures which enjoy some measure of success, e.g., radiation to solid tumors, antifolic acid drugs, and cytosine arabinoside for treatment of leukemias, actually operate by their effects on viral reproduction rather than by limiting cell division itself. In any case, it is imperative that studies designed to establish whether human tumors are, in effect, manifestations of infection with the equivalent of an otherwise silent, "temperate lysogenic virus" should be prosecuted with utmost vigor.

Morbidity and mortality from bacterial infections have been dramatically reduced by the availability of antibiotics. But this battle is never won. Resistant strains of almost every bacterial pathogen have repeatedly appeared. Each must be met with yet another antibiotic or combination thereof and the search for new, more effective antibiotics, largely conducted by the pharmaceutical industry, must be unceasing. No episode in the Viet Nam war is more dramatic, and certainly none more gratifying, than the successful development of therapy for a virulent, highly lethal form of malaria carried by the *A. falciparum* mosquito based on a combination of two drugs which affect two different aspects of the life cycle of the malarial plasmodium. There remain many infectious disorders, particularly in the tropics, such as schistosomiasis, for which no adequate drug is available. Appropriate agents must be sought, based on detailed understanding of the unique metabolism and life cycles of these organisms. If historical precedent is valid, there is good reason to be sanguine concerning the prospects in these regards, but the attack must be intensive and relentless.

Transplantation and Artificial Organs. Important advances will surely come from application of technology to deficiencies in the function of whole organs. An artificial lung, external to the body, can be used to replace the physical action of the muscles necessary for breathing; an artificial kidney can serve as a chemical device for removing metabolic products from the blood when the original excretory organs cannot perform that function. Artificial blood vessels made of synthetic tubing can serve as substitutes for defective natural vessels, and external artificial hearts can, at least for some hours, take over the pumping function of the inborn organ. And there is every reason to believe that each of these devices can be improved markedly in the future. But it should be emphasized that, while each of these is a triumph of bioengineering and invaluable to those who require them, each also represents a failure of biological research to have found a solution to the underlying biological problem.

If artificial structures are less adequate than natural ones, transplantation of organs from one person, alive or after death, to another offers another avenue to saving of life. Successful transplantation requires mitigation or abolition of the usual incompatibility of the transplanted tissue of the donor with the immune mechanisms of the host which otherwise results in rejection of the transplant as well as undesirable systematic reactions in the host. Experiments with chickens, mice, and cultured human blood cells as well as the heroic measures used in successful human heart and kidney transplants indicate that such antagonistic effects can be minimized. There is a limited number of tissue types, in the sense of serving as antigens, which elicit production of antibodies which then react with and damage the transplant. Although this number is large compared with classical blood types, it is small enough to permit the development of reliable typing procedures so that donor and recipient may be matched reasonably closely. In addition, a growing number of drugs is available to depress the production of antibodies. A combination of these procedures should significantly improve future management of such patients. It will be clear, however, that this approach, while dramatic in the extreme, is of limited value. It is inconceivable that hundreds of thousands of such operations can or should be performed annually. For coronary artery disease, prevention and early therapy of atherosclerosis must surely be the more fruitful long-term approach. Moreover, a useful mechanical heart, responsive to body needs, as a replacement for a seriously defective heart offers more promise than does homotransplantation for the medium term while avoiding the serious ethical problems occasioned by the latter procedure. Nevertheless, ever improving ability to perform and manage transplantation should be of continuing value in some endocrine diseases, in nephritis, and an occasional heart patient.

These insights and techniques are capable of prolonging life beyond the normal span but they create great new difficulties. Millions of individuals would profit from the transplantation of organs or from the use of "spare parts," but for years the supply of these and of the medical teams required for their installation will be inadequate to fill the demand. The ethical conflicts which the physician faces are crushing when he is forced to decide who is to benefit and who is to be denied vital help. Currently the occasions for such decisions are still rare since the numbers of available natural organs or substitute mechanical "organs" are so limited. In the future, yet other new life-saving devices will be invented, and the problems of assigning them to specific patients while withholding them from others will increase in frequency. Even if such devices could be made available in large numbers, the cost of keeping a small fraction of the population alive by these means may be so high a fraction of the gross national product as to compete seriously with other needs for the well-being of the population.

The Ethics of Terminal Medical Care. Another difficulty goes even deeper. Relatively little progress has been made in prolonging the adequate functioning of the human brain. The perpetuation of the physical workings of many parts of the body has not been accompanied by a perpetuation of its normal mental aspects. The death of individual neurons in the central nervous system is an attribute of the "normal aging process" and brain damage occurs not infrequently in consequence of trauma or illness. Here lies a great challenge for basic research and the beneficial application of the insights to be hoped for. Some of the best minds among biologists, psychologists, and physical scientists have recently turned their efforts to neurophysiology and brain function. Their studies should help to understand the riddle of the physical basis of the mind while helping also to discover the basis for procedures for alleviating the tragic situation of keeping the body alive without the full mental attributes which characterize a normal person. One may hope for progress in prolonging the physical and mental health of the aged, but then the problem of disharmonious functioning will simply be displaced to the end period of a more extended life span. Biology, the science of life, has to be complemented by new insights into the biology of death. The application of such insights will intensify concern with questions which already demand answers. Is society justified in keeping the aged alive when those mental functions which distinguish human beings from vegetating bodies have ceased? Where is the limit of anguish and material burden which the relatives of such aged persons and society at large can bear, a problem which is increasing in frequency and severity?

Research in aging involves the whole range of biological phenomena, from a study of the molecular changes of such substances as the collagen in our connective tissues and bones to the study of the most complex functioning of the central nervous system with its basis for consciousness, learning, reasoning, memory and other psychological attributes. It is imperative that such research be prosecuted as vigorously as possible. It should be clear, however, that there are no indications, as yet, that the aging process can be delayed, or mitigated, except in a most limited way. Support of the aged cannot be considered separately from economic and demographic facts. The success enjoyed by other aspects of medicine places in society ever larger numbers of aged, nonproductive individuals. Some continue to enjoy life but to some life is a burden. The cost and effort to provide care for this group become an increasingly large fraction of total goods and services. A highly advanced civilization will have to find an appropriate solution to this problem. Meanwhile, the need for support of research which will benefit the health of the newborn and of young productive people in general competes for the personnel and material resources required for research on aging. The need for dedicating large-scale support to children and adolescents may limit the effort society can devote to keeping the aged alive beyond a reasonable state.

Moreover, similar considerations must also apply to the dedication of resources to the care of nonproductive individuals as compared with that of potentially productive persons. Viral diseases of childhood, congenital malformations, hereditary disease, leukemias of childhood, endocrine dyscrasias, demyelinating diseases which strike young mothers, trauma, accidents, etc., all appear more worthy of attention than do the afflictions of advanced age. But these are harsh decisions and should not be made in an absolute manner. Our nation has the resources and can afford attack on the entire front. Moreover, as we have already noted, research cannot be forced. Alert clinical investigators in sufficient numbers should be poised to apply new understanding flowing from basic research to alleviation of the human condition as opportunity affords, avoiding feckless attempts to apply the inapplicable.

Genetic Diseases. The main illnesses of man have changed greatly in importance during the last hundred years. Infectious diseases have been combated effectively as their biological nature became clarified. For example, malaria was recognized as being caused by mosquito-borne protozoa, tuberculosis by bacteria, and influenza by viruses. Sulfa drugs and the antibiotics were found to kill the infectious agents without damaging the host. Other diseases, like rickets, pellagra, and scurvy, were shown to be caused not by the presence of an abnormal agent but by the absence of normally required substances, the vitamins. Improved nutrition in the light of this knowledge has greatly reduced the incidence of such deficiency diseases in the developed nations. However, "kwashiorkor," the consequence of protein deficiency, and xerophthalmia, due to deficiency of vitamin A, afflict tens of millions of the young in the tropical and subtropical countries around the globe. Resolution of this problem does not require further understanding of human biology; it requires a vast effort to upgrade education, agricultural practice, and the economies of these nations.

Increasingly, diseases which plague man are "inborn errors" which, as the effects of abnormal genotypes, lead to gross congenital malformations or to subtle derangements of metabolism. Many of these inborn errors are now understood in biochemical terms. Take the example which we considered earlier, phenylketonuria, a rare but serious inherited condition in which a specific enzyme, formed in the liver of normal persons, is not synthesized in the livers of affected individuals. A single gene, present in normals and absent or present in a defective mutant form in phenylketonurics, is responsible for the difference. The result of the absence of the enzyme is accumulation of the amino acid, phenylalanine, which normally is transformed by the enzyme into some other substance. This accumulation results in brain damage expressing itself in mental defect. The presence of this genetic defect can be discovered soon after birth by the presence of an abnormal derivative of phenylalanine in the urine or by an excess of phenylalanine in the blood. It took twenty years to unravel the biochemistry and genetics of the disease. Only then did it become possible to devise a treatment for it. Phenylalanine, a constituent of proteins, is essential in our diet. If, beginning in early infancy, a phenylketonuric individual is given a special diet very low in phenylalanine, development may proceed in improved fashion and the mental abilities of the child may approach normality.

It is hardly more than ten years since phenylketonuria has been treated this way and the last word has not yet been said about the real degree of success. Nevertheless, phenylketonuria is an example of the modern attack on genetic disease. Although the defective gene itself which is responsible for the absence of the enzyme cannot be "cured," its effect can be circumvented in greater or lesser degree. In diabetes, a disease with a complex genetic basis involving more than one gene, the defect is overcome to a considerable extent by furnishing the body with insulin from the outside. In galactosemia, the ingestion of milk sugar generates a problem, evident as stunted physical and mental growth and cataracts. Avoidance of milk and use of a synthetic formula containing cane sugar is all that is required. Or, in a congenital malformation such as cleft lip and palate, plastic surgery can not only save the life of severely affected infants but also produce an esthetically acceptable appearance. Clearly, a euphenic solution has to be discovered separately for each untoward genetic effect. Only a few such solutions have been found and further search will be an important area of biological effort. There is reason to expect that future work will extend the range of euphenics to many errors which are presently beyond repair. In turn this will engender the serious problem, considered earlier, of protecting the gene pool.

One special class of genetic disorder warrants specific comment. A variety of serious disorders is the expression of a deranged chromosomal pattern, broken chromosomes, or an extra chromosome (trisomy), which can now be detected during uterine life or at birth. The survival of such an infant is an emotional and economic burden to its parents and a drain on the society which must support and maintain it in an institution for its entire life.

Regeneration. After the first few years of life, accidents are a leading cause of death. Even more frequent are damaging accidents which maim or cripple. Whereas human amputees are doomed to empty sleeves or trouser legs, some lower forms—the lobster or newt—can perform prodigious feats of regeneration, replacing entire limbs. There are few leads to indicate the underlying basis for this ability in a variety of species as compared to man's incapacity. But it would seem that a determined effort in this regard is certainly warranted. The boon to humanity would be huge, indeed, were it to find any success.

Early Environmental Influences

Inadequate environments may lead to defects in genetically adequate persons whereas an appropriate environment may minimize the consequences of genetic defectiveness. Recently, much attention has centered on the effects of early environmental influences.

As commonly used, "early influences" denotes the conditioning of behavior by all the experiences of very early life. Early experiences, however, do more than condition behavioral patterns, they also profoundly and lastingly affect many biological characteristics of the adult. Events during the prenatal and early postnatal period condition the initial growth rate, maximum adult size, efficiency in utilization of food, resistance to malnutrition, to infection, and to other forms of stress.

Early influences affect some of the most obvious characteristics of human populations. Throughout the past century, for example, there has been a constant trend toward greater size and earlier sexual maturity of children. This phenomenon was first detected in the United States, then in other Western countries; it is now particularly striking in Japan and in other areas that have adopted Western ways of life. Evidence for increased growth is provided by the greater heights and weights of children at each year of age, by the faster growth rates during adolescence for both boys and girls, and by earlier onset of the menses.

Early nutritional influences, exaggerated by infection, can also affect later growth, mental ability, and general health in a deleterious manner. This is readily documented in the underprivileged areas of the world; very high infant mortality, slow growth during childhood and adolescence, with physical and mental lethargy continuing throughout life are among the pathological manifestations commonly observed in all seriously deprived social groups. These disorders are not racially determined. For example, they are found alike among the deprived Indians of Central America and among the populations of European origin who share the Indians' ways of life. In contrast, these manifestations are rare among both groups when born and raised in social and economic environments similar to those now prevailing in the prosperous communities of the United States and Europe. And there is every reason to believe that similar influences are at work among the urban and rural disadvantaged sector of American society, creating individual handicaps which can never be overcome.

The most important effects of the environment are those experienced during very early childhood, or the last trimester of fetal life. Most importantly, when environmental phenomena act adversely on the human organism in early life, their anatomical, physiological, and psychological effects are to a large extent irreversible; the fact that the various tissues and organs develop at different rates accounts for the existence of several "critical" periods in giving complete or partial irreversibility to responses that the developing organism makes to environmental forces. In the human species, the critical periods for the development of various mental capacities probably occur before the age of 6 to 8, and, most critically during the first year, a phenomenon of great relevance to the determination of "intelligence" in different socioeconomic and ethnic groups. Effects of the environment are much more likely to be reversible when experienced after the end of differentiation and development.

Virtually all effects of prenatal and early postnatal influences so far recognized in human populations occur also in other animal species. A large variety of stimuli, acting on the pregnant animal during gestation or on the young shortly after birth, affect diverse phenotypic expressions throughout adult life. Exposure to toxic agents, malnutrition, undernutrition or overnutrition, overt or subclinical infections, emotional disturbances of the mother or of the young, crowding, isolation, and other forms of social deprivation are some of the variables that have been used to design experimental models for the study of early influences. These influences have been studied with regard to their effects on anatomical structures, physiological characteristics, metabolic activities, behavioral patterns, and learning ability in adult life. In all cases "critical periods" have been recognized, differing as to initiation and duration depending upon the nature of the early influence and of the effect studied.

Nevertheless, the body of knowledge concerning the effects of early influences is superficial and episodic. Even the phenomena that have been most extensively studied—such as imprinting, the fixation during a critical period of a young animal's life of a stimulus which invariably elicits a particular response—are poorly understood albeit highly reproducible in their details. In the absence of broad scientific generalizations, it is not possible to extrapolate from one animal species to another, let alone to man. Yet there is no doubt that very early influences are of great importance in human life as recognized by the earliest psychiatrists and repeatedly documented since. Knowledge of these potentialities points to the safest and most effective way of affecting the mental as well as the physical development of man. At the same time, if improperly exploited by an authoritarian government, they could be of enormous danger to society.

Future studies of the effects of early influences should be conducted at several different levels.

1. Epidemiological observations in man, taking advantage of the fact that different human societies exhibit a wide range of customs with regard to gestation, parturition, lactation, physical and behavioral management during the early postnatal period. These differences in social patterns can be considered as experiments on man, performed without awareness of their consequences, demanding careful description and analysis.

2. Development and refinement of experimental models in various animal species. To yield the greatest scientific rewards, these models should use laboratory animals of known genetic and experiential history, observed throughout their life spans and, preferably, for several successive generations. Such longitudinal studies will require appropriate animal quarters, extensive facilities for recording and retrieving information, and, possibly, a new type of scientific organization.

3. Detailed analysis of the mechanisms through which early influences exert their lasting effect.

The Delivery of Medical Care

We cannot leave the subject of the future of medicine without noting that a substantial fraction of American society, the urban and rural disadvantaged, today lack access to medical care of the quality available to their more privileged fellow citizens. Many may be permanently limited by the experiences of very early life. Chronic illness, excess rates of infant and maternal mortality, and unnecessarily foreshortened life spans are their lot. Humane considerations, loss of potential productivity, and the heavy burden upon the rest of society all argue for early amelioration of these circumstances. No agency of our society has either the knowledge or the means to do so. Hence, we urge the organization and implementation of a series of substantial field trials addressed to the design of an appropriate system of medical care for this segment of society.

Controlled Sex Determination

More than a half-century has passed since it was learned that a man produces two kinds of sperm cells in about equal numbers. In addition to 22
chromosomes which are visibly alike in all sperm, half the nuclei possess the
relatively large X chromosome and half the small Y chromosome. In conception, X-bearing sperm are female-determining, Y-bearing sperm male
determining. It may be possible to separate the two kinds of sperm by biological or purely physical methods such as differential centrifugation. Admittedly, no success has been attained yet, in spite of some promising leads.
If success comes, insemination with the X or Y fraction of semen would
then assure control of the sex of the offspring. Application to animal
breeding could be of considerable economic importance as in the production of dairy cattle. If applied to man, subtle psychological changes in the
population might be expected. It is likely that no great deviation from a
1:1 sex ratio would result since most parents of more than one child seem
to desire children of both sexes. The sequence of sexes in a family may,
however, change considerably. Instead of the random sequence of boys and
girls, the majority of firstborn might be boys and that of secondborn girls.
Since position in the birth order has an effect on both physical and personality traits of the developing offspring, the consequences of the firstborns
being all boys and secondborns all girls might well be reflected in behavioral
shifts of the population. If widely available, this could also serve as an adjunct to programs of population control by assuring offspring of the desired sexes to all families.

An alternative method for deliberate choice of the sex of offspring is
technically feasible even now, albeit less attractive. Relatively simple surgical procedures permit determination of the sex of the young fetus. A
family which desires to limit its size should be permitted the option of such
inspection and, having one boy, for example, abort the next fetus if it is
not a girl.

Differential Fertility

From time to time serious questions are raised about the long-range biological and social effects of differential fertility* on the characteristics of populations. These questions arise because there is generally an inverse relation
between fertility and socioeconomic status, measured in terms of occupational status, education, or income, and because there are differences in the
fertility of the major "races" of man. There are also substantial differences
in the fertility of the major religious groups. Maximum fertility is found
among Moslems, with Hindus and Buddhists next. Christians as a group
have lower fertility, and, among Christians in the United States, Catholics

have higher fertility than Protestants. In worldwide terms, however, Catholics run the gamut from very low fertility, e.g., in North Italy, to the highest fertility in the world in some parts of Latin America. In general, Jews exhibit the lowest fertility of any of the world's major religious groups.

A few sweeping propositions can be ventured.

1. Many data are available descriptive of the differences in the fertility of broad socioeconomic, racial, and regional groups, but little is known about the significance of these differences for either the social or the biological heritage.

2. In biological terms, it is probable that differences in reproductive performances among individuals of varying characteristics within all groups are much more important than differences in the average performance between the highly heterogeneous social groupings for which data are readily available.

3. In the developed world, as birth rates have declined since the mid-nineteenth century, the inverse relation between socioeconomic status and fertility first become stronger and then weakened. The small-family pattern has tended to occur first in the urban upper classes, and only later to spread throughout society. As governments in the newly developing countries mount national programs to spread the practice of family planning, it is likely that the trend in the lower social strata of the populations will follow those of the upper strata more closely.

4. In the white population of the United States the "class" differences narrowed substantially with the postwar rise of the birth rate, which was more pronounced in the urban and upper-class groups than in the rural and lower economic strata. The inverse relation remains, however, partly because of an earlier age at marriage in the lower economic groups. It is probable that much of the higher fertility of the lower status and income groups would disappear if contraceptive information and services were made readily available.

5. In the United States, the fertility of Negroes exceeds that of the white population mainly as a correlate of their lower educational, economic, and social status. When similar educational, income and occupational groups are compared, the differences are greatly reduced and even reversed.

From a genetic viewpoint differences in fertility among groups of people are important only when these groups differ in their genetic endowments. From the societal standpoint only those genetic differences count which bear on the intellectual, behavioral, and social attributes characteristic of man.

---

* In this context, the word "fertility" is employed in its demographic usage, indicating the number of offspring produced per 1000 of population, and not in the sense of the opposite to sterility.

Selection and the Variability of Man

Even without scientific knowledge of genetics, man created a great variety of genetically different strains of domesticated animals and plants by selecting for desired types and breeding. The wild ancestors of cattle, dogs, chickens, wheat, and corn, for example, appeared rather uniform. Nevertheless, close inbreeding has shown that a great amount of concealed genetic variation was present beneath the apparent uniformity—variation which enabled man to select for traits which appeared desirable. Such selection led to the establishment of cattle specialized for milk or for meat production, the astonishing manifoldness of races in dogs, and chickens bred for high egg laying or for high meat yield. At the same time, selection led to disease resistance, heat tolerance and other physiological states. Plant strains were selected for adaptation to many climatic and soil conditions, as well as for yields which surpass by far those attained in the wild state.

But, in man, selection occurred without conscious direction. Different groups of mankind differ from one another in many ways; the significance of most of these differences is unknown or only incompletely understood. Why do the average body sizes of populations vary from the pygmies of Africa to the tall Watusi of the same continent, from the shorter southern Mediterraneans to the taller Scots? Why do the facial features of Orientals differ from those of the Caucasians? It is possible that some of these differences arose by the chance sampling of genetic types in the distant past, followed by long periods of physical, hence genetic, isolation. Other differences have been presumed to be the result of natural selection. Dark pigmentation of the skin is an asset in the tropics where it protects the tissues against excess ultraviolet radiation. Light pigmentation is an asset in northern regions where enough ultraviolet light must penetrate the surface to transform dihydrocholesterol into vitamin D. Long limbs serve as radiators of heat in desert peoples while short extremities conserve body heat in arctic climates. What is useful, natural selection preserves, and what is of negative value, it rejects.

While it is obvious that the racial groups of mankind differ from one another in specific ways, the multitude of differences in facial features, body build, height, and other physical as well as mental traits readily indicate the great heterogeneity of each major population group. Indeed, the extensive overlap of these groups with respect to many genetically determined traits is as impressive as the differences which distinguish between the groups. Moreover the polymorphic nature of any human group—and that of every other species studied intensely, e.g., cattle, chickens, flies—has become dramatically clear in recent years. Every human group contains a great variety of genes for alternative blood substances, serum proteins, hemoglobin, and enzymes; and new polymorphisms are constantly added to our knowledge. Thus, in every population there are people belonging to blood group M, others to N and still others to MN. Why should there be a variety of genes determining these properties instead of a single type best fitted to survival and therefore having become fixed by natural selection? What is the biological and sociological significance of polymorphism? The inability to answer these questions for most, if not all, human polymorphisms indicates fundamental gaps in our understanding of the genetics of human populations. There must exist selective forces which operate to retain variety of genes rather than to eliminate all but one of each kind. How these forces act specifically, so as to enhance survival of a gene under certain genetic or environmental circumstances and to decrease its survival under other circumstances, is unclear and will have to be established in each individual case. If we do not know how we became extensively polymorphic in the past or how we retain this polymorphism at present, we cannot expect to predict the genetic future.

The complexity of selective forces is such that to gain the necessary understanding there are required longitudinal studies, from birth to death, of exceedingly large cohorts; analysis of the data will require the use of powerful computers. The biological insights to be so gained should elucidate the causes of the great load of biological losses in the form of spontane-- ous abortions, stillbirths, deaths before the end of the reproduction period, reduced fertilities, and infertility.

Notwithstanding the complexity of genetic population dynamics, gross interference with natural conditions is clearly possible. It would not take many generations to breed Caucasians whose average adult body size is four feet or average Japanese of six feet. We could breed for obesity or leanness, blue eyes or black, wavy or wiry hair, and any one of the obvious physical attributes in which human beings vary. Presumably, we could also breed for mental performance, for special properties like spatial perception or verbal capacity, perhaps even for cooperativeness or disruptive behavior, even, conceivably, for high scores in intelligence tests. Most of these traits vary not only genetically but also under the influence of environmental factors, as, for example, size and weight with food, or mental scores with impressed social attitudes and educational opportunities. This, however, does not negate genetic components in the determination of the variety of traits. The "heritability" of a trait, which is a measure of the part which genes play in the observed variability of the trait, may be large or small. Although more research with respect to heritability of human traits is needed, it is abundantly clear that selection could be effective even with traits of quite low heritability.

Man, although potentially able to select his own genetic constitution, has not yet made use of this power. Selection is a harsh process. To make speedy progress, reproduction should be limited primarily to those who possess genotypes for the desired traits. But who will decide what is desirable? How much genotypic and phenotypic variability would be optimal in the human society? Who would dare to prohibit procreation to a majority of men and women, limiting this activity only to an elite group? And to whom would society entrust such decisions? May we expect changes in attitudes of whole societies so that they would accept the self-control of human evolution at the cost of forgoing the private decisions of most people to propagate themselves in their own children? It is extremely unlikely that such changes in attitudes will come soon. The future of man, however, may well extend over incomprehensibly long times, long enough not only to ponder these possibilities but also to explore them in actuality.

In order to overcome some of the objections to all-out self-selection by man, the late H. J. Muller advocated partial selection for the betterment of mankind. Muller proposed deep-freeze storage of the sperm of the most distinguished men. Such storage was to extend over a long period, perhaps decades after the death of the sperm donors, in order to give perspective to the judgment of their being unusually distinguished. The sperm of those who withstood the test of time were then to be made available to married couples. The wife and the donor would become biological parents while the husband would, like an adoptive parent, influence the child by his personal attributes. This scheme has a low genetic efficiency as compared with procedures in animal breeding. Its emotional appeal too is limited. Yet its control over man's genetic future, granting its limitations, would be accomplished by methods which leave room for free choice. Moreover, the procedure is already employed in numerous cases of infertility of a husband, without, however, using the opportunity to choose unusually distinguished sperm donors. Careful selection of the mothers by an appropriate agency and subsequent inbreeding might, however, accomplish the goal of a "superior" breed of man exhibiting the criteria chosen, but this was not essential to Muller's suggestion since the loss of free choice diminishes the social acceptability of the scheme.

A much more efficient and a most revolutionary way of selecting for specific human genotypes has been suggested on the basis of experiments with frogs and other amphibians—experiments whose original purpose had nothing to do with plans for genetic selection. It is possible to remove the haploid nucleus (half the adult member of chromosomes) of a frog egg before fertilization, and, instead of fertilizing it with sperm, implant the diploid nucleus (a complete nucleus with a double set of chromosomes, one from each parent) of a body cell from a frog embryo. Such an egg can develop into a normal frog. It has the same genetic constitution as the frog embryo whose body cell provided the transplanted nucleus. If the method of nuclear transplantation with subsequent full development should become successful utilizing the nuclei of body cells of adult individuals, and if it could be applied to man, a most powerful means of controlling the genetic constitution of future generations would become available. Since the nucleus of a body cell retains the totality of one's genes, a child produced by an enucleated egg which had been supplied with the nucleus of an adult body cell would, genetically, be an identical twin of the donor of that body cell. Moreover, any desired number of genetic twins could be produced. It would require the collection of unfertilized eggs from the oviducts of many women, removal of the egg nuclei, and replacement by the nuclei of body cells of the chosen man or woman. This would be followed by return of the eggs to the uteri of women who then would undergo normal pregnancies. In this way one could produce multiple identical copies of any person judged admirable.

Technically, it is still a long way from the use of frog eggs to those of humans, but what can be done in frogs today will surely be possible in man tomorrow. The biological problem now is primarily one of skill and development of detailed procedures. The next step would probably be the extension of the techniques from amphibians to laboratory mammals. Once successful in mice or rabbits there could be practical applications to animal breeding. Prize bulls or cows could be perpetuated by identical "offspring" derived from their body cells. From thence, technically, the steps toward potential human use would not be difficult, and if there were a strong wish to make such potentialities a reality, it could probably be accomplished within a few decades. At this time, there is need to ponder the personal and social implications of this biologically possible procedure. Powerful social forces would as surely resist adoption of such practice as they would a deliberately undertaken breeding program with selected human beings. At the present moment of extremely dangerous population growth, social pressures are best directed to lower reproduction, in general, without qualitative considerations. But one day, when populations are stable, world peace is the norm, and man's social and political institutions are sufficiently mature to assure that biological understanding will not be utilized to perpetuate injustice or strengthen dictatorship but, rather, to expand human potential, man will be free to guide his own evolutionary destiny.

There is no doubt that much of the seeming variability of mental, behavioral, and social traits can be accounted for by graded differences in nongenetic factors such as wealth and poverty, intellectual stimulation and its absence, or environmental encouragement and discouragement as well as malnutrition in early life. A major task before mankind is to see that these nongenetic factors are adjusted so that each individual realizes his genetic potential to the fullest. At the same time, however, while the performance of unchanged genotypes may be improved in this way, intensive studies of the existing genetic variability should make possible the design of realistic blueprints for the control of man's biological makeup. These plans will rest on a future deeper understanding of the "gene pool," the genic content of populations quite apart from its actual existence in living individuals.

In abstract terms, control of the genetic future of man consists of manipulation of the gene pool. In concrete terms such manipulation is accomplished by specified reproductive patterns of individuals. Although the hypothetical production of multiple identical copies discussed above may become technically feasible, there can be no certainty that a given genotype, successful under one set of conditions, would be equally successful under different circumstances. The future of man is more likely to be rich and exciting, to progress to greater possibilities, by exploring the variety of the gene pool than by standardizing on some uniform *Homo sapiens*. And although it might be feasible, we forcefully reject the abhorrent thought of breeding subsets of humans specifically adapted to the performance of various tasks, thereby creating a highly efficient but antlike society.

The brain of man has not increased significantly in size since his Cro-Magnon ancestor, perhaps not for many millennia before. When one day man accepts responsibility for his acknowledged power to control his own genetic destiny, the choice between various plans must be based on value judgments. When he begins to use the power to control his own evolution, man must clearly understand and define the values toward whose realization he is to strive.

Man's view of himself has undergone many changes. From a unique position in the universe, the Copernican revolution reduced him to an inhabitant of one of many planets. From a unique position among organisms, the Darwinian revolution assigned him a place among the millions of other species which evolved from one another. Yet, *Homo sapiens* has overcome the limitations of his origin. He controls the vast energies of the atomic nucleus, moves across his planet at speeds barely below escape velocity, and can escape when he so wills. He communicates with his fellows at the speed of light, extends the powers of his brain with those of the digital computer, and influences the numbers and genetic constitution of virtually all other living species. Now he can guide his own evolution. In him, Nature has reached beyond the hard regularities of physical phenomena. *Homo sapiens*, the creation of Nature, has transcended her. From a product of circumstances, he has risen to responsibility. At last, he is Man. May he behave so!

APPENDIX

Panels of the National Academy of Sciences Survey Committee on the Life Sciences

Chairman of Survey Committee
Dr. Philip Handler
National Academy of Sciences

Origins of Life

Chairman
Dr. Norman H. Horowitz
California Institute of Technology

Dr. Frank D. Drake
Cornell University

Dr. Stanley L. Miller
University of California, San Diego

Dr. Leslie E. Orgel
The Salk Institute for Biological
  Studies

Dr. Carl Sagan
Cornell University

Molecular Biology

Chairman
Dr. Sol Spiegelman
Columbia University College of
  Physicians and Surgeons

Dr. K. C. Atwood
University of Illinois

Dr. Paul Berg
Stanford University

Dr. Edwin S. Lennox
The Salk Institute for Biological
  Studies

Dr. Cyrus Levinthal
Columbia University

Dr. Charles A. Thomas, Jr.
Harvard Medical School

The Materials of Life and Their Transformations

Chairman
Dr. Hans Neurath
University of Washington
  School of Medicine

Dr. Konrad Bloch
Harvard University

Dr. Erwin Chargaff
Columbia University College of
  Physicians and Surgeons

Dr. Eugene A. Davidson
Milton S. Hershey Medical Center
Pennsylvania State University

929

Dr. Bernard L. Horecker
Albert Einstein College of Medicine,
  Yeshiva University

Dr. Daniel E. Koshland, Jr.
University of California, Berkeley

Dr. Henry Lardy
University of Wisconsin

Cellular and Subcellular Structure and Function

Chairman
Dr. David M. Prescott
University of Colorado

Dr. Bernard D. Davis
Harvard Medical School

Dr. Harry Eagle
Albert Einstein College of Medicine,
  Yeshiva University

Dr. Maurice Green
St. Louis University School of
  Medicine

Dr. George E. Palade
Rockefeller University

Dr. Herbert Stern
University of California,
  San Diego

Developmental Biology

Chairman
Dr. James D. Ebert
Carnegie Institution of Washington

Dr. Alfred J. Coulombre
National Institutes of Health

Dr. Mac V. Edds, Jr.
Brown University

Dr. Paul B. Green
University of Pennsylvania

Dr. Clifford Grobstein
University of California
  School of Medicine, San Diego

Dr. William S. Hillman
Brookhaven National Laboratory

Dr. Clement L. Markert
Yale University

Dr. Heinrich Ursprung
Swiss Federal Institute of Technology

Function of Tissues and Organs

Chairman
Dr. Horace Davenport
University of Michigan Medical
  School

Dr. Roy O. Greep
Harvard Medical School

Dr. John B. Hanson
University of Illinois

Dr. Teru Hayashi
Illinois Institute of Technology

Dr. Anton Lang
Michigan State University

Dr. William G. Van der Kloot
New York University School of
  Medicine

Anatomical Sciences

Chairman
Dr. Don W. Fawcett
Harvard Medical School

Dr. David Bodian
Johns Hopkins University School
  of Medicine

Dr. Milton Hildebrand
University of California, Davis

Dr. Arnold Lazarow
University of Minnesota Medical
School

Dr. Ronald Singer
University of Chicago School of
Medicine

Dr. W. Gordon Whaley
University of Texas

Structure and Function of the Nervous System

Chairman
Dr. Stephen Kuffler
Harvard Medical School

Dr. Edward V. Evarts
National Institute of Mental Health

Dr. Eric R. Kandel
New York University School of
Medicine

Dr. Irwin J. Kopin
National Institute of Mental Health

Dr. Vernon B. Mountcastle
Johns Hopkins University School
of Medicine

Dr. Walle J. H. Nauta
Massachusetts Institute of Technology

Dr. Sanford L. Palay
Harvard Medical School

Dr. William Alden Spencer
New York University School of
Medicine

Behavioral Biology

Chairman
Dr. Daniel S. Lehrman
Rutgers University

Dr. Benson E. Ginsburg
University of Connecticut

Dr. Stephen Glickman
University of California, Berkeley

Dr. Donald Griffin
Rockefeller University

Dr. Peter H. Klopfer
Duke University

Dr. Carl Pfaffmann
Rockefeller University

Dr. Kenneth D. Roeder
Tufts University

Dr. Eliot Stellar
University of Pennsylvania School
of Medicine

Dr. Hans-Lukas Teuber
Massachusetts Institute of Technology

Ecology

Chairman
Dr. Arthur Hasler
University of Wisconsin

Dr. George A. Bartholomew
University of California, Los Angeles

Dr. John E. Cantlon
Michigan State University

Dr. LaMont C. Cole
Cornell University

Dr. Charles F. Cooper
University of Michigan

Jared J. Davis
U.S. Atomic Energy Commission

Dr. Edward S. Deevey, Jr.
Dalhousie University

Dr. David M. Gates
Missouri Botanical Gardens

Dr. Robert Inger
Field Museum of Natural History
Chicago

Dr. Robert C. Lasiewski
University of California, Los Angeles

Dr. Richard S. Miller
Yale University

Dr. John E. Ross
University of Wisconsin

Dr. Frederick E. Smith
University of Michigan

Dr. Kenneth E. F. Watt
University of California, Davis

Evolutionary Mechanisms and Population Biology

Chairman
Dr. James F. Crow
University of Wisconsin

Dr. Richard C. Lewontin
University of Chicago

Dr. G. Ledyard Stebbins
University of California, Davis

The Diversity of Life

Chairman
Dr. Ernst Mayr
Harvard University

Dr. Richard D. Alexander
University of Michigan

Dr. J. Ralph Audy
University of California Medical
   Center

Dr. W. Frank Blair
University of Texas

Dr. Paul Illg
University of Washington

Dr. Edward F. Knipling
U.S. Department of Agriculture

Dr. M. J. Lavoipierre
University of California, Davis

Dr. Curtis W. Sabrosky
U.S. Department of Agriculture

Dr. Bobb Schaeffer
The American Museum of Natural
   History

Dr. William C. Steere
New York Botanical Garden

Biological Science and the Production of Food and Fiber

Chairman
Dr. Sterling B. Hendricks
U.S. Department of Agriculture

Dr. R. W. Allard
University of California, Davis

Dr. F. N. Andrews
Purdue University

Dr. Nyle C. Brady
Cornell University

Dr. Theodore C. Byerly
U.S. Department of Agriculture

Dr. Karl Maramorosch
Boyce Thompson Institute for
   Plant Research

Dr. John L. McHugh
   U.S. Fish and Wildlife Service

Dr. William T. S. Thorp
University of Minnesota

Biological Science and the Advancement of Medicine

Chairman
Dr. John B. Hickam
Indiana University School of Medicine

Dr. Karl H. Beyer
Merck Sharpe and Dohme Research
   Laboratories

Dr. Richard O. Burns
Duke University School of Medicine

Dr. Albert H. Coons
Harvard Medical School

Dr. Ben Eiseman
Denver General Hospital

Dr. Martin Goldberg
University of Pennsylvania Medical
   School

Dr. Lester Goodman
National Institutes of Health

Dr. David A. Hamburg
Stanford University School of
   Medicine

Dr. Seymour J. Kreshover
National Institutes of Health

Dr. Norman Kretchmer
Stanford University School of
   Medicine

Dr. Irving M. London
Albert Einstein College of Medicine
Yeshiva University

Dr. Kenneth S. McCarty
Duke University School of Medicine

Dr. Maclyn McCarty
Rockefeller University

Dr. Charles R. Park
Vanderbilt University School of
   Medicine

Dr. Oscar D. Ratnoff
Case Western Reserve University
   School of Medicine

Dr. Michael B. Shimkin
University of California, San Diego

Dr. Madison S. Spach
Duke University School of Medicine

Dr. Delford Stickel
Duke University School of Medicine

Dr. Lewis Thomas
Yale University School of Medicine

Dr. John Waldhausen
University of Pennsylvania
   School of Medicine

Dr. Maxwell M. Wintrobe
University of Utah College of
   Medicine

Dr. James B. Wyngaarden
Duke University School of Medicine

Human Development and Changes with Time

Chairman
Dr. Albert I. Lansing
University of Pittsburgh School
   of Medicine

Dr. Robert A. Aldrich
University of Washington School
   of Medicine

Dr. Albert Damon
Harvard University

Dr. Leonard Hayflick
Stanford University School of Medicine

Dr. Heinz Herrmann
University of Connecticut

Dr. Howard C. Taylor, Jr.
Columbia University College of
   Physicians and Surgeons

Biology and Industrial Technology

Chairman
Dr. Ernest H. Volwiler
Abbott Laboratories

Dr. Arnold O. Beckman
Beckman Instruments, Inc.

Dr. Otto K. Behrens
Eli Lilly and Company

Dr. Robert D. Coghill
Stanford Research Institute

Dr. Karl Folkers
University of Texas

Dr. Carl H. Krieger
Campbell Institute for Food Research

Dr. Emil M. Mrak
University of California, Davis

Dr. J. R. Porter
University of Iowa, College of
   Medicine

Dr. William A. Skinner
Stanford Research Institute

Dr. John A. Zapp, Jr.
E. I. duPont de Nemours and
   Company

Biology and Education

Chairman
Dr. Donald Kennedy
Stanford University

Dr. Donald H. Bucklin
University of Wisconsin

Dr. Thomas Eisner
Cornell University

Dr. Garrett Hardin
University of California,
   Santa Barbara

Dr. Colin S. Pittendrigh
Stanford University

Dr. Howard Schneiderman
University of California, Irvine

Biology and Renewable Resources

Chairman
Dr. David Pimentel
Cornell University

Dr. John E. Bardach
University of Michigan

Dr. John L. Buckley
Executive Office of the President
Office of Science and Technology

Dr. René Dubos
Rockefeller University

Dr. W. T. Edmondson
University of Washington

Dr. Walter S. Hopkins
U.S. Forest Service

Dr. Justin W. Leonard
University of Michigan

Dr. George Sprugel, Jr.
Illinois Natural History Survey

Dr. Earl L. Stone
Cornell University

Dr. Daniel Q. Thompson
Cornell University

Biology and the Future of Man

Chairman
Dr. Curt Stern
University of California, Berkeley

Dr. Theodosius Dobzhansky
Rockefeller University

Dr. René Dubos
Rockefeller University

Dr. David R. Goddard
University of Pennsylvania

Dr. Joshua Lederberg
Stanford University School of
   Medicine

Dr. James V. Neel
University of Michigan Medical
  School

Dr. Frank W. Notestein
The Population Council

Dr. Roger Revelle
Harvard University

The Role of Computers in the Life Sciences

Chairman
Dr. Allen Newell
Carnegie-Mellon University

Dr. G. Octo Barnett
Harvard Medical School

Dr. Jerome R. Cox, Jr.
Washington University School
  of Medicine

Dr. Max V. Mathews
Bell Telephone Laboratories

Dr. Bruce Waxman
Health Services and Mental Health
  Administration

Environmental Health

Chairman
Dr. Norton Nelson
New York University
  School of Medicine

Dr. Roy E. Albert
New York University
  School of Medicine

Dr. C. O. Chichester
University of California, Davis

Dr. Merrill Eisenbud
New York University
  School of Medicine

Dr. James Daniel Hardy
Yale University Medical School

Dr. Theodore F. Hatch
University of Pittsburgh

Dr. Harold C. Hodge
University of Rochester
  School of Medicine

Dr. James McCarroll
University of Washington

Dr. Richard E. Marland
Consumer Protection & Environmental
  Health Service

Dr. J. Carrell Morris
Harvard University

Dr. Richard L. Riley
Johns Hopkins University

Dr. Michael B. Shimkin
University of California, San Diego

Dr. James H. Sterner
University of Texas School of Public
  Health

Dr. James G. Wilson
Children's Hospital Research
  Foundation

Dr. James L. Whittenberger
Harvard University School of
  Public Health

Dr. John A. Zapp, Jr.
E. I. duPont de Nemours and
  Company

Special Consultants to the Study

Dr. Stephen Aldrich
Central Intelligence Agency

Dr. Ira Baldwin
University of Wisconsin

Dr. John H. Dingle
Case Western Reserve University
  School of Medicine

Dr. David Goldman
The Medical College of Pennsylvania

Dr. H. Orin Halvorson
University of Minnesota

Dr. Riley D. Housewright
United States Army

Executive Secretary NAS/NRC

Dr. Herbert B. Pahl (1967-1969)
Dr. Laura H. Greene (1969-1970)